JOHN RAMSAY'S CATALOGUE OF
BRITISH DIECAST MODEL TOYS

SIXTH EDITION

Swapmeet Publications
PO Box 47
Felixstowe, Suffolk IP11 7LP
Phone 01394 670700
Fax 01394 670730

SWAPMEET TOYS AND MODELS LTD. T/A SWAPMEET PUBLICATIONS
REG. NO. 1715966 REG. OFFICE: 36 REMBRANDT WAY, BURY ST EDMUNDS, SUFFOLK. DIRECTORS E.J. RAMSAY, S.E. RAMSAY, CO SEC M.J. RAMSAY B.A.

Originator and Editor
John Ramsay

Technical Editor
John King

1st Edition published 1983
2nd Edition published 1986
3rd Edition published 1988
Update published 1989
4th Edition published 1991
5th Edition published 1993
6th Edition published 1995

ISBN 0 - 9509319 - 9 - 3

Typeset by Swapmeet Toys and Models Ltd, Colchester and printed in Great Britain by Spottiswoode Ballantyne Ltd, Colchester

CONTENTS

COLOUR SECTIONS – CONTENTS

Cover Picture:- 280 Series Dinky Toys Van sold by Christie's, South Kensington, London for £12,650 (World Record Price for single model).

OFFICIAL COMPANY ACKNOWLEDGEMENTS

The names 'MATCHBOX', 'MODELS of YESTERYEAR', 'SUPER-KINGS', and 'The DINKY COLLECTION' are trademarks of the Tyco-Matchbox Group of companies and are subject to extensive trademark registrations (Marca Registrada) 1987 and 1988.

The names 'CORGI TOYS', 'CARS of The 50s', 'CORGITRONICS', 'ROCKETS' and 'CORGI JUNIORS' are acknowledged as trademarks of Mattel Ltd.

The name 'CORGI CLASSIC' is acknowledged as the trademark of Corgi Classics Ltd.

The names 'MODELS of DAYS GONE' and 'MARATHONS' are acknowledged as trademarks of Lledo Plc.

'EXCLUSIVE FIRST EDITIONS' is acknowledged as a trademark of Gilbow (Holdings) Ltd.

'HORNBY DUBLO' is acknowledged as a trademark of Hornby Hobbies Ltd.

'BRITAINS' is acknowledged as the trademark of Britains Ltd.

INTRODUCTION

Since the publication of the 5th Edition of the Catalogue two years ago, there has been an accelerated growth in the number of models sold at auction. Furthermore the high levels of world wide publicity achieved by high auction results has naturally encouraged even more would be sellers to sell their collections at auction.

Not only have the number of auctions increased, but so too has the quality of the collections offered for sale. Some of the prices achieved have been quite outstanding with both Christie's of South Kensington and Vectis Model Auctions selling models and sets for world record prices.

One of the benefits of the large number of quality items sold, has been the amount of new model information which has emerged, often as a result of better catalogue descriptions being given by the auction houses.

In addition the regular saleroom prices do help to underpin market price levels, although too much credence should not be given to any one individual auction price.

During the past two years all the major diecast manufacturers have been very active. As a result collectors have had a wide range of superb new models to chose from e.g. the Corgi Classic 'Chipperfield Circus' releases.

Change within the market place has continued with the 1995 management buyout of 'Corgi Classics' from the international toy company Mattel. The new company will be known as Corgi Classics Ltd.

This new 6th Edition contains far more detailed information and colour pictures than the previous edition. The main catalogue improvements include:-

CORGI TOYS – Many new variations in the car sections and the 'Novelty' and 'Classics' sections have been totally revised. In addition there are new listings of 'Juniors' and 'Superhaulers', plus 'Corgi Cameos'.

DINKY TOYS – The car listings include many new variations obtained from the various specialists auctions plus new information on the different box types and how to identify early post-war models.

MATCHBOX TOYS – The '1-75' Series regular wheel issues have been totally revised and the 'King Size' listings enhanced.

E.F.E. – Exclusive First Editions. The listings have been brought up to date and contain all the new 1995 issues.

LLEDO – 'Models of Days Gone'. The listings have been brought up to date and contain many new variations.

NEW LISTINGS – These include Benbros 'Qualitoys', Timpo Toys and Lone Star Railways. Many thanks to Robert Newsom for providing all the information. In addition listings of Wardie 'Master Models' and 'Fun Ho' models have been included.

TRAIN SECTION – Thanks to Dave Jowett the catalogue now includes a 'WRENN RAILWAYS' listing and this has been combined with the revised 'HORNBY DUBLO' section into a new section purely for train collectors.

COLOUR PAGE SECTIONS – The Catalogue now contains six separate colour sections totalling forty eight pages, which largely enables each chapter to have its own colour sections.

As stated in the 5th Edition, the success of the Catalogue is in no small way due to the splendid level of support and information supplied by both the trade and collectors alike.

As a result this 6th Edition represents the combined efforts of many people over a period of fifteen years to produce the best possible catalogue for the benefit of all.

MARKET PRICE RANGE GRADING SYSTEM

Based on the findings of the Market Surveys undertaken since 1983 virtually all the models have been given a 'Market Price Range'.
The price gap between the lower and higher figures indicates the likely price range a collector should expect to pay for the model.
Models qualifying for a price at the top end of the range could include:
- Boxed models where both the model and the box are in pristine condition,
- A scarce or unusual colour,
- An unusual component such as special wheels, e.g., spun hubs on some Dinky Toys cars,
- A model with pristine decals where this is unusual, e.g., Dinky Toys Guy Van No.514, 'Lyons Swiss Rolls',
- A model in an unusual or special box,
- A model priced by a trader who disagrees with the price range quoted in the Catalogue (which is only a guide).

PRICES FOR MODELS IN LESS THAN MINT BOXED CONDITION

Many boxed models seen for sale fail to match up to the exacting standards on which the Market Price Range has been based, having slight model or box damage. In these instances models may be priced at 50% to 60% of the Market Price Range shown, and this is particularly relevant when a model is common. Boxed models with considerable damage or unboxed models will be priced at a much lower level.

Note: It cannot be over-emphasised that irrespective of the price guidance provided by this Catalogue, collectors should not always expect to see prices asked within the price ranges shown. Traders will ask a price based on their trading requirements and will NOT be governed by any figures shown in this Catalogue, nor could they be reasonably expected to do so.

MODELS NOT GIVEN A 'MARKET PRICE RANGE'

It has not been possible to give every model a price range and these exceptions are as follows:

NPP   No Prices Possible

This is shown alongside models never encountered in the survey and about which there is doubt as to their actual issue, even though a model may have been pictured in a catalogue. This particularly applies to Spot-On models and the odd Dinky Toy. Readers will appreciate that unlike postage stamps or coins, no birth records are available in respect of all the die-cast models designed or issued.

NGPP   No Grading Possible at Present

Where a model or gift set is particularly rare and no price information whatsoever is possible, no price grading has been shown as the Compiler believes that this is carrying rarity and value assessment into the realms of pure guesswork.

As and when information becomes available concerning these rarities it will be included in the Catalogue.

GSP   Gift Set Price

If a model forms part of a Set (and is not available separately) the price range will be shown against the entry in the relevant Gift Set section and will refer to the complete set.

NRP   Normal Retail Price

This is shown alongside models which have been recently issued or for models which have yet to attain a real collectable value. One would not expect to see asking prices for models in this grade set higher than a few pounds unless a model happens to be particulary large, e.g. a common gift set containing several models.

NPE   No Price Estimate

This coding is shown against models and gift sets which were never encountered in the survey and about which no up to date asking price or auction price information was obtained. The price shown is therefore the Compiler's estimate of what it would cost should the model come into the market. This grading particularly applies to many of the pre-war Dinkies and also to the Spot-On model range.

Consequently because of rarity considerations, expect to see large price fluctuations occur over and above the catalogue estimate, especially at auctions.

DESCRIPTION OF MODEL COLOURS

The descriptions of the various colours used to describe model colour variations have been derived from the following sources:-

i) Manufacturers' colour descriptions.

ii) Colours commonly used and known to refer to certain models over a period of many years.

iii) Colours which we in consultation with the trade or specialist collectors decide most closely describes a previously unrecorded genuine colour variation.

iv) Colours given a model by a bona fide auction house. If this model is a previously unrecorded colour variation we will include the variation in future catalogue listings provided that:-
   a) The auction house are themselves satisfied that the model is genuine and not a repaint.
   b) Specialist dealers and collectors who view the model are satisifed that the colour variation is genuine and is not a repaint.

SCARCE COLOURS AND VARIATIONS

Collectors or traders who know of other variations which they believe warrant a separate listing are invited to forward this information to the Editor together with any supporting evidence.

CLASSIFYING THE CONDITION OF MODELS AND BOXES

The condition of a model and its accompanying box does of course have a direct bearing on its value which makes accurate condition grading a matter of key importance.

Unlike other collecting hobbies such as stamps or coins, no one universal grading system is used to classify the condition of models and boxes.

Nevertheless, whilst several versions exist, there are really two main systems of condition classification in the UK as follows:

1. The 'Specific Condition' Grading System

The following example is fairly typical of the types of descriptions and gradings seen on Mail Order lists.

M	Mint
AM	Almost Mint
VSC	Very Slightly Chipped
SC	Slightly Chipped
C	Chipped
VC	Very Chipped

If a model is described as Mint Boxed, the condition of its box is not normally separately described. However, it is expected to be in first class and as near original condition as is possible, bearing in mind the age of the model concerned.

If a box is damaged the flaws are usually separately described. This method has always seemed to work out quite well in practice, for all reputable dealers automatically offer a 'Sale or Return if not satisfied' deal to their clients, which provides the necessary safeguard against the misrepresentation of the model's condition. The Compiler would stress that the foregoing is only an example of a mail order condition grading system and stricter box grading definitions are known to exist.

2. The 'General Condition' Grading System

This method is often used by auctioneers although it is also to be seen used on the occasional mail order list.

(M)	Mint
(E)	Excellent
(G)	Good
(F)	Fair
(P)	Poor

Usually these gradings are separately applied to describe firstly the condition of the model and secondly the condition of the box. From our observations and purely for guidance purposes, we would suggest the following descriptions approximately represent the different grades.

a) Model Condition Gradings

1. MINT (M)
The model must be complete and as fresh, new and original in appearance as when first received from the manufacturers.

2. EXCELLENT (E)
The model is almost in mint condition and is only barred from that classification by having a few slight flaws, e.g., slight paintwork chipping in unimportant areas.

3. GOOD (G)
The model is in a complete and original condition and retains an overall collectable appearance despite having a few chips or rubbed paintwork.

4. FAIR (F)
The model may not be in its original state having, for example, a broken bumper, replacement radiator or windscreen, or it may have signs of metal fatigue. The paintwork may be faded, well chipped, retouched or repainted. There may be signs of rust. Unless the model is rare it is in a barely collectable condition.

5. POOR (P)
The model may be damaged, incomplete, repainted, altered, metal fatigued, or have a rusted baseplate or heavily chipped paintwork, etc. Unless the model is rare it has little real value to a collector other than as a candidate for a complete restoration or use as spares.

b) Box Condition Gradings

1. MINT (M)
The box must be complete both inside and out and contain all the original packing materials, manufacturer's leaflet and box labels. It should look as fresh, new and original in appearance as when first received from the manufacturers.

2. EXCELLENT (E)
The box is in almost mint condition but is only barred from that classification by just the odd minor blemish, e.g., there may be slight damage to the display labels caused by bad storage. The original shop price label may have been carelessly removed and caused slight damage. The cover of a bubble pack may be cracked or there may be very slight soiling etc.

3. GOOD (G)
The box is complete both inside and out, and retains an overall attractive collectable appearance. Furthermore, despite showing a few signs of wear and tear, it does not appear 'tired'.

4. FAIR (F)
The box will have a 'tired' appearance and show definite signs of wear and tear. It may be incomplete and not contain the original packing materials or leaflets. In addition it may not display all the exterior identification labels or they may be torn or soiled or a box-end flap may be missing or otherwise be slightly damaged. In this condition, unless the model is particularly rare, it will not add much to the model's value.

5. POOR (P)
The box will show considerable signs of wear and tear. It will almost certainly be badly damaged, torn, incomplete or heavily soiled and in this condition, unless it is very rare, is of little value to a collector.

MODEL and BOX
VALUATION GUIDELINES

The research has produced the following comparative price information concerning the values of both unboxed models and separate boxes in the various condition classifications.

The guidelines have been based on the 'General Condition' grading system as described in the previous section. The percentage value ranges are designed to reflect the relatively higher values of the rarer models and boxes.

UNBOXED MODEL CLASSIFICATION	% VALUE OF MINT BOXED MODEL
Mint	50% - 60%
Excellent	40% - 50%
Good	20% - 40%
Fair	10% - 20%
Poor	0% - 10%

BOX CLASSIFICATION	% VALUE OF MINT BOXED MODEL
Mint	40% - 50%
Excellent	30% - 40%
Good	20% - 30%
Fair	10% - 20%
Poor	0% - 10%

Note: The same model may have been issued in two or more types of box (Yesteryears for example). The model in the earlier box is usually (though not always) the more valuable.

Rare Models and Sets

The exceptions to the foregoing guidelines are in respect of rare models or boxes, or models seldom found in first class condition such as some pre-war models. In these situations rarity commands a premium and the asking price or the price realised at auction will almost certainly reflect it.

SELLING MODELS TO THE TRADE

The model value figures produced by the Price Grading system always refer to the likely *asking prices* for models.

They have been prepared solely to give collectors an idea of the amount they might reasonably expect to pay for a particular model.

The figures given are *not* intended to represent the price which will be placed on a model when it is offered for sale to a dealer. This is hardly surprising bearing in mind that the dealer is carrying all the expense of offering his customers a collecting service which costs money to maintain.

Collectors should not therefore be surprised when selling models to the trade to receive offers which may appear somewhat low in comparison with the figures shown in the Catalogue.

Dealers are always keen to replenish their stocks with quality items and will as a result normally make perfectly fair and reasonable offers for models. Indeed, depending on the particular models offered to them, the actual offer made may well at times exceed the levels indicated in the Catalogue which are only *guidelines* and not firm figures.

One last point when selling models to the trade do get quotations from two or three dealers especially if you have rare models to be sold.

HOW TO USE THE CATALOGUE

a) Identifying models from their lettering

All lettering shown in CAPITAL LETTERS indicates the actual lettering on the model itself. It may appear in either the Model Type (vehicle) or Model Features (description) column. Similarly *lettering in Italics* indicates that it is shown on the actual model.

b) Abbreviations

In this the 6th Edition dependence on abbreviations has been greatly reduced but where necessary they are used to include information concisely. The Abbreviations list is near the back of the book.

CATALOGUE OMISSIONS

Accurate birth records do not exist in respect of all the die-cast models issued. Therefore whilst every effort has been made to provide comprehensive information it is inevitable that collectors will have knowledge of models which have not been included. Consequently the Compiler will be pleased to receive details of these models in order that they may be included in future editions. Naturally, supporting evidence regarding authenticity will be required.

This Catalogue has been prepared solely for use as a reference book and guide to the rarity and asking prices of die-cast model toys.

Whilst every care has been taken in compiling the Catalogue, neither the Compiler nor the publishers can accept any responsibility whatsoever for any financial loss which may occur as a result of its use.

CATALOGUE UPDATING
INFORMATION SERVICE

As this Catalogue is a biennial an updating service is provided by our sister publication the 'MODEL PRICE REVIEW'. The 'REVIEW' contains details of new model variations plus considerable information on Market Price changes.

In addition it also provides price information and model listings on a wide range of toys and models not listed in the 'British Diecast Catalogue', e.g. Tinplate, 'O' Gauge Trains, Scalextric and Toy Soldiers etc. The next 'REVIEW' will be available in the autumn of 1996 and may be obtained from good model shops, Menzies bookshops, or if in difficulty direct from Swapmeet Publications.

WHEN REPLYING TO ADVERTISEMENTS PLEASE MENTION JOHN RAMSAY'S CATALOGUE

WHEN REPLYING TO ADVERTISEMENTS PLEASE MENTION JOHN RAMSAY'S CATALOGUE

WHEN REPLYING TO ADVERTISEMENTS PLEASE MENTION JOHN RAMSAY'S CATALOGUE

WHEN REPLYING TO ADVERTISEMENTS PLEASE MENTION JOHN RAMSAY'S CATALOGUE

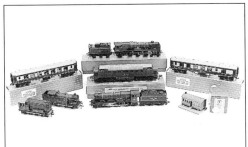

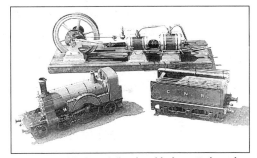
WHEN REPLYING TO ADVERTISEMENTS PLEASE MENTION JOHN RAMSAY'S CATALOGUE

WHEN REPLYING TO ADVERTISEMENTS PLEASE MENTION JOHN RAMSAY'S CATALOGUE

WHEN REPLYING TO ADVERTISEMENTS PLEASE MENTION JOHN RAMSAY'S CATALOGUE

Fine Diecasts & Toys at Phillips

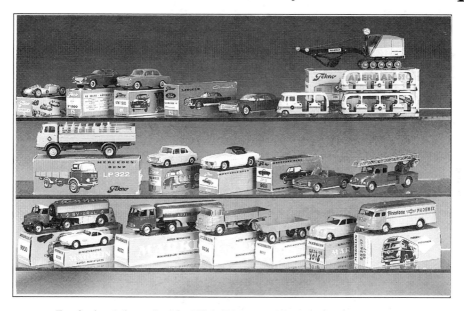

For further information on selling Diecast or Toys at auction please contact:
Kegan Harrison, Tel. (0171) 229 9090. Fax (0171) 792 9201

WHEN REPLYING TO ADVERTISEMENTS PLEASE MENTION JOHN RAMSAY'S CATALOGUE

WHEN REPLYING TO ADVERTISEMENTS PLEASE MENTION JOHN RAMSAY'S CATALOGUE

WHEN REPLYING TO ADVERTISEMENTS PLEASE MENTION JOHN RAMSAY'S CATALOGUE

BENBROS & ZEBRA TOYS

The following history and listings of Benbros and Zebra models have been provided by Robert Newson.

Benbros was started in the late 1940s by brothers Jack and Nathan Benenson, at Walthamstow in north-east London. They first called themselves "Benson Bros." and made diecast toys and lead figures (some of which are marked "Benson"). The name Benbros was adopted in 1951. One of their best known die-cast toys was a miniature coronation coach, copied from the Moko-Lesney coach. Their range of large die-cast toys was expanded during the 1950s with re-issues of various Timpo Toys, for which Benbros had acquired the dies.

The miniature "T.V. Series" was introduced in late 1954, packed in individual boxes which resembled a 1950s television set. By 1956 there were 24 models in the T.V. Series, and soon after this the packaging was changed to red and yellow "Mighty Midget" boxes. The Mighty Midgets were available up to 1965.

The Zebra Series was introduced in the 1960s in an attempt to update the range with better features and more accurate models. However, toy production was discontinued when Benbros was taken over in 1965.

Benbros "T.V. Series" and "Mighty Midgets"

Most models came in a very wide range of colours, so these have not been listed, but full details of colours and other variations are given in the illustrated booklet "Benbros T.V. Series & Mighty Midgets" by Robert Newson, which is still available from the author.

No.	Model	Description	Price	
1	Horse Drawn Hay Cart	With man and raves. Later models marked 'BENBROS'	£15-20	☐
2	Horse Drawn Log Cart	With man & 'log', 'Made in England' under horse	£15-20	☐
3	AA Motorcycle & Sidecar	With rider and separate windscreen. 'Made in England' under sidecar	£20-30	☐
4	Stage Coach with four horses	'KANSAS STAGE' cast in, separate driver on some, 'BENBROS' on later models	£15-20	☐
5	Horse Drawn Gipsy Caravan	No maker's name on model	£20-25	☐
6	Horse Drawn Milk Cart	Milkman and horse, 2 separate or cast-in churns, 'BENBROS' on later models	£15-20	☐
7	Three-wheeled Electric Milk Trolley	With milkman. 'EXPRESS DAIRY' cast in	£15-20	☐
8	Foden Tractor and Log Trailer	With log (wood dowel)	£15-20	☐
9	Dennis Fire Escape	Separate wheeled escape ladder	£15-20	☐
10	Crawler Bulldozer	with rubber tracks	£15-20	☐
11	Crawler Tractor with Hay Rake	Rubber tracks. Same basic casting as no. 10. No maker's name on model	£15-20	☐
12	Army Scout Car	Separate or cast-in driver	£10-15	☐
13	Austin Champ	Separate or cast-in driver	£15-20	☐
14	Centurion Tank	with rubber tracks	£15-20	☐
15	Vespa Scooter	With rider	£25-30	☐
16	Streamlined Express Loco	('TV Series' only). Runs on four concealed wheels	£15-20	☐
16	Chevrolet Nomad Station Wagon	('Mighty Midget' only). Most models have silver painted flash	£15-20	☐
17	Crawler Tractor with Disc Harrow	Rubber tracks. Same tractor as no. 11. No maker's name on model	£15-20	☐
18	Hudson Tourer	Same chassis as no. 16	£15-20	☐
19	Crawler Tractor and Trailer	Rubber tracks. Same tractor as nos. 11 and 17. No maker's name on model	£15-20	☐
20	Foden 8-wheel Flat Lorry	Early models in two-tone colours	£15-20	☐
21	Foden 8-wheel Open Lorry	Early models in two-tone colours	£15-20	☐
22	ERF Petrol Tanker	Similar to Matchbox 11a. No adverts or with 'Esso' transfer on one side	£15-20	☐
23	AEC Box Van	No transfers. Open rear end	£15-20	☐
23	Bedford Box Van	Without adverts or with 'Dunlop' transfers. Open rear end	£15-20	☐
24	Field Gun	Solid wheels. No maker's name on model. Working firing mechanism	£5-10	☐
25	Spyker	Similar to Charbens no. 2. Both models are marked with the maker's name	£5-10	☐
26	1904 Vauxhall 5 h.p.	Same chassis as no.25	£5-10	☐
27	1906 Rolls-Royce	Same chassis as no.25	£5-10	☐
28	Foden 8-wheel Flat Lorry with Chains	'Chains' are cast with the body	£15-20	☐
29	RAC Motorcycle & Sidecar	With rider and separate windscreen. 'Made in England' under side	£20-30	☐
30	AEC Army Box Van	Same casting as no. 23 in Military Green paint	£15-20	☐
30	Bedford Army Box Van	Same casting as no. 23 in Military Green paint	£15-20	☐
31	AEC Lorry with Tilt	Cast metal 'canvas' tilt, riveted in place	£15-20	☐
31	Bedford Lorry with Tilt	Cast metal 'canvas' tilt, riveted in place	£15-20	☐
32	AEC Compressor Lorry	Usually painted Yellow	£15-20	☐
32	Bedford Compressor Lorry	Usually painted Yellow	£15-20	☐
33	AEC Crane Lorry	No hook cast	£15-20	☐
33	Bedford Crane Lorry	No hook cast	£15-20	☐
34	AA Land Rover	'AA ROAD SERVICE' cast in, open rear end	£15-20	☐
35	Army Land Rover	No lettering on sides, open rear end	£15-20	☐
36	Royal Mail Land Rover	'ROYAL MAIL E-II-R' cast in, open rear end	£15-20	☐
37	Wolseley Six-Eighty Police Car	A little smaller than Morestone/Budgie no. 5	£15-20	☐
38	Daimler Ambulance	Similar to Matchbox no. 14b. Civilian or military paint	£20-25	☐
39	Bedford Milk Float	Similar to Matchbox no. 29a	£15-20	☐
40	American Ford Convertible	Windscreen frame and seats cast with body	£15-20	☐
41	Army Hudson Tourer	No. 18 in Military-Green paint	£15-20	☐
42	Army Motorcycle & Sidecar	With rider and separate windscreen. 'Made in England' under sidecar. 'AA' or 'RAC' cast on sidecar, i.e. this is the same casting as no. 3 or no. 29.	£20-30	☐
43	Bedford Articulated Box Van	Without adverts or with 'Dunlop' transfers, open rear end	£15-20	☐
44	Bedford Articulated Lowside Lorry	First version has hinged tailboard, later fixed	£15-20	☐
45	Bedford Articulated Low Loader	With log (wood dowel)	£15-20	☐
46	Bedford Articulated Petrol Tanker	Without adverts or with 'Esso' transfer on one side	£20-30	☐
47 ?	Bedford Articulated Crane Lorry	No hook cast	£15-20	☐
48	Bedford Articulated Lorry with Chains	'Chains' are cast with the model	£15-20	☐
49	Karrier Bantam Bottle Lorry	Similar to Matchbox 37a. 'Drink Coca-Cola' transfers. No maker's name	£30-40	☐
50 ?	RAC Land Rover	'RAC ROAD SERVICE' cast in, open rear end	£20-30	☐

Other Benbros Vehicles — Qualitoys

This list includes all the other vehicles in the Benbros range, mostly large scale items. Many carried the name "Qualitoy" as well as Benbros, and most were individually boxed. Dating of these models is quite difficult, since there were few contemporary adverts, and the only catalogues known are trade price lists for 1964 and 1965. The Timpo re-issues were probably no earlier than 1952, and the various motorcycles were introduced in late 1955. Where a retail price is shown (in shilling and pence) the model was still available on the 1964 and 1965 price lists.

Model	Description	Price	
Coronation Coach with 8 horses	ER cast on doors, MADE IN ENGLAND on drawbar. Later boxed marked Zebra Toys. 116 mm. (3s 7d)	£25-30	☐
State Landau with 4 horses	Two separate footmen. MADE IN ENGLAND under coach. 105 mm. (3s 7d)	£25-30	☐
Father Christmas Sleigh	With 4 reindeer. Metallic green or metallic blue. 110 mm. (2s 6d)	£60-80	☐
Covered Wagon with 4 bullocks	Re-issue of a model by L. Brooks (Toys) Ltd. (1958). Hollow-cast lead bullocks (diecast on the Brooks model). MADE IN ENGLAND lengthwise under wagon. Cloth canopy. Green wagon, Yellow shaft & wheels, Red cowboy. 186 mm.	£60-80	☐
Covered Wagon with 4 horses	Same wagon as above. Canopy plain or with BUFFALO BILL'S COVERED WAGON or CALGARY STAMPEDE COVERED WAGON printed. Red or Green wagon with Yellow shaft or metallic Green or metallic Blue with Red shaft. Yellow wheels. Two barrels. Metal or plastic cowboy holding whip. 186 mm. (4s 8d)	£60-80	☐
Rickshaw with 2 Passengers	Pulled by Ostrich or Zulu. Shown in the Joplin book* under Crescent, but believed in fact to be Benbros. About 150 mm.	£60-80	☐
Roman Chariot with 2 horses	With figure. Metallic Green or Yellow with Red wheels. About 135 mm.	£60-80	☐
Horse Drawn Farm Cart with man	Re-issue of Timpo model. Light Green or Yellow cart	£50-60	☐
Horse Drawn Water Wagon	Re-issue of Timpo model. Light Green wagon	£50-60	☐
Horse Drawn Log Wagon with log	Yellow with Red wheels, or Red with Yellow wheels, or Orange with Red wheels. 225 mm.	£60-70	☐
Stephenson's Rocket Loco & Tender	Metallic Brown or Silver plated loco. Tender metallic Green, Metallic Blue, Orange or Red. 105 mm.	£30-40	☐
Caterpillar Tractor	Copy of early Lesney model. Red or Yellow or metallic Blue, rubber tracks, 97 mm. (3s 6d)	£30-40	☐
Caterpillar Bulldozer	Copy of early Lesney model. Red tractor with Black blade, or metallic Blue with Red or Yellow blade. Rubber tracks. 118 mm. (4s 11d)	£30-40	☐
Caterpillar Excavator	With driver. Orange tractor with Green shovel or metallic Blue with Red shovel. Red or Green driver. Rubber tracks. 138 mm. (4s 11d)	£30-40	☐
Ferguson Tractor with driver	No name on model. Yellow or Red with unpainted wheels; metallic Green or Yellow with Red wheels; Orange with Black or Blue wheels. Driver Green, Brown, Blue, metallic Blue or Grey. 73 mm. (2s 6d)	£25-30	☐
Ferguson Tractor with Cab and Shovel	With driver. No name on model. Red, Yellow or dark Green with unpainted wheels. Green or Brown driver. 100 mm.	£35-40	☐
Ferguson Tractor & Log Trailer	With driver and log. Tractor details given above. Red trailer with yellow wheels. Trailer length 179 mm. (4s 3d)	£40-50	☐
Ferguson Tractor with Roller	With driver. No name on model. Roller is the former Timpo horse-drawn roller with changes to the die to provide a drawbar. Tractor details above. Red trailer with yellow rollers. Trailer length 109 mm. (3s 6d)	£40-50	☐
Ferguson Tractor with Harrow	With driver. No name on model. Harrow is the former Timpo horse-drawn harrow with changes to the die to provide a drawbar. Tractor details above. Red or Yellow trailer, length about 110 mm. (3s 6d)	£40-50	☐
Euclid Dumper Lorry	Copy of Dinky no.965. Metallic Blue cab and chassis, Yellow or Orange tipper. 145 mm. (5s 10d)	£50-60	☐
Muir Hill Dumper with Driver	Orange with Green tipper, Blue wheels; Yellow with Red or Orange tipper, Blue wheels; metallic Green with Orange tipper, Blue wheels; or Red with Yellow tipper, Black wheels. 105 mm. (3s 11d)	£40-50	☐
A101 Army Open Land Rover & Field Gun	Land Rover has two figures cast, separate windscreen, metal wheels with rubber tyres. Field gun marked BENBROS, solid rubber wheels. Dark Brownish-Green. 111 mm. and 102 mm.	£60-80	☐
A102 Lorry with Anti-Aircraft Gun	Matt dark Green, Silver gun. 117 mm.	£25-30	☐
A103 Lorry with Radar Scanner	Matt dark Green, Silver radar dish. 117 mm.	£25-30	☐
A104 Lorry with Searchlight	Matt dark Green. 117 mm.	£25-30	☐
A105 Armoured Car & Field Gun	Dark Brownish-Green or matt dark Green. Field gun same as A101. 96 mm. and 102 mm.	£30-40	☐
A106 Army AEC Lorry with Tilt	SUNDERLAND cast on cab sides. Dark Brownish-Green or matt dark Green, Green cloth tilt. 132 mm.	£100-125	☐
A107 Army Closed Land Rover	Same basic casting as A101. Matt dark Green, Black roof. Opening side and rear doors. 111 mm.	£40-50	☐
220 AEC Flat Lorry with chains	SUNDERLAND cast on cab sides. Red cab and chassis, light Green, Blue, Beige or metallic Green body. 130 mm. (3s 6d)	£100-125	☐
221 Articulated Low Loader	Re-issue of Timpo model. Red or Green cab with Red, Yellow or metallic Green trailer. Also matt Dark Green cab and trailer. No name on model. 166 mm.	£25-30	☐
223 Land Rover "Royal Mail"	Red with Black roof. ROYAL MAIL E II R cast on sides. Opening side and rear doors, two figures cast inside. 111 mm.	£100-120	☐
224 Articulated Petrol Tanker	Re-issue of Timpo model. Red or Orange cab, metallic Green or Yellow trailer, "Motor Oil Esso Petrol" transfer. Or light Green cab, Red trailer, "United Dairies" transfer. Or Green cab, Red trailer, "Shell Petrol" label. No name on model. 146 mm. (3s 6d)	£30-40	☐
225 AEC Dropside Lorry	SUNDERLAND cast on cab sides. Red cab and chassis, light Green or Blue body. 132 mm. (3s 6d)	£75-100	☐
226 Petrol Tanker	Re-issue of Timpo model. Red cab and chassis with Red or Yellow tank; or light Green cab and chassis with Yellow tank. "Motor Oil Esso Petrol" or "Fina Petrol Goes a Long Way" transfer. No name on model. 117 mm. (3s 1d)	£30-40	☐
227 AEC Flat Lorry	Re-issue of Timpo model. SUNDERLAND cast on cab sides. Red cab and chassis, light Green, Blue or Cream body. 130 mm. (3s 1d)	£75-100	☐
228 AEC Lorry with Tilt	As no.225 with plain cloth tilt. 132 mm.	£75-100	☐
Forward Control Box Van	Re-issue of Timpo model. Green cab and chassis with light Green or Red body. "Pickfords Removals" labels; or Red cab, chassis and body. No name on model. 99 mm.	£30-40	☐

Articulated Box Van	Re-issue of Timpo model. Red or Green cab, Green, Red or Cream trailer. "Lyons Tea" transfers. No name on model. 145 mm.	£100-150 ☐
AA Land Rover	Same casting as A107 and 223. AA ROAD SERVICE cast on sides and roof sign. Opening side and rear doors, two figures inside. Yellow with Black roof or all Yellow. 111 mm. (5s 10d)	£100-125 ☐
310 Ruston-Bucyrus 10-RB Crane	Maroon and Yellow body, dark Green chassis and jib, rubber tracks. BENBROS cast underneath. Width of body 37 mm. (3s 6d)	£70-80 ☐
311 Ruston-Bucyrus 10-RB Excavator	Maroon and Yellow body, dark Green chassis and arms, rubber tracks. BENBROS cast underneath. Width of body 37 mm. (3s 6d)	£70-80 ☐
AEC Lorry with Ruston-Bucyrus Crane	SUNDERLAND cast on cab sides. Red cab and chassis, Yellow body. Crane as no.310 with Maroon and Yellow body, dark green jib. 128 mm. (5s 10d)	£100-125 ☐
AEC Lorry with Ruston-Bucyrus Excavator	SUNDERLAND cast on cab sides. Red cab and chassis, Yellow body. Excavator as no.311 with Maroon and Yellow body, dark Green arms. 128 mm. (5s 10d)	£100-125 ☐
AA Motorcycle and Sidecar	Black cycle, Yellow sidecar and windscreen. AA badge cast on sidecar and windscreen, TTC147 cast on number plates. 84 mm.	
	(i) Fixed front forks, windscreen with plastic glazing, dark Brownish-Green metal rider.	£75-100 ☐
	(ii) Steering front forks, windscreen with curved frame cast in place of glazing, plastic rider.	£75-100 ☐
RAC Motorcycle and Sidecar	Black cycle, Blue sidecar and windscreen. RAC badge cast on sidecar and windscreen. TTC147 cast on number plates. Steering front forks, windscreen with curved frame, plastic rider. 84 mm.	£75-100 ☐
Solo Motorcycle with Rider	Fixed front forks, TTC147 cast on number plates. 84 mm.	
	(i) Police Patrol – Maroon cycle, Black metal rider	£30-40 ☐
	(ii) Telegraph Boy – Red cycle, Red metal rider	£30-40 ☐
	(iii) Army Despatch Rider – Dark Brownish-Green cycle and metal rider	£30-40 ☐
	(iv) Rally Rider – Green cycle, Blue metal rider	£30-40 ☐
Solo Motorcycle with Rider	Steering front forks, TTC147 cast on number plates. Silver plated cycles with plastic riders in four versions – Police Patrol, Telegraph Boy, Army Despatch Rider and Rally Rider. 84 mm.	£30-40 ☐

*Reference: The Great Book of Hollow-Cast Figures by Norman Joplin (New Cavendish Books).

Benbros 'Zebra Toys'

Zebra Toys were introduced in the early 1960s and were manufactured along with the existing production of large scale Benbros vehicles. Zebra Toys were packaged in distinctive black and white striped boxes. Most of the models had jewelled headlights and some also had windows and plastic interiors.

The AA and RAC Mini Vans apparently had not been introduced when toy production by Benbros came to an end in 1965. They do not appear on a trade price list dated January 1965 but a small number of these models (probably a trial run) were sold off with the remaining toy stocks and are now in the hands of collectors.

In the following list, numbers in brackets are those shown on Zebra boxes. The other numbers are cast on the models themselves. There seems to be no connection between the two numbering systems! Original retail prices (quoted in shillings and pre-decimal pence) are those given in 1964 and 1965 trade price lists. These models are rare in today's market.

100 (16)	Foden Concrete Mixer	Red cab and chassis, Beige or Yellow barrel, 70 mm. (3s 1d)	£50-60 ☐
101 (36)	Scammell Scarab Articulated Van 'BRITISH RAILWAYS'	Maroon cab and trailer, Pale Orange or Mustard-Yellow tilt, 105 mm. (4s 4d)	£100-125 ☐
103 (10)	Jaguar 'E'-type	Metallic Light Green, Metallic Light Blue or Metallic Light Brown, 90 mm. (3s 0d)	£75-100 ☐
104 (30)	Routemaster Bus	Red, 'Fina Petrol goes a long way' adverts, 111 mm. (4s 11d)	£75-100 ☐
106 (34)	Heinkel Bubble Car	Red or Blue body, 100 mm. (4s 4d)	£75-100 ☐
107 (27)	Daimler Ambulance	Cream body, 101 mm. (4s 1d)	£75-100 ☐
(20)	Bedford Cattle Transporter	Red cab and chassis, Light Brown body, 101 mm. (4s 4d)	£50-60 ☐
	Lansing Bagnall Rapide 2000	Fork Lift Truck, Red body, 89 mm. (3s 6d)	£50-60 ☐
	Field Gun	Dark Green, 'BENBROS' cast on model, 102 mm. (2s 0d)	£15-20 ☐
	Police Patrol Motorcycle	(Triumph) 'Silver' plated, plastic rider, 'ENT 303' cast, 84 mm. (2s 6d)	£30-40 ☐
	Rally Motorcycle	(Triumph) 'Silver' plated, plastic rider, 'ENT 303' cast, 84 mm. (2s 6d)	£30-40 ☐
(3)	Army Despatch Motorcycle	(Triumph) 'Silver' plated, plastic rider, 'ENT 303' cast, 84 mm. (2s 6d)	£30-40 ☐
(4)	Telegraph Boy Motorcycle	(Triumph) 'Silver' plated, plastic rider, 'ENT 303' cast, 84 mm. (2s 6d)	£30-40 ☐
	RAC Triumph Motorcycle & Sidecar	Black bike, Blue sidecar, White fairing, plastic rider, 'ENT 303', 84 mm. (3s 5d)	£75-100 ☐
(6)	AA Triumph Motorcycle & Sidecar	Black bike, Yellow sidecar and fairing, plastic rider, 'ENT 303', 84 mm. (3s 5d)	£75-100 ☐
(60)	Austin Mini Van	'AA PATROL SERVICE', Yellow body. Opening side and rear doors	£150-200 ☐
	Austin Mini Van	'RAC', Blue body. Opening side and rear doors	£150-200 ☐

BRITAINS
MOTOR VEHICLES

by Mike Richardson

Most people are aware of the military vehicles made by Britains both before the War and after in 1/32 scale to go with their soldiers, but not so many are acquainted with the contemporary civilian models. Some of these models are only colour variations of the military versions, for example the 59F 'Four-wheeled Lorry with Driver' in the farm series is the same as 1335 'Lorry, Army, Four-wheeled type' but painted in a smart duotone colour scheme instead of khaki. Other models are only available in the civilian type, usually for the good reason that the army could not possibly have a use for a militarised version. A good example of this would be 1656 'John Cobbs Railton Wonder Car' (or 'Railton Mobil Special' as we know it!).

Britains are our oldest toy company which is still in business having been started in 1860 although the first of the famous soldiers did not appear until 1890. This still means over a hundred years continuous toy manufacture, surely a record. The motor lorry models appeared in late 1932 and were based on the Albion army lorries of the time with the familiar 'square' cab design which was to be a hallmark of the Britains lorries until the end of the decade. The range of 4, 6 and 10-wheel farm lorries are still illustrated in the 1940 catalogue. After the War the cab was brought up to date by a change to a more rounded Fordson type, not nearly so attractive.

The military ambulance was also used in civilian versions, a cream 'Corporation' and a blue 'Volunteer Corps' as alternative liveries to the khaki army one. The rarest version of this model is the red and black 'Royal Mail' van which was sold for a short time towards the end of the production run.

There are three civilian cars, a 'Two-seater Coupé' and two 'Sports Model Open Tourers' in the pre-war production. The coup and the open sports car without driver and passenger do not have military equivalents, but when the open sports car has people in it then it is either a 'Mobile Police Car with 2 Officers' (finished in green with black wings), or a 'Staff Car with 2 Officers' as the military offering. The occupants of the car are legless and their lower regions are covered with a tartan rug - how nice for them on cold days! After the War there was a one-piece casting version of the staff car and police car without the separate grilles of the pre-war models and these were rather plain by comparison.

The final group of models consists of the superb record cars 'Bluebird' and 'Railton Special'. These came out in the late 1930s and each is over 6 inches long. The Bluebird was produced in three versions; a) with fully detailed removable chassis, b) without this part, and c) a slightly smaller one (just over 5 inches), without underside detail. The Railton Mobil Special always had the removable chassis and was available painted silver for 1s.6d. or chrome plated for 2s.6d.

After the War two new farm tractor models appeared, a couple of Fordson Majors produced with the active co-operation of the Ford Motor Company. These are excellent models both finished in the correct shade of dark blue and with the name 'Fordson' applied to the front and sides of the radiator. One version has standard wheels but the other (rarer) one had the spiked or 'spud' wheels used on heavy ground.

All these models are to the same scale as the soldiers (1/32), but there is also a similar range in '00' gauge (1/76 scale) to go with model railways. The smaller models date mainly from the post-war era although a sports car and a fastback saloon were seen pre-war. The small scale trucks have a Fordson cab similar to the later large scale farm and army lorries.

The large scale pre-war models are very collectable and prices are consequently very high for rare items in excellent condition and with original lovely boxes. Some few years ago a batch of replicas of the coup were made here in England so exercise care when buying this model. Spare parts are, or have been available for most of these toys to enable repairs to be carried out.

In 1994 Christie's Auctions sold the Britains Archive Collection. See the colour section for pictures of some of the rare colour variations.

Britains Motor Vehicles   (pre-war issues)

The models were constructed of a lead based alloy and the main body parts were hollow cast. However, parts such as wings and running boards were die-cast individually by hand.
The Market Price Range figures refer to boxed models in excellent condition.

Civilian Vehicles

Ref. No.	Model Type	Model Features and Size	Market Price Range	
59 F	Four-wheeled Lorry with Driver	Back and doors open, rubber tyres, 6″	£150-200	☐
60 F	Six-wheeled Lorry with Driver	Two-tone Blue body, White cab roof, Silver radiator surround, back and doors open, White rubber tyres, 6″	£150-200	☐
61 F	Ten-wheeled Lorry with Driver	Back and doors open, rubber tyres	£200-250	☐
90 F	Builders Lorry	As 59 F plus builders name on side. 'DAVIS ESTATES LTD BUILDERS OF HOMES'.	£1600-2000	☐
91 F	Builders Lorry	As 60 F plus builders name on side. Never seen	NPP	☐
92 F	Builders Lorry	As 61 F plus builders name on side. Never seen	NPP	☐
1398	Sports Model Open Tourer	Cream body, Black chassis and wheels, White rubber tyres, 4.25″	£750-1000	☐
1399	Two-Seater Coupé (fitted bumpers)	Cream body, Tan roof, wings and running-boards, Black hubs, White tyres, 4.5″. (Also in other colours)	£1000-1250	☐
1413	Mobile Police Car with two Officers	2-piece casting, Green body, Black wings, White tyres, 4.75″. (Also in other colours)	£500-600	☐
1470	The Royal Household Set	Coronation State Coach, King George VI plus the Queen with twelve attendants	£300-500	☐
1513	Volunteer Corps Ambulance with Driver, Wounded Man and Stretcher	Blue body, 'AMBULANCE', Red/White cross, White tyres	£600-700	☐
1514	Corporation Type Motor Ambulance with Driver, Wounded Man & Stretcher	Cream body, 'AMBULANCE', Red/White cross, White tyres	£700-900	☐
1552	'ROYAL MAIL' Van with Driver	Post-Office Red body, Black bonnet, 'GR' plus crown design, White tyres	£1600-2000	☐

Military Vehicles

1333	Lorry, Army, Caterpillar Type with Driver	Military Green finish, rubber tyres, 6″	£150-200	☐
1335	Lorry, Army, Six-wheeled Type with Driver	Military Green finish, rubber tyres, 6″	£150-200	☐
1432	Tender, Army, Covered, Ten-wheeled (with Driver)	Military Green finish, White rubber tyres, 6″	£150-200	☐
1433	Tender, Army, Covered, Ten-wheeled Caterpillar Type (with Driver)	Military Green finish, White rubber tyres, 6″	£150-200	☐
1448	Car, Staff	Military Green car with 2 Staff Officers, White rubber tyres, 4¼″	£350-450	☐
1641	Underslung Heavy Duty Lorry (18 wheels) with Driver	Military Green finish, 10½″	£350-450	☐
1642	Underslung Heavy Duty Lorry (18 wheels) with Driver	with Mounted Searchlight, Military Green finish, 10½″	£350-450	☐
1643	Underslung Heavy Duty Lorry (18 wheels) with Driver	with Mounted Anti-Aircraft Gun (small)	£350-450	☐
1643	Underslung Heavy Duty Lorry (18 wheels) with Driver	with Mounted Anti-Aircraft Gun (large)	£600-800	☐
?	Underslung Heavy Duty Lorry (18 wheels) with Driver	with Mounted Barrage Balloon Winch	£900-1100	☐
?	Armoured Car with Gun	Military Green, solid metal wheels	£100-125	☐

Autogiro & Record Cars (1:43 scale)

1392	Autogiro	Blue body, other colours known including Miliary Gren with pilot and three detachable rotor blades	£750-950	☐
1936	Bluebird Record Car, Napier Campbell	Malcolm Campbell's car, lift-off body, detailed engine, White tyres	£150-175	☐
1939	Napier Railton	John Cobb's car, '350.20 mph World Land Speed Record'	£250-300	☐

'Lilliput' Series (1:76 scale)

LV 601	Roadster	Various colours	£60-70	☐
LV 602	Limousine	Various colours	£60-70	☐
LV 603	Flat Semi-Trailer	Various colours. Green	£25-35	☐
		Blue	£35-45	☐

'Motor and Road' Series

1313	Volunteer Corps 'AMBULANCE'	Finished in Blue, with wounded man and stretcher	£300-400	☐
2024	Light Goods Van with Driver	Various colours, 'BRITAINS LTD' logo	£400-500	☐

Britains Motor Vehicles   (post-war issues)

Ref. No.	Model Type	Model Features and Size	Market Price Range

'Farm' Series

59 F	Farm Tipping Lorry	with Driver. Light Green or Blue	**£150-250** ☐
127 F	Fordson 'MAJOR' Tractor	with Driver and spade-end wheels	**£200-250** ☐
128 F	Fordson 'MAJOR' Tractor	with Driver and rubber-tyred wheels	**£175-225** ☐

'Clockwork' Series

2041	Clockwork Unit	disguised as a 2-wheeled trailer. 'Will last 1½ minutes when fully wound and capable of driving any other vehicle 20-30 feet'	**£45-55** ☐
2045	Clockwork Van	Finished in various colours with 'BRITAINS LTD' logo	**£500-700** ☐

Military issues, 'The British Commonwealth of Nations' Series

1334	Four-wheeled Tipper Lorry	with Driver	**£150-200** ☐
1335	Six-wheeled Army Lorry	with Driver	**£150-200** ☐
1433	Covered Army Truck	Caterpillar Type with Driver	**£150-200** ☐
1448	Staff Car	with General and Driver	**£350-450** ☐
1512	Army 'AMBULANCE'	with wounded man and stretcher	**£150-200** ☐
1791	Motor Cycle Dispatch Rider	Sold unboxed	**£25-35** ☐
1877	Beetle Lorry and Driver		**£65-75** ☐

Post-war 'Lilliput' Series (1:76 scale)

LV 601	Open Sports Car	2.25″ long	**£60-70** ☐
LV 602	Saloon Car	2.25″ long	**£60-70** ☐
LV 603	Articulated Lorry	4″ long	**£60-70** ☐
LV 604	Fordson Tractor with Driver	1.5″ long	**£35-45** ☐
LV 605	Milk Float and Horse	with Milkman. 2.25″ long	**£45-55** ☐
LV 606	Tumbrel Cart and Horse	with Hay Racks and Carter. 2.75″ long	**£35-45** ☐
LV 607	Austin 3-ton Covered Military Truck		**£35-45** ☐
LV 608	Austin 3-ton Farm Truck		**£35-45** ☐
LV 609	Austin Military Champ		**£65-75** ☐
LV 610	Centurion Tank		**£35-45** ☐
LV 611	Self-propelled 25pdr. Gun		**£25-35** ☐
LV 612	Humber 1½ ton Military Truck		**£35-45** ☐
LV 613	Humber 1½ ton Military Truck	Covered version	**£35-45** ☐
LV 614	Farm Trailer		**£15-25** ☐
LV 615	Saracen Armoured Vehicle		**£15-25** ☐
LV 616	1½ ton Truck		**£35-45** ☐
?	Civilian Ambulance	Cream body with 'AMBULANCE' on sides, 'BRITAINS' on rubber tyres, Red plastic hubs	**£100-125** ☐

Post war Motor Cycle issue

9699	BMW Racing Combination	Red and Yellow with Black rider with White helmet	NGPP ☐

Acknowledgements

The Editor would like to express his thanks to Joe Kahn Collectors World, 87 Portobello Road, London and Mr E.W. Skinner of Kent for kindly supplying additional information.

The models listed were originally compiled for the catalogue by Mike Richardson with assistance from Norman Joplin and Steven Nagle.

BRITAINS AUCTION RESULTS

Romsey Auction Rooms
Auction Sale May 1995
Property of H.R.H. The Duke of Gloucester

1512 Army ambulance with driver, mint condition, unboxed £145

1433 Covered Army Tender, caterpillar type, fair condition, plus 1876 Bren gun carrier in good condition £95

1335 Six-wheeled Army lorry, with driver, tipping body, (khaki green), very good condition, unboxed £85

1334 Four-wheeled Army lorry with driver, tipping body, (dark green), very good condition, unboxed £52

1877 Beetle lorry with driver (dark green), good condition, unboxed £35

'The Royal Household' 1470 Coronation State Coach, King George VI and the Queen with twelve attendants (walking outriders (4), footmen (6) and Yeomen (2)). All good condition, unboxed £185

Set 137F Tractor with driver, mechanical clockwork trailer and tipping hay cart, good condition, unboxed £100

127F Fordson 'Major' Tractor with spiked wheels and driver. Dark blue with orange wheels. Good condition, unboxed £130

Vectis Model Auctions

1448 Army Staff Car with driver & passenger, lovely A in D picture box £190

1512 Army Ambulance but post-war issue in military green, lovely A apart from 2 chips on O/S in B + 'utility' type picture box £190

1877 Beetle Army Lorry khaki/light brown roof/driver, lovely A in B red covered box £190

2041 Clockwork Trailer light blue/brown B + in D box £30

1400 'Bluebird' Land Speed Record Car blue/silver, B in C box £100

127F Fordson Major Tractor dark blue/orange 'spud' wheels, B +, driver is B in C green picture box £120

Lilliput Vehicle Set B + except lorry is C, fixed by 'Blu-Tac' to replacement inner card, box lid is C £100

1512 Army Ambulance with driver and patient on stretcher, B, light yellow picutre label in maroon covered box, C, scarce £130

9402 State Open Road Landau with 6 grey horses & 7 figures, traces still in sealed packed, plus instructions, all A to A + mounted on purple inner printed card in B maroon covered box with coloured picture label B +, brilliant and very scarce £280

1513 Volunteer Corps Ambulance with driver and wounded man on stretcher, navy blue body/red plastic wheels/cream insignia each side, all A to A + in A red box with yellow picture label £690

1727 RA Mobile Howitzer Unit with 4.5″ Howitzer limber with 4 wooden 'shells' and Caterpillar lory with driver B + to A, Lorry is B, box is B £390

1460 Army Service Corps Horse Drawn Wagon with two seated personnel plus rider, red box with black/silver label, A, box B £300

1433 British Army Covered Tender Caterpillar type with driver, B maroon covered boxed, yellow picture label is B +, scarce £120

Christies Auction Results
South Kensington, London
Britains Archive Sale of Rare items

1398 Sports Model Open Tourer Motor Car red and black, 1938, E £3960

1399 Two-seater Coupe model Motor Car 1935, G £1980

60F Six Wheel Tipping Wagon with driver, round-nosed, split windscreen, rubber tyres and plastic hubs, E £935

127F Metal Wheeled Spade Lug Tractor 1948, E £264

1656 John Cobb's Railton Wonder Car in original box and Bluebird advertisement inside lid, with paper label, G-E, box G, label grubby £220

Clockwork Diecast and Tinplate Delivery Van red cab and cream body with 'Britains Ltd' transfers on sides, non-original key, c.1956 G, transfers rubbed – Not sold, estimate £500-600

Wallis & Wallis Results
Lewes, Sussex
Late July 1995

127F Fordson Major Tractor VGC £210

1433 Army Covered Tender GC £140

Underslung Lorry with Barrage Balloon GC £200

A pre-war Britains Mechanical Transport and Air Force equipment underslung lorry, well repainted in dark green with replacement axles and wheels. VGC (one wire connector AF, one hatch lid pull AF) £125

A pre-war Britains Mechanical Transport and Air Force underslung lorry, with anti aircraft gun load, in olive green. FC to QGC (some rusting and parts wheels and tyres replaced) £205

BRITAINS: Top row: No.145F Set, VGC, £205; 12F Timber Carriage, GC, £102; 8F Horse Rake, VGC, £105.
Middle Row: 20F Farmers Gig, VGC, £145; 9F Horse Roller, VGC, £75; 131F Milk Float, VGC, £95.
Bottom Row: 127F Fordson Major Tractor, VGC, £210; 4F Cart, VGC, £90.
Pictures kindly supplied by Wallis & Wallis, West Street Auction Galleries, Lewes, Sussex BN7 2NJ and reproduced by their kind permission.

CHAD VALLEY

DIECAST CLOCKWORK VEHICLES

The Chad Valley company (makers of board games and wooden toys) produced tinplate toy vehicles from 1932 incorporating the year in the registration number on the number plates. Their first 'Wee-Kin' diecast toy vehicles were produced around 1949 and had 'CV 1949' as the registration number. They were fitted with a key-wound clockwork motor and were designed more as toys than models having generic titles like 'Open Lorry' or 'Fire Engine'. The cars issued between 1951 and 1954 as Rootes Group promotionals are much better attempts at models and were sold at Rootes Group garages as well as normal toy shops. The tractors produced from 1952 are particularly fine and well detailed models.

The years shown below indicate the periods in which Chad Valley offered them for sale though not all the toys were available for the whole of the period and some were still in the shops well after production ceased in 1956.

Ref. No.	Year(s)	Model Type	Model Features and Size	Market Price Range	
220	1949-53	Razor Edge Saloon	Various colours, number plates 'CV 1949', approximate scale 1:43	£90-120	☐
221	1949-53	Traffic Control Car	Casting as 9220 plus loudspeaker, 'CV 1949', approximate scale 1:43	£90-120	☐
222	1949-53	Police Car	Casting as 9220 plus loudspeaker and 'POLICE' sign, 'CV 1949', scale 1:43	£90-120	☐
223	1949-53	Track Racer	'CV 1949' on number plates, no other details	£90-120	☐
224	1949-53	Double Decker Bus	Red body, number plates 'CV 1949', Approximate scale 1:76	£150-200	☐
225	1949-53	Open Lorry	Various colours, 'CV 1949' on number plates	£100-130	☐
226	1949-53	Low-Loader	Green/Red body, 'CV 1949' on number plates, 3 Cream-coloured packing cases	£100-130	☐
227	1949-53	Timber Wagon	'CV 1949', body has round bosses to fit milk churns or other 'loads'	£100-130	☐
228	1949-53	Cable Layer	Red cab, Green body, silver trim, number plates 'CV 1949'	£100-130	☐
229	1949-53	Breakdown Lorry	Number plates 'CV 1949', no other details	£100-130	☐
230	1949-53	Milk Float	Number plates 'CV 1949', load of eight milk churns	£125-150	☐
231	1949-53	Fire Engine	Red body, number plates 'CV 1949'	£100-130	☐
232	1949-53	Tower Repair Wagon	Number plates 'CV 1949', no other details	£100-130	☐
233	1949-53	Milk Tanker	Blue body and logo, White tank, number plates 'CV 1949'	£100-130	☐
234	1949-53	Petrol Tanker	Number plates 'CV 1949', no other details	£100-130	☐
236	1949-53	The Hillman Minx	Grey or Metallic Dark Blue body, Rootes Group promotional, 1:43 scale	£90-120	☐
237	1949-53	The Humber Super Snipe	Metallic Dark Green body, Rootes Group promotional, 1:43 scale	£90-120	☐
238	1949-53	The Sunbeam-Talbot	Light Blue or Metallic Dark Green, Rootes Group promotional, 1:43 scale. Base has the wording 'A Rootes Group Product' plus usual Chad Valley marks	£90-120	☐
239	1949-53	Dust Cart	Body has tinplate sliding side panels, number plates 'CV 1949'	£100-130	☐
240	1949-53	The Commer Avenger Coach	Blue or Red body marked 'A Rootes Group Product', 1:76 scale, promotional	£100-150	☐
242	1949-53	The Commer Hands	(Articulated 6-wheel) 'A Rootes Group Product', Red body with 'Commer Hands' sticker, promotional	£100-150	☐
507	1951-54	The Humber Hawk	Metallic Dark Blue, Metallic Dark Green, or mid-Green body, Rootes Group promotional, 1:43 scale	£90-120	☐
?	1951-54	Guy Van	Dark Blue, Cream body, Tinplate doors, 'LYONS ICE CREAM CADBY HALL LONDON W11', Tin rear door	£150-200	☐
?	1951-54	Guy Van	Red body, Blue hubs with Red 'CHAD VALLEY' logo, Tin doors	£150-200	☐
?	1951-54	Guy Van	Green body, Yellow, 'GUY MOTORS LTD', 'COMMERCIAL VEHICLE MANUFACTURERS' logo, Tin rear doors	£150-200	☐

Other issues (with or without Motor)

no ref.	1950-55	Massey Ferguson Tractor		£100-125	☐
no ref.	1950-55	Ford Tractor		£100-125	☐
no ref.	1950-55	Hillman Minx Saloon		£100-125	☐
no ref.	1950-55	Humber Super Snipe	Blue-Grey body	£75-95	☐
no ref.	1950-55	Guy Truck		£100-125	☐
no ref.	1950-55	Sunbeam Racer	Metallic Pink/Silver, RN '5'	£75-95	☐
no ref.	1950-55	Humber Hawk		£75-95	☐
no ref.	1950-55	Rolls-Royce Razor Edge	Razor Edge Saloon	£75-95	☐
no ref.	1950-55	Routemaster London Bus		£100-125	☐
no ref.	1950-55	Commer Avenger Coach		£100-125	☐
no ref.	1950-55	Guy Truck	'LYONS ICE CREAM'	£150-200	☐
no ref.	1950-55	Sunbeam Talbot Saloon	Metallic Pale Brown body	£75-95	☐
no ref.	1950-55	Guy Milk Tanker	Blue/Cream with 'MILK' logo	£75-95	☐
no ref.	1950-55	Guy Cable Lorry		£75-95	☐
no ref.	1950-55	Guy Petrol Tanker	'REGENT PETROL'	£100-125	☐
no ref.	1950-55	Guy 'FIRE' Engine		£100-125	☐
no ref.	1950-55	Guy Container Lorry		£75-95	☐
no ref.	1950-55	Guy Refuse Lorry		£75-95	☐

Chad Valley model Tractors

no ref.	1952	Fordson Major E27N	Dark Blue body, Orange wheels, rubber tyres (2 types of tread on rear) working steering, towbar with pin, clockwork wound by starting handle. Scale 1:16. Illustrated box or plain box with small label	£150-200	☐
no ref.	1954	Fordson Major DDN	Mid-Blue body, Orange wheels, rubber tyres, working steering, lifting bonnet, towbar/pin, hydraulic lift at rear (detachable centre arm) clockwork wound through rear wheel hub. Scale 1:16. Illustrated box or plain box with small label	£150-200	☐
		Static version:	As previous model but without clockwork operation. Illustrated box or plain box plus small label. The word 'working' is deleted from all sides of box	£150-200	☐
		Chrome version:	Static (non-clockwork) version in Chrome plate, with or without wooden plinth. Thought to be a ploughing trophy or Ford presentation model	£250-400	☐
no ref.	1955	Ford Dexta	Mid-Blue body, Orange wheels, radiator panels and 'Fordson Dexta' decal, not steerable, rubber tyres, hook, scale 1:16. Illustrated box	£400-600	☐

28

Ref. No.	Year(s)	Model Type	Chad Valley - continued	Market Price Range	
no ref.	1955	Ferguson	Green body, Red wheels, *Ferguson* decal on sides, working steering, hook, scale 1:16. Illustrated box inscribed *Ferguson*. Promotional	£500-700	☐
		Colour variation:..........	Grey body, Grey wheels, hydraulic lift at rear..	£600-800	☐
no ref.	1955	Fordson Major E27N................	Red and Yellow with driver, clockwork, scale 1:43, boxed. Made under licence by Raybro & Sturdy Products S.A. Johannesburg, South Africa (model marked 'Chad Valley GB')..	£50-100	☐

The introduction to the Chad Valley section was written by Sue Richardson who also provided the basic listing.
Additional listing information came from the Cecil Gibson archives.
The Editor would like to express appreciation to John G. Butler of Berkhamsted, Herts. for his assistance with the Chad Valley Tractors information.

CHARBENS TOYS

The name 'Charbens' was derived by combining the first part of the names of Charles and Benjamin Reid. The toys were manufactured at their 219 Hornsey Road premises in North London. The listings have been taken from the firm's 1960 Trade Catalogue.

'Old Crocks' Miniature series

OC.1	1960-	Darracq, 1904, 2-seater open car	£10-25	☐
OC.2	1960-	Spyker, 1904, 4-seater open car..................	£10-25	☐
OC.3	1960-	'Old Bill' Bus, 1914, Double-decker open-top..	£10-25	☐
OC.4	1960-	Ford, 1907, Ford Model 'T' car....................	£10-25	☐
OC.5	1960-	Vauxhall, 1907, 2-seater open car................	£10-25	☐
OC.6	1960-	De Dion Bouton, 1906, open 2-seater.......	£10-25	☐
OC.7	1960-	Panhard, 1898, 2-seater, tiller steering	£10-25	☐
OC.8	1960-	Rolls-Royce Silver Ghost, 1906, 4-seater open car	£10-25	☐
OC.9	1960-	Standard 6hp, 1903, 4-seater open car......	£10-25	☐
OC.10	1960-	Wolseley, 1902, 4-seater open car	£10-25	☐
OC.11	1960-	Packard Runabout, 1908, open 2-seater	£10-25	☐
OC.12	1960-	Vauxhall Hansom Cab, 1905, with steering wheel on roof!	£10-25	☐
OC.13	1960-	Straker Steam Lorry	£10-25	☐
OC.14	1960-	Stephenson's Rocket (locomotive)	£10-25	☐
OC.15	1960-	Rocket Trailer, Tender for OC.14...............	£10-25	☐
OC.16	1960-	Albion 1909, 2-seater open truck	£10-25	☐
OC.17	1960-	Rover, 1912, 2-seater open sports car	£10-25	☐
OC.18	1960-	Mercedes-Benz, 1911, open 2-seater..........	£10-25	☐
M.19	1960-	Horse Transport, A 1930s Horse-Box........	£10-25	☐
OC.20	1960-	Lanchester, 1910, 4-seater sports tourer.....	£10-25	☐
OC.21	1960-	Morris Cowley, 1922, 2-seater open car.....	£10-25	☐
OC.22	1960-	Daimler, 1900, rather tall 2-seater.............	£10-25	☐
OC.23	1960-	Autocar, 1904, open 3-wheeler..................	£10-25	☐
OC.24	1960-	Grenville Steam Car, 3 wheels, boiler........	£10-25	☐
OC.25	1960-	Napier, 1905, famous 2-seater racer...........	£10-25	☐
OC.26	1960-	Fire Engine, 'Dennis'-like Fire Escape.......	£10-25	☐
OC.27	1960-	Breakdown Crane Lorry, articulated	£10-25	☐
OC.28	1960-	Mercer Runabout, open 2-seater sports.....	£10-25	☐

Military models

M.30	1960-	Mobile Searchlight, Searchlight on 4-wheel trailer	£10-25	☐
M.31	1960-	Mobile Twin Bofor Gun, on trailer...........	£10-25	☐
M.32	1960-	Mobile Radar, Radar dish on trailer	£10-25	☐
M.33	1960-	Mobile Field Gun, Large gun on trailer	£10-25	☐
M.34	1960-	Mobile Rocket Gun, Salvo device on trailer..	£10-25	☐
M.35	1960-	Mobile Tank, Armoured car with flag.......	£10-25	☐

Miniature Truck series

6	1960-	Tractor...	NGPP	☐
8	1960-	Tipping Truck...	NGPP	☐
9	1960-	Coach	NGPP	☐
10	1960-	'ROYAL MAIL' Van...................................	NGPP	☐
11	1960-	Ambulance..	NGPP	☐
12	1960-	'CARTER PATERSON' Van, Green body, White/Red logo, Black wheels, 3½"..	NGPP	☐
13	1960-	'POLICE' Van	NGPP	☐

Picture kindly supplied by Christie's, South Kensington, London.

14	1960-	'POST OFFICE' Van	NGPP	□
15	1960-	Fire Escape	NGPP	□
L.40	1960-	Articulated Tanker, Also listed as a 'Road Tanker'.	£10-25	□
L.41	1960-	Articulated Lorry	£10-25	□
L.41	1960-	Tipping Semi-Trailer	£10-25	□
L.42	1960-	Six-wheeled Lorry	£10-25	□
L.43	1960-	Six-wheeled Tanker	£10-25	□

Note: 'CHARBENS' and 'COPYRIGHT' are marked on underside of models. The models are interesting and very difficult to find in good condition. Additional information on any Charbens products would be welcomed.

'Die-Cast Wheel Toys'

The models listed below are rarely seen in mint and boxed condition so there can be little helpful price guidance. Doubtless many of the models are scarce and asking prices would reflect this.

1	1960-	Tree Wagon, with 2 horses, 1 man	NGPP	□
2	1960-	Horse Roller, and man	NGPP	□
3	1960-	Grass Cutter, with horse and man	NGPP	□
4	1960-	Farm Haycart, with horse & 2 racks	NGPP	□
5	1960-	Farm Wagon, with horse & 2 racks	NGPP	□
6	1960-	Farm Tractor, and man	NGPP	□
7	1960-	Bakers Van, with horse and man	NGPP	□

8	1960-	Tip Lorry	NGPP	□
9	1960-	Motor Coach	NGPP	□
10	1960-	Royal Mail Van	NGPP	□
11	1960-	Ambulance	NGPP	□
12	1960-	Carter Paterson Van	NGPP	□
13	1960-	Police Van	NGPP	□
14	1960-	Post Office Van	NGPP	□
15	1960-	Fire Engine Set, with 3 firemen	NGPP	□
16	1960-	Covered Wagon, with 4 horses & driver	NGPP	□
17	1960-	Tree Wagon, with tractor & driver	NGPP	□
18	1960-	Grass Cutter, with tractor & 2 drivers	NGPP	□
19	1960-	Reaper & Tractor, with 2 drivers	NGPP	□
20	1960-	Crane & Loose Jib	NGPP	□
21	1960-	Muir-Hill Dumper, with driver	NGPP	□
22	1960-	Travelling Zoo Set	NGPP	□
26	1960-	Armoured Car	NGPP	□
27	1960-	Large Tractor	NGPP	□
28	1960-	Steam Roller	NGPP	□
29	1960-	Mincing Machine	NGPP	□
31	1960-	Cable Lorry, with trailer	NGPP	□
32	1960-	Alfa-Romeo Racing Car	NGPP	□
33	1960-	Bristol Cooper Racing Car	NGPP	□
34	1960-	Ferrari Racing Car	NGPP	□
35	1960-	Tree Wagon, with horse	NGPP	□
36	1960-	Horse Transport Box	NGPP	□
37	1960-	Rocket Gun on Lorry, with trailer	NGPP	□
38	1960-	Savings Bank, with gun to fire coin into bank	NGPP	□

WHEN REPLYING TO ADVERTISEMENTS PLEASE MENTION JOHN RAMSAY'S CATALOGUE

CORGI TOYS

INTRODUCTION

Corgi Toys were launched in 1956 by the Mettoy Company which had itself been founded in Northampton by Phillip Ullmann in 1953. The 'Mettoy' name was derived from the first three letters of 'Metal' plus 'toy' - the company's main product range being composed of lithographed metal toys. In 1948 Mettoy produced their first cast metal toys and called them 'Castoys'. The Castoy models contained a clockwork motor and when the first Corgi models were introduced they also contained a mechanism. This plus the introduction of windows gave Corgi a competitive edge against their great rivals Dinky Toys and helped Mettoy to successfully launch Corgi Toys onto the market place.

Each year the company promotes the 'Worlds Biggest Little Motor Show' at the Donnington Park Motor Racing Circuit, Leicestershire, England. This event takes place over two days and includes a large Toyfair plus the Corgi Collectors Club annual convention and dinner.

This new edition of the Catalogue includes the following improvements. The car sections contain many new variations and the 'Novelty, Film and TV' section has been totally revised and enhanced. The 'Corgi Junior' section has been enlarged and there are now listings of 'Super Juniors'; 'Cameos' and 'Superhaulers'. In addition the Auction Results section has been enlarged and contains firm evidence of the high collector interest and demand for quality Corgi Toys.

The Corgi Collectors Club led by Susan Pownall has gone from strength to strength and is now established in over a dozen countries worldwide. Members receive six bi–monthly magazines plus a free Club model each year. (See the advertisement on the inside of the rear cover for details of how to join the club).

In 1995 the year was marked by a number of major success stories. Firstly the new 'Chipperfield Circus' releases were fully sold out within weeks of their launch.

In March Corgi unveiled the 1:18 scale model of the new Rover MGF alongside the full size car at the Geneva Motor Show.

Also in 1995 the Corgi Heritage Centre, under the direction of Chris Brierley, opened at Heywood near Manchester. The centre is a unique showcase which features the complete Corgi history. A visit is a must for all die-cast collectors – there's much to see and buy.

Finally just as this 6th Edition was going to the printers, Corgi announced that a management buyout team, led by former Corgi Managing Director Chris Guest, had bought Corgi Classics from the international toy company Mattel. The new British company will be known as Corgi Classics Ltd and will focus its attention on the needs of the collector. We wish Chris Guest and his team every success in their endeavours.

Corgi Toys Identification

Corgi Toys were often referred to as 'the ones with windows', as they were the first manufacturer to produce models with that refinement. Some of their first models also had a mechanical motor. Spring suspension was introduced from 1959 and in 1960 the first die-cast model to have an opening bonnet. The first models were based on real cars of the period. Similarly, with the launch of the 'Corgi Major Toys' in 1959, models of real commercial vehicles were available and competed with the Dinky 'Supertoys' range.

In the 1960s Corgi produced many successful film and TV-related models. Probably the best remembered was the 'James Bond' Aston Martin which sold in huge quantities in the autumn of 1965. Indeed, such was the popularity of the model that a version was still available in 1992!

Corgi introduced many new features in the 1960s such as: jewelled headlights, opening bonnet revealing detailed engine, opening boot revealing spare, self-centring steering, ruby rear lights, etc. One particularly attractive model was the Midland Red Motorway Express Coach. The detailed interior even incorporated a toilet! Needless to say good examples of this model are highly sought after by bus collectors. Similarly the 'Chipperfields Circus' collection of models were beautifully produced and are highly prized today.

Innovations were frequent and imaginative in the 1960s. 'Golden Jacks' for instance, a built-in jacking system which enabled models to have 'Take-Off' wheels. And 'Trans-O-Lites' whereby light rays were captured and fed through prisms to illuminate the headlights. 'WhizzWheels' and the slightly larger scale of 1:42 were introduced in the 1970s.

A market strategy unique to Corgi was the launching a replica model car simultaneously with the real car. To date simultaneous launches have occurred with Austin Metro, Ford Escort, Triumph Acclaim, Ford Sierra and the MG Maestro 1600, which is a unique record. Corgi were the first die-cast manufacturers to introduce the dimensions of light, sound and movement into their models by using the micro-chip in their 'Corgitronic' range. The models 'come alive', for example by just pushing down on the rear axle or, in the case of the Road Repair Unit, by pressing the workman to activate the pneumatic drill sound. Others (like the Sonic Corgi Truck) can be operated from a remote control handset.

Mettoy Diecast Toys - The 'Castoys' series

Castoys were produced by the Mettoy Company between 1948 and 1958 and were instigated by a request from Marks and Spencers for a robust, long lasting toy. The models were made of zinc alloy and were initially advertised as 'Heavy Cast Mechanical Toys'. Generally, they had windows, a clockwork motor and brake, plus black rubber tyres on cast hubs.

Of the original issues, only two models, No. 840, the 'Eight Wheel Lorry' and 870 'Delivery Van' remained in production after 1951 and these were packaged in attractive Yellow/Red boxes which displayed a picture of the model inside. The later issues of the Delivery Van with their various attractive body designs are now rare and sought after items.

The following listing contains all the information available at present. The Editor would welcome any additional information on body colours and variations.

Ref. No.	Year(s)	Model Type	Model Features and Size	Market Price Range	
			Large Scale Models 1/35		
810	1948-51	Limousine	No models seen though body colour shown as Red in 1948 catalogue	NPP	☐
820	1948-51	Streamline Bus	Cream, Green or Red body with clockwork mechanism, Red pressed tin seating, solid rubber wheels, unpainted chassis. Registration No 'MTY 820'	£100-200	☐
	?	Later issue	Metallic Blue and Gold body with Silver raised roof section and base, Red door with Brown plastic male passenger. Destination board shows 'PRIVATE' and registration 'MTY 718'	£100-200	☐
			Metallic Brown and Pink body with Silver raised roof section and radiator, with Green female passenger	£100-200	☐
830	1948-51	Racing Car	Light Leaf Green, 6" long approx, 'METTOY' cast in base, tinplate hollow printed wheels with motor and brake	£100-200	☐
840	1948-58	8 Wheel Lorry	Metallic Blue cab with Grey rear body, Silver radiator and hubs	£100-200	☐
850	1948-51	Fire Engine	Red body, Silver ladder and crank	£100-200	☐
			Red body, Silver extending ladder, no crank	£100-200	☐
860	1948-51	Tractor	No models seen but shown in 1951 catalogue with Yellow body plus Red engine cover with Silver hubs and Black tyres, steering wheel and brake	£100-200	☐
870	1948-51	Delivery Van	No models seen but shown in 1948 catalogue with plain Dark Blue body	£100-150	☐
	1952-55	'EXPRESS DELIVERY' Van	Yellow body with Red logo and design on sides	£150-200	☐
	1955-58	'POST OFFICE TELEPHONES'	Green body with White logo and Royal crest in Gold, plus Silver two part extending ladder on the roof	£200-300	☐
	1955-58	'ROYAL MAIL'	Red body, Silver trim, Yellow logo and Royal crest	£200-300	☐
	1955-58	'AMBULANCE'	Cream body with Black logo on sides	£100-200	☐
	1956-58	'B.O.A.C.'	Blue body Silver trim, White 'Fly By B.O.A.C.' on roof	£300-400	☐
			Small Scale Model 1/45		
?	1955-57	Soft Drinks Van	Dark red body, Silver wheels, Logo on rear 'CWS SOFT DRINKS – THIRST COME – THIRST SERVED', number plate 'CWS 300'	£75-95	☐
			Special Issue for Marks and Spencer		
	1958	'VANWALL' Racing Car	1:18 scale diecast body, perspex screen and moulded driver, steering wheel, 'VANWALL' side transfers, with or without 'push and go' motor. No Mettoy logo on base but 'Vanwall the famous British Grand Prix Winner' cast in.		
			i) Green body, RN '7' or '18'	£200-300	☐
			ii) French Blue body, RN '20'	£200-300	☐

The 'Miniature Numbers' series

The range of models produced between 1951 an 1954 was based on just two vehicle types - the Standard Vanguard and the Rolls Royce. Models were issued in small and large sizes and featured a clockwork motor plus brake, adjustable steering and moulded grey plastic wheels. The steering is controlled by moving the central fog lamp sideways. They were packaged in attractive window boxes. The basic Standard Vanguard model was also issued as a Taxi, a Fire Chief's Car and a Police Car. The following listing has been taken from the 1951 Mettoy Catalogue and the Editor would welcome any additional information.

Ref. No.	Year(s)	Model Type	Model Features and Size	Market Price Range	
502	1951	Standard Vanguard Saloon	Shown with Green body in catalogue (2 7/8 inches long)	£50-75	☐
505	1951	Rolls-Royce Saloon	Red or Blue body, Silver trim (3 inches long)	£50-75	☐
510	1951	Standard Vanguard Police Car	Black with White 'POLICE' logo on doors; roof siren and bell	£50-75	☐
511	1951	Standard Vanguard Taxi	Shown in 1951 catalogue with Yellow body and Red roof rack	£50-75	☐
512	1951	Standard Vanguard Fire Chief	Red, White 'FIRE CHIEF' on doors; single Silver ladder on roof	£50-75	☐
602	1951	Standard Vanguard Saloon	Blue body shown in catalogue (large scale version of 502, 4¼ inches long)	£50-75	☐
603	1951	Standard Vanguard Saloon	As 602 but with automatic 'to and fro' bump feature	£50-75	☐
605	1951	Rolls-Royce Saloon	Yellow body shown in catalogue (large scale version of 505, 4½ inches long)	£50-75	☐
606	1951	Rolls-Royce Saloon	As 605 but with automatic 'to and fro' bump feature	£50-75	☐

Corgi Toys - Saloons, Estates and Sports Cars

Ref. No.	Year(s)	Model Type	Model Features and Size	Market Price Range	
200	1956-61	Ford Consul	Cream, Dark Green, Medium Tan or Dark Tan body, no suspension, 90 mm.	£80-100	☐
			Brownish-Grey body Light Greyish-Brown or Bright Green	£100-120	☐
			Two-tone Green, Green/Cream or Silver/Cream	£90-120	☐
			Green/Light Grey or Green/Pale Grey	£100-120	☐
200 M	1956-59	Ford Consul	Blue body, flywheel motor, 90 mm.	£100-120	☐
			Dark Green or Bright Green, flywheel motor, 90 mm.	£90-120	☐
C200	1976-78	BLMC Mini 1000	Blue/Silver body with Red and White arrow, 85 mm.	£20-25	☐
201	1956-63	Austin Cambridge	Pale Blue, Turquoise or Mid-Grey body, no suspension, 90 mm.	£100-120	☐
			Light Grey body	£120-140	☐
			Green/Cream, Metallic Green/Silver, or two-tone Green	£90-110	☐
201 M	1956-59	Austin Cambridge	Cream, Red, Slate Grey or Medium Grey body with motor, 90 mm.	£90-110	☐
			Orange body or Silver over Metallic Blue	£120-150	☐
202	1956-60	Morris Cowley	Bright Green or Grey body, no suspension, 91 mm.	£80-90	☐
			Blue body, no suspension, 91 mm.	£110-125	☐
			Grey/Blue or Blue/Cream body.	£80-100	☐
			Pale Green/Blue or White/Blue body	£100-120	☐
202 M	1956-59	Morris Cowley	Pale Green or Medium Green body, flywheel motor, 91 mm.	£100-120	☐
			Dark Green body or Off-White, flywheel motor	£80-100	☐
202	1970-72	Renault R16	Blue/Silver body, no suspension, 91 mm.	£15-20	☐
203	1956-60	Vauxhall Velox	Red, Cream or Yellow body, no suspension, 91 mm.	£80-100	☐
			Yellow/Red body	£100-125	☐
203 M	1956-59	Vauxhall Velox	Red or Yellow body, flywheel motor, 91 mm.	£100-120	☐
			Orange or Cream body, flywheel motor	£175-225	☐
203	1971-72	De Tomaso Mangusta	Green/Gold body, WhizzWheels, 99 mm.	£15-20	☐
204	1956-60	Rover 90	Pale Grey, Dark Grey, or Metallic Green body, no suspension, 97 mm.	£100-120	☐
			Cream or Off-White or Maroon/Grey body	£100-120	☐
			Metallic Cerise/Pale Grey body	£100-120	☐
			Metallic Rose/Pink body	£100-125	☐
			White/Red	£150-200	☐
204 M	1956-59	Rover 90	Metallic Green, Dark Green, Bright Green or Grey body, flywheel motor, 97 mm.	£100-120	☐
204	1972-74	Morris Mini-Minor	Dark Blue body with WhizzWheels, 73 mm.	£90-110	☐
			Metallic Blue body, WhizzWheels	£50-60	☐
			Orange body	£30-40	☐
205	1956-61	Riley Pathfinder	Red body, no suspension, smooth or shaped hubs, 97 mm.	£70-80	☐
			Blue body	£80-100	☐
205 M	1956-59	Riley Pathfinder	Red body, flywheel motor, 97 mm.	£100-120	☐
			Mid Blue body	£80-90	☐
			Dark Blue body	£70-85	☐
206	1956-60	Hillman Husky Estate	Tan or Greyish Light-Brown body, no suspension, 86 mm.	£50-75	☐
			Blue/Silver body, 86 mm.	£80-95	☐
206 M	1956-59	Hillman Husky Estate	Cream, Dark Blue or Grey body, flywheel motor, 86 mm.	£80-90	☐
207	1957-62	Standard Vanguard III	White/Red or Grey/Red, smooth or shaped hubs, 95 mm.	£70-85	☐
			Green up to roof with Red roof	£70-85	☐
			Green up to windows with Red top	£80-100	☐
207 M	1957-59	Standard Vanguard III	Yellow or Off-White body, flywheel motor, 95 mm.	£80-90	☐
			Cream body, Red roof	£100-120	☐
208	1957-60	Jaguar 2.4 litre	White body, no suspension, 95 mm.	£70-90	☐
208 M	1957-59	Jaguar 2.4 litre	Metallic Dark Blue body, flywheel motor, 95 mm.	£90-110	☐
208 S	1960-62	Jaguar 2.4 litre	Lemon body, with spring suspension, smooth spun wheels, 95 mm.	£60-70	☐
			Pale Lemon body, shaped spun wheels	£140-160	☐
210	1957-60	Citroën DS19	Yellow body, Red roof, Grey baseplate, 97 mm.	£60-70	☐
			Yellow body, Red roof, Silver baseplate with detailed drive shaft	£120-140	☐
			Metallic Green body, Black roof, Grey or Silver baseplate	£50-60	☐
			As previous but base has bulge to take flywheel motor. A 210M was never produced	£120-150	☐
210 S	1960-65	Citroën DS19	Red body, Grey baseplate, spring suspension, 97 mm.	£50-60	☐
211	1958-60	Studebaker Golden Hawk	Blue/Gold body, no suspension, smooth spun wheels, 104 mm.	£70-80	☐
			White/Gold	£75-85	☐
211 M	1958-59	Studebaker Golden Hawk	White/Gold body, flywheel motor, no suspension, smooth spun wheels	£60-70	☐
211 S	1960-65	Studebaker Golden Hawk	Gold ('plated') body, White flash, suspension, shaped spun hubs	£80-90	☐
			Gold (painted) body, shaped spun hubs	£100-140	☐
214	1959-62	Ford Thunderbird Hardtop	Pale Green body, Cream roof, '1959' on rear number plate	£55-65	☐
			Pale Green body, Cream roof, blank rear number plate	£75-85	☐
214 M	1959-61	Ford Thunderbird Hardtop	Pink body, Black roof, flywheel motor	£80-100	☐
			Pale Green body, Cream roof, flywheel motor	£175-200	☐
214 S	1962-65	Ford Thunderbird Hardtop	Metallic Grey/Red or Black/Red body, Lemon interior, with suspension	£60-70	☐
215	1959-62	Thunderbird Open Sports	White with Blue interior, smooth or shaped hubs, no suspension, 102 mm.	£60-70	☐
215 S	1962-65	Thunderbird Open Sports	Red body with Yellow interior and driver, with spring suspension	£55-65	☐
216	1959-62	Austin A40	Two-tone Blue body, no suspension, smooth hubs, 86 mm.	£65-75	☐
			Red body, Black roof, smooth hubs	£80-100	☐
216 M	1959	Austin A40	Red/Black body, flywheel motor, no suspension	£150-175	☐

Ref. No.	Year	Name	Description	Market Price Range	
217	1960-63	Fiat 1800 Saloon	Light Blue or Two tone Blue body, smooth or shaped hubs	£35-45	☐
			Light Tan body	£50-60	☐
			Pale Yellow/Brown or Mustard Yellow body	£40-50	☐
218	1960-62	Aston Martin DB4	Red or Yellow body, interior, suspension, smoothor shaped hubs, 95 mm.	£50-60	☐
	1961-62		Red or yellow body, interior, suspension, cast 'spoked' hubs	£60-70	☐
219	1959-62	Plymouth Suburban Sports	Cream/Brown body or Pink body with Brown roof, 104 mm.	£50-60	☐
220	1960-62	Chevrolet Impala	Red (Yellow interior) or Blue (Red or Yellow interior) smooth/shaped spun hubs	£35-40	☐
222	1959-60	Renault Floride	Dark Red, Maroon, Lime Green or Pale Metallic Green body, Red, White or Yellow vac-formed interior, smooth or shaped hubs, suspension, 91 mm....................	£40-50	☐
			Metallic Blue body, Red interior, shaped hubs	£50-60	☐
224	1961-66	Bentley Continental	Seats, opening boot with removable spare, steering, special lights, 108 mm.		
			Cream/Metallic Apple Green or Pale Green/White	£50-60	☐
			Two tone Green or Gold body..	£50-60	☐
			Black/Silver body	£65-75	☐
225	1961-66	Austin 7 (Mini) Saloon	Red body, windows, suspension, seats, steering wheel, 73 mm.	£50-60	☐
			Primrose-Yellow body, Red interior, smooth spun wheels	£175-225	☐
226	1960-71	Morris Mini Minor...................	Light Blue or Red body, suspension, smooth/shaped spun wheels	£50-60	☐
			Sky Blue body, Red interior, spun hubs	£200-250	☐
			Metallic Maroon body, suspension, detailed cast wheels, 73 mm.	£50-60	☐
			N.B. The Light Blue version of 226 was also supplied for a short time by a games manufacturer as part of table-top racing game. This version has a large drive-pin hole in the base and has 'rally' stickers on the bonnet. It was not separately boxed ...	NGPP	☐
228	1962-66	Volvo P-1800	Light Brown body, (Red interior) or Dark Red (Lemon interior) shaped spun hubs ..	£40-45	☐
			Pink or Dark Pink body	£55-65	☐
229	1961-66	Chevrolet Corvair	Blue or Gold body, smooth or shaped spun wheels, 97 mm............................	£40-50	☐
230	1962-64	Mercedes-Benz 220 SE Coupé...	Maroon (Lemon interior) or Cream (Red interior) shaped spun hubs, spare wheel in boot	£35-45	☐
			Black body, Lemon interior, shaped spun hubs, spare wheel in boot	£80-100	☐
231	1961-65	Triumph Herald........................	Gold top and bottom, White in centre, spun hubs, red seats, 90 mm.	£75-85	☐
			Mid Blue top and bottom, White in centre, red seats......................................	£65-75	☐
			All Pale Blue (other details required please)..	NGPP	☐
232	1961-65	Fiat 2100...................................	Two-tone Mauve body, Venetian blinds, suspension, special lights, 95 mm.	£35-50	☐
233	1962-72	Heinkel Trojan	Red, Orange, 'Pink', or Lilac body, 3 smooth spun hubs or detailed cast wheels	£50-60	☐
			Metallic Blue or Turquoise variation body, smooth spun wheels	£60-70	☐
234	1961-64	Ford Consul Classic	Cream/Pink or Gold, opening bonnet, detailed engine, suspension, 95 mm.	£45-55	☐
235	1962-66	Oldsmobile Super 88	Black/White or Metallic Steel Blue/White, suspension, 108 mm.....................	£45-55	☐
			Light Blue/White body..	£55-65	☐
236	1964-69	Motor School Austin A60........	Light Blue, 2 figures, steering control on roof, 'L' plates, 'Highway Code' leaflet	£50-60	☐
238	1962-67	Jaguar Mk.10...........................	Opening bonnet & boot, luggage, battery operated lights.		
			Pale Blue, Light Blue, Metallic Steel Blue, Emerald Green or Metallic Cerise Red	£70-80	☐
			Metallic Deep Blue or Metallic Bright Kingfisher Blue body	£70-80	☐
			Mid Green body	£100-125	☐
	1966		Silver body	£125-150	☐
239	1963-68	Volkswagen 1500 Karmann Ghia	Cream (Red interior) or Red (Yellow interior) spare wheel/suitcase in boot	£35-40	☐
			Gold body, Red or Yellow interior, spare wheel/suitcase in boot	£60-70	☐
240	1963-65	Fiat 600 Jolly............................	Light Blue body, detachable roof, suspension, figures, 79 mm.	£75-85	☐
			Dark Metallic Blue body	£75-85	☐
241	1963-69	Chrysler Ghia L64	Shaped spun or detailed cast wheels, Corgi dog on rear shelf, 108 mm.		
			Metallic Blue/White, Metallic Green, Metallic Copper, Metallic Yellow or Metallic Silver Blue	£40-50	☐
242	1965-66	Fiat 600 Jolly............................	Yellow body, driver, passenger, suspension, no canopy, 79 mm.	£75-95	☐
245	1964-68	Buick Riviera	Metallic Gold, 'Trans-O-Lites', spoked wheels, towing 'grab', 108 mm.	£40-50	☐
			Metallic Light Blue or Metallic Greenish Blue body, towing hook....................	£45-55	☐
			Pale Blue body, spun or cast hubs..	£40-50	☐
246	1965-68	Chrysler Imperial......................	Red or Dark Red body, Blue interior, spun-shaped or detailed cast hubs, 2 figures, golf trolley	£50-60	☐
			Metallic Turquoise body, Blue or Green interior, detailed cast hubs..................	£100-125	☐
247	1964-69	Mercedes-Benz Pullman	Metallic Maroon body, windscreen wipers, instruction sheet, 121 mm.	£35-45	☐
248	1965-67	Chevrolet Impala	Brown body, Cream roof/interior, Chrome side stripe, shaped spun wheels	£40-45	☐
249	1965-68	Morris Mini-Cooper.................	Black/Red body, wickerwork panels, spun or cast wheels, 73 mm.	£60-70	☐
251	1963-66	Hillman Imp	Blue body, opening window, luggage, 83 mm.	£40-45	☐
			Metallic Bronze body..	£60-70	☐
			Light Blue body with 'JENSON'S' logo. Dutch promotional	£300-400	☐
252	1963-66	Rover 2000	Metallic Blue body, suspension, special lights, 95 mm.	£40-50	☐
			Metallic Maroon	£60-70	☐
253	1964-68	Mercedes-Benz 220 SE Coupé...	Metallic Maroon, or Metallic Blue, luggage, spare wheel..................................	£65-75	☐
255	1964-68	Motor School A60......................	Dark Blue body, left-hand drive, 5 language leaflet, (USA issue of 236).............	£125-150	☐
C257	1985	Mercedes-Benz 500 SEC...........	White body, 'Magic Top' (fold-away roof)	£7-10	☐
C258	1985	Toyota Celica Supra.................	Brown body, Black base, opening doors and tailgate, 125 mm.	£7-10	☐
			Blue body	£7-10	☐
			Blue and Cream body with Red line	£7-10	☐
259	1966-69	Citroën 'Le Dandy'	Metallic Dark Maroon body with Yellow interior	£85-100	☐
			Metallic Blue body, White roof and boot	£100-120	☐
260	1969	Renault 16 TS...........................	Metallic Maroon, opening bonnet & hatchback, adjustable seats, 91 mm.	£25-35	☐
262	1967-69	Lincoln Continental...................	Metallic Gold/Black body, with picture strip for TV set	£50-60	☐
			Light Blue/Tan body, with picture strip for TV set	£110-130	☐
263	1966-69	Marlin Rambler Sports	Red/Black (or White/Blue in No.10 GS) suspension, tow-hook, 102 mm.	£35-40	☐
264	1966-69	Oldsmobile Toronado...............	Metallic Medium or Dark Blue body, smooth or cast spoked wheels, 108 mm. ..	£45-65	☐
273	1970	Rolls-Royce Silver Shadow	Metallic Silver/Blue, Golden Jacks, Take-Off wheels, spare, 120 mm.	£60-70	☐
			Metallic White over Metallic Blue..	£50-60	☐

Corgi Toys — Saloons, Estates and Sports Cars – continued

Ref. No.				Market Price Range	
C273	1982-83	Honda Ballade 'BSM'	Driving School car with Yellow body and Red side stripes	**£25-35**	☐
274	1970-72	Bentley T Series	Pink body, opening doors & bonnet, special lights, WhizzWheels, 120 mm.	**£40-50**	☐
275	1968-70	Rover 2000 TC	Metallic Lime Green body, Golden Jacks, spare on boot (opening cover) 95 mm.	**£40-50**	☐
			White body, Red interior, cast wheels, pictorial window box	**£120-150**	☐
			Metallic Maroon body	**£40-50**	☐
C275	1981-	Mini Metro	Blue or Red body, Yellow interior, opening doors & hatchback, 94 mm.	**£15-20**	☐
		Royal Wedding Mini Metro	As previous model but Mauve body with Silver 'Charles & Diana' crest	**£15-20**	☐
276	1968-70	Oldsmobile Toronado	Metallic Blue, Gold or Red body, Golden Jacks, cast Take-Off wheels, 108 mm.	**£40-50**	☐
C276	1982-	Triumph Acclaim	Metallic Blue body, steering control, 120 mm.	**£10-15**	☐
C277	1982-	Triumph Acclaim 'BSM'	Driving School car with Yellow/Red body, steering control, 118 mm.	**£10-15**	☐
C278	1982	Triumph Acclaim	Driving School Car, Yellow body, with steering control, 'CORGI MOTOR SCHOOL' logo	**£25-35**	☐
C279	1979-	Rolls-Royce Corniche	Metallic Dark Red body, opening doors/bonnet/boot, tilt seats, 114 mm.	**£20-25**	☐
	1985		Metallic Blue, Bright Red, Off-White/Cream, Cream or Silver/Grey body	**£20-25**	☐
	1987		Silver/Black body with chrome trim	**£20-25**	☐
C279/3	1990	Rolls-Royce	Gold body with White seats	**£5-8**	☐
			Royal Blue body with White seats	**£5-8**	☐
			Light and Dark Brown body	**£5-8**	☐
C280	1970-78	Rolls-Royce Silver Shadow	Opening doors/bonnet/boot, special lights, WhizzWheels, 120 mm.		☐
			Metallic Blue/Silver (1st issue) Metallic Mid-Blue or Gold body	**£25-35**	☐
281	1971-73	Rover 2000 TC	Metallic Purple, amber or clear roof, WhizzWheels, 95 mm.	**£25-35**	☐
			Metallic Purple body, Matt Black roof panel	**£25-35**	☐
283	1971-74	DAF 'City' Car	Red/Black body, White interior, opening doors/bonnet, WhizzWheels	**£20-25**	☐
C284	1970-76	Citroën SM	Metallic Gold or Metallic Mauve, opening doors, WhizzWheels, 112 mm.	**£20-25**	☐
C285	1975-81	Mercedes-Benz 240 D	Silver, Blue or Copper/Beige, (all Metallic) WhizzWheels, 127 mm.	**£10-15**	☐
C286	1975-79	Jaguar XJC V-12	Blue/Black, Red/Black, Red, Blue, Orange, (all Metallic) WhizzWheels	**£10-15**	☐
C287	1975-78	Citroën Dyane	Metallic Yellow/Black or Metallic Green/Black, duck decal, WhizzWheels	**£10-15**	☐
C288	1975-79	Minissima	Green and Cream body, opening doors & bonnet, 63 mm.	**£10-15**	☐
C289	1977-81	Volkswagen Polo	Metallic Green body, opening doors and hatchback, 97 mm.	**£10-15**	☐
C289	1977-81	Volkswagen Polo 'PTT'	As previous model but Yellow body. German issue	**£20-25**	☐
291	1977-78	AMC Pacer	Metallic Maroon body, opening doors & hatchback, 118 mm.	**£35-45**	☐
C293	1977	Renault 5 TS	Metallic Gold/Black trim or Metallic Orange/Black trim, 97 mm.	**£10-15**	☐
		French issue:	As previous model but Blue body with 'SOS MEDICINS'	**£60-70**	☐
C294	1980	Renault 5 TS Alpine	Black body with White stripe, opening doors and hatchback, 97 mm.	**£8-12**	☐
C299	1982	Ford Sierra 2.3 Ghia	Metallic Light Brown/Black stripe, Dark Brown or Grey interior, Brown or Dark Grey base. Issued in a special two-tone Blue 'Ford' box.	**£60-70**	☐
			As previous model but Metallic Light Brown, Metallic Blue, Red or Yellow body, packed in White/Red 'Ford' box or normal Black/Yellow/Red box	**£10-15**	☐
	1985		Metallic Silver or Yellow body	**£10-15**	☐
	1985		Red body, White broken ground	**£10-15**	☐
C299/4	1990	Ford Sierra	Pink body, *'MR TOMKINSON'S CARPETS'* logo	**£7-10**	☐
300	1956-63	Austin Healey 100-4	Red body, Cream seats or Cream body, Red seats, 86 mm.	**£70-85**	☐
			Blue body with cream seats	**£150-175**	☐
300	1970-72	Chevrolet Corvette Stingray	Lacquered-finish Bright Green or Dark Red body, Golden Jacks, luggage	**£75-95**	☐
			N.B. Models without box header cards contained instructions		
301	1956-59	Triumph TR2	Cream (Red seats) or Green (Cream seats) windscreen, 86 mm.	**£70-85**	☐
301	1970-73	Iso Grifo 7 litre	Metallic Blue body, matt Black bonnet, WhizzWheels, 102 mm.	**£40-50**	☐
302	1957-64	MG 'MGA'	Red (Cream seats) smooth spun wheels, 90 mm.	**£50-60**	☐
			Red body, shaped spun wheels	**£70-80**	☐
			Metallic Light or Mid-Green body (Cream or Yellow seats) smooth or shaped spun wheels	**£50-60**	☐
303	1958-60	Mercedes-Benz 300 SL open	White body, Blue seats, smooth wheels, Blue box	**£70-90**	☐
			Blue body, White seats, smooth wheels, Blue box	**£70-90**	☐
			Cream body, Blue seats, smooth wheels, Blue box	**£80-100**	☐
			N.B. Models in rare plain overprinted box plus £20-30		
304	1959-61	Mercedes-Benz 300 SL Hardtop	Yellow/Red body, smooth spun wheels, no suspension	**£90-110**	☐
			All Yellow body, smooth wheels	**£110-130**	☐
304	1971-73	Chevrolet Camaro	Dark Blue body, White bonnet band & detachable roof, special lights	**£30-40**	☐
305	1960-62	Triumph TR3	Metallic Olive or Cream body, Red seats, smooth or shaped hubs, 86 mm.	**£65-85**	☐
305S	1962-64	Triumph TR3	Light Green or Cream body, spring suspension, shaped spun wheels, 86 mm.	**£80-110**	☐
306	1971-73	Morris Marina 1.8 Coupé	Metallic Red (White seats) or Metallic Lime Green, WhizzWheels, 98 mm.	**£40-45**	☐
307	1962-64	Jaguar 'E' type	Red or Metallic Grey body with Red removable hard-top, 95 mm.	**£65-75**	☐
			Plum body, Red hard-top	**£70-90**	☐
310	1963-68	Chevrolet Corvette Stingray	Metallic Deep Pink, Yellow interior, shaped wheels, 90 mm.	**£40-50**	☐
			Silver body, wire wheels	**£40-50**	☐
			Bronze body	**£80-100**	☐
310	1984	Porsche 924 Turbo	Black body (Gold design, Red seats) or Red body with Porsche badge	**£10-15**	☐
311	1970-72	Ford Capri V6	Orange body, Gold wheels with Red hubs, Black interior, 102 mm.	**£80-100**	☐
			Orange body, WhizzWheels	**£50-60**	☐
			Red body, Black bonnet	**£40-50**	☐
312	1971-73	Marcos Mantis	Metallic Plum body, opening doors, spoked wheels, 110 mm.	**£25-35**	☐
313	1970-73	Ford Cortina GXL	Metallic Blue body, Black/White interior, Graham Hill figure, WhizzWheels, 102 mm.	**£50-60**	☐
			Bronze body, Black roof	**£50-60**	☐
			Yellow body, Black roof	**£150-175**	☐
			Metallic Pale Green body, Black roof	**£100-120**	☐
			Promotional Tan body with 'CORTINA' number plate	**£150-200**	☐
C314	1976-79	Fiat X1-9	Metallic Lime Green/Black or Silver/Black body, suspension, hook, 110 mm.	**£15-25**	☐
C314	1982-	Supercat Jaguar XJS-HE	Black body, Red or Tan interior, opening doors, 118 mm.	**£10-15**	☐
C315	1976-78	Lotus Elite	Red or Yellow with White seats, opening doors, suspension, 120 mm.	**£20-30**	☐

Corgi Toys — Saloons, Estates and Sports Cars – continued

Ref. No.	Year	Model	Description	Market Price Range	
316	1963-66	NSU Sport Prinz	Metallic Red (with Yellow seats) or Maroon body, suspension, 86 mm.	£30-40	☐
318	1981	Jaguar XJS	Blue/Cream body with Red line	£10-15	☐
	1988		Pale Blue body, Beige seats	£7-10	☐
318/8	1990	Jaguar XJS	Blue body with White seats	£7-10	☐
318	1965-68	Lotus Elan S2 Opentop	Dark Green body, Yellow stripe with Black or Red interior (GS37)	GSP	☐
			White body, Black interior (GS40)	GSP	☐
			Metallic Copper body	£150-200	☐
319	1967-68	Lotus Elan S2 Hardtop	Dark Green/Yellow top, or Blue/White top, smooth or cast wheels	£55-65	☐
			Red body, White top, cast wheels	£65-75	☐
			Red body, Red top, cast wheels	£75-85	☐
319	1978-82	Jaguar XJS	Metallic Plum/Black body, opening doors, suspension, 128 mm.	£15-20	☐
320	1965-67	Ford Mustang Fastback 2 + 2	Opening doors, suspension, Corgi dog, half-open window, 95 mm.		
			Silver (Red interior) or Metallic Deep Blue (White interior) detailed cast wheels	£40-50	☐
			Metallic Deep Blue or Light Green body, spoked wheels	£40-50	☐
			Metallic Lilac body, spoked wheels	£70-80	☐
321	1978-82	Porsche 924 Saloon	Metallic Green body with hook, 118 mm.	£30-40	☐
			Red body	£15-20	☐
			Metallic Light Brown body, Red interior	£60-70	☐
C325	1981-	Chevrolet Caprice	Metallic Light Green and Dark Green body, White-wall tyres, 150 mm.	£10-15	☐
			Metallic Silver over Dark Blue (US market)	£70-80	☐
327	1967-69	MGB GT	Red body with suitcase in opening boot, spoked wheels, tilting seats, 90 mm.	£60-70	☐
329	1980-	Opel Senator	Dark Blue or Bronze body, opening doors, 142 mm.	£10-15	☐
			Silver body	£25-30	☐
Q330/1	1989	Mini 30th Anniversary	Pearlescent Cherry Red, Austin-Rover mail-order model (17,500)	£8-10	☐
(Q24/1)	1989	Mini 30th Anniversary	Q330/1 Mini specially packaged with 'MINI' book	£45-55	☐
C330/10	1990	Mini 'AFTER EIGHT'	Dark Blue with Gold stripe, French export model (5,000)	£10-15	☐
332	1967-69	Lancia Fulvia Sports	Metallic Green, Metallic Blue, or Red, suspension, tilt seats	£30-45	☐
			Yellow/Black body	£60-75	☐
334	1968-70	Mini Cooper 'Magnifique'	Pearlescent Dark Blue or Green, jewelled lights, sunshine roof, 73 mm.	£35-45	☐
C334	1981-	Ford Escort 1.3 GL	Yellow, Red or Blue body, opening doors, suspension, 112 mm.	£10-15	☐
335	1968-69	Jaguar 4.2 litre 'E' type	Deep Red body, opening doors/bonnet/hatch, spoked wheels	£60-70	☐
			Metallic Blue body	£40-50	☐
338	1968-71	Chevrolet SS 350 Camaro	Golden Jacks & Take-Off wheels, sliding headlight cover, removable hardtop, Metallic Gold/Black or Metallic Yellow body, 102 mm.	£35-45	☐
C338	1980-	Rover 3500	Metallic Blue, Red/Black or Orange/Brown body, suspension	£10-15	☐
341	1968-70	Mini Marcos GT 850	Metallic Crimson (Cream seats) or Metallic Maroon body, Golden Jacks, 86 mm.	£30-40	☐
			Pale Blue body	£70-80	☐
342	1970-72	Lamborghini P400 Miura	Red/Black or Lemon Yellow, Black bull figure, WhizzWheels, spare wheel	£25-35	☐
343	1969-73	Pontiac Firebird	Metallic Silver/Black, Red seats, Gold/Red Take-Off wheels, Golden Jacks	£25-35	☐
343	1980-	Ford Capri 3 litre	Yellow or Silver body, Black designs, opening doors/hatchback, 124 mm.	£10-15	☐
C345	1981-	Honda Prelude	Metallic Lt. or Dk.Blue, Cream/Green or Metallic Yellow body, sunshine roof	£10-15	☐
C346	1982-84	Citroën 2cv Charleston	Yellow/Black or Burgundy/Black body, opening bonnet, chrome trim	£10-15	☐
347	1969-74	Chevrolet Astro Experimental	Metallic Dark Blue or Green body, Gold/Red wheels, driver & passenger	£30-40	☐
			As previous model but with WhizzWheels	£25-35	☐
C352	1986	BMW 325	White with Black logo. Swiss export model	NGPP	☐
353/1	1986	BMW 325	Red body, Black trim, opening features	NRP	☐
353/9	1990	BMW 325i	Black body with Red seats	NRP	☐
C370	1982	Ford Cobra Mustang	White body, Red interior, Blue/Red design	£10-15	☐
372	1970-72	Lancia Fulvia	Red/Black body, opening doors/bonnet, suspension, WhizzWheels, 91 mm.	£25-35	☐
C373	1981-	Peugeot 505	Red body, Silver or Black lining, opening doors, suspension, 127 mm.	£10-15	☐
C374	1970-73	Jaguar 'E' type 4.2 ltr 242	Red or Yellow body, WhizzWheels, 108 mm.	£30-40	☐
C374	1973	Jaguar 'E' type 5.3 litre	Yellow or Metallic Yellow body. 'New' on box label	£30-40	☐
375	1970-72	Toyota 2000 GT	Translucent 'candy' Blue or Purple body, aerial, WhizzWheels, 102 mm.	£25-35	☐
377	1970-73	Marcos 3 litre	Yellow/Black, or Metallic Blue body, WhizzWheels, 91 mm.	£25-35	☐
			White/Grey	£55-65	☐
378	1970-72	MGC GT	Red/Black body, opening doors and hatchback, WhizzWheels, 90 mm.	£60-75	☐
			Orange body, (this version in Gift Set 20)	GSP	☐
C378	1982-	Ferrari 308 GTS	Red body, pop-up headlights, opening engine cover, 115 mm.	£10-15	☐
			Black body	£15-20	☐
380	1970-72	Alfa Romeo P33	White body, Gold roll bar, Red seats, WhizzWheels, 95 mm.	£25-35	☐
381	1970-74	VW Beach Buggy	Metallic Red/White, Blue/White, Orange/White or Red/White, 2 skis, W/Wheels	£15-25	☐
382	1970-75	Porsche Targa 911S	Metallic Blue/Black or Metallic Green body, WhizzWheels, 95 mm.	£25-30	☐
			Metallic Silver-Blue body, only seen in Gift Set 20	GSP	☐
C382	1981-	Lotus Elite 2.2	Blue body, 'Elite 2.2', opening doors, number plates	£10-15	☐
383	1970-71	Volkswagen 1200	Red or Orange body with Green 'Flower Power' base and flower labels	£50-60	☐
383	1970-73	VW 1200 'ADAC'	Yellow/Black body, 'ADAC' logo (German equivalent of 'AA')	£120-140	☐
			Yellow/Black 'PTT', Swiss issue	£75-85	☐
383	1970-76	Volkswagen 1200	Orange or Red body, no labels	£25-35	☐
384	1970-73	Adams Brothers Probe	Metallic Maroon (Blue interior) or Metallic Gold body, WhizzWheels, 97 mm.	£25-35	☐
384	1983-84	Renault 11 GTL	Dark Cream body, Red interior, opening doors & boot, 110 mm.	£10-15	☐
			Maroon or Metallic Mauve body	£25-30	☐
385	1984	Mercedes 190 E	Silver/Black body, White seats, number plates, chrome trim	£10-15	☐
	1985		All-Silver body	£10-15	☐
386	1971-74	Bertone Barchetta	Yellow/Black 'RUNABOUT', aerofoil, WhizzWheels, 83 mm.	£25-35	☐
386/8	1990	Mercedes 2.3/16	Red body with Beige seats	NRP	☐
387	1970-73	Chevrolet Corvette Stingray	Metallic Blue body, Black bonnet, roof emblem, WhizzWheels, 99 mm	£40-50	☐
			Metallic Pink body, Black bonnet	£50-60	☐
388	1970-74	Mercedes-Benz C111	Orange/Black body, WhizzWheels, 104 mm.	£25-35	☐
389	1971-74	Reliant Bond 'BUG' 700 ES	Orange body, Orange/Black 'BUG' labels, Cream interior, 64 mm.	£25-35	☐
			Lime Green body	£50-60	☐

392	1973-74	Bertone Shake Buggy	Yellow/Green or Pink/Green, detailed engine, flag, 89 mm..........................	£25-35	☐
C393	1972-79	Mercedes Benz 350 SL	White body, Pale Blue interior with chrome, spoked wheels, 102 mm.	£35-45	☐
			Metallic Blue or Dark Blue body with chrome solid disc wheels	£35-45	☐
			Metallic Green body, ? wheels	£55-65	☐
394	1973-76	Datsun 240 Z.....................	Red/Black body, non-rally version, 102 mm.	£20-25	☐
C400	1974-77	Volkswagen 1200	Metallic Red body, 'CORGI MOTOR SCHOOL', Gold roof steering wheel, cones ...	£75-85	☐
			Metallic Blue body version	£30-40	☐
			Metallic Blue with 'CORGI FAHR SCHULE', German issue	£60-70	☐
C401	1975-77	Volkswagen 1200	Same as C400 but supplied with 24 'bollards' for miniature driving practice..............	£35-40	☐
424	1961-65	Ford Zephyr Estate	Two-tone Blue, suspension, luggage, smooth shaped spun wheels, 97 mm.	£45-55	☐
435	1986	Volvo 760 Turbo	Dark Blue or Silver body or Metallic Dark Brown body	£6-9	☐
C435/12	1990	Volvo 760 Turbo	Green body with White seats	£6-9	☐
440	1966-67	Ford Cortina Estate	Blue/Brown, opening tailgate, suspension, 2 figures, golf equipment, 95 mm.	£80-110	☐
C440	1988	Porsche 944 Saloon	Red body	NRP	☐
445		Plymouth Suburban Sports Station Wagon	Pale Blue body, Red roof, Silver stripe	£40-50	☐
C453	1984	Ford Escort RS 1600 i	White body, Red seats, Black design, 110 mm.	£10-15	☐
485	1966-69	Mini Countryman.....................	Sea-Green body, 2 surfboards on roof-rack, male figure, special leaflet, 79 mm.	£65-80	☐
491	1967-69	Ford Cortina Estate	Metallic Dark Grey, Brown 'wood' panels, shaped spun wheels	£60-70	☐
			As previous model but with cast detailed wheels	£60-70	☐
			Red or Metallic Blue body, Brown 'wood' panels, shaped spun wheels	£60-70	☐
600	1984	Ford Escort	All Red or Red/Black or Red/White body, opening doors, 110 mm.	£10-15	☐
601	1984	Fiat N-9	Red or Silver/Red body, opening doors, 110 mm.	£10-15	☐
602	1984	BL Mini 1000	Yellow body, with or without 'CITY', opening doors, 85 mm.	£10-15	☐
602	1984	BL Mini 1000	Chrome plated model, wooden plinth, in black 'Austin-Rover' box, 'Austin-Rover Mini 25th Celebration Donington Park - August 1984'	£70-80	☐
603	1984	Volkswagen Polo	Green/White or White body, opening doors, 90 mm.	£10-15	☐
604	1984	Renault 5	Dark Blue or Yellow body, with or without 'Le Car TL', 95 mm.	£10-15	☐
605	1984	Austin Mini Metro	Blue body, with or without 'TURBO', 90 mm.	£10-15	☐
611	1986?	Ford Escort.............................	with 'DATAPOST 66' logo	£10-15	☐
612	1986?	Ford Escort.............................	with 'DATAPOST 77' logo	£10-15	☐
613	1986?	Metro Saloon..........................	with 'DATAPOST 66' logo	£10-15	☐
614	1986?	Metro Saloon..........................	with 'DATAPOST 77' logo	£10-15	☐
C675/14	1990	BMW 635	Red/Black body, White-wall tyres	NRP	☐
C1009	1984	MG Maestro	Yellow body, White flash, 'AA SERVICE'	£10-15	☐

MAJOR PACK

1126	1961-65	Racing Car Transporter	Metallic Dark Blue body with 'ECURIE ECOSSE' in Yellow lettering	£150-200	☐
		later version:..................	with logo in Orange lettering	£90-110	☐
			with logo in White lettering	£90-110	☐
			with logo and raised ridges in Light Blue	£90-110	☐
		colour variant:	Metallic Light Blue body with 'ECURIE ECOSSE' in Red lettering	£90-110	☐

Corgi Toys   -   'Cars Of The '50s' series

Ref. No.	Year(s)	Model Type	Model Features and Size	Market Price Range	
C801	1982	1957 Ford Thunderbird............	White/Tan, Cream/Orange or Cream/Black, White-wall tyres, suspension	£10-15	☐
C802	1982	Mercedes 300 SL	Burgundy or Silver body, opening doors, suspension, 126 mm.	£10-15	☐
			Red body, no suspension	£10-15	☐
C803	1983	1952 Jaguar XK120 Sports	Red body/Black hood, suspension, spoked wheels, opening bonnet & boot	£10-15	☐
C803/1	1983	1952 Jaguar XK120 Rally	Cream body, rally number '56'	£10-15	☐
			White body, rally number '56'	£10-15	☐
C804	1983	Jaguar 'Coupé des Alpes'	Cream body, Grey/Black tonneau, rally plate & number '56' or '414'	£10-15	☐
			As previous model but with rear wheel 'spats'	£15-20	☐
C805	1983	'56 Mercedes 300SC Cabriolet ..	Black body, Tan hood, suspension, opening bonnet & boot	£10-15	☐
	1984		Maroon body	£10-15	☐
	1986		Beige body and hood	£10-15	☐
	1987		Grey body, Black hood, export model	£15-20	☐
C806	1983	'56 Mercedes 300SL Roadster...	Black body, Grey folded hood, suspension, opening bonnet & boot......	£10-15	☐
	1986		Black/Green body, Beige seats	£10-15	☐
	1986		Red body, Cream interior, export model	£15-20	☐
	1986		Blue body	£10-15	☐
C810	1983	1957 Ford Thunderbird............	White body, tinted windows, White-wall tyres, suspension, spare wheel	£10-15	☐
	1984		Pink body	£10-15	☐
	1987		Red body	£10-15	☐
			Cream body, Orange roof	£10-15	☐
			Black body, White flash, Red/White interior	NGPP	☐
C811	1984	1954 Mercedes SL	Silver body, suspension, opening doors and bonnet, 127 mm.	£10-£15	☐
	1986		Red body	£10-£15	☐
	1987		Grey body, export model	£10-£15	☐
C812	1985	1953 MG TF	Green body, Tan seats, opening bonnet, luggage rack, spare wheel	£10-£15	☐
C813	1985	1955 MG TF	Red body, Black hood, opening bonnet, luggage rack, spare wheel	£10-£15	☐
	1987		Cream body, Red mudguards, export model	£15-20	☐
C814	1985	1952 Rolls-Royce Silver Dawn..	Red/Black body, Brown seats, opening bonnet and boot	£10-£15	☐
	1986		White/Beige body	£10-£15	☐
	1986		Silver/Black body, export model	£15-20	☐

Ref. No.			*Corgi Toys — 'Cars of the '50s' series – continued*	Market Price Range	
C815	1985	1954 Bentley 'R' type	Black or Cream body, Beige hood, opening bonnet and boot, chrome trim	£10-£15	☐
	1986		Dark Blue and Light Blue body	£10-£15	☐
	1986		Cream/Brown body, export model	£10-£15	☐
			White body, Black roof...	£15-20	☐
C816	1985	1956 Jaguar XK120....................	Red body, Black tonneau, racing number '56', plastic chassis	£10-£15	☐
			Red body, Cream hardtop	£15-20	☐
C819	1985	1949 Jaguar XK120....................	White body, Black hood, racing number '7', plastic chassis...............................	£10-£15	☐
C825	1985	1957 Chevrolet Bel Air.............	Red body, White roof and flash, White-wall tyres..	£10-£15	☐
	1987		Black body, White roof and flash, export model	£15-20	☐
C869	1986	MG TF Racing Car	Royal Blue body, Beige seats, racing number '113', spare wheel, roll-bar	£10-15	☐
C870	1986	Jaguar XK120...........................	Green body, Yellow seats, racing number '6', export model	£15-20	☐

No.33 'RAC' International Rally 'Sun' Mini plus No.321 'Monte Carlo' BMC Mini Cooper 'S' with roof signatures. Models sold by Christie's of South Kensington, London. (See Corgi Auction Results section).

Model Identification

Mechanical Some early Corgi Toys were produced in either the normal form or with a friction type flywheel motor. Exceptions were the sports cars and trucks which could not be converted to take the flywheel. The mechanisms were not robust and were phased out in 1959.

Model Number and Name All Corgi models have *'CORGI TOYS'* on the underside and virtually all models have the name of the model there as well. Unlike Dinky Toys the model numbers are not shown on all models making them difficult to identify at times. However, models without numbers may be found in the catalogue by looking for them in their own thematic section, e.g: Saloon Car, Novelty, etc.

Windows All Corgi models have windows.

Construction Materials All models are comprised at least in part of a die-cast alloy.

Boxes July 1956 - Blue box, January 1959 - Yellow/Blue box (Two-tone cars were first to use them) December 1966 - Window box (2 square window ends) May 1973 - Angled window box (one square window end, coloured lines around box) 1980 - Yellow window box, 1987 New style Corgi logo box.

Ref. No.	Year(s)	Model Type	Model Features and Size	Market Price Range	
C100	1985	'PORSCHE' 956	Yellow/Black body, racing number '7', 'CASTROL', 115 mm.	£7-10	☐
C100/2	1986		Yellow body, racing number '7', 'TAKA-Q'	£7-10	☐
C100/3	1988		Black body, racing number '1', 'BLAUPUNKT'	£7-10	☐
C101	1985	Porsche 956	Red/White body, racing number '14', 'CANON'	£7-10	☐
C101/2	1985	Porsche 956	White body, 'Clipper' logo plus 4 Red stripes on bonnet & tail, 'ADMIRAL ENERGY GROUP Ltd' logo	£15-20	☐
C102	1985	Opel Manta 400	Red body, racing number '43', 'SHELL', 105 mm.	£7-10	☐
	1988		Black body, racing number '18', 'SHELL'	£7-10	☐
C102	1985		Yellow body, racing number '12', 'BRITISH TELECOM'	£7-10	☐
C102/4	1990	'VAUXHALL OPEL' Manta ...	White body, racing number '6', 'MOBIL' on bonnet	£7-10	☐
C103	1985	Opel Manta 400	White body, racing number '15', 'CASTROL'	£7-10	☐
C104	1985	Toyota Corolla 1600	White/Red body, Yellow racing number '16', 'LAING'	£7-10	☐
	1986		White/Red body, racing number '2', 'TOTAL'	£7-10	☐
C105	1985	Toyota Corolla 1600	Red body, Yellow design, racing number '8', 'DUNLOP'	£7-10	☐
	1986		Red body, Yellow design, racing number '5', 'TOTAL'	£7-10	☐
C106	1985	Saab 9000 Turbo	White body, Red/Yellow design, racing number '3'	£7-10	☐
C106/1	1987		Red body, White design 'FLY VIRGIN'	£7-10	☐
C106/3	1988		Black body, racing number '7', 'MOBIL'	£7-10	☐
C106/9	1990	Saab Turbo	White/Maroon body, racing number '4', 'FEDERAL EXPRESS'	£7-10	☐
C107	1985	Saab 9000	Red body, Yellow design, racing number '41', 'BRITAX'	£7-10	☐
C108	1985	Chevrolet Z-28	Red body, Yellow design, racing number '52', 'WEBER', 115 mm.	£7-10	☐
C109	1985	Chevrolet Z-28	White body, Black/Yellow bands, Red racing number '84', 115 mm.	£7-10	☐
C110	1985	BMW 635	White body with Union Jacks and racing number '6'	£7-10	☐
C110/1	1986		Red body, racing number '25', 'FERODO'	£7-10	☐
C110/2	1987		White body, racing number '2', 'MOTUL'.	£7-10	☐
C110/3	1988		White body, racing number '46', 'WARSTEINER'	£7-10	☐
C111	1985	BMW 635	White/Blue body, racing number '18', 'BRITAX'	£7-10	☐
	1986		White body, racing number '8', 'PIRELLI'	£7-10	☐
C113	1987	Saab 9000	Red body, C7PM (Swedish)	£7-10	☐
C139/2	1987	Porsche 911	Orange body, racing number '24', 'JAGERMEISTER'	£7-10	☐
C139/4	1988		Red/Blue body, racing number '91', 'DENVER'.	£7-10	☐
150	1957-61	Vanwall Racing Car	(Blue box) Light or Mid-Green body, Yellow seat, large 'VANWALL', Blue tinted screen, RN '3'.	£45-55	☐
			Mid-Green body, Silver seat, 'VANWALL' logo, clear screen, RN '1'	£45-55	☐
			Mid-Green body, Yellow seat, small 'VANWALL' logo, clear screen, RN '1' ..	£45-55	☐
		Black/Yellow box:	Red body, Yellow seat, large 'VANWALL' logo, Blue tinted screen, RN '1' ..	£45-55	☐
			Red body, Silver seat, small 'VANWALL' logo, clear screen, RN '1'.	£45-55	☐
150 S	1961-65	Vanwall Racing Car	Light or Mid-Red body, Silver seats/driver, clear screen, RN '25', shaped wheels.......	£45-55	☐
150	1972-74	Surtees TS9 Formula 1	Metallic Purple or Metallic Blue body, 'BROOKE BOND OXO' logo, 8-spoke WhizzWheels...............	£20-25	☐
			Metallic Turquoise body with cast 8-stud WhizzWheels	£15-20	☐
		Gift Set model:	Blue/Yellow body with 'DUCKHAMS', (in GS 29 only)	GSP	☐
C150/4	1990	Chevrolet Camaro	Blue body, Orange/Black design, racing number '1'	£7-10	☐
151	1958-60	Lotus XI Racing Car	Silver (Red seats), Red (Cream seats), or Turquoise (Red seats). Clear or Blue-tinted windscreen, RNs '1', '3', or none. Blue box with leaflet	£50-60	☐
151 S	1961-63	Lotus XI Racing Car	Silver or Dull Blue body, maroon seats, suspension, clear or Blue-tinted windscreen, RNs '1' or '3'. Blue/Yellow box, no leaflet	£40-50	☐
151 A	1961-63	Lotus XI	Blue body, Red/White design, Silver nose, Red seats, shaped wheels, clear screen, driver, RN '1'.	£45-55	☐
			Lemon body, racing number '3', driver, spring suspension	£35-45	☐
C151	1974-76	'YARDLEY' Mclaren M19A....	White body, RN '55', White drivers helmet, 8-spoke WhizzWheels...............	£20-25	☐
			White body, RN '55', White drivers helmet, 8-stud WhizzWheels	£15-20	☐
			Same but Blue stripe on White drivers helmet, 8-stud WhizzWheels, (GS30 only).......	GSP	☐
152	1958-60	BRM Racing Car	Dark or Mid-Green body, Yellow or Silver seat, clear or Blue windscreen, RNs '1', '3' or '7', smooth hubs. Blue box with leaflet	£50-60	☐
	1959-61		Dark or Mid-Green body, Silver seat, clear or Blue windscreen, RNs '1', '3' or '7', cast spoked hubs. Blue/Yellow box, no leaflet	£40-50	☐
152 S	1961-65	BRM Racing Car	Turquoise body, cast or shaped (spun) hubs, suspension, RNs '1', '3' or '7'. Blue/Yellow box, no leaflet	£40-45	☐
C152	1974-76	Ferrari 312 B2	Red body, 'Ferrari/Shell' logo, RN '5', White driver, Orange/Blue helmet, 8-spoke or 8-stud cast wheels...............	£15-20	☐
153	1960-62	Bluebird Record Car	Blue body, UK & US flags on nose, metal wheels, 127 mm.	£60-70	☐
153 A	1961-65	Bluebird Record Car	Blue body, UK & US flags on nose, plastic wheels, 127 mm.	£45-55	☐
		variant:	Blue body with two Union Jacks on nose, Black plastic wheels...............	£60-70	☐
153	1972-74	Team Surtees TS 9B	Red, RN '26', Blue or Blue/White driver (Rob Walker) 8-spoke wheels........	£15-20	☐
			Red body, 'NORRIS' logo, (GS30 only)	GSP	☐
154	1963-72	Ferrari Formula 1	Red/Silver body, racing number '36', driver, windscreen, 91 mm.	£25-30	☐
C154	1974-78	'JOHN PLAYER SPECIAL' Lotus...............	Black body, Gold trim, racing number '1' or '4', drivers Emerson Fittipaldi or Ronnie Petersen.		
			1: 'JPS' logo, Black/Red helmet, 8-stud wheels, 'Fittipaldi' on box............	£15-20	☐
			2: 'JPS' logo, Black or Blue helmet, 'Petersen' on box..................	£15-20	☐
			3: 'JPS TEXACO' logo, Red helmet..	£15-20	☐
			4: 'JPS TEXACO' logo, Black helmet, 12-spoke wheels, (GS32 only)........	GSP	☐
			5: 'JPS SHELL' logo, Black/Red helmet, (GS30 only).....................	GSP	☐
		Marks & Spencers issue:	No 'Corgi' on base, 'TEXACO' logo, Orange (?) helmet	GSP	☐
155	1965-68	Lotus Climax Racing Car	Green/Yellow body, racing number '1' or '4', suspension, driver, 90 mm. ..	£25-30	☐

Corgi Toys — Racing, Rally and Speed Cars – continued

Ref. No.				Market Price Range	
C155	1974-76	'SHADOW' F1 Racing Car	Black body, 'UOP' logo, RN '17', driver (Jackie Collins) White/Maroon helmet	**£15-20**	☐
156	1967-69	Cooper-Maserati Racing Car	Blue body, racing number '7', windscreen, White driver, 90 mm.	**£30-35**	☐
C156	1974-76	Graham Hill's Shadow	White/Red body, racing number '12', driver, *'EMBASSY RACING'*, 132 mm.	**£20-25**	☐
158	1969-72	Lotus Climax Racing Car	Red/White, racing number '8', suspension, driver, windscreen, 90 mm.	**£25-30**	☐
C158	1975-77	Elf Tyrrell Ford F1	Blue body, racing number '1', *'ELF'*, Jackie Stewart driving, 110 mm.	**£15-20**	☐
159	1969-72	Cooper-Maserati	Yellow/White, racing number '3', driver-controlled steering, 90 mm.	**£25-30**	☐
C159	1974-76	Indianapolis Racing Car	Red body, racing number '20', Patrick Eagle driving, 130 mm.	**£20-25**	☐
C160	1975-78	'HESKETH' 308 F1	White body, 'HESKETH' logo, White driver, Black helmet, 4-spoke or 8-stud wheels	**£15-20**	☐
		Marks & Spencers issue:	White body, no 'CORGI' on some, White driver, Orange helmet	**GSP**	☐
			Yellow body, 'CORGI TEAM' logo, Orange driver (James Hunt) Black helmet, Blue belts, (GS26 only)	**GSP**	☐
161	1972-75	Santa Pod 'COMMUTER'	Red/Silver 'Dragster' body, racing number '2', WhizzWheels, 123 mm.	**£20-25**	☐
161	1977	'ELF-TYRRELL' Project 34	Blue body, 'ELF' logo, Red or Blue helmet, 8-stud wheels, RN '4'.	**£15-20**	☐
162		Tyrell P34	Blue/White body, 'FIRST NATIONAL BANK' logo, White driver, Red or Orange helmet	**£15-20**	☐
		Marks & Spencers issue:	As previous model but no 'Corgi' on base, 8-stud wheels	**GSP**	☐
162	1971-72	'QUARTERMASTER' Dragster	Green and White body, aerofoil, driver, plastic wheels, 146 mm.	**£20-25**	☐
C163	1971-76	Santa Pod Dragster	White/Blue lift-off body, *'GLOWORM'*, driver, plastic wheels, 113 mm.	**£20-25**	☐
164	1972-75	Ison Bros 'WILD HONEY'	Yellow/Red 'Dragster' body, *'JAGUAR'*, WhizzWheels, 171 mm.	**£20-25**	☐
165	1974-76	Adams Brothers Dragster..........	Orange/Yellow body, 4 x V-8 engines, WhizzWheels.	**£20-25**	☐
166	1971-74	Ford Mustang......................	*'ORGAN GRINDER'*, Yellow/Green body, racing number '39', driver	**£20-25**	☐
C167	1973-74	U.S.A. Racing Buggy	White/Red body, racing number '7', driver, US flag, 95 mm.	**£30-35**	☐
C169	1974-76	Starfighter Jet Dragster	Blue/Silver body, *'FIRESTONE'*, 155 mm.	**£20-25**	☐
C170	1974-76	John Woolfe's 208 Dragster	Blue/Yellow body, *'RADIO LUXEMBOURG'*, racing driver, 146 mm.	**£20-25**	☐
190	1974-76	'JOHN PLAYER' Lotus	1:18 scale, Black/Gold, RN '1', driver, removable wheels, tools, 270 mm.	**£30-35**	☐
191	1974-77	'TEXACO MARLBORO' Mclaren	1:18 scale, White/Red, RN '5', removable wheels, tools, 245 mm.	**£30-35**	☐
C201	1979-82	Mini 1000 'TEAM CORGI'.....	Metallic Silver body, racing number '8', various adverts, 85 mm.	**£10-15**	☐
			Dark Blue body, ? racing number	**NGPP**	☐
203	1971-72	De Tomaso Mangusta	Metallic Dark Green, Gold stripes, racing number '1'	**£20-25**	☐
227	1962-63	Mini Cooper Rally	Blue body, White roof and bonnet, spun wheels, flags, RN '1', '3' or '7'...	**£175-225**	☐
			Blue body and bonnet, White roof otherwise as above	**£175-225**	☐
			Primrose Yellow body, White roof and bonnet, with flags and RN '7'	**£150-175**	☐
			Primrose Yellow body and bonnet, with flags and RN '1'	**£175-225**	☐
256	1971-74	VW 'EAST AFRICAN RALLY'	Red body, rally number '18', steering on roof, rhinoceros, 91 mm.	**£100-140**	☐
271	1969-70	Ghia Mangusta De Tomaso......	Blue/White body, Gold stripes, aerial, detailed engine	**£40-50**	☐
C281	1982-	'DATAPOST' Metro	Blue/White body, racing number '77', various adverts, 94 mm.	**£10-15**	☐
282	1971-74	Mini Cooper Rally	White/Black body, rally number '177', special lights, WhizzWheels, 73 mm.	**£55-65**	☐
C291	1982	Mercedes Benz 240 Rally Car ...	Muddy Cream body, rally number '5', roof rack, spare wheel	**£10-15**	☐
C299	1987	Sierra Rally........................	Black body, rally number '7', *'TEXACO'*	**£5-8**	☐
C300	1979-82	Ferrari 'DAYTONA'	Green, multicoloured flash, racing number '5', opening doors, 120 mm.	**£10-15**	☐
C301	1979-82	Lotus Elite Racing Car	Yellow/Red body, racing number '7', *'FERODO'*, 120 mm.	**£10-15**	☐
302	1969	Hillman Hunter Rally	Blue body, White roof, Matt-Black bonnet, RN '75', equipment, kangaroo 'Golden Jacks', Transfers, Toolbox, leaflet, Instructions	**£80-90**	☐
C302	1979-82	VW Polo	Metallic Brown/Red body, racing number '4', various adverts, 97 mm.	**£10-15**	☐
303	1970-72	Roger Clark's Capri	White/Black body, racing number '73', decal sheet, WhizzWheels, 102 mm.	**£25-35**	☐
303 S	1961-65	Mercedes-Benz 300 SL open	Off-White body, Yellow seats, shaped wheels, bonnet stripe, RN '1-12'.....	**£70-90**	☐
			Blue body, Yellow seats, shaped wheels, bonnet stripe, RN '1-12'	**£80-100**	☐
			N.B. As from 1963 all '303S' models included a driver in a Grey suit, White shirt and red bow tie, racing numbers '3' or '7'.		
			White body, Yellow seats, bonnet stripe, driver, shaped wheels	**£80-100**	☐
			Chrome (Gold) body, Yellow and Brown seats, bonnet stripe, driver, cast wheels	**£100-125**	☐
C303	1980-	Porsche 924 Racer	Orange body, racing number '2', *'PIRELLI'*, 118 mm.	**£10-15**	☐
304 S	1961-65	Mercedes-Benz 300 SL Hardtop	Chrome body, Red roof, stripe, smooth/shaped/spoked wheels, RN '3' or '7'.	**£70-85**	☐
305	1972-73	Mini Marcos GT 850	White/Red body, Blue/White stripes, racing number '7', 86 mm.	**£30-35**	☐
C306	1980-	Fiat X1/9S	Blue with Red/Yellow bands, racing number '3' or '6', 110 mm.	**£20-25**	☐
307	1981-	Renault Turbo	Yellow/Red body, racing number '8', *'CIBIE'*, other adverts, 100 mm.	**£7-10**	☐
C308	1972-76	Mini Cooper S........................	Yellow body, RN '177', rally plaques, roof-rack, 2 spare wheels, WhizzWheels	**£45-55**	☐
C308	1982-	BMW M1	Yellow body, racing number '25', *'GOODYEAR'*, detailed engine, 129 mm.	**£7-10**	☐
			Gold body. Only 144 thought to exist.	**NGPP**	☐
309	1962-65	Aston Martin DB4	Turquoise/White body, Yellow interior, flags, spun wheels, RN '1', '3' or '7'.	**£60-70**	☐
			Variation with spoked wheels	**£90-110**	☐
C309	1982-	VW 'TURBO'........................	White/Brown body, racing number '14', various adverts, 97 mm.	**£7-10**	☐
C310	1982-	'PORSCHE' 924 Turbo............	Black/Gold, opening doors and hatchback, *'GOODYEAR'*, 124 mm.	**£7-10**	☐
312	1964-68	'E' type Jaguar	Plated Gold or Silver, racing number '2', driver, suspension, spoked wheels	**£55-65**	☐
C312	1983-	Ford Capri 'S'	White, racing number '6', hinged parcel shelf, various adverts, 97 mm.	**£7-10**	☐
314	1965-71	Ferrari Berlinetta 250 LM	Red body, racing number '4', wire wheels, suspension, 95 mm.	**£25-35**	☐
315	1964-66	Simca 1000 Sports	Plated Silver, Red interior, RN '8', Red/White/Blue racing stripes	**£35-40**	☐
			Metallic Blue body, racing number '8', Red/White/Blue stripes	**£100-120**	☐
316	1971-73	Ford GT 70	Green/Black body, White interior, racing number '32', flag design	**£25-30**	☐
317	1964	'MONTE CARLO 1964' Mini Cooper S	Red body, White roof, Yellow interior, racing number '37', roof spotlight	**£125-150**	☐
			Red body, Pink roof variation	**£175-200**	☐
318	1965	'MONTE CARLO 1965' Mini Cooper S	Red body, White roof, 'AJB 44 B', racing number '52', no roof spotlight	**£125-150**	☐
318	1965-67	Lotus Elan S2 Open Top	Metallic Blue, racing number '8', driver, opening bonnet, tilt seats, *'I'VE GOT A TIGER IN MY TANK'* logo on boot lid	**£70-80**	☐

Ref. No.	Year	Model	Description	Market Price Range	
C318	1983-1985	'MOTUL' Jaguar XJS	Black/Red/White body, racing number '4', *'JAGUAR'*, 118 mm.	£7-10	☐
	1985	Export issue:	Green body, racing number '12' and *'DEUTCHSLAND'* logo	NGPP	☐
C318	1985		British Racing Green body with White band, racing number '12'	£7-10	☐
319	1967-68	Lotus Elan Hard Top	Blue/White or Green/Yellow lift-off body, racing number '3', 90 mm.	£60-70	☐
			Red body, White top	£60-70	☐
C319	1974-75	Lamborghini Miura	Silver/Purple/Yellow body, racing number '7', WhizzWheels, 95 mm.	£15-20	☐
321	1965	'MONTE CARLO 1965' Mini Cooper S	Red body, White roof, spotlight, RN '52', Box with 'MONTE CARLO WINNER' flash	£300-400	☐
			Red body, White roof with spotlight, RN '52'	£160-190	☐
321	1966	'MONTE CARLO 1966' Mini Cooper S	Red body, White roof with RN '2' and *'TIMO MAKINEN'* and *'PAUL EASTER'* signatures, no spotlight. Box flashed with '1966' sticker.	£300-400	☐
322	1965-66	'Monte Carlo' Rover 2000	Metallic Maroon/White body, RN'136', rally plaques, 95 mm.	£100-120	☐
			Model boxed in rare 252 box with 322 labels	£120-150	☐
	1967		White body, Red interior, Black bonnet with 'KNV 12E', spoked wheels, racing number '21', 'Rally Finish' label on box	£120-140	☐
323	1965-66	'MONTE CARLO 1965' Citroën DS19	Blue/White, rally plaques & number '75', suspension, 97 mm.	£100-120	☐
C323	1974-78	Ferrari Daytona 365 GTB/4	White/Red/Blue body, racing number '81', opening doors, 122 mm.	£10-15	☐
324	1966-69	Marcos Volvo 1800 GT	White (2 Green stripes) or Blue (2 White stripes) RN '7', spoked wheels	£40-45	☐
324	1974	Ferrari Daytona Le Mans	Yellow body, racing number '33', *'A.BAMFORD'*, 122 mm.	£10-15	☐
325	1966-69	Ford Mustang Competition	White body with double Red stripe (Blue interior). Shaped spun wheels, detailed cast wheels, wire wheels or cast 'alloy' wheels	£40-50	☐
			White body, double Red stripes, Gold 'alloy' wheels	£60-70	☐
		Note:	A sheet of four racing numbers (no.'4') enclosed with each model.		☐
328	1966-67	'MONTE CARLO 1966' Hillman Imp	Metallic Dark Blue/White, 'FRW 306 C', rally plaques & number '107'	£75-85	☐
329	1973-76	Ford Mustang	Green/White body, racing number '69', opening doors, suspension, 113 mm.	£25-30	☐
330	1967-69	Porsche Carrera 6	White/Red with racing number '1' or '20', suspension, 97 mm.	£25-30	☐
			White body, Dark Blue panels, Yellow engine cover, RN '60'	£75-85	☐
331	1974-76	'TEXACO' Ford Capri GT	White/Black body, racing number '5'. 102 mm.	£15-20	☐
333	1966	'SUN/RAC' Mini Cooper S	Red/White body, RN '21' and *'SUN RAC INTERNATIONAL RALLY'* decals. 222 box with White label '1966 RAC INTERNATIONAL RALLY' etc. in Blue	£150-200	☐
337	1967-69	Chevrolet Stock Car	Yellow body, racing number '13', suspension, 95 mm.	£25-30	☐
339	1967-72	'MONTE CARLO 1967' Mini Cooper S	Red body, White roof, roof rack, RN '177', shaped spun wheels, Austin grille	£180-220	☐
			As previous model but with cast detailed wheels	£140-160	☐
			Red body, cast detailed wheels, Morris grille	£130-150	☐
		Box types:	1st issue with correct 'flashed' 321 box, 2nd issue 'picture' box, 3rd issue later 'picture' box. (Special leaflet enclosed with each model).		
340	1967-68	'MONTE CARLO 1967' Sunbeam Imp	Metallic Blue, RN '77', shaped spun wheels, correct 'flashed' 328 box	£75-95	☐
			Metallic Dark Blue, cast detailed wheels, pictorial 340 box	£80-90	☐
C340	1981	Rover 'TRIPLEX'	White/Red/Blue, hinged parcel shelf, 140 mm.	£7-10	☐
C341	1981-	Chevrolet Caprice	Red/White/Blue body, racing number '43', *'STP'*, 150 mm.	£7-10	☐
344	1969-73	Ferrari Dino Sports	Yellow (number '23') or Red (number '30') WhizzWheels, 104 mm.	£30-35	☐
345	1969	MGC GT Competition Model	Yellow body, Black bonnet (with bulge) opening doors & tailgate, 90 mm. 'MGB GT' on box overprinted 'NEW MGC'. Self-adhesive numbers enclosed	£50-70	☐
		Gift Set version:	Orange body (Car Transporter Gift Set 48)	GSP	☐
348	1968-69	Mustang 'Pop Art' Stock Car	Blue with Red/Orange 'Flower-Power' labels, racing number '20'	£60-70	☐
C350	1985	Toyota Celica Supra	Red/White body, racing number '14', *'HUGHES'*, racing tyres. 112 mm.	£7-10	☐
C351	1985	Ford Sierra Pace Car	White body, Green/Yellow tampo-print design, warning lights, flags	£7-10	☐
C353	1987	BMW 325i Rally	White body, Green logo *'CASTROL'*	£7-10	☐
354	1986	BMW 325	White body, racing number '33', *'FAVRAUD'* logo	£7-10	☐
370	1982	Ford Cobra Mustang	White/Black/Red/Blue, *'MUSTANG'*, with or without tailgate stripe, 135 mm.	£15-20	☐
371	1970-73	Porsche Carrera 6	White/Red, racing number '60', plated Blue engine cover, WhizzWheels, 97 mm.	£15-20	☐
376	1970-72	Chevrolet Corvette Stock Car	Silver body, racing number '13', *'GO-GO-GO'*, WhizzWheels, 95 mm.	£30-35	☐
377	1970-73	Marcos 3 Litre	Yellow body, Black bonnet strip, Whizzwheels.	£30-35	☐
			White body, Grey roof, Whizzwheels		☐
			N.B. Model 324 conversion.		
C380	1983-	'BASF' BMW M1	Red/White body, racing number '80', aerofoil, opening engine cover, 129 mm.	£7-10	☐
C381	1983-	'ELF' Renault Turbo	Red/White/Blue, racing number '5', *'FACOM'*, 100 mm.	£7-10	☐
			Blue/White, racing number '13', *'ELF'*	£7-10	☐
383	1977-78	Volkswagen 1200 Rally	Blue body, rally number '5', chequered roof and sides	£10-15	☐
384	1978	Volkswagen 1200 Rally Car	Blue body, rally number '5', chequered stripes	£15-20	☐
385	1970-76	Porsche 917	Metallic Blue or Red body, racing number '3', WhizzWheels, 108 mm.	£15-20	☐
386	1987	Mercedes 2.3/16	White body, Black racing number '17', *'SERVIS'*	£5-8	☐
386/4	1988		As previous model but racing number '17', *'BURLINGTON AIR EXPRESS'*	£5-8	☐
394	1973-76	Datsun 240 Z	Red body, rally number '11', *'EAST AFRICAN SAFARI'*, 97 mm.	£15-20	☐
396		Datsun 240 Z	Red/White body, rally number '46', *'JOHN MORTON'*, WhizzWheels	£20-25	☐
397	1974-78	Porsche-Audi 917-10	White or Orange, racing number '6', *'CORGI'*, racing driver, 120 mm.	£10-15	☐
399	1985	Peugeot 205	Silver body, racing number '205', multi-coloured tampo-print design.	£7-10	☐
399/5	1988	Peugeot 205 T16	Yellow body, racing number '2', *'VATENEN'*	£7-10	☐
402	1985	BMW M1	Red/White body, racing number '101', *'CASTROL'*	£7-10	☐
403	1985	Ford Escort	White body, racing number '84', multicoloured print, *'TOTAL'*	£7-10	☐
404	1985	Rover 3500	Red body, racing number '13', *'DAILY MIRROR'*	£7-10	☐
	1986		Red body, racing number '1', *'TEXACO'*	£7-10	☐
420	1984	'BMW M1'	Blue/White body, racing number '11', *'LIGIER'S'*	£7-10	☐
	1985		White body, racing number '17', *'ESSO'*	£7-10	☐

Ref. No.	Year	Model	Model Features	Market Price Range	
422	1984	'RENAULT 5' TBA................	Blue body, racing number '25', 'BOSCH' and 'ELF'...	£7-10	☐
	1985		Dark Blue body, multicoloured print, racing number '18'.............................	£7-10	☐
423	1984	'BROOKLYN' Ford Escort......	Blue/White body, Red seats, racing number '69', 'SHELL'...........................	£7-10	☐
424	1984	'FORD MUSTANG'	Black body, Yellow/Red print, racing number '77', 'ESSO'.........................	£7-10	☐
426	1984	'HEPOLITE' Rover	Yellow/Red, racing number '4', 'FERODO'...	£7-10	☐
	1988		Yellow/Red body, 'DAILY EXPRESS'...	£7-10	☐
435/2	1987	Volvo 760 Turbo	White body, Blue/Yellow print, 'GILLANDERS'.......................................	£7-10	☐
C440	1988	'PORSCHE 944' Rally	White body, Red design..	£7-10	☐
C440/6	1990	Porsche 944 Rally	White body, Pink/Blue design, 'PIRELLI', rally number '44'	£4-7	☐
C447	1983	'RENEGADE' 4x4 Jeep.........	Yellow body, racing number '5'. (As 448 but without hood). In GS 36	GSP	☐
C448	1983	'RENEGADE' 4x4 Jeep.........	Yellow body, Red hood, racing number '5'..	£7-10	☐
C507	1987-?	Range Rover Rally...................	Navy Blue body, White roof, 'PARIS-DAKAR' logo.................................	£20-30	☐
602	1984	BL Mini 1000	Metallic Dark Blue, racing number '8'...	£20-25	☐
611	1985	Ford Escort	Red body, racing number '66', 'DATAPOST'...	£7-10	☐
612	**1985**	**Ford Escort ....**	**Red, 'DATAPOST', '77'...**	**£7-10**	☐
613	1985	Metro Saloon..........................	Red, 'DATAPOST', '66'..	£7-10	☐
614	1985	Metro Saloon..........................	Red, 'DATAPOST', '77'..	£7-10	☐
60317	1992	F1 Racing Car........................	Green/White body, 'FUJI FILM' logo, Boots promotional (35,000)............	NGPP	☐
?	?	Jaguar XJR9...........................	White body, 'Martin Brundle', 'J. Nielsen' and 'R. Bosel' roof signatures.		
			'CASTROL' logos, rally number '60', Petrol Co. promotional	£3-5	☐

Trophy Models (Marks & Spencers special issues)

The models were specially produced to be sold by Marks & Spencers in 1961. The set consisted of five vacuum plated 'gold' models taken from the existing Corgi product range, each mounted on a detachable black moulded base with a gold name label. The models were packaged in white boxes with red/grey design plus 'St.Michael Trophy Models' in red. They did not sell well at the time of issue but are keenly sought after by present day collectors.

Ref. No.	Year(s)	Model Type	Model Features and Size	Market Price Range	
150 S	1961	Vanwall Racing Car	Gold plated body, Red wheels and radiator grille	£100-200	☐
152	1961	BRM Racing Car	Gold plated body, Red wheels and radiator grille	£100-200	☐
300	1961	Austin-Healey Sports Car	Gold plated body, plastic windscreen, Red wheels and radiator grille	£100-200	☐
301	1961	Triumph TR2 Sports Car..........	Gold plated body, plastic windscreen, Red wheels and radiator grille	£100-200	☐
302	1961	MG 'MGA' Sports Car.............	Gold plated body, plastic windscreen, Red wheels and radiator grille	£100-200	☐

Marks & Spencers issues

In 1978 a series of special sets and single models were produced for sale through selected M & S stores. They were packed in attractive non-standard boxes and had unique liveries. They were not issued in great quantities.

Single models

Ref.	Year	Model	Features	Market Price	
8800	1978	Custom Van...............................	No details available..	£25-35	☐
8801	1978	Spindrift Helicopter..................	Black body with Yellow chassis, floats and rotor blades	£25-35	☐
8802	1978	Massey Ferguson Tractor.........	Red/Black body with White arms and Red shovel	£40-50	☐
8803	1978	Buick 'FIRE CHIEF' Car.......	Red body with 'City Fire Department' logo on bonnet..................................	£50-75	☐

Small sets

Ref.	Year	Model	Features	Market Price	
8000	1978	F1 Racing Set...........................	Includes 162 'ELF' Tyrrell (Dark Blue) and 160 Hesketh F1 (White)...........	£75-100	☐
8001	1978	Wings Flying Team	Includes 301 Lotus Elite (Green) and Nipper aircraft (White) on Grey trailer...	£100-150	☐
8002	1978	Motorway Police Patrol	C429 'POLICE' Jaguar (Green) and Blue Fiat X1-9	£60-80	☐
8003	1978	Spindrift Power Boat Team	301 Ferrari Daytona (Yellow) and Yellow power boat on trailer	£60-80	☐

Medium sets

Ref.	Year	Model	Features	Market Price	
8100	1978	Racing Team	C421 Land Rover (White with 'FORMULA' logo) 338 Rover, and 301 Lotus on trailer..	£100-150	☐
8101	1978	Wings Flying School	C421 Land Rover (Grey with 'WINGS' logo) Grey helicopter and Nipper aircraft on Grey trailer..	£100-150	☐
8102	1978	Motorway Breakdown..............	C429 'POLICE' Jaguar, 293 Renault 5 (Yellow) plus Berliet Wrecker with 'RESCUE BREAKDOWN SERVICES'...	£100-150	☐
8103	1978	Spindrift Power Boat Team	Includes Spindrift 301 Ferrari, Helicopter & Dinghy...............................	£100-150	☐

Large sets

Ref.	Year	Model	Features	Market Price	
8400	1978	Grand Prix Racing	Includes 160 Hesketh (White) 162 'ELF' Tyrrell (Dark Blue) Fiat X1-9 (Blue) and Land Rover (White with 'FORMULA 1 RACING TEAM' logo)............................	£250-350	☐
8401	1978	Wings Flying Club	Includes Land Rover, Helicopter, Tipsy Nipper aircraft on trailer plus Lotus Elite	£200-250	☐
8402	1978	Motorway Rescue.....................	Includes 'POLICE' Jaguar, Berliet Wrecker, Renault 5 and Fiat X1-9........	£200-250	☐
8403	1978	Spindrift Power Boat Team	Includes Ferrari Daytona (Yellow) Yellow power boat on trailer, Yellow/Black helicopter, plus M.F. Tractor and 'RESCUE' dinghy	£200-250	☐

WHEN REPLYING TO ADVERTISEMENTS PLEASE MENTION JOHN RAMSAY'S CATALOGUE

Corgi Classics - Cars (original issues)

A factory fire ended production in 1969 of this original series of 'Classics' cars. Boxes are of two types: one with separate lid with coloured line-drawings printed on it and containing a separate picture of the model; and type two which has the model attached to a sliding-drawer style base in an outer box with half-flaps (similar printing to 1st type).

N.B. Early issues have reference number 900 and changed to 9001 etc just before release.

Ref. No.	Year(s)	Model Type	Model Features and Size	Market Price Range	
9001	1964-69	1927 3-litre Bentley	British Racing Green, racing number '3', detachable hood, driver, 102 mm.	£30-40	☐
9002	1964-68	1927 3-litre Bentley	Red body, civilian driver, no racing number, detachable hood	£50-60	☐
9004	1967-69	'WORLD OF WOOSTER' Bentley	As previous model but in Green or Red and with Jeeves and Wooster figures	£70-90	☐
9011	1964-68	1915 Model T Ford	Black body, driver, passenger, spoked wheels, brass radiator, 86 mm.	£30-35	☐
9012	1965-68	Model T Ford	Version with Yellow/Black body, Black or Yellow wheels	£30-35	☐
9013	1964-69	1915 Model T Ford	Blue/Black body, detachable hood, spare wheel, driver cranks, 83 mm.	£25-35	☐
9014		1915 'LYONS TEA' Van	Appeared in 1967/68 catalogue but was not issued.	NGPP	☐
9021	1964-69	1910 38 hp. Daimler	Red body, driver and 3 passengers, folded hood, detailed chassis, 108 mm.	£25-35	☐
9022		1910 38 hp. Daimler	Appeared in the 1966 catalogue but not issued.	NGPP	☐
9031	1965-68	1910 Renault 12/16	Lavender/Black body with carriage lamps, spoked wheels, 102 mm.	£25-35	☐
9032	1965-69	1910 Renault 12/16	Same as previous model but Primrose Yellow and Black body	£25-35	☐
9041	1966-70	1912 Rolls-Royce Silver Ghost	Silver and Black body, carriage lamps, spoked wheels, 118 mm.	£25-35	☐
		variant:	Maroon body, Silver roof and bonnet	NGPP	☐

Corgi Classics Cars (re-introduced issues)

Some of the 'Classics' were re-introduced in 1985 when original tools were discovered. These later models are distinct from the originals as they have 'SPECIAL EDITION' on their baseplates and are packed in Grey/Red boxes which do not contain a picture of the model. The model numbers are different and 13,500 of each colour were made.

C860 (9041) 1985		1912 Rolls-Royce Silver Ghost	Silver, Black or Ruby Red body	£8-11	☐
C861 (9002) 1985		1927 3-litre Bentley open top	British Racing Green, Black or Ruby Red body	£8-11	☐
C862 (9031) 1985		1910 Renault 12/16	Yellow, Pale Blue, Cream or Brown body	£8-11	☐
C863 (9012) 1985		1915 Model T Ford	Black, Red or Blue body	£8-11	☐

Corgi Toys - Twin Packs ('Little and Large') (issued 1981-82)

These packs combine standard models with similar 'Junior' models. The models listed are known to have been featured and the compiler would welcome any further information.

1352 Renault 5 Turbo (307) Metro (C275)
1354 Texaco Lotus (C154) Junior 53
1355 Talbot Matra Rancho (457)
1356 Fiat XI/9 (306) Ford Escort (334)
1357 Golden Eagle Jeep (C441)
1359 Ford Escort (334) Junior 105
1360 Batmobile (267)
1361 Aston Martin James Bond Silver £100-£125

1362 James Bond Lotus Esprit (269)
1363 Buck Rogers (607)
1364 Space Shuttle 'NASA' (648)
1365 Routemaster Bus 'BTA' (469) & FX4 Taxi Various other logos used
1371 Volkswagen Turbo (309)
1372 Jaguar XJS (319)
1373 Ford Capri (312) Junior 61

1378 Porsche 924 Yellow
11380 Mercedes Sedan 240D Metallic Grey
1381 Ferrari 308GTS Red
1382 Ford Mustang (320)
1384 Ford Thunderbird Cream
1389 Ford Sierra (299) Junior 129
1397 BMW M1 'BASF' (380)
1402 Scania Tipper plus Dumper Truck

Corgi Truckers

A new series of 1:76 scale models

Ref. No.	Year(s)	Model Type	Model Features and Size	Market Price Range	
C1300/1	1989	MAN Container	Yellow/Blue body, 'YORKIE'	NRP	☐
C1301/1	1989	MAN Tanker 'BP'	White body, Yellow/Green design	NRP	☐
C1301/2	1989	MAN Tanker 'MOBIL'	Beige body, Blue/Red logo	NRP	☐
C1302/1	1989	MAN Tipper	All Orange	NRP	☐
C1303/1	1989	Ford Cargo Container	Yellow body, Orange tilt, 'SCHWEPPES'	NRP	☐
C1302/2	1989	Ford Cargo Container	White/Green body, '7 UP'	NRP	☐
C1304/1	1989	Ford Cargo Tanker	White/Blue/Yellow, 'DUCKHAMS OILS'	NRP	☐
C1304/2	1989	Ford Cargo Tanker	Yellow/Silver body, 'SHELL'	NRP	☐
C1305/1	1989	Ford Cargo Tipper	Grey/Green/Silver body	NRP	☐
C1305/2	1989	Ford Tipper	Red/Silver body	NRP	☐

Corgi Toys - Small Commercial Vehicles and Vans

Excluding models issued from 1987 as 'Corgi Classics' (see separate listing)

Ref. No.	Year(s)	Model Type	Model Features and Size	Market Price Range	
403	1956-61	Bedford 12 cwt Van	'DAILY EXPRESS' on Dark Blue body, 83 mm.	£80-100	☐
			As previous model but Deep Blue body	£100-120	☐
403 M	1956-59	Bedford 12 cwt Van	'K.L.G. PLUGS' on Red/Silver body, flywheel motor, 83 mm.	£125-150	☐
404	1956-62	Bedford Dormobile	Cream (Blue roof on some), Turquoise, Blue, Red, Metallic Red or yellow, smooth or ribbed roof, smooth or shaped hubs, 83 mm.	£65-85	☐
			Lemon-Yellow body with Blue roof	£100-125	☐
404 M	1956-59	Bedford Dormobile	Red, Metallic Red, Turquoise or Blue body, flywheel motor, 83 mm.	£65-70	☐
405	1981	Ford Transit Milk Float	'DAIRY CREST' logo on cab doors, 'MILK MNARKETING BOARD' logo on each side and 'MILK' on rear	£20-30	☐
C405	1982	Ford Transit Milk Float	'LOTTA BOTTLE' on Blue/White body, opening doors, 143 mm.	£10-15	☐
407	1957-61	Smiths Karrier Bantam	'HOME SERVICES HYGIENIC MOBILE SHOP', Pale Green/Red, 95 mm.	£65-80	☐
408	1957-59	Bedford 'AA' Service Van........	Yellow/Black, divided windscreen, smooth hubs, Blue box, leaflet	£80-90	☐
	1958-59		Yellow/Black, undivided windscreen, smooth or shaped hubs, Blue box, leaflet	£70-80	☐
	1959-62		Yellow/Black, undivided windscreen, shaped hubs, Blue/Yellow box, no leaflet	£60-70	☐
411	1958-62	Karrier Bantam Van.................	Yellow body, Grey plastic shutter, smooth wheels, 'LUCOZADE', Blue box	£70-80	☐
			As previous model but with shaped wheels, Blue/Yellow box	£80-90	☐
413	1957-62	Smiths Karrier Bantam Mobile Butchers	White/Blue van, 'FAMILY BUTCHERS', meaty decals, 93 mm. Blue box	£85-100	☐
421	1960-62	Bedford 12 cwt Delivery Van....	'EVENING STANDARD', Black body, Silver ridged roof, undivided windscreen, smooth hubs, 83 mm.	£80-90	☐
			'EVENING STANDARD', Black lower body, Silver upper body and ridged roof, undivided windscreen, smooth hubs	£100-120	☐
422	1960-62	Bedford 12 cwt Van	'CORGI TOYS', Yellow body, Blue roof, smooth or shaped wheels, 83 mm. ...	£100-130	☐
		reversed colours:	Blue body, 'CORGI TOYS', Yellow roof, smooth wheels	£300-400	☐
		variation:	Blue lower half with Yellow upper body, 'CORGI TOYS'	£300-400	☐
			Export issue with 'AUROBODE' logo.	NGPP	☐
C424	1977-79	Security Van	Black/Yellow/White body, 'SECURITY', windows with grilles, 100 mm.	£10-15	☐
426	1962-64	Karrier Bantam Van Circus Booking Office	Red/Blue body, 2 circus & office staff. 'Chipperfields Booking Office', 91 mm.	£80-120	☐
C426	1978-81	Chevrolet Booking Office Van ..	Yellow/Red/Blue body, 'PINDER-JEAN RICHARD', 2 loudspeakers	£25-35	☐
428	1963-66	Karrier Ice-Cream Van	Blue/White body, detailed chassis, salesman swivels. 'MR. SOFTEE', 91 mm. ...	£75-90	☐
431	1964-66	Volkswagen Pick-Up	Yellow/Red, suspension, 91 mm.	£45-55	☐
433	1962-64	Volkswagen Delivery Van	'VW' logo on front of Red/White body, seats, steering wheel, 91 mm.	£50-60	☐
			'VROOM & DREESMAN', Grey body, shaped spun wheels, Dutch promotional	£250-350	☐
434	1962	Volkswagen Kombi	Metallic two-tone Green body, Red or Yellow 'VW' badge and seats.	£45-55	☐
435	1962-63	Karrier Bantam Van.................	Blue/White/Yellow body, 'DRIVE SAFELY ON MILK', ...	£60-70	☐
437	1979-80	Chevrolet Van 'COCA-COLA'	Red body, White logo, tinted roof windows, crates.	£20-25	☐
441	1963-67	Volkswagen Van	Blue body with Trans-o-lite headlamps, 'CHOCOLATE TOBLERONE', 91 mm.	£65-75	☐
443	1963-65	Plymouth Suburban US Mail ...	Blue/White body, 'ADDRESS YOUR MAIL CAREFULLY', 104 mm.	£50-55	☐
447	1964-67	Ford Thames Van	Pale Blue/Cream van with salesman and boy, 'WALLS ICE CREAM', 90 mm. ...	£120-150	☐
450	1964-67	Austin Mini Van......................	Green body, opening doors and bonnet, 79 mm.	£50-60	☐
			Olive-Green body (slightly paler shade than previous model)	NGPP	☐
			Green body with White '2001' logo, (promotional)	NGPP	☐
452	1956-63	Commer Dropside Lorry..........	Red and Cream body, (raised ridge on some cab roofs), smooth or shaped hubs.	£65-75	☐
453	1956-60	Commer Refrigerated Van	Light or Dark Blue cab, Cream body, 'WALLS ICE CREAM'	£100-125	☐
454	1957-62	Commer Platform Lorry	Yellow/Silver or Metallic Blue/Silver, 120 mm.	£70-80	☐
455	1957-61	Karrier Bantam 2-ton...............	Blue, Red or Grey body, Red platform floor, smooth hubs...................	£70-80	☐
		variant:	Early Mettoy version, Red body with 'C.W.S. SOFT DRINKS' logo on rear ...	£100-125	☐
456	1960-63	E.R.F 44G Dropside Lorry.......	Yellow/Metallic Blue, smooth/shaped wheels, 120 mm.	£60-70	☐
457	1957-65	E.R.F 44G Platform Lorry	Two-tone Blue or Yellow/Blue body, smooth hubs	£60-70	☐
459	1958-60	E.R.F 44G Van	Yellow/Red, 'MOORHOUSES LEMON CHEESE', 117 mm.	£150-175	☐
462	1970	Commer Van 'CO-OP'	White/Blue promotional model, 90 mm.	£70-80	☐
462	1971	Commer Van 'HAMMONDS'..	Green/Blue/White promotional model, 90 mm.	£90-100	☐
465	1963-66	Commer Pick-Up Truck...........	Red/Orange or Green/Grey, Red interior, Trans-O-Lites, 90 mm.	£25-35	☐
466		Commer Milk Float	White cab, chassis and load; Blue rear roof and sides.	£35-45	☐
471	1965-66	Karrier Bantam Snack Bar	Blue/White, 'JOE'S DINER' with figure and opening hatch, 95 mm.	£70-85	☐
			Blue/White, 'PATATES FRITES'. Belgian issue	£130-160	☐
474	1965-67	'WALLS' Ice Cream Van.........	Musical version of model 447 (5 note chimes), without figures, 90 mm. ...	£80-100	☐
479	1968-71	Commer Mobile Camera Van	Blue/White body, 'SAMUELSON FILM COMPANY LTD', camera/operator/case ...	£80-90	☐
484	1967-71	Dodge Livestock Transporter ...	Beige/Green body, 'KEW FARGO', 5 figures, 140 mm.	£30-40	☐
C611	?	Ford Escort Saloon	with 'DATAPOST 66' logo	£10-15	☐
C612	?	Ford Escort Saloon	with 'DATAPOST 77' logo	£10-15	☐
C613	?	Metro Saloon	with 'DATAPOST 66' logo	£10-15	☐
C614	?	Metro Saloon....................	Metro Saloon with 'DATAPOST 77' logo	£10-15	☐
C615	?	Metro Van	Red body 'ROYAL MAIL' logo	£10-15	☐
C616	?	Chevrolet Van....................	Red body with 'PARCELS' logo	£10-15	☐

Ford Escort 55 Vans – **Market Price Range £8-15**

Type 1: Black plastic rear bumper (fitted to models before 1986)
Type 2: Metal rear bumper (fitted to models from mid-1986 to 1989)
Type 3: New one-piece moulded body (without opening rear doors) from 1989

Assume models to be Type 1 unless shown otherwise. The models feature a metal body with a plastic chassis and wheels. They have amber side & tail lights, opening rear doors (types 1 & 2) and beige (types 1,2,3) or black (2 & 3) interiors. White or brown interiors sometimes appear with type 1.
Model types shown in brackets. Liveries issued:-

C496 'ROYAL MAIL' (1, 2 & 3); C496/2 'POLICE' (2 & 3); C496/3 'BRITISH GAS' (2); C496/4 'BRITISH AIRWAYS' (2); C496/5 'NOTRUF' (2); C496/9 'BRITISH TELECOM' (2); C496/15 'HOOVER'; C496/16 'B.B.C.' (2); C496/17 'FORD' (2); C496/18 'BRITISH GAS' (2 & 3); C496/19 'BRITISH TELECOM' (3); C496/20 'UNIGATE' (3); C496/24 'PTT TELECOM' (3); C497 'RADIO RENTALS' (2); C498 'BRITISH GAS' (1); C499 'BRITISH TELECOM' (1); C503 'DUNLOP' (2); C503/7 'TELEVERKET' (2); C504 'JOHN LEWIS' (2); C512 'BOLTON EVENING NEWS' (2); C514 'CHUBB'; C514 'DIGBY'S' Light or Dark Blue; C515 'N.E.C.'; C532 'R.A.C.'; C534 'PIZZA SERVICE'; C537 'A.A.'; C543 'TELEVERKET'; C549 'HOTPOINT'; C557 'FIRE SALVAGE'; C559 'JAGO AUTOMOTIVE'; C560 'WILTSHIRE FIRE'; C561 'WAITROSE'; C562 'GAMLEYS'; C563 'McVITIES'; C564 'TELEVERKET'; C577 'PLESSEY'; C578 'BEATTIES'; C584 'MANCHESTER Eve. News'; C621 'POLICE'; C626 'CHUBB FIRE'; C632 'KAYS' (2); 91610 'A.A.' (3); 91611 'R.A.C.' (3); 91612 'ROYAL MAIL' (3); 91620 'YORKSHIRE GAS' (3); 91984 'AUTO FEDERATION' (3)

Mercedes 207-D Vans issued 1984-89 – **Market Price Range £5-10**

Liveries issues:-

C516 'BMX SERVICE'; C535 'ATHLON'; C539 'GROUP 4'; C548 'SECURITAS'; C554 'ROYAL MAIL'; 564 'PTT'; 568 'BF GOODRICH'; 576 'PEPSI'; C576/2 'PORSCHE RACING'; C576 'PARCELINE'; C576 'LEKER OG HOBBY'; C576 'OVERNITE TNT'; C576/10 'C.R. SMITH'; C588 'CURTIS HOLT'; C630 'KAYS'; C631 'BLUE ARROW'; C670 'ROYAL MAIL PARCELFORCE'.

Ford Transit Vans issued 1987-92 – **Market Price Range £5-10**

See also under 'Ambulance, Fire, Police and Rescue Vehicles' section.

656/1 'RAC'; 656/3 'AMBULANCE'; 656/4 'FORD'; 656/5 'A.A.'; 656/7 'POSTBIL'; 656/8 'POLISSI'; 656/9 'POLIS'; 656/12 'KTAS'; 656/16 'BUNDESPOST'; 656/18 'FALCK SERVICE'; C656/21 'LYNX'; C656/22 'POLICE'; C656/28 'NOTTINGHAM AMBULANCE'; 656/29 'CENTRE PARCS'; 656/30 'CENTRE PARKS'; 656/31 'UNICHEM'; 656/33 'McDOUGALL ROSE'; 656 'FIRE SERVICE'; 656 'KAYS'; 656 'AMBULANSE' (Norway); 656 'AMBULANSSI' (Finland); 91640 'S.WALES POLICE'; 91642 'NATIONAL BREAKDOWN FALKEN' (Denmark); 91647 'POLITI' (Denmark); 91647 'POLIS' (Swiss); 91657 'BELGIAN RED CROSS'.

Page from the 1963-64 Catalogue.

Corgi Toys - Large Commercial Trucks and Tankers

Excludes models issued from 1987 as 'Corgi Classics' (see separate listing)

Ref. No.	Year(s)	Model Type	Model Features and Size	Market Price Range	

Bedford Trucks

1100	1958-63	'S' Carrimore Low Loader........	Red cab, Blue trailer, drop-down ramps, operable winch, 220 mm................................	**£65-75**	☐
			Yellow cab, Blue trailer	**£75-85**	☐
1101	1957-63	'S' Carrimore Transporter........	Red cab, Blue transporter body, 'CORGI CAR TRANSPORTER'	**£65-75**	☐
			Blue cab, Yellow transporter body	**£75-85**	☐
1104	1957-63	'S' type Carrimore	Red cab, Silver trailer, detachable rear axle, operable winch, 220 mm.......................	**£65-75**	☐
		Machinery Carrier	Blue cab, Silver trailer	**£75-85**	☐
			Yellow cab, Black base, Silver Grey trailer	**£75-80**	☐
1104	1974-77	'TK' type Horse Transporter	Green or Metallic Green with Orange or Yellow trailer, 'NEWMARKET', 4 horses & boy, 256 mm.	**£60-75**	☐
1105	1962-66	'TK' type Car Transporter	Red cab, Blue trailer, collapsible decks, 'Corgi Car Transporter', 273 mm.	**£60-80**	☐
1110	1959-64	'S' type 'MOBIL' Tanker........	Red/White articulated body, detachable cab, 'MOBILGAS', 191 mm.	**£100-125**	☐
1110	1965-67	'TK' type 'SHELL' Tanker......	Blue/White articulated tanker, 'SHELL BENZEEN', Dutch model	**£1500-2000**	☐
1129	1962-65	'S' type 'MILK' Tanker	Blue/White articulated body, detachable cab, 191 mm.	**£100-125**	☐
1131	1963-66	'TK' type Carrimore Machinery Low Loader........	Blue/Yellow articulated body, detachable cab and rear axle, suspension......................	**£60-70**	☐
1132	1963-65	'TK' Carrimore Low Loader	Yellow/Red articulated body, detachable cab and rear axle, suspension, 241 mm.......	**£100-125**	☐
			Blue cab, Silver Grey trailer, Yellow rear	**£60-80**	☐
1140	1965-67	Bedford 'TK' Petrol Tanker.....	Red/Silver/White articulated body, tilting cab, 'MOBILGAS', 191 mm.	**£100-125**	☐
1141	1965-67	Bedford 'TK' Milk Tanker........	Blue/White articulated body, tilting cab, 'MILK', 191 mm.	**£100-125**	☐

Berliet Trucks

C1105	1977-81	Racehorse Transporter	Brown/White, 'NATIONAL RACING STABLES', 4 horses, 280 mm.	**£40-50**	☐
C1107	1979-	'UNITED STATES LINES'	Blue/White body, 2 Grey containers, jockey wheel, 290 mm.	**£35-45**	☐

Ford Trucks   These models feature a tilt cab which uncouples from the trailer section.

1108	1982	'MICHELIN'............................	Blue/White body, 2 containers, 243 mm.	**£20-25**	☐
1109	1979	'MICHELIN'............................	Blue/Black body, 2 containers, 243 mm.	**£20-25**	☐
1137	1966-69	'EXPRESS SERVICES'..........	Blue/Silver/Red body, 'H' series tilt-cab, 235 mm.	**£50-60**	☐
1138	1966-69	'CORGI CARS' Transporter	Red/Silver cab, two-tone Blue transporter body	**£50-60**	☐
1157	1976-81	'ESSO' Tanker	White/Red articulated body, 270 mm.	**£20-25**	☐
1158	1976	'EXXON' Tanker	White/Black body, 270 mm. German issue.	**£30-35**	☐
1159	1976-79	Ford Car Transporter	Blue/White or Green articulated body, 360 mm.	**£25-30**	☐
1160	1976	'GULF' Tanker	White/Orange articulated body, 270 mm.	**£25-30**	☐
1161	1979-80	'ARAL' Tanker	Blue/White/Black articulated body, 270 mm. German export model	**£25-30**	☐
1169	1982	'GUINNESS' Tanker	Cream/Brown/Black articulated body, 270 mm.	**£20-25**	☐
1170	1982	Ford Car Transporter	Red/White/Yellow articulated body, 360 mm..	**£20-25**	☐
1191	1985	'FORD QUALITY'	White cab, chassis and tampo print, 2 Blue containers	**£15-20**	☐
	1985	'BALLANTINES FINEST SCOTCH'..........	Container holds 6 miniatures. Available duty-free shops (20,000)...............................	**£45-55**	☐
	1985	'KAYS' Container Truck	Red/White body, Cerise/Black tampo print, Mail-order model (4,000)	**£10-15**	☐

Ford Cargo Box Vans   Issued 1985-86 – Market Price Range £5-10.

1190 'THORNTONS'; 1190 'EVER READY'; 1192 'LUCAS'; 1228 'THE NEW LEWIS'S'; 1249 'WHITES BAZAAR'.
'ARNOTTS BISCUITS', Australian issue (NGPP).

Mack Trucks

1100	1971-73	'TRANS-CONTINENTAL'	Orange cab, Black/Orange/Silver trailer, sliding doors, jockey wheel, 257 mm............	**£40-50**	☐
1106	1971-77	'A.C.L.' Container Truck.........	Yellow/Black/White body, 2 Red containers with White logo, 290 mm.	**£40-50**	☐
1151		'EXXON' Tanker	Red/White body, striped window box	**£60-70**	☐
1152	1971-75	'ESSO' Tanker..........................	White/Red/Blue articulated body, Gloster Saro Petrol Tanker (detachable)	**£40-50**	☐

'Royal Mail' Issues

617?		Leyland Artic Truck..................	'PARCELS' N.B. Not generally released – only seen in a Post Office Model Display Unit.	**NGPP**	☐
618		Mercedes Benz Artic Truck.......	'PARCELS'..	**£10-15**	☐

Scammell Trucks

Scammell Handyman Articulated Trucks   featuring 8 wheels and uncoupling trailer.

1146	1970-73	Carrimore Mk.V Tri-deck	Orange/White/Blue articulated transporter with 3 collapsible decks, 290 mm.	**£80-100**	☐
1147	1970-72	'FERRYMASTERS'.................	Yellow/White body, 'INTERNATIONAL HAULIERS', 235 mm.	**£50-60**	☐
1148	1969-72	Carrimore Mk.IV Car	Red/White transporter body with Yellow chucks	**£80-100**	☐
1151	1970	Co-operative Society................	Blue/White body, promotional	**£100-120**	☐

Scania Box Vans   Issued 1983-88 – Market Price Range £5-10.

1123 'KOHLER'; 1132 'SWEDISH POST'; 1132 'DANZAS'; 1133 Tipper Truck; 1134 'LANTMANNEN'; 1134 'CORGI'; 1146 'RYDER TRUCK RENTALS'; 1148 'SECURICOR PARCELS', 'BRS TRUCK RENTALS', 1150 'BRITISH SUGAR'; 1151 'HONDA'; 1182 'SUZUKI'; 1183 'ADIDAS'; 1183 'GLASSENHETER'; 1183 'BROSSARD'; 1238 'McCAIN'; 1238 'CADBURY'S'; 1238 'SECURICOR EXPRESS'; 1251 'B.O.C.'; 1251/2 'ROLO'; 1264 'ELF' Tanker.

N.B. Seddon Atkinson and Volvo Trucks are included in the Superhauler Listings.

Corgi Toys   -   Agricultural Models

Ref. No.	Year(s)	Model Type	Model Features and Size	Market Price Range	
50	1959-66	Massey-Ferguson 65 Tractor.....	Red bonnet, Pale Grey or Cream chassis, Red metal or plastic wheels, metal or plastic steering wheel, 79 mm.	£60-70	☐
C50	1974-77	Massey Ferguson 50B Tractor ..	Yellow/Black/Red body, windows, 138 mm.	£20-25	☐
51	1959-69	Massey-Ferguson Tipper Trailer....................	Red chassis, Yellow body, Red metal or plastic wheels, 102 mm.	£20-25	☐
			Red chassis, Grey body, Red metal or plastic wheels, 102 mm	£30-35	☐
53	1960-66	Massey-Ferguson 65 Tractor with Shovel........................	Red bonnet, Cream or Light Grey chassis, Red metal or Orange plastic wheels, operable shovel...............	£50-60	☐
54	1974	Massey Ferguson Tractor with Shovel	Yellow/Red or White/Red body, 150 mm.	£30-35	☐
54	1958-62	Fordson Half-Track Tractor	Blue body, Orange rollers and wheels, Black rubber tracks, lights in radiator grille, 91 mm. Plain 'early' box	£120-140	☐
			Same model but with Grey rubber tracks, lights at sides of grille, picture box	£120-140	☐
55	1961-63	Fordson Major Tractor............	Blue/Grey/Red body, 83 mm.	£50-60	☐
55	1977	David Brown Tractor.............	Black/Red/White body, steering wheel, 105 mm.	£20-25	☐
56	1961-63	Four-Furrow Plough	Red/Brown/Yellow body, 90 mm.	£15-20	☐
56	1977	Farm Tipper Trailer	Red/Yellow or Red/White body with drop-down tailboard, 130 mm.	£10-15	☐
57	1963-65	Massey Ferguson Tractor with Fork	Red/Silver/Cream body, driver, steering wheel, 127 mm.	£60-75	☐
58	1965-72	Beast Carrier...........................	Red, Cream and Blue body, 4 calves, 112 mm.	£20-25	☐
60	1964-66	Fordson Power Major Tractor..	Blue body, plough lifts, 83 mm.	£55-65	☐
61	1964-70	Four-Furrow Plough	Blue/Silver body, 90 mm.	£5-10	☐
62	1965-70	Ford Tipper Trailer	Red/Yellow body, 144 mm.	£10-15	☐
64	1965-69	Conveyor on Jeep	Red body, Yellow/White conveyor, farmhand figure, 197 mm.	£40-45	☐
66	1966-72	Massey Ferguson 165 Tractor...	Red/Blue/White body, engine sound, 76 mm.	£45-55	☐
67	1967-72	Ford Super Major Tractor.......	Blue/White/Silver body, 'FORD 5000', 90 mm.	£55-65	☐
69	1967-70	Massey Ferguson 165 Tractor and Shovel	Red/Blue body, Silver shovel, figure, 127 mm.	£55-65	☐
71	1967-72	Fordson Disc Harrow	Yellow/Red/Silver body, 90 mm.	£5-10	☐
72	1971-73	Ford 5000 Tractor and Towbar	As Corgi 67 but with frame, bucket and pipes, 90 mm.	£55-65	☐
73	1970-72	Massey Ferguson Tractor and Saw	As Corgi 66 plus Yellow rotating saw. 90 mm.	£60-70	☐
74	1969-72	Ford 5000 Tractor and Scoop...	As Corgi 67 plus Yellow/Silver scoop, 90 mm.	£55-65	☐
100	1957-61	Dropside Trailer....................	Yellow/Red/Grey body, 108 mm.	£10-15	☐
101	1958-61	Platform Trailer......................	Yellow/Grey or Blue/Grey body.	£10-15	☐
102	1958-59	Rice's Pony Trailer	Red body, Brown chassis, wire drawbar, smooth hubs, plastic pony.......	£50-60	☐
			Red body, Silver chassis, wire drawbar, smooth hubs, plastic pony	£40-50	☐
	1959-65		Red body, black chassis, wire or cast drawbar, smooth or shaped hubs	£30-40	☐
			Red body, Silver chassis, wire or cast drawbar, smooth or shaped hubs	£30-40	☐
			Cream body, Red chassis, wire or cast drawbar, smooth or shaped hubs	£30-40	☐
	1961-65		Tan/Cream body, Silver chassis, cast drawbar, shaped hubs..........	£30-40	☐
112	1969-72	Rice Beaufort Horse-Box	Blue/White horse-box with mare and foal.........	£25-30	☐

MAJOR PACKS (and large Agricultural Models)

1111	1959-60	M-F Combine Harvester..........	Red/Yellow, Yellow metal wheels, metal tines, 172 mm.	£70-80	☐
1111	1960-61	M-F Combine Harvester..........	Red/Yellow, Yellow metal wheels, plastic tines.........	£60-70	☐
	1961-62		Red/Yellow, Orange plastic wheels, plastic tines.........	£60-70	☐
C1112	1977-78	David Brown Tractor and Combine Harvester	Corgi 55 Tractor with Red/White/Black combine harvester, 220 mm.	£30-35	☐

HOW TO OBTAIN EXPORT MODELS: Please send a stamped addressed envelope to the Corgi Collectors Club (see inside cover page) who will supply a list of dealers who stock these models.

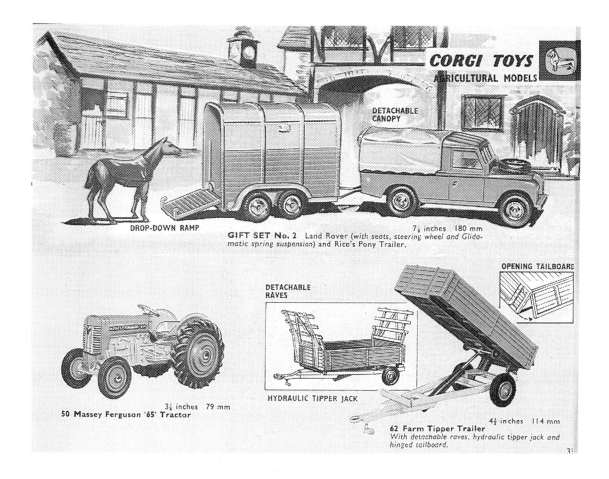

GIFT SET No. 2 Land Rover (with seats, steering wheel and Glida-matic spring suspension) and Rice's Pony Trailer.

DROP-DOWN RAMP

7⅛ inches 180 mm

CORGI TOYS
AGRICULTURAL MODELS

DETACHABLE CANOPY

OPENING TAILBOARD

DETACHABLE RAVES

HYDRAULIC TIPPER JACK

50 Massey Ferguson '65' Tractor
3⅛ inches 79 mm

62 Farm Tipper Trailer
With detachable raves, hydraulic tipper jack and hinged tailboard.
4½ inches 114 mm

Corgi Toys   -   Taxis

Ref. No.	Year(s)	Model Type	Model Features and Size	Market Price Range	
221	1960-63	Chevrolet Impala Cab	Yellow body, *'YELLOW TAXIS'*, smooth/shaped spun wheels, 108 mm.	£50-60	☐
C327	1980	Chevrolet Caprice Taxi	Yellow body, *'THINK TWA'*, fare table on door, 90 mm.	£10-15	☐
388	1987	Mercedes 190 Taxi	White or Beige body, Yellow/Black *'TAXI'* logo, export model	£5-10	☐
C411	1976-80	Mercedes Benz 240 D	Orange/Black or Off-White body, *'TAXI'* on roof, 127 mm.	£10-15	☐
			Cream and Black body (German issue)	NGPP	☐
418	1960-65	Austin FX4 Taxi	Black body, *'TAXI'* sign, smooth or shaped hubs, no driver, 97 mm.	£40-50	☐
			Black body, *'TAXI'* sign, smooth or shaped hubs, 'younger' driver figure	£35-45	☐
			Black body, *'TAXI'* sign, smooth or shaped hubs, 'older' driver figure	£30-40	☐
C425	1978	London Taxi	FX4 type taxi with Black body, *'TAXI'*, WhizzWheels, 121 mm.	£10-15	☐
425/1	1986	London Taxi	FX4 type taxi with Black body, *'RADIO CAB'*, Yellow design on door	£5-10	☐
430	1962-64	Ford Bermuda 'TAXI'	Ford Thunderbird, White body, Yellow and Red canopy, 102 mm.	£40-50	☐
			White body, Lime Green and Red canopy	£40-50	☐
			White body, Blue and Red canopy	£30-40	☐
			White body, Green and Pink canopy	£30-40	☐
			Metallic Blue/Red	£200-250	☐
434	1985	Mercedes 'TAXI'	Yellow body, Red taxi sign, chrome trim	£10-15	☐
450	1983	Peugeot Taxi	Beige with Blue label, *'739:33:33'*, (French issue)	£10-15	☐
451		Ford Sierra Taxi	Cream body. (No other details)	NGPP	☐
480	1965-66	Chevrolet Impala Taxi	Dark Yellow and Red body, Chrome stripe, shaped spun wheels, 108 mm.	£40-45	☐
			As previous model but with detailed cast wheels	£50-55	☐
507	1969	Chrysler Bermuda Taxi	Shown in catalogue but not issued	NGPP	☐
91812	1992	Taxi	Cream body, *'FINANCIAL TIMES'* logo	NGPP	☐

Corgi Toys - Emergency Vehicles
(Ambulance, Fire, Police & Rescue Vehicles)

Ref. No.	Year(s)	Model Type	Model Features and Size	Market Price Range	

Please see the 'Classics' section for more emergency vehicles which are listed there.
Emergency vehicles based on Ford Escort and Transit vans may also be found under those headings in the 'Corgi Small Commercials and Vans' section.

Ref. No.	Year(s)	Model Type	Model Features and Size	Market Price Range	
C106/13	1990	Saab 'BRANDWEER'	Red body, White side panels, 'ALARM', (Dutch export model)	£15-20	☐
209	1958-61	Riley Police Car	Black and Silver body, bell, 'POLICE', 97 mm.	£65-75	☐
213	1959-61	Jaguar Fire Service Car	Red body, bell, Grey aerial, roof sign, smooth spun wheels, 95 mm.	£80-90	☐
213s	1961-62	Jaguar Fire Service Car	As previous model but with suspension and shaped spun wheels	£100-120	☐
223	1959-61	Chevrolet Impala 'State Patrol'	Black body, Silver stripe, 'STATE PATROL', Grey aerial, 108 mm.	£35-45	☐
237	1962-66	Oldsmobile Sheriffs Car	Black body, White or Off-White roof, 'COUNTY SHERIFF', clear or Blue light	£50-60	☐
260	1979-81	Buick 'POLICE' Car	Blue/White body, 'CITY OF METROPOLIS', 2 flashing light bars	£10-15	☐
284	1982-83	Mercedes-Benz 240 D	Red body, 'NOTRUF 112', flashing lights, German export model	£10-15	☐
293	1980-81	Renault 5 TS	Light Blue/Dark Blue, 'S.O.S. MEDICINS'	£10-15	☐
295	1982-83	Renault 5 TS	Red/White 'SAPEURS POMPIERS', warning lights, French export model	£10-15	☐
297	1982-86	Ford Escort 'POLICE' Car	Light or Dark Blue, White doors, Blue warning lights	£10-15	☐
299	1985	Ford Sierra 'POLIS' Car	Blue/Yellow/Black body, warning lights, Swedish export model	£10-15	☐
299/7	1985	Sierra Ghia 2.3 'POLIS'	White/Black body with White logo, (Sweden)	£10-15	☐
C317	1986	Peugeot 'POLITI'	Black/White body, warning lights, Norwegian export model	£10-15	☐
C326	1980-81	Chevrolet Caprice Police Car	Black/White body, 'POLICE', suspension, 150 mm.	£10-15	☐
C332	1980-81	Opel Doctors Car	White/Red body, 'NOTARTZ', opening doors	£10-15	☐
C339	1980	Rover 3500 Police Car	White and Red body, 'POLICE', 140 mm.	£10-15	☐
353	1987	BMW 'NOTARTZ'	Red/White body, 2 Blue warning lights, German export model	£10-15	☐
357	1987	Ford Sierra 'BRANDCHEFF'	Red body, door badge, warning lights	£5-10	☐
C358/1	1987	Ford Sierra 'POLICE'	White body, Yellow/Black stripe, warning lights unit on roof	£10-15	☐
358	1987	Ford Sierra 'POLITI'	White body, Red/Blue logo, warning lights, export model	£10-15	☐
358	1987	Ford Sierra 'POLICE'	White body, Red logo, warning lights, Dutch export model	£10-15	☐
C358/3	1986	'RIJKSPOLITIE'	White body, White/Red bonnet, crest, roof beacon, (Holland)	£10-15	☐
C358/4	1986	'LEGIBIL'	White/Black body, 'LEGE', twin roof beacons, (West Germany)	£10-15	☐
361	1987	Volvo 'POLIS'	White body, Black/Yellow logo, Swedish export model	£10-15	☐
373	1970-76	Volkswagen 1200 Police Car	Black/White/Blue body, 'POLICE', WhizzWheels, 91 mm.	£10-15	☐
373	1987	Peugeot 'POLITI'	Black/White body, warning lights, export model	£10-15	☐
383	1970-73	VW 1200 'ADAC'	Yellow/Black body, 'ADAC' logo (Continental equivalent of 'AA')	£60-70	☐
386	1987	Mercedes 'POLIZEI'	Green/White body, 2 Blue warning lights, German export model	£10-15	☐
395	1972/73	Fire Bug	Orange body, Whizzwheels	£20-30	☐
402	1972-77	Ford Cortina Police Car	White/Red body, 'POLICE', warning lights, opening doors, 102 mm.	£25-35	☐
405	1956-60	Bedford Fire Tender	Green body, divided windscreen, Silver or Black ladder, 'A.F.S.', smooth or shaped hubs, 83 mm.	£80-100	☐
405 M	1956-59	Bedford Fire Tender	Red body, divided windscreen, Silver or Black ladder, 'FIRE DEPT', smooth or shaped hubs, 83 mm.	£90-110	☐
C405	1978-80	Chevrolet Ambulance	White/Orange, opening doors, ambulancemen, 119 mm.	£10-15	☐
C406	1980-81	Mercedes Bonna 'AMBULANCE'	White body, Red/Black design, opening doors, stretcher, ambulancemen	£10-15	☐
			German issue: Cream body, 'KRANKENWAGEN'	£10-15	☐
			Danish issue: Red/White/body, 'FALCK'	£10-15	☐
			Swedish issue: White/Red/Black body, 'SDL 951'	£10-15	☐
C406/2	1990	Mercedes Bonna	White/Red stripes, 'FALCK', (Danish export model)	£5-10	☐
412	1957-60	Bedford 'AMBULANCE'	Cream 'Utilicon' body, smooth hubs, 83 mm.	£60-70	☐
		variation:	N.B. A few examples of 412 were wrongly issued with 'HOME SERVICES' front labels.	NGPP	☐
C412	1976	Mercedes 'POLIZEI' Car	Green/White body, Blue roof lamp, German issue	£10-15	☐
414	1976-77	Jaguar XJ12-C	White/Blue body, 'COASTGUARD'	£10-15	☐
416	1959-62	R.A.C. Land Rover	Blue body, 'RADIO RESCUE', metal or plastic tilt, smooth or shaped hubs, Blue/Yellow box.	£70-80	☐
416s	1962-64	R.A.C. Land Rover	Blue body, plastic canopy, 'RADIO RESCUE', aerial, with suspension, 95 mm.	£55-65	☐
416s	1962-64	R.A.C. Land Rover	Blue body with plastic tilt, 'RADIO RESCUE', 'RAC' logo on bonnet and doors	£55-65	☐
			Yellow body, Grey plastic cover, Black 'TS RADIO' decals on doors, (TOURING SECOURS) decals on doors, Belgium issue	£275-325	☐
C416	1977-79	Buick Police Car	Metallic Blue body, 'POLICE', 2 policemen, 150 mm.	£15-20	☐
419	1960-63	Ford Zephyr Motorway Car	White body, 'POLICE', aerial, clear roof light, 97 mm.	£45-55	☐
			As previous model but Off-White body, big or small Blue roof light	£45-55	☐
		Export issues:	with 'POLITIE' logo (Dutch)	£160-190	☐
			with 'RIJKS POLITIE' logo (Dutch)	£350-450	☐
421	1977-79	'FOREST WARDEN'S' Land Rover	Red/White body, roof-rack, spare wheel, opening doors, 135 mm.	£15-20	☐
422	1977-80	Riot Police Wagon	Red/White body, number '6' & 'RIOT POLICE' on doors, water cannon	£15-20	☐
423	1960-62	Bedford Fire Tender	Red body, Black ladder, undivided windscreen, smooth or shaped hubs	£70-80	☐
			Red body, unpainted ladder, undivided windscreen, shaped hubs	£80-100	☐
424	1976-79	'SECURITY' Van	Black/Yellow/White body, mesh windows, WhizzWheels	£10-15	☐
C428	1978-79	Renault Police Car	Black/White body, 'POLICE', aerial, warning lights, 97 mm.	£10-15	☐
C429	1978-80	Police Jaguar XJ12-C	White/Red/Blue body, 'POLICE', aerial, warning lights, 127 mm.	£15-20	☐
C430	1978-80	Porsche 924 'Police'	Black/White body, 'POLICE', warning light, 118 mm.	£15-20	☐
C430	1978-80	Porsche 924 'Polizei'	White/Green body, 'POLIZEI', warning light, 118 mm.	£15-20	☐
C435/13	1990	Volvo 'POLIS'	White with Blue panels front & rear, flashing lights bar	£5-10	☐

50

Corgi Toys — Emergency Vehicles – continued

Ref. No.				Market Price Range	
437	1962-68	Cadillac Superior Ambulance....	Red body, Cream roof, shaped spun wheels, battery-operated flashing light...............	**£35-45**	☐
			White body, Blue roof, battery-operated Red flashing light, 114 mm.	**£55-65**	☐
C438	1987	Rover Sterling 800.....................	White body, Red stripe, *'POLICE'*, flashing lights bar	**£5-10**	☐
439	1963-65	Chevrolet Impala 'FIRE CHIEF'..................	Red body, White stripe, aerial, Orange roof light, firemen, 108 mm.		
			with White painted door labels with *'FIRE DEPT'*	**£60-70**	☐
			with White rectangular label on front doors *'FIRE DEPT'*	**£50-60**	☐
			with round Red label on front doors *'FIRE DEPT'*	**£50-60**	☐
448	1964-69	Austin Police Mini Van............	Blue body, *'POLICE'*, dog and policeman, 79 mm.	**£90-110**	☐
454	1984	Ford Sierra *'POLIZEI'*.............	Green/White body, Swiss export model	**£10-15**	☐
456	1986	Ford Sierra *'POLIZEI'*.............	Green/White body, German export model	**£10-15**	☐
461	1972-74	*'Police'* Vigilant Range Rover...	White/Blue, warning lights, policemen, *'POLICE'* emergency signs...........................	**£20-25**	☐
			White/Red body, *'LANGZAAM'*, policemen, emergency signs, Dutch model.............	**£20-25**	☐
463	1964-66	Commer *'AMBULANCE'*	Cream or White body, Red interior, Blue tinted windows and roof light, 90 mm.......	**£45-55**	☐
464	1963-	Commer 15 cwt *'POLICE'* Van	Dark Blue, *'COUNTY POLICE'*, window bars, clear roof light, leaflet	**£55-65**	☐
	1963-		As previous model but Metallic Light Blue, with Blue roof light	**£50-60**	☐
			Dark Blue, window bars, Red roof light, *'CITY POLICE'*, instruction leaflet.............	**£175-200**	☐
			Dark Blue, 'open' windows, Blue roof light, White *'POLICE'* cast into sides, instructions	**£45-55**	☐
			Deep Green body, *'POLICE'*, export model, opaque rear/side windows....................	**£400-500**	☐
			Metallic Green body, *'POLIZEI'*, German issue	**£150-175**	☐
			Metallic Blue body, *'SECOURS'*, French issue	**£150-175**	☐
			Metallic Blue body, window bars, *'RIJKSPOLITIE'*, Dutch issue	**£150-175**	☐
477	1966-67	Land Rover Breakdown...........	Red/Yellow/Silver, spare wheel on some, hook, WhizzWheels, 114 mm.	**£30-35**	☐
481	1965-69	Chevrolet Police Car	White/Black body, *'POLICE PATROL'*, Red roof lights, 2 policemen, 108 mm.	**£40-50**	☐
482	1966-69	Chevrolet Impala 'FIRE CHIEF'..................	Red over White body, Chrome stripe, bonnet logo, Blue light, Grey aerial		
			with rectangular *'FIRE CHIEF'* label on front doors, shaped spun wheels...............	**£40-50**	☐
			with round label on front doors *'FIRE CHIEF'*, shaped spun wheels	**£65-75**	☐
			with round label on front doors *'FIRE CHIEF'*, detailed cast wheels	**£55-65**	☐
482	1974-77	Range Rover Ambulance	White/Red/Blue body, *'AMBULANCE'*, stretcher, 2 ambulancemen	**£15-20**	☐
483	1979	Belgian Police Range Rover ...	White body, Red stripes, warning lights, policemen, emergency signs	**£10-15**	☐
C484	1978-80	AMC Pacer *'RESCUE'*............	White/Orange/Black body, number '35', special lights, 118 mm.	**£5-10**	☐
C489	1980	Volkswagen Police Car............	White/Green body, *'POLIZEI'*, opening doors and hatchback, 97 mm.	**£10-15**	☐
C490	1967-70	Volkswagen Breakdown...........	Beige/Red, tool-box, 2 spare wheels, 102 mm.	**£35-45**	☐
492	1966-69	VW *'POLIZEI'* Car.................	Green body, White roof, White *'POLIZEI'* on bonnet, No. '18' logo......................	**£40-50**	☐
492	1966-69	VW European Police Car.........	Dark Green body, White roof & wings, Red *'POLIZEI'*, Blue lamp, 91 mm.	**£40-50**	☐
			N.B. Box should contain 'True Scale Steering' Red/Yellow cardboard roof fitting.		
			All-White body, crest on doors, *'POLITIE'*, Blue lamp, Dutch model	**£100-150**	☐
506	1968-71	Sunbeam Imp 'Panda' Car	White body, Black bonnet and roof, Blue roof light	**£40-50**	☐
			White body, Black roof, 'luminous' door panels, Blue roof light	**£40-50**	☐
			Light Blue body, White roof, 'luminous' door panels, Blue roof light....................	**£50-60**	☐
509	1970-72	Porsche Targa Police Car.........	White/Red body, *'POLIZEI'*, siren, warning lights, 95 mm.	**£40-50**	☐
541	1986	Ford Sierra *'POLICE'*	Black/White body, Norwegian/Danish export model...................................	**£10-15**	☐
541	1987	*'POLITI'*	White with Blue/Yellow side stripes, (Norway)..	**£10-15**	☐
541/2	1988	Ford Sierra *'NOTRUF'*	Red body, warning lights, German export model	**£10-15**	☐
542	1987	Bonna *'AMBULANCE'*............	Red/White body, 2 warning lights, Norwegian export model	**£10-15**	☐
576	1988	Mercedes 207 D Van................	Red body, White *'POMPIERS'*, French export model	**£10-15**	☐
597	1986	Ford Sierra *'POLICE'* Car.......	White body, Yellow/Black logo, 2 warning lights	**£5-10**	☐
598	1986	Range Rover *'POLICE'*	White body, Yellow/Black print, 2 warning lights	**£5-10**	☐
619	1988	Land Rover	Red/White body, *'SAPEUR POMPIERS'*, export model	**£5-10**	☐
621	1986	Ford Escort *'POLICE'* Van	White body, Red/Black side flash, Blue logo	**£5-10**	☐
656	1987	Ford Transit Van	White/Red body, flashing lights bar, Red Cross, *'AMBULANCE'*.	**£5-10**	☐
656	1987	Ford Transit Van *'POLICE'*	Black body, White logo, Finnish export model	**£5-10**	☐
656	1987	Ford Transit Van *'FALCK'*.....	White body, 2 Red stripes, warning lights, export model	**£10-15**	☐
656	1987	Ford Transit Van	White/Red, *'AMBULANSE'*, flashing lights bar, Norwegian export model	**£10-15**	☐
C656/28	1990	Ford Transit	White/Yellow stripe, *'NOTTINGHAM AMBULANCE SERVICE'*	NRP	☐
C674/1	1988	*'AA'* Ford Transit...................	Breakdown truck with Yellow body, White stripe, Black rear lifting gear.	NRP	☐
C674/2	1988	*'RAC'* Ford Transit.................	Breakdown truck with White body, Red/Blue stripe, Black lifting gear..................	NRP	☐
C674/3	1988	*'POLICE'* Ford Transit............	Breakdown truck with White body, Red stripe, roof lights, Black lifting gear	NRP	☐
C674/4	1988	*'BARNINGSKAREN'* Transit	Red/Yellow breakdown truck, Black lifting gear, export model...........................	**£9-11**	☐
700	1974-79	Motorway Ambulance..............	White/Red body, *'ACCIDENT'*, Red Cross, 98 mm..	**£15-20**	☐
702	1975-79	Breakdown Truck	Red/Black, single bumper, hook, *'ACCIDENT'*, 100 mm.	**£10-15**	☐
703	1976-78	Hi-Speed Fire Engine	Red body, Yellow ladder, warning lights, 115 mm.	**£10-15**	☐
911	1976-80	Air-Sea Rescue Helicopter	Blue/Yellow body, Black 'flick-spin' rotor, *'N 428'*, operable winch	**£15-20**	☐
921	1975-81	Hughes OH-6A Helicopter.......	White/Red, *'POLICE'*, *'RESCUE'*, warning lights, 143 mm.	**£15-20**	☐
921/1	1979-80		White/Blue, *'POLIZEI'*, 'flick-spin' rotor, operable winch, German issue	**£15-20**	☐
921/2	1979-80		White/Blue, *'POLITIE'*, 'flick-spin' rotor, operable winch, Dutch issue	**£15-20**	☐
921/4	1979-80	*'ADAC'* Helicopter..................	Yellow body, *'D-HFFM'*, 'flick-spin' rotor, operable winch	**£15-20**	☐
921/6	1979-80	Swiss Red Cross Helicopter	Red body, Black blades, 'flick-spin' rotor, operable winch	**£15-20**	☐
924	1977-81	Air-Sea Rescue Helicopter	Orange/Yellow/Black body, *'RESCUE'*, 150 mm.	**£15-20**	☐
927	1978-79	Surf Rescue Helicopter	Blue/White body, *'SURF RESCUE'*, 156 mm.	**£15-20**	☐
931	1979-80	Jet Ranger Helicopter..............	White/Red body, *'POLICE RESCUE'*, 'flick-spin' rotor, operable winch	**£15-20**	☐

MAJOR PACKS (Emergency Vehicles)

1103	1976-81	*'PATHFINDER AIRPORT CRASH TRUCK'*............	Red/Silver, *'AIRPORT FIRE BRIGADE'*, operable pump & siren, Orange decal	**£35-45**	☐
			As previous model but non-working siren, Brick-Red decal.............................	**£35-45**	☐
			Red/Silver, operable pump & siren, *'new YORK AIRPORT'* logo................................	**£35-45**	☐

Ref. No.				Market Price Range	
C1118	1981-83	'AIRPORT FIRE SERVICE'...	Red body, *'EMERGENCY UNIT'*, operable water pump............	£40-50	☐
1120	1984	Dennis Fire Engine....................	Red body, turntable, warning lights, Yellow plastic ladder, crest design	£10-15	☐
1126	1977-81	'SIMON SNORKEL' Dennis Fire Engine	Red/White/Yellow, turntable, ladder, 6 firemen, 265 mm.	£25-30	☐
1127	1964-74	'SIMON SNORKEL' Bedford TK Fire Engine	Red/Yellow/Silver, turntable, ladder, 6 fireman, 252 mm.	£70-80	☐
1140	1982	Ford Transit Wrecker...............	White/Red, *'24 Hour Service'*, operable winch, hook, 131 mm.	£10-15	☐
			As previous model but logo changed to *'RELAY'*.	£10-15	☐
	1982		Red/Yellow body, *'ABSCHLEPPDEENST'*, export model	£10-15	☐
	1987		Red body, Gold *'FALCK'* logo, Danish export model	£10-15	☐
	1987		Red body, Yellow side panels, *'VIKING'*, export model	£10-15	☐
1142	1967-74	'HOLMES WRECKER'...	Red/White/Blue, Grey or Gold twin booms, ladder, 2 spare wheels 114 mm.	£70-80	☐
C1143	1969	'AMERICAN LA FRANCE'...	Articulated Fire Engine in Red/White/Yellow, shaped spun or detailed cast wheels, 4-part extending ladder, 5 firemen, plain early box	£70-80	☐
			As previous model but in later striped window box	£50-60	☐
1144	1975-78	Berliet Wrecker Recovery.........	Red/White/Gold body, with Gold or Grey hoists, 130 mm.	£50-60	☐
2029	1985	Mack Fire Engine....................	Red body, 4 warning lights, *'HAMMOND FIRE DEPT'*	£10-15	☐
91822	1992	'FALKEN' Ford Transit..........	White body, Blue/Gold stripes, Black lifting gear, export model	£9-11	☐

Page from 1969 Corgi Catalogue Ref C2017/9/68.

Ref. No.	Year(s)	Model Type	Model Features and Size	Market Price Range	

Unless described otherwise, all models in this listing are finished in Military-Green or Olive-Drab camouflage.

Ref. No.	Year(s)	Model Type	Model Features and Size	Market Price Range	
C290	1977-80	Bell Army Helicopter	Red crosses, Black rotor, 'ARMY' markings, 160 mm.	£15-20	☐
350	1958-62	Thunderbird Missile	Red/White guided missile, Air Force Blue loading trolley, 140 mm.	£100-125	☐
351	1958-62	R.A.F. Land Rover	Blue/Silver, R.A.F. roundel, spare wheel, windows, 95 mm.	£40-50	☐
352	1958-62	R.A.F. Vanguard Staff Car......	Blue/Silver Standard Vanguard with R.A.F. roundel, 95 mm.	£40-50	☐
353	1959-61	Decca Radar Scanner	Blue/Orange, scanner rotates, 83 mm.	£25-35	☐
354	1964-66	Commer Military Ambulance ...	Red crosses, seats, steering wheel, suspension, Army driver, 90 mm.	£40-50	☐
355	1964-65	Commer Van 'MILITARY POLICE'................	Battery-operated flashing light, suspension, Army driver, 90 mm.	£70-80	☐
356	1964-66	VW Personnel Carrier	'US PERSONNEL', seats, suspension, Army driver, 91 mm.	£40-60	☐
357	1964-66	Land Rover Weapons Carrier...	Military Green, Lemon interior, aerial, spun wheels, White star, 95 mm.	£120-140	☐
358	1964-68	1961 Oldsmobile Staff Car	Army driver and 3 passengers, White star, 'HQ STAFF', suspension, 108 mm.	£50-60	☐
359	1964-66	Commer Army 'FIELD KITCHEN'	Military Green, Blue interior, U.S. star on roof, driver/attendant, 91 mm.	£80-100	☐
414	1961-64	Bedford Military Ambulance	Red crosses, windows, 83 mm.	£50-60	☐
500	1963-64	US Army Land Rover	Rare version of model 357, 95 mm.	£200-250	☐
C900	1974-78	German Tiger Mk.I Tank	Brown/Green, Rubber tracks, fires shells (12 supplied) aerial, '144', 103 mm. ...	£15-20	☐
C901	1974-78	Centurion Mk.I Tank..............	Rubber tracks, fires shells (12 supplied) aerial, Union Jacks, 121 mm.	£15-20	☐
C902	1974-80	American M60 A1 Tank	Rubber tracks, fires shells (12 supplied) 115 mm.	£15-20	☐
C903	1974-80	British Chieftain Tank............	Fires shells (12 supplied) rubber tracks, 125 mm.	£15-20	☐
C904	1974-78	German King-Tiger Tank	Rubber tracks, fires shells (12 supplied) Black crosses, 'B 34', 120 mm.	£15-20	☐
C905	1975-76	Russian SU100 Tank Destroyer...........................	Grey, Fires shells (12 supplied) rubber tracks, Red Star, 112mm.	£15-20	☐
C906	1975-76	Saladin Armoured Car	Rubber tracks, fires shells (12 supplied) elevating gun, 108 mm.	£15-20	☐
C907	1976-80	German Rocket Launcher........	Steel Blue/Red, half-track, detachable limber, fires rockets (12) 167 mm.	£15-20	☐
C908	1977-80	French AMX Recovery Tank ...	Crane, lifting dozer blade, equipment, 3 figures, 127 mm.	£40-50	☐
C909	1977-80	Tractor Gun & Trailer	Sand-coloured British gun and trailer, fires shells (12 supplied) 280 mm.	£25-35	☐
C910		Bell Army Helicopter	Military-Green helicopter with Army markings, Black or Green rotor.	£15-20	☐
C922	1975-78	Casualty Helicopter	Red/White/Yellow Sikorsky helicopter, number '3', Red crosses	£15-20	☐
C923	1975-78	Sikorsky Sky Crane	Military-Green helicopter, Red cross, 'ARMY' marking, 160 mm.	£15-20	☐

MAJOR PACKS - (and large Military and R.A.F. models)

Ref. No.	Year(s)	Model Type	Model Features and Size	Market Price Range	
1106	1959-61	Karrier Decca Radar Van........	Cream body, 4 Orange bands, rotating scanner, aerials, 134 mm.	£80-100	☐
			Cream body, 5 Orange bands, rotating scanner, aerials, 134 mm.	£80-100	☐
1108	1958-61	Bristol Bloodhound Guided Missile & Launching Ramp	with lifting mechanism and Yellow/Red/White Guided Missile, RAF markings.........	£65-75	☐
1109	1959-62	Bristol Bloodhound Guided Missile & Loading Trolley	with lifting mechanism and Yellow/Red/White Guided Missile, RAF markings.........	£65-75	☐
1112	1959-62	Corporal Guided Missile on Launching Ramp.............	Military-Green mechanical base, White missile, Red rubber nose cone, instructions ...	£80-100	☐
	1960-62		As previous model but with separately boxed 1408 Percussion head and instructions	£100-120	☐
1113	1959-62	Corporal Guided Missile Erector Vehicle......................	with lifting mechanism and Guided Missile, spare wheel, 292 mm.	£90-120	☐
1115	1958-62	Bristol Ferranti Bloodhound.....	Yellow/Red/White Guided Missile with RAF markings.............................	£40-50	☐
1116	1959-62	Bloodhound Launching Ramp....	Military-Green launching ramp for 1115. Rotates, has lifting mechanism	£70-80	☐
1117	1959-62	Bloodhound Loading Trolley....	for use with model 1115. Military-Green, spare wheel, drawbar pivots	£25-35	☐
1118	1959-62	International 6x6 Army Truck..	Military-Green with British markings (US markings on box picture), 140 mm.	£90-110	☐
1124	1960-62	Launching Ramp for Corporal Guided Missile	Military-Green, operable and adjustable mechanisms, in plain 'Temporary Pack' box	£25-35	☐
1133	1965-66	Troop Transporter....................	International Six wheeled truck, 'US 7811332', hook, 140 mm.	£125-150	☐
1134	1965-66	'US ARMY' Fuel Tanker	Bedford 'S' Type Artic, US Army star, 'NO SMOKING', 191 mm.	£200-250	☐
1135	1965	Heavy Equipment Transporter..	Bedford Carrimore, Military Green, US Army star, driver, Red interior, 241 mm.	£200-250	☐

DRIVER AND THREE PASSENGERS

4¼ inches 108 mm

358 H.Q. Staff Car
With seats, steering wheel, Glidamatic spring suspension, driver and three passengers.

DETACHABLE CAB

7½ inches 191 mm

1134 Army Fuel Tanker
This articulated model has a detachable driving cab.

DRIVER

3⅝ inches 91 mm

356 Personnel Carrier
With seats, steering wheel, Glidamatic spring suspension and driver.

Models pictured in the 1966 Corgi Catalogue.

Ref. No.	Year(s)	Model Type	Model Features and Size	Market Price Range	
107	1967-70	Batboat on Trailer.....................	Black boat (tinplate fin cover) with Batman and Robin figures, gold trailer (suspension, cast wheels). Blue/yellow pictorial box also contains black accessory towing hook for attachment to Batmobile	£60-70	☐
	1974-81		Black boat (plastic fin) with Batman and Robin figures, gold trailer (no suspension, Whizzwheels)...	£50-60	☐
201	1970-72	The Saint's Volvo	White body, White 'Saint' logo on red label, WhizzWheels, driver, Red/Yellow 'window' box	£50-60	☐
258	1965-68	The Saint's Volvo	White body, Black 'Saint' logo (transfer), Red interior, driver, spun hubs, Blue/Yellow card box	£70-85	☐
258	1968-70	The Saint's Volvo	White body, white 'Saint' logo on Red label, Red interior, driver, cast hubs, Blue/Yellow card box	£50-60	☐
258	1968-70	The Saint's Volvo	As previous version but white 'Saint' logo on blue label	NGPP	☐
C259	1979-80	Penguinmobile	White car with 'The Penguin' figure under Red/Yellow parasol, 95 mm. Black/Yellow 'window' box	£25-30	☐
C260	1979-81	Superman Police Car	Blue/White body (150 mm), *'CITY OF METROPOLIS'* markings, Black/Yellow pictorial window box	£35-40	☐
261	1965-69	James Bond's Aston Martin......	Gold body with James Bond at the wheel, passenger seat ejector (with figure). Accessories: envelope with 'secret instructions', spare passenger, self-adhesive '007' badge, (plus 'Model Car Makers to James Bond' Corgi Catalogue in earlier boxes). From the film 'Goldfinger'.	£90-110	☐
261	1979-81	Spiderbuggy and Green Goblin...	Red/Blue jeep body (150 mm.) with crane, Spiderman and Green Goblin figures. Black/Yellow pictorial window box.	NGPP	☐
262	1979-80	Captain Marvel's Porsche	White with flames and stars, driver, 120 mm. Black/Yellow 'window' box...................	£40-45	☐
263	1979-81	Captain America's Jetmobile.....	White/Red/Blue body (155 mm.), with driver, Red wheels, Black/Yellow 'window' box	£20-25	☐
264	1979-82	The Incredible Hulk Truck	Hulk in Red cage on Mazda pick-up, 120 mm. Black/Yellow 'window' box................	£20-25	☐
264	1979-82	The Incredible Hulk Truck	As previous model but Hulk in Grey cage	£40-50	☐
265	1979-82	Supermobile..............................	Blue/Red/Silver body, (148 m.), Superman at the controls, moving fists'. Black/Yellow pictorial 'window' box contains 10 spare rockets and instruction leaflet.........	£20-25	☐
266	1968-72	Chitty Chitty Bang Bang...........	Chrome, Brown and Red body (162 m), Red/Yellow retractable 'wings', figures of Caractacus Potts, Truly Scrumptious, a boy and a girl. Pictorial Blue/Yellow 'window'box comes in two sizes	£140-170	☐
	1992		25th Anniversary replica model on 'mahogany' display stand. Direct mail offer from Corgi..	£70-80	☐
266	1979-83	Spider Bike	Red/Blue motorcycle (115 m.), Spiderman rider, Black wheels, Black or Red handlebars/forks, Black or Blue seat and fairing, amber or clear windshield, rocket launchers		
			Box (1) Black/Yellow pictorial 'window' box with header card, 10 spare rockets.......	£25-30	☐
			Box (2) Black/Yellow 'window' box without header card, 10 spare rockets	£20-25	☐
			Box (3) Black/Red/Yellow 'window' box without header card, 10 spare rockets	£20-25	☐
266	1980-82	Spider Bike	As previous model but with white wheels	£40-50	☐
267	1966-67	Batmobile.................................	Black body (usually gloss, some matt), Red 'Bat' logo on doors and on gold cast wheels, Batman and Robin figures, 'pulsating exhaust flame', instruction sheet concealed in base, 12 spare rockets (Red or Yellow), self-adhesive 'Batman' badge. Pictorial card box with diorama, earliest versions had 'features' leaflet within.	£150-200	☐
	1967-72		Same model but with towing hook cast into base. Blue/Yellow 'window' box............	£100-140	☐
	1973		As previous model but with Red WhizzWheels and without pulsating 'flame' effect. Blue/Yellow 'window' box..	£250-350	☐
	1974-77		As previous model but with Black WhizzWheels and without pulsating 'flame' effect. Copyright information cast in base. Dark Blue/Yellow 'window' box (header card on some), spare rockets, no instruction sheet..	£50-60	☐
	1977-79		As previous casting but with wider WhizzWheels, no Robin figure. Black/Red/Yellow 'window' box..	NGPP	☐
268	1978-80	Batman's Batbike	Black/Red rocket-firing motorcycle with Red or Grey Batman figure. Black/Yellow 'window' box (header card on some), spare rockets	£40-50	☐
	1980-83		As previous versions but in Black/Red/Yellow 'window' box	£30-40	☐
268	1967-72	The Green Hornet's 'Black Beauty'..	Black body, Green interior, driver and Green Hornet figures, transfer on roof, spun or detailed hubs. Fires missile from front, radar scanner from rear. Four of each, plus 'secret instructions' are in Blue/Yellow pictorial card box	£180-200	☐
269	1977-83	James Bond Lotus Esprit	White body, Black windows, operable fins and rocket mechanism. From the film 'The Spy Who Loved Me'.		
			Early pictorial 'window' box with plain base must contain instruction sheet and 10 spare rockets..	£65-80	☐
			Later pictorial 'window' box has instructions printed on base, contains 10 spare.......	£55-65	☐
	1977		10 gold-plated versions of 269 were presented to VIPs at the film's launch. The models had special mountings and boxes..	NGPP	☐
270	1968-76	James Bond's Aston-Martin DB5..	Silver body (slightly larger than 261). Same features as 261 plus: revolving number-plates and extending tyre slashers. Accessories: envelope containing 'secret instructions'. ejectable passenger, self-adhesive '007' badge (different from 261), set of number plates. Variations include Gold or Silver coloured bumpers, metal or plastic spoked rear wheels.		
			Box (1) model sits on card platform under vac-formed bubble (fragile, few made)......	£150-200	☐
			Box (2) Blue/Yellow 'window' box (some with card 'upstand' till 1973, few made).....	£140-170	☐
			Box (3) Black/Blue/Yellow 'window' box (1973-76)...	£120-140	☐

Corgi Toys — *Novelty, Film & TV Related – continued*

Ref. No.				Market Price Range	
270	1977-78	James Bond Aston-Martin DB5	As previous version but with fixed number plates, 'solid' chrome WhizzWheels, no tyre-slashers, no 'secret instructions'. Box has symetrical window, ejectable passenger lodged in box inner	£100-125	☐
C271	1978-83	James Bond Aston-Martin	Silver body (⅓ scale), Whizzwheels ('spoked' detail or 'alloy racing').		
			Early Black/Yellow boxes had '1:36' printed on window tag	£50-60	☐
			Later Black/Yellow boxes did not have the window tag	£50-60	☐
			Final boxes were Black/Red/Yellow	£40-50	☐
?	1991-92	James Bond Aston-Martin	Reissue of previous model in clear plastic display box with plastic '007' badge	£15-20	☐
C272	1981-83	James Bond Citroën 2cv	Yellow body, opening bonnet. From film 'For Your Eyes Only'		
			Box (1) Black/Red/Yellow 'window' box with pictorial header card	£35-45	☐
			Box (2) Black/Red/Yellow 'compact' box with pictorial top flap	£35-45	☐
272	1981-83	James Bond Citroen 2cv	Gold plated version with retailer's prize certificate (25 only)	£750-1000	☐
277	1968-72	'MONKEES' Monkeemobile	Red body, White roof, Yellow logo, cast detailed wheels, plus figures of Mike, Mickey, Davy and Pete. Blue/Yellow 'window' box	£150-200	☐
			In Blue/Yellow 'window' box with clip-in cardboard header	£300-400	☐
			N.B. Pre-production model with plastic engine exists.		
278	1981-	Dan Dare's Car	Red/Yellow space vehicle. Planned but not produced	NPP	☐
C290	1976-77	Kojak Buick	Bronze body (various shades, 150 mm.), 4-spoke or disc type wheel hubs, 'gunfire' sound, self-adhesive 'Lieutenant' badge, figures of Kojak (no hat) and Crocker (blue jacket). Black/Yellow pictorial 'window' box	£50-65	☐
	1977-80		As previous model but figure of Kojak has a hat and Crocker had a Black jacket. 'New' tag on some boxes	£30-35	☐
C292	1977-82	Starsky & Hutch Ford Torino	Red/White body (150 mm.), figures of Starsky, Hutch, and a suspect. Black/Yellow pictorial 'window' box	£30-35	☐
	1986		Reissued as an export model (20,000)	£10-15	☐
298	1982-83	Magnum P.I. Ferrari	Red Ferrari 308GTS with 4-spoke or disc wheels. Black/Red/Yellow pictorial 'window' box	£20-25	☐
C320	1978-81	The Saint's Jaguar XJS	White body, standard or 'dished' WhizzWheels. Black/Yellow 'window' box (yellow or black inner)	£30-35	☐
336	1967-69	James Bond's Toyota 2000 GI	White body, rocket launchers in boot. From film 'You Only Live Twice'. Diorama box must have card reinforcements to protect aerial, envelope with 'secret instruction', self-adhesive '007' badge, spare rockets	£150-200	☐
C342	1980-82	'PROFESSIONALS' Ford Capri	Silver/Black body (124 mm.), tinted windows, tinted windows, dished or disc wheel hubs, figures of Cowley, Bodie, Doyle. Black/Yellow pictorial 'window' box	£35-45	☐
348	1968-69	Ford Mustang 'POP ART' Stock Car	Blue body and interior, 5 Red/Yellow psychedelic labels with racing number '20'. Never appeared in catalogues	£50-60	☐
C348	1980-81	'Vegas Thunderbird	Red body (124 mm.), with Dan Tanner figure. Black/Yellow pictorial 'window' box	£35-45	☐
349	1967-67	'POP ART' Morris Mini	Red body, Yellow interior, 4 psychedelic labels, *MOSTEST* logo. Model not generally released or shown in catalogues, few only produced	£700-900	☐
391	1972-72	James Bond Ford Mustang Mach I	Red body, White interior and base, WhizzWheels (2 types known). From film *'Diamonds Are Forever'*. Red/Yellow 'window' box has James Bond '007' Red sticker label	£125-175	☐
391	1972-73	Fire Bug	Orange body, Yellow ladder, *'FIREBUG'*, WhizzWheels, 83 mm.	£15-25	☐
423	1978-78	'ROUGH RIDER'	Yellow Chevrolet van, motorcycle side labels	20-25	☐
426	1962-64	'CHIPPERFIELDS CIRCUS' Mobile Booking Office	Karrier Bantam in red and blue, with clown and circus posters, spun hubs. Blue/yellow card box	£110-140	☐
C426	1978-82	'JEAN RICHARD' Booking Office	Yellow/Red Chevrolet van, detailed or 4-spoke WhizzWheels, 122 mm.	£20-30	☐
431	1978-79	'VANATIC'	White Chevrolet van, polychromatic side labels	£20-25	☐
C432	1978-79	'VANTASTIC'	Black Chevrolet, Yellow/Red design	£20-25	☐
C433	1978	'VANISHING POINT'	Chevrolet van shown in 1978 catalogue but not issued	NPP	☐
C434	1978-80	'CHARLIE'S ANGELS' Custom Van	Pink Chevrolet van, Yellow or Brown interior, 4-spoke or disc wheels. Black/Yellow pictorial 'window' box	£20-30	☐
C435	1979-80	'SUPERMAN' Van	Metallic Silver Chevrolet 'SuperVan'. Black/Yellow pictorial 'window' box (printing variations seen)	£20-30	☐
C436	1979-80	'SPIDERVAN'	Blue Chevrolet van, 'Spiderman' design, 4-spoke or disc wheels. Black/Yellow pictorial 'window' box	£20-30	☐
C437	1979-80	'COCA COLA'	Red Chevrolet van, White design, tinted roof windows, crates	£20-25	☐
			N.B. Various other labels were designed for the Chevrolet 'van' series. Some prototype labels were printed but not officially used. Some of these may have found their way on to repainted van castings — they are NOT official Corgi issues. Logos include: 'Apache Patrol', 'Light Vantastic', 'Vanilla Treat', 'Cosmos', 'Columbia', 'Aquarius', 'Centaur', 'Colorama', 'Rocket Van', 'Centaur', plus 4 other unlettered 'psychedelic' designs.		
436	1963-65	Citroën 'WILDLIFE SAFARI'	Yellow Citroën ID19, driver & passenger, detailed interior, roof luggage, 'Wild Life Reservation' logo	£50-60	☐
447	1965-66	'Wall Ice Cream Van'	Ford Thames van in Blue/Cream, salesman, boy, spare transfers. Blue/Yellow card box, inner base, leaflet	£120-150	☐
472	1964-66	'VOTE FOR CORGI' Land Rover	Corgi 438 in Green/Yellow, Blue/Yellow card box	£65-75	☐
474	1965-68	Musical 'Walls Ice Cream Van'	Ford Thames van in Blue/Cream, musical movement, diorama but no figures. Blue/Yellow card box	£80-100	☐
475	1964-65	Citroën Olympic Winter Sport	White/Yellow Citroën Safari, '1964', roof-rack, skier, skis, 108 mm. Diorama 'By Special Request' box	£70-80	☐

Ref. No.	Year	Name	Description	Market Price Range	
475	1965-68	'CORGI SKI CLUB' Citroën ...	Off-White body, Red roof-rack, 4 Yellow skis & 2 poles, bonnet transfer, Brown dashboard/rear seats, Green front seats, 108 mm.	£70-80	☐
475	1965-68	'CORGI SKI CLUB' Citroën ...	White body, Yellow Roof-rack, 4 Red skis and 2 poles, Green dashboard/rear seats, Brown front seats	£70-80	☐
479	1967-71	Commer Mobile Camera Van...	Blue/White, spun hubs, camera and operator, 'Samuelson Film Services', equipment case box	£80-90	☐
479	1967-71	Commer Mobile Camera Van...	As previous model but with detailed cast hubs	NGPP	☐
486	1967-69	'KENNEL CLUB' Truck.........	White/Orange Chevrolet Impala with 'Vari-View' dachshund picture plus 4 dogs	£50-60	☐
487	1965-69	'CHIPPERFIELDS' Parade Vehicle	472 Land Rover in Red/Blue, *CIRCUS IS HERE*, label, chimpanzee, clown, Blue/yellow card box	£100-125	☐
497	1966-66	The Man From UNCLE's 'Thrush Buster' Oldsmobile ...	White body, 'UNCLE' logo, gun sound, figures of Napoleon Solo and Ilya Kuriakin. Blue/Yellow pictorial card box has 3-D 'Waverley' ring	£300-400	☐
497	1966-69	'The Man From UNCLE's 'Thrush-Buster' Oldsmibile....	Metallic purplish blue body, 'UNCLE' logo, cast or plastic spotlights, gun sound, figures of Solo and Kuryakin. Blue/Yellow pictorial card box has 3-D 'Waverley' ring	£120-150	☐
499	1967-69	1968 Winter Olympics Citroën..	White/Blue car 'Grenoble Olympiade', Red or Yellow roof rack, Yellow or Red skis/poles, male tobaganist, female skier. Blue/Yellow 'window' box	£85-100	☐
503	1964-70	'CHIPPERFIELDS' Giraffe Transporter...............................	Red/Blue Bedford 'TK', cast or spun wheels, 2 giraffes, 97 mm. Blue/Yellow card box	£50-75	☐
	1970-71		As previous model but larger 'stepped' front wheels	£60-85	☐
510	1970-72	Citroën Team Managers Car	Red, 'Tour De France', figures, spare wheels, 'Paramount'	£45-60	☐
511	1970-71	'CHIPPERFIELDS' Poodle Truck	Blue/Red Chevrolet Pick-Up, *PERFORMING POODLES* labels, female trainer, 4 white and 2 Black poodles, Blue/Yellow 'window' box	£250-300	☐
513	1970-72	Citroën 'Alpine Rescue' Car	White/Red car, Yellow roof-rack, St. Bernard, sled, skis, male figure, 108 mm., Blue/Yellow 'window' box	£150-200	☐
607	1963-68	'CHIPPERFIELDS' Elephant Cage..	A Corgi Kit with Brown plastic cage and elephant parts, instruction leaflet, Blue/Yellow card box	£30-40	☐
647	1980-83	Buck Rogers Starfighter	White/Blue, 150 mm., Yellow retractable wings, Wilma Dearing and Tweaky figures, Black/Yellow pictorial 'window' box, 10 spare rockets	£20-25	☐
648	1981-82	NASA Space Shuttle	White/Black body, 'U.S.A. Satellite', pictorial hatch, 156 mm.	£20-25	☐
C649	1979-82	James Bond Space Shuttle.........	White body (C468 casting), separate satelite (early versions retained by nylon strap). From film 'Moonraker'. Larger pictorial Black/Yellow box	£20-25	☐
700	1974-80	Motorway Service Ambulance ..	White/Red futuristic vehicle, WhizzWheels	£8-12	☐
701	1974-80	Inter-City Mini-Bus..................	Orange body, Yellow labels, WhizzWheels	£8-12	☐
801	1969-69	Noddy's Car	Yellow/Red car with dickey-seat, cast wheel hubs and chrome bumpers. Figures of Noddy, Big-Ears, and black-faced Golly. Pictorial Blue/Yellow, 'window' box	£750-1000	☐
			As previous model but Golly has Grey or Light Tan face	£200-400	☐
	1969-73		As previous model but with Master Tubby (light or dark brown) instead of Golly.....	£200-400	☐
802	1969-72	Popeye's Paddle-Wagon	Yellow/White body, Red wings, Blue paddle covers, White or Yellow rear wheels, anchors, moving figures of Popeye, Olive Oyl, Swee'Pea, Bluto and Wimpey. Blue/Yellow pictorial 'window' box	£300-350	☐
803	1969-70	The Beatles Submarine..............	Yellow/White, psychedelic design, hatches (Yellow rear, White front) open to show John, Paul, George & Ringo, pictorial window box with Blue-Green inner lining	£250-300	☐
	1970-71		As previous model but with Red hatch covers	£200-250	☐
	1970-71		With one red hatch and one white hatch	£300-400	☐
804	1975-78	Noddy's Car	Red/Yellow car, no dickey-seat, no rear bumper. Figure of Noddy only. Dark Blue/Yellow pictorial 'window' box	£80-100	☐
805	1970-71	The Hardy Boys Rolls Royce ...	9041 Silver Ghose casting in Red, Blue and Yellow, plated wheels. Bubble-pack of five Hardy Boys figures also contained in the Blue/Yellow 'window' box	£125-150	☐
806	1970-72	Lunar Bug	Red/White/Blue, 'Lunar Bug', windows, drop-down ramps, 127 mm.	£80-100	☐
807	1971-73	Dougal's Magic Roundabout Car	Yellow/Red, with Brian, Dougal and Dylan, 118 mm. Yellow/Blue 'window' box with decal sheet	£120-140	☐
807	1973-74	Dougal's Car	As previous model but in Black/Yellow 'window' box, with decal sheet	£120-140	☐
808	1971-73	Basil Brush's Car......................	Red/Yellow car with hand-painted Basil figure, 'Laugh tapes' and soundbox are in separate printed box within pictorial Blue/Yellow 'window' box	£80-100	☐
809	1973-73	Dick Dastardly's Car................	Purple/Yellow racing car with Dick and Muttley figures. Dark Blue/Yellow 'window' box	£80-100	☐
811	1972-73	James Bond Moon Buggy	Blue/White body, Yellow WhizzWheels, Red rotating scanner, Blue/Yellow pictorial window box	£200-250	☐
H851	1972-74	Magic Roundabout Train	Red/Blue, Mr Rusty and Basil in the locomotive (engine sound), Rosalie and Paul in the carriage and Dougal in the van, 311 mm. Blue/Yellow pictorial 'window' box with Blue nylon tow-rope	£150-200	☐
H852	1972-74	The Magic Roundabout...........	Red/White/Blue working roundabout with Swiss musical movement playing the TV theme. Dylan, Paul, Rosalie, Florence and Basil figures. 200 mm. Blue/Yellow pictorial card box	£350-450	☐
H853	1972-74	Magic Roundabout Playground................................	(820 mm.), contains a modified H852, H851 (with the figures), plus Zebedee, Dylan, four kids, see saw, park bench, 3 Blue and 3 Orange shrubs and 2 flowers. Operating carousel and track. Theme music plays when Dylan is wound up.	£500-600	☐
H859	1972-74	Mr. McHenry's Trike	Red/Yellow trike and trailer. Mr McHenry and pop-up Zebedee figures, 117 mm. Blue/Yellow pictorial 'window' box with blue nylon towing cord and instruction sheet	£100-130	☐
860-868	1972-74	Magic Roundabout individual figures:..............	860 Dougal, 861 Florence, 862 Zebedee, 863 Mr Rusty, 864 Brian Snail, 865 Basil, 866 Ermintrude the Cow, 868 Dylan the Rabbit. Each:	£20-40	☐

Ref. No.		Corgi Toys — Novelty, Film & TV Related – continued		Market Price Range	
C925	1976-81	Batcopter	Black body, Red 'Bat' rotors, Batman figure, operable winch, 143 mm.	£25-30	☐
C926	1978-80	Stromberg Helicopter	Black body/rotors, ten spare rockets. From film 'The Spy Who Loved Me'. Black/Yellow 'window' box..	£25-30	☐
927	1978-80	Chopper Squad Helicopter........	White/metallic Blue Jet Ranger helicopter, operating winch. Black/Yellow pictorial 'window' box...	£25-30	☐
C928	1981-82	Spidercopter.............................	Blue/Red body, (142 mm.), 'spider legs', retractable tongue, Black/Yellow pictorial 'window' box...	£25-30	☐
C929	1979-80	'DAILY PLANET' Jetcopter....	Red/White body (156 mm.), rocket launchers, Black/Yellow pictorial 'window' box contains 10 spare rockets.)..	£15-20	☐
C930	1972-80	'Drax' Jet Ranger Helicopter	White body, 'Drax' logo, ten spare rockets. From film 'Moonraker'. Black/Yellow 'window' box..	£20-25	☐

The Exploration Range

D2022	1980	'SCANOTRON'	Green/Black/Yellow	£15-25	☐
D2023	1980	'ROCKETRON'.......................	Blue/Yellow, Black tracks	£15-25	☐
D2024	1980	'LASERTRON'	Orange/Black/Yellow	£15-25	☐
D2025	1980	'MAGNETRON'......................	Red/Black	£15-25	☐

The Muppets Show Models

D2030	1979-80	Kermit's Car............................	Yellow car with a famous Green frog, bubble-packed..	£40-45	☐
	1980-82		Same model but in Red/Yellow pictorial 'window' box..	£35-40	☐
D2031	1979-80	Fozzie Bear's Truck.................	Red/Brown/White truck, Silver or Black hooter, bubble-packed	£35-40	☐
	1980-82		Same model but in Red/Yellow pictorial 'window' box..	£30-35	☐
D2032	1979-80	Miss Piggy's Sport Coupé	Pink sports car, Red or Pink dress, bubble-packed	£40-45	☐
	1980-82		Same model but in Red/Yellow pictorial 'window' box..	£35-40	☐
D2033	1979-80	Animal's Percussionmobile........	Red traction-engine, Yellow or Red wheels, Yellow or Black chimney, Yellow or Silver cymbal. Bubble-packed	£35-40	☐
	1980-82		Same model but in Red/Yellow pictorial 'window' box...	£30-35	☐

MAJOR PACKS (Corgi Novelty, Film & TV-related models)

1121	1960-62	'CHIPPERFIELDS' Crane Truck...........................	Red body, Raised Blue log and wheels, operable grey tinplate jib and hook, instruction leaflet. Blue/Yellow lidded box with packing...	£100-125	☐
	1963-69		Red body, raised Blue logo and wheels, operable chrome tinplate jib and hook, instruction leaflet. Blue/Yellow card box with end flaps..	£100-125	☐
1123	1961-62	'CHIPPERFIELDS' Circus Cage..........................	Red body, Yellow chassis, smooth hubs, red diecast end and middle sliding doors, 2 plastic lions, animal name decals, instruction sheet. Blue/Yellow lidded box with packing	£45-55	☐
	1963-68		Red body, Yellow chassis, smooth or spun hubs, Blue plastic end and middle sliding doors, 4 animals (lions, tigers or polar bears), animal name decals. Blue/Yellow card box with end flaps...	£45-55	☐

Gift Set No.23 'Chipperfields Circus' Set. Sold by Wallis & Wallis, Lewes, Sussex.

Ref. No.				Market Price Range	
1130	1962-70	'CHIPPERFIELDS' Horse Transporter	Bedford TK truck, Red/Blue, Green or Red 'horse-head' design at rear, cast or spun hubs, 6 Brown or Grey horses, Blue/Yellow card box........	£100-130	☐
	1970-72		As previous model but with larger 'truck' wheels	£100-130	☐
1139	1968-72	'CHIPPERFIELDS' Menagerie Transporter	Scammell Handyman Mk.III, Blue/Red cab, Blue trailer with 3 plastic cages, 2 lions, 2 tigers and 2 bears. Blue/Yellow pictorial 'window' box, spare self-adhesive securing tape for animals	£175-225	☐
1144	1969-72	'CHIPPERFIELDS' Crane & Cage with Rhino.....	Red/Blue Scammell Handyman Mk.III, 'COME TO THE CIRCUS' on n/s, silver jib & hook, stepped 'truck' front wheels on some, Grey rhinoceros in plastic cage. Blue/Yellow 'window' box	£200-250	☐
C1163	1978-82	Human Cannon Truck	Red and Blue body, 'MARVO' figure, 130 mm.	£30-40	☐
C1164	1980-83	Berliet 'DOLPHINARIUM'	Yellow/Blue cab and trailer, Clear plastic tank, 2 dolphins, girl trainer. Black/ Yellow 'window' box with header card on some	£45-55	☐
9004	1967-69	'The World of Wooster' Bentley	Green 9002 Bentley with figures of Jeeves and Wooster, plated wheels. Bubble-packed in display base	£70-90	☐

Twin Packs (Circus, Film and TV-related models)

1360	1982-?	Batmobile..................................	267 plus a Corgi juniors version. Black/Red/Yellow 'window' box	NGPP	☐
1361	197?-?	James Bond Aston-Martin	271 plus a Corgi Juniors version. Black/Red/Yellow 'window' box	NGPP	☐
1362	197?-?	James Bond Lotus Esprit	269 plus a Corgi Juniors version. Black/Red/Yellow 'window' box	NGPP	☐
1363	1982-83	Buck Rogers 'Little and Large Set'	(647) plus a smaller version. Black/Yellow pictorial 'window' box	NGPP	☐

Corgitronics and Corgimatics

Ref. No.	Year(s)	Model Type	Model Features and Size	Market Price Range	

These models have 'Battery-operated Micro-Chip Action'.

C1001	1982	HCB Angus Firestreak	Red/Yellow/White, 'RESCUE', electronic siren, on/off switch 165 mm.	£40-50	☐
C1002	1981	Sonic Corgi Truck Set	Yellow/White/Black/Red, 'SHELL SUPER OIL', 'BP OIL', remote control	£20-25	☐
C1002	1981	'YORKIE' Truck Set	White/Yellow/Blue/Orange, 'MILK CHOCOLATE YORKIE', remote control..........	£20-25	☐
C1003	1981	Ford Road Hog........................	Black, Yellow/White twirls, 2-tone horn, press-down start, 150 mm.	£10-15	☐
C1004	1981	'Beep Beep Bus'	Red, 'BTA WELCOME TO BRITAIN', 2-tone horn, press-down start, 123 mm.	£20-25	☐
	1983		Red body with 'WELCOME TO HAMLEYS' logo	£20-25	☐
C1005	1982	Police Land Rover...................	White/Blue, 'POLICE', electronic siren, press-down start, 132 mm.	£10-15	☐
C1006	1982	'RADIO WEST' Roadshow.....	'Your Local Radio 605', AM radio, advertised but not issued............................	NGPP	
C1006	1982	'RADIO LUXEMBOURG'......	Red/White, 'RTL 208', AM radio, 3 loudspeakers, 123 mm.	£20-25	☐
C1007	1982	Road Repair Unit Land Rover & Trailer............	Yellow/Red/Silver, 'ROADWORKS', press start, road drill & sound	£10-15	☐
C1008	1982	Fire Chief's Car	Red/White/Yellow/Silver, 'FIRE DEPARTMENT', press-down start, siren................	£10-15	☐
C1009	1983	MG Maestro 1600	Yellow/Red, press start, working front and rear lights, 118 mm.	£15-20	☐
			Red/Black body. Sold in Austin Rover Group box	£20-25	☐
C1024	1983	'Beep Beep Bus'	Red, 'BTA', supplied exclusively to Mothercare shops	£20-25	☐
1121	1983	Ford Transit Tipper Lorry.......	Orange/Black, Flashing light and working tipper	£20-25	☐

Corgi Toys   -   Aircraft

Ref. No.	Year(s)	Model Type	Model Features and Size	Market Price Range	

Note: Helicopters and Space Vehicles are listed in the Emergency Services, Novelty and Military Sections.

650	1973-80	'B.O.A.C.' Concorde Airliner....	White/Blue with Gold tail design, all-card box with 'BRITISH AIRWAYS'	£50-60	☐
			White/Blue with Red/White/Blue tail, display stand...................................	£10-15	☐
651	1973-81	'AIR FRANCE' Concorde	White/Blue with Gold tail design, all-card box	£70-80	☐
			White body, Red/White/Blue tail, display stand......................................	£10-15	☐
652	1973-81	'JAPAN AIRLINES' Concorde	White/Red/Blue/Black, all-card box	£200-250	☐
653	1973-81	'AIR CANADA' Concorde	White/Red/Blue/Black, all-card box	£145-195	☐
1301	1973-77	Piper Cherokee Arrow..............	Yellow/Black with White wings, or White/Blue, 'N 286 4 A'	£35-45	☐
1302	1973-77	Piper Navajo............................	Red/White or Yellow/White, 'N 9219 Y'...	£35-45	☐
1303	1973-77	Lockheed F104A Starfighter	Silver or Camouflage with Black crosses	£35-45	☐
1304	1973-77	Mig-21 PF..............................	Blue or Silver, number '57', Red stars, retractable undercarriage	£35-45	☐
1305	1973	Grumman F-11a Tiger	Blue 'NAVY', or Silver with U.S. stars	£35-45	☐
1306	1973-77	North American P51-D Mustang	Silver or Camouflage, Black props, U.S. stars, moveable control surfaces	£35-45	☐
1307	1973-77	Saab 35 X Draken	Silver or Camouflage, retractable undercarriage, Swedish Blue/Yellow markings..	£35-45	☐
1308	1973-77	BAC (or SEPCAT) Jaguar.......	Silver or Camouflage, retractable wheels, moveable control surfaces	£35-45	☐
1309	1973-77	'B.O.A.C.' Concorde	Dark Blue/White, retractable wheels	£35-45	☐
1310	1973-77	'AIR FRANCE' 'BOEING 707B'	White/Blue body, Silver wings, retractable wheels	£35-45	☐
1311	1973-77	Messerschmitt ME410	All Silver body, Black Iron Crosses on wings & fuselage	£35-45	☐

6th EDITION
'BRITISH DIECAST MODEL TOYS CATALOGUE'
USERS SURVEY

Whether you are a collector or trader we would greatly value your views on this new Edition and would ask you to kindly complete and return this questionnaire.

We hope to publish the results of this survey and for the three most helpful and constructive replies we receive we shall be giving a years free subscription to the collecting magazine or newspaper of their choice. If necessary do please use a separate sheet for your replies.

1. What do you MOST like about the Catalogue?

....

....

2. What do you LEAST like about the Catalogue?

....

....

3. Is the Catalogue now too big?
   Would you like to see it split up into 2 volumes, i) Pre 1970 issues ii) Post 1970 issues?
   iii) Individual sections e.g. Dinky Toys?

....

....

4. Do you own model listings, Catalogues or pictures of models not currently listed?

....

....

5. Would you like the database made available on disc or CD-ROM for use on a personal computer?

....

NAME & ADDRESS (BLOCK CAPITALS PLEASE)..

....

....

Kindly return the form to:- Swapmeet Publications, PO Box 47, Felixstowe, Suffolk, England. IP11 7LP.

WINNERS OF THE 5th EDITION 'NEW INFORMATION' COMPETITION

As so much excellent new information has been provided the number of winners increased to four as follows:-

Ray Holcroft of Lancashire for Dinky Toys information. Wilf Bainbridge of Scotland and Keith Harbour of Middlesex for Corgi Toys information. Dave Jowett of Nottingham for Wrenn Railways model listings.

Grateful thanks to all who took the time and trouble to send in new information.

| --- | --- | --- | --- | --- | --- |
1312	1973-77	Boeing 727 'TWA'......	White body, Silver wings, retractable wheels	**£35-45**	☐
1313	1973-77	Japanese Zero-Sen A6M5......	Green or Silver with Red circles, retractable wheels	**£35-45**	☐
1315	1973-77	'PAN-AM' Boeing 747......	White body, Silver wings, hinged nose, retractable wheels	**£35-45**	☐
1315/1	1973-77	'BRITISH AIRWAYS' Jumbo	Boeing 747, White/Silver, Blue logo, hinged nose, retractable wheels......	**£35-45**	☐
1316	1973-77	McDonnell Douglas F-4c5......	Phantom II in Silver or Camouflage with retractable undercarriage	**£35-45**	☐
1320	1978-80	'BRITISH AIRWAYS' VC-10..	White/Silver with Red tail, Blue logo, retractable wheels......	**£35-45**	☐
1325	1978-80	'SWISSAIR' DC-10......	White/Silver with Red stripe and tail, retractable wheels	**£35-45**	☐

Corgi Toys - Roadmaking Vehicles and Cranes

Ref. No.	Year(s)	Model Type	Model Features and Size	Market Price Range	
54	1974	Massey Ferguson Shovel......	Orange/White tractor body, Silver shovel, *'Block Construction'*, 150 mm.	**£35-45**	☐
109	1968-69	'PENNYBURN' Trailer......	Blue body, Yellow chassis, 76 mm.	**£30-35**	☐
403	1974-79	Thwaites Skip Dumper......	Yellow/Green tipping body, driver, WhizzWheels, 83 mm.	**£25-35**	☐
406	1971-75	Mercedes-Benz Unimog......	Yellow/Green or Yellow/Red body, detachable top, suspension, hook, 91 mm.	**£25-35**	☐
409	1971-75	Unimog Dumper......	White/Red or Blue/Yellow body, suspension, hook, 104 mm.	**£20-30**	☐
C409	1981	'ALLIS CHALMERS' Forklift	Yellow body, pallets/load/driver, 112 mm.	**£15-20**	☐
413	1976-78	Mazda Motorway Maintenance......	Yellow/Black body, figure, road signs, bollards, decal sheet enclosed.	**£25-35**	☐
458	1958-66	E.R.F. Earth Dumper......	Red and Yellow body, 'E.R.F.' cast-in, smooth or shaped hubs, 95 mm.	**£40-45**	☐
459	1974-78	Raygu Rascal Roller......	Yellow/Green body, *'Road Roller'*, 125 mm.	**£20-25**	☐
460	1959-61	E.R.F. Neville Cement Tipper ..	Pale Yellow and Silver body, metal or plastic fillers, smooth or shaped hubs, 95 mm.	**£45-55**	☐
483	1968-72	Dodge Tipper Truck......	Yellow/Black or White/Blue body, *'KEW FARGO'*, spun or cast wheels, 136 mm.	**£25-35**	☐
494	1967-72	Bedford Tipper......	Red/Yellow body, rear view mirror, 102 mm.	**£35-45**	☐
		variant:	Red body, Silver tipper	**£65-75**	☐

MAJOR PACKS (Corgi Roadmaking Vehicles and Cranes)

Ref. No.	Year(s)	Model Type	Model Features and Size	Market Price Range	
C1101	1976-81	Mobile Crane......	Yellow/Blue body, *'Warner & Swasey'*, 150 mm.	**£25-30**	☐
1102	1958-62	'EUCLID' TC-12 Tractor......	Yellow or Pale Lime-Green, Pale Grey tracks, 159 mm. Box has inner lining	**£80-90**	☐
			As previous model but with Black tracks.	**£50-60**	☐
C1102	1974-76	'BERLIET' Bottom Dumper	Yellow and Orange body, *'Road Construction'*, 287 mm.	**£30-35**	☐
1103	1960-63	'EUCLID' Crawler Tractor......	Yellow or Pale Lime-Green, Pale Grey tracks, 111 mm.	**£80-90**	☐
			As previous model but with Black tracks.	**£50-60**	☐
1107	1963-66	'EUCLID' with Dozer......	Yellow or Pale Lime-Green, Grey tracks, driver, 159 mm.	**£60-70**	☐
			Yellow body, Black tracks, driver	**£70-90**	☐
1110	1976-80	'JCB' Crawler Loader......	Yellow/White body, Red working bucket, Black tracks, driver	**£15-20**	☐
1110	1976-80	J.C.B. Crawler......	Yellow and White body, driver, 115 mm.	**£15-20**	☐
			Light Blue/Orange with Light Blue chassis, driver.	**£15-20**	☐
			Yellow body, Light Blue cab, Red bucket.	**£15-20**	☐
			Red body, Light Blue cab and bucket	**£15-20**	☐
C1113	1981-86	'HYSTER' Handler......	Yellow or Black/White main body, *'US Lines'*, hoist, 212 mm.	**£15-20**	☐
	1986-87		Yellow or Black/White main body, *'SEALINK'*, container, export model	**£10-15**	☐
	1986-87		White/Dark Blue/Yellow, *'MICHELIN'*, container	**£10-15**	☐
1119	1983	Mercedes Load Lugger......	Yellow/Red body, *'CORGI'*	**£15-20**	☐
1121	1983	Ford Transit Tipper......	Orange/Beige body, *'CORGI'*, (Corgimatic)	**£15-20**	☐
1122	1984	Mercedes Mixer......	Orange body, Black stripes	**£10-15**	☐
1122	1985		Orange body, White revolving drum, Black/Yellow design	**£10-15**	☐
1128	1963-76	'PRIESTMAN' Cub Shovel......	Red/Yellow body, driver, 165 mm.	**£30-35**	☐
1128	1984	Mercedes Tipper......	Yellow cab, Red tipper, 6 wheels, *'BLOCK'* logo	**£10-15**	☐
1128	1985	Mercedes Tipper......	Black body, White logo *'TARMAC'*	**£10-15**	☐
1145	1970-76	Unimog Goose Dumper......	Yellow/Red body, *'406'*, 171 mm.	**£30-35**	☐
1150	1971	Mercedes 406 Snowplough......	Unimog in Green/Black, 2 Red flags, Orange/Silver plough	**£30-35**	☐
			Unimog vehicle, Yellow cab and back, Red chassis, Silver snow-plough, 2 Red flags	**£30-35**	☐
1152	1983-	'BARRATT' Tipper......	Green/White body, tipper section tips, 145 mm.	**£5-10**	☐
1153	1973-74	'PRIESTMAN' Crane......	Red/Orange body, *'Higrab'*, 230 mm.	**£45-55**	☐
C1153	1983-84	'WIMPEY' Tipper Truck......	Green/Silver body, tipping section tips, 145 mm. (Scania)	**£5-10**	☐
C1153	1984		Yellow body	**£5-10**	☐
C1153	1985	'LAING' Tipper Truck......	As previous model but with Yellow body and Black logo	**£5-10**	☐
1154	1974-76	Priestman Crane Truck......	Yellow/Red body, Silver boom, hook, 240 mm.	**£45-55**	☐
1154	1979	'BLOCK CONSTRUCTION'......	Orange/Yellow crane, White body, brick pallet load	**£25-35**	☐
C1155	1975-79	'Skyscraper' Tower Crane......	Yellow/Red body, Black tracks, 340 mm.	**£35-40**	☐
1156	1977-80	Volvo Concrete Mixer......	Yellow/Red body, *'RAPIER'*.	**£20-25**	☐
1156	1980		Orange/White body, *'BLOCK CONSTRUCTION'*	**£15-20**	☐

Corgi Toys - Miscellaneous models
Jeeps, Land Rovers, Pick-ups, Caravans, Motor Cycles, Go-Karts, Trailers, Public Service Vehicles, etc

Ref. No.	Year(s)	Model Type	Model Features and Size	Market Price Range	
C46	1983-	Super Kart	Blue or Orange main body, Red/Silver racing driver	£5-10	☐
100	1957-61	Dropside Trailer	Cream/Red or Yellow body, drawbar, 108 mm.	£10-15	☐
101	1958-61	Platform Trailer	Grey/Yellow body, drawbar and axle swivel, 108 mm.	£10-15	☐
104	1965-66	Dolphin 20 Cabin Cruiser	Blue/White boat, Red trailer, helmsman, 136 mm.	£20-25	☐
C171	1982-	Street Bike	Red, Silver and Black body, multicoloured swirl	£5-10	☐
C172	1982-	'POLICE' Bike	White/Black/Silver body	£5-10	☐
C173	1982-	Cafe Racer	Silver and Black racing number '26', '750 cc Class'	£5-10	☐
289	1976	VW Polo 'DBP'	Yellow/White, Blue roof beacon, left-hand drive, WhizzWheels, (German issue)	NGPP	☐
383	1970-73	VW 1200 'PTT'	Yellow Swiss Postal livery, (Swiss issue)	£100-150	☐
383	1970-73	VW 1200 'ADAC'	Yellow/White 'ADAC' livery, (German issue)	£100-150	☐
406	1957-63	Land Rover Pick-Up	Yellow with Black roof, smooth or shaped hubs, Blue box, leaflet	£55-65	☐
			All Cream, smooth hubs, Blue box, leaflet	£55-65	☐
			All Green, smooth hubs, Blue box, leaflet	£55-65	☐
			Yellow with Black roof, smooth or shaped hubs, Blue/Yellow box, no leaflet	£45-55	☐
			Yellow body with Red seats, Grey steering wheel, smooth hubs	£80-90	☐
			Metallic Blue, Cream roof, smooth or shaped hubs, Blue/Yellow box, no leaflet	£45-50	☐
			Dark Green body, spun hubs	£100-125	☐
409	1959-63	Forward Control Jeep	Light Blue body, Red grille, smooth or shaped hubs, 91 mm.	£25-35	☐
C415	1976-78	Mazda Camper	Red body with drop-down tailboard, White caravan, 140 mm.	£25-30	☐
417	1963-65	Land Rover Breakdown	Red/Yellow, 4 strut bumper, smooth wheels, 'BREAKDOWN SERVICE'	£40-50	☐
417s	1963-65	Land Rover Breakdown	As previous model but with solid bumper, shaped wheels, suspension	£35-45	☐
C419	1978-79	Covered Jeep CJ5	Green with White plastic top, 100 mm.	£15-20	☐
420	1962-66	Ford 'Airborne' Caravan	Ford Thames in Two-tone Green, Brown interior or Blue/Pale Grey, Red interior or Blue/Green, Brown interior	£40-50	☐
			Two-tone Lilac, Beige interior	£70-80	☐
C421	1977-79	Land Rover Safari Hardtop	Orange/Black body, roof rack with ladder, spare wheel, 114 mm.	£15-20	☐
		Land Rover Safari Hardtop	A variant of C421 with 'FOREST FIRE WARDEN'	£15-20	☐
431	1964-66	Volkswagen Pick-Up	Yellow/Red, seats, steering wheel, suspension, 91 mm.	£45-55	☐
434	1963-66	Volkswagen Kombi	Two-tone Green, Red or Yellow seats, 91 mm.	£45-55	☐
438	1963-77	Land Rover	Red, Dark Green or Metallic Green body with either Grey, Dark Grey or Cream plastic canopy, spare wheel on bonnet, 95 mm.	£50-60	☐
438	19?-?	Land Rover 'LEPRA'	Promotional Metallic Green body and Cream canopy, Red 'LEPRA' logo, promotional	£200-250	☐
		Promotional Land Rover	with '10 MILLIONTH CORGI LAND ROVER' label	£50-75	☐
C440	1979-	Mazda Custom Pick-Up	Orange/Yellow/Red, US flag, 120 mm.	£10-15	☐
C441	1979-82	'GOLDEN EAGLE' Jeep	Brown/Tan or Gold/White, detachable roof, spare wheel on some, 100 mm.	£10-15	☐
C447	1983	'RENEGADE' Jeep	Yellow with Red hood	£10-15	☐
C448	1985	4 x 4 'RENEGADE' Jeep	Red/White body, roll bar, 100 mm.	£5-10	☐
C457	1981-83	Talbot Matra Rancho	Red/Black or Green/Black, opening doors and boot, tilt seats, 120 mm.	£10-15	☐
C457	1984	Talbot Matra Rancho	Green or White/Blue body, Brown seats, 120 mm.	£5-10	☐
470	1965-72	Forward Control Jeep	Blue/Grey or Mustard Yellow, suspension, left-hand drive, 91 mm.	£30-35	☐
477	1966-67	Land Rover Breakdown	Red/Yellow/Silver, spare wheel on some, hook, WhizzWheels, 114 mm.	£30-35	☐
478	1965-69	Jeep Tower Wagon	Green, Yellow and Silver body, figure, 129 mm.	£20-25	☐
C490	1967-70	Volkswagen Breakdown	Tan/Red, tool-box, 2 spare wheels, 102 mm.	£40-50	☐
C490	1976-79	Touring Caravan	White and Blue body, opening doors, drawbar, 125 mm.	£10-15	☐
C493	1976-78	Mazda B 1600 Pick-Up	Blue body, drop-down tailboard, 120 mm.	£10-15	☐
C495	1983-	4x4 Mazda 'OB TRUCK'	Blue/Black, 'Corgi Cruiser', drop-down tailboard, 121 mm.	£5-10	☐
C495	1985	4x4 Mazda	As previous model but Blue/White body, 'SURF RIDER'	£5-10	☐
C501	1984	Range Rover	Beige and Dark Brown body	£5-10	☐
C507	1987	Range Rover Rally	Navy Blue body, White roof, 'PARIS - DAKAR' logo	£20-30	☐
C522		Range Rover	Red/White/Blue, 'STIMOROL'	NGPP	☐
C567	1984	Range Rover	White body, 'PARIS MATCH', and 'VSD'	£7-10	☐
C619	1986	Range Rover	Dark Beige body, Black ladder, roof-rack, luggage	£5-10	☐
			Red body, 'ROYAL MAIL' logo	£10-15	☐
Q619/3	1990	'NORWEB' Land Rover	White with 3 Black side stripes, spare wheel	NRP	☐
681	1971	Stunt Bike	Gold engine, Silver WhizzWheels, Mauve/Yellow rider, Red trolley (19,000 made)	NGPP	☐

MAJOR PACKS (Miscellaneous Corgi models)

1106	1984	'CORGI' Loadlugger	Yellow body and chassis, Red 'BIG BIN'	£10-15	☐
1114	1984	Mercedes Gritter	Yellow/Black body and plough, ladder	£10-15	☐
1114			Yellow/Black body with Red stripes, 'MOTORWAY MAINTENANCE'	£10-15	☐
1115	1985	Parisienne Refuse Truck	Green body, 'PARIS' logo, export model	£10-15	☐
1116	1979	S & D Refuse Collector	Orange or Red body, 'City Sanitation', 151 mm.	£15-20	☐
1116/2	1988		Blue cab, White tipper, 'BOROUGH COUNCIL'	£5-10	☐
1117	1980	'FAUN' Street-sweeper	Orange/Yellow vehicle with operator	£15-20	☐
			All-Yellow version	£15-20	☐
1119	1960-62	HDL Hovercraft 'SR-N1'	Blue/Grey/White body, Yellow rudders and wheels	£30-35	☐
1150	1974-77	Unimog with Snow Plough	Yellow/Brown body, Silver blade, 2 flags, 155 mm.	£30-35	☐
C522/2	1986?	Ruby Anniversary Land Rover	Maroon body with '40TH ANNIVERSARY' on bonnet. Special box	NGPP	☐

Corgi Toys Gift Sets

Ref. No.	Year(s)	Set Name	Contents	Market Price Range	
1	1957-62	Transporter and 4 Cars	1101 Blue/Yellow Bedford Carrimore Transporter plus 201 Austin Cambridge, 208 Jaguar 2.4, 301 Triumph TR2 and 302 MGA, plus 2 Yellow/Black 'Corgi Toys' dummy boxes	£500-600	☐
1	1957-62	Transporter and 4 Cars	1101 Red/Two-tone Blue Transporter, 200 Ford Consul, 201 Austin Cambridge, 204 Rover 90, 205 Riley Pathfinder, 2 Yellow 'Corgi Toys' dummy boxes	£400-500	☐
C1	1983	Ford Sierra Set	Ford Sierra 299 with Blue body and Blue/Cream Caravan	£20-30	☐
C1/2	1985	'London Scene'	469 'LONDON STANDARD', Sierra Police Car and 425/1 Taxi	£15-20	☐
2	1958-66	Land Rover and Pony Trailer Set	438 Land Rover (Green, Beige tin tilt) and 102 Pony Trailer (Red/Black)	£150-175	☐
		colour change:	As previous but with All Red Land Rover	£200-250	☐
		colour change:	As previous set but Light Brown Land Rover (Cream plastic tilt) Light Brown/Cream trailer	£70-80	☐
2	1971-73	Unimog Dumper and Shovel	1128 and 1145	£30-35	☐
C2		Fire Set	no details at present	£15-20	☐
3	1959-62	Land Rover with Thunderbird Missile	Contains 350 and 351	£200-250	☐
3	1967-69	Batmobile and Batboat	1st issue: 267 Batmobile plus 107 Batboat, in plain window box with 4 figures	£250-300	☐
3	1979	2nd issue:	267 Batmobile and 107 Batboat in pictorial window box, only 2 figures	£100-125	☐
C3	1986-88	'British Gas' Set	Contains Blue/White Ford Cargo Van, Ford Escort Van (2nd), plus compressor	£20-25	☐
4	1959-62	Bristol Ferranti Bloodhound Guided Missile Set	Contains: 351, 1115, 1116, 1117 (see 'Military Vehicles' section)	£250-350	☐
4	1974-75	Country Farm Set	Models 50, 62 and equipment	£40-50	☐
5	1959-60	Racing Car Set	150 (Red) 151 (Blue) 152 (Green). All have flat spun wheels	£150-200	☐
5	1960-61	Racing Car Set	150 (Red) 151 (Blue) 152 (Green). All have cast spoked wheels	£150-200	☐
5s	1962-63	Racing Car Set	150s (Red) 151a (Blue) 152s (Turquoise). 'Gift Set 5s' stickers on box	£150-200	☐
5	1967-72	Agricultural Set	484 Livestock Transporter and pigs, 438 Land Rover (no hood) 62, 69, accessories 1490 skip & churns, 4 calves, farmhand & dog, 6 sacks	£150-200	☐
6	1959-62	'Rocket Age' Set	Contains: 350, 351, 352, 353, 1106, 1108, 1117 (see 'Military' section)	£600-800	☐
6	1967-69	Cooper Maserati Racing Set	Contains 490 VW Breakdown Truck plus 156 on trailer	£70-90	☐
7	1959-63	Tractor and Trailer Set	Contains 50 and 51	£70-80	☐
7	1968-75	'DAKTARI' Set	438 Land Rover in Green with Black Zebra stripes. 5 figures: Paula, Dr Marsh Tracy with chimp Judy on his lap, a Tiger on the bonnet, and Clarence The Short-Sighted Lion (with spectacles!)	£75-85	☐
8	1959-61	Combine Harvester, Tractor & Trailer Set	Contains 1111, 50 and 51	£200-250	☐
8	1960-74	'Lions Of Longleat' Set	Land Rover, keeper, 3 lions, dens and meals (with early wheels)	£100-125	☐
			As above but with WhizzWheels	£70-80	☐
C8/2		Police Set		£15-20	☐
9	1959-62	Corporal Guided Missile Set	Contains: 1112, 1113, 1118 (see 'Military Vehicles' section)	£300-400	☐
9	1968-72	Tractor, Trailer and Shovel Set	Contains 66, 69 and 62	£100-125	☐
9		3 Racing Minis Set	Yellow, White and Blue, numbers/stripes/adverts, special Red 'Hamleys' box	£90-110	☐
10	1968-69	Rambler Marlin and Kayaks Set	Blue/White 319 with Trailer and 2 Canoes	£100-130	☐
10	1974-78	Centurion Tank and Transporter Set	Contains 901 and 1100 Mack articulated transporter	£70-80	☐
10	1982	Jeep Set	Red 441 plus two motorcycles on trailer	£20-25	☐
C10	1985	Sierra & Caravan Set	C299 2.3 Sierra plus Pale Brown caravan with Blue/Grey strip	£25-35	☐
11	1960-64	E.R.F. Dropside and Trailer	456 and 101 with cement and planks load	£125-150	☐
			As above but with WhizzWheels	£60-70	☐
11	1971-75	London Gift Set	Contains 418 Taxi with 468 'OUTSPAN' and 226 Mini	£75-95	☐
C11	1980	London Gift Set	C425 Taxi with C469 Bus 'B.T.A.' and policeman	£30-35	☐
12	1961-66	Circus Gift Set	1121 Circus Crane Truck and 1123 Circus Cage, plus instructions	£150-175	☐
12	1968-70	Grand Prix Racing Set	155, 156 and 330 with Volkswagen tender, trailer and equipment	£200-250	☐
12	1970-72	Grand Prix Racing Set	158, 159 and 330 (or 371) with Volkswagen tender, trailer and equipment. The artwork on the box and the vac-formed base are different from previous issue	£200-250	☐
C12	1981-	Glider and Trailer Set	345 with Trailer and Glider	£30-40	☐
13	1964-67	Fordson Tractor & Plough Set	Contains 60 and 61	£75-85	☐
13	1969-72	Renault 16 'PARAMOUNT' Film Unit	White/Black body, 'TOUR DE FRANCE' logos, camera/operator, cyclist	£75-85	☐
13	1981-82	Tour De France 'RALEIGH' Team Car	373 Peugeot, White body, Red/Yellow 'RALEIGH' and 'TOTAL' logos, racing cycles and Manager with loudhailer	£50-60	☐
C13	?	'RAC' Ford Escort & Caravan Set	Flashing light in middle or front of van roof	£40-50	☐
C13	?	'AA' Ford Escort & Caravan Set	Flashing light in middle or front of van roof	£40-50	☐
14	1961-65	Tower Wagon Set	409 Jeep, Yellow cradle, lamp standard & electrician	£60-70	☐
14	1969-73	Giant 'DAKTARI' Set	Gift Set 7 items plus 503 and 484 transporters	£200-250	☐
15	1963-64	Silverstone Set	150s, 151a, 152s, 215s, 304s, 309, 417s, 3 buildings, plain box (no picture)	£750-100	☐
15	1964-66	Silverstone Set	150s, 154, 152s, 215s, 304s, 309, 417s, 3 buildings, layout shown on box	£750-100	☐
15	1968-76	Land Rover & Horsebox Set	Contains 438, 112, horse and foal	£50-60	☐
16	1961-66	'ECURIE ECOSSE' Set	1126 Transporter with 3 racing cars with instruction leaflet.		☐
		i)	Metallic Dark Blue 1126 Transporter (with Orange lettering) 150 Vanwall (Red, no.'25') 151 Lotus Eleven (Blue, number '3') 152 BRM (Turquoise, no.'3')	£200-250	☐
		ii)	Metallic Dark Blue 1126 Transporter (with Yellow lettering) 150s Vanwall, 151a Lotus Eleven (Blue, no. '7') 152s BRM	£300-350	☐

61

Ref. No.	Year	Name	Description	Market Price Range	
	1965	iii).........	Metallic Light Blue 1126 Transporter (with Red lettering) 150s Vanwall, 152s BRM, 154 Ferrari (Red, no.'36')...	£200-250	☐
		iv).........	Metallic Dark Blue 1126 Transporter (with Light Blue lettering and ridges) 150s Vanwall, 152s BRM, 154 Ferrari..	£200-250	☐
17	1963-67	Ferrari Racing Set	Contains 438 Land Rover in Red with Green canopy, plus Red 154 Ferrari F1 on Yellow trailer...	£85-95	☐
17	1976-81	Military Set	Contains 904, 906, 920 (see 'Military Vehicles' section)..........................	£40-50	☐
C17	1986	'BRITISH TELECOM' Set......	Ford Cargo Box Van, Ford Escort Van and a Compressor	£15-20	☐
18	1961-63	Ford Tractor and Plough Set....	Contains 55 and 56	£70-80	☐
18	1976-77	Emergency Gift Set	Contains 402, 481, C921 (see 'Emergency Vehicles' section)..................	£40-50	☐
C18/1	?	3 Mini Racers Set	with *'CHELSEA'*, *'PARK LANE'* and *'PICADILLY'* logos..........................	£20-30	☐
C18/2	?	Mini Special Editions Set	with *'RED HOT'*, *'RITZ'* and *'JET BLACK'* logos......................................	£20-30	☐
	Note:.....		C18/1 and C18/2 were sold (in long 'window' boxes) exclusively by Woolworths.		
19	1962-68	'CHIPPERFIELDS' Cage Set...	438 Land Rover (plastic tilt) and 607 Elephant and cage on trailer	£150-175	☐
19		'R.N.L.I.' Set	438 Land Rover plus Orange dinghy on trailer with *'Mumbles Lifeboat'* logo	£45-65	☐
C19	1972-77	Land Rover & Nipper Aircraft	438 Land Rover (Blue/Orange) Yellow/Red or All-Orange plane *'23'* on trailer.........	£45-55	☐
19	1973-77	'CORGI FLYING CLUB'.......	Blue/Orange Land Rover (438) with aircraft	£60-70	☐
C19	1979-82	Emergency Gift Set	Contains C339 and C921	£30-40	☐
C19	1980-82	Emergency Gift Set	Contains C339 and C931 in Red/White liveries	£35-45	☐
C19/7	1990	Norwegian 'AMBULANSE' Set	White Ford Transit Van & Saab 9000 *'POLITI'*	£30-40	☐
C19/8	1990	Swedish 'AMBULANS' Set	White/Red Ford Transit & White/Blue Saab 9000 *'POLIS'*	£30-40	☐
C19/9	1990	Swedish Breakdown Set	Red/Yellow Ford Transit *'Bjarnings'*, Black Saab 9000 *'BRANDCHEF'*	£30-40	☐
20	1961	Golden Guinea Set	Gold-plated 224 Bentley Continental, 234 Ford Consul, 229 Chevrolet Corvair, Catalogue, 2 Accessory Packs..	£150-200	☐
20	1973	Tri-Deck Transporter Set	1st issue contains 1146 Transporter with 210 'Saint's' Volvo, 311 Ford Capri, 343 Pontiac, 372 Lancia, 377 Marcos, and 378 MGC GT (rare Orange version)	£500-600	☐
20		Tri-Deck Transporter Set	late issue with WhizzWheels (sold in Harrods) contains 377 Marcos (Silver Green), 382 Porsche Targa (Silver Blue), 201 Volvo (Orange 'Saint' label), 313 Ford Cortina GXL (Bronze/Black), 334 Mini (Orange), plus retailers pull-out leaflet illustrating Transporter..	£500-600	☐
C20	1978-80	Emergency Gift Set	Contains C429, C482, C921 (see 'Emergency Vehicles' section)...............	£30-40	☐
C20/2	1986	A.A. Set	Ford Escort and Transit Vans, Ford Transit Breakdown..........................	£15-20	☐
C20/3	1986	'A.A.' Set	Range Rover plus caravan 'Information Centre'	£15-25	☐
21	1962-66	E.R.F. Dropside and Trailer	456 and 101 with milk churns and self-adhesive accessories	£175-225	☐
21	1969-71	'CHIPPERFIELDS' Circus Set..	Contains 1144 Crane & Cage and 1139 Menagerie Transporter	£750-1000	☐
C21	1980-82	Superman Set.............................	Contains 260, 265 and 925..	£100-125	☐
C21/2	1986	R.A.C. Set	Range Rover, Ford Escort Van and Ford Transit Breakdown	£15-20	☐
22	1962-66	Farming Models Set	111, 406, 51, 101, 53, 1487, 1490, accessories & GS18..........................	£600-700	☐
C22	1980-82	James Bond Set	Contains 269, 271 and 649...	£125-150	☐
C22	1986	'ROYAL MAIL' Set	Ford Cargo & Escort Vans, Austin Mini Metro *'DATAPOST'*................	£15-20	☐
23	1962-66	'CHIPPERFIELDS'...................	1st issue: 1121 Crane Truck, 2 x 1123 Animal Cages (2 lions, 2 polar bears) plus Gift Set 19 and 426 Booking Office	£400-500	☐
	1964	2nd issue:.....	as 1st issue but 503 'TK Giraffe Truck' replaces 426 Booking Office	£350-450	☐
C23	1980-82	Spiderman Set	Contains 261, 266 and 928...	£90-110	☐
24	1963-68	Commer Constructor Set	2 cab/chassis units, 4 interchangeable bodies, milkman, accessories.........	£80-95	☐
24	1976-	Mercedes and Caravan Set.......	Contains 285 and 490 with colour change 1980	£25-35	☐
25	1963-66	BP or Shell Garage Set	Contains Garage with 5 various cars, figures and accessories	£150-200	☐
25	1969-71	Racing Car and Tender Set......	Contains 159 and Volkswagen Tender	£80-90	☐
25	1980	Talbot Rancho Set	457 plus two motorcycles on trailer...	£15-20	☐
26	1971-75	Beach Buggy Set.....................	381 plus Sailing Boat	£30-40	☐
26	1981-83	Corgi Racing Set	457 Talbot Matra Rancho, 160 Hesketh (Yellow) on 'Corgi Racing Team' trailer......	£35-45	☐
27	1963-72	Priestman Shovel on Machinery Carrier	1128 and 1131 (Bedford Machinery Carrier)..	£90-110	☐
C27		Emergency Set	no details	£15-20	☐
28	1963-66	Transporter and 4 Cars	1105 Bedford TK Transporter with 222 Renault Floride, 230 Mercedes-Benz, 232 Fiat, 234 Ford Classic, 2 dummy 'Corgi Toys' boxes, instructions. Pictorial box	£400-500	☐
28	1963-66	Mazda Dinghy Set....................	493 Mazda plus dinghy and trailer...	£40-45	☐
C28	1987	Post Set	Contains 656/2, Red Sierra (racing number '63') or Brown Saab 9000	£20-25	☐
29	1963-64	Massey Ferguson Tractor and Trailer Set........	Contains 50, 51, driver..	£65-75	☐
C29	1981	'CORGI' Pony Club.................	Contains 441 Jeep, 112 trailer, girl on pony, 3 jumps, 3 hay bales	£25-35	☐
29	1975-76	Ferrari Racing Set	Contains 323 and 150, *'DUCKHAMS'*..	£60-75	☐
30	1973-73	Grand Prix Gift Set	'Kit' versions of 151 Yardley (1501), 154 JPS (1504), 152 Surtees (1502) plus 153 Surtees (1503)? in unique Norris livery. Mail order only	£150-200	☐
C30	1978-80	Circus Gift Set	Land Rover and Trailer..	£50-60	☐
31	1965-68	Buick Riviera Boat Set.............	245 Buick, Red boat trailer, and Dolphin Cabin Cruiser towing water skier	£100-125	☐
C31	1977-80	Safari Land Rover Set..............	C341 Land Rover with animal trailer, Warden and Lion..........................	£30-40	☐
32	1965-68	Tractor, Shovel and Trailer Set	Contains 54 and 62	£100-125	☐
C32	1976-79	Lotus Racing Set	Black/Gold C301 Lotus Elite, and C154 JPS Lotus on trailer..................	£50-75	☐
C32	1979-83	Lotus Racing Set	Black/Gold C301 Lotus Elite, and C154 Texaco Lotus on trailer.............	£50-75	☐
C32	1989-90	3 Model Set	Contains Concorde, Taxi and Routemaster Bus 'STANDARD'	£20-30	☐
33	1965-68	Tractor & Beast Carrier	Contains 55 and 58	£100-125	☐
?	1968-72	Tractor & Beast Carrier	Contains 67 and 58	£70-80	☐
C33	1980	'DLRG' Rescue Set..................	White/Red 421 Land Rover and boat on trailer	£25-30	☐
34	1977-79	Tractor and Tipping Trailer	Contains 55 and 56	£25-35	☐

Ref. No.			*Corgi Toys — Gift Sets – continued*	Market Price Range	

Ref. No.				Market Price Range	
35	1965-68	London Gift Set	418 Taxi with 648 *'Corgi Toys'* and policeman	£80-100	☐
C35	1978-79	'CHOPPER SQUAD' Surf Boat	Contains 927, 419, trailer, rescue boat	£30-40	☐
36	1967-70	Marlin Rambler Set	Contains 263 and Boat	£45-65	☐
36	1967-70	Oldsmobile Toronado Set	Contains 276 (Greenish-Blue) Chrome trailer, Yellow/Blue speedboat, 3 figures	£120-140	☐
36	1983	Off-Road Set............................	447 (Dark Blue/Cream, racing number '5') plus power-boat on trailer..................	£25-35	☐
C36	1976-78	Tarzan Set...........................	Includes Light Green 421 Land Rover, paler Green 'zebra' stripes, Tarzan, Jane, Cheetah (chimp) boy, dinghy with hunter, elephant, snake, vines, trailer (same colours as Land Rover) with White cage	£90-120	☐
37	1966-69	'Lotus Racing Team'	490 VW Breakdown Truck, Red trailer with cars 318, 319, 155, plus 2 sets of racing numbers ('5' and '9') a 1966 illustrated checklist and a pack of cones....................	£200-250	☐
37	1979-82	Fiat X-19 Set	Fiat X-19 and Boat 'Carlsberg'	£30-40	☐
38	1977-78	Mini Camping Set	Mini with 2 figures, tent, barbecue	£35-45	☐
38	1965-67	'1965 Monte Carlo Rally'.........	318 Mini Cooper 'S', 322 Rover 2000, and 326 Citroën DS19. Monte Carlo emblem on each bonnet	£400-500	☐
C38	1980-	Jaguar XJS Set	319 with Powerboat on Trailer	£20-30	☐
40	1967-69	The Avengers Set.....................	John Steed & his Bentley, Emma Peel & her Lotus Elan, 3 Black umbrellas	£300-400	☐
C40	1977-80	Batman Gift Set....................	Contains 107, 267, 925...........................	£175-225	☐
41	1966-68	Ford 'H' Series Transporter and six Cars	1138 Transporter (Red/Two-tone Blue), 252 Rover 2000 (Metallic Plum), 251 Hillman Imp (Metallic Bronze), 440 Ford Cortina Estate (Metallic Blue/Brown 'wood' panels), 204 Morris Mini-Minor (Light Blue), 321 Austin Mini Cooper 'S' (Red, RN '2', '1966 Monte Carlo Rally', with roof signatures), 180 Morris Mini Cooper 'S' (Black/Red, 'wickerwork' panels). (Only sold by mail order)	£300-400	☐
C41	1977-81	Silver Jubilee Set.....................	The State Landau with Their Majesties (and a Corgi!)............................	£15-20	☐
C42	1979-80	Agricultural Set	Contains C34, C43, Silo/Elevator	£45-55	☐
C43	1979-80	Silo and Conveyor Set	Silo and Conveyor 'CORGI HARVESTING COMPANY LTD'	£40-50	☐
C43	1985	'TOYMASTER' Transport Set ..	Contains C496 'ROYAL MAIL', C515 'BMX' plus Volvo 'TOYMASTER' truck......	£20-25	☐
C44	1978-80	Metropolitan Police Set.............	421 Land Rover, 112 Horsebox plus Policeman on horse	£40-50	☐
45	1966	'All Winners' Set	261 James Bond's Aston-Martin, 310 Chevrolet Stingray, 324 Marcos Volvo 1800GT, 325 Ford Mustang Competition, 314 Ferrari Berlinetta. 9,000 sets sold	£300-400	☐
C45	1978-80	Royal Canadian Police Set........	R.C.M.P. Land Rover (421), Trailer (102) & 'Mountie' on horse	£75-85	☐
46	1966-69	'All Winners' Set	264 Oldsmobile Toronado (Metallic Blue), 307 Jaguar 'E'-type (Chrome finish, RN '2', driver), 314 Ferrari Berlinetta (Red, RN '4'), 337 Chevrolet Stingray (Yellow, RN '13'), 327 MGB GT (Red/Black, suitcase, accessories)	£200-250	☐
47	1966-69	Ford Tractor & Conveyor Set...	Contains 67, trailer with conveyor belt, figure, accessories	£75-80	☐
C47	1978-80	Pony Club Set.......................	421 Land Rover & Horsebox in Metallic Bronze, girl on pony figure	£25-30	☐
48	1967-68	Ford 'H' series Transporter and six Cars	1159 Transporter (Orange/Silver/Two-tone Blue) with 252 Rover 2000 (Metallic Maroon), 251 Hillman Imp, 440 Ford Cortina Estate, 180 Morris Mini Cooper 'S' (with 'wickerwork' panels), 204 Morris Mini-Minor (Metallic Maroon), 321 Mini Cooper 'S' ('1966 Monte Carlo Rally'), Red/White, RN '2'	£200-250	☐
	1968	'SUN/RAC' variation..............	Same as previous set but the 321 'Monte Carlo' Mini Cooper is replaced by 333 SUN/RAC Rally Mini Cooper. In addition the 251 Hillman Imp is changed to Metallic Gold with White stripe and the 204 Mini Minor is now Metallic Blue with RN '21'	£300-400	☐
48	1969	Scammell Transporter and six Cars	1148 Transporter (Red/White) with 378 MGB (Yellow/Black), 340 Sunbeam Imp (1967 Monte Carlo, Metallic Blue, RN '77'), 201 Saint's Volvo P1800 (White with Orange label), 180 Morris Mini Cooper 'S' (with 'wickerwork' panels), 339 Mini Cooper 'S' ('1967 Monte Carlo Rally', RN '177'), 204 Morris Mini-Minor (Metallic Maroon), plus bag of cones and leaflet	£500-600	☐
C48	1978-81	'JEAN RICHARD PINDER' Circus Set	Contains C426, C1163, C30, ringmaster, artistes, animals, seating, and cardboard cut-out 'Big-Top' circus tent	£100-125	☐
C48/1	1986	Racing Set...............................	C100/2 plus 576/2	£20-25	☐
C49	1978-80	'CORGI FLYING CLUB' Set ...	Green/White Jeep (419) with Blue/White Nipper Aircraft	£25-35	☐
C51	1978-80	'100 Years of the Car' Set........	3 Mercedes: C805 (White) C806 (Black) C811 (Red). (Originally for Germany).........	£20-25	☐
?	1978-80	'The Jaguar Collection' Set	C804 (Cream), C816 (Red), C318 (Mobil Green/White). Sold in 'UNIPART' stores ..	£30-35	☐
C54	1978-80	Swiss Rega Set......................	Bonna Ambulance and Helicopter	£30-35	☐
C55	1978-80	Norway Emergency Gift Set	Police Car, Breakdown Truck, Ford Transit Ambulance	£12-18	☐
C56	1978-80	Swedish Set	Ford Sierra 'POLIS', Bonna Ambulance	£12-18	☐
C57	1978-80	Swedish Set	Contains Volvo and Caravan	£12-18	☐
C57	1978-80	Volvo 740 and Caravan	Red Volvo, White/Red/Blue Caravan. Swedish export set	£15-20	☐
C61	1978-80	Swiss Fire Set	1120 Dennis Fire Engine, Sierra 'POLITZEI', Escort Van 'NOTRUF'......................	£30-35	☐
C62	1986	Swiss Services Set	C564 'PTT', Box Van 'DOMICILE', VW Polo 'PTT'. Export Set	£20-25	☐
C63	1986	French Set................................	Bonna Ambulance, Peugeot 505, Renault 5 'POLICE'	£30-35	☐
C63	1986	Emergency Set	Mercedes Ambulance (White body, Blue designs and roof lights, Fire Chief Car ('Sapeurs Pompiers') 'POLICE' Car (White body, Black doors, Blue roof light)	NGPP	☐
64	1965-69	FC Jeep 150 & Conveyor Belt ..	Jeep (409) Yellow/White Conveyor	£40-45	☐
C65	1978-80	Norway Set	Ford Transit Ambulance plus Helicopter	£12-18	☐
C67/1/2/3	1978-80	Cyclists Sets	Sold in France, 2 Cars, 2 Bicycles	£15-20	☐
C70	1978-80	Danish 'FALCK' Set	Bonna Ambulance and Ford Breakdown Truck	£15-20	☐
C72	1978-80	Norway Set	Contains C542 plus Helicopter 'LN OSH'	£12-18	☐
C73/1	1990	Swedish 'POLIS' Set................	White/Blue Volvo 740 & Red/White Jet Ranger Helicopter	£12-18	☐
C330/2-5		Mini 30th Anniversary	4 Minis with 'ROSE', 'SKY', 'FLAME' or 'RACING' logos, interior colours vary	£40-50	☐
?		Mini 30th Anniversary	Model of a Mini with Anniversary Book	£35-45	☐
C330/6-9		Four Mini Set..........................	Silver ('CITY'), Blue ('MAYFAIR'), Maroon ('MAYFAIR'), Pale Yellow ('CITY')	£20-30	☐
1151	1970	Scammell 'Co-op' Set	Contains 1147, 466 & 462 in Blue/White livery. Promotional in brown box	£200-250	☐
C1412	?	Swiss Police Set	Range Rover and Helicopter 'POLITZEI'	£18-22	☐

63

Ref. No.			*Corgi Toys — Gift Sets – continued*	Market Price Range	
?	1985	Wiltshire Fire Brigade	Dennis Fire Escape plus Escort Van both in red (650)...........................	£45-55	☐
?	1985	Race Team Set...........................	'ADMIRAL ENERGY GROUP Ltd' logos on 501 Range Rover (White), Porsche 956 (White) on trailer...............................	£35-45	☐
?	1980	Construction Site Set................	Contains 54 with 440 (Mazda Pick-Up)...	£30-35	☐
?	1988	'ROYAL MAIL' Set	Post Office Display Set not sold to the public includes 611, 612 & 496 Escort Vans, 613, 614 & 615 Metro Vans, 616 General Motors (Chevrolet) Van, 617? Leyland Artic and 618 Mercedes Benz Artic, plus Juniors 39, 90/1/2/3/4................	NGPP	☐
?	1992	Set of 4 Minis...........................	Black Mini ('Check'), White Mini ('Designer'), Red Mini ('Cooper'), Metallic Blue Mini ('Neon')	£12-14	☐

Gift Sets pictured in the 1969 Corgi Catalogue.

CORGI TOYS

GS 6 Rocket Age Gift Set

Early Corgi Display Stand (£325)

No 1110 Bedford 'S' Type
Tanker (Dutch Issue)
'Shell Benzeen'
with special box (£2000)

*Above models sold by Vectis Model Auctions, 35 Castle Street,
East Cowes IOW. Pictures reproduced by their kind permission*

GS 15 Silverstone Set (2nd Issue) Gift Set
Pictures GS 6 & GS 15 kindly supplied by Wilf Bainbridge of Scotland

CORGI TOYS

321 Monte Carlo Mini in special 'Flashed' box plus
317 Monte Carlo Mini in picture box

333 'Sun' Rally Mini Special 'flashed' Austin Seven box, plus
the scarce 321 1966 Monte Carlo Mini with autographs in
special 'flashed' 321 box

227 Mini Cooper in Blue/White and Lemon/Yellow with white
roof only. Blue version also known with white roof only.
(Note dished wheels on fixed face axles)

GS 17 — What might have been? The early Corgi idea that
eventually became the Red/Beige Land Rover 438 and the
154 Ferrari F1.

332 International Rally Rover with No 21 (as Mini)
but on both sides

281 Rover 2000 TC Series 2 with box type grill and whizz
wheels in the usual purple shade

Pictures kindly supplied by Wilf Bainbridge of Scotland to whom the Editor wishes to express his grateful thanks

CORGI TOYS

324 Marcos Volvo 1800 GT in white and the less common blue livery

330 Porsche Carrera 6 in the more unusual colours of white/blue with yellow perspex engine cover

Pictures kindly supplied by Wilf Bainbridge of Scotland

No 1132 Bedford TK 'Carrimore' Low Loader in the scarce yellow/red livery

Gift Set 27 — Machinery Carrier with Bedford tractor unit and 'Priestman Cub' shovel

No 1131 Bedford TK 'Carrimore' Detachable Axle Machinery Carrier

No 1107 Euclid TC 12 Tractor — Hard to find in good condition

The above four models sold by Lacy Scott, Risbygate Street, Bury St. Edmunds in 1995. Pictures reproduced by their kind permssion

'The Great Book of Corgi' Routemaster Bus variations — the common yellow/blue and the rare all yellow.
Picture kindly supplied by Gerry Savage of Corgi Collector Club

CORGI TOYS

Gift set 38 (£300)

Gift set 5 (£190)

805 Hardy Boys Rolls Royce (£170)

Gift set No 16 (£200)

Yellow Submarine (Red Hatches) (£360)

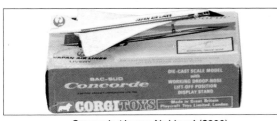

Concorde 'Japan Air Lines' (£200)

Gift Set 12 (£200)

Bus Collectors Society
'SKYRIDER' RM (£350)

Minis L-R i) 317, (£235), ii) 321, (£200), iii) 333, (£240), iv) 339, (£110), v) 339, (£130)

Models on this page sold in May, 1995 by Vectis Model Auctions at their Guildford saleroom. The pictures have been reproduced by their kind permission. At the time of the sale the condition of the models/boxes was excellent

CORGI CLASSICS

97377 JPS Lotus 72D (Emerson
Fittipaldi) ('The Donnington Collection')

97343 Morris 1000 Traveller
'Bomb Disposal'

97770 Morris Mini Van
'Hamleys'

97346 Morris 1000 Pick-up
'Tarmac'

97317 Foden 8-wheel Beer Lorry
'Scottish & Newcastle Breweries'

97328 AEC 8-wheel Tanker
'Major'

97368 Scammell Highwayman Heavy
Breakdown Truck 'Pickfords'

Scammell Scarab Articulated Truck
'Eskimo Foods'

97327 Atkinson 8-wheel Truck
'Eddie Stobart'

97367 Scammell Highwayman
Articulated Tanker 'Pointer'

97334 Atkinson 8-wheel Flat Truck
'Lucozade'

97336 Daimler CW Double Decker Bus
'Glasgow Corporation'

CORGI CLASSICS

97347 Bedford OB Coach
'Malta'

97342 Burlingham Seagull Coach
West Coast'

97315 Guy Arab Double Decker B us
'London Transport' Wartime Livery

97341 Leyland Atlantean Double Decker
Bus 'Maidstone & District'

98165 Ford Cortina
'London Transport Radio Control Car'

97364 Leyland Tiger Cub Single Deck
Bus 'North Western'

97399 Simon Snorkel Fire Appliance
'Cleveland County'

98486 Mack Fire Truck
'Paxtonia Fire Co.'

97360 AEC Merryweather Pumper
'Rotherham'

98484 Mack Fire Truck
'Chicago Fire Dept.'

97204 Guy Arab Bus with reversed
side adverts

97915 Scammell Highwayman & Trailers

97204 Guy Arab Bus picture kindly supplied by Mr J. W. Sanders of Derbyshire. NB See further Corgi Toys pictures in the Miscellaneous Models colour section

THE CORGI HERITAGE CENTRE
53 YORK STREET, HEYWOOD, NR. ROCHDALE, LANCS, OL10 4NR
TEL: 01706 365812 FAX: 01706 627811
A CORGI CLASSICS VENTURE IN CO-OPERATION WITH CHRIS BRIERLEY MODELS

VISIT THE NEW CORGI HERITAGE CENTRE

- The complete range of Corgi Classics
- Selected obsolete Corgi Models
- Mail order service
- Standing order facilities
- Discounts for Corgi Collector Club members on selected items
- Regular Corgi Collector Club presence, facilities for joining the Club on the spot & Club merchandise available

MUSEUM OF CORGI MODELS
PAST & PRESENT

- Discover the fascinating history of Corgi models through exhibits and graphic displays, original point of sale and catalogues
- See how your Corgi model is made – stage by stage
- Be one of the first to see the new Corgi 1:18 scale MGB and compare it with the real thing
- A Hornby Railway display complementing the Corgi Original Omnibus vehicles
- The Corgi Heritage Centre offers you the chance to discover the fascinating history of Corgi die-cast model vehicles. It's a collector's heaven, and one visit will inspire you to add some 'Classic' pieces to the collection you already have, begin a collection for a relative or a friend, or even start collecting for the very first time.

(Closed Tuesdays and Sundays at present)

The Corgi Heritage Centre, 53 York Street, Heywood, Nr Rochdale, Lancs. OL10 4NR.
Tel: 01706 365 812, Fax: 01706 627 811.

Disabled access.   Free car park at rear.

Easy to get by road and rail.

1d: Customer Exclusive Models

Note: These models are listed for the sake of completeness but there is little real opportunity of collectors obtaining them as very few were issued (usually 50 or less). Market Price Range NGPP.

C468 'RED ROSE COFFEE'
C469 'METTOY SALES CONFERENCE'
C469 'M.G.M.W. DINNER'
C469 'QUALITOYS VISIT'
C469 'VEDES VISIT TO SWANSEA'
C469 'MARKS & SPENCER VISIT SWANSEA'
C469 'HAROLD LYCHES VISIT'

C469 'METTOY Welcomes SWISS BUYERS to SWANSEA'
C469 'FINNISH VISIT TO SWANSEA'
C469 'M.G.M.W. DINNER'
C469 'OCTOPUSSY'
C469 'MARRIOT HOTELS'
C469 'CHARLIE'S ANGELS'

C469 'CORGI COLLECTORS Visit'
C469 'REDDITCH'
C469 'SKYRIDER BUS Collectors Society'
C469 'WHATMAN PAPER'
C469 'COLT 45 SALES CONFERENCE'
C469 'SKYRIDER'
C461 'MANNHEIM VISIT 1986'.

1e: Electronic Issues

Ref. No.	Year(s)	Model Name	Body Colour, Fleetname, Route, Other Details	Market Price Range
1004	1981	'CORGITRONICS First In ELECTRONIC DIE-CAST'	Red, London Transport, '11'	**£15-20** ☐

Other issues will be found combining 'BTA', 'HAMLEYS', 'OXO', etc with the 'CORGITRONICS' logo. See that section for details.

2: Metrobus Mk.2 Double-Decker Bus issued 1988-93

Market price Range as shown otherwise under £15.

Ref. No.	Model Name	Market Price Range		Ref. No.	Model Name	Market Price Range	
C675/1	'WEST MIDLANDS TIMESAVER'	**£20-25**	☐	97051	'INVICTAWAY'	GSP	☐
C675/2	'READING TRANSPORT			97064	'ROLLER COASTER'	GSP	☐
	GOLDLINE'	**£15-20**	☐	97065	'STAGECOACH'	GSP	☐
C675/3	'W. MIDLANDS TRAVEL'	**£15-20**	☐				

C675/4 'BEATTIES'
C675/5 'THE BEE LINE'
C675/6 'YORKSHIRE TRACTION'
C675/7 'WEST MIDLANDS'
C675/9 'NEWCASTLE BUSWAYS'
C675/10 'LONDON TRANSPORT'
Q675/12 'MAIDSTONE'
Q675/13 'EAST KENT'
Q675/14 'GM BUSES'
Q675/15 'NATIONAL GARDEN FESTIVAL'

C676/16 'STRATHCLYDE'
91702 'AIRBUS'
91848 'Yorkshire Rider'
91850 'READING'
91852 'STEVENSONS'
91853 'BRADFORD'
91854 'HALIFAX'
91855 'W.YORKS'
91856 'SUNDERLAND'

91857 'NEWCASTLE'
91858 'LEEDS'
91859 'WY PTE'
91860 'HUDDERSFIELD TRAMWAYS'
91861 'TODMORDEN'
91862 'BRADFORD Centenary'
91863 'HUDDERSFIELD'
91864 'GREY & GREEN'
91865 'YORKS RIDER'.

3: Plaxton Paramount Coaches issued 1985–93

Market Price Range as shown otherwise under £15

Ref. No.	Model Name	Market Price Range		Ref. No.	Model Name	Market Price Range	
C791	'SWISS PTT'	**£15-20**	☐	97064	'SEAGULL'	GSP	☐
C769/6	'POHJOLAN LIJKENNE'	**£25-30**	☐	97065	'STAGECOACH'	GSP	☐
97051	'INVICTAWAY'	GSP	☐				

C769 'NATIONAL EXPRESS'
C770 'HOLIDAY TOURS'
C771 'AIR FRANCE'
C771 'SAS'
C773 'GREEN LINE'
C774 'RAILAIR LINK'
C774 'ALDER VALLEY'
C775 'CITY LINK'
C776 'SKILLS SCENICRUISERS'
C777 'TAYLORS TRAVEL'

C792 'GATWICK FLIGHTLINE'
C793/1 'INTASUN EXPRESS'
C1223 'PHILIPS'
C769 'CLUB CANTABRICA
C769/4 'S.A.S.'
C769/5 'GLOBAL'
C769/7 'SCOTTISH CITYLINK'
C769/8 'BLUEBIRD EXPRESS'
91908 'S.A.S.'
91909 'FINNAIR'

91911 'APPLEBY'
91913 'VOYAGER PLAXTON'
91914 'SPEEDLINK'
91915 'TELLUS'
91916 'EAST YORKS'
91917 'HIGHWAYMAN'
91918 'SOUTHEND'
91919 'SHEARINGS'
91920 'NOTTINGHAM'.

4: Ford Transit Minibus issued 1988-89

Market Price Range £5-10

C676/1 'BLUEBIRD'; C676/2 'SOUTH WALES TRANSPORT'; C676/3 'BADGERLINE'; C676/4 'FALCK SYGETRANSPORT'; C676/5 'ROYAL MAIL'; C676/6 'CHASERIDER'; C676/7 'BRITISH AIRWAYS'; C676/10 'AMBULANS'; C676/11 'POLIS'; C676/12 'OXFORD'; 701 'INTER-CITY'.

5: Major Models - Coaches

Ref.	Year	Model Name	Body Details	Market Price	
1120	1961-62	'MIDLAND RED COACH'	Red/Black, uncast wheels, 'Birmingham - London Motorway Express'	**£125-150**	☐
C1168	1983	'GREYHOUND'	Red/White/Blue, 'Americruiser'	**£15-20**	☐
C1168	1983	'MOTORWAY EXPRESS'	White/Brown/Yellow/Red, Limited Edition	**£10-15**	☐
C1168	1983	'EURO EXPRESS'	White/Red/Blue, Limited Edition	**£15-20**	☐
C1168	1983	'ROVER BUS'	Blue, 'Chesham Toy and Model Fair', LE	**£10-15**	☐
			As previous model but Cream body	**£20-25**	☐
C1168	1983	SWISS 'PTT'	Confirmation required — was this issued?		☐

6: Miscellaneous

508   1968-69   Commer 2500 Minibus   Orange/White/Green body, 'HOLIDAY CAMP' logo .... **£45-55** ☐

Corgi Toys - Accessories

CORGI KITS

601	1961-68	Batley 'LEOFRIC' Garage.........................	**£15-20**	☐
602	1961-66	'AA' and 'RAC' Telephone Boxes.............	**£20-25**	☐
603	1961-66	Silverstone Pits......................................	**£25-30**	☐
604	1961-66	Silverstone Press Box.............................	**£25-30**	☐
605	1963-67	Silverstone Club House and Timekeepers Box	**£25-35**	☐
606	1961-66	Lamp Standards (2)..................................	**£5-10**	☐
607	1963-67	Circus Elephant and Cage........................	**£20-25**	☐
608	1963-66	'SHELL' Filling Station Building	**£20-25**	☐
609	1963-66	'SHELL' Filling Station Forecourt Accessories..	**£20-25**	☐
610	1963-66	Metropolitan Police Box and Public Telephone Kiosk..................................	**£20-25**	☐
611	1963-66	Motel Chalet	**£20-25**	☐

SPARE WHEELS (for 'Take-off Wheels' models)
Nos 1341 - 1361 were bubble-packed on card

1341	1970	for 344 Ferrari Dino Sport. Shown in 1969 catalogue but model issued with WhizzWheels....................................	**£10-15**	☐
1342	1968	for 300 Chevrolet Corvette.......................	**£10-15**	☐
1351	1968	for 275 Rover 2000 TC	**£10-15**	☐
1352	1968	for 276 Oldsmobile Toronado		
		for 338 Chevrolet Camaro		
		for 343 Pontiac Firebird. Shown in 1969 catalogue but not issued with 'Take-off Wheels'..............................	**£10-15**	☐
1353	1970	for 342 Lamborghini P400		
		for 302 Hillman Hunter Rally.................	**£10-15**	☐
1354	1970	for 273 Rolls Royce Silver Shadow...........	**£10-15**	☐
1361	1968	for 341 Mini Marcos GT 850 (This was the first 'Take-Off Wheels' model)..	**£10-15**	☐

SPARE TYRE PACKS

1449	1970-71	New Standard 15 mm.	**£10-15**	☐
1450	1958-70	Standard 15 mm......................................	**£10-15**	☐
1451	1961-70	Utility Vehicles 17 mm.	**£10-15**	☐
1452	1961-70	Major Models 19 mm.	**£10-15**	☐
1453	1965-70	Mini Cars 13 mm.....................................	**£10-15**	☐
1454	1967-70	Tractor wheels (Rear) 33 mm.	**£10-15**	☐
1455	1967-70	Tractor wheels (Front) 19 mm.	**£10-15**	☐
1456	1967-70	Racing wheels (Rear) 16 mm.	**£10-15**	☐
1457	1967-70	Racing wheels (Front) 14 mm.	**£10-15**	☐
1458	1967-70	Commercial (Large) 24 mm......................	**£10-15**	☐
1459	1967-70	Commercial (Medium) 19 mm..................	**£10-15**	☐

SELF-ADHESIVE ACCESSORIES

1460	1959	'A' Pack (66 items) including Tax Discs, Number Plates, 'GB' & 'Running-In' labels, etc	**£10-15**	☐
1461	1959	'B' Pack (36 items) including White-wall tyre trim, 'Styla Sportsdiscs', Number Plates..	**£10-15**	☐
1462	1959	'C' Pack (69 items) including Number Plates, Commercial & Road Fund Licences (A,B & C) 20mph & 30mph Speed Limit Plates & Trailer Plates, etc	**£10-15**	☐
1463	1959	'D' Pack (100 items) including Number, Corps Diplomatique & 'L' Plates, Touring Pennants.......................................	**£10-15**	☐
1464	1961	'E' Pack (86 items) including Assorted Badges, Take-Off Wheels, Trade & Licence Plates	**£10-15**	☐

CORGI 'CARGOES' (bubble-packed on card)

1485	1960	Lorry Load - Planks.................................	**£10-15**	☐
1486	1960	Lorry Load - Bricks.................................	**£10-15**	☐
1487	1960	Lorry Load - Milk Churns........................	**£10-15**	☐
1488	1960	Lorry Load - Cement...............................	**£10-15**	☐
1490	1960	Skip and 3 Churns...................................	**£10-15**	☐

FIGURES

1501	1963-69	Racing Drivers and Pit Mechanics (6).................................	**£10-15**	☐
1502	1963-69	Silverstone Spectators (6)	**£10-15**	☐
1503	1963-69	Race Track Officials (6)...........................	**£10-15**	☐
1504	1963-69	Press Officials (6)	**£10-15**	☐
1505	1963-69	Garage Attendants (6).............................	**£10-15**	☐

MISCELLANEOUS

1401	1958-60	Service Ramp (operable)	**£15-20**	☐
1445	1962	Spare Red bulb for 437 Ambulance...........	**£2-3**	☐
1441	1963	Spare Blue bulb for 464 Police Van..........	**£2-3**	☐
1443	1967	Red flashing bulb for 437 Ambulance	**£2-3**	☐
1444	1967	Blue flashing bulb for 464 Police Van.......	**£2-3**	☐
1445	1967	Spare bulb for TV screen in 262 Lincoln...	**£2-3**	☐
1446	1970	Spare tyres for 1150 Snowplough..............	**£2-3**	☐
1480	1959	Spare nose cone for Corporal Missile.........	**£2-3**	☐
1497	1967	James Bond Spares (2 Bandits and lapel badge for 261).......................................	**£15-25**	☐
1498	1967	James Bond Spares (Pack of missiles for 336 Toyota)..	**£10-15**	☐
1499	1967	Green Hornet Spares (Pack of missiles and scanners for 268)	**£10-15**	☐
	1960s	Corgi Club Badge. Gold Corgi dog on Red background	**£20-25**	☐

'Husky' and 'Corgi Juniors' series   (1965-1975)

'Husky' models were introduced by Mettoy Playcraft in 1965 to compete with the Matchbox 1-75 range. These small-scale models have plenty of detail and action-features and the range includes cars, commercials, military and Film/TV specials.

The models have either a plastic or die-cast chassis together with various types of regular wheels and WhizzWheels. Models could only be obtained from 'Woolworths' stores and were only sold in blister packs.

Production under the 'Husky' trade name ceased in 1969 and the range was reissued in 1970 as 'Corgi Juniors'. To facilitate this change, 'HUSKY' was removed from the baseplates which were then re-engraved 'CORGI JUNIORS'.

The models were mostly fitted with 'WhizzWheels' to enable them to be used on the 'Rocket Track' and to compete against the new Matchbox 'Superfast' range. Corgi Juniors were blister packed on blue/white card for the 'regular' issues and red/white card for the 'specials'. Each pack incorporated a 'Collectors Card' picture of the real vehicle and these could be cut out and pasted into a special collectors album. Whilst 'Husky' and 'Corgi Juniors' in mint condition blister packs are no longer cheap, plenty of low priced unboxed models are available hence this range offers the younger collector plenty of scope.

Ref. No.	Year(s)	Model Type	Model Features and Size	Market Price Range	

Husky models and Corgi Juniors issued 1965-1975

Ref. No.	Year(s)	Model Type	Model Features and Size	Market Price Range	
1-a	1965-67	Jaguar Mk.10	Metallic Royal Blue or Medium Blue, 'Husky' on base/GPW, 65 mm.	£20-25	☐
1-b	1967-69	larger version:	Metallic Dark Blue or Mid or Pale Yellow, 'Husky' on base, metal or Grey plastic wheels	£10-15	☐
1-c	1970-72	Reliant TW9 Pick-Up	Orange body, WhizzWheels, 'Juniors' on base	£8-12	☐
1-d	1973-75	Grand Prix Racer	Metallic Green/White, WhizzWheels, 'Juniors' on base	£5-8	☐
2-a	1965-67	Citroën Safari with Boat	Pale Yellow car with Brown boat, Grey plastic wheels, 'Husky' on base	£20-25	☐
2-b	1967-68	larger casting:	Metallic Gold, Brown or Blue boat, Grey plastic wheels, 'Husky' on base, 70 mm.	£10-15	☐
2-c	1970-73	Corgi Juniors issue:	Blue or Yellow body, metal or Grey plastic wheels	£8-12	☐
3-1	1965-68	Mercedes 220	Pale Blue body, Grey plastic wheels, 'Husky' on base	£10-15	☐
3-2	1965-69	VW 1300 'POLICE' Car	White/Black body, 'Husky' on base	£20-25	☐
	1970-74	Corgi Juniors issue:	As previous model with or without 'Juniors' on base	£10-15	☐
3-3	1975	VW 1300 'POLICE' Car	White body, WhizzWheels, 'Juniors' on base	£8-12	☐
4-a	1965-67	Jaguar Mk.10	Red body, 'FIRE CHIEF' on doors, 'Husky' on base	£20-25	☐
4-b	1967-69	larger casting:	otherwise as previous model, 'Husky' on base, 70 mm.	£15-20	☐
4-c (E4)	1970-75	Zetor 5511 Tractor	Orange/Red body, non-WhizzWheels, 'Juniors' on base	£20-30	☐
5-1	1965-69	Lancia Flamina	Mauve body, opening bonnet, Grey plastic wheels, 'Husky' on base	£10-15	☐
5-2	1968-69	Willys Jeep	Metallic Green with Grey or Yellow windscreen, non-WhizzWheels, 'Husky'	£10-15	☐
	1970-73	Corgi Juniors issue:	Brown or Orange body, non-WhizzWheels, 'Juniors' on base	£8-12	☐
6-1	1965-67	Citroën Safari Ambulance	White body with Red cross, warning lights, 'Husky' on base	£20-25	☐
6-2	1967-69	Ferrari Berlinetta 250GT	Red body, spoked wheels, 'Husky' on base	£20-25	☐
6-3	1970-73	De Tomaso Mangusta	Yellow or Purple body, WhizzWheels, 'Juniors' on base	£10-15	☐
7-1	1965-67	Buick Electra	Red body, Grey plastic wheels, 'Husky' on base	£20-25	☐
7-2	1968-69	Duple Vista 25 Coach	Green/White or Red/White body, 'Husky' on base	£20-25	☐
	1970-73	Corgi Juniors issues:	Yellow/White, Purple/White or Orange/White	£10-15	☐
7-a	1965-67	Ford Thunderbird Open Top	Pink/Black body, Grey plastic wheels, 'Husky' on base	£20-25	☐
7-b	1966-68	Ford Thunderbird Hard Top	Yellow with Blue removable top, 'Husky' on base	£10-15	☐
8-1	1968-69	Farm Tipper Trailer	Yellow/Red body, 'Husky' on base	£5-7	☐
9-1	1965-68	Buick 'POLICE' Car	Light or Dark Blue body, Red logo, 'Husky' on base	£15-20	☐
9-2	1968-69	Cadillac Eldorado	Blue body with tow hook, 'Husky' on base	£10-15	☐
	1970-72	Corgi Juniors issues:	Metallic Green or White/Black body, 'Juniors' on base	£8-12	☐
10-1a	1965-69	Guy Warrior Coal Truck	Red body, Blue windows, rear corner windows, 'Husky' on base	£20-25	☐
10-1c	1967-69	casting change:	Red body but no rear corner windows, 'Husky' on base	£15-20	☐
10-2	1973-75	Ford GT-70	Orange body, opening hatch, detailed engine, 'Juniors' on base	£9-12	☐
11-1a	1966-67	Forward Control Land Rover	Green/Brown body, Blue windows, rear corner windows, 'Husky' on base	£10-15	☐
11-1b	1967-69	casting change:	Metallic Green/Brown, no rear corner windows, 'Husky' on base	£10-15	☐
11-2	1970-74	Austin Healey LM Sprite	Red body, racing number '50', WhizzWheels, 'Juniors' on base	£30-40	☐
12-1	1965-67	VW Pick-Up Tower Wagon	Yellow/Red with Blue windows, 'Husky' on base	£15-20	☐
12-2	1968-69	Ford Tower Truck	Yellow or White body, Grey plastic wheels, 'Husky' on base	£10-15	☐
12-3	1970-73	Reliant-Ogle Scimitar	White or Metallic Blue, WhizzWheels, 'Juniors' on base	£20-25	☐
13-a	1965-69	Guy Warrior Sand Truck	Yellow/Brown with rear corner windows, 'Husky' on base	£15-20	☐
13-b	1967-68	casting change:	As previous model but without rear corner windows, 'Husky' on base	£10-15	☐
13-b	1968-69	colour variation:	Blue/Brown, with or without rear corner windows	£10-15	☐
13-c	1970-73	Corgi Juniors issues:	Green/Brown or White/Brown, 'Juniors' on base	£8-12	☐
14		Guy Warrior Petrol Tanker			
14-a	1965-67	'SHELL'	Yellow/White body, with rear corner windows, metal wheels, 'Husky' on base	£20-25	☐
14-b	1967-68	'SHELL'	As previous model but without rear corner windows, 'Husky' on base	£15-20	☐
14-c	1968-69	'ESSO'	White body, metal wheels, no rear corner windows, 'Husky' on base	£15-20	☐
14-d	1968-69	'GULF'	No other details available	£15-20	☐
14-e	1970-75	Corgi Juniors issue:	As 14-c with metal wheels or WhizzWheels, 'Juniors' on base	£9-12	☐
15-1	1965-67	Volkswagen Pick-Up	Turquoise body with Brown removable canopy, 'Husky' on base	£10-15	☐
15-2a	1967-69	Studebaker TV Car	Yellow or Metallic Blue with Blue windows, 'Husky' on base	£25-30	☐
15-2b	1970-71	Corgi Juniors issue	Green or Yellow body, WhizzWheels, 'Juniors' on base	£10-15	☐
15-3(E15)	1973-74	Mercedes 'SCHOOL BUS'	Metallic Blue body, WhizzWheels, 'Juniors' on base	£9-12	☐
16-a	1965-67	Dump Truck	Aveling Barford, Yellow or Red body, 'Husky' on base	£8-10	☐
16-b	1971-75	Land Rover Pick-Up	Metallic Green, tinted windows, WhizzWheels, 'Juniors' on base	£6-9	☐

Husky and Corgi Juniors (1965-1975) – continued

Ref. No.				Market Price Range	
17-1a	1965-67	Guy Warrior 'MILK' Tanker ...	White body with rear corner windows, oval tank, 'Husky' on base..............	£20-25	☐
17-1b	1967-68	casting change:	As previous model but without rear corner windows, 'Husky' on base	£15-20	☐
17-1c	1968-69	casting change:	White or Cream body, square tank, no rear corner windows, 'Husky', 71 mm.	£15-20	☐
17-2(E17)	1970-75	VW 1300 Beetle	Metallic Green with flower designs, WhizzWheels, 'Juniors' on base..........	£10-15	☐
18-1a	1965-67	Jaguar 'E'-type 2 + 2	Gold plated or Silver plated body, 'Husky' on base, 75 mm.	£30-40	☐
18-1b	1967-69	Jaguar 'E'-type 2 + 2	Gold plated in various shades, 'Husky' on base	£30-40	☐
18-2	1973-75	Wigwam Camper Van	Orange or Blue body, WhizzWheels	£12-15	☐
19-1a	1965-69	Commer Walk-Thru Van	Green with Red doors and Grey driver, sliding doors, 'Husky' on base	£10-15	☐
19-1b	1968-69	Commer Walk-Thru Van	All Red body and door, 'Husky' on base	£15-20	☐
19-2	1969-70	Speedboat on Trailer	Red/Cream, 'HUSKY' on hull, Gold trailer	£8-11	☐
19-2	1970-73	Corgi Juniors issues:	Red/Cream, Blue trailer with 'Juniors' on base, WhizzWheels or metal wheels	£5-7	☐
20-1	1965-68	Ford Thames Van	Red body with Yellow ladder & TV aerial, opening rear door, 'Husky' on base	£15-20	☐
20-2a	1968-69	VW 1300	Blue with Black luggage on roof, 'Husky' on base	£20-25	☐
20-2b	1970-71	Corgi Juniors issues:	Brown or Red body, WhizzWheels, 'Juniors' on base	£9-12	☐
21-1a	1965-67	Military Land Rover	Olive body, star on cab roof, rear corner windows, 'Husky' on base	£15-18	☐
21-1b	1967-69	casting change:	As previous model but without rear corner windows, 'Husky' on base	£11-14	☐
21-2	1968-69	Jaguar 'E'-type 2 + 2	Metallic Maroon body, spoked wheels, 'Husky' on base	£30-40	☐
21-3	1970-74	Mini Cooper 'S' 1300	Metallic Purple body, WhizzWheels, 'Juniors' on base	£10-15	☐
22-1	1965-68	Military Ambulance	Citroën Safari with Olive body, Red cross on roof, Blue warning lights, 'Husky'	£10-15	☐
22-2a	1968-69	Aston Martin DB6	Metallic Gold or Purple body, 'Husky' on base	£30-40	☐
22-2b	1970-71	Corgi Juniors issue:	Metallic Green body, 'Juniors' on base	£30-40	☐
22-3(E22)	1973-75	Formula 1 Racer	Yellow body, racing number '3', Union Jack decals, WhizzWheels	£10-15	☐
23-1	1965-67	US Army Tanker	Guy Warrior, Olive body, star on cab, Blue windows, 'Husky' on base	£20-25	☐
23-2a	1967-69	Loadmaster Shovel	Orange or Yellow with plated parts, 'Husky' on base	£9-12	☐
23-2b	1970-73	Corgi Juniors issue:	Yellow body, 'Juniors' on base	£7-10	☐
24-1	1966-69	Ford Zephyr Estate Car	Blue or Metallic Red body, opening tailgate, 'Husky' on base	£20-25	☐
24-2	1971-74	Aston Martin DBS	Green body, WhizzWheels, 'Juniors' on base	£10-15	☐
25-a	1966-69	S & D Refuse Van	Light Blue or Dark Red body, 'Husky' on base	£10-15	☐
25-b	1970-73	Corgi Juniors issue:	Orange body, 'Juniors' on base	£8-11	☐
26	1966-69	Sunbeam Alpine Hard Top ...	Metallic Bronze/Blue or Red/Blue, removable hardtop, 'Husky' on base	£30-40	☐
27-1a	1966-69	Bedford TK Lorry	Dark Red or Orange body, 'Husky' on base	£15-20	☐
27-1b	1970-72	Corgi Juniors issue:	Orange body, 'Juniors' on base	£10-15	☐
27-2(E27)	1973-75	Formula 5000 Racing Car	Black body, White driver, WhizzWheels, 'Juniors' on base	£7-10	☐
28-a	1966-69	Ford Breakdown Truck	Blue body, plated parts, hook, 'Husky' on base	£9-12	☐
28-b	1970-71	Corgi Juniors issue:	Blue or Green body, hook, 'Juniors' on base	£7-10	☐
29-1	1966-69	ERF Cement Lorry	Yellow/Red with rotating drum, 'Husky' on base	£15-20	☐
29-2a	1970-71	ERF Fire Engine	Red body, metal wheels or WhizzWheels but no windows, 'Juniors' on base ..	£15-20	☐
29-2b	1972-75	new casting:	Large cab with Blue windows, WhizzWheels, 'Juniors' on base	£10-15	☐
30-a	1966-69	Studebaker Ambulance..........	(Wagonaire) White, Red crosses, stretcher, metal wheels, 'Husky' on base ..	£15-20	☐
30-b	1970-73	Corgi Juniors issue:	White with metal wheels or WhizzWheels, 'Juniors' on base	£10-15	☐
31-1	1966-69	Oldsmobile Starfire Coupé	Metallic Blue or Green body, opening boot, 'Husky' on base	£15-20	☐
31-2(31)	1970-79	Land Rover Breakdown..........	Purple or Blue body with 'WRECKER' or 'CRASH TRUCK' logo, 'Juniors' on base	£5-7	☐
32-1	1966-69	VW Luggage Elevator	White/Yellow or Red/Blue, 'Husky' on base	£15-20	☐
32-2	1970-72	Lotus Europa.....................	Metallic Green body, WhizzWheels, 'Juniors' on base	£12-16	☐
33-1a	1967-69	Farm Trailer	Olive or Turquoise trailer with 4 calves, drop-down tailgate, 'Husky' on base	£5-7	☐
33-1b	1970-72	Corgi Juniors issue:	Orange body, 'Juniors' on base	£4-6	☐
33-2	1970-74	Jaguar 'E'-type 2 + 2	Yellow or Blue body, WhizzWheels, 'Juniors' on base	£15-20	☐
34-a	1967-69	BM Volvo 400 Tractor..........	Red/Yellow body, Red or Black smoke stack, 'Husky' on base	£12-15	☐
34-b	1970-72	Corgi Juniors issue:	As previous model but with 'Juniors' on base	£9-12	☐
35-a	1966-69	Ford Camper	Metallic Blue or Yellow with sliding door and detailed interior, 'Husky' on base	£11-15	☐
35-b	1970-73	Corgi Juniors issue:	Green or Red body, WhizzWheels, 'Juniors' on base	£8-11	☐
36	1967-69	Fire Engine	Simon Snorkel, Red body with operating boom, 'Husky' on base	£12-16	☐
37-a	1969	NSU R080	Metallic Blue with opening bonnet and detailed interior, 'Husky' on base ..	£12-16	☐
37-b	1970-73	Corgi Juniors issues:	Metallic Blue, Purple, Orange or Pink, WhizzWheels, 'Juniors' on base	£8-12	☐
38-a	1968-69	Single Horse Box	Rice's Beaufort, Green with White pony, drop-down tailgate, 'Husky' on base	£8-11	☐
38-b	1970-71	Corgi Juniors issues:	Red or Bronze body, WhizzWheels, 'Juniors' on base	£6-9	☐
39-a	1968-69	Jaguar XJ-6	Yellow body with Red tow hook, 'Husky' on base	£30-40	☐
39-b	1970-73	Corgi Juniors issues:	Yellow body (metal wheels) Silver or Maroon body (WhizzWheels) 'Juniors'	£10-15	☐
40-a	1968-69	Ford Transit Caravan	Green/White or Red/White, detailed interior, 'Husky' on base	£14-17	☐
40-b	1970-72	Corgi Juniors issues:	Blue or Grey (WhizzWheels) or Yellow (metal or WhizzWheels) 'Juniors' on base	£10-14	☐
41	1969	Porsche Carrera	Never seen with 'HUSKY' baseplate..	NGPP	☐
	1970-73	Corgi Juniors issues:	White body, metal wheels or WhizzWheels, 'Juniors' on base	£10-15	☐
42-1	1971-72	Euclid Dump Truck	Yellow/Red body, Black plastic wheels or WhizzWheels, 'Juniors' on base ...	£9-12	☐
42-2	1972-76	Terex Rear Dump Truck........	Red/Yellow, Yellow/Red or Blue/Beige, 'Juniors' on base	£7-10	☐
43	1970-75	Farm Tractor with Blade	Massey-Ferguson 3303, Yellow body, 'Juniors' on base	£8-11	☐
44	1970-75	Road Roller	Raygo Rascal 600, Blue/Orange, 'Juniors' on base................................	£7-10	☐
45	1970-74	Mercedes Benz 280 SL	Silver (metal wheels) Yellow, Metallic Blue or Red with WhizzWheels, 'Juniors' on base	£7-9	☐
46	1970-74	Jensen Interceptor..............	Metallic Maroon or Green, or Orange body, WhizzWheels, 'Juniors' on base..	£15-20	☐
47	1971-75	Scammell Concrete Mixer	Blue/White/Red body..	£8-11	☐
48	1970-73	ERF Tipper Truck	Red/Silver or Blue/Yellow, 'Juniors' on base	£8-11	☐
49	1971-75	Pinifarina Modulo	Yellow body with Maroon stripe, 'Juniors' on base	£10-14	☐
50	1971-74	Ferrari 512 S.....................	Maroon/White or Maroon/Silver, racing number '6', WhizzWheels, 'Juniors'	£8-11	☐
51	1971-73	Porsche 917	Gold/Red body, WhizzWheels, 'Juniors' on base	£15-20	☐
52	1971-73	Addams Probe	Metallic Purple body, WhizzWheels, 'Juniors' on base	£7-10	☐
54	1972-75	Container Truck	Ford D1000, Red/Orange or Red/Yellow, WhizzWheels............................	£8-12	☐
55	1971-73	Double Decker Bus	Daimler Fleetline, Red body, 'ESSO UNIFLO', WhizzWheels....................	£10-15	☐
56	1971-73	Fire Chief's Car	Ford Capri, Red/White, 'FIRE' or 'FIRE CHIEF' logo, WhizzWheels, 'Juniors'	£8-11	☐
57	1971-73	Cadillac Eldorado................	'HOT RODDER', Pink body, exposed engine, WhizzWheels, 'Juniors' on base	£7-10	☐
58 (E58)	1971-75	Beach Buggy	Metallic Red body, WhizzWheels, 'Juniors' on base..............................	£5-7	☐
59	1971-73	'FUTURA'	Orange body, Yellow/Black logo, WhizzWheels, 'Juniors' on base..............	£5-7	☐

Ref. No.	Year(s)	Model Type	*Husky & Corgi Juniors (1965-1975)* – *continued*	Market Price Range	
60	1971-73	VW Beetle Hot Rod	Orange body, WhizzWheels, 'Juniors' on base	£6-8	☐
61	1971-75	'SHERIFF's Car	Mercury Cougar XR7 with WhizzWheels & 'Juniors' on base	£7-10	☐
62	1971-73	Volvo P-1800	Red/Black, WhizzWheels, 'Juniors' on base	£9-12	☐
63	1971-74	Ford Escort Rally	Metallic Blue, racing number '6', WhizzWheels, 'Juniors' on base	£9-12	☐
64	1971-73	Morgan Plus 8	Yellow or Red body, WhizzWheels, 'Juniors' on base	£15-20	☐
65	1971-73	Bertone Carebo	Purple body, Amber windows, WhizzWheels, 'Juniors' on base	£8-10	☐
67	1971-73	Ford Capri Dragster	Yellow body, *'HOT PANTS'*, Union Jack label, WhizzWheels, 'Juniors' on base	£6-9	☐
71	1971-73	US Racing Buggy	Blue body, Stars & Stripes livery, WhizzWheels, 'Juniors' on base	£6-9	☐
72	1971-75	Mercedes-Benz C111	Red body, Blue windows, WhizzWheels, 'Juniors' on base	£6-8	☐
73	1971-73	Alfa-Romeo P33	Blue body, clear windscreen, WhizzWheels, 'Juniors' on base	£7-10	☐
74	1972-75	Bertone Barchetta	Orange with Black stripe, WhizzWheels, 'Juniors' on base	£6-8	☐
75	1972-75	Super Stock Car	Silver with Union Jack design, WhizzWheels, 'Juniors' on base	£5-7	☐
76 (76)	1974-75	Military Jeep	Military Green with White star and driver, WhizzWheels, 'Juniors' on base	£6-9	☐
77	1971-73	Ital Manta	Pink body, clear windows, WhizzWheels, 'Juniors' on base	£7-10	☐
77	1971-75	Marcos	Orange body, Amber windows, WhizzWheels, 'Juniors' on base	£6-8	☐
78	1971-73	Old MacDonald's Lorry	Red cab, Silver bonnet, Brown truck body	£14-18	☐
80-1	1974-75	Porsche Carrera	White body, racing number '4', Red/Blue design	£7-10	☐

Novelty, Film & TV related Specials

Ref. No.	Year(s)	Set Name	Contents	Market Price Range	
1001a	1968-69	James Bond Aston Martin DB6	Metallic Grey body, Grey plastic wheels, 'Husky' on base	£100-125	☐
1001b	1970-72	Corgi Juniors issue:	As previous model but WhizzWheels, 'Juniors' on base	£100-120	☐
1002a	1968-69	Batmobile	Black body, Blue canopy, Grey plastic wheels, 'Husky' on base	£100-125	☐
1002b	1970-72	Corgi Juniors issue:	As previous model but WhizzWheels, 'Juniors' on base	£10-125	☐
1003a	1968-69	Batboat on Trailer	Black/Red plus Gold trailer, Grey plastic wheels, 'Husky' on base	£60-70	☐
1003b	1970-72	Corgi Juniors issue:	As previous model but WhizzWheels, 'Juniors' on base	£40-50	☐
1004a	1968-69	Monkeemobile	Red/White, 'MONKEES', exposed engine	£100-125	☐
1004b	1970-72	Corgi Juniors issue:	As previous model but WhizzWheels, 'Juniors' on base	£100-125	☐
1005a	1968-69	'Man From UNCLE' Car	Blue car with 2 figures, metal wheels, 'Husky' on base	£100-125	☐
1005b	1970-71	Corgi Juniors issue:	As previous model but WhizzWheels, 'Juniors' on base	£100-125	☐
1006a	1968-69	Chitty Chitty Bang Bang	Yellow/Orange or Orange/Yellow, spoked wheels, 'Husky' on base	£100-125	☐
1006b	1970-72	Corgi Juniors issue:	As previous model but WhizzWheels, 'Juniors' on base	£100-125	☐
1007	?	'Ironsides' Police Van	'Juniors' on base, Blue body, 'SAN FRANCISCO' logo, 2 figures	£175-200	☐
1008	1971-72	Popeye Padde Wagon	Yellow body with Popeye, Olive Oyl & Sweet Pea figures	£75-95	☐
1010	1971-73	James Bond's Volkswagen	Orange body, Green stripe, 'CORGI' & No '5' labels, WhizzWheels	£75-95	☐
1011		James Bond Bobsleigh	Yellow body with Black/Yellow chequer label. White/Black nose label '007', Blue figure with Yellow goggles/helmet	£175-200	☐
1012		S.P.E.C.T.R.E. Bobsleigh	Orange body, boards head label on nose, Brown figure with Black helmet & Green goggles	£175-200	☐

Major Models

Ref. No.	Year(s)	Model Type	Description	Market Price Range	
2001	1968-69	'HUSKY' Multi Garage	A set of four garages, (no cars) 'Husky' on base	£15-20	☐
	1970-75	Corgi Juniors issue:	As previous model but with 'CORGI' logo, 'Juniors' on base	£10-15	☐
2002	1967-69	'HUSKY' Car Transporter	Hoynor Mk.II, White/Blue/Orange, detachable cab, 'Husky' on base	£20-30	☐
	1970-72	Corgi Juniors issue:	As previous model but with 'CORGI' logo, 'Juniors' on base	£15-20	☐
2003a		Machinery Low-Loader	Red/Blue/Yellow, detachable cab, drop-down ramp, 'Husky' on base	£20-30	☐
2003b	1970-73	Corgi Juniors issue:	As previous model with metal wheels or WhizzWheels, 'Juniors' on base	£15-20	☐
2004a	1968-69	Removals Delivery Van	Red or Blue cab, plated box, *'HUSKY REMOVALS'*, metal wheels, 'Husky' on base	£30-40	☐
2004b	1970-72	Corgi Juniors issue:	As previous model but *'CORGI REMOVALS'*, WhizzWheels, 'Juniors' on base	£20-30	☐
2006	1970-79	Mack 'ESSO' Tanker	White body and tank, WhizzWheels, 'Juniors' on base	£8-11	☐

Husky and Corgi Juniors Gift Sets

3001	1968-69	4 Garage Set	Contains 23, 27, 29, or 9, 30 or 36	£50-70	☐
3002	1968-69	Batmobile Set	1002 Batmobile and 1003 Batboat on trailer	£100-150	☐
3002	1970	'Club Racing' Set	Juniors set of 8 racing cars inc. Mini Cooper 'S' (Metallic Mauve), Ford Capri, Morgan, etc.	£100-150	☐
3003	1968-69	Car Transporter Set	2002 Husky Car Transporter plus 16, 26, 6-2, 21-2, 22-2, 26	£100-150	☐
3004	1968-69	4 Garage Set	Contains 23-2, 29	£50-75	☐
3004		James Bond 'OHMSS' Set	Contains 1004, 1001, 1011, 1012 plus un-numbered VW Beetle in Red with Black No.'5' on White circle on sides. (From film 'On Her Majesty's Secret Service')	£600-750	☐
3005	1968-69	Holiday Time/Leisure Time	Contains 2-2, 5-2, 7-2, 15-2, 19-2, 20-2, 21-2, 35-1	£125-150	☐
3006	1968-69	Service Station	Contains 14-c, 22-2, 28	£50-75	☐
3007	1968-69	'HUSKY MULTIPARK'	In 1968 catalogue but not issued	NPP	☐
3008	1968-69	Crime Busters Set	Contains 1001, 1002, 1003, 1005	£350-450	☐
	1970	Corgi Juniors issue	As previous set	£300-400	☐
3011		Road Construction Set	Gift Set containing seven models	£100-125	☐

Gift Sets & Twin Packs – 1975-1991

These are many and various and include the reference numbers:- J200-J260; J3001-J3184, 92210-92695, 3013-3123.
Normally these sets are worth the sum total of the individual models. Rare sets to look out for include:-

3019/1 1983-84 James Bond 'Octopussy' Set £50-75   3080 1980/82 Batman Set £100-150
3030 1976-77 James Bond 'Spy Who Loved Me' Set £50-75   3082 1980/82 James Bond 'Goldfinger' Set £100-125

Husky Accessories

1561/2	1968-69	Traffic Signs		£20-30	☐
1571	1968-69	Pedestrians		£10-15	☐
1572	1968-69	Workmen		£10-15	☐
1573	1968-69	Garage Personnel		£10-15	☐
1574	1968-69	Public Servants		£10-15	☐
1580	1968-69	Husky Collector Case	storage for 48 models	£10-15	☐
1585	1968-69	Husky Traveller Case	opens to form Service Station (this item never seen)	NPP	☐
2001	1968-69	'HUSKY' Multi Garage	A set of four garages, (no cars) 'Husky' on base	£15-20	☐
	1970-75	Corgi Juniors issue:	As previous model but with 'CORGI' logo, 'Juniors' on base	£10-15	☐

Husky and Corgi Juniors Catalogues and listings

Ref. No.	Year(s)	Publication	Cover Features and Details	Market Price Range	

HUSKY CATALOGUES

Mettoy Playcraft (Sales) Ltd 1966

	1966	Leaflet (single fold)	Red, illustrating No.1 Jaguar Mk.10 on cover and Nos.1-29 inside. '1/9 each'	£20-25	☐
same ref.	1966	Leaflet (Belgian issue)	As previous leaflet but Nos.1-32 shown, printed in French	£20-25	☐
same ref.	1966	Booklet (10 pages)	Front/rear covers feature a row of garages and cars. Good pictures of 1002 Batmobile and 1001 James Bond's Aston-Martin, plus Nos.1-36	NGPP	☐
no ref.	1967	Catalogue (24 pages)	Cover features boy with Husky vehicles and sets. Good pictures of all the rare models and Gift Sets plus accessories and models 1-41	£30-40	☐

CORGI JUNIORS CATALOGUES

Mettoy Playcraft 1970

		Catalogue (16 pages)	Blue cover with 10 models featured. Contains excellent pictures of all the rare early models including GS 3004 James Bond 'O.H.M.S.S.' Set etc.	£30-40	☐

Collectors Notes

Corgi Rockets

This model range was issued between 1970 and 1972 to compete against Mattel 'Hot Wheels' and similar products. The models had 'WhizzWheels' and featured a special 'Tune-Up' system which increased the play value and speed of the virtually frictionless wheels. In addition they were very robust, being advertised as 'four times stronger' than most other diecast racers. To begin with seven Corgi Juniors were adapted as Rockets and five of those received a superb vacuum metallised finish.

A range of accessories was also issued in the form of 'Speed Circuits' etc, and each car was issued with a special 'Golden Tune-Up Key' which released the base. The bubble-packed models are difficult to find in top condition and the prices reflect their scarcity.

Ref. No.	Year(s)	Model Type	Model Features and Size	Market Price Range	
D 901	1970-72	Aston-Martin DB-6	Metallic Deep Gold body, Green interior	£30-40	☐
D 902	1970-72	Jaguar XJ-6	Metallic Green body, Cream interior	£30-40	☐
D 903	1970-72	Mercedes-Benz 280 SL	Metallic Orange body, White interior	£30-40	☐
D 904	1970-72	Porsche Carrera 6	Orange-Yellow body, Black number '19'	£30-40	☐
D 905	1970-72	'The Saint's Volvo P1800	White body, Blue/White 'Saint' label on bonnet	£40-50	☐
D 906	1970-72	Jensen Interceptor	Metallic Red body, Yellow interior	£30-40	☐
D 907	1970-72	Cadillac Eldorado	Metallic Copper body, White interior	£30-40	☐
D 908	1970-72	Chevrolet Astro	Metallic Red/Black body	£30-40	☐
D 909	1970-72	Mercedes-Benz C111	Red or Blue body, White interior	£20-30	☐
D 910	1970-72	Beach Buggy	Orange body, Black interior	£20-30	☐
D 911	1970-72	Marcos XP	Gold body, Chrome interior	£20-30	☐
D 913	1970-72	Aston-Martin DBS	Metallic Blue, Yellow interior	£30-40	☐
D 916	1970-72	Carabo Bertone	Metallic Green/Blue, Orange interior	£20-30	☐
D 917	1970-72	Pininfarina Alfa-Romeo	Metallic Purple/White	£20-30	☐
D 918	1970-72	Bitzzarini Manta	Metallic Dark Blue, White interior	£20-30	☐
D 919	1970-72	'Todd Sweeney' Stock Car	Red/Purple, Yellow/Black front, RN '531'	£50-75	☐
D 920	1970-72	'Derek Fiske' Stock Car	White/Red, Silver bonnet, Red logo, RN '304'	£50-75	☐
D 921	1970-72	Morgan Open Sports	Metallic Red body, Black seats	£30-40	☐
D 922	1970-72	Rally Ford Capri	Yellow body, Orange/Black stripe, RN '8'	£30-40	☐
			Green body, Black bonnet, (GS 2 model)	£30-40	☐
D 923	1970-72	'James Bond' Ford Escort	White body, Pale Blue stripes, 'JAMES BOND', White '007' and 'SPECIAL AGENT' logos. (From film 'On Her Majesty's Secret Service')	£100-150	☐
D 924	1970-72	Mercury Cougar XR7	Red body with Black roof, Yellow interior	£30-40	☐
		'James Bond' issue:	Red/Black with Yellow side flash, interior and skis on roof rack. (From film 'On Her Majesty's Secret Service')	£150-200	☐
D 925	1970-72	'James Bond' Ford Capri	White body with Black/White check design, 2 bonnet stripes and RN '6'. (From film 'On Her Majesty's Secret Service')	£100-150	☐
D 926	1970-72	Jaguar 'Control Car'	Metallic Brown body, Red roof blade, 'DAILY MIRROR' labels on doors, '1970 Mexico	£75-100	☐
D 927	1970-72	Ford Escort Rally	White body, Red RN '18', 'DAILY MIRROR' labels on doors, '1970 Mexico World Cup Rally Winner'	£100-150	☐
D 928	1970-72	Mercedes 280 SL 'SPECTRE'	Black body with Red 'S.P.E.C.T.R.E.' logo, plus boars head design	£100-150	☐
D 930	1970-72	Bertone Barchetta	Metallic Green over White body, Red interior	£20-30	☐
D 931	1970-72	'Old MacDonalds Truck'	Yellow cab, Brown rear, Silver engine	£75-100	☐
D 933	1970-72	'Holmes Wrecker'	White cab, Gold/Red rear assembly with Red *AUTO RESCUE*. (Not seen)	NGPP	☐
D 937	1970-72	Mercury Cougar	Metallic Dark Green body, Yellow interior and spoiler	£20-30	☐

Corgi Rockets Gift Sets

D 975	1970	Super Stock Gift Set 1	Contains D 905, D 919, Trailer and 3 figures	NGPP	☐
D 976	1970	Super Stock Gift Set 2	Contains Green/Black D 922, D 920, Trailer and 3 figures	NGPP	☐
D 977	1970	Super Stock Gift Set 3	Contains D 926, D 919, D 920 and 5 figures	NGPP	☐

The listing above has been prepared from a Corgi Rockets 1970 catalogue. The sets themselves have not been seen and further information is required.

D 978		'O.H.M.S.S.' Gift Set	Models of cars in the James Bond film 'On Her Majesty's Secret Service': D 923 and D 925 (as driven in the ice-racing scene) D 924 (as driven by 'Tracey') D 928 (as driven by the Chief of 'S.P.E.C.T.R.E.')	£500-750	☐

Corgi Rockets 'Speedsets' and 'Speed Circuits' Track Layouts

D 2051	1970	Action Speedset	One car, 'Autostart', 12 ft of track	NGPP	☐
D 2052	1970	Super Autobatics Speedset	One car, 'Autostart', 16 ft of track plus 'leaps' etc	NGPP	☐
D 2058	1970	Race-Abatic Speedset	Two cars, 'Autostart', 2 x 16 ft of track plus 'leaps' etc	NGPP	☐
D 2071	1970	Jetspeed Circuit	One car, 'Superbooster', 16 ft of track plus 'leaps' etc	NGPP	☐
D 2074	1970	Triple-Leap Speed Circuit	One car, 19 ft, 6 in. of track plus 'leaps' etc	NGPP	☐
D 2075	1970	Grand Canyon Speed Circuit	One car, 12 ft of track	NGPP	☐
D 2079	1970	World Champion Speedset	Two cars, 2 x 16 ft of track, 2 Boosters	NGPP	☐

Corgi Rockets Accessories

D 1931 Superleap,   D 1934 Autofinish,   D 1935 Connections (3)   D 1936 Space Leap,   D 1937 Autostart,   D 1938 Super Crossover,   D 1945 Adaptors (3) D 1963 Track (16ft)   D 1970 Super Booster,   D 1971 Hairpin Tunnel,   D 1976 Quickfire Start,   D 1977 Lap Counter,   D 1978 Pitstop,   D 1979 Spacehanger Bend

Corgi Rockets catalogues

no ref.	1969	8-page booklet	listing the first 7 issues, Green model on cover	£20-25	☐
no ref.	1970	16-page booklet	listing most issues, good pictures of rare models, sets and accessories	£30-35	☐

Corgi Juniors 1975-1991

The following listing represents the best information available to us. The listing is in no way complete and the Editor would welcome further details on other variations/issues and price levels.

Market Price Range — Scarcer items as shown, otherwise under £15
Models have WhizzWheels.

E1	1977-83	Mercedes-Benz 220D Ambulance, White or cream....................		☐	E51	1976-78	Volvo 245 Estate Car, Metallic green, White or Blue tailgate......................		☐
E2	1980-81	Blake's Seven Liberator	£50-75	☐	E52-1	1976-79	Mercedes Benz 240D 'TAXI'...........		☐
E3	1977-81	Stromberg's Helicopter		☐	E52-2	1982-83	Scooby Doo's Vehicle	£20-25	☐
E4	1975-79	Zetor Farm Tractor..........................	£15-20	☐	E53	1977-79	'FIRE' Launch................................		☐
E5	1980-82	NASA Space Shuttle........................		☐	E54-1	1980-82	'CORGI' Formula 1 Racer, Black car, Yellow or White driver		☐
E6	1979-80	'Daily Planet' Helicopter.................		☐					
E7	1976-80	Dumper Truck, Red/Yellow or Blue/ Yellow...................................		☐	E54-2	1976-78	(54) Ford D1000 Container Truck, Red/Yellow or Red/Orange...........		☐
E7	1976-80	Dumper Truck, Yellow/Red or Yellow/ Black..................................		☐	E55	1976-80	Refuse Truck, Blue/Yellow, Bronze/ Blue or Green/White		☐
E8	1979-83	Rover 3500		☐	E56	1979-80	Chevrolet 'SPIDERVAN'	£20-25	☐
E9	1975-80	'POLICE' Range Rover		☐	E57-1	1975-77	Ferrari 512s, Blue body, number '6'......		☐
E10	1977-81	Triumph TR7, White/Blue	£20-25	☐	E57-2	1979-80	Spiderbike....................................	£20-25	☐
		Triumph TR7, Silver/Red body...........	£20-25	☐	E58	1976-78	Beach Buggy..................................		☐
		Triumph TR7, Orange body............	£15-20	☐	E59-1	1980-83	Tom's Cart....................................	£15-20	☐
E11	1979-85	Supermobile....................................		☐	E59-2	1977-79	Mercedes-Benz 240D 'POLIZEI' Car.....	£15-20	☐
E12	1980-82	Jeep		☐	E59-3	1982-84	Mercedes-Benz 240D, Blue or Red or White...................................		☐
E13-1	1976-78	Rough Terrain Truck, Red or Blue body..		☐	E60	1977-79	James Bond Lotus Esprit................	£30-40	☐
E13-2	1980-81	Buck Rogers Starfighter..................	£25-35	☐	E61-1	1979-81	Buick Regal 'SHERIFF' Car............	£15-20	☐
E14	1975-76	(14d) 'ESSO' Tanker	£20-25	☐	E61-2	1980-82	Ford Capri 3-litre...........................	£15-20	☐
E14-2	1977-80	Buick Royal 'TAXI'		☐	E62	1977-80	AMC Pacer, Metallic Blue or Red body..		☐
E15	1975-84	(15-3) Mercedes 'SCHOOL BUS', Yellow or Red body......................		☐	E63	1977-80	'SURF RESCUE' Helicopter		☐
E16-1	1975-77	Land Rover Pick-Up........................		☐	E64	1980-82	'The Professionals' Ford Capri........	£15-20	☐
E16-2	1980-82	Rover 3500 'POLICE' Car................		☐	E65	1976-81	Caravan Trailer		☐
E17-1	1975-77	(17-2) Volkswagen 1300 Beetle.........	£15-20	☐	E66-1	1976-79	Centurion Tank..............................		☐
E17-2	1979-81	Metropolis 3500 'POLICE' Car.........	£20-30	☐	E66-2	1980	Ice Cream Van...............................		☐
E18	1977	Snowmobile, not seen......................	NGPP		E67-1	1976-80	Road Roller...................................		☐
E19	1980-82	Pink Panther Motorcycle		☐	E67-2	1980-83	Popeye's Tugboat	£20-25	☐
E20-1	1976-78	Site Cement Mixer..........................		☐	R68	1977-79	Kojak's Buick Regal	£20-25	☐
E20-2	1977-80	Penguinmobile................................	£15-20	☐	E69	1976-80	Batmobile	£20-30	☐
E21	1977-80	Charlie's Angels Chevrolet Van........	£15-20	☐	E70-1	1976-80	Cougar 'FIRE CHIEF'....................		☐
E22-1	1975-77	(22-3) Formula 1 Racer....................		☐	E70-2	1977-81	Ford Torino 'FIRE CHIEF'.............		☐
E22-2	1981-82	'PARAMEDIC' Van		☐	E71	1980-85	London Austin 'TAXI'		☐
E23	1979-81	Batbike	£50-75	☐	E72-1	1975-77	(72) Mercedes C111........................		☐
E24	1979-80	'SHAZAM' Thunderbolt	£30-40	☐	E72-2	1979-83	Jaguar XJS, Blue or Red body.........		☐
E25	1979-80	'CAPTAIN AMERICA' Porsche 917	£30-40	☐			Jaguar XJS, Red body, White 'MOTOR SHOW' logo...................	£20-30	☐
E26	1977-90	ERF Fire Tender, Yellow body.........		☐					
E27	1976-80	(27/2) Formula 5000 Racing Car...........		☐	E73	1980	'DRAX' Helicopter		☐
E28-1	1975-76	Hot Rodder....................................		☐	E74	1978-80	'RYDER TRUCK RENTAL' Leyland Van...		☐
E28-2	1977-80	Buick Regal 'POLICE' Car, White or Black body.................................		☐	E75	1977-80	Spidercopter.................................	£20-30	☐
E29	1975-80	Simon Snorkel Fire Engine..............		☐	E76	1976-78	(76) Military Jeep...........................		☐
E30	1976-83	Mobile Cement Mixer, Green/Yellow, Blue/White or Red/Silver...............		☐	E77	1977-80	Poclain Digger, Yellow/Red or White/ Red..		☐
E31	1975-79	Land Rover Breakdown, Red body, 'WRECKER TRUCK'....................		☐	E78	1976-81	Batcopter......................................		☐
					E79-1	1975-76	Land Rover Military Ambulance..........		☐
		Land Rover Breakdown, Blue body, 'CRASH SERVICE'		☐	E79-2	1980-83	Olive Oyl's Aeroplane		☐
E32	1970-74	The Saint's Jaguar XJS...................	£50-75	☐	E80	1979-80	'MARVEL COMICS' Van	£20-25	☐
E33	1979-80	'WONDERWOMAN's Car..................	£20-30	☐	E81	1975-83	Daimler Fleetline London Bus, various logos, with or without faces at windows......................................		☐
E34-1	1975-78	Sting Army Helicopter.....................		☐					
E34-2	1980	'HERTZ' Chevrolet Van...................		☐					
E35-1	1975-79	Air Bus Helicopter		☐	E82-1	1975-78	Can-Am Racer, Metallic Blue..........		☐
E35-2	1983-87	Tipper Truck, Silver/Blue or Red/ Brown..		☐	E82-2	1981-82	Yogi Bear's Jeep...........................	£20-30	☐
					E83-1	1975-77	'COMMANDO' Armoured Car.........		☐
E36-1	1975-77	Healer-Wheeler 'AMBULANCE'..........		☐	E83-2	1980-81	'GOODYEAR' Blimp......................		☐
E36-2	1979-80	'COCA-COLA' Chevrolet Van............		☐	E84-1	1975-78	Daimler Scout Car.........................		☐
E37	1976-79	Porsche Carrera 'POLICE' Car.........		☐	E84-2	1980-83	Bugs Bunny Vehicle	£15-20	☐
E38	1980-83	Jerry's Banger...............................	£20-25	☐	E85	1975-78	Skip Truck....................................		☐
E39	1975-77	Jaguar 'E' Type..............................	£35-45	☐	E86	1974-809	Fiat C1-9, Green body	£25-35	☐
E40-1	1977-80	Army Red Cross Helicopter		☐			Fiat X1-9, Gold body, racing number '4'................................	£15-20	☐
E40-2	1979-81	James Bond's Aston-Martin	£50-75	☐					
E41	1979-81	James Bond Space Shuttle	£15-20	☐			Fiat X1-9, Gold body, racing number '9', 'FIAT'......................		☐
E42	1977-81	'RESCUE' Range Rover		☐					
E43	1976-80	Massey-Ferguson 3303 Farm Tractor with Blade, Orange/Black, Yellow/Red or all Yellow..............................	£20-30	☐	E87	1975-80	Leyland Truck, 'COCA-COLA'		☐
							Leyland Truck, 'PEPSI-COLA'		☐
							Leyland Truck, 'WEETABIX'............		☐
E44-1	1976-78	Raygo Rascal 600 Road Roller		☐			Leyland Truck, 'W.H. SMITH'..........		☐
E44-2	1979-80	Starship Liberator	£50-75	☐	E88	1975-80	Mobile Crane.................................		☐
E45	1977-81	Starsky and Hutch Ford Gran Torino ...	£15-20	☐	E89	1975-82	Citroën Dyane, dark Yellow or Gold or Purple...		☐
E46	1976-80	'POLICE' Helicopter, White or Metallic Blue body...................................		☐	E90	1977-79	'FIREBALL' Chevrolet Van.............		☐
E47	1978-80	'SUPERVAN' (Chevrolet)		☐	E91a	1977-79	'GOLDEN EAGLE' Chevrolet Van		☐
E48	1975-79	Shovel Loader, red.........................		☐	E91b	1980-81	'VANTASTIC' Chevrolet Van (new casting)		☐
E49-1	1977-79	Tipping Lorry................................		☐					
E49-2	1981-83	Woody Woodpecker's Car................		☐	E92	1977-81	Volkswagen Polo, Metallic Lime or darker Green body........................		☐
E50	1979-80	'Daily Planet' (Leyland) Van, Red or Silver..	£10-20	☐	E93-1	1977-78	Tugboat..		☐
					E93-2	1980-81	Dodge Magnum	£15-20	☐

Ref. No.	Year	Description	Market Price Range
E94-1	1975-77	Porsche 917	
E94-2	1978-80	'ADIDAS' Chevrolet Van	
95	1977-82	'COCA-COLA' Leyland Van	
96-1	1975-78	Field Gun, military Green	
96-2	1980-83	Ford Thunderbird, Red or Cream of Green body	
97-1	1977-78	'EXXON' Petrol Tanker	£25-35
97-2	1977-80	'TEXACO' Petrol Tanker	
		'SHELL' Petrol Tanker	
		'BP OIL' Petrol Tanker	
98-1	1975-77	Marcos	
98-2	1977-79	Mercedes-Benz Mobile Shop	
98-3	1980-81	'POLICE' Helicopter	
99	1979-81	Jokermobile	£30-40
100	1981-83	Hulk Cycle	£30-40
102	1981-83	Renault 5 Turbo	
103	1981-83	Ford Transit Wrecker	
104	1981-83	Ford Mustang Cobra	
105	1981-83	Ford Escort 1.3GL, Metallic Green or Blue body	
E107	1981-83	Austin Metro, Metallic Dark Blue or Medium Blue body	
E108	1981-83	Locomotive	
E111	1981-83	Passenger Coach	
E112	1981-83	Goods Wagon	
E113	1982-83	Paddle Steamer	
E114	1981-83	Stage Coach	
E115	1981-83	James Bond 2cv Citroën	£20-30
E116	1982	Mercedes-Benz 'ESPANA 82'	
E117	1982	Chevrolet 'ESPANA 82' Custom Van	
E119	1983	Fire Engine, 'FLUGHAFEN-FEURWEHR' (German Issue)	£15-20
120	?	Leyland Van, 'Eiszeit' (German Issue)	£15-20
120	1983	Ice Cream Van, 'FRESHLICHE' (German Issue)	£15-20
121	1983	Chevrolet Van, 'TECHNISCHER' (German Issue)	£15-20
E123	1982-83	'AIRPORT RESCUE' Tender	
124	1982-83	Mercedes-Benz 500SL	
125	1982-83	Ford Transit Lorry	
E125	1983	Ford Dropside Truck	
126	1982-83	Ford Transit Breakdown, 'ABSCHIEPPDIENST', (German Issue)	£15-20
127	1982-83	'ADAC' Service Car, (German Issue)	£20-25
128	1982-83	Fred's Flyer	£25-35
129	1982-83	Ford Sierra 2.3 Ghia, Blue, Red or Silver body	
131	1982-83	Ferrari 308GTS, 'Magnum PI'	£25-35
133	1982-83	Buick Regal 'POLICE' Car, 'Magnum PI'	£25-35
134	1982-83	Barney's Buggy, Red/Orange, (The Flintstones')	£25-35
135	1982-83	Austin Metro 'DATAPOST'	
E136	1982-82	Ferrari 308GTS, Red or Black	
E137	1982-84	VW Turbo	
E138	1982-84	Rover 3500	
E139	1982-84	Porsche 911 Turbo	
E140	1982-84	Ford Mustang Cobra	
E141	1982-84	Ford Capri S 'ALITALIA'	
E143	1983-84	Leyland 'ROYAL MAIL' Van	
E144	1983-84	'BRITISH GAS' Van	
E145	1983-84	'BRITISH TELECOM' Van	
E146	1983-84	Ford Transit Pick-Up, 'Wimpey'	
E147	1983-84	Leyland 'ROADLINE' Lorry	
E148	1983-84	USS Enterprise	
E149	1983	Klingon Warship	
E150	1983	'Simon and Simon' Police Car	
E151	1983	Wilma'a Coupé	£25-35
E152	1983	'Simon and Simon' 1957 Chevy	
E156	1983	1957 Chevy	
E160	1983	VW Hot Rod	
E161	1983	Opel Corsa, 1.3SR	
E170	?	Vauxhall Nova	
E174	1983	Quarry Truck	
175	?	Ford Escort	
E175	1983	Pipe Truck	
176	?	Ford Capri 'S'	
E177	1983	'Corgi Chemco' Tanker	
E178	1983	'Corgi' Container Truck	
E179	1983	Chevy Corvette, Yellow or Aqua Blue	
E180	1983	Pontiac Firebird SE	
181	?	Mercedes 300sl	
E182	1983	4x4 Renegade Jeep	
E183	1983	Renegade Jeep with Hood	
E184	1983	Range Rover	
E185	1983	Baja Off Road Van	
190	1983	Austin Metro	
190	1983	Buick Regal	
191	1983	Rover 3500	
192	1983	Triumph TR7, 'British Airways'	
192	1983	Mercedes 'Arabic' Ambulance	
193	1983	Chubb 'Arabic' Fire Truck	
195	1983	Leyland Van 'Arabic Miranda'	£15-25
E196	1983	'Police Tactical Force' Van	
198	1983	James Bond Citroën 2cv	£15-25
201	1983	Chevrolet Van 'Arabic Team'	£15-25
E203	1983	Fiat X1.9, Orange/Red or Yellow	
E204	1983	Renault 5 Turbo	
E205	1983	Porsche 911	
E206	1983	Buick Regal	
208	1983	Ford Sierra 'Notartz'	£15-25
209	1983	Leyland Van 'DBP'	
210	1983	Matra Rancho 'Safari Park'	
211	1983	Ford Escort 'Fahrschule'	£15-25
212	1983	VW pole 'Siemens'	
219	1983	Ford Sierra 'Polizei'	£15-25
222	1983	Chevrolet Van 'Swissair'	
223	1983	Matra Rancho 'Safari Park'	
224	1983	Chevrolet Van 'Rivella'	£15-25
226	1983	Ford Transit Wrecker 'Abschleppdienst'	£15-25
228	1983	Leyland Van 'Waser Papeterie'	£15-25
250	1983	Simon Snorkel 'Brandbil'	£15-25
252	1983	Ford Transit Wrecker 'Falck'	£15-25
253	1983	Mercedes Ambulance 'Falck'	£15-25
254	1983	Mercedes 240D 'Falck'	£15-25
?	?	Leyland Van 'Geest', on special card	£20-30
?	?	Chevrolet Van 'Unichem'	£15-25

Corgi Juniors 'J' Series

Ref. No.	Year	Description	Market Price Range
J1	1984	NASA Space Shuttle	
J1	1988	Ford Capri, 'Duckhams'	
J2	1984-85	Dump Truck	
J2	1988	Iveco Tanker, 'Esso'	
J3	1984-85	Triumph TR7, Black and Red/Blue	
J4	1984	Starfighter, (Buck Rogers)	
J4	1988	Ford Transit Van, 'Kremer Racing'	
J5	1984-85	'Holiday Inn' Bus, Green or White	
J6	1984	Rover 'Police' Car	
J7	1984	ERF Fire Engine	
J8	1984-85	Simon Snorkel Fire Engine	
J9	1984-85	Mobile Cement Mixer	
J9	1988	Iveco Container, 'Mars'	
J10	1984	Aston-Martin DB5, Red	
J10	1985	Aston-Martin DB5, Yellow, 'DB6'	
J11	1984	Volvo Estate Car, White	
J11	1985	Volvo Support Car, White, 'Castrol'	
J12	1984	Skip Truck, Red/White	
J12	1988	Iveco Tanker, 'BP Oil'	
J13	1984	Refuse Truck, Yellow/Grey	
J13	1988	Iveco Truck, 'Pepsi'	
J14	1984	Mercedes 240D	
J14	1985	Mercedes 240D Rally Car	
J15	1984	Lotus Esprit	
J15	1988	Ford Transit Van, 'Police'	
J16	1984	Ford Capri, White, Silver or Blue	
J16	1988	BMW 3251 Saloon, Red	
J17	1984	london FX4 Taxi	
J18	1984-85	Jaguar XJS, White, Silver or Green	
J19	1984	Matra Rancho, Green/Black or Blue	
J20	1984-88	London Bus, Red	
J39	1988	Chevrolet 'ROYAL MAIL' Van	
J62	1985	Mobile Shop	
J63	1988	Ford Transit Van, 'Royal Mail'	
J64	1988	Land-Rover 110, Yellow, 'AA'	
J66	1988	Land-Rover 110, White, 'Police'	
J73	1988	Ford Escort XR3i	
J74	1988	Land-Rover 110, White, 'Safari Rally'	
J77	1988	Ferrari Testarossa, White	
J79	1988	Mercedes 300E Ambulance	
J81	1988	Buick, Blue, 'Police NYPD'	
J85	1988	Porsche 935 Racer	
J86	1988	Porsche 935 Racer	
J88	1988	Porsche 935, Red, no markings	
J89	1988	Mercedes 2.3/16 Racer, White, 'Servis'	
J90	1988	Mercedes 2.3/16 Saloon, Red	
J90	1988	Escort 'DATAPOST', '66'	
J91	1988	Jaguar XJ40, White, 'Police'	
J91	1989	Escort 'DATAPOST', '77'	

Ref. No.					Market Price Range
J92	1988	Metro 'DATAPOST', '66'.......................	☐		
J93	1988	Jaguar XJ40, White, 'Jaguar'.................	☐		
J93	1989	Metro 'DATAPOST', '77'.......................	☐		
J94	1988	Mercedes 300E Estate, Red	☐		
J94	1989	Metro Van 'ROYAL MAIL'.....................	☐		
J95	1988	Mercedes 300E Estate Taxi, light Greyish-Yellow....................................	☐		
J97	1988	Land-Rover 110, Red, 'Fire Salvage'	☐		
J98	1988	Porsche Targa, Red..............................	☐		
J99	1988	Porsche Targa. White, 'Turbo'	☐		

900 Series Issues

90010	1991	Ford Transit Van 'Kremer Racing'	☐	
90013	1991	Ford Transit Van 'Police', Dark Blue	☐	
90015	1991	Ford Transit Van 'RAC', White.............	☐	
90030	1991	ERF Fire Engine, Red/Silver.................	☐	
90035	1991	Simon Snorkel Fire Engine, Red/White	☐	
90040	1991	Iveco Container Truck 'Wispa'...............	☐	
90065	1991	Iveco Tanker 'Shell'	☐	
90076	1991	BMW 325i, Metallic Silver-Blue	☐	
90100	1991	Matra Rancho, Yellow, 'M'	☐	
90125	1991	Ford Transit Wrecker 'Police'	☐	
90126	1991	Ford Transit Wrecker 'Kremer Racing'	☐	
90145	1991	BMW M3, Black/White........................	☐	
90160	1991	Ford Sierra, Metallic Blue	☐	
90190	1991	Ferrari Testarossa, Red, 'Ferrari'...........	☐	
90200	1991	Corvette, Black/Red, 'Flame' design	☐	
90201	1991	Corvette, Red/White, 'Vette'.................	☐	
90300	1991	Pontiac Firebird, Silver, Red bodyline ...	☐	
90301	1991	Pontiac Firebird, Yellow/Black, 'Fire Bird'...	☐	

90310	1991	Military Jeep, Olive body, Brown top	☐	
90360	1991	US Custom Van, Black/Red, 'Team Racing'	☐	
90371	91	Land-Rover, 'Coastguard', Dark Blue/ Yellow	☐	
90374	1991	Land-Rover, 'Emergency – Fire', Red....	☐	
90390	1991	Mercedes Ambulance, White, red crosses..	☐	
90420	1991	Buick 'Police' Car, Black/White	☐	
90421	1991	Buick 'Fire Chief' Car, Red/White........	☐	
90430	1991	Volvo 760 Saloon, Metallic Grey	☐	
90440	1991	Porsche 935 Racer, Red, '33'	☐	
90460	1991	Mercedes 2.3/16, Blue, 'Mobil', 'Koni'...	☐	
90461	1991	Mercedes 2.3, Red..............................	☐	
90470	1991	Jaguar XJ40, 'Police', White.................	☐	
90471	1991	Jaguar XJ40, Metallic Bronze...............	☐	
90500	1991	Helicopter, 'Police', White/Black	☐	
90520	1991	Ford Thunderbird, Black, 'chrome' spare wheel.......................................	☐	
90540	1991	Ford Mustang, Blue, 'Goodyear', '77'....	☐	
90541	1991	Ford Mustang, White, Red stripes, '7' ...	☐	
90550	1991	BMW 850i, Black................................	☐	
90560	1991	Ferrari 348 TB, Red.............................	☐	
90570	1991	Mercedes 500sl, White.........................	☐	
90580	1991	Jaguar XJR9, White/Purple, 'Jaguar'.....	☐	
91000	1991	MAN Container Truck 'Perrier', Dark Green..	☐	
91020	1991	MAN Tanker 'Texaco', White................	☐	
91040	1991	MAN Open Back Tipper, Yellow...........	☐	

Twin Pack Issues E2501–2595 and J200–260

These are Corgi Juniors bubblepacked in pairs from 1977 approx. The market price range is equivalent to the sum of the individual model prices for each model. Rare issue E2519 Batman Set £100-150.

42

76

Corgi Super Juniors & Superhaulers

Ref. No.	Model Type	Model Features	Market Price Range	

FORD D SERIES TRUCK issued 1970-75

Ref. No.	Model Type	Model Features	Market Price Range	
2002	Car Transporter	White cab, Blue chassis, Red deck	£20-25	☐
		Red cab and chassis, White deck	£40-50	☐
2003	Low Loader	Blue cab, trailer and chassis	£20-25	☐
2004	'CORGI' Removals Van	Red cab and chassis, Silver trailer	£40-50	☐
		Light Blue cab and chassis, Silver trailer	£40-50	☐
2007	Low Loader	Red cab and chassis, Blue trailer with Orange Junior digger load	£25-35	☐
2012	Low Loader	Military Green with U.S. vehicle	NGPP	☐

FORD D SERIES TRUCK SETS 1970-76

Ref. No.	Model Type	Model Features	Market Price Range	
3003	Car Transporter Set	White or Red cab plus 5 Juniors	£40-50	☐
3011	Low Loader Set	Red cab plus 6 Juniors	£50-60	☐
3024	Low Loader Setr	Blue cab, Yellow trailer (1976), 6 Juniors	£50-60	☐
3025	Car Transporter Set	Yellow cab, Orange deck (1976), 5 Juniors	£30-35	☐

MACK TRUCKS issued 1971-75

Ref. No.	Model Type	Model Features	Market Price Range	
2006	'ESSO' Tanker	White cab & tank	£10-15	☐
2010	'EXXON' Tanker	White cab and tank	£20-25	☐
2011	'US' Army Tanker	Military Green body	£20-25	☐
2027	'RYDER RENTALS'	Yellow cab and Box Trailer	£10-15	☐

MERCEDES TRACTOR UNITS, CAR TRANSPORTER issued 1976

Ref. No.	Model Type	Model Features	Market Price Range	
2014/15		White cab and deck, Blue chassis	£20-25	☐
2015		White cab, Yellow deck, Red chassis	£20-25	☐

N.B. Car Transporter Sets 3023, 3015, 3105 – £30-35.

TANKERS issued 1983-84

Market Price Range — as shown otherwise £10-15. Liveries issued:-
1130 'CORGI CHEMCO' Red or White cab; 1166 'GUINNESS'; 1167 'DUCKHAMS'; 1130 'SHELL' Yellow or White cab; 1167 '7 UP' £20-30.

BOX TRAILERS issued 1978-85

Market Price Range as shown otherwise £10-£15. Liveries issued:-
1166 'ARIA DAIRY'; 1129 'ASG SPEDITION', 'BRITISH HOME STORES' £20-30; 2020 'BIRDS EYE', 'CARTERS LEMON DELINER' £25-35; 1131 'CHRISTIAN SALVESON'; 1129 'CORGI' Black or White cab, 1146 'DUNLOP', 2028 'GERVALS DANONE', 1139 'HALLS FOOD'; 1175 'INTERNATIONAL DISTRIBUTORS MEETING' £70-80; 1178 'MAYNARDS'; 1202 'PICKFORDS HOMESPEED' £70-80; 1144 'ROYAL MAIL PARCELS', 1111 'SAFEWAY' £15-20; 1137 'SOUKS SUPERMARKET' £25-30 (Saudi issue); 1175 'TI RALEIGH'; 1177 'WEETABIX'; 1145 'YORKIE'; 1176 'ZANUSSI'.

MERCEDES SETS

Ref. No.	Model Type	Model Features	Market Price Range	
1403	'CORGI CHEMCO'	Plus Junior Van	£25-30	☐
3128	'DUCKHAMS' & 'YORKIE'	Plus 10 Juniors	£40-50	☐
1200	'DUCKHAMS' & 'GUINNESS' Tanker	Plus 3 Scammells	£40-50	☐

SCAMMELL 4x2 LANDTRAIN TRACTOR UNITS — TANKERS issued 1985

Market Price Range £10-12.
1185 'DUCKHAMS'; 1141 'SHELL' Yellow or Orange Cab.

BOX TRAILERS issued 1984

Market Price Range as shown otherwise £10-12. Liveries issued:-
1186 'LUCAS CAV FILTERS' £15-20; 1186 LUCAS GB TRUCK RACING £15-20; 1186 'McVITIES' Blue or Orange cab, 'NORMANS SUPERMARKET £20-25; 1144 'ROYAL MAIL PARCELS', 'T.I. RALEIGH'; 1177 'WEETABIX'; 1145 'YORKIE' Yellow or Red cab; 1175 'ZANUSSI' £35-45.

SCAMMELL 4x2 SETS

1200 Contains 1177 RALEIGH, 1177 WEETABIX 7 1186 McVITIES £23-45
N.B. See also 'Corgitronic' Scammell issues.

SCAMMELL 6x4 LANDTRAIN TRACTOR UNIT

Ref. No.	Model Type	Model Features	Market Price Range	
J3700	Car Transporter	'COCA COLA RACE TEAM' U.S. issue	£30-40	☐

BOX TRAILERS issued 1986-92

Market Price Range as shown otherwise £8-15. Liveries issued:-
1247 'BF GOODRICH'; 1246 'COCA COLA' (UK issue) Grey shadow on wavyline; 3300c 'COCA COLA' (US issue) No Grey shadow on White wavy line on trailer £20-25; 52/2 'CORNING'; 1246 'DR PEPPER'; 1246/8 'FAO SCHWARTZ' £20-25; 1246/6 'FRANCOIS AVRIL' £20-25; 'HERSHEY'S CHOCOLATE' Purple or Dark Brown cab; 71500 '7 UP'; 91320 'WEETABIX'; 1246/1 'YORKIE'.

SCAMMELL 6x4 Sets

Ref. No.	Model Type	Model Features	Market Price Range	
3004	'YORKIE'	Plus Volvo and 2 Juniors	£20-25	☐
J3500/600	'COCA COLA'	Plus 3 Juniors	£30-35	☐

FLATBED TRAILER issued 1986

Market Price Range £7-10.
1220/1 Red cab and flatbed with load (also 'BP' offer model).

VOLVO F12 'Globetrotter' TRACTOR UNIT

Three cab types:- Type 1: cast marker lights with or without airfoil; Type 2: Cast air horns and marker lights; Type 3: cast marker lights plus chrome air horns.

CAR TRANSPORTERS issued 1984-92

Market Price Range £7-10.
1193 Red cab, White deck, Red chassis; 1222 Red, Blue or Yellow cab; 91380 Red or White cab.

CAR TRANSPORTER SETS 1984-92

Tractor units issued with Red, Blue, White or Yellow cabs. The Market Price Range is £10-15.

TANKERS issued 1986-92

Market Price Range as shown otherwise £8-12. Liveries issued:-
1264 'BP' White cab; 1265 'BP' Green cab £15-20 (New Zealand issue); 91341 'BP' Green with White cab roof, 'BURMAH' £75-100; 'DUCKHAMS', Yellow or Blue cab, 'GULF' White or Silver cab; 1265/4 'NESTE', 1250/2 'NOROL', 1250/3 'POLO', 'SHELL' Red or Yellow cab; 91355 'TESCO', 1250 & 1265/1/2 'TEXACO' Red or White cab. Tanker Set issued 1987/88 'TEXACO' £12-15.

BOX TRAILERS issued 1985-89

Market Price Range as shown otherwise £8-12. Liveries issued:-
1197 'ASG SPEDITION'; 1227 'BEEFEATER' £25-35; 1225 'BILSPEDITION' £20-25; 1232 BOSCH PLATINUM £20-25; 1212 'BRITISH HOME STORES', 'BRITISH TELECOM'; 1233 'CADBURYS DAIRY MILK'; 1224 'CADBURY'S FLAKE'; 1248 'CARTERS LEMONADE LINER' £15-20; V20 'COCA COLA' 1000 only British Home Stores issue £30-40; 91350/5 'EDDIE STOBART', 'FEDERAL EXPRESS'; 1231/31 'FREIA CHOCOLATE'; 1231/23 'FRIZZY PAZZY'; 1245 'FUJI FILM'; 1231/13 'GAMINO'; 1231/18 'GATEWAY'; 1206 'HILLARDS' £40-50 (2500 certificated); 1196 'HOTPOINT'; 91310 'HULA HOOPS'; 1231/29 'INTERMARCHE' £20-25; 1217 'KAYS'; 1231 'KAYS'; 1194 'LEE COOPER'; 1231 'LO COST'; 1231/19 'MARABOU CHOCOLATE'; 1231 'MARS'; 1231 'MARS' Brown or Black cab; 1231 'McCAIN'; 91300 'ORANGINA'; 1211 'RILEYS'; 1188 'ROYAL MAIL PARCELS'; 1231 'ROYAL MAIL DATAPOST'; 1231 'ROYAL MAIL PARCELFORCE'; 1231 'SAFEWAY'; 1231/37 'SAS CARGO' £20-25; 91301 'SNICKERS' £20-25; 1231/22 'STEIFF'; 1231/6 'TESCO'; 1212 'TNT OVERNITE' £80-90; 1231/1 'WEETABIX'; 1231 'WIMPY' Red or White cab; 1231/5 'WOOLWORTHS'; 'YORKIE'.

VOLVO BOX TRAILER SETS

Market Price Range £6-9. Each contains 2 Super haulers plus matching Juniors. Issued 1987-94.
J3167 'WIMPY' & 'WEETABIX'; J3167/4 'WHITE ARROW'; J3167/6 'KAYS'; J3184 ROYAL MAIL DESPATCH CENTRE'; J3186 'ROYAL MAIL DATAPOST'; J3189 'BRITISH TELECOM'; C43 'TOYMASTER' Superhauler plus 2 Juniors £25-35; C43 'WEETABIX' Superhauler plus Routemaster & Junior; V37 'EDDIE STOBART' Superhauler plus Transit Van.

CORGI CLASSICS – VOLVO BOX TRAILERS issued 1993-94

Market Price Range £7-10.
98100 'SWIFT SERVICE'; 98101 'AMTRAK'; 98102 'UNITED TRANSPORT'; 98103 'P&O FERRYMASTERS'; 98304 'CHRISTIAN SALVESON'; 98305 'EXEL LOGISTICS'; 98306 'DODDS TRANSPORT'; 98307 'LYNX PARCELS'.

SEDDON ATKINSON 400 SERIES TRACTOR UNITS

3171 Car Transporter 'GLOBETROTTER' (Saudi Arabia issue) £15-20.

TANKERS issued 1987-92

Market Price Range as shown otherwise £8-12.
1251/1 'BOC CENTENARY'; 1264/1 'BP'; 1264/2 'ELF'; 1251/2 'ROLO'; 1264/1 'CADBURYS' £75-100.

BOX TRAILERS issued 1987-92

Market Price Range as shown otherwise £7-10.
91424 'ASDA'; 1238/9 'CADBURYS CHOCOLATE'; 1238/2 'CADBURYS FLAKE'; 1238/13 'CADBURYS WISPA'; 1238/7 'FEDERAL EXPRESS'; SA4 'GATEWAY' £35-40; 91430 'KIT-KAT'; 1238/10 'LYNX'; 1238/10 'MARS'; 1238/1 'McCAIN'; 91420 'PERRIER'; 1238/4 'RADIO 1 ROADSHOW'; 1238 'ROYAL MAIL PARCELS'; 1238/6 'ROYAL MAIL DATAPOST'; 1238/14 'ROYAL MAIL PARCELFORCE' Red Shadowing; 91422 'ROYAL MAIL PARCELFORCE' Grey shadowing; 1238/3 'SECURICOR'; 1238/3 'SILENTNIGHT'; 91310 'SMARTIES'; 1238/12 'WIMPY'.

SEDDON ATKINSON SETS issued 1988-91

Market Price Range £15-20.
3184 'ROYAL MAIL DESPATCH CENTRE' Superhauler plus 4 Juniors; 92625 'ROYAL MAIL PARCELFORCE' Superhauler x 2 plus 2 Juniors; 3087 'WIMPY' Superhauler plus 2 Juniors; 3167 'WIMPY' Superhauler plus 4 Juniors; 'SECURICOR' No details, NGPP.

KENWORTH T600 & T800 AERODYNE TRACTOR UNITS issued 1993-94

Single models are certificated. Sold as Race Image. Collectables in the U.S.A.
91385 'VALVOLINE' £10-15; 81388 'QUAKER STATE' £10-15; 91389 'TEXACO HAVOLINE' £25-30; 91390 'PLASTIKOTE' £25-30; 91591 'LOTUS' RACE SET Superhauler plus 2 Juniors etc. £15-20; 93016 'FUJI FILM' RACE SET Superhauler plus 4 Juniors etc £20-25; 98404 'RAYBESTOS' NGPP; 98405 'DUPONT' NGPP; 98511 'VALVOLINE' NGPP; 98516 'WESTERN AUTO' plus Drag car; 98518 'OLDSMOBILE' NGPP; 98519 'SUPER CLEAN' NGPP; 98521 'SLICK 50' NGPP.

FORD AEROMAX TRACTOR UNITS issued 1994

Single models certificated. Sold as Race Image collectables in the U.S.A.
91391 'CITGO' NGPP; 98400 'MAXWELL HOUSE' NGPP; 98401 'MOTORCRAFT LAKE SPEED' NGPP; 98520 'MOTORCRAFT BOB GLIDDEN' NGPP.

CORGI/KIKO TOYS BRAZIL

Kiko Toys manufactured models for the South American market using Corgi Junior models in 1985/6

KK1	Low Loader	with Junior digger, White cab..	**£30-40** ☐
KK2	'ATLANTIC OIL'	White/Blue Tanker	**£30-40** ☐
KK3	'SATURNO' (ZANUSSI)	Black cab/trailer	**£30-40** ☐

RECOMMENDED READING

'CORGI SUPER JUNIOR and SUPERHAULER GUIDE' provides full details plus pictures of all the variations compiled by Andy and Pat Browning, 3 Waterside Terrace, Ninn Lane, Great Chart, Ashford, Kent TN23 3DD. Tel: 01233-643461. N.B. All the profits from this publication go to a childrens charity.

The Editor would like to express his appreciation to Andy Browning for his help with the Superhauler listings.

Qualitoys

A range of sturdy vehicles made up from the same basic parts. First issued in 1969 they were aimed at the pre school age group.

They were publicized as being from the 'makers of Corgi Toys' and did not form part of the Corgi range as such. They have no great collectable value.

Q701 Pick Up Truck
Q702 Side Tipper
Q703 Breakdown Truck
Q704 Tower Wagon

Q705 Horse Box
Q706 Giraffe Transporter
Q707 Fire Engine
Q708 Pick Up Trailer

1962 Catalogue Ref:- C/100/62 U.K. Edition.

Corgi Toys Catalogues - (United Kingdom Editions)

Information taken from the Cecil Gibson Archives and this Catalogue compiler's own collection of reference material.
Note: 'Concertina' leaflets were issued with models sold in the early Blue boxes.

The Editor would especially like to express his appreciation for the catalogue updating information received from Mr Mark Atkinson of Essex.

Ref. No.	Year(s)	Publication	Cover Features and Details	Market Price Range	
no ref.	1956	Concertina leaflet	Blue cover, famous Corgi dog, shows first 14 models, no prices	£15-20	☐
no ref.	1956	Concertina leaflet	Blue cover with Red/Gold Corgi dog. Depicts first 14 models and shows prices of both normal and mechanical models	£20-25	☐
50/157/K1	1957	Concertina leaflet	Blue cover with Red/Gold Corgi dog. Depicts ten models and lists the mechanical models in red	£5-10	☐
40/257/K1	1957	Concertina leaflet	Blue cover with Red/Gold Corgi dog. Depicts ten models but does not list mechanical models	£5-10	☐
40/257/K2	1957	Concertina leaflet	As previous leaflet but with the addition of 208	£5-10	☐
50/557/K3	1957	Concertina leaflet	As 40/257/K2 plus 100,150,408, 454, 'WOW! CORGI TOYS' logo	£5-10	☐
100/1057/K3	1957	Concertina leaflet	Blue cover showing 100, 150, 207, 208, 302, 405, 408, 455	£5-10	☐
50/1057/K4	1958	Concertina leaflet	Blue cover, 'WOW! CORGI TOYS' logo. Listings include models 102, 406/7, and first 'MAJOR' toy (1101)	£15-20	☐
50/1157/K4	1958	Concertina leaflet	Cover shows 102, 210, 406, 407, 412, 1101, 'WOW! CORGI TOYS' logo	£5-10	☐
52/258/K5	1958	Concertina leaflet	Cover shows GS 1 & 2, 101, 211, 302, 457, 459, 1100, 1401, 1450	£5-10	☐
52/258/K6	1958	Concertina leaflet	As previous leaflet plus 350, 351	£5-10	☐
300/658/K7	1958	Concertina leaflet	Shows GS 3, 151, 209, 458, 'NEW CORGI TOYS' logo & prices	£5-10	☐
25/257/C1/UK	1957	Four-fold leaflet	'Blue box' 208 Jaguar on cover, 15 model pictures inside	£75-100	☐
25/257/C2/UK	1957	Four-fold leaflet	As previous leaflet but with 24 model pictures	£75-100	☐
50/1057/C3/UK	1957	Four-fold leaflet	Shows GS 1 Bedford Transporter and 6 cars on Blue/Yellow cover with details of 100, 150, 200-8, 210, 300-2, 403-8, 412, 452-5, 1101	£25-30	☐
25/1157/C4/UK	1957	Four-fold leaflet	As previous leaflet plus 101 and 102	£25-30	☐
no ref.	1958	Four-fold leaflet	As previous leaflet plus 211. No prices, car listing or ref. no.	NGPP	☐
650/858/C8	1958	Catalogue	First 'book' catalogue. Cover depicts boy playing with Bloodhound Missile, many other vehicles	NGPP	☐
no ref.	1959	Four-fold leaflet	Blue cover with 'THE ROCKET AGE WITH CORGI TOYS'. (This leaflet was issued with Rocket Age models)	£15-20	☐
no ref.	9/1959	Interim leaflet	Lists 152, 50 Tractor, 350 Thunderbird, new TT van & accessories	NGPP	☐
U.K. 9/59	1959	16 page Catalogue	Cover features Massey Ferguson Tractor No 50 and BRM Racer No 152. Agricultural & 'MAJOR' issues (No.1100 etc) are listed	£30-40	☐
no ref.	1959	Single page leaflet	Features Renault Floride features plus 'STRAIGHT FROM THE MOTOR SHOW' logo	£10-15	☐
no ref.	1959	Two fold leaflet	Features 'AUTHENTIC ROCKET AGE MODELS' logo & models plus 1102 Tractor Dozer.	£10-15	☐
no ref.	1960	Interim leaflet	Depicts M1 Motorway scene	£5-10	☐
U.K. 9/60	1960	20 page Catalogue	Cover has motorway bridge scene & Corgi models. This catalogue was the first with listings of 'CHIPPERFIELDS'	£30-40	☐
U.K. 9/61	1961	24 page Catalogue	Racetrack scene on cover. Listings and pictures include new Sports Cars, Express Coach and Kits	£20-25	☐
no ref.	1962	Two-fold Checklist leaflet	Front cover depicts Blue/Yellow 'CORGI TOYS' plus seven models and their features. Red/Grey interior plus first check list	£15-20	☐
C/100/62	1963	32 page Catalogue	Cover depicts schoolboy (in red cap and blazer) crossing road with Corgi dog. No catalogue date is shown on front cover	£75-100	☐
no ref.	1963	32 page Catalogue	Same cover as C/100/62 but boy's cap and blazer are Blue. The date '1963-64' is shown on front cover	£15-20	☐
Playcraft Toys Ltd 1964					
	1964	Two-fold Checklist leaflet	Blue/Yellow 'Corgi Toys' design on cover featuring 241 Ghia	£15-20	☐
Playcraft Toys Ltd 1964					
	1965	40 page Catalogue	Cover logos: 'CORGI TOYS', 'CORGI CLASSICS', '1965'. Contains Classics and first Routemaster in the listings	£15-20	☐
Mettoy Playcraft (Sales) Ltd 1965					
	1965	Two-fold Checklist leaflet	Six model cars from six different nations are featured on the cover	£5-10	☐
Playcraft Toys Ltd 1965					
	1966	40 page Catalogue	Cover depicts model 261 James Bond's Aston Martin DB5. Contents give details of special Rallye Monte Carlo issues. 'Price 3d'	£15-20	☐
C2038/66	1966	Leaflet	Cover proudly states 'MODEL CAR MAKERS TO JAMES BOND'	£8-12	☐
C2039/4/66	1966	Four-fold Checklist leaflet	Similar to previous with 'MODEL CAR MAKERS TO JAMES BOND'. The contents feature 1127 Simon Snorkel etc	£10-15	☐
C2017/9/66	1967	48 page Catalogue	The cover & contents are dominated by Film & TV related models of 'BATMAN' & 'THE AVENGERS' etc. Also contains details of a model never issued - 498 Mini Countryman	£15-20	☐
Mettoy Playcraft (Sales) 1967					
	1967	Three-fold Checklist leaflet	Cover shows 'NEW' in 5 languages & 1142 Holmes Wrecker. Listings include 1967 Monte Carlo Rally winners	£15-20	☐
C/2017/7/67	1967-68	48 page Catalogue	Model 262 Lincoln Continental makes up the covers. 'Price 6d'. 2 models shown but not issued: 9022 Daimler 38 with Hood, & 9014 Model 'T' Van 'Lyons Tea' (eventually issued as Corgi Classic C865 in Feb 1986)	£10-15	☐
C2017/9/68	1968	48 page Catalogue	Cover features 268 'Chitty Chitty Bang Bang'. Listings include 803 'Yellow Submarine' and 'Take-off Wheels' issues	£15-20	☐
Mettoy Playcraft (Sales) Ltd 1969					
	1969	Seven-fold Checklist leaflet	'Concorde' model on cover plus 302 Hillman Hunter. Listings include 'Corgi Comics', 'CHIPPERFIELD' and Scammell Transporter Set No.48	£5-10	☐

Ref. No.	Year(s)	Model Type	*Corgi Toys Catalogues – continued*	Market Price Range	
The Mettoy Co Ltd 1970	1970	48 page Catalogue	Cover depicts 388 Mercedes Benz C111, first 'WhizzWheels' models listed	£5-10	☐
1970 Mettoy Co Ltd	1971	Two-fold Checklist leaflet	6 WhizzWheels models on the cover, final 'Take-Off Wheels' issues listed	£5-10	☐
C2017 Petty 7/71/LOI7b	1972	48 page Catalogue	Cover shows 1972 Car models. Excellent 'CORGI COMICS' pictures inside	£5-10	☐
C2017 Petty 7/71/LOI7B (2nd)	1972	48 page Catalogue	Cars across both covers	£5-10	☐
1973 Mettoy Co Ltd	1973	40 page Catalogue	F1 Racing Cars featured on the cover. Good Racing/Rally pictures within	£5-10	☐
1974 Mettoy Co Ltd	1974	40 page Catalogue	'John Player' Lotus on cover, good Military & Aircraft pictures	£5-10	☐
1975 Mettoy Co Ltd	1975	Three-fold leaflet	Helicopters, Noddy's Car, etc on the cover. Numbers given 'C' prefix.	£5-10	☐
1976 Mettoy Co Ltd	1976	Three-fold leaflet	First page features 'KOJAK'. Good Roadmaking and Public Services listings	£5-10	☐
C2210	1977	48 page Catalogue	Silver Jubilee Coach on cover. Large section listing Corgi 'Juniors'	£5-10	☐
The Mettoy Co Ltd	1978	48 page Catalogue	James Bond's Lotus on cover, 'JEAN RICHARD' models within	£5-10	☐
C2250	1979	48 page Catalogue	James Bond's Space Shuttle C649 'MOONRAKER' is featured on the cover, and 'SUPERMAN' & 'THE MUPPETS' are listed inside	£5-10	☐
C2270	1980	48 page Catalogue	Rover 3500 'POLICE' C339 & C1001 HCB ANGUS are the cover features. Good listings of Emergency vehicles includes foreign 'POLICE' issues	£5-10	☐
C2285	1981	32 page Catalogue	'CORGI' container on cover. Listings feature Film/TV models	£5-10	☐
C2337	1982	32 page Catalogue	Cover features 'Gull-wing' Mercedes (C802), 'Corgitronics' within	£5-10	☐
The Mettoy Co PLC	1983	36 page Catalogue	Boxed models on cover, new Mercedes & Scania trucks inside	£5-10	☐
no ref.	1984	32 page Catalogue	'CORGI '84' & boxed models on cover. Large scale '800' series cars listed. This was the last catalogue to display Corgi Dog emblem.	£3-5	☐
no ref.	1985	48 page Catalogue	Cover shows new 'CORGI' trade name logo. The new 'CLASSICS' Commercials range is listed.	£3-5	☐

Overseas Editions of Corgi Catalogues

These are known to have been produced for the USA, Belgium, Eire, Kenya/Uganda, Sweden, Holland, Singapore/ Malaya, France, Denmark and Italy.

Usually the catalogues were identical to the UK editions but included a checklist providing details in the language or currency of the country concerned. Unlike UK editions, no Catalogue price was shown on the cover. However, the 1966 French edition was an exception in that it was printed entirely in French. It is not known whether any overseas editions were published after 1967/68.

The market price range of overseas editions is likely to be similar to corresponding UK editions. However, unique items in pristine condition would attract a premium.

OVERSEAS ISSUES RECORDED TO DATE

25/257/C2/ SM	1957	Four-fold Leaflet	Issued in Singapore/Malaya	NGPP	☐
7/1058/Cb	1957	16-page Catalogue	Issued in Kenya/Uganda/Tanganyika	NGPP	☐
10/658/C5	1958	Leaflet	Issued in Eire	NGPP	☐
no ref.	8/1959	16-page Catalogue	Issued in Belgium (printed in French)	NGPP	☐
no ref.	1966	48-page Catalogue	Issued in France, same cover as C2017/9/66, (printed in French)	NGPP	☐
C2017/9/68	1966	48-page Catalogue	Issued in France, same cover as C2017/9/68	NGPP	☐

TRADE CATALOGUES

Catalogues for trade purposes have been produced for some years and occasionally are offered for sale to collectors. No information is available on catalogues issued before 1980 but those from the 1980-90 decade tend to be in the £5 to £15 range.

Corgi Toys shop display and 'point-of-sale' items

Ref. No.	Year(s)	Item	Details	Market Price Range	
no ref.	1957-59	Display stand, wooden	Ten cream 'corrugated' hardboard shelves, pale blue display background with yellow/blue plastic 'CORGI TOYS' sign screwed to top of display, (30″ x 29″ x 12″)	£200-300	☐
no ref.	1957-59	Display card/sign	Tin/cardboard, yellow/blue with gold 'dog' logo, 'Wow! Corgi Toys - The Ones With Windows'	£50-60	☐
no ref.	1957-59	Display card/sign	As previous item but with 'new Corgi Major Toys - The Ones With Windows'	£50-60	☐
no ref.	1957-59	Counter display unit	Two shelf stand with Blue backing logo 'CORGI TOYS', 'THE ONES WITH WINDOWS' 'MODEL PERFECTION' & 'NEW' plus the early gold Corgi dog on red background	£300-400	☐
no ref.	1957-59	Counter display unit	Cardboard, single model display card, 'new - CORGI TOYS' logo	£50-60	☐
no ref.	1957-59	Counter display unit	Cardboard, 2 tier unit with 'new - CORGI MAJOR TOYS' in yellow/blue design	£200-300	☐
no ref.	1957-59	Counter display unit	Cardboard, 2 tier unit, 'COLLECT CORGI TOYS' and 'new MODELS EVERY MONTH' logos in yellow/blue design	£200-300	☐

Ref. No.	Year(s)	Model Type	*Corgi Toys — Shop Display – continued*	Market Price Range	
no ref.	1957-59	Counter display unit............	Cardboard, Renault Floride (222) pictorial display card with *'1959 MOTOR SHOW'* and *'EARLS COURT'* logos	**£75-100**	☐
no ref.	1957-59	Counter display unit............	Cardboard, Citroën (475) pictorial display card with *'new - THE CITROEN'* and *'OLYMPIC WINTER SPORTS'* logos	**£75-100**	☐
no ref.	1957-67	Metal Display stand	Tiered stand 75cm x 3½cm x 4.5cm high, three 'CORGI TOYS' and Black logos, plus three early gold Corgi dog emblems	**£175-200**	☐
no ref.	1960-61	Window sticker....................	*'new MODELS EVERY MONTH'*	**£15-20**	☐
no ref.	1966-69	Window sticker....................	Window bills advertising new releases	**£15-20**	☐
no ref.	1960-69	Oblong sign........................	Glass or plastic with *'CORGI TOYS'* and *'PRECISION DIE-CAST SCALE MODELS'* logos plus gold Corgi 'dog' logo in blue/yellow/red design	**£75-100**	☐
no ref.	1961	Corgi Dog...........................	Moulded dog standing on hind feet holding a 'CORGI CHRISTMAS CARD'..........	NGPP	☐
no ref.	1968-83	Metal Display stand	Tiered stand 75 cm x 3½cm c 4.5 cm high, with three 'CORGI TOYS' Black/Yellow logos, plus three White/Red late Corgi dog emblems	**£145-175**	☐
no ref.	1971-73	Oblong sign........................	Plastic, with *'CORGI'* and *'TESTED BY THE CORGI TECHNOCRATS'* logos plus white Corgi 'dog' logo on red square, yellow background plus 3 'Technocrats' faces	**£50-75**	☐
C2001/2	1963-65	Display stand, rotary...........	For self-selection, 7 tray unit, large *'CORGI TOYS'* header sign	NGPP	☐
C2003	1963-65	Display stand, rotary...........	Self-selection, 4 columns, 4 compartments (45" x 30") large *'CORGI TOYS'* header boards..	NGPP	☐
C2004	1963-65	Display stand, rotary...........	Self-selection, 4 column, 72 compartments (72" x 30").....................................	NGPP	☐
C2005	1963-65	Display stand, rotary...........	Self-selection, 2 column, 36 compartments (72" x 30").....................................	NGPP	☐
C2006	1963-65	Display stand, rotary...........	Self-selection, 2 column, 36 compartments (55" x 30").....................................	NGPP	☐
C2007	1963-65	Display stand, moulded plastic	Large counter display to house up to 50 models, large black header display board with *'NATURALLY CORGI TOYS'* on yellow/blue background, and *'JOIN THE CORGI MODEL CLUB'* on display front	**£200-300**	☐
C2008	1960s	Display stand, revolving...........	Glass fronted large electric display to house 100-120 models with light and dark simulated wood panels with four *'CORGI'* logos, (38" x 24" x 24")	**£400-600**	☐
C2009	1957-66	Showcase, glass....................	Three glass shelves, three 'CORGI TOYS' logos (black/blue) plus gold Corgi 'dog' logo on red background, (20" x 15" x 9")	**£200-300**	☐
E9051	1970s	Corgi Juniors Unit	Yellow plastic (21¾" x 21¾"), displays 48 models, logo 'LOOK FOR WHIZZWHEELS MODELS'..	**£100-150**	☐

NB. The Editor would welcome any further information on Corgi display material.

Acknowledgements

The Editor would like to express appreciation to the following collectors, traders and manufacturers, who very kindly took the time and trouble to provide information about new entries and colour variations.

Peter Clawson, Lincs
Bruce Nally, Australia
Gerry Savage, Cornwall
Susan Pownall, Corgi Collectors Club
Adrienne Fuller, Corgi Toys
Keith Harbour, Middlesex
R. Smith, Kent
Ken Crawley, Warks.
A Slight, Staffs.
Jim Whittaker, Lancs.
David Towner, Kent
R. E. Doubleday, Essex
Alan Peebles, Sussex
B. C. Whittaker, Yorks
Terry Clancy, Eire
John Marshall, California, U.S.A.
Mr Hughes, Gloucs.
Eric Impey, Yorks.
John Hepburn, Gloucs.
Tony Robinson, Derbyshire
R. Welburn, Yorks.

Wilf Bainbridge, Scotland
David Graves, West Midlands
Mr Davis, Donnington
Michael Clarke, London
David Whyte, Scotland
Ray Holcroft, Lancs.
C. Bettinson, Lincs.
Chris Fuller, Kent
R. Webber
Peter Naylor, Scotland
Bruce Wheaton, Canada
Mike Clarke, London
Mike Tipton, Staffs.
Peter Harrison, Carterton
Andy and Pat Browning, Kent
J. W. Saunders, Derbyshire
M. A. Chalmers, Essex
Ray Strutt, Collectors Gazette
George Hatt, Trowbridge
Chris Brierley, Heywood

Corgi Classics Commercials

This excellent series was introduced in 1985 and features finely engineered models of classic vehicles. Great care has been taken to achieve faithful modelling of the original vehicle using authentic liveries wherever possible.

N.B. All Commercials 1/50; Cars 1/43.

A.E.C. CABOVER BOX VANS

C897/1	1987	'CARTER PATERSON', *'Atora For Xmas'*	£10-15	☐
C897/2	1987	'JOHN KNIGHT', *'Hustler Soap'*	£10-15	☐
897/3	1987	'LMS EXPRESS PARCELS', *'Puck Matches'*	£60-70	☐
897/4	1988	'DUCKHAMS WEARCURE', Silver/White	£9-12	☐
897/5	1988	'AMPLION RADIO', Two-tone Blue	£11-13	☐
897/6	1988	'WEETABIX', Yellow/White/Red	£9-12	☐
C897/7	1988	'MARS', Brown/Cream/Red	£9-11	☐
897/8	1988	'HIS MASTERS VOICE', Silver/Dark Green	£18-24	☐
D897/9	1988	'INTERNATIONAL', Green/Yellow/Black	£9-12	☐
D897/10	1988	'POTTERS ASTHMA CURE', 'BP' promotional	£9-11	☐
D897/11	1988	'JOHN BARKER', Dark Brown/White	£12-15	☐
D897/12	1989	'ROYAL MAIL', Red/Black	£22-27	☐
D987/13	1989	'GPO TELEPHONES', (see GS D15/1)	GSP	☐
D897/14	1990	'G.W.R.', Dark Brown/White	£9-11	☐
D897/15	1990	'UNITED DAIRIES', see Gift Set D67/1	GSP	☐
97140	1991	'SOUTHERN RAILWAY', *'Express Parcels Service'*	£10-15	☐
97754	1993	'LMS RAILWAY', see Set 97754	GSP	☐

A.E.C. CABOVER TANKERS

C945/1	1987	'FLOWERS BREWERY', Cream/Green	£12-14	☐
C945/2	1987	'GAYMERS CIDER', Dark Blue/Red	£12-14	☐
C945/3	1988	'CARLESS CAPEL', Dark Green/Cream	£6-8	☐
C945/4	1988	'DUCKHAMS OILS', Blue/Silver	£6-8	☐
C945/5	1988	'SOMERLITE OIL', Light Blue/White	£10-14	☐
C945/6	1989	'REDLINE GLICO', Red/Black	£9-12	☐
D945/7	1990	'SHELL', see Gift Set D9/1	GSP	☐
D945/8	1990	'MOBILGAS'	£9-12	☐
D945/9	1990	'MOBILGAS'	£9-12	☐
C945/10	1988	'BP PETROLEUM', 'BP' promotional	£15-20	☐
D945/12	1990	'UNITED DAIRIES', see Gift Set D67/1	GSP	☐
97442	1991	'JOHN SMITHS BREWERY', (Gift Set)	GSP	☐

A.E.C. MERCURY TRUCKS and TANKERS

97894	1994	'PICKFORDS'	£17-19	☐
97896	1995	'CHIPPERFIELDS'	NGPP	☐
97931	1995	'GREENALL WHITLEY' Flatbed	£35-45	☐
97932	1995	'N.E. GAS BOARD'	£22-26	☐

A.E.C. MERCURY TRUCKS with TRAILERS

97889	1995	'CHIPPERFIELDS'	NGPP	☐
97891	1993	'BILLY SMARTS'	£24-28	☐
97892	1993	'S. HOUSEMAN'	£20-24	☐
97893	1993	'J. AYERS'	£20-24	☐
97895	1994	'B.R.S.'	£18-20	☐

A.E.C. REGAL HALF-CAB COACHES

97020	1992	'WYE VALLEY' Motors	£14-16	☐
97069	1993	'WHITTLES', see Set 97069	GSP	☐
97070	1992	'SILVER SERVICE', see Set 97070	GSP	☐
97075	1992	'SOUTH WALES', see Set 97075	GSP	☐
97180	1991	'GREY-GREEN', Grey/Green	£14-16	☐
97181	1991	'TIMPSONS', Cream/Brown	£14-16	☐
97184	1991	'SHEFFIELD', Off-White/Red	£9-11	☐
97185	1992	'WEST RIDING', Cream/Green	£11-14	☐
97186	1992	'GREY CARS', Grey/Cream/Red	£14-16	☐
97187	1992	'HANSON', Red, Cream flash	£8-10	☐
97189	1991	'OXFORD', Cream/Maroon, Kays LE	14-16	☐

97190	1991	'LEDGARD', Blue/Black, GUS LE	9-11	☐
97191	1991	'ROSSLYN MOTORS', Red/Black	£8-10	☐
97193	1992	'CARNEYS', White body, Red roof	£8-10	☐
97194	1992	'HARDINGS', Mid-Blue/Dark Blue	£9-11	☐
97196	1993	'STANLEY FIELD', TT-Green	£8-10	☐
97197	1993	'WESTERN WELSH', White/Red	£14-16	☐
97750	1991	'EAST KENT'	GSP	☐
98161	1993	'EASTERN COUNTIES', Cream/Black	£11-14	☐
98162	1993	'WALLACE ARNOLD', Cream/Red	£14-16	☐

A.E.C. REGENT DOUBLE-DECKER BUS

D41/1	1990	'BARTONS', Red/Cream, (See Gift Set D41/1)	GSP	☐
D47/1	1990	'BEANO', Red/Yellow, (see Gift Set D47/1)	GSP	☐
C599	1987	'TRUSTEE SAVINGS BANK', Dark Blue/Cream, 'Nottingham City', 4,200	£25-35	☐
C599/1	1986	'WISK', Red/Yellow	£20-25	☐
D599/1	1989	'WESTERN', Red/White, *'Wallaces Sausages'*	£10-15	☐
C599/1	1987	'WOODHAMS SCOOTERS', Dark Blue/Cream, 'EASTBOURNE', 4900	£34-38	☐
C599/3	1987	'HUNTLEY & PALMERS', Brown/White, 'LEICESTER CITY', 4,000	£30-35	☐
		As previous model but no White windows	£40-45	☐
C599/4	1988	'GLASGOW', Green/Brown, *'Crown Wallpapers'*	£17-25	☐
C599/5	1988	'RHONDDA', Red/Yellow, *'Premium Bonds'*, 3,700	£15-20	☐
C599/6	1989	'MORECAMBE', Green/White, 'HEYSHAM', 5,000	£14-18	☐
C599/7	1989	'BRADFORD', Blue body, White banks, 5,000	£14-18	☐
C599/8	1989	'HANTS & DORSET', Dark Green/Cream, in Gift Set D4/1	GSP	☐
C599/9	1990	'WESTERN', No details available	£12-15	☐
D559/10	1990	'BRIGHTON & HOVE', Red/Cream body, 'Tamplins Ales', 5,100	£12-15	☐
D559/11	1990	Green-Yellow, *'Irish Independent'*	£8-10	☐
D599/12	1990	'BATTLE OF BRITAIN', RAF Blue, *'Wings for Victory'*	£8-10	☐
Q599/13	1990	'HALIFAX', Green/Red, 59, *'Websters XL'*, 5,300	£8-10	☐
C634	1986	'MAPLES', Red, new 'bolt head' wheels	£20-25	☐
C643	1986	'NEWCASTLE ALE', Yellow/White body	£20-25	☐
96980	1991	'STEVENSONS', Yellow/Black, 'UTTOXETER'	£8-10	☐
96983	1991	'LIVERPOOL Corp', Green/White, 'Littlewoods'	£8-10	☐
	1991	'ROCHDALE', Blue/White	£8-10	☐
97001	1993	'P.M.T.', Red/White, 'Stoke'	£7-10	☐
97002	1993	'SHEFFIELD', Cream, *'Double Diamond'*	£7-10	☐
97003	1993	'West BRIDGEFORD', Maroon/Cream, 'Say CWS'	£7-10	☐
97050/A	1993	'DEVON GENERAL'	GSP	☐
97050/B	1993	'THOMAS BROS'	GSP	☐
97062	1991	'OXFORD', Red/Black body	£7-10	☐
	1993	'OXFORD', No details as present	£7-1'	☐
	1993	'CORGI', Blue/Cream Club model, 'Meridian Way, Leicester'	£10-15	☐
97064	1993	'TRAVEL CARD', Red/White, in 'Blackpool Set 97064	GSP	☐
97065	1993	'STAGECOACH', White, in 'Stagecoach' Set 97065	GSP	☐

A.E.C. REGAL IV BUSES

97018	1995	'DUNDEE'	£11-14	☐

A.E.C. RELIANCE

97900	1995	'DEVON GENERAL'	£8-10	☐
97130	1995	'OXFORD'	£8-10	☐

AMERICAN CLASSIC BUSES

98462	1994	YC743 Greyhound 'ATLANTA'	£16-19	☐

Vintage Bus
Yellow coach YC743 issues etc.

98460	1994	YC743 'WORLDS FAIR'	£19-24	☐
98461	1994	YC743 'BATTLE of BRITAIN'.............	£19-24	☐
98463	1994	YC743 'GREYHOUND' 'CHICAGO'		☐
		(1700)	£50-60	☐
98464	1994	YC743 'BURLINGTON' Whaleine	£19-24	☐
98465	1994	YC743 'BURLINGTON', pin-stripe	£19-24	☐
98467	1995	YC743 'NEW JERSEY'	£19-24	☐
98468	1994	YC743 'CHAMPLAIN'	£19-24	☐
98470	1995	YC743 'SILVERSIDE'	£19-24	☐
98471	1995	YC743 'BATTLE of BRITAIN'	£19-24	☐
98472	1995	YC743 'W.A.C.'	£19-24	☐
98473	1995	YC743 'WAVES'	£19-24	☐
98600	1995	TD4502 'PACIFIC GREYHOUND'	£19-24	☐
98601	1995	TD4502 'PACIFIC GREYHOUND'	£19-24	☐
98602	1995	TD44505 'GREYHOUND LINES'........	£19-24	☐
98603	1995	TD4506 'DETROIT'	£19-24	☐
98604	1995	TD4507 'FIFTH AVENUE'	£19-24	☐
97635	1995	TD4502 'LOS ANGELES'	£19-24	☐

Modern Bus

98421	1995	MCI Demo Bus...............................	£28-33	☐
98422	1995	MCI 'PETER PAN Trailways'............	£28-33	☐
98427	1995	MCI 'PETER PAN Birthday Bus'	£28-33	☐
98431	1995	Bank version of 98427	£28-33	☐
98432	1995	Bank version of 98421	£28-33	☐
98650	1995	MCI 'CALIFORNIA'	£28-33	☐
98651	1995	MCI 'THRASHER Bros'	£28-33	☐
98652	1995	MCI 'SEA WORLD'	£28-33	☐
98653	1995	Bank version of 98652	£28-33	☐
98654	1995	Bank version of 98651	£28-33	☐
98655	1995	Bank version of 98650	£28-33	☐
98431	1995	TD	£28-33	☐

ATKINSON TRUCKS and TANKERS

97162	1995	'POLLOCK'	£20-25	☐

ATLANTEAN BUS

97052/B	1994	'DEVON GENERAL'	GSP	☐
97230	1994	'RIBBLE-GAY HOSTESS'	GSP	☐
97231	1994	'HULL'	GSP	☐

BEDFORD 'CA' VANS

D981/1	1989	'PICKFORDS', see Kays Set D74/1	GSP	☐
D981/2	1989	'CAMBRIAN NEWS', White/Black	£6-9	☐
D981/3	1990	'A.A.', Yellow/Black	£6-9	☐
D981/4	1989	'EXPRESS DAIRIES', White/Blue	£6-9	☐
D981/5	1989	'DANDY', see D14/1 Set....................	GSP	☐
D981/6	1989	'BEANO', see D14/1 Set....................	GSP	☐
D981/7	1990	'COLLECTOR CLUB 1990', Yellow/		
		Blue...	£10-15	☐
D981/9	1990	'EVENING NEWS', Yellow/Black	£6-9	☐
D981/10	1990	'EVENING STANDARD', Silver/		
		Black..	£6-9	☐
D981/11	1990	'The STAR', Red body	£6-9	☐
D981/12	1990	'GAS', see GUS Set D54/1..................	GSP	☐
96900	1991	'MANCHESTER EVENING NEWS',		
		Yellow/Black................................	£6-9	☐
97740	1991	'The TIMES', see 97740 Set................	GSP	☐
98754	1991	'The ADVENTURE', Yellow	£6-9	☐
98965	1992	'EAGLE', see Set 98965.....................	GSP	☐
96904	1994	'RAC RADIO RESCUE'	£7-9	☐
96905	1995	'CHIPPERFIELDS' Booking Office......	NGPP	☐
98106	1995	'POLICE'	£7-10	☐
98906	1995	'BLACKBURN Fire Brigade'	£7-10	☐

BEDFORD DORMOBILES

D982/1	1989	Cream/Blue....................................	£6-9	☐
D982/2	1989	Red/Cream....................................	£6-9	☐
D982/3	1990	Cream/Green..................................	£6-9	☐
D982/4	1991	Brown/Cream.................................	£6-9	☐
96920	1991	'POLICE', Dark Blue, beacon	£6-9	☐
96923	1994	'ST JOHN'S AMBULANCE'	£6-9	☐

BEDFORD 'O' ARTICULATED TRUCKS

97300	1993	'BILLY SMARTS', Grey/Green	NRP	☐
97301	1994	'LONDON BRICK Co Ltd'.................	£12-16	☐
97303	1994	'CHIPPERFIELDS' Truck	NGPP	☐
97887	1995	'CHIPPERFIELDS' Horsebox..............	NGPP	☐

BEDFORD 'O' SERIES BOX VANS

C822/1	1988	'PERSIL', Green/White	£11-14	☐
C822/2	1988	'TATE & LYLE', Blue/White/Red........	£11-14	☐
C822/3	1988	'GILLETTE', Green/Black/Red............	£11-14	☐
D822/4	1989	'CARTER PATERSON', *'Solidox'*		
		Green body, Green roof....................	£14-17	☐
		Green body, Red roof......................	£35-40	☐
D822/5	1989	'MILLERS', (total production 3,200)		
		Cream/Green (Red wings).................	£14-16	☐
		Same but Black wings......................	£16-19	☐
		Same, logo partly hidden	£35-40	☐
D822/6	1990	'SHELL', see Set D17/1	GSP	☐
		Same but 5 rivet base......................	GSP	☐
D822/7	1989	'CADBURYS', Chocolate/Red.............	£14-17	☐
D822/8	1989	'MALTESERS', Brown/White/Red.......	£16-19	☐
D822/9	1989	'ROYAL MAIL', see D7/1 Set............	GSP	☐
D822/10	1990	'TERRYS OF YORK', Dark Red	£16-19	☐
D822/11	1990	'L.N.E.R.', Blue/Black	£11-14	☐
		Same but no front body print.............	NGPP	☐
822/12	1990	'TOYMASTER', Yellow/Red (own		
		shops)...	£24-28	☐
D822/13	1990	'BRITISH RAILWAYS', see Set D46/		
		1	GSP	☐
D822/16	1990	'WHITBREAD', see Set D94/1	GSP	☐
97120	1991	'LMS', Crimson/Black	£8-10	☐
97123	1991	'NSPCC', Green/Yellow/Black	£8-10	☐
97125	1993	'GPO Telephones', Olive-Green/Black ..	£8-10	☐
97126	1993	'NATIONAL COAL BOARD', White/		
		Red..	£8-10	☐
97781/A	1993	'TATE & LYLE', see Gift Set 97781	GSP	☐
97124	1992	'YOUNGSTERS TOY SHOPS'............	£10-12	☐
97200/A	1991	'BRS PARCELS'	GSP	☐
97714/B	1994	Military Green (D-Day Set)................	GSP	☐
97735/A	1992	'WILSONS OF KENDALL'.................	GSP	☐
97752/A	1992	'RUDDLES BREWERY'.....................	GSP	☐

BEDFORD 'OB' COACHES

C949/1	1987	'NORFOLKS', Green, (Pale Yellow		
		stripe) small *'Ipswich'*	£34-38	☐
		brighter Yellow or Dark Green stripe,		
		large *'Ipswich'*..............................	£34-38	☐
C949/2	1987	'ROYAL BLUE', Beige/Blue, small		
		'Exeter'	£80-90	☐
		large *'Exeter'*, Blue door line	£53-58	☐
		no Blue line, lower fleetline...............	£53-58	☐
C949/3	1987	'ALEXANDER BLUEBIRD', Cream/		
		Dark Blue....................................	£40-50	☐
C949/4	1987	'GREY CARS', Grey/Cream/Red..........	£16-19	☐
C949/5	1987	'CROSVILLE', Cream/Green...............	£24-28	☐
C949/6	1987	'SOUTHDOWN', Green/Cream............	£145-175	☐
C949/7	1987	'EASTERN COUNTIES', Cream/Red ..	£20-24	☐
C949/8	1988	'SOUTH MIDLAND', Red/White.........	£23-26	☐
C949/9	1988	'PREMIER', with Blue bonnet.............	£27-30	☐
		without Blue bonnet........................	£50-75	☐
C949/10	1988	'HIGHLAND', see Set C89.................	GSP	☐
C949/11	1988	'EAST YORKSHIRE', Cream/Blue.......	£18-20	☐
D949/12	1989	'CLASSIC CARS', Grey/Maroon	£30-35	☐
D949/13	1989	'HANTS & SUSSEX', Maroon/Red,		
		Dark Cream stripe	£30-35	☐
		with Light Cream stripe...................	£30-35	☐
Q949/14	1989	'WALLACE ARNOLD', Cream/Red	£18-22	☐
D949/15	1989	'MACBRAYNES', Red/Green/Cream ...	£35-40	☐
D949/16	1989	'HANTS & DORSET', see D4/1 Set.....	GSP	☐
D949/17	1990	'GREENSLADES', Cream/Green.........	£8-10	☐
D949/18	1990	'DEVON GENERAL', Maroon/Cream ..	£8-10	☐
Q949/19	1990	'SOUTHERN VECTIS', Dark Green	£18-22	☐
D949/20	1990	'RAF AIR PASSENGER COACH',		
		see Set D35/1	GSP	☐
Q949/22	1990	'BOULTONS of SHROPSHIRE', Red		
		or Cream/Maroon..........................	£11-13	☐
D949/23	1990	'HOWARDS TOURS', Cream/Red,		
		Kay's..	£11-13	☐
D949/24	1990	'SOUTHERN NATIONAL', Cream/		
		Green, Kay's	£11-13	☐
D949/25	1990	'EASTERN NATIONAL', Cream,		
		Green base line.............................	£8-10	☐
		Cream, no base line........................	£8-10	☐
D949/26	1990	'WEST YORKSHIRE', Cream/Red,		
		Grattans......................................	£12-14	☐
D949/27	1990	'BRITISH RAILWAYS',		
		Maroon/Cream, *'Melstead'*	£17-22	☐
		Maroon/Cream, *'Bristol'*	£15-20	☐
Q949/28	1990	'YORK FAIR', see Set Q55/1	GSP	☐

Ref. No.	Year	Description		Price
D949/29	1990	'BARTONS TRANSPORT', Set D41/1	GSP	☐
Q949/30	1990	'WESTERN NATIONAL', Cream/ Green	£17-22	☐
949/31	1991	'BRITISH RAILWAYS', Maroon/ Cream, (P & K Models)	18-22	☐
Q949/32	1990	'CORGI ON THE MOVE', Set D82/1	GSP	☐
Q949/33	1990	'STANDERWICK', see Set Q57/1	GSP	☐
97070	1992	'SILVER SERVICE', see Set 97070	GSP	☐
97075	1992	'SOUTH WALES', Cream/Red	£10-13	☐
97078	1993	'CORKILLS COACHES', Green/Black, in Gift Set	GSP	☐
97078	1993	'De VANENBURG', Red/Black, in Set	GSP	☐
97079	1993	'PREMIER', in 70th Anniversary Set	GSP	☐
97100	1991	'ISLE of MAN TOURS', TT-Blue	£9-11	☐
97101	1991	'SCILLY ISLES', Cream/Blue, *'Vic's Tours'*	£11-13	☐
97103	1991	'SKILLS of NOTTINGHAM', TT-Green, (A.B.Gee)	£8-10	☐
97104		'BRONTE' Bus Co., no details	£7-11	☐
97105	1992	'FELIX', Maroon body, Red trim	£11-13	☐
97106	1992	'BIBBYS', Black body, White roof	£11-13	☐
97107	1992	'MURGATROYD', Cream/Pale Blue	£11-13	☐
97108	1992	'GRANVILLE TOURS', TT-Blue	£14-17	☐
97109	1993	'WHITTAKERS Tours', Cream/Red/ Pale Blue	£8-10	☐
97111	1993	'MEREDITH', White/Yellow, 'Malpas'	£8-10	☐
97113	1993	'WARBURTONS', Black/Pale Grey	£8-10	☐
97697/B	1993	'METROPOLITAN POLICE'	GSP	☐
97698	1993	'Metropolitan Police', in Set 97698	GSP	☐
97741	1991	'J.M.T.', see Set 97741	GSP	☐
97741	1991	'PIONEER', see Set 97741	GSP	☐
97765	1993	'WILES', Pale Blue/White, (in Set)	GSP	☐
98163	1993	'GREY-GREEN', Grey/Green, 'Clacton'	£11-13	☐
98164	1993	'EDINBURGH', Maroon/White	£11-13	☐
no ref.	1992	'SMITH'S COACHES', Cream/Red, (only 3 made)	NGPP	☐

BEDFORD 'OB' PANTECHNICONS

Ref. No.	Year	Description		Price
C953/1	1987	'PICKFORDS', Dark Blue, '3401'	£34-39	☐
D953/1	1989	'PICKFORDS', no number, Set D74/1	GSP	☐
C953/2	1987	'WARING & GILLOW', Green/White/ Black	£60-70	☐
C953/3	1987	'FRASERS of IPSWICH', Black/ White/Grey	£40-50	☐
C953/4	1987	'STEINWAY & SONS', Green/Black	£20-25	☐
C953/5	1988	'GRIFF FENDER', Blue/Off-White	£9-11	☐
C953/6	1988	'DUCKHAMS', Green/White, 'NOL'	£9-11	☐
C953/7	1988	'CAMP HOPSON', Cream body	£28-33	☐
Q953/8	1990	'MICHAEL GERSON', Dark Green/ Black (Certificated)	£19-24	☐
D953/9	1989	'STYLO', Blue/Black/Red	£19-22	☐
D953/10	1989	'WEETABIX', Yellow/Brown	£24-27	☐
D953/11	1990	'SHELL THE WINNER', see Set D17/1	GSP	☐
D953/12	1989	'BISHOPS MOVE', Yellow/White	£25-30	☐
		Same but with thicker lettering	£25-30	☐
D953/13	1990	'WYLIE & LOCKHEAD', Black/ White	£23-26	☐
D953/14	1990	'ARTHUR BATTY', Green body	£9-11	☐
D953/15	1990	'YORK FAIR 1765-1990', see Set Q55/1	GSP	☐
D953/16	1990	'LEE BROTHERS', Green/White, Silver wheels	£20-25	☐
		with standard wheels	£13-16	☐
Q953/17	1990	'SLUMBERLAND BEDS', Set Q57/1	GSP	☐
D953/20	1990	'CORGI ON THE MOVE'	GSP	☐
97080	1991	'JOHN JULIAN', Dark Blue/Cream	£9-11	☐
97081	1991	'BREWER & TURNBULL', Blue/ White (Certificated)	£16-18	☐
97082	1991	'PICKFORDS', curved 'Pickfords'	£11-13	☐
97083	1991	'BLACKPOOL TOWER CIRCUS', 'Charlie Cairoli'	£15-20	☐
97084	1991	'GRATTANS' Mail Order	£9-11	☐
97085	1991	'SLUMBERLAND BEDS', Deep Red, normal body	£10-12	☐
97086	1992	'FREEBORNS', White/Orange/Brown	£11-13	☐
97087	1992	'BARNARDO'S', White/Green	£11-13	☐
97088	1993	'WHITE & Co.", 'Portsmouth'	£11-13	☐
97089	1993	'JOHN MASON', 'Liverpool Philharmonic'	£11-13	☐
97090	1991	'RILEYS', 'Billiard Tables'	£11-13	☐
97091	1991	'G.H.LUCKING & SONS', Blue/ White	£11-13	☐
97195	1992	HOWELLS & SON, Red/Black/White	£11-13	☐

Ref. No.	Year	Description		Price
97092	1995	'CHIPPERFIELDS CIRCUS'	NGPP	☐
	1995	'GOING FOR GOLD' Corgi voucher promotion	NGPP	☐
97093	1994	'HAPPY BIRTHDAY' Direct or Club model	NGPP	☐

BURLINGHAM SEAGULL COACHES

Ref. No.	Year	Description		Price
97069	1993	'WHITTLES', Blue/Red, in Gift Set	GSP	☐
97170	1993	'SEAGULL', Grey/Black, 'Blackpool'	£12-14	☐
97171	1993	'NEATH & CARDIFF'	£12-14	☐
97172	1993	'STRATFORD BLUE'	£12-14	☐
	1993	'WOODS of BLACKPOOL'	£12-14	☐
97173	1993	'RIBBLE', Cream and Red	£12-14	☐
97174	1993	'YELLOWAY', Yellow/Orange	£12-14	☐
	1993	'STRATFORD BLUE', Cream/Dark Blue	£12-14	☐
	1993	'YORK BROTHERS', Dark Blue/Red, in Set	£12-14	☐
97175	1994	'DON EVERALL'	£12-14	☐
97176	1994	'KING ALFRED'	£12-14	☐
97177	1994	'NORTHERN ROADWAYS'	£12-14	☐
97178	1995	'COLISEUM COACHES'	£12-14	☐

CHIPPERFIELDS CIRCUS

Ref. No.	Year	Description		Price
96905	1995	Bedford 'CA' Booking Office	NGPP	☐
97022	1995	AEC Regal Living Coach	NGPP	☐
97092	1995	Bedford 'OB' Pantechnicon	NGPP	☐
97303	1994	Bedford 'OB' Articulated Truck	NGPP	☐
97885	1995	Scammell, Pole Trailer & Caravan	NGPP	☐
97886	1995	Scammell Crane Truck	NGPP	☐
97887	1995	Bedford 'O' Articulated Horsebox	NGPP	☐
97888	1995	Foden Pole Truck & Caravan	NGPP	☐
97889	1995	AEC Animal Truck & Trailer	NGPP	☐
97896	1995	AEC Pole Truck	NGPP	☐
97915	1995	Scammell and two Trailers	NGPP	☐
97957	1995	ERF Flatbed Lorry	NGPP	☐

N.B. Because of strong collector interest a Market Price Range has yet to be established for the 'CHIPPERFIELDS' issues.

DAIMLER CW UTILITY BUS

Ref. No.	Year	Description		Price
97820	1994	'WEST BROMWICH'	£20-22	☐
97822	1994	'DERBY CORPORATION'	£18-20	☐
97827	1994	'SHEFFIELD'	£20-22	☐
97829	1995	'DOUGLAS'	£18-20	☐

DAIMLER DUPLE COACHES

Ref. No.	Year	Description		Price
97821	1994	'SWAN MOTORS'	£10-12	☐
97825	1994	'BURWELL & DISTRICT'	£10-12	☐
97823	1994	'BLUE BUS SERVICES'	£10-12	☐
97830	1995	'SCOUT'	£10-12	☐

DAIMLER FLEETLINE BUS

Ref. No.	Year	Description		Price
97824	1994	'BIRMINGHAM'	£22-25	☐
97826	1994	'MANCHESTER'	£22-25	☐
97828	1995	'ROCHDALE'	£22-25	☐

ERF TRUCKS and TANKERS

Ref. No.	Year	Description		Price
97930	1994	'BLUE CIRCLE'	£20-25	☐
97940	1994	'EDDIE STOBART'	£65-75	☐
97942	1995	'FLOWERS' Flatbed	£22-26	☐
97957	1995	'CHIPPERFIELDS' Flatbed	£22-27	☐
97980	1994	'ESSO PETROLEUM'	£20-25	☐

FIRE SERVICE APPLIANCES

Ref. No.	Year	Description		Price
C1143/2	1990	La France Aerial Ladder, see 97320		
97320	1991	La France Aerial Ladder, Bright Red, open cab	£16-22	☐
97321	1992	La France Aerial Ladder, Crimson/ White, closed cab	£15-17	☐
97322	1993	La France, closed, 'CHICAGO'	£15-17	☐
97323	1993	La France, closed, 'CARNEGIE', Blue	£15-17	☐
97324	1993	La France, open cab, 'ORLANDO'	£15-17	☐
97325	1993	La France, closed, 'DENVER', White body	£15-17	☐
97326	1994	La France Pumper, 'ORLANDO'	£14-16	☐
97331/A	1993	La France, open, 'SCOTTDALE', in Gift Set	GSP	☐
97331/B	1993	La France, closed, 'SOUTH RIVER', in Gift Set	GSP	☐
97352	1993	AEC Ladder Truck, 'STOKE-on-TRENT'	£19-22	☐

Ref. No.	Year	Description	Price	
97353	1994	AEC Turntable, *'DUBLIN'*	£20-24	☐
96906	1995	Bedford CA *'BLACKBURN'*	£7-10	☐
96854	1995	'Morris Motors' Pick-Up	£8-12	☐
97355	1992	AEC Merryweather Pumper, Red/ Silver, wheeled escape *'NOTTINGHAM'*	£19-22	☐
97356	1993	AEC Pump Escape, *'NOTTINGHAM'*, *'DUNKIRK'*	£19-22	☐
97357	1993	AEC Pump Escape, *'HERTS'*	£19-22	☐
97358	1993	AEC Pump Escape, *'CLEVELAND'*	£19-22	☐
97359	1994	AEC Tender, *'DUBLIN'*	£19-22	☐
97360	1995	AEC Pump Tender, *'ROTHERHAM'*	£19-22	☐
97385	1993	AEC Ladder Truck, *'CARDIFF'*	£19-22	☐
97386	1993	AEC Ladder Truck, *'BRISTOL'*	£19-22	☐
97387	1994	La France Ladder, *'DENVER'*	£19-22	☐
97389	1994	Fire Chief Car, *'CHICAGO'*	£9-12	☐
97392	1994	Simon Snorkel, *'W. GLAMORGAN'*	£25-28	☐
97393	1995	La France Pumper, *'WAYNE'*	£9-12	☐
97395	1995	La France Pumper, *'VERO BEACH'*	£9-12	☐
97397	1995	Fire Chief Car, *'PENSACOLA'*	£9-12	☐
97398	1995	La France Ladder, *'JERSEY CITY'*	£20-25	☐
97399	1995	Simon Snorkel, *'CLEVELAND'*	£25-28	☐
98450	1995	Mack B Pumper, *'CHICAGO'*	£12-15	☐
98451	1995	Mack CF Pumper, *'BERWICK'*	£12-15	☐
98452	1995	White Tanker *'VOLUNTEER'*	£12-15	☐
98475	1995	VW Fire Marshall Van	£8-10	☐
98484	1994	Mack CF Pumper, *'CHICAGO'*	£12-15	☐
98485	1995	Mack CF Pumper, *'NEPTUNE'*	£12-15	☐
98486	1995	Mack B Pumper, *'PAXTONIA'*	£12-15	☐

FODEN TRUCKS and TANKERS

Ref. No.	Year	Description	Price	
97781	1993	'TATE & LYLE', see Gift Set 97781	GSP	☐
97950	1993	'GUINNESS', Black/Gold/Red	£65-77	☐
97951	1993	'Milk Marketing Board', Dark Blue/ White	£24-27	☐
97952	1993	'HOVIS', White/Black, Red wheels	£24-27	☐
97955	1994	'GUINNESS' with chains	£55-65	☐
97956	1994	'PICKFORDS' Flatbed	£34-45	☐
97970	1994	'REGENT'	£34-39	☐
97971	1994	'ROBSONS'	£22-26	☐

FORD POPULAR VANS

Ref. No.	Year	Description	Price	
D980/1	1989	'S.A. PEACOCK', Green/Black	£8-10	☐
D980/2	1989	'FULLERS', Grey/Red	£8-10	☐
D980/3	1989	'LUTON MOTOR Co', Green/Brown... with lighter Brown wings	£6-9 / £6-9	☐ ☐
D980/4	1989	'CORGI CLUB 89', Dark Blue/Black....	£6-9	☐
D980/5	1989	'SIGNSMITH', see Grattans Set D23/1	GSP	☐
D980/6	1989	'FRASER COOK Ltd', see Grattans Set D23/1	GSP	☐
D980/7	1989	'LEWIS EAST Ltd', see Grattans Set D23/1	GSP	☐
D980/8	1989	'C. PEARSON', Green/Black	£6-9	☐
D980/9	1989	'COLMANS MUSTARD', Kays Set D72/1	GSP	☐
D980/10	1989	'BOWYERS', see Kays Set D72/1.......	GSP	☐
D980/11	1989	'PICKFORDS REMOVALS', see Kays Set D74/1	GSP	☐
D980/12	1989	'D. SHELDON', Maroon/Black	£6-9	☐
D980/13	1990	'LIMA FURNITURE Ltd', Brown body	£6-9	☐
D980/14	1990	'CAMBRIAN FACTORY Ltd'	£6-9	☐
D980/15	1990	'ABBEYCOLOR', Maroon/Black	£6-9	☐
D980/16	1990	'ROYAL MAIL', Red/Black	£6-9	☐
D980/17	1990	'NATIONAL COAL BOARD', see GUS Set D54/1	GSP	☐
96860	1991	'EASTBOURNE MOTORS', Blue/ Grey	£6-9	☐
96862	1991	'ROYAL MAIL', Red/Black	£6-9	☐
96863	1993	'SUNLIGHT SOAP', White/Red	£6-9	☐
96865	1992	'BEEZER', 'Colonel Blink'	£6-9	☐
98109	1991	'ROYAL MAIL', Red/Black	£6-9	☐
98755	1991	'HOTSPUR', 'Willie Wallop'	£6-9	☐
96866	1994	'GAS'	£6-9	☐
98973/A	1992	'CAPTAIN AMERICA'	GSP	☐
99808	1993	'ROYAL MAIL' Re-run of D980/16	£6-9	☐

FORD MODEL 'T' VANS

Ref. No.	Year	Description	Price	
C865	1986	'LYONS TEA', Blue/White	£8-11	☐
C865/1	1987	'NEEDLERS', Brown/Red, billboards...	£8-11	☐
C865/2	1986	'LYONS TEA', As C865 but Black roof	£100-150	☐
C865/2	1987	'DRUMMER DYES', Yellow/Red, billboards	£8-11	☐

Ref. No.	Year	Description	Price	
C865/3	1987	'KALAMAZOO', Red, billboards.........	£8-11	☐
C865/4	1987	'PEPSI COLA', White/Blue/Red, billboards	£8-11	☐
C865/5	1987	'TWININGS', Black, Kay's	£8-11	☐
D865/6	1988	'AMBULANCE', see Set C88	GSP	☐
D865/7	1989	'KAYS', White/Grey, Kay's	£8-11	☐
D865/8	1989	'ROYAL LAUNDRY', see Set C90...	GSP	☐
	1989	'SUNLIGHT LAUNDRY', see Set C90	GSP	☐
C865/11	1989	'STEIFF', Brown/Black, billboards.........	£8-11	☐
D865/12	1989	'A 1 SAUCE', see Set D71/1	GSP	☐
D865/13	1989	'APS MEDICINES', see Set D71/1	GSP	☐
Q865/14	1990	'NAAFI', Blue/Black	£40-50	☐
Q865/15	1990	'JOHN MENZIES', Green/White	£8-11	☐
Q865/17	1990	'WHITBREAD', see Set D94/1	GSP	☐
C873	1986	'ZEBRA GRATE POLISH', Yellow, zebra design	£8-11	☐
C874	1987	'CORGI COLLECTOR CLUB', *2nd Anniversary*	£12-15	☐
C875	1986	'SCHOKOLADE GOLD', *'Stollwerck'*..	£8-11	☐
C876	1986	'DICKINS & JONES', Green/White/ Yellow	£16-20	☐
C877	1986	'ROYAL MAIL', Red/Black	£16-20	☐
C965	1986	'FORDS 75th Anniversary', Blue/ White, Yellow windows/logo	£8-11	☐
C965	1986	'FORDS 75th Anniversary', same but White logo	£11-14	☐
C966	1986	'FORDS 75th Anniversary', same but White windows/logo	£40-50	☐
	1987	'SWAN VESTAS', see Gift Set C69......	GSP	☐
	1987	'THE TIMES', see Gift Set C49.........	GSP	☐
	1987	'KAY & Co.', see Gift Set C68	GSP	☐
	1987	'T.C. BENNETT', see Set C50	GSP	☐
	1987	'H & C MAILES', see Set C50	GSP	☐
	1987	'T.J. POUPART', see Set C50	GSP	☐
97464	1992	'CADBURYS', Purple/Cream, Woolworths promotional	£8-11	☐
97469	1995	'RCA VICTROLA'	£8-10	☐
97751/A	1992	'BASS BREWERY' (Kays)	£8-11	☐
97753/A	1992	'TERRY OF YORK'	£8-11	☐

FORD MODEL 'T' TANKERS

Ref. No.	Year	Description	Price	
C864	1986	'PRATTS MOTOR SPIRIT', Green/ Yellow/Red	£8-11	☐
C864/1	1987	'STALEY SALES CORP.', Black/ Silver	£10-12	☐
C864/2	1987	'RIMMER BROS Ltd', Green/Black	£10-13	☐
C864/3	1987	'SAN FRANCISCO', Red/Gold, *'Fire'*..	£8-11	☐
C864/4	1987	'NATIONAL BENZOLE', Beige body..	£15-18	☐
C872	1986	'DOMINION', TT Blue/Yellow	£9-12	☐
C880	1986	'BP MOTOR SPIRIT', Green/Yellow.....	£9-12	☐
C864/6	1988	'OLYMPIC GASOLINE', Green/ Yellow, Kay's	£8-11	☐
D864/7	1989	'TEXACO', see Set D71/1	GSP	☐
D864/8	1989	'SOMERLITE', see Set D71/1	GSP	☐
97049B	1994	'YELLOWSTONE PARK'	GSP	☐

GUY ARAB Double Deck Buses

Ref. No.	Year	Description	Price	
97076/A	1992	'W.ALEXANDER', Red, 'Perth', in Set	GSP	☐
97077/A	1992	'E. LANCASHIRE', Red/Black, in Set...	GSP	☐
97198	1992	'SOUTHDOWN', Green/Cream.........	£28-32	☐
97199	1992	'BIRKENHEAD', Blue/White...............	£20-24	☐
97201	1993	'BIRMINGHAM', Blue/Cream...............	£22-27	☐
97202	1993	'MAIDSTONE', Green/Cream...............	£20-24	☐
97203	1993	'LONDON TRANSPORT', 'Dagenham'	£20-24	☐
97204	1993	'COVENTRY', Dark Maroon/Black	£18-20	☐
N.B. Variation with 'FLOWERS KEG BITTER' logo on the nearside exists.				
97205	1993	'BOURNEMOUTH', Yellow/Blue.........	£20-24	☐
97206	1993	'NORTHERN GENERAL', Red/ White	£20-24	☐
97208	1993	'YORKSHIRE', Red/Black	£18-20	☐
97209	1993	'WALSALL', Mid-Blue/Black	£14-16	☐
97310	1993	'SOUTHAMPTON'	£17-19	☐
97052	1994	'DEVON GENERAL'	GSP	☐
97311	1994	'MIDLAND RED'	£18-20	☐
97311	1994	'WOLVERHAMPTON'	£18-20	☐
97313	1994	'PAISLEY & DISTRICT'	£18-20	☐

KARRIER 'W' TROLLEY BUSES

Ref. No.	Year	Description	Price	
97870	1994	'NEWCASTLE'	£20-24	☐
97871	1995	'BRADFORD'	£20-24	☐

LEYLAND ATLANTEAN BUSES

97052	1994	'DEVON GENERAL'	£20-24	☐
97230	1994	'RIBBLE', 'Gay Hostess'	£20-24	☐
97231	1994	'HULL'	£20-24	☐
97232	1995	'WALLASEY'	£20-24	☐
97233	1995	'DEVON GENERAL' open	£20-24	☐

LEYLAND TIGER CUB BUSES

97810	1995	'LEICESTER'	£11-14	☐

LEYLAND TIGER Coaches

97076/B	1992	'W.ALEXANDER', Blue/Black, in Set ..	GSP	☐
97077/B	1992	'E. LANCASHIRE', Dark Green, in Set 'Robinsons'	GSP	☐
97079	1992	'PREMIER', in 70th Anniversary Set	GSP	☐
97192	1992	'RIBBLE', Cream/Red	£15-17	☐
97210	1993	'MAYPOLE', Dark Green/Cream	£15-17	☐
97211	1993	'BARTONS', Red/Maroon	£15-17	☐
97212	1993	'ELLEN SMITH', White/Red	£15-17	☐
	1993	'PREMIER', Cream/Red, in Set	GSP	☐
97213	1994	'RED & WHITE'	£15-17	☐
97214	1994	'SKILL'S 75th'	£15-17	☐
97216	1994	'The DELAINE'	£15-17	☐

MACK TRUCKS and VANS
(see also under 'FIRE APPLIANCES')

C906/1	1987	'MACK PARTS', Green/Cream	£9-11	☐
C906/2	1987	'SUNSHINE BISCUITS', Blue/Black	£9-11	☐
C906/3	1987	'WHITE ROCK', Yellow/Black/Red	£9-11	☐
C906/4	1987	'BUFFALO FIRE DEPT', Red/Black	£9-11	☐
C906/5	1987	'PEPSI COLA', Blue/White/Red	£9-11	☐
C906/6	1988	'STANLEY TOOLS', Yellow/Red/White	£9-11	☐
C906/7	1988	'PEERLESS LIGHT', Cream/Maroon/Blue	£9-11	☐
C906/8	1988	'BOVRIL', Cream/Black/Red	£9-11	☐
C906/9	1988	'CARNATION', Red/White	£9-11	☐
C906/10	1988	'GULDENS MUSTARD', Yellow/White/Red	£9-11	☐
98453	1995	'BREYER'	£10-12	☐
98454	1995	'WILTON FARM'	£10-12	☐
98481	1995	'GOODYEAR'	£10-12	☐

MINI VANS

96950	1994	'ROYAL MAIL'	£7-9	☐
96951	1994	'POLICE'	£7-9	☐
96952	1994	'RAC Radio Rescue'	£7-9	☐
96953	1994	'AA Road Service'	£7-9	☐
96956	1994	'Surrey Police'	£7-9	☐
96955	1994	'CORGI CLASSICS' (Club model)	£8-10	☐

MORRIS MINOR 1000 VANS

C957/1	1987	'ROYAL MAIL', Red, plastic base	£18-20	☐
C957/1	1987	same but metal base	£18-20	☐
C957/2	1987	'GAS', Green body, 'Mr Therm'	£12-15	☐
C957/3	1987-88	'CORGI Collector Club 3rd Anniversary', 1st type wheels	£14-17	☐
		with 2nd type wheels	£20-25	☐
C957/4	1988	'CASTROL', Green/White	£12-16	☐
C957/5	1989	'MICHELIN', Bright Yellow	£12-16	☐
C957/7	1988	'MACFISHERIES', Blue/White	£14-16	☐
C957/8	1989	'GRATTANS', see Grattans Set C91	GSP	☐
C957/9	1989	'TELEGRAPH & ARGUS', see Grattans Set C91	GSP	☐
C957/10	1989	'MITCHELLS', see Grattans Set C91	GSP	☐
C957/11	1989	'APPLEYARDS', Pale Green	£6-8	☐
D957/12	1989	'D. MORGAN', Blue body	£6-8	☐
D957/13	1989	'KIMBERLEY CLARK', Blue, 'HI-DRI'	£6-8	☐
D957/15	1989	'POLICE' Van, see Set D13/1	GSP	☐
D957/16	1989	'FRYS COCOA', see Kays Set D72/1	GSP	☐
D957/17	1989	'RINGTONS TEA', see Kays Set D72/1	GSP	☐
D957/18	1989	'ROYAL MAIL', see D7/1 Set	GSP	☐
D957/19	1989	'PICKFORDS', see D74/1 Set	GSP	☐
D957/20	1989	'GUERNSEY POST OFFICE', Blue	£14-16	☐
D957/21	1989	'7 UP', White van	£6-8	☐
D957/22	1990	'BISHOPS REMOVALS', (as 96845)		
D957/23	1991	'A. DUNN & SON', Issued as 96844		

D957/24	1990	'B.A.T.R.', White/Red (with cert)	£70-80	☐
D957/25	1990	'ROYAL AIR FORCE', see Set D35/1..	GSP	☐
D957/26	1990	'NAMAC 25' (Dutch) White/Red, 'England' on base	£22-27	☐
		'China' on base	£15-20	☐
D957/27	1990	'GPO TELEPHONES', Yellow/Blue	£8-12	☐
C958/1	1987	'POST OFFICE TELEPHONES', Olive Green, plastic base	£20-25	☐
C958	1987	same but metal base	£18-22	☐
D958/2	1989	'GPO TELEPHONES', see D15/1 Set ...	GSP	☐
C959	1987	'SMITHS CRISPS', Dark Blue/White, Black interior	£9-11	☐
		with Brown interior	£9-11	☐
C959/6	1988	'FOYLES FOR BOOKS', Red body	£9-12	☐
96837	1991	'MAIDSTONE & DISTRICT'	£6-9	☐
96840	1991	'BRISTOL WATER', Green body	£6-9	☐
96842	1991	'P.O. TELEPHONES', Yellow/Blue	£6-9	☐
96844	1991	'A.DUNN & SON, Blue, (was D957/23)	£6-9	☐
96845	1991	'BISHOPS REMOVALS', Yellow, (intended D957/22)	£6-9	☐
96846	1992	'TIGER', *'Roy of the Rovers'*	£6-9	☐
96847	1993	'COLMANS', Red/Yellow, *'Mustard'* .	£6-9	☐
97740	1991	'The SUNDAY TIMES', see 97740 Set	GSP	☐
98104	1993	'ROYAL MAIL', Red/Black	£6-9	☐
98756	1991	'The ROVER', Orange van	£6-9	☐
96848	1993	'BIRDS CUSTARD', Yellow/Red/Blue	£6-9	☐
96849	1994	'A.A. SERVICE'	£6-9	☐
96852	1994	'GAYDON 1994 SHOW'	£10-12	☐
96855	1995	'Wiltshire Police'	£8-11	☐
98756	1991	'The ROVER'	£6-9	☐
97541/A	1993	'ROYAL MAIL EPSOM' (Set 97541)	GSP	☐
97541/B	1993	'P O TELEPHONES' (Set 97541)	GSP	☐
97541/C	1993	'POSTAL ENGINEERING' (Set 97541)	GSP	☐
97697/A	1993	'POLICE'	GSP	☐
97722/B	1994	'POLICE SOUTH GLAMORGAN'	GSP	☐
98960/A	1992	'BIFFO THE BEAR'	GSP	☐
98972/A	1992	'SPIDERMAN'	GSP	☐

MORRIS MINOR 1000 PICK-UPS

96850	1994	'WIMPEY'	£7-9	☐
96851	1995	'LONDON BRICK Co Ltd'	£7-9	☐
96854	1995	'MORRIS MOTORS Fire Brigade'	£8-12	☐

MORRIS 'J' VANS

D983/1	1990	'POST OFFICE TELEPHONES', Olive	£8-11	☐
D983/2	1990	'ROYAL MAIL', Red/Black	£8-11	☐
D983/3	1991	'COLLECTOR CLUB '91'	NGPP	☐
D983/4	1991	'Metropolitan Police', see 96883 below		☐
D983/5	1991	'WALLS ICE CREAM', Cream/Blue	£6-9	☐
D983/6	1990	'ELECTRICITY', see GUS Set D54/1...	GSP	☐
D983/7	1990	'BEANO', see D47/1 Set	GSP	☐
D983/8	1990	'BRITISH RAILWAYS', see Set D46/1	GSP	☐
96880/2	1991/3	'PICKFORDS', Dark Blue body	£8-11	☐
96882	1991	'ROYAL MAIL', Red/Black	£8-11	☐
96883	1990	'Metropolitan Police', (was D983/4)	£6-9	☐
96887	1992	'The TOPPER', '4d Every Friday'	£6-9	☐
96891	1993	'MORRIS SERVICE', 'BMC' logo	£6-9	☐
96892	1993	'BOVRIL', Blue/Black	£6-9	☐
96893	1994	'ROYAL MAIL'	£8-11	☐
96894	1994	'P O TELEPHONES'	£8-11	☐
96886	1994	'FAMILY ASSURANCE'	£8-11	☐
97200/B	1991	'BRS EXPRESS PARCELS'	GSP	☐
97695/C	1992	BMC COMPETITION DEPT	GSP	☐
97714/A	1994	'ROYAL AIR FORCE' (D-Day Set)	GSP	☐
97735/B	1992	'THE CUMBERLAND'	GSP	☐
97746/B	1991	'CORGI' (Set 97765/B)	GSP	☐
97765/B	1993	'W FORBES'	GSP	☐
98758	1992	'WIZARD', *'The Bumper Boys Paper'* ...	£8-11	☐
98759/B	1991	'KORKY THE CAT'	GSP	☐
98960/B	1992	'BERYL THE PERIL'	GSP	☐
98970/B	1992	'THE X-MEN/THE BLOB'	GSP	☐
98972/B	1992	'SPIDERMAN'	GSP	☐
99140	1993	'GPO Telephones', Olive-Green/Black ...	£8-11	☐

1926 RENAULT BOX VANS

C824		'MARCEL GARDET', Blue body	£8-11	☐
C824/3	1988	'THE LIPTON', Dark Blue/Brown	£11-14	☐
C902	1985	'ROYAL MAIL', Red/Blue/Gold, with or without cab scuttle	£40-50	☐

C917	1986	'COURVOISIER', Green/Gold/Red	**£7-9**	☐
97000	1991	'PERRIER WATER', Green/White	**£7-9**	☐

RENAULT CANVAS BACKED TRUCKS

C922	1986	'GALERIES LAFAYETTE', White/ Green	**£8-11**	☐
C925	1986	'GERVAIS DANONE', Blue/Yellow	**£20-25**	☐

RENAULT OPEN TRUCKS

C823/1	1985	'JULES COLARD', Blue/Gold/White	**£7-9**	☐
C824/1	1988	'HERLOIN', Grey/Blue/Red	**£8-11**	☐

RENAULT BEER LORRIES

D889/1	1989	'STELLA ARTOIS', Red/White/Black	**£8-11**	☐

SCAMMELL HIGHWAYMAN TRUCKS

97840	1995	'SHELL-MEX BP' Tanker	**£35-40**	☐
97885	1985	'CHIPPERFIELDS' Tractor, Pole Trailer & Caravan	NGPP	☐
97886	1995	'CHIPPERFIELDS' Crane Truck	NGPP	☐
97915	1995	'CHIPPERFIELDS' Tractor and two Trailers	NGPP	☐
97920	1994	'EDWARDS' Tractor, 2 Trailers	**£35-45**	☐

SCAMMELL SCARAB Articulated Vehicles

97910	1993	'RAIL FREIGHT', Yellow/Black	**£12-14**	☐
97911	1993	'BRITISH RAILWAYS', Maroon/ Cream	**£12-13**	☐
97913	1994	'RAIL FREIGHT', Grey	**£11-13**	☐
97914	1994	'BRS PARCELS SERVICE'	**£11-13**	☐
97917	1995	'WATNEYS'	**£15-18**	☐
97912	1994	'ROYAL MAIL' Limited Edition	**£15-18**	☐
97916	1994	Corgi 10th Anniversary Club model	**£15-18**	☐

SUNBEAM 'W' TROLLEY BUSES

97800	1994	'READING CORPORATION'	**£20-24**	☐
97801	1995	'MAIDSTONE'	**£20-24**	☐

THORNEYCROFT BOX VANS (without billboards)

C821	1985	'WAKEFIELD CASTROL', Green/ Black	**£12-16**	☐
C821/1	1988	'HEIDELBERGER', Green/Gold/ White	**£9-12**	☐
C828	1985	'GAMLEYS', Blue/Red/Silver	**£18-24**	☐
C830	1985	'W & R JACOB', Rust/White/Gold	**£34-38**	☐
C831	1985	'HUNTLEY & PALMERS', Blue/ Gold/White	**£9-11**	☐
C832	1985	'CORGI 1st ANNIVERSARY', Blue Corgi Club model		
		1: 'Kingsway, Fforestfach Ind.Est.'	**£30-35**	☐
		2: 'Kingsway Ind.Est., Fforestfach'	**£30-35**	☐
C833	1985	'MACFARLANE LANG', Green/ Gold	**£9-11**	☐
C834	1985	'LYONS SWISS ROLLS', Dark Blue	**£40-50**	☐
C839	1985	'NURDIN & PEACOCK', Blue/Silver, with A4 certificate & plinth	**£30-35**	☐
C840	1985	'ALLENBURYS', Red/White	**£15-20**	☐
C841	1985	'PEEK FREANS', Green/Cream, Orange scuttle	**£9-11**	☐
		without cab scuttle	**£50-60**	☐
C842	1985	'CARTER PATERSON', Green/Red	**£12-15**	☐
C843	1985	'EDDERSHAWS', Brown/Gold	**£9-11**	☐
C845	1985	'DUCKHAMS OIL', Silver body with spoked wheels	**£9-11**	☐
		with disc wheels	**£9-11**	☐
C846	1985	'IND COOPE', Green/Black/Gold	**£12-14**	☐
C847	1985	'KEILLERS', Cream body	**£13-17**	☐
C848	1985	'NEWS OF THE WORLD', Black/ Silver	**£13-17**	☐
C849	1987	'GOODYEAR', Blue/Brown, (for USA)	**£35-38**	☐
C853	1985	'M. A. RAPPORT', Maroon/Cream	**£18-24**	☐
C854	1985	'LINCOLNSHIRE Ambulance', White	**£9-11**	☐
C855	1985	'LINCOLNSHIRE FIRE', Red	**£9-11**	☐
C856	1985	'LINCOLNSHIRE POLICE', Black	**£9-11**	☐
C859/6	1987	'KAYS', Maroon/Beige, Kay's	**£15-20**	☐
D859/12	1990	'SHELL OIL', see Set D9/1	GSP	☐
C907	1986	'HP SAUCE', Red/White/Gold	**£12-16**	☐
C910	1986	'SMALL & PARKES', Black/White	**£12-16**	☐
C911	1986	'PERSIL', Green/Red, German export	**£9-11**	☐
C913	1986	'DEWARS WHISKY', Red/White	**£9-11**	☐
C914	1986	'LIPTONS TEA', Blue/Gold/Red	**£9-11**	☐
C915	1986	'OXO', Red/White	**£9-11**	☐
C924	1986	'SAFEWAY', Red/Black	**£14-17**	☐
C926	1986	'DOUBLE DIAMOND', Black/Gold	**£14-16**	☐
C931	1986	'STEPNEY TYRES', Red/Gold	**£14-17**	☐
C932	1986	'PURITAN SOAP', Yellow/Black	**£9-11**	☐
C933	1986	'BUY PUNCH', Red/Black	**£20-25**	☐
C968	1986	'RADIO STEINER', Blue, no cab scuttle, Swiss	**£14-17**	☐

Promotional Issues presented to factory visitors and not sold through normal outlets:

		'SWANSEA BANKERS', Beige, no cab scuttle, 20 issued	NGPP	☐
		'MARCONI', White/Blue, 20 issued	NGPP	☐

THORNEYCROFT BOX VANS (with billboards)

C859	1986	'THORLEYS CATTLEFOOD', Yellow/Red	**£9-11**	☐
C859/1	1987	'SCOTTS EMPIRE BREAD', Blue/ Red	**£9-11**	☐
C859/2	1987	'CHIVERS JAMS', Green/Cream/Blue	**£9-11**	☐
C859/3	1987	'ARNOTTS BISCUITS', Australian export model, 8,200 (5,000 with Certs)	**£40-50**	☐
C859/4	1987	'GOODYEAR', C849 with billboards	**£9-11**	☐
C859/5	1987	'GRATTANS 75th', Green, no scuttle	**£24-29**	☐
C859/6	1987	'KAYS', see Gift Set C68	GSP	☐
C859/7	1989	'LEDA SALT', Grey/Black	**£9-11**	☐
C859/8	1988	'VOLVOLUTUM', Green/Brown/ Yellow	**£9-11**	☐
C859/9	1988	'ASDA', Blue/Yellow	**£9-11**	☐
C859/10	1988	'BATCHELORS PEAS', Green/Cream	**£15-19**	☐
C859/11	1988	'LEA & PERRINS', Orange/Brown	**£9-11**	☐
C859/12	1989	'SHELL OIL & PETROL', see Set D9/1	GSP	☐
C859/13	1989	'McDOUGALLS', Brown/Red	**£20-25**	☐
C859/16	1990	'ASDA', *'25th Birthday'*	**£9-11**	☐
C929	1986	'GAMLEYS', Green/Black/Red	**£12-15**	☐
97754	1993	'LMS RAILWAY', see Set 97754	GSP	☐

97150,1,2,3,4,5 1992 'ROYALS' Six souvenir vans in various colours and representing different castles or royal residences. Each has 'Queen's 40th Anniversary' logo. Normal retail price (**£8-12**)

THORNEYCROFT BEER TRUCKS

C867	1986	'THOMAS WETHERED', Green/Red	**£8-11**	☐
C867/1	1987	'CHARLES WELLS', Brown/Cream	**£8-11**	☐
C867/2	1987	'TOOHEYS PILSNER', Red/White	**£8-11**	☐
		Blue/White version	**£8-11**	☐
C867/3	1987	'SWAN LAGER', Black/Red	**£8-11**	☐
C867/4	1988	'CARLSBERG', Green/White	**£8-11**	☐
C882	1986	'ST. WINIFREDS', Red body	**£8-11**	☐
C883	1988	'TAUNTON CIDER', Green/Red/ Yellow	**£8-11**	☐
C867/5	1990	'CHARRINGTONS', see Set D52/1	GSP	☐
C867/6	1990	'GREENE KING', see Set D51/1	GSP	☐
97742	1991	'JOHN SMITHS BREWERY', in Set	GSP	☐

THORNEYCROFT CANVAS BACKED TRUCKS

C827	1985	'G.W.R.', Brown/Cream, no 'GWR'	**£25-30**	☐
		with 'GWR', (Kay's)	**£25-30**	☐
C836	1985	'L.M.S.', Maroon/Cream	**£25-30**	☐
C837	1985	'SOUTHERN RAILWAY', Olive/ Cream	**£25-30**	☐
C838	1985	'L.N.E.R.', Blue/Cream	**£25-30**	☐
C923	1986	'FIELD AMBULANCE', Olive-Green	**£12-15**	☐
C923/2	1986	'TROESCH', Green/Brown, Swiss	**£190-220**	☐

THORNEYCROFT OPEN TRUCKS

C820/1	1985	'EAST ANGLIAN FRUIT Co', Brown	**£5-8**	☐

THORNEYCROFT DOUBLE DECKER BUS

1st type: 4 top-rail supports,
2nd type: 8 top-rail supports.

C858	1986	'SANDEMANS', Red 1st type	**£12-14**	☐
C858	1986	2nd type body	**£12-14**	☐

Ref. No.			Market Price Range	
C858/1	1987	'NATIONAL MOTOR MUSEUM', Red/White 2nd type	£12-14	☐
		Red body, Red cab canopy	£25-30	☐
C858/2	1987	'CHARLIE CHAPLIN', Yellow/Red 2nd type	£12-14	☐
C858/3	1987	'PALM TOFFEE', Green, 2nd type	£12-14	☐
C858/4	1987	'IDRIS SODA WATER', Black/ Yellow	£12-14	☐
C858/5	1987	The TIMES', Red body	£12-14	☐
C858/6	1987	'L. & N.W.R.', Brown/Yellow/White	£12-14	☐
C858/7	1988	'OAKEYS KNIFE POLISH', Red/ White	£10-12	☐
C858/8	1988	Military Bus, Kay's Set C88	GSP	☐
C858/9	1988	'BAXTERS', Kay's Set C89	GSP	☐
C858/10	1988	'SCHWEPPES', 'BP' & Corgi PRM	£20-25	☐
C858/11	1988	'GREAT EASTERN RAILWAY', White/Red	£20-25	☐
C884	1986	'BEER IS BEST', Red/White, 1st type	£14-16	☐
C885	1986	'THOMAS TILLING', Yellow/Black, 1st type	£20-25	☐
C885	1986	same but 2nd type	£20-25	☐
C886	1986	GRANTS MORELLO CHERRY BRANDY, Red, 1st type	£20-25	☐
		with reversed advert logos	£20-25	☐
C975	1986	'ALLENBURYS PASTILLES', Orange/Rust	£12-14	☐
96985	1992	'EAST SURREY', Blue/White/Red	£10-12	☐
96986	1993	'BRIGHTON & HOVE', Blue/Red	£10-12	☐
96987	1993	'GENERAL' 'SCHWEPPES'	£10-12	☐
96988	1993	'BEAMISH', Dark Red/White/Black	£10-14	☐
96991	1995	'SHEFFIELD' (Corgi direct)	NGPP	☐
96996	1995	'TILLING' (Corgi direct)	NGPP	☐
96992	1995	'NORFOLKS' (Corgi direct)	NGPP	☐
96993	1995	'YELLOWAYS' (Corgi direct)	NGPP	☐
96989	1995	'GENERAL' (Corgi direct)	NGPP	☐
96994	1995	'SOUTH WALES' (Corgi direct)	NGPP	☐

CORGI TRAMLINES

A range of Tram models in '00' gauge (1:76 scale) introduced in 1988.

SINGLE DECK TRAMS (open platforms)

C990/1	1988	'SOUTHAMPTON CORPORATION', Red/White	£12-14	☐
C990/2	1988	'SHEFFIELD CORPORATION', Dark Blue/White	£12-14	☐
D990/3	1989	'DERBY CORPORATION', Green/ White	£12-14	☐
D990/4	1989	'WOLVERHAMPTON', Green/White	£14-16	☐
D990/6	1990	'MAIDSTONE CORPORATION', White/Yellow	£12-14	☐
97263	1994	'ASHTON-U-LYNE'	£14-16	☐

OPEN TOP TRAMS
(Double deck, open platforms, no roof)

C991/1	1988	'L.C.C.', Red/White/Black	£15-20	☐
D991/2	1988	'BLACKPOOL CORPORATION', White/Green, 3 saloon end colours:		
		1: Green ends,	£10-15	☐
		2: White ends,	£10-15	☐
		3: White AND Green ends	£13-16	☐
D991/3	1989	'BATH ELECTRIC', Beige/Blue	£13-16	☐
D991/4	1989	'BOURNEMOUTH', Brown/Yellow	£15-20	☐
D991/5	1989	'BURTON & ASHBY', White/Brown	£15-20	☐
D991/6	1990	'CROYDON', Brown/Cream/Red	£13-16	☐
Q991/7	1990	'GARDEN FESTIVAL', Brown/ Cream	£13-16	☐
D991/8	1990	'LLANDUDNO', Green/Cream, (also 97242)	£16-19	☐
97240	1991	'LOWESTOFT', Dark Brown/Cream	£10-13	☐
97241	1991	'SOUTH METROPOLITAN', Dark Green/Cream	£10-13	☐
97290	1992	'HULL', Maroon/White	£10-13	☐
97291	1992	'SOUTH SHIELDS', Maroon/Cream	£10-13	☐
98150	1993	'LOWESTOFT', Maroon/Cream	£10-13	☐
98151	1993	'S. METROPOLITAN', Green/Cream	£10-13	☐

CLOSED TOP TRAMS
(double-decker with roof, open platforms to lower deck)

C992/1	1988	'LEEDS CITY TRANSPORT', Red/ White	£14-16	☐
C992/2	1988	'GLASGOW CORPORATION', Yellow/White	£14-16	☐
C992/3	1988	'L.C.C.', Red/White, GUS model	£14-16	☐

C992/4	1988	'BLACKPOOL', White/Green, Kay's	NGPP	☐
C992/5	1988	'BRADFORD', Cream/Blue, Grattans	£27-32	☐
D992/6	1989	'SOUTHAMPTON', Red/White	£14-16	☐
D992/7	1989	'BIRMINGHAM', Cream/Dark Blue	£33-38	☐
D992/8	1990	'LONDON TRANSPORT', Red/White	£14-16	☐
97260	1991	'BIRKENHEAD', Maroon/White	£14-16	☐
97261	1991	'SOUTH SHIELDS', Blue/Cream, (also D992/9)	£10-13	☐
98152	1993	'GLASGOW', White/Red/Yellow	£10-13	☐
98153	1993	'LONDON'	£10-13	☐
98154	1993	'DOVER', Green/White	£14-16	☐
97267	1994	'GRIMSBY'	£14-16	☐
97268	1994	'L.C.C.'	£14-16	☐
97270	1994	'BOLTON/ACDO'.	£14-16	☐

FULLY CLOSED DOUBLE DECK TRAMS
(with roof and enclosed platforms)

D993/1	1989	'PORTSMOUTH', Maroon/White	£14-16	☐
D993/2	1989	'DOVER', Green/White	£14-16	☐
D993/3	1991	'COVENTRY', Red/White	£10-13	☐
97262	1993	'BLACKPOOL', Green/Cream	£10-13	☐
97263	1992	'ASHTON UNDER LYNE'	£10-13	☐
97264	1992	'CARDIFF'	£10-13	☐
97285	1992	'LEICESTER', Maroon/Cream	£10-13	☐
97286	1992	'SUNDERLAND', Red/White	£10-13	☐
97287	1992	'NOTTINGHAM'	£10-13	☐
97288	1992	'SHEFFIELD', Blue/White	£10-13	☐
97296	1992	'LIVERPOOL'	£10-13	☐
97265	1994	'BELFAST'	£14-16	☐
97273	1994	'BLACKPOOL PLEASURE BEACH'	£10-13	☐
97293	1992	'NEWCASTLE EVENING C'	£10-13	☐

Commemoratives/Promotionals

D37/1	1990	'PENNY POST', '150th Anniversary', special box	£13-16	☐
	1993	'BRITISH TRAM CO.', promotionals for regional newspapers: 'Nottingham', 'Newcastle', 'Leicester', 'Sunderland', 'Sheffield', 'South Shields, 'Hull'	NGPP	☐

TROLLEY BUS

97800	1994	'READING/SUNBEAM'	£20-24	☐
97870	1994	'NEWCASTLE/KARRIER'	£20-24	☐

VOLKSWAGEN VAN

D985/1	1990	Delivery Van	£6-9	☐
98757	1991	'THE SKIPPER'	£6-9	☐
96960	1991	'BOSCH AUTO ELECTRICAL'	£6-9	☐
96961	1992	'THE LION/CAPTAIN CONDOR'	£6-9	☐
98965/B	1992	'EAGLE/DAN DARE'	£6-9	☐
96965	1992	'CORGI COLLECTORS CLUB'	£6-9	☐
98973/B	1992	'CAPTAIN AMERICA'	GSP	☐

VOLVO SUPERHAULERS

98100	1994	'SWIFT SERVICES'	NGPP	☐
98101	1994	'AMTRAK'	NGPP	☐
98102	1994	'UTC'	NGPP	☐
98103	1994	'P & O FERRYMASTERS'	NGPP	☐
98304	1994	'CHRISTIAN SALVESON'	NGPP	☐
98305	1994	'EXEL LOGISTICS'	NGPP	☐
98306	1994	'DODD'S TRANSPORT'	NGPP	☐
98307	1994	'LYNX'	NGPP	☐

VINTAGE TRUCK

98449	1995	White Tanker, 'THE PETROL CORPORATION'	£16-19	☐
98453	1995	White Battle Truck, 'TRIPLE XXX'	£16-19	☐
98458	1995	White Beer Truck, 'JACOB RUPPERT'	£16-19	☐
98457	1995	White Soda Truck, 'WHITE ROCK'	£16-19	☐
98456	1995	White Sacks Truck, 'SCHEIWE'S COAL'	£16-19	☐
98455	1995	White Canvas Back Truck, 'P.R.R.'	£16-19	☐

YELLOW COACH 743

See listed under 'American Classic Buses'.

Corgi Classics Cars

Listed alphabetically

AUSTIN-HEALEY 3000 Sports Car

D733/1	1990	Hard-Top, Red/White	£8-10	☐
D733/2	1990	Hard Top, see D53/1 Kays Set	GSP	☐
D734/1	1990	Open Soft-Top, Blue body	£8-10	☐
D735/1	1990	Closed Soft-Top, Pacific-Green/Grey	£8-10	☐
96200	1991	Hard Top, Turquoise/White, rack	£8-10	☐
96220	1991	Open Top, Metallic Blue/Cream, rack	£8-10	☐
96240	1991	Open Top, Cream, luggage rack	£8-10	☐
97681/A	1992	Hard Top, Silver/White (GS 97681)	GSP	☐
97709/B	1993	Hard Top, Red/White (GS 97709)	GSP	☐
97730/A	1992	Hard Top, Red/White, RN '76'	GSP	☐
97730/B	1992	Hard Top, Green body, RN '18'	GSP	☐
97730/C	1992	Open Top, Blue/Turquoise, RN '414'	GSP	☐

N.B. 97730A/B/C are part of GS 97730 Austin Healey Set.

99050	1993	Open Top, Pale Blue	£8-10	☐
99051	1991	Soft Top, Dark Green/Grey, rack	£8-10	☐
99928/A	1992	Open Top, Chrome plated (1000 only)	NGPP	☐
99928/B	1992	Soft Top, Chrome plated (1000 only)	NGPP	☐

N.B. 99928A/B form part of GS 99928.

CHEVROLET BEL AIR

C532	1994	Blue or Black	£5-8	☐
C582/2	1989	Chevrolet Bel Air, Pale Blue, Silver fin	£8-10	☐
C582/2	1989	Chevrolet Bel Air, Black/White, Silver fin	£8-10	☐
96570	1992	Chevrolet Bel Air, Gold, 'Millionth'	£8-10	☐
96570	1992	Chevrolet Bel Air, Pale Blue, White fin	£8-10	☐
96570	1994	Blue or Gold	£5-8	☐
97389	1994	'CHICAGO' logo	£7-10	☐
97396	1994	'HIGHWAY PATROL' logo	£7-10	☐
97397	1995	'PENSACOLA' logo	£7-10	☐

FERRARI 250 GTO

D739/1	1990	250 GTO Sport, Red, number '151'	£8-10	☐
D740/1	1990	250 GTO Road	£8-11	☐
96320	1990	Re-run of D740/1	£8-10	☐
97690/A	1991	Pale Green body, RN '15'	GSP	☐
97690/B	1991	Grey body, RN '10'	GSP	☐
97690/C	1991	Blue body, RN '5'	GSP	☐

N.B. 97690 A/B/C form GS 97690 Racing Ferrari's Set.

97708/A	1993	Red body, RN '165' (GS 97708)	GSP	☐
98124	1993	250 GT Road, Red, no number	£8-10	☐

FORD CORTINA and Lotus Cortina

D708/1	1989	Lotus Cortina, White/Green, (also in Gift Set D53/1)	£8-10	☐
D708/2	1989	Ford Cortina, Maroon body	£8-10	☐
D708/3	1989	Lotus Cortina, Monaco Red	£8-10	☐
D708/4	1989	Ford Cortina, Aqua Blue	£8-10	☐
D708/5	1989	Rally car, see Set D16/1	GSP	☐
D708/6	1990	Police car, White, 'POLICE'	£8-10	☐
D708/7	1990	Ford Cortina, Black body	£8-10	☐
D708/8	1990	Ford Cortina, Spruce-Green body	£8-10	☐
96501	1994	French Blue body	£8-10	☐
96760	1991	Rally car, Red/Gold, (Sir John Whitmore)	£10-12	☐
96763	1992	Rally car, Red/Black, (Roger Clark)	£10-12	☐
96764	1992	Rally car, Cream/Green, (Jim Clark)	£10-12	☐
97709/A	1993	Red body, RN '29'	GSP	☐
98130	1993	Lotus Cortina, White/Green stripe	£8-10	☐
98266	1994	Chrome plated, mounted on plinth, (1000 only), certificated	NGPP	☐

FORD POPULAR Saloon

C701/1	1988	Grey-Blue	£8-10	☐
C701/3	1989	Black	£8-10	☐
C701/5	1989	Fawn	£8-10	☐
D701/6	1989	Rally car, see Gift Set D16/1	GSP	☐
D701/7	1989	Pale Green	£8-10	☐
D701/8	1990	Grey	£8-10	☐
D701/9	1990	Winchester Blue	£8-10	☐
98132	1993	Black	£8-10	☐
98132	1993	Black C701/3 Renumbered/China	£8-10	☐
98264	1993	Chrome plated, mounted on plinth, certificated (1000 only)	NGPP	☐
96481	1994	Sage Green	£8-10	☐
97714/C	1994	'ROYAL NAVY' (D-Day Set)	GSP	☐

FORD SIERRA COSWORTH

96012	1994	'SPENDER' logo	£9-11	☐

FORD THUNDERBIRD

C810/2	1994	Black body	£6-9	☐

FORD ZEPHYR Mk.II Saloon

D710/1	1989	Black body	£8-10	☐
D710/2	1989	Blue body	£8-10	☐
D710/3	1989	Monaco Red	£8-10	☐
D710/4	1989	Regency Grey	£8-10	☐
D710/5	1989	Black body, 'POLICE'	£8-10	☐
D710/6	1990	Maroon body	£8-10	☐
D710/7	1990	Pompadour Blue	£8-10	☐
D710/8	1990	Blue/Grey R.A.F. (GS D35/1)	GSP	☐
D710/9	1990	White/Black RN '47' (GS D36/1)	GSP	☐
D710/10	1990	Yellow body, RN '117' (GS D36/1)	GSP	☐
D710/11	1990	Dark Green body, RN '97' (GS D36/1)	GSP	☐
96721	1991	Rally car, White, (Anne Hall)	£8-10	☐

FORD ZODIAC Mk.II Saloon

D709/1	1989	Maroon/Grey	£8-10	☐
D709/2	1989	Two-tone Blue	£8-10	☐
D709/3	1989	Yellow/White	£8-10	☐
D709/4	1989	Red/White	£8-10	☐
D709/5	1989	Yellow/White body, RN '21', (GS D16/1)	GSP	☐
98135	1993	Yellow/White, D709/3 re-run	£8-10	☐
D709/6	1990	Black/Blue	£8-10	☐
D709/7	1990	Two-tone Green	£8-10	☐
		Grey/Yellow (very few made)	NGPP	☐
D709/8	1990	Ermine White/Grey	£8-10	☐

JAGUAR 'E'-type

97700	1991	Soft Top, Dark Blue, RN '110'	GSP	☐
?	1991	Soft Top, Red body, Tan top	£8-10	☐
96042	1991	Soft Top, Cream/Black	£8-10	☐
96043	1991	Open Top, Black, Cream interior	£8-10	☐
96080	1991	Open Top, Signal Red (GS 97702)	GSP	☐
97680/A	1991	Open Top, Grey body	GSP	☐
97680/B	1991	Soft Top, Red body, Tan top	GSP	☐

N.B. 97680 A/B form part of GS 97680 '30th Anniversary of the 'E' Type Jaguar'

97701/A	1991	Soft Top, Grey body, Black top, RN '170'	GSP	☐
97701/B	1991	Soft Top, Red body, Black top, RN '108'	GSP	☐

N.B. 97701 A/B form part of GS 97701 'Racing 'E' Types'

96081	1992	Open Top, Primrose, Red interior	£8-10	☐
96082	1992	Soft Top, Silver, (Ken Baker)	£8-10	☐
98120	1993	Soft Top, British Racing Green	£8-10	☐
98121	1993	Open Top, Silver Blue	£8-10	☐
99927/A		Open Top, Chrome plated, (part of GS 99927 & GS 99969)	GSP	☐
99927/B		Soft Top, Chrome plated (part of set 99969)	GSP	☐

JAGUAR Mk.II Saloon 1959

C700/1	1988	Red body, Silver or Yellow box inners	£12-14	☐
C700/3	1988	Black, CLE of 7,000	£12-14	☐
D700/4	1989	Metallic Fawn	£9-11	☐
D700/5	1989	Green body	£9-11	☐
D700/6	1989	Metallic Blue	£9-11	☐
D700/7	1989	Metallic Grey	£9-11	☐
D700/8	1989	Silver-Blue (96560)	£9-11	☐
D700/9	1990	Willow-Green body	£9-11	☐
D700/11	1990	Rally car, see Kays Set D53/1	GSP	☐
C706/1	1988	Police car, Black, 'POLICE'	£14-16	☐
D706/2	1989	Police car, see Kays Set D75/1	GSP	☐
96680	1991	Rally car, Black, (Stirling Moss)	£14-16	☐
96881	1991	Rally car, Cream, (John Coombes)	£14-16	☐
96682	1991	'Inspector Morse', Maroon, Black roof	£20-25	☐
97700/A	1992	Silver body	GSP	☐
97702/A	1992	Dark Red on plinth	NGPP	☐
98131	1993	Silver Blue (97700A Re-run)	£14-16	☐
97697/A	1993	White 'POLICE'	GSP	☐
97708/B	1993	Ivory, RN '82'	GSP	☐
98131	1993	Silver Blue (97700 Re-run)	£9-11	☐

Ref. No.	Year	Description	Price	
98263	1993	Chrome plated, mounted on plinth (1000 only)...........................	NGPP	☐
96683	1994	Old English White..................................	£9-11	☐
97721/A	1994	Black/White body.................................	GSP	☐

JAGUAR XK 120

96040	1991	Open Top, White body	£8-10	☐
96041	1991	Open Top, British Racing Green............	£8-10	☐
96044	1991	Soft Top, Black, White top....................	£8-10	☐
96060	1991	Open Top, Black body...........................	£8-10	☐
97681/B	1991	Open Top, Light Green body (GS 97681)	GSP	☐
97700/C	1991	Open Top, Cream body, RN '153' (GS 97700).....................................	GSP	☐
97703/A	1991	Soft Top, Cream body, RN '65'............	GSP	☐
97703/B	1991	Soft Top, Green body, RN '64'.............	GSP	☐
97703/C	1991	Open Top, White body, RN '166'	GSP	☐
N.B. 97703A/B/C form set 97703 R.A.C. Rally set.				
97706/A	1993	Open Top, Blue body, RN '16'..............	GSP	☐
97706/B	1993	Open Top, White body, RN '7'..............	GSP	☐
97706/C	1993	Open Top, Red body, RN '8'	GSP	☐
N.B. 97706A/B/C/ form set 97706 'Jaguar XK120 Set 'First Time Out'				
99927/B	1992	Soft Top, Chrome plated, part of set 99927 (1000 only)	NGPP	☐
98900	1994	Open Top, Chrome plated	£8-10	☐

MERCEDES-BENZ 300SL ROADSTER

96410	1993	Open Top, Red, Cream seats.................	£8-10	☐
96411	1993	Open Top, Dark Grey, Red seats...........	£8-10	☐
96415	1993	Soft Top, Ivory, Black top....................	£8-10	☐
96416	1993	Soft Top, Silver, Black top	£8-10	☐

M.G. 'MGA'

D730/1	1990	Hard-Top, Silver/Black	£8-10	☐
D730/2	1990	Hard-Top, see Kays Set D53/1	GSP	☐
D731/1	1990	Open Soft-Top, British Racing Green ...	£13-16	☐
D732/1	1990	Closed Soft-Top, Red/Black	£8-10	☐
96140	1991	Hard-Top, Red, luggage rack	£8-10	☐
96160	1991	Open Top, Black, luggage rack	£8-10	☐
96180	1991	Soft Top, White/Grey, luggage rack.......	£8-10	☐
97695/A	1992	White body, Black top, RN '324', in 'Abingdon' Set...........................	£8-10	☐
97695/B	1992	Red body, Black top, RN '38', in 'Abingdon' Set...........................	£8-10	☐
99929/A	1992	Open Top, Chrome plated, GS 99929 (1000 only)................................	NGPP	☐
99929/B	1992	Soft Top, Chrome plated, GS 99929 (1000 only)................................	NGPP	☐
99046	1993	Hard Top, Silver/Black	£8-10	☐
99048	1993	Closed Soft-Top, Red/Black	£8-10	☐
97722/A	1994	Hard Top, White body 'POLICE' (GS 97722)	GSP	☐

MINI - COOPER

94140	1992	Red/White, 'Monte Carlo', RN '37'	£8-10	☐
94141	1992	Black/White, RN '7'..............................	£8-10	☐
97708/C	1993	Red body, RN '8'..................................	GSP	☐
97709/C	1993	Red body, RN '38'................................	GSP	☐
97712/A	1993	Red body, RN '52'................................	GSP	☐
97712/B	1993	Red body, RN '37'................................	GSP	☐
97712/C	1993	Red body, RN '177'..............................	GSP	☐
N.B. 97712A/B/C/ form GS 97712 Monte Carlo Winners Set.				
97713/A	1993	Red body...........................	GSP	☐
97713/B	1993	Blue body	GSP	☐
97713/C	1993	White body	GSP	☐
N.B. 97713A/B/C for GS 97713 Italian Job Set.				
98137	1993	Black body with basketweave panels......	£7-9	☐
98136	1993	Almond-Green/White............................	£8-10	☐
98137	1993	with 'wickerwork' panels......................	£8-10	☐
97721/B	1994	White body, 'DURHAM POLICE'...........	GSP	☐
98128	1994	British Racing Green/White body	£7-9	☐
98139	1994	Red body...	£7-9	☐

MORRIS MINOR 1000 CONVERTIBLE

96750	1994	Snowberry White body	£8-10	☐
96751	1994	Clipper Blue body	£8-10	☐
96752	1994	Porcelaine Green body..........................	£8-10	☐
96753	1994	Frifford Grey body................................	£8-10	☐
96754	1994	Highway Yellow body	£8-10	☐
96755	1995	Rose Taupe body	£8-10	☐
96757	1995	With 'Lovejoy' Box, Dark Blue body.....	£9-11	☐

MORRIS MINOR 1000 Saloon

C702/1	1988	'B.S.M.', Black, with 'L' plates.............	£12-14	☐
C702/2	1988	Dark Blue	£12-14	☐
D702/4	1989	'Millionth Minor', Lilac body...............	£9-11	☐
D702/5	1989	Maroon..	£9-11	☐
D702/6	1990	Almond-Green (see 98134)....................	£9-11	☐
D702/7	1990	Ivory body	£9-11	☐
D702/8	1990	Clipper Blue	£9-11	☐
D702/9	1990	(79137) Sage Green, Not issued............	NPP	☐
C703/1	1988	'Panda' Car, Blue/White, 'POLICE' separate hubs, thin end of sign attached to roof, no mirror/wiper detail, thick quarterlights	£15-20	☐
		integral (larger) hubs, detailed windscreen, thick end of sign attached to roof, thin quarterlights	£20-25	☐
		NB. Ist issue castings with 2nd type wheels exist.		
96740	1991	Rally car, Cream, (Pat Moss)	£12-14	☐
96741	1992	'Himalayan Rally' car, Dark Blue.........	£12-14	☐
96742	1993	Rally car, 'London to Peking'	£12-14	☐
98134	1993	Almond Green (reissued D702/6)	£9-11	☐
97698/A		'POLICE' (small hub caps)....................	GSP	☐
98262	1993	Chrome Plated, mounted on plinth (1000 by Direct Mail only)	NGPP	☐
96744	1994	with 'POLICE' logo	£8-10	☐
96745	1994	Black body	£8-10	☐
96746	1994	Red body, RN '323'	£10-12	☐
96756	1994	'Bristol Omnibus'	£10-12	☐
96758	1994	'Some Mothers Do Ave Em'	£9-11	☐
96759	1994	'MERTHYR TYDFIL POLICE'...............	£8-10	☐
98134	1994	Almond Green body	£8-10	☐

MORRIS MINOR 1000 TRAVELLER

96870	1994	Green body	£8-10	☐
96871	1994	Black body	£8-10	☐
96873	1994	'EDINBURGH POLICE'.........................	£8-10	☐
96874	1994	White body...	£8-10	☐

PORSCHE 356b SPEEDSTER

D741/1	1990	Hard-Top, Red/Black	£6-9	☐
D742/1	1990	Open Soft-Top, White/Black	£6-9	☐
D743/1	1990	Closed Soft-Top, Black, Red seats	£6-9	☐
96360	1990	Open Top, Blue, Black hood	£6-9	☐
98122	1993	Closed Soft-Top, Black body & hood	£6-9	☐
98123	1993	Open Top, Silver, Black hood	£6-9	☐

SAAB 96 Saloon

D711/1	1990	Dark Red..	£8-10	☐
D711/2	1990	Light Blue..	£8-10	☐
D712/1	1990	Rally car, Red, (Erik Carlsson)	£11-13	☐
96662	1991	Rally car, Light Blue, (Pat Moss)..........	£9-11	☐
99045	1993	Maroon..	£8-10	☐

TRIUMPH TR3a Sports Car

D736/1	1990	Hard-Top, Red, Black top	£8-10	☐
D737/1	1990	Open Soft-Top, see 99053 (below).........		☐
D738/1	1990	Closed Soft-Top, Yellow/Black..............	£8-10	☐
96300	1991	Closed Soft-Top, Red/Black, rack	£8-10	☐
99052	1993	Hard Top, Red body, Black top	£8-10	☐
99053	1990	Open Soft-Top, Pale Blue	£8-10	☐
99054	1993	Closed Soft-Top, Cream, Black top	£8-10	☐

Corgi Classics Gift Sets

Note: All Gift Sets include numbered certificates unless indicated by 'no Cert'.

Ref. No.	Year(s)	Set Name	Contents	Market Price Range	
D4/1	1989	'Transport of the Early 50s'	OB Coach & Routemaster Bus, 'HANTS & DORSET' Dark Green/Cream, 4,800	£35-40	☐
D7/1	1989	'ROYAL MAIL' Set	Bedford OB Box Van & Morris Minor Van in Post Office Red, 4,600	£36-42	☐
D9/1	1989	'SHELL 1910-1940'	Grattans Set, Thorneycroft Box Van 'SHELL OIL' , 'SHELL PETROL' & AEC Cabover Tanker 'YOU CAN BE SURE OF SHELL', 4,400	£20-25	☐
D13/1	1989	'Police Vans' Set	Two Morris 1000 Vans: a White one with 'DOG SECTION' and a Black version with 'GATESHEAD POLICE INCIDENT VAN', 4,500	£22-25	☐
D14/1	1989	'DANDY & BEANO' Set	2 Bedford CA Vans: a Yellow 'DANDY', and a Blue 'BEANO', 4,400	£30-40	☐
D15/1	1989	'GPO Telephones' Set	AEC Cabover & Morris Minor Van in Olive-Green GPO livery, 4,400	£33-38	☐
D16/1	1989	'RALLYING WITH FORD'	3 Fords: Yellow/White Zodiac (RN '21') Monaco Red Zephyr (RN '29') and a Pale Green Popular (no rally number). 3,400	£28-33	☐
D17/1	1989	'SHELL 1950-1960'	Yellow/Red Bedford OB Box Van & White/Yellow OB Pantechnicon, 5,000	£22-26	☐
D19/1	1989	'SHELL 1910-40' Set	No details	£15-18	☐
D23/1	1989	Ford Popular Van Set	Purple/Black van 'FRASER COOK Ltd', Black van 'LEWIS EAST Ltd', and a Light Blue/Black van 'SIGNSMITH'. Grattans Mail-Order Set, 5,000	£25-28	☐
D35/1	1990	'50th Anniversary of the Battle of Britain' Set	Airforce-Blue Bedford OB Coach & Morris Minor Van, Black Ford Zephyr (some Zephyrs were issued with Zodiac grilles). 13,000	£21-24	☐
D36/1	1990	'Racing Zephyrs' Set	Three Ford Zephyrs, 1: White body, Black bonnet, RN '47', 'ENGLAND' 2: Yellow body & wheels, RN '117', 3: Black body & wheels, RN '97', 8,000	£17-19	☐
D37/1	1990	'PENNY POST'	Red/Black fully closed Tram, '150th Anniversary', 'Penny Black' design	£16-18	☐
D41/1	1990	'BARTONS TRANSPORT'	Red Bedford OB Coach & Red/Cream AEC Double-Decker Bus, 12,000	£16-19	☐
D46/1	1990	'Vehicles of the '50s & '60s'	Maroon/Cream OB Box & Morris 'J' vans, 'BRITISH RAILWAYS', 13,000	£12-15	☐
D47/1	1990	'BEANO 1990'	'Bash Street Kids' AEC Bus, & 'Minnie the Minx' Morris J Van, 15,000	£17-20	☐
C49	1986	'Transport of The 30s' Set	'The TIMES' Thorneycroft Bus and Ford Model T Van, 8,900	£15-19	☐
C50	1987	'Transport of The 30s' Set	'London Markets' Set (5,000, no Cert) containing 3 Ford Model T Vans: 'SMITHFIELD', 'COVENT GARDEN' and 'BILLINGSGATE'	£15-20	☐
D51/1	1990	'GREENE KING' Set	Mid-Green AEC Tanker & Thorneycroft Beer Truck, Kays Mail-order, 4,900	£18-22	☐
D52/1	1990	'CHARRINGTONS' Set	Orange/Black AEC Tanker & Thorneycroft Truck, Kays Set, 5,000	£18-22	☐
D53/1	1990	4-piece 'Rally' Set	Blue Jaguar Mk.II ('3') White/Grey Ford Cortina (no RN) Red/White Austin-Healey ('66') Blue/Black MGA ('48') Kays Set, 4,500	£24-28	☐
D54/1	1990	4-piece 'Utilities' Set	Kay's Set with Bedford CA Van (Green, 'GAS'), Ford Popular Van (Red/Black), Morris J Van, (Blue/Black), Morris Minor Van (Green/Black) 5,000	£33-38	☐
Q55/1	1990	'YORK FAIR' Set	Bedford OB Coach with Yellow/Pink/White body and Clown design, and Bedford OB Pantechnicon in Cream/Blue, '225 Years', 5,300	£30-36	☐
Q57/1	1990	'The Northern Collection'	Contains Bedford OB Coach 'RIBBLE/STANDERWICK' and Q953/17 OB Pantechnicon 'SLUMBERLAND', 4,900	£18-22	☐
C67/1	1991	'Systeme' Rally Set	Export set	£10-13	☐
C67/2	1991	'Peugeot' Rally Set	Export set	£10-13	☐
D67/1	1990	'UNITED DAIRIES' Set	Orange AEC Cabover Van, White AEC Cabover Tanker, 7,500	£13-16	☐
C68	1987	'Transport of The 30s' Set	Thorneycroft & Ford T Vans 'KAYS', (Kays Mail-order Set) 5,000	£35-40	☐
C69	1987	'Transport of The 30s' Set	Mail-Order Set, Thorneycroft & Ford T Vans 'BRYANT & MAY', 10,000	£15-18	☐
D71/1	1989	'Ford Model 'T' Set	Kays Mail-Order Set: Blue 'SOMERLITE' & Red 'TEXACO' tankers with Red/Brown 'A1 SAUCE' van & White/Black 'APS MEDICINES' van. 2,500	£17-20	☐
D72/1	1989	'Minor & Popular Vans' Set	2 Morris Vans: 'RINGTONS TEA' & 'FRYS COCOA & CHOCOLATE', with 2 Ford Popular Vans: 'COLMANS MUSTARD' and 'BOWYERS WILTSHIRE SAUSAGES'. 3,400 (Kays Mail-Order Set)	£28-33	☐
D74/1	1989	'PICKFORDS' Set	OB Pantechnicon, Ford Popular & Morris Minor vans, Kays Set, 3,500	£60-70	☐
D75/1	1989	'Police Cars' Set	Kays Mail-Order 3-car Set: White Jaguar Mk.II, Blue/White 'PANDA' Morris Minor, and Black Ford Zephyr. 3,100	£35-40	☐
D82/1	1990	'CORGI ON THE MOVE'	Dark Blue/White Bedford OB Coach and Pantechnicon, (Corgi Club members model, personalised certification)	£18-23	☐
C88	1988	'Military Gift Set'	Thorneycroft Bus '2nd Division', Ford T Van 'Order of St.John', Kays Set, 6,000	£25-30	☐
C89	1988	'60 Years of Transport'	3 models: Thorneycroft Bus 'BAXTERS' with OB Coach 'HIGHLAND' and, Green/White Tram 'FORD FOR VALUE', Kays Mail-order set, 3,100	£140-160	☐
C90	1988	'Model T Ford Utility' Set	'ROYAL LAUNDRY' & 'SUNLIGHT' vans, Kays Mail-order, 8,600	£12-16	☐
C91	1989	'Morris Minor Vans' Set	3 vans: Green 'GRATTANS' van with Cream/Brown 'MITCHELLS' and Yellow 'TELEGRAPH & ARGUS', (Grattan's Mail-order LE, 5,000)	£65-75	☐
D94/1	1990	'WHITBREAD' Set	Bedford OB Box Van and Ford Model T Van in Brown/Black livery, 5,800	£12-15	☐
91356	1994	Eddie Stobart Gift Set	No details	£16-19	☐
93715	1992	3-piece Mini Set	Red, Silver and Green Minis sold only by Woolworths	£30-35	☐
96445	1993	'Goldfinger' Set	30th Anniversary of Goldfinger, James Bond Aston Martin	£22-24	☐
96990	1992	AEC Bus Set	Yellow/Dark Blue AEC Double-Decker and AEC Regal coach, both with AEC logos	£15-18	☐
96995	1992	'IAN ALLAN' Set	Red AEC Double Deck Bus and Green/White Bedford CA van	£22-24	☐
97049	1994	'YELLOWSTONE National Park'		£19-22	☐
97050	1993	Regent Bus Set	2 open top buses (White/Red and Cream/Blue)	£15-18	☐
97051	1993	Invictaway Set	Dark Blue Metrobus, Cream/Green Plaxton	£15-18	☐
97052	1994	'DEVON GENERAL' Set		£35-40	☐
97053	1994	'YORK Bros' Set		£17-19	☐
97055	1994	'THAMES VALLEY'	Original Omnibus	£17-19	☐
97056	1994	'CROSVILLE'	Original Omnibus	£17-19	☐
97057	1995	'SOUTHDOWN'	Leyland PSI/ECW & Leyland Leopard	£24-28	☐
97061	1991	'COVENTRY' Bus Set	A.E.C. Double-Decker ('VERNONS') and Bedford OB coach in Maroon	£14-16	☐
97063	1991	'YELLOWAYS' Set	Yellow/Orange Bedford OB coach and A.E.C. Regal coach	£17-20	☐
97064	1993	'BLACKPOOL' Bus Set	AEC Routemaster 'Travel Card', Metrobus 'Roller Coaster', Plaxton 'Seagull'	£18-11	☐
97065	1993	Stagecoach Set	Routemaster, Metrobus, Plaxton. White/Orange/Red/Blue livery	£18-22	☐
97066	1993	'Routemasters in Exile'	Scotland: Kelvin, Clydesdale, Perth, Strathtay	£18-22	☐
97067	1993	'Routemasters in Exile'	Midlands: K & M Gagg, East Midlands, Confidence, United Counties	£18-22	☐

Ref. No.				Market Price Range	
97068	1994	'Routemasters in Exile'.............	North: Burnley/Pendle, Manchester, East Yorkshire, Carlisle...............................	£18-22	☐
97069	1993	'WHITTLES' Set............	Burlingham Seagull and AEC Regal coaches in Dark Blue/Red livery........................	£22-24	☐
97070	1992	'SILVER SERVICE' Set..........	AEC Regal and Bedford OB coaches both in Silver and Blue livery..........................	£22-24	☐
97071	1992	'DEVON' Bus Set	AEC Double-Decker (Red/White) & AEC Regal coach (Cream/Green).....................	£20-24	☐
97072	1992	'GOSPORT & FAREHAM'.....	AEC DD & Regal coach in Spruce-Green/Black 'PROVINCIAL' livery......................	£22-27	☐
97074	1994	'Routemasters in Exile'.............	South: Southampton, Kentish, Capital, Southend...............................	£18-22	☐
97075	1992	'SOUTH WALES' Bus Set	Maroon/Red AEC Regal and Cream/Red OB Coach	£19-23	☐
97076	1992	'W.ALEXANDER' Bus Set ...	Red Guy Arab double decker and Mid-Blue Leyland Tiger	£28-33	☐
97077	1992	'EAST LANCASHIRE' Set.....	Red/Black Guy Arab and Dark Green Leyland Tiger..............................	£22-25	☐
97078	1993	'Corkills - de Vanenburg'.........	Bedford coaches in Maroon/Black, and Turquoise/Black, 'Hotel Kasteel', (Dutch)	£19-22	☐
97079	1993	'PREMIER' Set.......................	70th Anniversary Set (Tiger and OB)..............................	£22-26	☐
97086	1992	'FREEBORNS'........................	Bedford OB Pantechnicon, Grattans mail-order..............................	£13-16	☐
97106	1992	'BIBBYS'	Bedford OB Coach, 'Ingleton', Kays mail-order................................	£13-16	☐
97107	1992	'MURGATROYD'	Bedford OB Coach, Grattans mail-order................................	£13-16	☐
97185	1992	'WEST RIDING'	AEC Regal Coach, Grattans mail-order................................	£13-16	☐
97200	1991	'BRS' Set	Green/Black Bedford OB Box & Morris 'J' vans. Kays LE 5,000	£15-19	☐
97331	1992	La France Set	Green open backed and Yellow closed Fire Engines	£24-28	☐
97351	1992	AEC Ladder Set	AEC Ladder Truck and Bedford CA Van 'Bristol'	£24-28	☐
97391	1992	AEC Pumper Set	AEC Fire Engine and Bedford CA Van 'Bristol'...............................	£24-28	☐
97541	1991	'ROYAL MAIL' Set	3 Minor Vans	£24-27	☐
97680	1991	'30 Years of the 'E' type'	Light Grey open & Red closed 'E' types...............................	£16-18	☐
97681	1991	'Stirling's Choice' Set	Silver Austin-Healey ('7') & Green Jaguar XK120 (open) special box.............	£15-18	☐
97690	1991	'Ferrari' Set	Light Green ('15'), Dark Blue ('5'), Light Grey ('10'), Kays LE 5,000	£20-25	☐
97695	1992	'Abingdon' Set	Dark Green Morris 'J' van 'BMC', White MGA ('324'), Red MGA ('38')..................	£23-27	☐
97696	1993	'R.A.C.' Set	Bedford CA van and Mini Cooper............................	£15-18	☐
97697	1993	Leicestershire & Rutland Police Set	Morris 1000 Van and Jaguar Mk.II, both in White with Black 'Police' logos............	£14-16	☐
97698	1993	'Metropolitan Police' Set........	Bedford OB Coach and Morris 1000 Car...............................	£16-18	☐
97700	1991	'Jaguar Through the Years'	Black 'E' type ('110'), White open XK120, Light Blue Mk.II...................	£20-24	☐
?	1991	'Jaguar XK120' Set	Cream (closed, '65'), White (open, '166'), Green (closed, '64'), GUS 5,000	£16-18	☐
97701	1991	'Racing 'E' types' Set	Grey (Black top, '170'), Red (Black top, '108'), special box, 7,500	£16-18	☐
97702	1992	'Jaguar Collection'.................	A Maroon Mk.II, a Green XK120 and a Red 'E' type, on wood plinth	£20-24	☐
97706	1993	Jaguar XK120 Set	'First Time Out'. 3 XK120s (Red '8', White '7', Blue '6')........................	£17-20	☐
97708	1993	Tour de France Set..................	Jaguar Mk.II ('82'), Ferrari GTO ('165'), Mini-Cooper ('8')..................	£17-20	☐
97709	1993	Alpine Rally Set	Ford Cortina ('29'), Austin-Healey ('95'), Mini-Cooper ('38')....................	19-23	☐
97712	1992	'Monte Carlo Mini' Set............	3 Red/White Minis, Rns '37', '52', '177'	£18-22	☐
97713	1992	'The Italian Job'	3 Minis from the film - Red, White, Blue	£24-27	☐
97714	1994	'D-DAY' Set..........................		£36-44	☐
97721	1994	'Durham Police' Set.................		£17-19	☐
97722	1994	'S.Glamorgan Police' Set........		£17-19	☐
97730	1992	'Austin-Healey' Set.................	3 competition Austin-Healeys, Red ('76'), Green ('18'), Green ('414')................	£22-27	☐
97735	1992	'CUMBRIAN' Set....................	Bedford OB Van plus Morris 'J' Van in Red and White......................	£16-19	☐
97740	1991	'The TIMES' Set.....................	Contains Bedford CA van and Morris Minor Van............................	£11-13	☐
97741	1991	'ISLAND TRANSPORT'........	Two Bedford OB coaches: 'J.M.T.' and 'PIONEER' liveries	£11-13	☐
97742	1991	'JOHN SMITHS BREWERY'	Contains Thorneycroft Beer Truck and A.E.C. Tanker	£15-18	☐
97746	1991	'TOYMASTER' Set.................	Yellow/Red Bedford 'CA' & Blue 'CORGI' Morris 'J' vans, (own shops only)........	£15-19	☐
97747	1991	'WEBSTERS' Brewery Set......	Blue/Red AEC Cabover Tanker & Thorneycroft Truck, GUS LE 5,000	£22-26	☐
97749	1991	'BRITISH RAIL' Gift Set	Fordson 8 and Bedford 'CA' van in Maroon/Cream livery, special box	£14-18	☐
97750	1992	'EAST KENT' Set...................	Bedford OB and AEC Regal coaches in Dark Red livery......................	£16-20	☐
97751	1992	'BASS' Brewery Set	Red/Black Thorneycroft & Blue/Black Ford 'T' Van, (Kays)......................	£17-20	☐
97752	1992	'RUDDLES' Brewery Set	Bedford OB Box Van and Thorneycroft Beer Truck............................	£17-20	☐
97753	1992	'TERRYS of YORK' Set.........	Thorneycroft Box Van plus Ford Model 'T' Van	£13-16	☐
97754	1993	'LMS Railway' Set..................	AEC Cabover and Thorneycroft van in Maroon/Black 'LMS' livery............	£19-22	☐
97755	1992	'WHITBREAD' Brewery Set....	AEC Tanker and Thorneycroft van in Dark Brown/Black......................	£23-26	☐
97765	1993	'STRATHBLAIR' Set..............	'Wiles' Bedford coach and 'Forbes' Morris 'J' van............................	£14-17	☐
97781	1993	'TATE & LYLE'.....................	Foden Tanker and Bedford OB Van	£30-40	☐
97885	1995	'CHIPPERFIELDS'.................	Scammell, Pole Trailer & Caravan	NGPP	☐
97888	1995	'CHIPPERFIELDS'.................	Foden Pole Truck & Caravan	NGPP	☐
97891	1992	'BILLY SMARTS'...................	White/Green *'Circus'* Truck and Trailer..............................	£18-22	☐
97892	1993	'S.HOUSEMAN'.....................	Brown/White Truck and Trailer, *'York'*..............................	£18-22	☐
97893	1993	'J.AYERS'.............................	Red Truck and Trailer, *'Modern Amusements'*...............................	£18-22	☐
97920	1994	'EDWARDS'..........................	Scammell and two Trailers	£50-60	☐
98759	1991	'DANDY' Set.........................	Morris 'J' van and Bedford 'CA' van	£12-15	☐
98960	1992	'BEANO' Set	Morris 1000 van ('Biffo') and Morris 'J' van ('Beryl The Peril').............	£16-19	☐
98965	1993	'EAGLE' Set	Volkswagen van and Bedford CA van	£14-17	☐
98970	1992	'X Men' Set	Bedford Van plus Morris 'J' Van	£14-17	☐
98972	1992	'Spiderman' Set	Morris 'J' Van and Morris 1000 Van	£14-17	☐
98973	1992	'Captain America' Set	White/Red VW Van and Two-tone Blue Ford Popular Van............................	£14-17	☐
032/A/ 96041	1991	The Classic British Sports Car Collection'	8 cars on wooden plinth: 96041, 96060, 96160, 96180, 96220, 96300, 99051, 99053. Originally a Sunday magazine direct-mail offer, then through Corgi Club	£30-35	☐
	1993	'Premier Albanian' Set	Leyland Tiger and Bedford OB Coaches with 'PREMIER' logo	£17-19	☐
?	1993	La France Pumper Set	'SCOTTDALE' (open, Green) and 'SOUTH RIVER' (closed, Orange)......................	£30-35	☐
	1993	'Connoisseur Collection 'E'-type Jaguars..................	One open, one closed, Chrome plated, Black plinth, Black box. CLE of 5,000 direct-mailed	£48-55	☐

'Original Omnibus Company' ('00' scale, 1/76)

AEC REGENT II/WEYMANN Double Deck

97814	1995	'LONDON TRANSPORT'	£8-11	☐

AEC REGENT Mk.5/MCW ORION Double Deck

97943	1995	'DOUGLAS CORPORATION'	£8-11	☐

AEC RELIANCE/MARSHALL Single Deck

97904	1995	'LEICESTER CITY'	£8-11	☐

AEC RELIANCE/WEYMANN Single Deck

97130	1994	'OXFORD'	£8-11	☐
97900	1994	'DEVON GENERAL'	£8-11	☐
97902	1995	'POTTERIES'	£8-11	☐

BRISTOL 'K' Double Deck

97851	1995	'HANTS & DORSET'	£8-11	☐
97854	1995	'WESTERN NATIONAL'	£8-11	☐
97856	1995	'WEST YORKSHIRE'	£8-11	☐

BRISTOL K5G/ECW Double Deck

97859	1995	'BRISTOL TRAMWAYS'	£8-11	☐

BRISTOL K6B/ECW Double Deck

97858	1995	'CALEDONIAN'	£8-11	☐

BRISTOL 'L' Single Deck

97850	1995	'MERTHYR TYDFIL'	£8-11	☐
97852	1995	'MAIDSTONE & DISTRICT'	£8-11	☐
97855	1995	'UNITED AUTO'	£8-11	☐

BRISTOL L5G/ECW Single Deck

97860	1995	'BATH TRAMWAYS'	£8-11	☐
97867	1995	'NORTH WESTERN'	£8-11	☐
97868	1995	'EASTERN COUNTIES'	£8-11	☐
97869	1995	'LINCOLNSHIRE'	£8-11	☐

B.U.T. TROLLEYBUS/WEYMANN

97811	1995	'NOTTS & DERBY'	£8-11	☐
97813	1995	'BRIGHTON CORPORATION'	£8-11	☐

LEYLAND LEOPARD Single Deck

97835	1994	'RIBBLE'	£8-11	☐
?	1994	'MIDLAND RED' (Corgi Show model)	NGPP	☐

Gift Sets included in the Classic Gift Sets listing.

LEYLAND LEOPARD/WILLBROOK Single Deck

97903	1994	'LONDONDERRY & LOUGH SWILLY'	£8-11	☐
97905	1995	'SAFEWAY SERVICES'	£8-11	☐

LEYLAND PS1/ECW Single Deck

97836	1995	'EAST YORKSHIRE'	£8-11	☐
97838	1995	'BIRCH BROS'	£8-11	☐

LEYLAND PD1A/ECW Double Deck

97836	1995	'EASTERN COUNTIES'	£8-11	☐
97837	1995	'NORTH WESTERN'	£8-11	☐

LEYLAND PD2/MCW ORION Double Deck

97941	1995	'St HELENS CORPORATION'	£8-11	☐
97945	1995	'RIBBLE'	£8-11	☐

LEYLAND PS2/MCW ORION/BMMO Double Deck

97944	1995	'NEWCASTLE CORPORATION'	£8-11	☐

ORIGINAL OMNIBUS ACCESSORIES

?	1994	Bus Garage (Corgi direct mail)...............	£7-10	☐

Specification List of Bodywork Variations

ECW SINGLE DECK
Bristol L:- Bristol Radiator, Mudguards
Leyland PSI:- Leyland Radiator, Mudguards

ECW DOUBLE DECK
Bristol K:- Bristol Radiator, Mudguards
Leyland PDI:- Leyland Radiator, Mudguards

WEYMANN
Regent II:- AEC Exposed Radiator, Mudguards, Headlights, Bonnet
Trolleybus:- Booms, Side Vents, Flat Front, Headlights

MCW ORION
Regent V:- AEC Enclosed Radiator, Mudguards, Tin Front, Headlights, Bonnet
BMMO:- Leyland Enclosed Radiator, Mudguards, Tin Front, Headlights, Bonnet
St. Helens:- Leyland Enclosed Radiator, Mudguards, Tin Front, Headlights, Bonnet
Leyland PD2:- Leyland Exposed Radiator, Mudguards, Headlights, Bonnet.

WHEN REPLYING TO ADVERTISEMENTS PLEASE MENTION JOHN RAMSAY'S CATALOGUE

1995 Classics July–December New Issues

Ref No.	Description
FIRE	
97399	Simon Snorkel – Cleveland County
97361	AEC Ladder – New Zealand
97337	Mini Van – Fawley refinery
PUBLIC TRANSPORT	
97341	Leyland Atlantean – Maidstone & District
97336	Daimler CW – Glasgow
97315	Guy Arab – London Wartime
97316	Karrier W – Ipswich
97363	Weymann Bus – Edinburgh
97364	Weymann Bus – North Western
97347	Bedford OB – Maltese
97340	Burlingham Seagull – Trent
97342	Burlingham Seagull – West Coast
97179	Burlingham Seagull – Banfields
98165	Ford Cortina – London Transport
97365	Blackpool Tram
96888	Morris J Van – Southdown
ROAD TRANSPORT	
97334	Atkinson 8 wheel rigid/crates – Lucozade
97366	Atkinson 8 wheel/trailer/load – Tennant
97367	Highwayman Round Tanker – Pointer
97335	Scammell Scarab – Eskimo Foods
97368	Highwayman Crane – Pickfords
97329	Bedford Artic – BRS Red
97328	AEC Eliptical Tanker – Major
97369	AEC Truck/Trailer – Eddie Stobart
97327	Atkinson 8 Wheel Rigid – E Stobart
BREWERY RANGE	
97370	AEC 4 wheel flatbed/barrels – Federation
97371	Bedford O Van – Cameron
97319	ERF Tanker – Bass Worthington
97318	Scammell Scarab/Barrels – Websters

Ref No.	Description
97317	Foden Chains/Barrels – Scottish & Newcastle
97372	Atkinson Tanker – Mackeson
97309	Foden 8 Wheel Rigid/Load – BRS – Special for Classic Toys Magazine
CHARACTER	
96655	James Bond Aston Martin – 1/43 Original
96656	James Bond Aston Martin – 1/43 Gold
96657	James Bond Aston Martin 1/36
LIGHT COMMERCIAL	
97772	Mini Van – Burberry's
97771	Mini Van – Cavendish Woodhouse
97770	Mini Van – Hamley's
MORRIS RANGE	
97343	Traveller – Bomb Disposal
97345	Pick Up – Tarmac
97346	Pick Up – Blue Circle
97344	Conv. Open – Black
97379	Traveller – Collector Club
GUS MAIL ORDER	
97897	Highway 2 Pole Trailers – Billy Smarts for GUS Catalogue
ORIGINAL OMNIBUS	
97095	Lancashire Holiday Set
97096	Capital & Highlands Set
97097	Bridges & Spires Set
DONNINGTON COLLECTION	
97378	Surtees TS9B
97377	Lotus
97376	Ferrari 312
97375	Shadow DN1
97374	Surtess TS9
97373	Hesketh 308
	Ford Cortina – Corgi Rally

RECOMMENDED ADDITIONAL READING ON CORGI CLASSICS

The Catalogue Editor is indebted to George Hatt the author of 'The Corgi Classics Collectors Guide' for providing much invaluable information. Classics collectors are strongly advised to purchase a copy of George's book for it contains considerable additional information plus colour photographs of rare items.
Send to: 16 Horse Road, Hilperton, Trowbridge, Wiltshire, BA14 7PE. Tel: 01255 768821.

Late New Issues

ERF Celebration Day Model. Issued to mark the Corgi Company becoming independent again on 7th August 1995. (Available January 1996).

Classic Toys Magazine promotional model. Foden Lorry 'BRITISH ROAD SERVICES'. Limited Edition of 5000 (Certificated). Available October 1995.

Corgi Donnington Collection; a re-issued series of famous Formula One cars of the seventies
97373 Hesketh 308/Ford Cosworth V8, Jackie Oliver
97374 Surtees TS9/Ford Cosworth V8, John Surtees
97375 Shadow DN1/Ford Cosworth V8, James Hunt
97376 Ferrari 312B/Ford Cosworth V8, Mario Andretti
97377 Lotus 72D/Ford Cosworth V8, Emerson Fittipaldi
97378 Surtees TS9B/Ford Cosworth V8, Mike Hailwood

1995 Corgi Collector Club Model Morris Traveller with Corgi logos, see picture inside rear cover.

New 1/18th scale Rover MGF launched in March 1995.
Variations:- MGF 1.8i VVC; Open and closed top versions; Full range of MGF colours. Retail Price £25.

Chipperfield Circus Figures. Six White metal figures representing a prominent artiste in the circus world.
Set 1 issued in Spring 1995
Set 2 issued in Autumn 1995
Both sets hand painted.

Corgi Cameos

A range of low cost models, which were first issued in 1990 as 'The Village Cameo Collection' and individually sold through retail outlets. In addition they were also used as promotional models. In 1992 Corgi Direct became responsible for sales, and the models have been marketed in sets of ten via press and TV publicity campaigns and have been released in a wide variety of colour shades and promotional logos.

At this stage it is impossible to provide price guidance for either the individual models or the sets, some of which are limited editions of 10,000 pieces. The following listing provides a basic collectors listing. Many other colour variations exist and collectors requiring this information should refer to the recommended reading at the end of the section.

SALOON CARS
(2nd colours shown, denote roof colour)

Citroen 2CV – Cream/Brown, Blue/Grey with/without 'KELLOGGS' logo; Green/Grey, Dark Red/Black with 'CADBURYS' logo, Bright Red/Black or Yellow/Grey.

Mini Cooper Blue, Cream (2nd Corgi Convention promotional). Grey, Dark Green – Cadbury 'Sixties' Set, Light Green, Red/White 'FINA PETROL', All Red (no logo), Purple/White 'DRINKA PINTA MILKADAY' Cadburys 'Sixties' Set, White or Yellow.

Morris Minor Blue, Brown, Green with/without 'KELLOGGS' logo, Green (Cadburys Sixties Set), Pink or White.

Volkswagen Beetle Beige, Blue, Maroon, Orange Cadburys 'Sixties' Set, Dark Orange, Off-White or Yellow with/without 'KELLOGGS' logo.

COMMERCIAL VEHICLES
A.E.C. Cabover Van – Logos issued

'ANGLO PAK' – 'FINA' Set 3
'BOUNTY' – Chocolate Set (10,000)
'CADBURY'S' – CO-OP Set
'CADBURY'S' – Set 97426
'CADBURY'S DAIRY MILK' – Set 97436
'CAMWALL'
'CARTER PATERSON'
'CHARRINGTONS'
'COLMANS MUSTARD'
'CRUNCHIE' – Set 97435
'DRUMMER DYES' – 'FINA' Set
'DUNLOP TYRES'
'FYFFES'
'G.W.R. PARCELS'
JOHN KNIGHT – 'FINA' Set
'LIFEBUOY' – 'Unilever' Set (10,000)
'MARS' – Chocolate Set (10,000)
'MERRY CHRISTMAS' – Christmas Set (20,000)
'METROPOLITAN RAILWAY' – Set 97833
'OMO' – 'Unilever' Set (10,000)
'PEEKFREANS' – 'FINA' Set 2
'PICKFORDS'
'ROYAL MAIL' – 'ROYAL MAIL' Set
SETH WILKINSON — Set C26
'STABILO SCHWAN' – German promotional
'THE HOLLY & THE IVY' – Christmas Set
'J. WARD'
'WHITBREAD TROPHY' – Whitbread Set
'3rd DIVISION' – D. Day Set (10,000)
'12th CORPS' – D. Day Set (10,000)

BEDFORD BUS

'B.E.A.'
'B.O.A.C.'
'BLUEBIRD'
'BOURNEVILLE' – Set 97435
'CLASSIC CARS'
'CROSVILLE'
DEVON GENERAL – FINA Set 1
DOROTHY HOLBROOK
'EASTERN NATIONAL' – FINA Set 3 with/without 3934 fleet No.
'FIRE DEPT' 3 – FINA Set 2
'GUARDS ARMOURED DIVISION' – D. Day Set (10,000)
'HEINZ BEANS'
'KIT-KAT' – Chocolate Set (10,000)
'LUX' – Unilever Set (10,000)
'OSRAM LAMPS'
'QUALITY STREET' – Chocolate Set (10,000)
'RAPID ROAD'
'RIVER VALLEY'
'SILENT NIGHT' – Christmas Set (20,000)
'SOUTHERN RAILWAY' – Set 97833
'STELLA ARTOIS' – Whitbread Set (10,000)
'VIM' – Unilever Set (10,000)

'WHITBREAD' – Whitbread Set (10,000)
'34th TANK BRIGADE' – D. Day Set (10,000)

MODEL T-FORD VAN

'AERO' – Chocolate Set (10,000)
'BLACK MAGIC' – Chocolate Set (10,000)
'CADBURY'S ROSES' – Set 97436
'CADBURY'S THE CHOCOLATE' – On Pack Offers
'COMMANDO BRIGADE' – D. Day Set (10,000)
'CORGI' – Set 97426
'CORGI' – Gaydon Show Special
'CHUPA CHUPS'
'CITY AND SUBURBAN'
G. DAVID – FINA Set 3
'DULUX PAINT'
'DONCASTER MUSEUM'
'FRESHBAKE'
'GRATTANS' – Set C26
'HUDSONS SOAP' – Unilever Set (10,000)
'JOHNNIE WALKER' (Gold or Maroon jacket)
'KING OF THE ROAD'
'KLEENEZE'
'KELLOGGS'
L.N.E.R. – Set 97833
'LANDBRO' – FINA Set 3
'L.M.S.'
'LONDON MAIL'
'LIPTONS TEA'
'MACKESON STOUT' – Whitbread Set (10,000)
'MURPHY'S IRISH STOUT' – Whitbread Set (10,000)
'NATIONAL GARDEN FESTIVAL'
'NOEL' – Christmas Set (20,000)
'PERSIL' – Unilever Set (10,000)
'PICKFORDS' – Pickfords Set
'PRINCES SPREAD'
'RIPLEY CO-OP' – Ripley 'Co-op' Set
'ROBERTSON'
'ROYAL MAIL' – Royal Mail Set
ROYAL FAMILY Issues – H.R.H. The Queen; H.R.H. Prince Phillip; H.R.H. Prince Charles; H.R.H. Lady Diana
'SEASONS GREETINGS' – Christmas Set (20,000)
'SMITHS CRISPS' – FINA Set 2
'THE SKETCH' – FINA Set 1
'WEBSTERS'
'YULETIDE GREETINGS' – Christmas Set (20,000)
'ZEBRA POLISH'
'2ND ARMY' – D. Day Set (10,000)

MORRIS TANKER

W. BUTLER – FINA Set 3
CADBURY'S – Set 97426
CADBURY'S – Set 97436
'CARLESS CAPEL'
'CHRISTMAS CHEER' – Christmas Set (20,000)
'CHRISTMAS WISHES' – Christmas Set (20,000)
'CO-OP' – Ripley 'Co-op' Set
'CORNISH CREAM'
'DOUBLE DIAMOND'
'ELF PETROL'
'FINA PETROL' – FINA Sets 1 or 2
'FLOWERS FINE ALE' – Whitbread Set (10,000)
'FOSTERS LAGER'
'GALAXY' – Chocolate Set (10,000)
'HEINEKEN LAGER' – Whitbread Set (10,000)
'KNIGHTS CASTILE' – Unilever Set (10,000)
'MILKY WAY' – Chocolate Set (10,000)
'RINSO' – Unilever Set (10,000)
'SHELL'
'SOMERLITE OIL'
'7TH or 79TH ARMOURED DIVISION' – D. Day Set (10,000)

MORRIS PICK UP TRUCK

'B.B' – FINA Set 3
'BEACH GROUPS' – D. Day Set (10,000)
'BODDINGTONS' – Whitbread Set (10,000)
'CADBURY'S DRINKING CHOCOLATE' – Ripley 'Co-op' Set
'CADBURY'S FRUIT & NUT' – Set 97435
'CHARLES WELLS'
'FERROCRETE' – FINA Set 2
'GAYMERS CIDER'
'G.W.R.' – Set 97833
'HARRY FIRTH' – Set C26

'MILKY BAR' – Chocolate Set (10,000)
'MORRIS COMMERCIALS'
'ROLO' – Chocolate Set (10,000)
'PEACE ON EARTH' – Christmas Set (20,000)
'J. SMITH'
'SUNLIGHT SOAP' – Unilever Set (10,000)
'SURF'
'SUTTONS SEEDS'
"THORLEY'S – FINA Set 1
'WELSH BITTER' – Whitbread Set (10,000)

RECOMMENDED ADDITIONAL READING ON CORGI CAMEOS

The Editor is indebted to George Hatt author of 'The Corgi Classics Collectors Guide' for providing much invaluable information. George's Guide contains a detailed listing of all the 'Corgi Cameo' models, colours and variations and collectors are strongly advised to obtain a copy. Send to: Digbys Publications, 16 Horse Road, Hilperton, Trowbridge, Wiltshire, BA14 7PE. Tel: 01255 768821.

Corgi Toys Auction Results

LACY SCOTT AUCTION RESULTS

Display Shelf for 'Classic Cars of the 50's, M **£45**
Chipperfields Circus Crane Truck and cage (12), BDG **£50**
James Bond Aston Martin DB5 (261), BDM **£60**
Marks & Spencer Issue Wings Flying Team (8001), BM **£90**
Marks & Spencer Issue Wings Flying School (8101), BM **£115**
Lotus Mark II Le Mans racing car (151), G **£50**
Tarzan Gift Set (36), BM **£75**
Gift Set 48 Car Transporter with six cars (251) Hillman Imp, metallic green instead of blue (204), Mini Minor metallic blue and 321 RN21 (BM) **£480**
Grand Prix Silverstone Pits Kit (603) BDM **£40**
Silverstone Press Box BDM **£45**
Silverstone Timekeepers Box BDM **£40**
Musical Walls Ice Cream Van (474), BM **£80**

WALLIS & WALLIS AUCTION RESULTS

803 Beatles Yellow Submarine original display window box, with inner display packing. Mint. **£150**
Gift Set 23: Chipperfields Circus containing long wheel base Land Rover (503), crane truck (1121) 2 x animal cages (1123) with 2 lions and 2 polar bears, elephant and cage on trailer (607) and Bedford giraffe transporter with 2 giraffes, original box and packing. VGC-Mint **£360**
336 James Bond Toyota 2000 GT white, red aerial and pennant missile firing mechanism in boot, complete with James Bond in blue and firing pistol and driver 'AKI' in grey. Model from the film 'You Only Live Twice' in original packet (packet torn). In original picture box and packing. VGC **£190**
469 Routemaster Double Decker Bus red, 'Mettoy Welcomes Swiss Buyers to Corgi Factory Swansea May 1977' adverts, boxed. VGC-Mint............. **£145**
469 Routemaster Double Decker Bus red, 'Vedes Visit to Mettoy Swansea 12th June 1978' adverts. Bus No 12, boxed. Mint. **£150**
471 Silver Jubilee Routemaster LT Double Decker Bus silver, 'Qualitoys Visit to Northampton March 1977' adverts, boxed. Mint **£150**
471 Silver Jubilee Routemaster LT Double Decker Bus silver, 'Marks and Spencer Visit to the Mettoy Company Swansea' adverts, boxed, Mint... **£150**
Original 1960s Corgi Display Cabinet measuring 72" x 36" x 4½", wood construction with 'Corgi Toys' and logo to top, complete with 6 original and 6 additional shelves. GC to VGC **£280**
Corgi Major Gift Set No 4 'Bristol Bloodhound' guided missile with launching ramp, loading trolley and RAF Land Rover, original box. GC **£100**
Tour De France Gift Set 13: with Renault R16, Paramount film unit and cyclist, original display box. Mint **£100**
Chipperfields Land Rover and Elephant Cage Trailer Gift Set 19: complete with cage, elephant, boxed with inner display box and original packing. Mint **£120**
Volkswagen Racing Club Gift Set 6: including Breakdown truck, trailer and Cooper Maserati F1 Racing car, original display box. Mint **£100**
Corgi Major Gift Set No 16: Ecurie Ecosse Racing Car Transporter and 3 racing Cars, transporter in dark metallic blue with orange 'Ecurie Ecosse', a Vanwall F1 GP (150S) red, No 25; a Lotus Mk Eleven Le Mans racing car (151A) in blue No 7; and a BRM F1 Grand Prix racing car (152S) in turquoise, No 7. Original boxes. VGC **£250**

227 Morris Mini Cooper competition model, blue, white roof, white bonnet with crossed flags, No 1 to sides, red interior, associated box. VGC to Mint. **£260**
227 Morris Mini Cooper competition model in blue with white roof, all blue bonnet with crossed flags, No 7 to sides, yellow interior, original box. VGC to Mint. **£260**

VECTIS MODELS AUCTION RESULTS

BOXED CARS

204 Morris Minor royal blue/whizz wheels, A, yellow & red window boxed **£120**
313 Ford Cortina GXL met. pale green/black with Graham Hill figure & box, scarce, A **£100**
513 Citroen Safari 'Alpine Rescue' with St Bernard & guide, sledge & skis, A **£220**
200M Ford Consul Saloon Flywheel mid blue, lovely A with white wall tyres applied over FSP (easily removable but an official Corgi accessory), with early catalogue leaflet in B box **£110**
202M Morris Cowley mid green/with FSP/flywheel, A in B box **£110**
204M Rover 90 met. green/FSP/flywheel, B + in C box, very scarce colour **£110**
227 Morris Mini Cooper blue/white bonnet & roof/bonnet flags/red interior/SP, thin No 1, A in B box **£220**
227 Morris Mini Cooper lemon/white roof & bonnet/flags/1/red interior/SP, B + in B box. **£150**
227 Morris Mini Cooper lemon/white roof & bonnet/flags/7/red interior/SP, B + ... **£180**
236 Austin A60 'Driving School' extremely rare pre-production version in grey with maroon side stripe & interior/yellow plastic roof wheel with 'Corgi Motor School' cast into sides/two interior figures/SP, A in B standard box with Corgi 'Junior Highway Code' leaflet, brilliant! **£750**
317 1964 Monte Carlo Rally Mini Cooper 'S', red/37/pink roof with spotlight/ lemon interior/SP, A in C 'plain' box, rare **£210**
318 1965 Monte Carlo Rally Mini Cooper 'S' red/52/white roof/sump guard, B + to A in 317 'plain' printed box. **£150**
321 1966 Monte Carlo Rally BMC Mini Cooper 'S', red/2/roof signatures/sump guard/SP, good B in B 'flashed' box (one end flap is C) **£200**
322 Rover 2000 International Rally Finish white/black bonnet/21/cast wheels, A in similar box and condition to last lot, very scarce **£160**
333 1966 RAC/SUN Rally BMC Mini Cooper 'S' red/white roof/21/sump guard/SP, A in B+ mounted 'flashed' box, very scarce **£280**
339 1967 Monte Carlo Rally BMC Mini Cooper 'S' Austin grille, red/177/white roof with roof rack and two spare wheels/sump guard/cast wheels, A in B + card picture box **£120**
440 Ford Cortina Estate 'Golfing' red/brown panels/white interior, all A in B box. **£95**
275 Rover 2000 TC white/red interior/black spare wheel cover on boot/cast wheels/'golden jacks', A in B + pictorial window box, rare **£150**
31 The 'Riviera' Set with Buick Riviera pale blue/red interior/wire wheels/hook/ red trailer/FSP/dolphin cruiser with sailor plus water skier, all A on B + inner pictorial stand in B box with instructions. **£280**
321 1965 Monte Carlo Mini Cooper 'S' red body & interior/white roof/52/SP, A in B + box, scarce **£180**
321 1965 Monte Carlo Mini Cooper 'S' same condition as above but in earlier flashed 317 box with 'Special Release MONTE CARLO WINNER' label, red body & interior/white roof/52/SP **£360**

323 Citroen in 1965 Monte Carlo livery, light blue/white roof, A in B + box £100
334 Mini Cooper 'Magnifique' met. green/sunshine, roof/CW, A pictorial window boxed £40
Gift Set No 16 Ecurie Ecosse Racing Transporter light blue letters/met. dark blue body/SP, B + with **No 150S Vanwall** red, **No 151A Lotus Eleven** blue and **No 152S BRM** turquoise, all B + in B to B + boxes, inner lining in B +, box is B, scarce £270

NOVELTY, FILM & TV RELATED
336 James Bond Toyota 2000 GT with secret documents, A to A + in A box £200
261 James Bond's Aston Martin gold complete with secret instructions, spare figure, badge and catalogue, all A with B + inner stand in A box £110
808 'Basil Brush and His Car' A to A + boxes £130
852 'Magic Roundabout' Carousel 4 children & Dylan, working order, A to A + in good C picture box (could be improved to virtually A), very scarce .. £440
267 Batmobile First Issue A to A + with all inner packing, unopened instructions, in B picture box £180
336 James Bond Toyota 2000 GT complete with sealed secret instructions etc, all A but boot lid stays open £120
497 Man from U.N.C.L.E. with ring, all A in B + box £110
426 Mobile Booking Office A apart from slight roof rubs in B + to A box £110
1139 Scammell Menagerie Trailer B + to A, outer yellow & blue windows box is C £160
Gift Set 12 Circus Crane Truck and Animal Cage, B + to A, long picture box is B £120
107 Batboat & **No 267 Batmobile** later version with **Batman** alone, both A in B striped window box and B plain window box respectively £80
266 Chitty, Chitty, Bang, Bang original issue with 4 figures, wings, inner stand & scene in pictorial window box, all A, box is B £180
267 Batmobile scarce 1st issue with BATWHEELS both figures, lovely A on inner pictorial stand with sealed instructions, outer picture box is B to C £150
277 Monkeemobile with **The Monkees** cast wheels, A to A + window box £700
851 Magic Roundabout Train with Mr Rusty, 2 children and Dougal, A in B to B + window box £200
851 Magic Roundabout Train with Dylan, 4 children and Dougal, B + to A with inner lining in B to C picture box, rare £330
Gift Set No 40 'The Avengers' with Steed and red Bentley, Emma Peel and white Lotus/3 plastic umbrellas, inner pictorial stand, all B + to A in B pictorial box, scarce £345
Glass Shop Display Cabinet with 'Corgi Toys' moulded into glass, 3 shelves £320
9004 'World of Wooster' Bentley with Jeeves and Wooster figures, A in B pictorial window box £140
Metal Box Shop Sign with original box, lovely A, box is B, rare £330

MILITARY
1133 US Troop Transporter white stars etc, A in B + 'end flap' box £110
1134 Bedford 'S' Type US Army Fuel Tanker 'NO SMOKING' etc/SP, B + to A with inner lining in B + box, very scarce £160
Gift Set 4 Bloodhound Missle C; **Launching Ramp** B +; **Loading Trolley** B +; and **RAF Land Rover** FSP, A, inner lining is B, repaired box lid is C, scarce set £140

CORGI ROCKETS
from HM SECRET SERVICE all in sealed bubble packs on pictorial cards with numbered key
923 Ford Escort Stock Car white/whizz wheels/7 .... £120
925 Ford Capri as above but No 6 .... £100
928 Mercedes 280SL black/black plastic wheels/ SPECTRE label £120

COMMERCIALS
403M Bedford Van 'KLG' with flywheel, red/FSP, lovely A in B + blue box, very scarce £120
421 Bedford Van 'Evening Standard' black/silver roof/FSP, B + to A boxed £85

421 Bedford Van 'Evening Standard' black lower body/silver reminder, A in B + to A box, scarce £170
422 Bedford Van 'Corgi Toys' yellow/blue roof/FSP, B + to A in B box £130
422 Bedford Van 'Corgi Toys' blue lower body/yellow remainder, A, very scarce £440
422 Bedford Van 'Corgi Toys' blue body/yellow roof, B in B + box, rare £320

EXPORT ISSUES
All in UK issue boxes unless stated
416S 'Touring Secours' Land Rover 'TS' logo black doors/yellow/grey plastic canopy/aerial/hook/red interior/SP, B + in 'RAC' box yellow label 'Touring Secours' £320
419 Ford Zephyr Motorway Patrol Car 'POLITIE' white/small blue roof light/aerial/red interior/FSP, B + ... £190
419 Ford Zephyr Motorway Patrol Car 'RIJKS POLITIE' white/small blue roof light/aerial/red interior/SP, A rare £440
422 Bedford Van all blue 'AVRO BODE'/FSP-B £210
433 VW Delivery Van 'Vroom & Dreesmann' grey/lemon interior/SP, A in B box, rare £190
464 Commer Police Van 'RIJKS POLITIE' met blue/large blue flashing roof light/red interior/'grilled' rear & side windows/SP, B + very scarce £180
464 Commer Police Van 'Police' dark green/opaque rear and side windows, rare B + (one end flap is C) £320
471 Smiths Karrier Mobile Canteen 'Patates Frites' deep blue/SP, A in B box £220
492 VW European Police Car 'Politie' white/'chrome' roof light/SP/2 figures/ light brown interior, B + and steering wheel is loose, in A box, rare £100
1110 Bedford 'S' Type Fuel Tanker, 'SHELL BENZEEN' blue/white/SP, lovely B + in special 'Shell Chemicalien' presentation box, B £2000
1140 Bedford TK 'Mobilgas' Petrol Tanker red/white advert with blue letters/SP, B + with inner lining in B to B + box, scarce so good £150

BUSES
468 Routemaster New South Wales Govt. Transport Dept. Livery green/cream/ brown roof/ 'Naturally Corgi Toys' with driver & clippie/SP, B + with leaflet, rare £570

LACY SCOTT, BURY ST. EDMUNDS
July 1995 Sale

A **Chipperfields Set**, 1st issue (23), BDM £290
A **Chipperfields Circus mobile booking office** (426), BM £100
A **Walls Ice Cream Van** on Ford Thames (447), BM £105
A **Chipperfields Circus half set** 96905, 97393, 97886, 97896, 97915 & 97957, BM & collector album and booklet, M £190
A **Popeye paddle wagon** (802), BM £220

WALLIS & WALLIS, LEWES, SUSSEX
Late July 1995

2 Corgi Chipperfield vehicles: Circus horse transporter with horses (1130); and Land Rover with elephant and cage on trailer GS No.19. In original boxes, GC to VGC, minor chipping, boxes worn and damaged £160
A **Corgi Monte Carlo Mini Cooper S** (339) in its special "1967" issue box with paperwork. VGC to mint, minor wear to box £100
A **scarce Corgi Monte Carlo BMC Mini Cooper S** (321) 1966 Rally version, with autographs on roof, in original special issue box, VGC to mint, minor wear £200
An **original Corgi Chitty Chitty Bang Bang** (266) all complete with figures, front and rear wings, in original box, VGC, minor damage to box £145
A **Corgi gift set No.40 "The Avengers"** complete with 2 original umbrellas, in original display box with packing, VGC, minor wear to box £310

Collectors Notes

CRESCENT TOYS

The Crescent Toy Company Limited

The company was founded in July 1922 by Henry G. Eagles and Arthur A. Schneider in a workshop 30 feet square at the rear of a private house at 67 De Beauvoir Crescent, Kingsland Road, London N1. They manufactured model soldiers, cowboys, kitchen sets, etc. from lead alloy. These were hollow castings, hand painted, packed one dozen to a box, and sold to wholesalers at six shillings per dozen boxes.

The small firm prospered and eventually opened up a factory in Tottenham. With the second World War came a ban on metal toys and production was changed to munitions. After the War the firm resumed making metal hollow cast toys and in addition marketed the diecast products of a firm called DCMT (Die Casting Machine Tools Ltd). As a consequence early post-war models had 'DCMT' cast into the underside of the body.

In 1948 the firm opened a modern factory on a 4¼ acre site at Cymcarn, a Welsh mining village near Newport, Monmouth (now Gwent) and two years later transferred all production there, maintaining only an office in London. From this time Crescent toys made their own diecast products without 'DCMT' on them. Hence it is possible to find the same models with or without 'DCMT' cast in. Die Casting Machine Tools went their own way and from 1950 produced models under the name of 'Lone Star'.

Crescent Toys will be best remembered for their excellent ranges of military models and farm equipment but probably most of all for their superb reproductions of the racing cars of the 1950s. The following post-war model listings have been extracted from a unique collection of original trade catalogues (1947-80) most kindly provided by Mr.J.D.Schneider, the former Managing Director of Crescent Toys Ltd. All of the original research and actual compiling of the lists was undertaken by Ray Strutt of the 'Collectors Gazette'.

EARLY POST-WAR MODELS

223	1948	Racing Car, Various colours	£25-35	☐
422	1949	Sports Car, Assorted colours	£30-40	☐
423	1949	Oil Lorry, Various colours	£30-40	☐
424	1949	Truck Lorry, Various colours	£30-40	☐
425	1949	Saloon Car, Assorted colours	£30-40	☐
800	1947-49	Jaguar, Bright colours	£35-45	☐
802	1947-49	Locomotive, Assorted colours	£25-35	☐
803	1947-48	Locomotive, Silver	£25-35	☐
804	1948-49	Police Car, Black	£35-45	☐
1221	1949	Fire Engine, Red body	£40-50	☐
-		Garages, Retailing at 1/-, 1/6, 2/6 and 4/-. Complete with Modern Pumps, Motor Cars and Garage Attendants, 'CRESCENT GARAGES' logo	NGPP	☐
FC 330		Domestic Iron and Stand	£10-15	☐

FARM EQUIPMENT

1802	1949-60	Tractor and Hayrake, various colours	£65-75	☐
1803	1967-74	Dexta Tractor and Trailer, various colours	£45-55	☐
1804	1950-59	Tractor and Disc Harrow, various colours	£55-65	☐
1805	1950-61	Tractor, Various colours	£55-65	☐
1806	1950-60	Hayrake, various colours	£5-10	☐
1807	1950	Disc Harrow, various colours	£5-10	☐
1808	1950-56	Platform Trailer, various colours	£5-10	☐
1809	1950-56	Ricklift Trailer, various colours	£5-10	☐
1809	1962-80	Dexta Tractor, various colours	£25-35	☐
1810	1950-80	Box Trailer/Farm Trailer, (No.148 1968-74) various colours	£15-20	☐
1811	1950-67	Animal Trailer/Cattle Trailer, (No.148 1968-71) various colours	£10-15	☐
1811	1975-81	Dexta Tractor and Trailer, various colours	£15-20	☐
1813	1950	Timber Wagon (Horse Drawn) various colours	£75-95	☐
1814	1950-60	Plough Trailer, (No.150 1968-71) various colours	£10-15	☐
1815	1950	Hayloader, various colours	£10-15	☐
1816	1950	Roller Harrow, various colours	£5-10	☐
1817	1950-56	Timber Trailer, various colours	£10-15	☐
1818	1954-60	Tipping Farm Wagon, various colours	£10-15	☐
1819	1954-55	Large Farm Wagon, various colours	£25-35	☐

DIECAST ACTION TOYS

1222	1954-59	Builders & Decorators Truck, (Red handcart) unpainted ladder & bucket, Beige builder figure on Green base	NGPP	☐
1268	1954-59	Mobile Space Rocket, various colours	NGPP	☐
1269	1954-59	Mobile Crane, various colours	£30-40	☐

1272	1954-59	Scammell Scarab & Box Trailer, various colours	£70-80	☐
1274	1954-59	Scammell Scarab & Low Loader, various colours	£70-80	☐
1276	1955-59	Scammell Scarab & Oil Tanker, various colours	£70-80	☐
2700	1956-60	Western Stage Coach, various colours	£70-80	☐
2705	1955	Western Stage Coach, various colours	NGPP	☐
-		Scammell Scarab Set, Mechanical Horse, Box Trailer and Low Loader	NGPP	☐

MILITARY MODELS

(All are in military colours unless described otherwise)

155	1960-68	'Long Tom' Artillery Gun	£15-20	☐
235	1946	Cannon, operable	NGPP	☐
F 355	1938	Tank and Cannon Set	NGPP	☐
650	1954-59	Military Set, Two No.696 British Tanks, one No.698 Scout Car and one No.699 Russian Tank	NGPP	☐
NN656/2	1938-40	Field Gun and Gunner	NGPP	☐
NN692	1938-40	Deep Sea Diver, with equipment	NGPP	☐
NN693	1938-40	Searchlight Unit, with Officer and two Soldiers	NGPP	☐
NN694	1938-40	Rangefinder Unit, with Officer and Soldier	NGPP	☐
F 695	1946	Howitzer, unpainted, with spring and plunger, 'CRESCENT' cast-in	£10-12	☐
696	1954-59	British Tank	£30-40	☐
698	1954-56	Scout Car	£20-30	☐
699	1954-56	Russian Tank	£30-40	☐
NN700	1938-40	Royal Engineers Set, with 2 Soldiers and Telegraph Pole	NGPP	☐
K 703	1938-40	Field Wireless Unit, 2 Soldiers	NGPP	☐
K 704	1938-40	R.A.M.C. Stretcher Party, with 2 Soldiers and Patient	NGPP	☐
1248	1957	Field Gun	£5-10	☐
1249	1958-79	18-pounder Quick-Firing Gun	£10-15	☐
1250	1958-80	25-pounder Light Artillery Gun	£10-15	☐
1251	1958-80	5.5" Medium Heavy Howitzer	£10-15	☐
1260	1976-79	Supply Truck	£30-40	☐
1263	1962-80	Saladin Armoured Scout Car	£20-30	☐
1264	1975-80	Scorpion Tank	£12-16	☐
1265	1977-80	M109 Self-Propelled Gun	£12-15	☐
1266	1978-79	Recovery Vehicle	£12-15	☐
1267	1958-63	'Corporal' Rocket and Lorry	£50-60	☐
1270	1958-60	Heavy Rescue Crane	£40-50	☐
1271	1958-60	Long Range Mobile Gun	£20-30	☐
1271	1976-80	Artillery Force	£15-20	☐
2154	1962-74	Saladin Armoured Patrol, (No.1270 1975-80)	£10-15	☐

HISTORICAL MODELS (in Regal colours)

1300	1975-76	Royal State Coach	£20-30	☐
1301	1977-79	Royal State Coach, (Commemorative box)	£20-30	☐
1302	1977	Royal State Coach & Figures	£20-30	☐
1450	1956-60	Medieval Catapult	£20-30	☐
1953	1954-60	Coronation State Coach	£30-40	☐

Miniature 'WILD WEST' Transport

906	1956	Stage Coach, various colours	£30-40	☐
907	1956	Covered Wagon, various colours	£30-40	☐

GRAND PRIX RACING and SPORTS CARS

1284	1956-60	Mercedes-Benz, all-enveloping Silver body	£80-100	☐
1285	1956-60	B.R.M. Mk.II, Bright Green	£80-100	☐
1286	1956-60	Ferrari, Orange-Red	£80-100	☐
1287	1956-60	Connaught, Dark Green	£80-100	☐
1288	1956-60	Cooper-Bristol, Light Blue	£80-100	☐
1289	1956-60	Gordini, French Blue	£80-100	☐
1290	1956-60	Maserati, Cherry Red	£80-100	☐
1291	1957-60	Aston-Martin DB3s, White/Light Blue	£80-100	☐
1292	1957-60	Jaguar 'D' type, Dark Green	£80-100	☐
1293	1958-60	Vanwall, Dark Green	£80-100	☐
6300	1957	Racing Cars Set, nos.1284 - 1289 as above in display box	NGPP	☐
	1958-60	Same set but 1290 replaces 1284	NGPP	☐

LONG VEHICLES (various colours)

1350	1975-80	Container Truck	£20-25	☐
1351	1975-80	Petrol Tanker	£20-25	☐
1352	1975-80	Girder Carrying Truck	£20-25	☐
1353	1975-80	Flat Platform Truck	£20-25	☐

'TRUKKERS' (various colours)

1360	1976-81	Cement Mixer	£5-20	☐
1361	1976-81	Covered Truck	£5-20	☐
1362	1976-81	Tipper Truck	£5-20	☐
1363	1976-81	Recovery Vehicle	£5-20	☐
1364	1976-81	Super Karrier	£5-20	☐

CRESCENT TOY SHIPS

BATTLESHIPS

		H.M.S. 'King George V'. Grey hollow cast, with main armament only, boxed	£15-20	☐
-		Same but additional separately cast secondary armament	£15-20	☐
		H.M.S. 'Vanguard'. Grey/Black/White, solid casting, 'CRESCENT' cast-in	£5-7	☐
Q 3	1940	Battleship Set, Battleship plus 4 Sailors	NGPP	☐
S 3	1940	Warships Set, Battleship and Destroyer plus 8 Sailors	NGPP	☐
NN 691		H.M.S. 'Malaya', Grey hollow cast body, with Black funnels, boxed	£15-20	☐

AIRCRAFT CARRIERS

-	H.M.S. 'Victorious', Grey hollow cast body, separate unpainted aircraft, boxed	£20-25	☐
NN 667	H.M.S. 'Eagle', Grey hollow cast body, separate unpainted aircraft, Union Jack sticker attached to box	£10-15	☐

OTHER WARSHIPS

	'H' or 'I' Class Destroyer. Unpainted solid cast body, 'CRESCENT' cast in bow	£15-20	☐
	'H' or 'I' Class Destroyer. As previous model plus 3 lead figures of naval personnel	£20-25	☐
	'V & W' Class Destroyer. Grey hollow cast body	£2-3	☐

A 34		Gunboat. Grey hollow cast body	£2-3	☐
234	1946	Submarine. Unpainted body with conning tower and deck gun, 4"	£10-15	☐
C 310		'County' Class Cruiser, 'Cumberland', Grey hollow cast	£7-9	☐
K 664		'County' Class Cruiser, Grey hollow cast body	£7-9	☐
K 665		War Transport Ship, Grey hollow cast body, boxed	£15-20	☐

PASSENGER SHIPS

'Queen Mary'. Black/White/Red hollow cast body, boxed	£15-20	☐
'Dunnottar Castle'. Mauve/White/Red, hollow cast body, boxed	£25-30	☐
'Athlone Castle'. Mauve/White/Red, hollow cast body, boxed	£25-30	☐

'Dunnottar Castle' and 'Athlone Castle' were part of the 'Union Castle' fleet and the models were sold in souvenir boxes, probably on board.

MISCELLANEOUS

'Tower Bridge'. Solid cast model of the famous landmark, various colours	£5-10	☐

MODEL IDENTIFICATION. Crescent Ships are of rather crude manufacture and have virtually no identifying features. Only the H.M.S. 'Vanguard' and the 'H' or 'I' Class Destroyer are known to have 'CRESCENT' cast in. A few of the early models had a little paper 'Crescent' half-moon label.
Ship models were packed in cream cardboard boxes of varying quality.

CRESCENT AIRCRAFT

O 2	1940	Spitfire Set. 2 Spitfires with 2 Pilots and 2 Mechanics	£50-75	☐
Q 2	1940	Spitfire Set. As previous set but with a different reference number	£50-75	☐
U 2	1940	Aircraft Set. 5 Aircraft plus 3 Pilots and 6 Groundcrew	£75-100	☐
FC 38	1946	Aeroplane, Spitfire	£5-10	☐
FC 89	1946	Aeroplane, Mosquito	£5-10	☐
FC 90	1946	Aeroplane, Lightning, 3" x 2" with U.S. markings	£5-10	☐
FC 179	1946	Khaki Bomber	£5-10	☐
FC 372	1946	Aeroplane, Lightning, 4.75" x 3" with U.S. markings	£5-10	☐
FC 663	1946	North Sea Patrol, Aeroplane and two men including Pilot	£20-25	☐

A rare Crescent Garage Set (c.1949) with wooden garage, cast motorist's shop, three vehicles etc. in original Green box. Sold by Christies, South Kensington, London.

Acknowledgements.

Thanks are due to the following contributors for additional information on Crescent toys:
Jack Barker, Blackpool, Lancs.   Brian Smart, Chelmsford, Essex.   Ray Pearson, Northwich, Cheshire

DINKY TOYS

INTRODUCTION

During the course of the period 1994-95 some of the finest collections ever to come to auction have been sold. These have included collections containing examples of almost every pre-war motor vehicle, set and accessory produced. In addition the post-war model auctions have been very comprehensive and have included previously unrecorded variants as well as rare colours and export issues. The impact of all this information on the catalogue listings has been considerable, particularly in respect of the pre-war and early post-war car listings which have been greatly enhanced. Other improvements in this edition include new information and diagrams on how to identify early post-war cars and new information on Box Types for cars and pre-war Gift Sets.

Probably the highlight of the auction sales was the Christies 'Hemley Collection' Sale, when a world record price for a single model of £12,650 was paid for the very rare green, 28 series, 2nd type 'Bentalls Department Store' promotional Delivery Van (see cover picture). At a previous sale £14,200 was paid for a 24 series set, again a world record.

Similarly, high prices were also achieved by Vectis Model Auctions for post-war models in rare colours, e.g. 189 Triumph Herald, all Red (£1,700) and 501 Diesel Wagon, Red/Black (£5,200). See the extended Auction Results section for the details.

All pre-war issues must be considered rare and market prices have reflected this. Similarly the prices paid for the early post-war issues have also increased considerably. One of the benefits of the large volume and quality of items sold, has been the amount of new model identification information which has emerged, particularly in respect of the early post-war car issues.

Overall the demand for top quality Dinky Toys remains very strong.

HISTORY OF DINKY TOYS

In 1931 Meccano Ltd introduced a series of railway station and trackside accessories to accompany their famous 'HORNBY' train sets. These 'Modelled Miniatures' were in sets numbered 1 - 22 and included railwaymen, station staff, passengers and trains. Set number 22 was comprised of six vehicles which were representative rather than replicas of actual vehicles. It was first advertised in the Meccano Magazine of December 1933.

At about this time 'Tootsie Toys' of America were introducing model vehicles into the United Kingdom and they were proving to be very popular. Consequently Meccano Ltd decided to widen their range of products and issue a comprehensive series of models to include vehicles, ships and aircraft. 'Modelled Miniatures' therefore became 'Meccano Dinky Toys' and set number 22 the first set of 'Dinky Cars'. The first 'Dinky Toys' advertisement appeared in the April 1934 edition of the Meccano Magazine. The first Dinky car produced after the change of name was 23a in April 1934. It was probably based on an early MG but was again generally representative rather than an accurate model. Set 22 cost 4/- and consisted of: 22a Sports Car, 22b Sports Coupé, 22c Motor Truck, 22d Delivery Van, 22e Tractor and 22f Tank and is today highly sought after.

The range of models produced grew quickly so that the Meccano Magazine of December 1935 was claiming that there were 200 varieties to choose from! Although the phrase 'Dinky Toys' became a household name, the actual range was of course far greater and was not limited to cars; it even included dolls house furniture. Indeed, by the time the famous Binns Road factory in Liverpool finally closed its doors in November 1979 over 1000 different designs had been produced. Pre-war models are rare today and fetch high prices, which reflects how difficult it is to find a model in really good condition. This is because so many 1930s models were made from an unstable alloy which has tended to crystallize and disintegrate. Fortunately the post-war models do not suffer from the same problem and much of today's collecting interest is centred around the delightful models produced in the fifties and sixties with Gift Sets being particularly sought after.

In 1987 the Dinky trade name was bought by Matchbox who were at the time part of the Universal International Co. of Hong Kong. They introduced the 'Dinky Collection' in 1988 with some very fine models in a constant scale of 1:43. On the 7th May 1992 it was announced in the 'New York Times' that 'Tyco Toys Inc.' had acquired by merger the 'Universal Matchbox Group' and with it the famous 'Dinky Toys' brand name.

Model Identification

Common Features. There are several features common to various groups of models and to avoid unnecessary repetition in the 'Features' column they are shown below. Exceptions to these general indications are noted in the listings.

'Dinky Toys', 'Meccano Ltd', or 'Meccano Dinky Toys'.
These wordings are to be found cast or stamped on the base-plate or chassis or in the case of early models without a base they are cast into the model itself. Some very early models have 'HORNBY SERIES' cast-in (notably those in the 22 series).

Wheel hubs. Solid one-piece wheel/tyre castings were fitted to the 'Modelled Miniatures' and first pre-war 'Dinky Toys'. They had 'Hornby' or 'Meccano' cast onto their rims and were covered in a thin colour wash or silver-plated. This casting was soon replaced with more realistic cast hubs (having a smooth convex face) fitted with white (sometimes coloured) rubber tyres. Pre-war hubs may be black, coloured or sometimes silver-plated. Post-war hubs were of the 'ridged' type having a discernible ridge simulating a nave-plate or hub cap and were usually fitted with black rubber tyres. They were only painted, never silver-plated.

Supertoy hubs and tyres. When Supertoys were introduced in 1947 the ridged type of hub was used on the Fodens with black 'herringbone pattern' tyres, and on the Guys with smooth black tyres. Fodens graduated to the use of 'fine radial-tread' tyres first in black, later in grey, then to black again but with a more chunky 'block' tread. Supertoys later acquired plastic hubs and plastic tyres.

Wheel materials. Lead was used originally for a short time, the majority of models from the mid-1930s to the early 1960s having diecast mazak hubs. Small models like motor-cycles or the 35b Racer were fitted with solid one-piece wheel/tyre moulding (white or black rubber pre-war, black post-war). In 1958/9 spun aluminium hubs were introduced and some models (such as 131, 178, 179, 180, 181, 182 and 290 Bus) appeared fitted with either type. Plastic hubs replaced the diecast versions on racing cars numbered 230-235 while the Austin A30 and Fiat 600 were given solid one-piece wheel/tyre plastic injection mouldings.

Speedwheels were introduced in the 1970s and some model can be found fitted with metal wheels or Speedwheels. The former are more collectable.

Model Number and Name. Model numbers appear on many Dinky Toys baseplates but by no means on all. The model name however appears on virtually every post-war Dinky Toy. Pre-war models usually had neither (though the 38 and 39 series are exceptions having the model name on their baseplates).

Windscreen. Pre-war and early post-war models had tinplate or celluloid windscreens. Moulded plastic windscreens appeared in the 1950s on open car models.

Baseplates. Assumed to be of tinplate or diecast metal unless described otherwise. Plastic moulded baseplates are generally restricted to a few models made after 1970.

Abbreviation RN. Racing or Rally Number.

Construction Materials. All models assumed to be constructed at least in part of a diecast alloy. Some pre-war models were made of a lead alloy like the 22 and 28 series plus the few odd models such as 23 a Racing Car and 23m Thunderbolt Speed Car. The Blaw-Knox Bulldozer was one of the very few produced (right at the end of its production) in plastic.

Windows. The first Dinky to be fitted with plastic window glazing was the Austin A105 Saloon. Some models in production at the time were fitted with glazing later on and may therefore be found with or without windows.

Hooks were not fitted to the first Supertoys Foden models (1947). Small hooks were fitted in early 1948, the usual (larger) hook appearing in mid-1948.

Axles were all 'crimped' pre-war and on these series of models post-war: 23, 25, 29, 30, 34, 35, 36, 37, 38, 39, 40 and 280. Otherwise models had rivet-ended axles until the advent of Speedwheels. Early Guy models had tinplate clips to retain the front axles.

Size of models is usually shown in millimetres and refers to the longest overall measurement (usually the length). In the case of pre-war models slight inaccuracies may occur from expansion of the casting as it ages in the course of time.

The Scale of Dinky Toys was originally 1/43 (with a few exceptions). Supertoys Foden and Guy vehicles (introduced in 1947) were in a scale of 1/48 while military models issued from 1953 were smaller at 1/60. Most aircraft models before 1965 were around 1/200 and ships 1/1800. In the late 1960s and early 1970s the 1/36 scale was introduced.

Dinky Numbering System. The dual/triple reference numbers used on some Dinky Toys and Supertoys (for example 409/521/921 Bedford Articulated Lorry) refers to the basic model type and casting and not to model colours. The renumbering by Meccano was an administration process to re-catalogue production of existing lines and introduce new models. New colours on existing castings which arise at about the time of renumbering are therefore coincidental with it rather than a consequence of it.

PRE-WAR MODELS IDENTIFICATION FEATURES TO LOOK FOR:

1: Wheel hubs generally smooth, not ridged
2: Axles were crimped, not rivetted
3: Base-plates often bare metal (unpainted)
4: Criss-cross chassis (see diagrams)
5: Wing-mounted spare wheel on cars
6: Smooth white (occasionally coloured) tyres
7: Slots in chassis for tinplate figures (36 series)
8: Tinplate radiator grilles
9: Stairs on 29 series Bus absent post-war
10: Thinner axles used pre-war

CLASSIFYING THE EARLY MODEL TYPES

In addition to the details given in the earlier sections, the age and category of a particular model is determined by features such as:—
i) The type of chassis or Base Plate.
ii) The type of Radiator Shell and Bumper.
iii) Body features such as the front of a Lorry, Van or Bus.

Diagrams of all of these features are included in each relevant section.

INFORMATION REQUIRED:- RUBBER STAMP DATES SHOWN ON BOXES.
The Editor would welcome any information on this subject i.e. when did the practice commence and finish.

How to Identify Early Post War Issues

Acknowledgement: The following information has been supplied by Hugo Marsh of Christies of South Kensington, London (see Sept '94 'Barnes Collection' catalogue).

Post War 30 Series
Cicra 1946 — Open chassis with smooth black wheel hubs.
Circa 1948 — Plain chassis with ridged black wheel hubs.

36 Series
Circa 1946 — Moulded chassis with smooth black wheel hubs.
Circa 1948 — Moulded chassis with black ridged wheel hubs.

38 Series
Circa 1946 — With pre-war lacquered metal base, silvered sidelights, smooth black hubs, spread spigots not rivets.
Circa 1946 — Solid steering wheels, smooth black hubs, silvered sidelights, black painted baseplate.
Circa 1947 — 1st variation. As above with silver edged windscreen.
Circa 1948/9 — Open or solid steering wheel with ridged wheel hubs, black painted baseplate.
Circa 1950 — As above with coloured wheel hubs.

39 Series
Circa 1946 — Bare metal baseplate, smooth black wheel hubs, silver door handles.
Circa 1948 — Black painted baseplate, ridged black wheel hubs.
Circa 1950 — As above with coloured wheel hubs.

N.B. The Editor would welcome details of colour variations not included in the early post-war listings.

Model Boxes

Dinky Cars
Apart from sets and special issues (pre-war) the early models were sold unboxed from the retailers trade boxes until 1953/54 approx. As a result models spanning this period were sold both unboxed and boxed, e.g. 40 Series Models in boxes showing both the early and late reference numbers may attract a premium, e.g. 40a (158).

N.B. The colour spot on the end of the first type Yellow card box should always match the model inside. See also section on Trade Boxes.

NOTE: Circa 1964-67 some motor cars and sports cars were boxed in cellophane and card boxes, which proved to be fragile and easily damaged. Originally these boxes were issued with card protection strips for removal by the shopkeeper. Known issues:- 110, 111, 112, 113, 114, 115, 127, 128, 133, 151, 161, 170, 171, 172, 215.

Circa 1966-68. Motor cars, sports cars and racing cars issued in hard 'see thru' plastic cases with lift off lid. Models known to have been issued in these boxes include:- 116, 129, 131, 132, 152, 153, 154, 158, 161, 163, 164, 175, 187, 188, 189, 190, 208, 210, 213, 216, 220, 221, 224, 261 Ford Taunus 17 German 'Police' car and 262 VW Swiss PTT car.

Circa 1972-76. Various cars issued in original vacuform packs with card bases, known issues include:- 129, 178, 226, 227, 342 and 344.

Circa 1976-79. Various cars issued in original cellophane and card boxes, known issues included:- 112, 120, 122, 123, 180, 207, 211, 221, 124, 128, 192, 208, 201, 203, 206, 222, 223, 226.

The editor would be pleased to receive details of other models not listed.

Small Commercial Vehicles
Apart from sets the early models were sold unboxed from retailers trade boxes until 1953/4 approx. As a result models spanning this period were sold both unboxed and boxed e.g. 31a (450) boxes showing early and late reference numbers e.g. 30j/412 may attract a premium. The colour spot shown on the end of the first type of yellow box should match the model inside. See also the section on Trade Boxes.

Gift Sets
Sets: 001-006
Housed in Green card boxes with plain Yellow inserts.

Sets: 1, 2, 3, 4, 5, 6
c.1934: Purple marbled 'Modelled Miniatures' box.
c.1939: Green box with pictorial insert.
c.1936: Blue patterned 'MECCANO DINKY TOYS' box.
Post-war: Green box with plain insert.

Sets: Series-24, 25 and 30
c.1934: Purple marbled 'Modelled Miniatures' box.
c.1935: Purple marbled 'MECCANO DINKY TOYS' box with Yellow/Red label picturing eight assorted cars & lorries. Purple insert with Gold script on two central lines 'MECCANO DINKY TOYS No '24', '25' or '30'.
N.B. The 24 Series sets also contained a purple packing card stating 'PLEASE REMOVE THIS PACKING CARD TO DISPLAY CONTENTS'.
c.1936: Blue patterned box lid with Yellow/Red label picturing eight assorted cars & lorries. Purple insert with no Gold Script on 25 Series (no details available on 24 and 30 Series).

Sets: 12, 42, 43, 44 and 49 (Pre-war issue)
Blue landscape boxes with inner Blue/Green pictorial inserts.

Sets: 151, 152, 156, 161, 162
Grey/Blue or Blue (152) display boxes with inner scenic backdrop and packing boards.

Trains
Sets 17, 18, 19, 20, 21
1st c.1933: Purple marbled 'ladder' box, 'HORNBY SERIES MODELLED MINIATURES' on large colour label. This box type only applies to Set 21.
2nd c.1936: Blue patterned 'ladder' box with 'MECCANO DINKY TOYS' on large colour label picturing the set contained within. Colour spot on end label denotes colour of set within.
3rd c.1939: Plain Blue 'landscape' box without a colour label. Green/Blue pictorial insert. Code No 1045 dated 11·38 on end label. N.B. only used in Set 19.

More information required on boxes

Much more information exists on Dinky boxes especially the rare issues. Please send in any new information you may have.

Dinky Toys Cars

Model Identification - continued

Dinky Toys Cars chassis types 1934-1950

1934-1935 'Criss-Cross' Chassis 1st type	1935-1936 'Criss-Cross' Chassis 2nd type	1936-1940 Open Chassis	1946-1947 Plain Chassis	1948-1950 Moulded Chassis

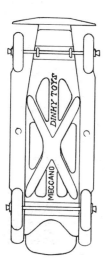 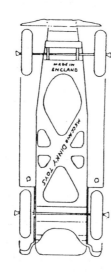 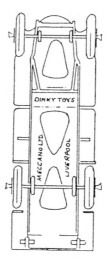 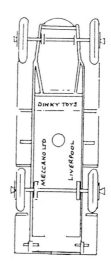 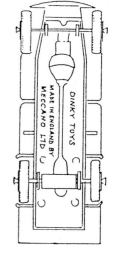

N.B. Both the 1st and 2nd type criss-cross chassis were produced with and without a spare wheel slot.

24 Series Radiator Grille Types

1st Type With diamond shape in centre of bumper No radiator badge or over-riders 1934-38	2nd Type 'Bentley' style, no diamond shape in bumper No radiator badge or over-riders 1934-38	3rd Type 'Bentley' style, with radiator badge and over-riders 1938-40

N.B. The 1st and 2nd Type Grilles will be found on both the 1st and 2nd Types of chassis. The later 3rd Type will be found with the 2nd Type chassis.

1st Type	2nd Type	3rd Type

1948-50	1950-52	1952-59

Note: Pre-war wheel hubs may be smooth diecast or the rare chrome (Tootsie Toy type) hubs which attract a premium.

22a	1933-35	Open top Sports Car	'Modelled Miniature' with 'HORNBY SERIES' cast into lead body, solid metal wheel/tyre castings (thinly painted in metallic blue, purple, green, yellow or red, or not painted at all) lead windscreen surround, tinplate radiator (grille may be same colour as body, or overpainted with the colour of the mudguards), 82 mm.		
			Blue body, Yellow seats and mudguards	£400-500	☐
			Blue body, Red seats and mudguards	£400-500	☐
			Cream body, Red seats and mudguards	£400-500	☐
			Cream body, Green seats and mudguards	£400-500	☐
			Cream body, Blue seats and mudguards	£400-500	☐
			Red body, Cream seats and mudguards	£150-250	☐
			Yellow body, Green seats and mudguards	£400-500	☐
			Orange-Brown body, Cream seats and mudguards	£150-200	☐
22b	1933-35	Closed top Sports Coupé	'Modelled Miniature' with 'HORNBY SERIES' cast into lead body, solid metal wheel/tyre castings (coloured or plain, as 22a) tinplate radiator (painted in main body colour) 82 mm.		
			Cream body, Red roof and mudguards or Green roof and mudguards	£400-500	☐
			Red body, Blue roof and mudguards	£400-500	☐
			Red body, Cream roof and mudguards	£400-500	☐
			Yellow body, Green roof and mudguards	£400-500	☐
22g	1935-41	Streamline Tourer	Model has cast steering wheel and windscreen, smooth diecast hubs or chrome hubs which may be painted as body colour or a contrasting colour, 85 mm.		
			Body colours: Green, Red, Light or Dark Blue, Cream, Buff or Black	£150-200	☐
22h	1935-41	Streamlined Saloon	Red, Blue or Cream saloon version of 22g (no steering wheel) 85 mm.	£150-200	☐
23	1934-35	Racing Car	1st casting. Lead body, no racing number or driver, coloured tyres on some, 0, 2, 3 or 4 exhausts stubs, 94 mm.		
		variations:	Cream or White body with either Blue, Cream, Green, Orange or Red top flash	£200-300	☐
			Yellow body with Blue upper body flash, 3 exhaust stubs	£200-300	☐
23a	1935-41	23 re-issued:	1st casting. Diecast body, no driver, no racing number, Black or White tyres, 4 exhausts, 94 mm.		
		variations:	White body and wheels, Blue top flash and circle on nose	£100-150	☐
			Cream body and wheels, Red top flash and circle on nose	£100-150	☐
			Blue body, White top flash and circle on nose	£100-150	☐
			Orange body, Green top flash and circle on nose	£100-150	☐
			Yellow body, Dark Blue top flash and circle on nose	£100-150	☐
			Brown body, Cream top flash	£100-150	☐
		2nd casting:	With driver plus raised circles for racing numbers, 6 exhausts in fishtail, 94 mm.		
		colour type 1:	With minor colour sidestripes and perhaps coloured tyres,		
		colour type 2:	Broad nose flash, even width top rear flash,		
		colour type 3:	Broad flash at cockpit and pointed ends top flash, plus circle on nose		
		variations:	(type 3) White body, Blue nose/circle/top flash, number '2'	£100-150	☐
			(type 3) Cream body, Red nose/circle/top flash, number '3'	£100-150	☐
			(type 3) White body, Green nose/circle/top flash, number '6'	£100-150	☐
			(type 3) Orange body, Green nose/circle/top flash, number '4'	£100-150	☐
			(type 1) Cream body, Red stripes, number '9', ('Humbug' version)	£100-150	☐
			(type 2) Blue with White 'humbug' stripes and driver racing number 11	£300-400	☐
			(type 2) Yellow body, Dark Blue top flash, racing number '7'	£100-150	☐
			(type 2) Blue body, White top flash, racing number '11'	£100-150	☐
		casting variation:	With driver, raised racing number circle on nearside only, no detailed exhaust,		
			Orange body, Green nose circle, Green racing number '4'	£100-150	☐
			Orange body, long Green upper body flash, 3 exhaust stubs, Green RN '4' or '10'	£100-150	☐
			Yellow body, long Dark Blue upper body flash, chrome hubs	£100-150	☐
23a	1946-52	3rd casting:	With transverse body ribs, no raised circle for racing numbers, and only issued in colour type 3, with or without racing numbers		
			Red body, Silver nose circle, top flash and side circle (Red RN '4'), Red hubs	£30-35	☐
			Silver body, Red nose circle, top flash and side circle (Silver RN '4'), Red hubs	£30-35	☐
		note:	Details of any other 23a colour are welcomed		
23b	1935-41	Hotchkiss Racing Car	Blue body, Dark Blue, Red or Silver flash & racing number '2' or '5', 96 mm.	£300-400	☐
	1935-41		Yellow (Blue flash and RN), Orange (Green flash and RN), or Green (Yellow flash and RN)	£300-400	☐
	1946-48		Red with Silver flash and RN '5', or Silver with Red flash and RN '5'	£40-50	☐
23c	1936-38	Mercedes Benz Racing Car	Red, Light Blue, Yellow or Green, plain clipped-in base, with or without racing numbers, driver cast-in, Black hubs, treaded tyres, 92 mm.	£100-150	☐
	1938-40		As previous model but with rivetted baseplate bearing information	£100-150	☐
	1946-50	('Large Open Racing Car')	Re-issued 23c in Blue or Silver, various racing numbers, 92 mm.	£40-50	☐
23d	1936-38	Auto Union Racing Car	Red, Blue, Light Blue, Pale Green, Yellow or Silver body, plain clipped-in tinplate base, various Black racing numbers on roundels, driver slotted-in, Black hubs, herringbone pattern tyres, 100 mm.	£100-150	☐
	1938-41		As previous model but with rivetted baseplate bearing information	£40-50	☐
	1946-50		Re-issued 23d with Silver body, Red racing number '2', no driver	£40-50	☐
23e	1936-38	'Speed Of The Wind' Racing Car	Red, Blue, Light Blue, Green, Yellow or Silver body, plain clipped-in tinplate base, driver, various racing numbers, Black herringbone tyres & hubs, lead versions exist, 104 mm.	£75-95	☐
	1938-41		As previous model but with rivetted baseplate bearing information	£40-50	☐
	1946-49		Re-issue of 23e in Red or Silver, rivetted informative baseplate	£30-40	☐

Ref. No.			*Dinky Toys — Cars – continued*	Market Price Range
23e (221)	1950-54		Silver body & wheels, plain base	£30-40 ☐
23f (232)	1952-54	Alfa-Romeo Racing Car	Red body, White racing number '8', Red diecast hubs, 100 mm...............	£70-85 ☐
23g (233)	1952-54	Cooper Bristol Racing Car........	Green body, White racing number '6', Green diecast hubs, 89 mm..........	£70-85 ☐
23h (234)	1953-54	Ferrari Racing Car....................	Blue body, Yellow nose, racing number '5' and diecast hubs, 101 mm.......	£70-85 ☐
23j (235)	1953-54	H.W.M. Racing Car.................	Green body, Yellow racing number '7', Green diecast hubs, 99 mm.........	£70-85 ☐
23k (230)	1953-54	Talbot-Lago Racing Car	Blue body, Yellow racing number '4', Blue diecast hubs, 103 mm...........	£70-85 ☐
23m	1938-41	'Thunderbolt' Speed Car	Silver body (Black detailing), Union Jacks on tail, Silver coloured baseplate in original box dated 2·38, code: A2247, 126 mm.	£100-150 ☐
23n (231)	1953-54	Maserati Racing Car	Red, White flash & racing number '9', Red diecast hubs, 94 mm.	£70-85 ☐
23p	1939-40	Gardner's MG Record Car.......	Dark Green, White flash and 'MG' logo, Union Jacks, 'MG Magnette' on base, lacquered unpainted tinplate baseplate, Yellow box, dated 9·39, 104 mm.	£150-200 ☐
	1946-47		Dark Green, Union Jacks, no flash, 'MG Record Car' on base, not boxed...............	£100-125 ☐
23s	1938-40	Streamlined Racing Car	Light Green (Dark Green detailing), lead, 126 mm.	£400-500 ☐
			Light Blue (Dark Blue or Silver detailing), lead	£400-500 ☐
			Orange body, lead.............	£400-500 ☐
			Light Green, Light Blue or Orange body, mazuk.	£75-100 ☐
23s (222)	1948-54		Light, Mid or Dark Green, or Dark Blue, Silver flashes.	£30-40 ☐
			Silver body with Red, Green or Blue flashes................	£30-40 ☐
			Red body with Silver or Black flashes, Black base	NGPP ☐
24a	1934-40	Ambulance................................	See 'Fire, Police & Ambulance Vehicles' Section	
24b	1934-38	Limousine	Types 1 or 2 criss-cross chassis, types 1, 2 or 3 grille, no sidelights, no spare wheel, 3 side windows, 3 'stacked' parallel horizontal bonnet louvres. Plated chrome, Blue or Black hubs, 98 mm.	
		body/chassis colours:......	Maroon/Dark Maroon, Maroon/Grey, Maroon/Black, Blue/Yellow, Dark Blue/Black, Yellow/Brown	£1000-1500 ☐
	1937-40	casting change:	Same colours but no spare wheel slot, 3 parallel bonnet louvres, open chassis, 'Bentley' grille and bumper...	£200-400 ☐
24c	1934-38	Town Sedan............................	Types 1 or 2 criss-cross chassis, types 1, 2 or 3 grille, spare wheel, no sidelights, separate windscreen/steering wheel casting, plated chrome, Blue or Black hubs, 97 mm.	
		body/chassis colours:......	Green/Black, Green/Yellow, Pale Green/Red, Dark Blue/Dark Blue, Cream/Dark Blue, Cream/Black, Dark Blue/Black	£1000-1500 ☐
	1937-40	casting change:	Same colours but open chassis, no spare wheel slot, narrower boot, shorter door handles..	£200-400 ☐
24d	1934-38	Vogue Saloon	Types 1 or 2 criss-cross chassis, types 1, 2 or 3 grille, with spare wheel, no sidelights. Plated chrome, Blue or Black hubs, 97 mm.	
		body/chassis colours:......	Blue/Dark Blue, Blue/Black, Blue/Maroon, Cream/Blue, Brown/Green, Pink/Green, Green/Blue, Red/Grey..............	£1000-1500 ☐
	1937-40	casting change:	Same colours but open chassis, higher 'domed' roofline........................	£200-400 ☐
24e	1934-38	Super Streamlined Saloon	Types 1 or 2 criss-cross chassis, types 1, 2 or 3 grille, no spare or sidelights, 12 bonnet louvres. Plated chrome, Blue or Black hubs, 97 mm.	
		body/chassis colours:......	Maroon/Black, Red/Dark Red, Red/Black, Green/Red, Green/Blue, Red/Brown	£1000-1500 ☐
	1937-40	casting change:	As previous model but with 13 bonnet louvres.	£200-400 ☐
24f	1934-38	Sportsmans Coupé....................	Criss-cross chassis, with spare wheel, no sidelights, 97 mm. Colours: Blue/Blue, Blue/Black, Yellow/Brown, Cream/Dark Blue, Brown/Buff	£1000-1500 ☐
	1937-40	casting change:	Open chassis, higher 'domed' roofline, no spare wheel	£200-400 ☐
24g	1934-38	Sports Tourer 4 Seater	Types 1 or 2 criss-cross chassis, types 1, 2 or 3 grille, spare wheel hub cast-in, no sidelights, open tinplate windscreen, separate dashboard/steering wheel casting. Plated chrome, Blue or Black hubs, 100 mm.	
		body/chrome colours:.....	Yellow/Black, Yellow/Blue, Blue/Brown, Cream/Green, Cream/Brown, Black/Cream, Blue/Maroon	£1000-1500 ☐
	1937-40	casting change:	Open chassis, filled-in windscreen, cast impression of spare	£200-400 ☐
24h	1934-38	Sports Tourer 2 Seater	Types 1 or 2 criss-cross chassis, types 1, 2 or 3 grille, spare wheel hub cast-in, no sidelights, open tinplate windscreen, separate dashboard/steering wheel casting. Plated chrome, Blue or Black hubs, 98 mm.	
		body/chassis colours:......	Red/Red, Green/Green, Yellow/Green, Yellow/Blue, Yellow/Black, Black/Cream, Cream/Green, Red/Green	£1000-1500 ☐
	1937-40	casting change:	Open chassis, filled-in windscreen, cast impression of spare	£200-400 ☐

NOTE: The rarest of the 24 Series have coloured tyres matching the body colour and a higher value can be expected.

Ref. No.			*Dinky Toys — Cars – continued*	Market Price Range
25j	1947-48	Jeep	Red or Green body, Red wheels and tail-lights, 68 mm.	£75-95 ☐
			Aqua Blue or Sky Blue body, Yellow or black wheels, Red tail-lights	£100-150 ☐
25y (405)	1952-54	Universal Jeep	Green or Red body with hook, Maroon hubs, spare wheel on side. 83 mm..........	£65-75 ☐
27d (340)	1950-54	Land Rover	Green, Dark Blue or Orange body, tinplate windscreen frame, driver, 90 mm.	£50-60 ☐
	1952-53	Gift Set model:....	Dark Brown body. Only in Gift Set No.2, Commercial Vehicles Set.	GSP ☐
27f (344)	1950-54	Estate Car	Pale Brown body with Dark Brown panels, rear axle pillars, Fawn hubs, 105 mm......	£60-70 ☐
27m (341)	1950-54	Land-Rover Trailer	Orange body (Beige wheels), Green body (Green wheels), Dark Blue (Blue wheels)....	£20-30 ☐
30a (32)	1935-40	Chrysler 'Airflow' Saloon..........	No chassis, separate bumper units, lead versions exist, 103 mm.	
			Turquoise, Maroon, Cream, Green, Blue, Red, (wheels may be any colour)...........	£200-300 ☐
			Rare issues with plated chrome wheels	£300-400 ☐
	1946		Cream or Green body, smooth hubs, White tyres	£150-200 ☐
	1946-48		As previous model but Blue, Cream or Green body (wheels usually Black)...........	£125-150 ☐
30b	1935-40	Rolls Royce	Open chassis, no sidelights, authentic radiator, 101 mm. Colours:	
	1935-40		Cream/Black, Red and Dark Red, Blue/Black, Dark Blue/Black, Fawn/Black, Red/Black, All Black	£200-400 ☐
			Yellow/Brown, Red/Red, Grey/Grey, Green/Green, Pale Green/Black	£200-400 ☐
			Light Blue body, smooth black wheel hubs, Open chassis.........	£300-400 ☐

Ref. No.	Year	Name	Description	Market Price Range
	1946		Fawn body, smooth hubs, open chassis	£100-150 ☐
	1946-50		Plain (closed) chassis, Navy Blue/Black or Greyish-Brown/Black	£100-150 ☐
30c	1935-40	Daimler........................	Open chassis, no sidelights, authentic radiator, 98 mm. Colours:	
	1935-40		Cream/Black, Blue/Black, Dark Blue/Black, Yellow/Black, Fawn/Black........	£200-400 ☐
			Turquoise/Black, Fawn/Black, Light Green/Black................................	£2005-400 ☐
			Pink/Maroon, Red/Red..	£175-250 ☐
	1946		Sand body, smooth black wheel hubs, Open chassis............................	£300-400 ☐
			Green or Fawn body, open chassis, smooth or ridged hubs...................	£130-150 ☐
	1946-50	Daimler........................	Plain (closed) chassis, Dark Green/Black, Cream/Black, Greyish-Brown/Black, Grey/Black, Light Green/Black.........................	£70-85 ☐
			Medium Green body with Pale Green hubs....................................	£80-120 ☐
30d	1935-40	Vauxhall........................	Open chassis, no sidelights, spare wheel, 'Egg Box' or 'shield' grille, 98 mm.	
			Green/Black, Blue/Black, Grey/Black, Yellow/Black, Brown/Black..........	£200-400 ☐
	1935-38		Green/Green, Grey/Grey, Yellow/Brown, Cream/Brown, Tan/Brown...........	£200-400 ☐
	1938-40	radiator change:......	As previous model but with 'shield' grille, Black chassis..................	£200-400 ☐
			With 'shield' radiator and coloured chassis................................	£200-400 ☐
	1946		Green body, smooth black wheel hubs, Open chassis........................	£100-150 ☐
	1946-50		Plain (closed) chassis, no spare wheel, 'shield' radiator, Green/Black, Brown/Black, Maroon/Black, Yellow/Black, Grey/Black, Olive-Green/Black, Blue/Black......................	£70-85 ☐
			Variation with Silver cast ridged hubs, thick axles, with Dark Olive Green body, black chassis.......................................	£200-250 ☐
30e	1935-48	Breakdown Car........................	See 'Commercial vehicles and Vans' section	
30f	1936-41	Ambulance........................	See 'Fire, Police and Ambulance' vehicles section	
30g	1936-50	Caravan	See Caravan section	
32 (30a)	1934-35	Chrysler 'Airflow' Saloon.........	Maroon (lead) body, no chassis, separate bumper units, 103 mm.	£200-250 ☐
			Maroon (diecast) body, no chassis, separate bumper units, 103 mm.	£200-250 ☐
34a	1935-40	'Royal Air Mail' Service Car	See 'Commercial Vehicles and Vans' section	
35a	1936-40	Saloon Car........................	Some versions may have spare wheel cover in darker shade of main colour — Blue, Maroon, Grey, Yellow, Red, Turquoise, Black or White solid rubber wheels, 51 mm.	£90-120 ☐
	1946-48		Grey or Blue body (spare wheel cover not enhanced), Black rubber wheels only	£70-85 ☐
35az	1939-40	Fiat 2-seater Saloon................	Red, Blue or Green, White rubber wheels, 'Simca 5' cast inside. French issue........	£80-100 ☐
35b	1936-39	Racer................................	Red, Silver, Yellow or Blue body, with or without driver, White solid rubber wheels, Red grille & steering wheel, 57 mm.	£50-70 ☐
35b (200)	1939-40		Silver body, Red grille, Brown driver, solid Black rubber wheels only	£50-70 ☐
			Silver body, Red grille, Silver driver, solid Black rubber wheels only........	£50-70 ☐
			Green body, Black tyres...	£100-125 ☐
35c	1936-40	MG Sports Car........................	Red, Green, Turquoise, Blue or Maroon, Silver detailing, White solid rubber wheels, 52 mm.	£90-120 ☐
	1946-48		Red or Green body, Silver on radiator only, Black rubber wheels only	£70-100 ☐
35d	1938-40	Austin 7 Car (open tourer)	Wire windscreen frame, Black or White rubber wheels, Silver radiator & steering wheel, hole for driver, 50 mm., Blue, Turquoise, Grey, Lime Green, Maroon or Yellow, (Yellow may have Orange spare wheel cover)	£50-70 ☐
	1946-48		Blue, Fawn, Grey or Yellow body, Silver on radiator only, Black rubber wheels only	£50-70 ☐
36a	1937-41	Armstrong-Siddeley Limousine with Driver and Footman.............	Detailed chassis with slots, tinplate figures, sidelights, 97 mm. Red/Dark Red, Grey/Dark Grey, Maroon/Dark Maroon	£1000-1500 ☐
	1946		Grey body, Black smooth wheel hubs, Moulded chassis with or without slots	£100-150 ☐
36a	1947-50	Armstrong-Siddeley	(no slots or figures), Mid-Blue/Black, Grey/Black, Maroon/Black, Red/Maroon, Sky Blue/Black, Powder Blue/Black, Saxe-Blue/Black, Olive-Green/Black, Ridged hubs, moulded chassis........	£70-100 ☐
			Turquoise body, moulded chassis, ridged hubs........	£140-170 ☐
36b	1937-41	Bentley 2 seat Sports Coupé with Driver and Footman	Detailed chassis with slots, tinplate figures, sidelights, 94 mm. Cream/Black, Yellow/Maroon, Grey/Grey........	£1000-1500 ☐
	1946		Light Green or Saxe Blue body, smooth black wheel hubs, Moulded chassis with or without slots........	£200-300 ☐
36b	1947-50	Bentley (no slots/figures)	Green/Black, Blue/Black, Grey/Black, Fawn/Black, Light Fawn/Black, moulded chassis, ridged hubs........	£70-100 ☐
			Light Blue, moulded chassis, ridged hubs	£125-150 ☐
36c	1937-41	Humber Vogue Saloon with Driver and Footman ... with Driver & Footman........	Detailed chassis with slots, tinplate figures, sidelights, 91 mm. Green/Dark Green, Blue/Dark Blue, all Royal Blue	£1000-1500 ☐
	1946		Early post war issues with smooth Black hubs, moulded chassis with or without slots........	£100-150 ☐
36c	1947-50	Humber Vogue	Brown/Black, Blue/Black, Grey/Black, Maroon/Black, (no slots/figures)	£90-125 ☐
			Light Blue and Black body, moulded chassis, ridged hubs	£175-225 ☐
36d	1937-41	Rover Streamlined Saloon with Driver and Footman	Detailed cast chassis with slots, tinplate figures, sidelights, Black hubs, 94 mm. Green/Dark Green, Red/Maroon	£1000-1500 ☐
	1946		Early post war issues with smooth Black hubs & moulded chassis with or without slots........	£100-150 ☐
36d	1947-50	Rover (no slots/figures)	Dark, Mid or Bright Blue/Black, Light or Mid-Green/Black	£70-100 ☐
			Green body with Light Green hubs........	£100-125 ☐
36e	1937-41	British Salmson 2 seater Sports with Driver	Detailed chassis, cast driver, Black hubs, solid windscreen, sidelights, 93 mm. (spare wheel on some, 96 mm.) Royal Blue/Black, Blue/Dark Blue, Black/Red, Grey/Dark Grey, (hole in seat for driver)........	£1000-1500 ☐

Ref. No.		*Dinky Toys — Cars – continued*	Market Price Range
	1946	British Salmson	Early post war issues with smooth Black hubs, moulded chassis .... £100-150 ☐
			Rare Brown issues.. £100-150 ☐
36e	1947-50	British Salmson 2 seater Sports	Red/Black, Light or Mid-Green/Black, Fawn/Black, Mid-Blue/Black, Sky-Blue/Black or Saxe-Blue/Black, No hole in seat .... £70-80 ☐
			Red or Brown body, moulded chassis, ridged hubs .... £250-300 ☐
36f	1937-41	British Salmson 4 seater Sports with Driver	Detailed chassis, cast driver, sidelights, Black hubs and solid windscreen, cast-in spare wheel, 96 mm.
			Red/Maroon, Green/Dark Green, (hole in seat for driver) .... £1000-1500 ☐
36f	1947-50	British Salmson 4 seater Sports	Light or Mid-Green/Black, Brown/Black, Grey/Black, Fawn/Black, (no hole) .... £70-100 ☐
			Brownish-Grey/Black or Light Grey/Black .... £70-100 ☐

N.B. Early Post War Issues 38 & 39 Series – see the Model Identification section for details.

Ref. No.			Market Price Range
38a	1940-41 1946	Frazer Nash BMW Sports Car Special Issue	Red (Maroon seats), Dark Blue (Fawn seats), lacquered metal base, 82 mm. .... £150-175 ☐
			Dark Blue body, Light Blue seats, spread spigot not rivet 'Hornby Series' tinplate sheet.. £200-300 ☐
		Regular Issues	With Black base, smooth hubs .... £75-100 ☐
	1947-50		Light or Dark Blue (Fawn or Grey seats), Black base .... £70-100 ☐
			Grey (Fawn or Blue seats), or Grey (Red seats & wheels), Black base.................... £70-100 ☐
			Light Grey (Blue seats, Black wheels), Blue with Putty seats .... £70-100 ☐
38a (100)	1950-55		Same as previous models but made for export only (renumbered in 1954).................... NGPP ☐
38b	1940-41	Sunbeam Talbot Sports............	Red (Maroon tonneau), Red or Black wheels, lacquered metal base, 92 mm. .... £150-175 ☐
	1946		Grey body, Fawn seats or Green with Dark Green seats .... £300-400 ☐
	1947-49		Red/Maroon or Maroon/Grey, Black baseplate .... £70-100 ☐
			Light Green/Green, Brown/Blue, Black baseplate .... £70-100 ☐
			Light Grey (Grey or Dark Blue tonneau), Black wheels, Black baseplate .... £70-100 ☐
			Dark Grey (Grey or Light Blue tonneau), Black wheels, Black baseplate .... £70-100 ☐
			Yellow body and ridged hubs with matt Fawn tonneau, Black painted baseplate .... £200-300 ☐
			Yellow body and ridged hubs with Matt Green tonneau, Black painted baseplate .... £200-300 ☐
			Dark Blue body, Light Grey tonneau, Black wheels and baseplate .... £70-100 ☐
			Light Blue body, Dark Grey tonneau, Black wheels and baseplate .... £70-100 ☐
			Brown body, Blue tonneau .... £70-100 ☐
	1950		Late post war issues with coloured hubs, eg. Yellow body, Green tonneau, Yellow hubs .... £200-250 ☐
38b (101)	1950-55		As previous models but made for export only (renumbered in 1954) .... NGPP ☐
38c	1946	Lagonda Sports Coupé............	Early post war issues.. £200-300 ☐
	1947-50		Green (Black seats), or Green/Dark (Green seats), Black baseplate .... £70-100 ☐
			Grey (Fawn seats), or Grey (Maroon seats)... £70-100 ☐
			Maroon (Dark Blue seats), Black baseplate, 102 mm. .... £70-100 ☐
			Light Grey (Dark Grey seats), or Mid-Grey (Grey seats) .... £70-100 ☐
38c (102)	1950-55		As previous models but made for export only (renumbered in 1954) .... NGPP ☐
	1950		Late post war issues with coloured hubs, eg. Maroon body with Green hubs............. £200-250 ☐
38d	1940-41	Alvis Sports Tourer	Green body, Black seats & wheels or Maroon body, Red seats, lacquered metal baseplate, 95 mm. .... £150-175 ☐
	1946		Early post war issues.. £200-300 ☐
	1947-50		Green/Dark Green, Green/Brown, Black painted base .... £70-100 ☐
			Green body, Black seats and wheels, Black painted base .... £70-100 ☐
			Green body, Black seats, Green wheels, Black painted base .... £70-100 ☐
			Maroon/Grey, Red hubs, Maroon/Red, Light Blue/Dark Blue, Black base.................. £100-150 ☐
			Blue/Grey, Grey/Blue, Black painted base .... £70-100 ☐
	1950		Late post war issues with coloured hubs, eg. Maroon body with Grey hubs .... £200-250 ☐
38d (103)	1950-55		As previous models but made for export only (renumbered in 1954) .... NGPP ☐
38e	1940 ?	Triumph Dolomite..................	Planned and catalogued but not issued. .... NPP ☐
38e	1946	Armstrong Siddeley Coupé	Early post war issues.. £200-300 ☐
	1947-50		Grey/Blue, Light Grey/Blue, Black painted baseplate, 96 mm. .... £70-100 ☐
			Light Grey/Green, or Grey/Dark Green .... £70-100 ☐
			Bright Green/Grey, Red/Maroon, Cream/Blue, Black painted baseplate.................... £70-100 ☐
	1950		Late post war issues with coloured hubs, e.g. Light Green, Apple Green hubs or Mid or Light Green and Grey with Mid Green hubs, or Light Grey and Dark Green with Grey hubs.. £200-250 ☐
38e (104)	1950-55		As previous models but made for export only (renumbered in 1954) .... NGPP ☐
38f	1940-41	Jaguar (SS100) Sports Car	Khaki/Blue, Blue/Grey, Light Blue/Grey, Grey/Blue, Grey/Black, Red/Maroon, Dark Brown/Black, 2 windscreens, clear lacquered baseplate, 80 mm. .. £150-175 ☐
	1946		Early post war issues.. £75-100 ☐
	1947-50		Light or Dark Blue body, Grey or putty seats, Black painted baseplate .... £70-100 ☐
			Brown body, Black seats, Black painted baseplate or Red body .... £70-100 ☐
	1950		Late Post-war issues with coloured hubs, e.g. Light Blue body, putty seats, Blue hubs.. £150-180 ☐
38f (105)	1950-55		As previous models but made for export only (renumbered in 1954) .... NGPP ☐
39a	1939-41	Packard Super 8 Tourer	Light Green, Grey, Black, Yellow, Blue, lacquered baseplate, 107 mm. .... £150-175 ☐
	1946		Early post war issues.. £100-150 ☐
	1947-50		Brown, Green or Olive-Green body, Black painted baseplate .... £70-100 ☐
	1950		Late post war issues with coloured hubs .... £200-250 ☐
39b	1939-41	Oldsmobile 6 Sedan	Black, Maroon, Yellow, Mid Blue, Light or Mid-Grey or Green, lacquered baseplate, 100 mm. .... £150-175 ☐
	1946		Early post war issues.. £100-150 ☐

Ref. No.				*Dinky Toys — Cars – continued*	Market Price Range	
	1947-50			Grey, Brown, Cream, Violet Blue, Green or Fawn body, Black painted base............	**£70-100**	☐
	1947-50		U.S. issue	Light Blue body, Black ridged hubs, oval baseplate support, open rear baseplate.......	**£200-300**	☐
	1950			Late post war issues with coloured hubs	**£200-250**	☐
	1952		Export issue	Sand body and hubs, oval front supports, closed rear baseplate.................	**£200-300**	☐
39bu	1950-52	Oldsmobile Sedan (US issue)		Cream with Dark Blue wings or two-tone Blue, Black painted baseplate.................	**£700-900**	☐
				Cream body, Tan wings, Black painted baseplate, Blued axles, oval studs, closed rear baseplate	**£700-900**	☐
		Variation		With oval cast front supports, no tow hook hole, non blued steel axles................	**£700-900**	☐
39c	1939-41	Lincoln Zephyr Coupé		Grey, Yellow Red or Green body, lacquered baseplate, 106 mm.	**£150-175**	☐
	1946			Early post war issues	**£100-150**	☐
	1947-50			Grey, Brown, Maroon or Red body, Black painted baseplate	**£70-100**	☐
	1950			Late post war issues with coloured hubs e.g. Light 'Riley' Green with darker Green hubs	**£200-250**	☐
39cu	1950-52		US issue:	Red body and ridged hubs, Maroon wings, Black painted baseplate................	**£1000-1250**	☐
39cu	1950-52		US issue:	Cream body and ridged hubs, Brown wings, Black painted baseplate................	**£1000-1250**	☐
39cu	1950-52		US issue:	Tan with Brown wings, Black painted baseplate........................	**£1000-1250**	☐
39d	1939-41	Buick Viceroy Saloon		Grey, Green, Maroon, Cream or Blue, lacquered baseplate, 103 mm.	**£150-175**	☐
	1946			Early post war issues	**£100-150**	☐
	1947-50			Light or Dark Green, Maroon, Fawn, Blue, Beige or Grey body, Black base	**£70-100**	☐
				Mustard body, Black painted baseplate	**£150-200**	☐
				Apple Green body and hubs	**£300-400**	☐
	1950			Late post war issues with coloured hubs, eg. Light 'Riley' Green with darker green hubs	**£200-250**	☐
39e	1939-41	Chrysler Royal...........................		Yellow, Green, Dark Blue or Grey body, lacquered baseplate, 106 mm.	**£150-175**	☐
	1946			Early post war issues	**£100-150**	☐
	1947-50			Light Blue, Mid-Blue, Dark Blue, Light Green, Mid-Green, Dark Green or Dark Grey body, Black wheels and baseplate	**£70-100**	☐
				As previous models but with Silvered baseplate........................	**£250-350**	☐
				Cream body, Green hubs, Black painted baseplate	**£100-150**	☐
	1950			Late post war issues with coloured hubs, eg. Light 'Triumph 1800' Blue with blue hubs	**£200-250**	☐
39eu	1950-52	Chrysler Royal (US issue).........		Yellow with Red wings, Yellow hubs or two-tone Green body with Light Green hubs, Black baseplate, Blued axles	**£700-900**	☐
39f	1939-41	Studebaker State Commander...		Yellow, Green or Dark Grey body, lacquered baseplate, 103 mm.	**£150-175**	☐
	1946			Early post war issues	**£100-150**	☐
	1947-50			Yellow body, Black smooth wheels	**£400-500**	☐
				Mid-Blue, Green, Olive or Maroon body, Black baseplate	**£70-100**	☐
				Grey or Light Grey body, Black wheels	**£70-100**	☐
				Dark Maroon body, Black wheels	**£70-100**	☐
				Very Dark Blue body, Black wheels	**£70-100**	☐
				Tan body, Black wheels	**£120-150**	☐
	1950			Late Post-war issues with coloured hubs	**£200-250**	☐
40a (158)	1947-55	Riley Saloon		Dark Blue, Light Blue, Cream, Dark Grey, Light Grey, Light Green, Mid Green or Dark Green, large or small print on Black painted baseplate, 93 mm.	**£100-125**	☐
40b	1948-49	Triumph 1800 (Renown)		Light Blue, Fawn, Grey, rear axle pillars, Black baseplate, 91 mm.	**£90-120**	☐
				Black body, rear axle held by pillars, Black baseplate	**£1500-2000**	☐
40b (151)	1949-55			Mid Blue, Dark Blue, Beige, Grey or Tan, rear axle held by baseplate	**£90-120**	☐
40d (152)	1949-54	Austin (A40) Devon		Light Blue, Mid Blue, Dark Blue, Light Green (Cream hubs), Dark Green, Red, Maroon, Tan, large or small print on Black base	**£90-120**	☐
				Dull Green, Fawn wheels	**£90-120**	☐
				Greyish-Green, Beige wheels	**£90-120**	☐
40e	1948-50	Standard Vanguard		Tan body, 'open' rear wheel arches, small print on base, with rear axle clip, name inside roof, 99 mm.	**£90-120**	☐
				Variation with no name inside roof	**£150-200**	☐
	1950-52			Tan or Light Blue, 'closed' rear wheel arches, small print on base	**£90-120**	☐
40e (153)	1952-54			Light Blue, Dark Blue, Fawn, Cream or Tan, 'ridged' boot lid, large base print.........	**£90-120**	☐
				Tan body, Red hubs, open rear wheel arches	**£180-220**	☐
				Maroon body and hubs, with spats, no lettering under roof and large lettering on base, circa 1953	**£750-1000**	☐

40e (153) Standard Vanguard Base variations

1948-1950 Small Print with rear axle clip	1950-1952 Small Print with no rear axle clip	1952-1959 Large Print on base

| 40f (154) | 1951-54 | Hillman Minx .... | | Light Green, Dark Green, Light Tan or Dark Tan body, Cream or Green hubs, large base print, 88 mm. | **£90-120** | ☐ |
| | | | | Dark Tan, Grey hubs .... | **£150-200** | ☐ |

Ref. No.		Name	Description	Price
40g (159)	1950-54	Morris Oxford	Dark Green, Light Green hubs or Very Dark Green, Grey or Light Green hubs, large or small base print, 93 mm.	**£90-120**
			Fawn, Light Tan or Grey body, large or small print on base	**£90-120**
			Mid-Blue body (similar shade to the 481 'Ovaltine' Bedford CA Van)......................	**£1500-2000**
40j (161)	1949-53	Austin (A40) Somerset	Light Blue, Mid Blue, Dark Blue or Red body, Mid Blue hubs, 89 mm.	**£90-120**
101	1957-60	Sunbeam Alpine (touring)........	Pink body, Tan seats, Cream diecast hubs, Grey driver, 94 mm.	**£150-200**
			Turquoise body, Blue seats, Light Blue diecast hubs, Grey driver	**£150-200**
			Turquoise body, Blue seats, spun aluminium hubs, Grey driver	**£150-200**
102	1957-60	MG Midget (touring finish)	Orange body, Red seats and diecast hubs, Grey driver, 83 mm.	**£175-225**
			Light Green body, Tan seats, Cream diecast hubs, Grey driver	**£175-225**
			Late issues with spun wheels........................	**£200-250**
103	1957-60	Austin Healey 100 (touring)......	Red body, Grey seats, diecast hubs and driver, 85 mm.	**£145-175**
			Cream body, Red seats and diecast hubs, Grey driver	**£145-175**
104	1957-60	Aston Martin DB3S (touring)...	Pale Blue body, Blue seats, Dark Blue cast hubs, Grey driver, 87 mm.	**£145-175**
			Pink body, Red seats and diecast hubs, Grey driver.	**£145-175**
105	1957-60	Triumph TR2 (touring finish) ...	Grey body, Red seats and diecast hubs, 84 mm.	**£100-125**
			As previous issue but with spun hubs in 'plain' printed box.	**£200-300**
			Primrose-Yellow body, Green seats and diecast hubs, Grey driver	**£140-160**
	1959-60		As previous models but with spun aluminium hubs	**£145-175**
106 (140a)	1954-58	Austin A90 Atlantic	Light Blue body, Cream seats, Cream wheels, 95 mm.	**£125-150**
			Light Blue body, Red seats, Red wheels	**£100-125**
			Light Blue body, Dark Blue seats, Cream wheels	**£110-140**
			Black body, Red seats & wheels, White tyres	**£100-125**
			Red body, (reported but never seen)	NGPP
107	1955-59	Sunbeam Alpine (competition finish)	Light Blue, Tan or Cream seats, Cream wheels, '26', racing driver, 94 mm.	**£75-85**
			Cerise body, Grey seats, Cream wheels, RN '34', racing driver	**£75-85**
108	1955-59	MG Midget (competition)........	Red body, Tan seats, Red wheels, RN '24', racing driver, 83 mm.	**£100-125**
			White body, Maroon seats, Red wheels, RN '28', racing driver	**£100-125**
			U.S. Issue, Red body and wheels, Tan seats, dashboard & tonneau, no driver as per special box picture........................	**£300-400**
109	1955-59	Austin Healey 100 (competition finish)	Cream body, Red seats and hubs, racing driver & number '23', 85 mm.	**£80-95**
			Yellow body, Blue seats and hubs, racing driver & number '21'	**£80-95**
110	1956-59	Aston Martin DB3S (competition finish)	Metallic Grey body, Blue seats and hubs, racing driver & number '20', 87 mm.	**£80-95**
			Metallic Turquoise body, Red seats and hubs, racing driver and number '22'	**£80-95**
			Light Green body, Red interior, Red ridged wheels, RN '22'	**£250-350**
110	1966-67	Aston Martin DB5	Metallic Red, Cream or Black seats, '110' on base, spoked wheels, 111 mm.	**£70-85**
	1967-71		Metallic Red or Blue, Cream or Black seats, plain base, spoked wheels	**£70-85**
111	1956-59	Triumph TR2 Sports Car (competition finish)	Pink body, Blue seats and hubs, racing driver & number '29', 84 mm.	**£90-110**
			Turquoise body, Red seats and hubs, racing driver & number '25'	**£90-110**
112	1961-66	Austin Healey Sprite II	Red body, suspension & fingertip steering, spun hubs, 78 mm.	**£65-75**
		South African issues:	Turquoise, Pink, Light Blue or Dark Blue body, spun hubs	**£500-750**
113	1962-69	MG 'MGB'	Cream body, Red seats, Grey plastic driver, 85 mm.	**£70-80**
	1966	South African issue:	Mid-Blue body (Red interior), or Red body, spun hubs	**£500-750**
114	1963-71	Triumph Spitfire	Sports car with Blue lady driver (plastic), spun hubs, 87 mm.	
	1963-66		Metallic Silver-Grey body (Red seats), or Red body (Cream seats)	**£65-80**
	1966-70		Metallic Gold body with Red seats and 'Tiger In Tank' on bootlid	**£70-80**
	1966-70		Metallic Gold body, without bootlid logo	**£60-70**
	1970-71		Metallic Purple body	**£100-125**
115	1965-69	Plymouth Fury Sports..............	White open body, suspension & steering, driver & passenger, 122 mm.	**£70-80**
116	1966-71	Volvo P 1800 S	Red or Dark Metallic Red, Silver or Gold wheels, suspension, 105 mm.	**£40-50**
120	1962-67	Jaguar 'E' type........................	Red, detachable Black hardtop/optional Cream or Grey folded soft-top, 92 mm.	**£60-70**
			Metallic Blue & White, Black, Grey or Cream body	**£60-70**
			Metallic Light Blue & Black body, Cream seats	**£850-1350**
122	1977-78	Volvo 265 DL Estate..............	Metallic Blue or Cream with '265DL' wing badges, 141 mm.	**£15-20**
	1979-80		Orange version without '265 DL' (Polistil, made in Italy, Brown card box)	**£15-20**
123	1977-80	Princess 2200 HL......................	Metallic Bronze with black roof side panels or white with black panels, plastic wheels, 128 mm.	**£15-20**
			All over White version	**£30-40**
124	1977-79	Rolls-Royce Phantom V............	Metallic Light Blue, boot opens - bonnet does not (see 152), 141 mm.	**£30-40**
127	1964-66	Rolls-Royce Silver Cloud Mk3	Metallic Blue or Metallic Green, suspension & steering, 125 mm.	**£60-70**
	1966-69		Metallic Gold	**£60-70**
	1969-72		Metallic Red	**£60-70**
128	1964-67	Mercedes-Benz 600	Metallic Red body, suspension & steering, 3 figures/luggage, 147 mm.	**£35-40**
	1967-75		As previous model but with Black roof, driver only	**£25-30**
	1975-79		Metallic Blue body, driver, suspension & fingertip steering, 147 mm.	**£25-30**
129	?-?	MG Midget (U.S. issue)	White body, Maroon seats, Red hubs, no driver or racing number (see 108)	**£400-500**
			Red body, Tan seats, Red hubs, no driver or racing number (see 108)	**£400-500**
129	1965-72	Volkswagen 1300 Sedan	Metallic Blue body, spun hubs, suspension & fingertip steering, 100 mm.	**£30-40**
	1972-76		Metallic Blue body, plastic Speedwheels	**£30-40**
130	1964-66	Ford Consul Corsair	Red or Metallic Red body, suspension & steering, spun hubs, 106 mm.	**£45-55**
	1966-69		Light Blue, suspension & fingertip steering, spun hubs	**£45-55**
131	1956-61	Cadillac Eldorado......................	Pink (Grey seats), Yellow (Red seats), driver, diecast hubs, 118 mm.	**£90-120**
	1962-63		As previous models but with spun aluminium hubs	**£90-120**

Ref. No.	Year	Model	Description	Market Price Range	
131	1968-70	Jaguar 'E' type 2 + 2	White body, suspension, tilting seats, cast spoked wheels, 112 mm.	£70-80	☐
	1970-75		Bronze body, cast spoked wheels or plastic wheels	£70-80	☐
	1975-76		Metallic Purple, Speedwheels	£40-50	☐
	1976-77		Bronze body, Speedwheels	£40-50	☐
	1977-77		Metallic Red or Post Office Red body, Speedwheels	£40-50	☐
132	1955-61	Packard Convertible	Light Green/Red, or Light Brown/Red, driver, 112 mm.	£80-110	☐
132	1967-74	Ford 40 RV	Metallic Silver, Blue, Metallic Green, Red/Yellow, spun wheels, 96 mm.	£25-35	☐
			N.B. Early models have red headlight recesses.		
133	1955-60	Cunningham C5R	White (Tan seats), or Off-White (Blue seats), Blue driver, 99 mm.	£70-80	☐
			As previous models but with spun aluminium hubs	£70-80	☐
133	1964-66	Ford Cortina	Metallic Gold/White, spun hubs, 101 mm, (issued to replace 139)	£40-50	☐
	1966-68		Pale Yellow body, spun hubs	£40-50	☐
134	1964-68	Triumph Vitesse	Metallic Blue or Metallic Green, with white side stripe, spun hubs, 85 mm.	£60-70	☐
135	1963-69	Triumph 2000 Saloon	Red interior, Grey base, spun hubs, wipers, luggage, 105 mm.		
		normal colours:	Metallic Green with White roof or Metallic Blue with White roof	£55-65	☐
		Gift Set 118 colour:	White body, Blue roof	GSP	☐
		promotional colours:	Black body, Cactus-Green roof	£800-1000	☐
			Black body, White roof	£800-1000	☐
			Blue Grey body, Black roof	£800-1000	☐
			Light Green body, Lilac roof	£800-1000	☐
			Brown body, Light Green roof	£800-1000	☐
			British Racing Green, White roof	£800-1000	☐
			White body, Light Green roof, Blue interior	£800-1000	☐
			Cherry Red body, White roof, Blue interior	£800-1000	☐
			White body, Black roof, Blue interior	£1000-1500	☐
			Dark Green body, Cactus-Green roof	£900-1300	☐
			White body, Light Grey roof	£600-700	☐
136	1964-65	Vauxhall Viva	White body, suspension & fingertip steering, 93 mm.	£30-35	☐
	1965-68		Deep Metallic Mid Blue body	£30-35	☐
	1969-73		Pale Metallic Blue body	£30-35	☐
137	1963-66	Plymouth Fury Convertible	Grey/Cream, Green/Cream, Pink/Cream, Blue/Cream, Two-tone Green, Metallic Light Green/Metallic Dark Green, 122 mm.	£60-80	☐
			Dark Blue/White, detachable hard-top, spun aluminium hubs	£70-80	☐
			Blackish-Green, Pale Green top, Red interior, spun hubs	£80-100	☐
138	1963-66	Hillman Imp	Metallic Silver Green body, luggage, spun hubs, cast headlamps, 85 mm.	£30-40	☐
	1966-68		Metallic Red body, luggage, spun hubs, jewelled or plastic headlamps	£30-40	☐
	1968-73		Metallic Blue body, luggage, spun hubs, jewelled or plastic headlamps	£30-40	☐
139	1963-64	Ford Cortina	Pale Blue body, suspension & steering, cast headlamps, 101 mm.	£45-55	☐
	1964-65		Metallic Blue body	£45-55	☐
	1966	South African issue:	Green body, spun hubs, Fawn interior	£500-600	☐

NOTE: South African Dinky Toys — The boxes are printed in both English and Afrikaans, and with the distributors name.

Ref. No.	Year	Model	Description	Market Price Range	
139a (170)	1949-54	Ford Fordor Sedan	Yellow, Red, Green or Tan body, (all with matching wheels), 102 mm.	£70-90	☐
			Brown body, Red wheels	£70-90	☐
			Red body, Maroon wheels	NGPP	☐
139am	1950-54	US Army Staff Car	(170m) Ford Fordor in Olive drab with White stars on roof and doors	£175-250	☐
			Variant without stars (Canadian Market)	NGPP	☐
139b (171)	1950-54	Hudson Commodore	Dark Blue body, Stone roof & wheels, 111 mm.	£80-100	☐
			Dark Blue body, Fawn roof and wheels	£80-100	☐
			Cream body, Maroon roof & wheels	£80-100	☐
			Royal Blue body, Stone roof and wheels	£100-125	☐
			Fawn lower body, Light Blue roof, as per 151 (40b) Triumph Renown Blue	NGPP	☐
140a (106)	1951-54	Austin A90 Atlantic	Blue body, Dark Blue seats, 95 mm.	£100-125	☐
			Dark Blue body, Red seats	£100-125	☐
			Pink body, Cream seats and wheels	£100-125	☐
140b (156)	1951-54	Rover 75 Saloon	Maroon (Maroon wheels), or Cream (Cream wheels), 101 mm.	£70-90	☐
140	1963-69	Morris 1100	Light Blue or Dark Blue body, suspension & suspension, spun hubs, front number plate may have surrounding casting or not, 87 mm.	£30-40	☐
	1966	South African issue:	White body, Blue roof or Light Caramel, Red interior	£500-750	☐
141	1963-67	Vauxhall Victor Estate Car	Yellow or Maroon body, suspension & steering, spun hubs, 92 mm.	£30-40	☐
	1966	South African issue:	Pink body with Blue interior, spun hubs	£500-750	☐
142	1962-68	Jaguar Mk 10	Metallic Blue or Light Blue, suspension, spun aluminium hubs, 107 mm.	£40-50	☐
	1966	South African issue:	Green body with White roof, spun hubs	£500-750	☐
143	1962-67	Ford Capri	Turquoise body, White roof, suspension, luggage, spun hubs, 90 mm.	£50-60	☐
144	1963-67	Volkswagen 1500	Off-White or Bronze body, suspension, luggage, spun hubs, 93 mm.	£30-40	☐
			Metallic Green body	£400-600	☐
145	1962-67	Singer Vogue	Metallic Light Green body, suspension & steering, spun hubs, 93 mm.	£40-50	☐
			Yellow body, Red interior, spun hubs	£1500-2000	☐
146	1963-67	Daimler 2.5 litre V8	Metallic Pale Green body, suspension & steering, spun hubs, 95 mm.	£50-60	☐
147	1962-69	Cadillac 62	Metallic Green or Blue body, suspension & steering, spun hubs, 113 mm.	£50-60	☐
148	1962-62	Ford Fairlane	(Non-metallic), Pale Green, closed windows, spun hubs, White tyres, 111 mm.	£50-60	☐
	1962-65		(Non-metallic), Pale Green, open windows, spun hubs, White tyres	£50-60	☐
	1965-67		Light or Dark Metallic Green, open windows, spun hubs, White tyres	£50-90	☐
	1966	South African issue:	Bright Blue body, open windows, spun hubs, White tyres	£500-750	☐
	1966	South African issue:	Greyish-Lilac, spun hubs, no base number, White tyres	£800-1000	☐

Ref. No.	Year	Name	Description	Market Price Range	
149	1971-75	Citroën Dyane	Bronze body, Black roof, suspension, Speedwheels, 91 mm.	£25-30	☐
	1971-75		Light Grey body, Dark Grey or Black roof, suspension, Speedwheels	£25-30	☐
150	1959-64	Rolls-Royce Silver Wraith	Two-tone Grey body, suspension, spun hubs, Chrome or metal bumpers, 117 mm.	£40-50	☐
			Later issues with plastic bumpers	£35-45	☐
			N.B. Similar model F551 'Made in France'		
151 (40b)	1954-59	Triumph 1800 (Renown)	Light Blue, Light Blue wheels, rear axle held in baseplate, 91 mm.	£80-100	☐
			Light Blue, Dark Blue wheels	£80-100	☐
			Pale Brown (Green wheels), or Grey (Blue wheels)	£80-100	☐
151	1965-69	Vauxhall Victor 101	Yellow, Metallic Red or Lime Green, suspension, spun hubs, 105 mm.	£50-60	☐
152 (40d)	1954-56	Austin (A40) Devon	Red (Red wheels), Dark Blue or Dark Green body, 86 mm.	£80-100	☐
			Greyish-Green or Greenish-Grey (same colour or Brown wheels)	£80-100	☐
	1956-60		Deep Yellow lower body, Blue upper body, Dark Blue wheels	£200-250	☐
			Pink lower body, Lime Green upper body, Light Cream wheels	£200-250	☐
			Mid Blue body, Mid Blue ridged wheels	£600-800	☐
152	1965-67	Rolls Royce Phantom V	Dark Blue body, chauffeur and 2 passengers, spun hubs, 141 mm.	£40-50	☐
	1967-77	design change:	Dark Blue or Black body with Chauffeur but no passengers	£25-30	☐
153 (40e)	1954-59	Standard Vanguard	Blue, Brown, Tan, Cream or Fawn, ridged boot, large print on base	£80-110	☐
			White (White wheels), ridged boot lid, large print on base	£80-110	☐
			Maroon (Brown wheels), ridged boot lid, large print on base	£2000-3000	☐
	1959-59		As previous models but having enlarged boot lid lamp casting	£80-110	☐
153	1967-71	Aston Martin DB6	Metallic Silver Blue body, suspension, steering, 111 mm.	£40-45	☐
			Metallic Green body	£60-70	☐
154 (40f)	1954-56	Hillman Minx	Brown (Cream wheels), 87 mm.	£80-90	☐
			Tan body, (Blue wheels)	£80-90	☐
			Light Green (Light Green wheels)	£80-90	☐
	1956-59		Blue lower body, Pink upper body, Dark Blue wheels	£200-250	☐
	1956-59		Bright Green lower body, Cream upper body	£125-150	☐
	1956-59		Olive-Green lower body, Cream upper body	£125-175	☐
			Lime Green lower body, Cream upper body	£200-250	☐
154	1966-69	Ford Taunus 17M	Yellow & White body, suspension, steering, tilt seats, windows, 110 mm.	£25-35	☐
155	1961-66	Ford Anglia 105E	Turquoise or Green body, Red interior, suspension, windows, spun hubs, 81 mm.	£60-70	☐
			Turquoise body, Pale Blue interior	£100-150	☐
	1966	South African issue:	Deep Cream body, Red interior, spun hubs	£500-750	☐
156 (140b)	1954-56	Rover 75	Ivory body, Ivory or Light Blue hubs, 101 mm.	£80-110	☐
			Red (Red wheels), or Maroon (Red wheels)	£80-110	☐
	1956-59		Dark Green lower, Light Green upper body, Light Green wheels	£90-120	☐
	1956-59		Ivory lower, Light Blue upper body, Ivory wheels	£100-125	☐
	1956-59		Ivory lower, Dark Blue upper body, Ivory wheels	£200-250	☐
	1956-59		Ivory lower, Mid-Blue upper body, Beige wheels	£175-200	☐
156	1968-71	Saab 96	Metallic Red or Metallic Blue body, suspension, spun hubs, 98 mm.	£50-75	☐
157	1954-57	Jaguar XK120	Greyish-Green (Fawn wheels), or Red (Red wheels), 97 mm.	£90-110	☐
			Yellow (Yellow wheels), or White (Fawn wheels)	£200-250	☐
	1957-59		Turquoise lower body, Cerise upper body, Cerise wheels	£200-250	☐
	1957-59		Yellow lower body, Grey upper body, Grey wheels	£200-250	☐
	1959-62		Greyish-Green body, spun aluminium hubs, lighter Yellow box	£200-250	☐
			Red body, spun aluminium hubs	£200-250	☐
157	1968-73	BMW 2000 Tilux	Blue/White, suspension, special lights, spun hubs, 121 mm.	£30-40	☐
			Metallic Blue with Gold upper half, pictorial box lining	£90-120	☐
158 (40a)	1954-60	Riley Saloon	Cream body, Green wheels, large print on base, 93 mm.	£100-125	☐
			Light Green body, Mid-Green wheels, large print on base	£100-125	☐
158	1967-70	Rolls-Royce Silver Shadow	Metallic Red, suspension, spun hubs, 125 mm.	£30-40	☐
	1970-73		Metallic Blue, suspension, opening doors/bonnet/boot	£20-25	☐
159 (40g)	1954-56	Morris Oxford	Grey body with Grey hubs, 93 mm.	£80-110	☐
			Dark Green body (Dark Green hubs), or Light Green body	£80-110	☐
			Mid Blue body, Mid Blue ridged wheels	£700-900	☐
			Pale Brown (Sand) body with matching ridged wheels	£700-900	☐
	1956-59		Cream lower body, Green upper body, Green wheels	£150-200	☐
	1956-59		Dark Pink lower body, Cream upper body, Beige wheels	£150-200	☐
159	1967-70	Ford Cortina Mk.II	White body, suspension, tilting seats, spun aluminium hubs, 105 mm.	£40-50	☐
160	1958-62	Austin A30	Turquoise or Tan body, smooth or treaded solid grey plastic wheels, 77 mm.	£80-110	☐
160	1967-74	Mercedes-Benz 250 SE	Metallic Blue body, suspension, steering, working stop-lights, 117 mm.	£25-35	☐
161 (40j)	1953-56	Austin (A40) Somerset	Light Blue body, Mid-Blue wheels, 89 mm.	£80-110	☐
			Mid-Blue body, Light Blue wheels	£80-110	☐
			Dark Blue body, Mid Blue hubs, 40J on baseplate, dual numbers on box with Blue Spot	£300-400	☐
			Dark Red body, Dark Red wheels	£80-110	☐
	1956-59		Red lower body, Yellow roof, Red wheels	£150-200	☐
	1956-59		Black lower body, Cream roof, Cream wheels	£150-200	☐
161	1965-69	Ford Mustang Fastback	White (Red seats), 'MUSTANG' badge on wings, steering, 111 mm.	£40-50	☐
	1969-73		Yellow body, Blue seats, cast-in logo replaces decal badge	£30-40	☐
			Orange body (without decal), Speedwheels	£25-35	☐
162	1956-60	Ford Zephyr (Mk I)	Cream and Dark Green body, Cream wheels, 96 mm.	£65-80	☐
			Two-tone Blue body, Light Blue wheels	£65-80	☐
			Cream and Light (Lime), Green body	£65-80	☐
162	1966-70	Triumph 1300	Metallic Blue, suspension, fingertip steering, spun aluminium hubs, 93 mm.	£40-50	☐
163	1956-60	Bristol 450 Coupé	British Racing Green body, Light Green wheels, RN '27', 98 mm.	£40-65	☐

Ref. No.			*Dinky Toys — Cars – continued*	Market Price Range	
163	1966-71	Volkswagen 1600 TL................	Red or Dark Metallic Red, suspension, cast detailed hubs, 102 mm............................	£30-40	☐
			Metallic Blue body, Speedwheels...	£30-40	☐
164	1957-60	Vauxhall Cresta	Maroon lower body, Beige upper body, Cream wheels, 96 mm.	£80-100	☐
	1957-60		Green lower body, Grey upper body, Grey wheels...	£80-100	☐
164	1967-71	Ford Zodiac Mk.IV	Silver body, suspension, steering, 4 opening doors, 114 mm.	£30-40	☐
			Pale Metallic Blue body, suspension & fingertip steering	£30-40	☐
			Metallic Bronze body, Red interior, suspension & fingertip steering	£120-150	☐
165	1959-60	Humber Hawk..............................	Maroon/Cream or Green/Black, no front number plate casting, 102 mm.	£60-70	☐
	1959-63		Maroon/Cream or Green/Black, with front number plate casting	£60-70	☐
			Black lower & all Green upper body, spun wheels, with front number plate	£150-200	☐
165	1969-76	Ford Capri...............................	Metallic Green, Blue or Purple, Speedwheels, suspension, 102 mm......................	£30-40	☐
166	1958-63	Sunbeam Rapier..............	Orange lower body, Cream upper body, Cream wheels, 89 mm.	£80-100	☐
			Mid-Blue lower body, Turquoise upper body, Mid-Blue wheels.............................	£70-80	☐
166	1967-70	Renault R16	Metallic Blue, suspension & fingertip steering, spun hubs, 99 mm........................	£20-35	☐
167	1958-63	A.C. Aceca Sports Coupé	Grey body, Red roof, Red wheels, 89 mm.	£70-80	☐
			Cream body, Reddish-Maroon roof, Silver cast hubs..	£200-250	☐
			Cream body, Brown roof, Cream or Beige wheels or spun aluminium hubs	£70-80	☐
			Pale Yellow body, Maroon roof, spun aluminium hubs	£80-90	☐
			All Cream body, spun aluminium hubs. (Lighter Yellow box with Cream spot).........	£200-250	☐
			Cream body, Maroon roof, spun aluminium hubs	£200-250	☐
168	1959-63	Singer Gazelle Saloon...............	Brown lower, Pale Yellow upper body, spun aluminium hubs, 92 mm......................	£80-100	☐
			Dark Green lower, Grey upper body, spun aluminium hubs	£70-80	☐
168	1968-70	Ford Escort	Pale Blue or White, cast detailed hubs, 97 mm.	£30-40	☐
	1970-74		Metallic Red body, spun aluminium hubs..	£30-40	☐
	1974-75		Metallic Blue body, Speedwheels...	£30-40	☐
169	1958-63	Studebaker Golden Hawk	Green/Cream body, Cream wheels or spun hubs, White tyres, 106 mm...................	£70-80	☐
			Tan/Red body, Cream wheels or spun hubs, White tyres....................................	£70-80	☐
169	1967-69	Ford Corsair 2000 E	Silver body, Black textured roof, suspension & steering, 108 mm.........................	£45-55	☐

Two paint schemes exist for two-colour issues on models 170, 171 and 172:
1: Lower colour covers wing tops and doors up to windows (generally known as 'Highline') and
2: Lower colour extends only up to ridge on wings/doors ('Lowline').

170 (139a)	1954-56	Ford Fordor	Single colours: Tan (Red wheels), or Green, Yellow or Red, 102 mm.	£70-90	☐
	1956-58		('Highline'), Red lower body, Cream upper body...	£150-200	☐
	1956-58		('Highline'), Blue lower body, Pink upper body...	£150-200	☐
	1958-59		('Lowline'), Red lower body, Cream upper body...	£150-200	☐
	1958-59		('Lowline'), Blue lower body, Pink upper body...	£150-200	☐
170m	1954-54	Ford US Army Staff Car	(139am) Military Green, US issue, renumbered 675	£175-250	☐
170	1964-70	Lincoln Continental...................	Metallic Orange with White roof, or Blue with White roof, 127 mm.	£60-80	☐
170	1979	Granada Ghia..........................	Never issued		
171 (139b)	1954-56	Hudson Commodore Sedan	Dark Blue body, Fawn or Stone roof, Fawn wheels, 111 mm.	£80-100	☐
			Cream body, Maroon roof	£80-100	☐
	1956-58		('Highline'), Turquoise lower body with Red upper body, Red wheels..................	£150-200	☐
			('Highline'), Blue lower body, Red upper body, Red wheels...............................	£200-250	☐
			('Highline'), Grey lower body with Blue upper body, Blue wheels.......................	£150-200	☐
	1958-59		('Lowline'), Turquoise lower body with Red upper body, Red wheels..................	£200-250	☐
			('Lowline'), Grey lower body with Blue upper body, Blue wheels	£200-250	☐
171	1965-68	Austin 1800..............................	Pale Blue or Metallic Blue, suspension, steering, spun hubs, 101 mm.................	£50-60	☐
172	1954-56	Studebaker Land Cruiser	Light Green (Green wheels), or Blue (Fawn wheels), 107 mm.	£90-110	☐
	1956-58		('Highline'), Cream lower body, Maroon upper body, Cream wheels....................	£125-175	☐
			('Highline'), Cream lower body, Tan upper body, Cream wheels.........................	£125-175	☐
	1958-59		('Lowline'), Cream lower body, Maroon upper body, Cream wheels....................	£125-175	☐
			('Lowline'), Cream lower body, Tan upper body, Cream wheels	£125-175	☐
172	1965-69	Fiat 2300 Station Wagon	Blue, TT Blue or White/Blue, suspension, steering, spun hubs, 108 mm...............	£40-50	☐
173	1958-60	Nash Rambler Station Wagon ..	Turquoise/Maroon, number on baseplate, 101 mm.	£50-60	☐
			Pink/Blue, number on baseplate...	£50-60	☐
	1960-62		Turquoise/Maroon, without number on baseplate...	£50-60	☐
			Pink/Blue, without number on baseplate..	£50-60	☐
173	1969-73	Pontiac Parisienne	Metallic Maroon or Blue, retractable aerials, Speedwheels, 132 mm...................	£45-55	☐
174	1958-63	Hudson Hornet..........................	Red/Cream body, Grey wheels or spun aluminium hubs, 111 mm.......................	£70-85	☐
			Yellow/Grey body, Grey wheels or spun aluminium hubs	£70-85	☐
174	1969-73	Ford Mercury Cougar..............	Red body, cast or Speedwheels, retractable aerial, 122 mm...............................	£25-30	☐
			Blue or Metallic Dark Blue body, cast or Speedwheels.....................................	£25-30	☐
175	1958-61	Hillman Minx	Grey body, Blue roof and boot, Blue wheels or spun hubs, 88 mm......................	£75-85	☐
			Tan body, Green roof and boot, Cream wheels or spun hubs	£75-85	☐
175	1969-73	Cadillac Eldorado.....................	Metallic Purple/Black or Metallic Blue/Black, Speedwheels, 133 mm...................	£30-45	☐
176	1958-63	Austin A105 Saloon	First Dinky Toys car to have windows. Body sides have a contrasting side flash. Treaded tyres may be Black or White. 102 mm.		
	1958-59		Cream body, Dark Blue side flash, Cream wheels	£80-90	☐
			Grey body, Red side flash, Red wheels	£80-90	☐
	1959-63		Cream body, Dark Blue roof and side flash, Cream wheels or spun hubs............	£120-150	☐
			Grey body, Red roof and side flash, Red wheels or spun hubs..........................	£120-150	☐
176	1969-74	N.S.U. Ro80	Metallic Red body, spun hubs, luminous seats, working lights, 114 mm.	£30-40	☐
			Metallic Blue body	£100-150	☐

Ref. No.				Market Price Range	
177	1961-66		Opel Kapitan	Blue body, suspension, fingertip steering, spun hubs, 100 mm.	£30-45	☐
	1966	South African issue:	Dark Blue body.	£500-750	☐
	1966	South African issue:	Pale Yellow body, Red interior	£500-750	☐
178	1959-63		Plymouth Plaza	Light Blue body, Dark Blue roof and side stripe, spun hubs, 108 mm.	£80-90	☐
				Pink body, Green roof and side stripe, spun hubs, ...	£80-90	☐
				Light Tan body, Light Green roof and flash, spun hubs	£200-250	☐
				Pale Blue body with White roof and side stripe, suspension, spun hubs	£150-200	☐
178	1975-79		Mini Clubman	Bronze body, opening doors, jewelled headlights on some, 82 mm.	£40-50	☐
				Red body version	£100-125	☐
179	1958-63		Studebaker President	Pale Blue body, Blue stripe, Cream wheels or spun hubs, 108 mm.	£80-100	☐
				Yellow body, Blue stripe, Cream wheels or spun hubs	£80-100	☐
179	1971-75		Opel Commodore	Metallic Blue body, Black roof, suspension, Speedwheels, 107 mm.	£45-55	☐
180	1958-63		Packard Clipper	Fawn/Pink body, Cream wheels or spun hubs, White tyres, 108 mm.	£80-100	☐
				Orange/Grey body, Cream wheels or spun hubs, White tyres	£80-100	☐
				All Green body, White tyres	£80-100	☐
180	1979-80		Rover 3500	White body, plastic chassis & wheels, 131 mm. Made in Hong Kong	£15-20	☐
181	1956-70		Volkswagen Saloon	Grey, Air Force Blue or Lime Green, Dark Blue or Green wheels, 90 mm.	£40-70	☐
				Light Blue, spun aluminium hubs.	£40-70	☐
				Light Blue hubs, Blue hubs, Lighter Yellow box	£150-200	☐
	1966	South African issues:	Cream, Light Green or Light Blue, spun hubs.	£500-750	☐
182	1958-66		Porsche 356a Coupé	Light Blue, Cream, Red or Cerise, Cream wheels or spun hubs, 87 mm.	£100-125	☐
				Deep Pink body with matching ridged wheel hubs	£150-200	☐
				Deep Pink body, spun wheel hubs.	£150-200	☐
	1966	South African issue:	Plum body, spun aluminium hubs	£500-750	☐
183	1958-60		Fiat 600	Red body, smooth or treaded solid Grey plastic wheels, 71 mm.	£55-65	☐
				Light Green body, smooth or treaded solid Grey plastic wheels	£50-60	☐
183	1966-72		Morris Mini Minor Saloon	Metallic Red with gloss black roof or Metallic Red or Blue with matt Black roof. Box contains 'Meccano Automatic Transmission' leaflet, spun hubs, 75 mm.	£50-60	☐
				Metallic Red body and roof, Speedwheels	NGPP	☐
	1966	South African issue:	Red body and roof or Mid Blue body, spun hubs	£500-750	☐
184	1961-65		Volvo 122 S	Red body, suspension, windows, plastic wheels, 97 mm.	£60-70	☐
				As previous model but with White body.	£200-250	☐
	1966	South African issue:	Greyish Lilac with White interior	£500-650	☐
	1966	South African issue:	Greyish Green with White interior or Pale Green, Fawn interior	£500-650	☐
185	1961-63		Alfa Romeo 1900	Red or Yellow body, suspension & steering, spun hubs, 102 mm.	£40-50	☐
186	1961-67		Mercedes-Benz 220 SE	Light Blue or RAF Blue, suspension, steering, spun hubs, 102 mm.	£30-40	☐
	1966	South African issue:	Greyish Light Blue with Cream interior	£500-750	☐
187	1959-64		VW Karmann Ghia Coupé	Green/Cream, Red/Black or Yellow/Green, suspension, 96 mm.	£40-60	☐
187	1968-77		De Tomaso Mangusta 5000	Red and White body with racing number '7', 102 mm.	£20-25	☐
188	1968-74		Jensen FF	Yellow or Green body, suspension, steering, special lights, 121 mm.	£30-45	☐
189	1959-64		Triumph Herald Saloon	Green/White, spun aluminium hubs, 86 mm.	£50-60	☐
				Blue/White, spun aluminium hubs.	£45-60	☐
		special issues:		Blue/White, Magenta, Dark Blue or Lilac	£1000-2000	☐
		special issue:		Red lower, White upper body, plain printed box with Red spot	£2000-2500	☐
		special issue:		Greyish-Green, Pale Whitish-Green roof, plain box with correct colour spot	£1500-2000	☐
		special issue:		Pinkish-Brown body with Pale Grey roof	£750-1000	☐
		special issue:		Dark Grey body and roof, Pale Grey bonnet and boot	£1500-2000	☐
		special issue:		All Red body in plain box with red spot	£1500-2000	☐
		special issue:		Very Dark Blue body, Pale Blue hubs	£400-800	☐
		special issue:		Pale Lilac body, Bluish White roof in box with Blue and White spot	£600-800	☐
				N.B. Special Issues Box Type – Models issued in standard boxes.		
189	1969-76		Lamborghini Marzal	Green/White, Yellow/White or Red/White, cast detailed hubs, 137 mm.	£20-25	☐
	1976-78			Metallic Blue/White or Dark Metallic Green/White, Speedwheels	£20-25	☐
190	1970-74		Monteverdi 375 L	Metallic Red body with opening doors, Castwheels or Speedwheels, 116 mm.	£20-25	☐
191	1959-64		Dodge Royal Sedan	Cream body with Brown flash, spun hubs, 111 mm.	£50-75	☐
				Cream body with Blue flash, spun hubs, lighter Yellow box	£150-200	☐
				Light Green body with Black flash, spun hubs	£50-75	☐
192	1959-64		De Soto Fireflite	Grey/Red, spun aluminium hubs, 114 mm.	£80-100	☐
				Sea Green/Fawn, spun aluminium hubs	£80-100	☐
192	1970-80		Range Rover	Bronze, various colours of interior, cast detailed or Speedwheels	£15-20	☐
				Black or Yellow body, Speedwheels	£15-20	☐
193	1961-69		Rambler Station Wagon	Yellow/White body, suspension, steering, Black roof-rack, spun hubs, White tyres, 102 mm.	£40-45	☐
	1966	South African issue:	Pink/Mauve, All Mauve, or Lime-Green body	£500-750	☐
	1966	South African issue:	Pale Lilac body, Black roof or Pale Blue, Cream roof	£600-800	☐
	1966	South African issue:	Light Greyish-Green body, Black roof, Red interior	£600-800	☐
194	1961-67		Bentley 'S' Coupé	Grey (Red or Maroon seats), or Gold (Cream seats), suspension, driver, 113 mm.	£55-75	☐
	1966	South African issue:	Avocado Green body, Dark Red seats, spun hubs	£600-800	☐
	1966	South African issue:	Cream body, Red interior, spun hubs	£500-750	☐
195	1960-66		Jaguar 3.4 Mk.II	Maroon, Cream or Grey body, suspension. First with fingertip steering, 95 mm.	£60-80	☐
		South African issue:	Pale Bluish-Grey body, White interior or Red body, White interior	£600-800	☐
196	1963-70		Holden Special Sedan	Bronze/White or Turquoise/White, suspension & steering, 108 mm. .... N.B. First model with jewelled headlights.	£35-50	☐
	1966	South African issue:	White body, Turquoise roof	£500-750	☐

Ref. No.				Market Price Range	
197	1961-71	Morris Mini Traveller	White or Mid Green body with 'wood' trim, Red or Yellow interior, 72 mm.............	£40-50	☐
			Dark Green body with 'wood' trim, Yellow interior	£250-350	☐
			Lime Green body	£200-300	☐
			Fluorescent Green body, Red interior, spun hubs	£120-130	☐
			Luminous Pink body	£140-160	☐
198	1962-69	Rolls-Royce Phantom V...........	Metallic Green and Cream body, Blue chauffeur, spun hubs. First model with		
			Metallic paint & opening windows, 125 mm.	£55-65	☐
			Cream upper body, Grey lower body with Blue chauffeur, spun hubs	£55-65	☐
			Two tone Grey body, Blue chauffeur, spun hubs.	£60-75	☐
	1966	South African issue:	Dark Grey over Metallic Cream body, Red interior..	£500-750	☐
			Green or Two-Tone Grey	£500-750	☐
			Pale Grey body, Ivory roof, Red interior	£500-750	☐
199	1961-71	Austin 7 Countryman...............	Blue body with 'wood' trim, suspension & steering, windows, 72 mm................	£40-50	☐
	1970-71		Fluorescent Pinkish-Orange	£120-130	☐
200 (35b)	1954-57	Midget Racer..........................	Silver body, Red grille, Brown driver, solid Black rubber wheels, 57 mm.	£25-35	☐
200	1971-78	Matra 630 Le Mans	Blue body, racing number '5', '9' or '36', Speedwheels....................................	£15-20	☐
201	1979-80	Plymouth Stock Car.................	Blue body, racing number '34', wide plastic wheels, 135 mm.	£15-20	☐
202	1971-75	Fiat Abarth 2000	Fluorescent Red/White body, opening doors, Speedwheels, 91 mm.	£15-20	☐
202/2	1979-80	Customised Land Rover...........	Yellow body with white crash guard. White or Black (344 casting)	£30-40	☐
203	1979-80	Customised Range Rover........	Black body, Yellow/Red design, White plastic chassis/crash guard, 115 mm.....	£20-25	☐
204	1971-74	Ferrari 312 P	Metallic Red body & opening doors, Speedwheels, RN '60', 99 mm.	£20-25	☐
			Metallic Red body, White opening doors, Speedwheels, RN '60'	£20-25	☐
205 (230)	1962-64	Talbot Lago Racing Car	Blue, Red or Yellow plastic hubs, RN '4', bubble-packed (230 on base)	£200-300	☐
205	1968-73	Lotus Cortina Rally	White/Red, RN '7', suspension & FS, screw or rivet in base, 105 mm.	£40-60	☐
206 (231)	1962-64	Maserati	Red/White, Red or Yellow plastic hubs, bubble-packed (231 on base)	£200-300	☐
206	1978-80	Customised Corvette................	Red/Yellow or White/Black, plastic chassis and wide wheels, 113 mm.	£15-20	☐
207 (232)	1962-64	Alfa Romeo Racing Car	Red body, Red plastic hubs, bubble-packed, (232 on base), 100 mm................	£200-300	☐
207	1977-80	Triumph TR7 Rally.................	White/Red/Blue, RN '8', plastic chassis & wheels, 'Leyland', 98 mm.	£15-20	☐
208 (233)	1962-64	Cooper Bristol Racing Car......	Dark Green, Red plastic wheel hubs, bubble-packed, (233 on base), 89 mm.	£200-300	☐
	variant:	....	As previous model but with Green metal hubs..	£150-200	☐
208	1971-75	VW Porsche 914	Yellow body, cast detailed wheel hubs, 89 mm.	£25-30	☐
	1976-80		Metallic Blue/Black body, Speedwheels...	£25-30	☐
209 (234)	1962-64	Ferrari Racing Car	Blue, Yellow triangle, Yellow plastic hubs, bubble-packed, (234 on base)........	£200-300	☐
210 (239)	1962-65	Vanwall....................................	Green, Yellow plastic hubs, bubble-packed, (239 on base), 95 mm.	£200-300	☐
210	1971-73	Alfa Romeo 33	Red body with Black doors and racing number '36'	£25-30	☐
211	1976-76	Triumph TR7 Rally.................	Metallic Blue-Green body, opening doors, plastic wheels, 98 mm.	£75-100	☐
		promotional issue:	White body, British Leyland promotional..	£25-30	☐
	1976-78		Red or Yellow body, Pale Grey bumpers & interior	£25-30	☐
	1978-80		Red or Yellow body, Black bumpers & interior	£25-30	☐
212	1965-70	Ford Cortina Rally..................	White with Black bonnet, 'Castrol', RN '8', suspension, 102 mm.	£45-60	☐
213	1970-73	Ford Capri Rally.....................	Metallic Red body, Black bonnet, spotlights, wing mirrors, Speedwheels	£40-50	☐
	1973-75		Bronze body, Black bonnet, spotlights, wing mirrors, Speedwheels	£40-50	☐
214	1966-69	Hillman Imp Rally	Blue body with racing number '35', suspension & steering, 86 mm.	£45-55	☐
215	1965-66	Ford GT Racing Car	White body with racing number '7', spun hubs, 96 mm.	£20-30	☐
	1966-70		White body with racing number '7', Silver spoked wheels................................	£20-30	☐
	1970-74		Green body, Silver or Gold spoked wheels	£20-30	☐
			Yellow or Metallic Blue, removable bonnet, Silver or Gold spoked wheels	£20-30	☐
216	1967-69	Dino Ferrari	Red body, Silver or Gold spoked wheels, 98 mm.	£20-30	☐
	1969-75		Metallic Blue/Black, Silver or Gold spoked wheels or Speedwheels.................	£20-30	☐
217	1968-70	Alfa Romeo Scarabeo OSI.......	Red body, Silver spoked wheels, 132 mm..	£15-20	☐
	1969-74		Red, Orange or Green body, Speedwheels	£15-20	☐
218	1969-73	Lotus Europa............................	Yellow body, Blue panels/roof, chequered flags, Gold engine, 96 mm.	£25-30	☐
	1973-75		Yellow/Black body or Metallic Blue body, Silver engine, Speedwheels............	£25-30	☐
219	1977-79	Leyland Jaguar XJ-5.3 Coupé..	White body, 'Leyland' decal, 137 mm. (Made in Hong Kong)............................	£10-15	☐
219	1978-79	'Big Cat' Jaguar.......................	White/Red, Black 'Big Cat' decal. (This model was not boxed).........................	£10-15	☐
220 (23a)	1954-56	Small Open Racing Car	Silver (Red wheels), or Red (Silver wheels), RN '4', 94 mm.	£25-30	☐
220	1970-73	Ferrari P5	Red body with opening doors, 96 mm.	£20-25	☐
	1973-75		Red body with opening doors, Speedwheels	£20-25	☐
221 (23e)	1954-56	'Speed Of The Wind' Racing Car	Silver diecast body with plain baseplate, 104 mm.	£30-40	☐
221	1969-76	Corvette Stingray.....................	Metallic Bronze body, Silver or Gold spoked wheels, 113 mm.	£20-30	☐
	1976-78		Red or White body, Black bonnet, opening doors, Speedwheels........................	£10-15	☐
222 (23s)	1954-56	Streamlined Racing Car	Silver body with Red, Blue or Green trim, 105 mm.	£30-40	☐
222	1978-80	Hesketh 308 E	Dark Blue or Bronze, RN '2', cast-detailed or Speedwheels, 132 mm.	£15-20	☐
		promotional issue:	As previous model but in 'OLYMPUS CAMERAS' box, (Swiss)	£50-75	☐
223	1970-75	McLaren M8A Can-Am...........	White body, Metallic Blue engine cover, cast detailed wheels, 94 mm.	£20-25	☐
	1976-78		Metallic Green body, Black engine cover, Speedwheels....................................	£20-25	☐
224	1970-74	Mercedes-Benz C111	White or Metallic Dark Red, cast wheels or Speedwheels, 102 mm.	£20-25	☐
225	1971-76	Lotus F1 Racing Car	Metallic Red body with racing number '7', 127 mm.	£15-20	☐
	1976-77		Lime-Green or Metallic Blue body with racing number '7'................................	£15-20	☐
226	1972-75	Ferrari 312 B2	Red body with racing number '5', 121 mm.	£15-20	☐
	1976-80		Bronze or Gold body, Black, White or Yellow rear wing, racing number '5'......	£15-20	☐
227	1975-77	Beach Buggy	Yellow/Grey, Yellow/White, Green/Grey or Pink/Black body, 105 mm.	£15-20	☐
228	1970-72	Super Sprinter..........................	Blue/Silver or Blue/Orange body, suspension, Speedwheels, 115 mm.	£15-20	☐

Ref. No.	Year	Name	Description	Market Price Range	
230 (23k)	1954-60	Talbot Lago Racing Car	Blue body, Yellow racing number '4', Blue diecast hubs, 103 mm.	£70-85	☐
	1960-62		Blue body, Yellow racing number '4', spun aluminium hubs	£70-85	☐
	1962-64		Blue body, RN '4', Red or Yellow plastic hubs, (boxed, see 205)	£70-85	☐
231 (23n)	1954-60	Maserati Racing Car	Red body, White flash and RN '9', Red diecast hubs, 94 mm.	£70-85	☐
	1960-62		Red body, White flash and racing number '9', spun aluminium hubs	£70-85	☐
	1962-64		Red body & plastic hubs, White flash & RN '9', (boxed, see 206)	£70-85	☐
	1962-64		Red, Yellow plastic hubs, White flash & RN '9', (boxed, see 206)	£70-95	☐
232 (23f)	1954-60	Alfa Romeo Racing Car	Red body, White racing number '8', Red diecast hubs, 100 mm.	£70-85	☐
	1960-62		Red body, White racing number '8', spun aluminium hubs	£70-85	☐
	1962-64		Red body, White RN '8', Red plastic hubs, (boxed, see 207)	£70-85	☐
233 (23g)	1954-60	Cooper Bristol Racing Car	Green body, White flash and RN '6', Green diecast hubs, 89 mm.	£70-85	☐
	1960-62		Green body, White flash and racing number '6', spun aluminium hubs	£70-85	☐
	1962-64		Green body & plastic hubs, White flash and RN '6', (boxed, see 208)	£70-85	☐
234 (23h)	1954-60	Ferrari Racing Car	Blue body, Yellow nose, diecast hubs & RN '5', 101 mm.	£70-85	☐
	1960-62		Blue body, Yellow nose and racing number '5', spun aluminium hubs.	£70-90	☐
	1962-62		Blue body, Yellow triangle on nose, RN '5', spun hubs, boxed	£100-125	☐
	1962-64		Blue, Yellow triangle on nose, Yellow plastic hubs, (boxed, see 209)	£100-125	☐
		South African issue:	Red body, RN '36', spun hubs (same as UK issue but with dimpled rivets) in South African box	£150-250	☐
235 (23j)	1954-60	H.W.M. Racing Car	Light Green body, Yellow RN '7', Green diecast hubs, 99 mm.	£70-85	☐
236	1956-59	Connaught Racing Car	Pale Green body, Mid-Green wheels, RN '32', White driver, 96 mm.	£60-70	☐
237	1957-60	Mercedes Benz Racing Car	White body, Red wheels or spun hubs & RN '30', Blue driver, 98 mm.	£70-80	☐
	1960-62		Cream body, Red wheels or spun hubs, RN '30', Blue driver	£50-60	☐
	1962-64		Cream body, plastic hubs, RN '30', Tan driver	£50-60	☐
238	1957-60	Jaguar 'D' type	Turquoise body, White driver, RN '4', Blue diecast wheels, 87 mm.	£70-80	☐
	1960-62		Turquoise body, White driver, RN '4', spun aluminium hubs	£50-70	☐
	1962-65		Turquoise body, White or Yellow driver, RN '4', Blue plastic hubs	£50-70	☐
239	1958-60	Vanwall Racing Car	Green body, Green wheels, White driver, racing number '35', 95 mm.	£70-85	☐
	1960-62		Green body, White driver, RN '35', spun aluminium hubs	£70-85	☐
	1962-65		Green body, White or Tan driver, RN '35', Yellow plastic hubs	£70-85	☐
	1962-65		Green body, Yellow driver, RN '35', Yellow plastic hubs	£70-85	☐
240	1963-70	Cooper Racing Car	Blue/White, RN '20', spun aluminium hubs, suspension, 80 mm.	£30-35	☐
241	1963-70	Lotus Racing Car	Green body with racing number '36', suspension, spun hubs, 80 mm.	£30-35	☐
242	1963-71	Ferrari Racing Car	Red body, RN '36', suspension, opening engine cover, spun hubs, 89 mm.	£30-35	☐
243	1963-71	B.R.M. Racing Car	Green, Yellow opening engine cover, RN '7', suspension, spun hubs, 82 mm.	£30-35	☐
	1963-71		Metallic Green, Yellow opening engine cover, racing number '7'	£30-35	☐
260	1971-72	VW 'Deutsche Bundespost'	Yellow body (129 casting), German export model, 100 mm.	£100-150	☐
262	1959-60	Volkswagen 'PTT' Car	Yellow/Black (181 casting, fixed doors), 'PTT' logo, cast hubs, Swiss export model, 90 mm.	£500-750	☐
	1960-62		Yellow/Black (181 casting, fixed doors), 'PTT' logo, spun aluminium hubs, Swiss export model, 90 mm.	£500-750	☐
	1962-66		Yellow/Black, (181 casting, fixed doors), 'PTT' logo, plastic hubs, Swiss export	£500-750	☐
	1966-68	129 casting:	Yellow/Black, opening doors, spun hubs, hard plastic case.	£150-200	☐
	1968-72	129 casting:	Yellow/Black, opening doors, plastic hubs, 100 mm., Swiss export	£40-50	☐
	1972-76		Yellow/Black, opening doors, Speedwheels, Swiss export	£40-50	☐
340 (27d)	1954-66	Land Rover	Green body, Brown interior and metal wheels. Tan cast driver, 92 mm.	£50-60	☐
	1966-69		Orange body, Green interior and plastic hubs, Blue, cast or plastic driverl	£50-60	☐
	1969-71		Red body and plastic hubs, Yellow interior, Blue plastic driver	£50-60	☐
	1971		Red body, Blue plastic driver, Green plastic hubs	£70-80	☐
341 (27m)	1954-66	Land-Rover Trailer	Orange body (Red wheels), or Green body (Green wheels)	£20-30	☐
342	1966-72	Austin Mini-Moke	Metallic Green, Grey canopy with 1 or 2 windows, bubble-packed or boxed, 73 mm.	£25-40	☐
	1972-75		Metallic Greenish-Blue, 1 canopy window, Speedwheels, bubble-packed or boxed, 76 mm.	£25-30	☐
344 (27f)	1954-61	Estate Car	Brown/Fawn body, rear axle pillars, 104 mm.	£60-70	☐
344	1970-72	Land Rover Pick-Up	Metallic Blue or Metallic Red body, bubble-packed, 108 mm.	£15-20	☐
	1973-78		Metallic Blue or Metallic Red body, Speedwheels, bubble-packed.	£15-20	☐
370	1969-76	Dragster	Yellow/Red, driver, 'FIREBALL', 'INCH-PINCHER', starter unit, 113 mm.	£30-35	☐
405 (25y)	1954-66	Universal Jeep	Red or Green body, diecast hubs, tinplate windscreen frame, 83 mm.	£30-40	☐
	1966-67		Orange body, red plastic hubs, boxed in late lighter yellow box	£200-300	☐
448	1963-68	Chevrolet El Camino Pick-Up with Trailers	Turquoise/White/Red Pick-up & 2 trailers, 'Acme Trailer Hire', 256 mm.	£150-230	☐
449	1961-69	Chevrolet El Camino Pick-up	Green/White, suspension, fingertip steering, windows, 111 mm.	£55-65	☐
			Red/Yellow, suspension, fingertip steering, windows, 111 mm.	£55-65	☐
		South African issue:	All-Turquoise body, spun hubs	£500-750	☐
		South African issue:	Cream over Chocolate Brown lower body, spun hubs	£500-750	☐
		South African issue:	Turquoise over Cream lower body, spun hubs	£500-750	☐
475	1964-66	Model 'T' Ford	Blue body, Yellow panels and wheels, driver/female passenger, 79 mm.	£40-50	☐
476	1967-69	Morris Oxford (Bullnose)	Yellow body, Blue chassis, Fawn hood, driver, 92 mm.	£40-50	☐
516	1965-66	Mercedes Benz 230 SL	Metallic Red, Cream roof, windows, 85 mm. (French issue)	£65-85	☐
675 (170m)	1954-?	Ford US Army Staff Car	Military Green, US issue	£175-250	☐

Dinky Cars made by Meccano, Paris, France and sold in Britain

24kz	1939-40	Peugeot Car	Red or Blue, tinplate front bumper, rubber tyres for UK	NGPP	☐
518	1962-65	Renault 4L	Brown or Grey body, suspension, steering, windows, 85 mm. (French issue)	£65-85	☐
524	1965-67	Panhard 24c	Dark Metallic Grey body, (French issue)	£65-85	☐
530	1965-66	Citroën DS19	Light Green body, Light Grey roof. (French issue)	£65-85	☐
535	1962-65	2cv Citroën	Blue body, suspension, steering, windows, 88 mm. (French issue)	£65-85	☐
550	1962-65	Chrysler Saratoga	Pink/White body, windows, suspension, steering, 129 mm. (French issue)	£65-75	☐
551	1959-64	Rolls Royce Silver Wraith	Same as UK issue 150 'Made in France'	£75-85	☐
553	1962-65	Peugeot 404	Green or White, suspension, steering, windows, 102 mm. (French issue)	£65-75	☐
555	1962-65	Ford Thunderbird Convertible..	White, driver, windscreen, suspension, steering, 121 mm. (French issue)	£65-75	☐

Dinky Toys Cars made in Hong Kong

57/001	1965-67	Buick Riviera	Blue body with White roof and interior, opening bonnet and tailgate	£80-100	☐
57/002	1965-67	Chevrolet Corvair Monza	Red body, Black roof, opening bonnet and rear engine cover, 107 mm.	£100-125	☐
57/003	1965-67	Chevrolet Impala	Yellow body with White roof, opening bonnet and tailgate	£100-125	☐
		US/Canadian issue:	Yellow body with Yellow roof.	£100-125	☐
57/004	1965-67	Oldsmobile Dynamic '88'	Blue body. This model replaced Dodge Polara shown in the catalogue	£100-125	☐
57/005	1965-67	Ford Thunderbird	Blue body with White roof	£100-125	☐
57/006	1965-67	Nash Rambler Classic	Green body with Silver roof trim, opening bonnet, tailgate and windows	£80-100	☐
180	1979-80	Rover 3500	White body with opening doors, plastic wheels, 131 mm.	£10-15	☐
219	1978-79	'Big Cat' Jaguar	White/Red, Black 'Big Cat' decal. (This model was not boxed)	£15-25	☐

Dinky Toys made in Italy by Polistil under licence to Dinky Tri-ang

122	1979-80	Volvo Estate Car	Orange body, Brown card box	£15-20	☐
243	1979-80	Volvo 'Police' Car	White body, Brown card box	£15-20	☐

Dinky 1:25 Scale Models Vacuform packed with card bases

2162	1973-76	Ford Capri	Metallic Blue, Black roof, suspension, windows, number plates, 175 mm.	£65-75	☐
2214	1974-76	Ford Capri Rally Car	Red, Black roof & bonnet, RN '12', suspension, windows, 175 mm.	£65-75	☐
2253	1974-76	Ford Capri Police Car	White/Orange, 'POLICE', Blue light, suspension, windows, 175 mm.	£65-75	☐

Sections containing other Dinky Cars

For other models derived from cars see these sections:
Fire, Police and Ambulance vehicles, Military vehicles, Gift Sets,
Buses, Taxis and Trams, Dinky Action Kits, 'Mini-Dinky' models,
Dinky Toys issued by Airfix Products, Novelty, Space and Film/TV-related models, 'Dinky Dublo' models.

MATCHBOX (Matchbox Miniatures) Dinky Toys

Matchbox bought the Dinky Toys trademark in early 1987. Prior to the launch of 'The Dinky Collection' in 1988, the following Matchbox miniatures were released in blister packs which carried the 'Dinky Toys' logo:
MB17 VW Golf, MB44 Citroën Cv15, MB51 Firebird SE, MB60 Toyota Supra, MB69 '84 Corvette, MB74 Fiat Abarth.
The models have 'Matchbox' bases.

'Mini-Dinky' models

These were issued in 1968 and were made in Hong Kong and Holland. Each model was sold with a free red plastic garage. All the cars and commercial vehicles have special features. The models listed are illustrated in the 1968 US issued 3-page fold-out leaflet which advertised them as 'Swinging Value' at 59 cents and 69 cents. The Market Price Range is £30-40 each. N.B. Racing cars 60 and 61 made by Best Box of Holland (now EFSI).

10 Ford Corsair, Yellow or Metallic Gold
11 Jaguar 'E' type, Red or Metallic Maroon
12 Corvette Stingray, Blue or Metallic Dark Blue
13 Ferrari 250 LM, Red or Metallic Maroon
14 Chevrolet Chevy II, Yellow or Metallic Maroon
15 Rolls-Royce Silver Shadow, Blue
16 Ford Mustang, White, Cream or Metallic Blue
17 Aston Martin DB6, White
18 Mercedes Benz 230 SL, Gloss or Matt White/Black
19 MGB Roadster, Blue
20 Cadillac Coupé De Ville, Silver or White
21 Fiat 2300 Station Wagon, Blue or Yellow/White
22 Oldsmobile Toronado, Metallic Pale Blue
23 Rover 2000, Blue
24 Ferrari Superfast, Red
25 Ford Zephyr 6, Silver

26 Mercedes 250 SE, White or Bronze
27 Buick Riviera, Blue
28 Ferrari F 1, Red, '7'
29 Ford F 1, White
30 Volvo 1800s, Blue
31 Volkswagen 1600TC, Blue or Metallic Green
32 Vauxhall Cresta, Silver or Dark Green
33 Jaguar, Red
57 Chevrolet Corvair Monza Club Coupé, Red/Black
60 Cooper, Blue '10'
61 Lotus Racing Car, Green, '4'
94 International Bulldozer, Yellow
95 International Skid Shovel, Yellow
96 Payloader Shovel, White
97 Euclid R40, Yellow
98 Michigan Scraper, Yellow
99 Caterpillar Grader, Orange

N.B. Cars fitted with Flexomatic Independent Suspension.

Models 94-99 Construction Vehicles are illustrated in a US issued 'Mini-Dinky' fold-out launch leaflet '1'.

-           Case .... 'Mini-Dinky' 12-Car Collector Case, with models .... **£400-600** ☐

No.262 Rare 'non-opening' version of the Swiss 'PTT' car.
Picture kindly supplied by Christie's, South Kensington, London.
(Note:- This is not a picture of a Mini-Dinky)

Matchbox Dinky - 'The Collection'

Manufactured by Matchbox International Ltd in Macau

DY 1	1988	1967 Jaguar 'E' type (soft-top)..	British Racing Green, 'J 916', White-wall tyres	£12-15	☐
DY 1 B	1991		Yellow body, Black hood	£10-12	☐
	1995		Black body	£10-12	☐
	1992	pewter model:	Unpainted pewter model on wooden plinth	£30-35	☐
DY 2	1989	1957 Chevrolet Bel Air............	Red body, White roof, Silver stripe, 'ASA 174', White-wall tyres	£10-£1	☐
			Dark Red variant reported but not seen (Australian issue)	NGPP	☐
DY 3	1989	1965 MGB GT	Blue body, Black roof, 'PGY 323C'	£10-14	☐
	1992		Orange body	£15-18	☐
	1995		Red body	£10-12	☐
DY 4	1989	1950 Ford E83W 10 cwt Van....	'HEINZ 57 VARIETIES', Yellow body, Black roof, '618 APH'	£8-10	☐
	1990		'RADIO TIMES', Green body, Gold logo 'Journal of the BBC'	£12-14	☐
DY 5	1989	1949 Ford V8 Pilot..................	Black body, Silver trim, 'HOY 712'	£12-15	☐
DY 5 B	1992		Silver body	£8-10	☐
DY 5 C	1993		Tan body	£8-10	☐
DY 6	1989	1951 Volkswagen Saloon..........	Light Blue body, Grey roof, '111A-46003'	£18-20	☐
DY 6 B	1991		Black body with Grey roof	£12-15	☐
DY 6 C	1992		Red body with Grey roof	£12-15	☐
DY 7	1989	1959 Cadillac Coupé De Ville ...	Metallic Deep Red body, White roof	£12-15	☐
DY 7 B	1991		Pink body	£10-12	☐
DY 8	1989	1948 Commer 8 cwt Van..........	'SHARPS TOFFEES', Red body	£10-14	☐
DY 8 B	1991		'HIS MASTERS VOICE', Dark Blue body	£10-12	☐
DY 9	1989	1949 Land Rover....................	Green body, Cream canopy, 'EOP 999'	£12-15	☐
DY 9 B	1991	'AA' Land Rover	Yellow/Black body, 'AA' emblem	£12-15	☐
DY 10	1989	Mercedes Konferenz Coach	Cream/Dark Blue, 'REISEBURO RUOFF', 'STUTTGART', special box, (1:50)........	£25-30	☐
DY 11	1990	Tucker Torpedo....................	Metallic Red or Metallic Light Blue body, Silver trim, White-wall tyres	£10-12	☐
DY 12	1990	1955 Mercedes 300 SL..............	Off-White body, Silver trim	£8-12	☐
DY 12 B	1992		Black body, Silver trim	£7-10	☐
DY 13	1990	Bentley Continental	Metallic Light Blue, Silver trim	£8-10	☐
DY 13 B	1992		Dark Blue, Silver trim	£7-10	☐
DY 14	1990	Delahaye 145	Dark Metallic Blue body	£8-12	☐
DY 14B	1992		Dark Red body	£7-10	☐
DY 15	1989	1953 Austin A40 Van................	'BROOKE BOND TEA', Bright Red, (Brooke Bond promotional in plain box)	£10-12	☐
DY 15	1990	1953 Austin A40 Van................	'BROOKE BOND TEA', Bright Red, (standard issue, normal box)	£7-10	☐
DY 15 B	1991		'DINKY TOYS', Cream/Yellow body	£8-12	☐
DY 16	1990	1967 Ford Mustang Fastback ...	Metallic Green body or White with Red seats	£8-12	☐
DY 17	1990	1939 Triumph Dolomite...........	Red body & hubs, Black hood, opening dicky-seat, special box	£12-15	☐
DY 18	1988	1967 Jaguar 'E' type (open)	Red body	£10-12	☐
DY 19	1990	1973 MGB GT V8..................	Maroon body, Black seats, alloy wheels	£10-12	☐
DY 20	1991	1955 Triumph TR4..................	White body, Black seats, Silver trim	£10-12	☐
DY 21	1991	1964 Mini Cooper S	Off-White body, Black roof, Silver trim	£10-12	☐
DY 22	1991	1952 Citroën 15cv	Black body, Silver trim	£8-12	☐
DY 22 B	1992		Off-White body, Silver trim	£7-10	☐
DY 23	1991	Chevrolet Corvette	Red body, White side panel	£8-12	☐
DY 23 B	1993		Bronze body, Cream side panel	£7-10	☐
DY 24	1991	1973 Ferrari 246 Dino..............	Red body	£7-10	☐
DY 25	1991	1958 Porsche 356a	Silver body	£7-10	☐
DY 26	1991	Studebaker Hawk	Gold body, White side flash, Silver trim	£12-15	☐
DY 27	1991	Chevrolet Bel Air Open Top.....	Light Blue body, White and Blue seats	£12-15	☐
			Light Blue body, White and Brown seats	£70-80	☐
DY 28	1992	1969 Triumph Stag..................	White body	£12-15	☐
	1995		Metallic Green	£10-12	☐
DY 29	1992	1953 Buick Skylark..................	Light Blue body	£7-10	☐
DY 30	1992	Austin Healey 100	British Racing Green body	£10-12	☐
DY 31	1993	1955 Ford Thunderbird............	Red body	£10-12	☐
DY 32	1993	1957 Citroën 2cv..................	Grey body	£15-18	☐
	1991	Sports Cars Set 1	Three models on wooden plinth, colours unique to set: DY 25, (Red body), DY 12 (Silver body), DY 24 (Metallic Blue body)	£25-30	☐
	1992	Sports Cars Set 2	Three models on wooden plinth, colours unique to set: DY 20, (Red body), DY 18 (Cream body), DY 30 (Metallic Light Blue)	£20-25	☐
DY 921	1992	Jaguar 'E' Type	Cast in pewter, unpainted, special box, 'DINKY' on plinth	£25-30	☐
DY 921	1992	Jaguar SS100	Cast in pewter with 'MATCHBOX' on plinth	£25-30	☐

N.B. 1995 New Issues: Jaguar XK120, Karmann Ghia, Mercedes 300SL Convertible.

Code 2 Models (Production numbers shown in brackets)

DY5	?	Ford V8 Pilot	Black body with 'RETRO MOBIL FEVRIER 92' on roof	NGPP	☐
DY8	1991	Commer 8cwt Van..................	'MOTORFAIR' (2000)	£30-35	☐
DY18	?	Jaguar 'E' Type	Open Red body with bonnet decal 'AUTO PASSION MENSUEL DE LA VOMURE DE COLLECTION'	NGPP	☐
DY21	1991	Mini Cooper 'S'	'CLASSIC CAR SHOW' (1000)	£45-50	☐
DY28	1992	Triumph Stag......................	'CLASSIC CAR SHOW' (2000)	£20-30	☐
DY8	1994	Commer 8cwt Van..................	'CLASSIC TOYS' special box (2000)	£20-30	☐
DY4	1995	Ford E83 W 10 cwt Van	'THE DUTCH DINKY SOCIETY' in Red or two shades of Green with Black roof (300)	£50-60	☐
DY21	1994	Mini Cooper S 'Police Car'......	White body, special box (2000)	£20-30	☐
DY21	1995	Mini Cooper Rally Car............	Green body, White roof, special box, RN '13' in white circle (2000)	£20-30	☐

Dinky Toys — Commercial Vehicles and Vans

25 Series Trucks 1934-50 Wheel types The first pre-war issues have cast metal wheels followed by chrome (rare) or diecast hubs with large white tyres. The early post-war issues c.1946 have smooth hubs and large black tyres. 1947-50 issues have ridged black hubs with large black tyres. The last issues c.1949-50 have coloured hubs and attract a premium. Similarly early cast or chrome hubs also attract a premium.

Identification of casting types

LORRIES   (25 series):

Type 1 - (1934-36), 'criss cross' chassis (usually black), tinplate radiator, no headlamps, no front bumper, 'smooth' cast hubs (various colours) with large white tyres. 105 mm.

Type 2 - (1936-46), 'open' chassis (usually black), diecast radiator with headlamps but no front bumper, 'smooth' cast hubs (various colours), with large white tyres. 105 mm.

Type 3 - (1947-48), 'closed' chassis (only in black), diecast radiator with headlamps but no front bumper,'smooth' or 'ridged' wheel hubs (only in black) ,with black tyres. 105 mm.

Type 4 - (1948-50), detailed chassis (only in black), diecast radiator with headlamps and with bumper, 'ridged' wheel hubs (only in black), with black tyres. 110 mm.

Dinky Toys 25 series Lorry types 1934-1950

1st type 1934-1936 Tinplate radiator without headlights No bumpers Open chassis	2nd type 1936-1946 Diecast radiator without headlights No bumpers Open chassis	3rd type 1947-1948 Diecast radiator without headlights No bumpers Plain (closed) chassis	4th type 1948-1950 Diecast radiator without headlights and front bumper Moulded chassis

  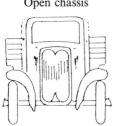   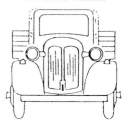

Dinky Toys 25 series chassis types 1934-50

1934-1936 Open Chassic	1936-1946 Open Chassis	1947-1948 Plain Chassis	1948-1950 Moulded Chassis

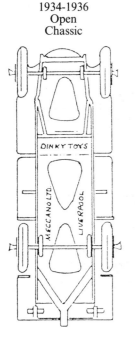 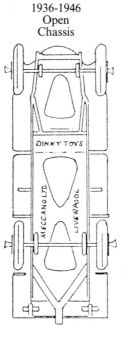 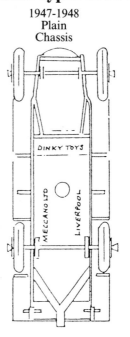 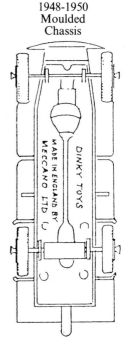

Dinky Toys - Commercial Vehicles and Vans
Identification of Casting Types (continued)

Dinky Toys Heavy Commercials cab types 1947-1964

1947-1952
Foden 'DG' (1st type) cab
Exposed radiator
Colour flashes on sides

1952-1964
Foden 'FG' (2nd type) cab
Radiator behind grille
No colour flashes on sides

1947-1956
Guy 1st type cab
Exposed radiator
No gusset at either
side of number plate

1956-1958
Guy 2nd type cab
Exposed radiator
With gusset at each
side of number plate

1958-1964
Guy 'Warrior' cab
Radiator behind grille
Restyled front with
sidelights in wings

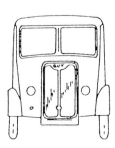

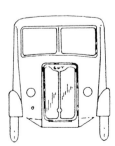

Identification of Casting Types – continued

VANS   (28 series and 280 series):

Type 1 - **(1933-35)**, two-piece lead body with *'HORNBY SERIES'* (early issues) or *'DINKY TOYS'* cast-in under cab roof, tinplate radiator, no headlamps, thinly-painted coloured solid wheel/tyre castings (some silver plated), 84 mm. Note that coloured wheels tend to attract a premium to the price of the model.

Type 2 - **(1935-39)**, one-piece diecast body, cast-in shield-shaped radiator, rear wheel spats, cast 'smooth' wheel hubs with rubber tyres (usually white), 81 mm. All carried advertising.

Type 3 - **(1939-41)**, one-piece diecast body with rear wheel spats, cast 'smooth' wheel hubs (various colours) with black tyres, open rear windows, 83 mm. All carried advertising.

Type 3 - **(1947-54)**, one-piece diecast body with rear wheel spats, cast 'ridged' wheel hubs (usually black) with black tyres, filled-in rear windows, 83 mm. No advertising. Most of post-war Type 3 have a cast boss under the roof to take the loudspeakers on 34c.

1st type 1933-1935 2-piece lead casting Metal wheels/tyres Tinplate radiator without headlights No bumpers	2nd type 1935-1939 Single diecasting Metal hubs with white rubber tyres Cast-in radiator No bumpers	3rd type 1939-41, 1947-54 Single diecasting Metal hubs with rubber tyres Cast-in radiator and front bumper
	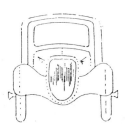	

FORD TRANSIT VANS CASTINGS:

Type 1 - **(1966-74)**,   has sliding driver's door, opening hinged side door, and twin rear doors.
Type 2 - **(1974-78)**,   non-sliding driver's door, one side-hinged door, one top-hinged rear door.
Type 3 - **(1978-80)**,   as Type 2 but with a slightly longer bonnet (18 mm.)

For other models derived from commercial vehicles see these sections:
Fire, Police and Ambulance vehicles, Military vehicles, Farm and Garden, Buses, Taxis and Trams, Dinky Action Kits, Dinky Toys issued by Airfix Products, Novelty, Space and Film/TV-related models, 'Dinky Dublo' models, Road-making Equipment, Gift Sets.

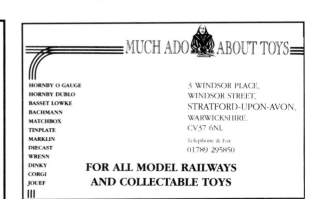

WHEN REPLYING TO ADVERTISEMENTS PLEASE MENTION JOHN RAMSAY'S CATALOGUE

Dinky Toys
Commercial Vehicles and Vans

Ref. No.	Year(s)	Model Type	Model Features and Size	Market Price Range	
14a (400)	1948-54	B.E.V. Truck	Mid-Blue body with Blue wheels, Fawn driver, hook, 85 mm............	£30-35	☐
			Grey body (with Blue, Grey or Red wheels), Fawn driver, hook............	£30-35	☐
14c (401)	1949-54	Coventry Climax Fork Lift.......	Orange, Brown or Dark Red body, Green forks, Fawn driver, 108 mm.	£25-30	☐
14z	1938-40	Three-wheel Delivery Van	'Triporteur' with Green, Red, Grey, Blue or Yellow body, Black hubs, White tyres, driver is always a different colour from van, French model	NGPP	☐
22c	1933-35	Motor Truck..........................	2-piece lead body, tinplate radiator, 'HORNBY SERIES' cast-in, metal cast coloured wheels, 90 mm.		
			Blue cab (Red or Yellow truck body), or Red cab (Green, Blue or Cream truck body)	£300-400	☐
			Blue cab (Yellow truck body)........................	£300-400	☐
			Yellow cab, (Blue truck body)........................	£900-1000	☐
22c	1935-40	Motor Truck..........................	Orange-Red, Maroon, Green or Blue (diecast one-piece), body, open rear window, coloured diecast hubs, 84 mm.	£100-125	☐
	1935-40		Dark Blue body, chrome hubs........................	£125-150	☐
	1945-47		Red, Green or Brown body, open rear window, Black diecast hubs........	£60-70	☐
	1948-50		Red, Green or Brown body, closed rear window, Black diecast hubs.......	£60-70	☐
22d	1933-34	Delivery Van..........................	Lead body, tinplate radiator, 'HORNBY SERIES' cast-in, 84 mm.		
			Orange/Blue body or Blue/Yellow body, no advertising, Type 1	£900-1200	☐
	1934-34		As previous models but with 'DINKY TOYS' cast-in	£400-500	☐
	1934	Interim variant......................	Orange and Blue body (interim variant between the plain 22d, Delivery Van and the yellow 28n Meccano Delivery Van. (See the October 1934 Meccano Magazine).......	£2000-2500	☐
22d (28n)	1934-35	Delivery Van 'MECCANO'	Yellow body (lead), 'Meccano Engineering For Boys' in Red & Black, Type 1, 84 mm. 22d till April 1935, renumbered 28n.	£900-1200	☐
25a	1934-36	Wagon	Maroon, Green, Red or Blue body, Black chassis, Type 1	£300-400	☐
	1936-40		Maroon, Green, Red or Blue body, Black or Red chassis, Type 2	£100-125	☐
	1936-40		Blue body with Orange chassis, Type 2...................	£150-200	☐
	1946		Grey, Green or Blue, Type 2, smooth hubs................	£60-70	☐
	1947-48		Grey, Green, Red, Orange or Blue body, Black chassis, Type 3	£60-70	☐
	1948-50		Grey, Green, Light Blue, Orange, Cream or Red body, Black chassis, Type 4	£60-70	☐
25b	1934-36	Covered Wagon......................	Blue body, Cream tilt, Black chassis, Type 1	£300-400	☐
	1936-40		Green body, Green, Cream or Yellow tilt, Black chassis, Type 2	£100-150	☐
			Cream/Yellow or Fawn/Cream, Black chassis, Type 2	£100-150	☐
			Orange body, Cream tilt, Green chassis, Type 2.............	£150-200	☐
	1936-40	Covered Wagon 'CARTER PATERSON' ...	Green body, Blue hubs, Green tilt, Black chassis, Type 2, 'Express Carriers London'	£300-350	☐
		'CARTER PATERSON' ...	Green body, Blue hubs, Type 2, 'Special Service To The Seaside'............	£400-500	☐
		'MECCANO'	Green body, Cream tilt, Black chassis, Type 2, 'Engineering For Boys'........	£250-300	☐
			Variation with chrome hubs.....................	£500-600	☐
		'HORNBY TRAINS'	Fawn body, Cream tilt, Black chassis, Gold lettering, Type 2	£250-300	☐
	1945-47	Covered Wagon......................	Green/Green, Grey/Light or Dark Grey, Blue/Grey, Black chassis, Type 3	£70-100	☐
	1947-50		Green/Green, Grey/Grey, Cream/Red, Yellow/Blue, Black chassis, Type 4	£70-100	☐
25c	1934-36	Flat Truck..........................	Dark Blue body, Black chassis, Type 1	£150-200	☐
	1936-40		Green or Stone body, Black chassis, Type 2................	£100-125	☐
	1946		Fawn, Green or Grey body, smooth hubs, Type 2	£60-70	☐
	1947-48		Green, Blue or Grey body, Black chassis, Type 3............	£60-70	☐
	1948-50		Green, Blue, Orange or Stone body, Type 4................	£60-70	☐

Note: Pre-war 1934-40 Truck issues – Some will be found with a '20 mph' disc on the rear.

Ref. No.	Year(s)	Model Type	Model Features and Size	Market Price Range	
25d	1934-35	Petrol Tank Wagon	Same chassis casting as other 25 series lorries but with hook removed.		
		(plain)	Red body, no advertising, Black chassis, Type 1	£200-250	☐
		'SHELL BP'	Red body, Black chassis, Type 1	£400-500	☐
		'ESSO'	Green body, Black chassis, Type 1	£400-500	☐
		'POWER'	Green body, Black chassis, Type 1	£400-500	☐
		'PRATTS'......................	Green body, Black chassis, Type 1	£400-500	☐
		'CASTROL'	Green body, Black chassis, Blue hubs, Red logo, Type 1	£400-500	☐
		'TEXACO'	Red body, Black chassis/hubs, White logo 'PETROLEUM & PRODUCTS', Type 1	£400-500	☐
	1936-46	'PETROL'	Red body, Black chassis, Black or White lettering, Type 2	£150-200	☐
		'SHELL BP'	Red body, Black chassis, Blue or chrome hubs, Type 2	£250-300	☐
		'MOBILOIL'	Red body, Black chassis, Type 2	£250-300	☐
		'TEXACO'	Red body, Black chassis, Type 2	£250-300	☐
		'PETROL'	Green body, Black chassis, Type 2	£250-300	☐
		'ESSO'	Green body, Black chassis, Black or Blue wheels, Gold lettering, Type 2	£250-300	☐
		'POWER'	Green body, Black chassis, Type 2	£250-300	☐
		'CASTROL'	Green body, Black chassis, Black or Blue wheels, Red lettering, Type 2	£250-300	☐
		'REDLINE GLICO'	Blue body, Black chassis, Red panel, Gold lettering, Type 2	£250-300	☐
	1945	'POOL' (Wartime)	Grey body, White wheels, Black chassis, Black lettering, Type 2........	£400-500	☐
	1945-46	'POOL' (Wartime)	Grey body, Black chassis, Type 2....................	£300-400	☐
	1945-46	'PETROL' (Wartime)........	Grey body, Type 2, ...	£300-400	☐
	1946-47	'PETROL'	Red or Green body, Black chassis, Type 3	£100-150	☐
	1947-48	'PETROL'	Orange body, Type 4	£300-400	☐
	1948-50	'PETROL'	Red, Light Green or Mid-Green body, Black chassis, Type 4........	£70-100	☐
	1948 ?	'PETROL'	Yellow body, Black chassis, Type 4....................	£200-300	☐

Ref. No.				Market Price Range	
25e	1934-35	Tipping Wagon	Maroon/Yellow body, Black chassis, Type 1	£150-200	☐
	1936-40		Maroon/Yellow, Brown/Turquoise or Fawn/Fawn body, Black chassis, Type 2	£100-125	☐
	1946		Grey, Green or Fawn, Type 2	£60-70	☐
	1947-48		Grey, Stone, Green or Yellow body, Black chassis, Type 3	£60-70	☐
	1948-50		Grey, Stone or Brown body, Black chassis, Type 4	£60-70	☐
	1948-50		Blue/Pink body, Black chassis, Type 4	£60-70	☐

Note: Early Post-war 25 series Trucks variations exist with smooth hubs and large Black tyres.

25f	1934-35	Market Gardeners Lorry	Green body, Black chassis or Yellow body, Green chassis, Type 1	£150-200	☐
	1936-40		Green or Yellow body, Black chassis, Type 2	£100-125	☐
			Green body, Yellow chassis, Type 2	£150-200	☐
	1945-47		Green, Grey or Yellow body, Black chassis and hubs, Type 3	£100-120	☐
	1947-50		Green, Grey, Yellow or Red body, Black chassis/hubs, Type 4	£70-100	☐
			Orange body, Black chassis/hubs, Type 4	£150-200	☐
			Yellow body, Black chassis, Yellow hubs, Type 4	£100-125	☐
25g	1935-40	Trailer	Dark Blue or Green body with cast-in hook, tinplate drawbar, 69 mm	£35-40	☐
	1946-47		Green, Stone, Pale Blue or Orange body, cast-in hook, tinplate drawbar	£15-20	☐
	1947-48		Green, Stone, Pale Blue or Orange body, cast-in hook, wire drawbar	£15-20	☐
	1948-49		Green, Stone, Pale Blue or Orange body, tinplate hook, wire drawbar	£15-20	☐
25g (429)	1950-54		Green or Red body with tinplate hook and wire drawbar	£15-20	☐
25m (410)	1948-54	Bedford Tipper Truck	Green cab and body, Green wheels, crank-handle operates tipper, 100 mm	£100-130	☐
			Green cab and truck body, Black wheels	£80-90	☐
			Orange cab and truck body, Green wheels	£100-130	☐
			Orange cab and truck body, Black wheels	£80-90	☐
			Cream cab and truck body, Red wheels	£300-400	☐
			Yellow cab, Royal Blue truck body, Yellow wheels	£250-350	☐
			Red cab, Cream truck body, Red wheels	£80-90	☐
			N.B. Models with windows attract a premium.		
25r (420)	1948-54	Forward Control Lorry	Red, Green, Grey, Cream, Light Blue or Orange body, Black wheels, 107 mm	£60-70	☐
			Cream body, Blue wheels, 107 mm	£90-120	☐
25s	1937-40	Six-wheeled Wagon	Brown body, no tilt, holes in seat (but no figures), 101 mm	£100-125	☐
			Royal Blue body	£200-250	☐
	1945-48		Brown (various shades), Green or Dark Blue body, Grey or Light Blue tilt, with or without holes for figures (but no figures)	£100-125	☐
25t	1945-47	Flat Truck & Trailer	(25c Flat Truck (Type 3), and matching 25g Trailer), Green, Blue, Orange or Stone..	£140-160	☐
	1947-50		(25c Flat Truck (Type 4), and matching 25g Trailer), Green or Orange	£120-140	☐
25v (252)	1948-54	Bedford Refuse Wagon	Fawn body, Green opening hatches and rear door, 106 mm	£80-90	☐
25w (411)	1949-54	Bedford Truck	Green cab and truck body, Green wheels, 100 mm	£80-90	☐
			Dark Green cab, Light Green truck body, Light Green wheels	NGPP	☐
25x (430)	1949-54	Commer Breakdown Lorry	'DINKY SERVICE', operable crane, 123 mm.		
			Dark Grey cab with Ocean Blue back, (packed in Orange box)	£100-120	☐
			Dark Grey cab with Royal Blue back, (in Orange box)	£100-120	☐
			Dark Brown cab with Mid or Dark Green back, (in Orange box)	£100-120	☐
			Mid Tan cab with Mid or Dark Green back, (in striped box)	£100-120	☐

Note: Models housed in boxes with the correct picture and end colour spot and displaying dual numbers e.g. 30J/412 attract a premium.

28 series DELIVERY VANS
Note that coloured metal cast wheels on 1st type vans tend to attract a price premium.

28a	1934	'HORNBY TRAINS'	Orange body, *Hornby Trains* logo, 1st Type	£700-900	☐
28a		'HORNBY TRAINS'	Yellow body, *Hornby Trains British & Guaranteed* in Gold		
	1934-35		Type 1, 84 mm.	£500-600	☐
	1935-36		Type 2, 81 mm.	£250-350	☐
28a		'GOLDEN SHRED'	Cream body, *Golden Shred Marmalade* on right hand side, *Silver Shred Marmalade* on left hand side		
	1936-39		Type 2, 81 mm.	£600-800	☐
	1939-41		Type 3, 83 mm.	£300-400	☐
28b		'PICKFORDS'	Dark Blue, *Pickfords Removals & Storage, Over 100 Branches* in Gold		
	1934-35		Type 1, 84 mm.	£500-600	☐
	1935	'PICKFORDS'	Dark Blue late version with diecast hubs, white tyres, Type 1	£700-900	☐
	1935-35		Type 2, 81 mm.	£300-400	☐
28b		'SECCOTINE'	Blue body, *Seccotine Sticks Everything* in Gold		
	1935-39		Type 2, 81 mm.	£300-400	☐
	1939-41		Type 3, 83 mm.	£300-400	☐
28c		'MANCHESTER GUARDIAN'	*The Manchester Guardian* in Gold		
	1934-35		Black/Red body, Type 1, 84 mm.	£500-600	☐
	1935-39		Red body, Type 2, 81 mm.	£300-400	☐
	1939-41		Red body, Type 3, 83 mm.	£300-400	☐
28d		'OXO'	Blue body, *Beef In Brief* and *Beef At Its Best* in Gold		
	1934-35		Type 1, 84 mm.	£500-600	☐
	1935-39		Type 2, 81 mm.	£300-400	☐
	1939-41		Type 3, 83 mm.	£500-700	☐
28e		'ENSIGN LUKOS'	Orange body, *Ensign Cameras* and *Ensign Lukos Films* in Gold		
	1934-35		Type 1, 84 mm.	£500-600	☐
28e		'FIRESTONE'	*Firestone Tyres* in Gold		
	1934-35		White body, Type 1, 84 mm.	£500-600	☐
	1935-39		Blue or White body, Type 2, 81 mm.	£300-400	☐
	1939-41		Blue or White body, Type 3, 83 mm.	£200-300	☐

Ref. No.	Year	Name	Description	Market Price Range	
28f		'PALETHORPES'	Pale Grey-Blue body, Pink sausage decal, 'Palethorpes Royal Cambridge' on van sides, 'Palethorpes Model Factory' on rear		
	1934-35		Type 1, 84 mm.	£500-700	☐
	1935-38		Type 2, 81 mm.	£400-500	☐
28f		'VIROL'	Yellow body, 'Give Your Child A Virol Constitution' in Black		
	1938-39		Type 2, 81 mm.	£600-800	☐
	1939-41		Type 3, 83 mm.	£300-400	☐
28g		'KODAK'	Yellow body, 'Use Kodak Film To Be Sure' in Red		
	1934-35		Type 1, 84 mm.	£500-600	☐
	1935-39		Type 2, 81 mm.	£300-400	☐
	1939-41		Type 3, 83 mm.	£600-800	☐
28h		'SHARPS TOFFEES'	'Sharps Toffee, Maidstone' in Gold		
	1934-35		Black/Red body, Type 1, 84 mm.	£500-600	☐
	1935-35		Red body, Type 2, 81 mm.	£400-500	☐
28h		'DUNLOP'	Red body, 'Dunlop Tyres' in Gold		
	1935-39		Type 2, 81 mm.	£300-400	☐
	1939-41		Type 3, 83 mm.	£300-400	☐
28k		'MARSH & BAXTER'	Dark Green body, 'Marshs Sausages' and pig logo in Gold		
	1934-35		Type 1, 84 mm.	£500-600	☐
	1935-39		Type 2, 81 mm.	£300-400	☐
	1939-41		Type 3, 83 mm.	£500-600	☐
28L		'CRAWFORDS'	Red body, 'Crawfords Biscuits' in Gold		
	1934-35		Type 1, 84 mm.	£500-600	☐
28m		'WAKEFIELD'S CASTROL'	Green body, 'Wakefield Castrol Motor Oil' in Red		
	1934-35		Type 1, 84 mm.	£500-600	☐
	1935-39		Type 2, 81 mm.	£300-400	☐
	1939-41		Type 3, 83 mm.	£800-1000	☐
28n		'MECCANO'	Yellow body, 'Meccano Engineering For Boys' in Red & Black		
	1934-35		Type 1, 84 mm. Was 22d	£500-600	☐
	1935-35		Type 2, 81 mm.	£300-400	☐
28n		'ATCO'	Green body, 'Atco Lawn Mowers Sales and Service' in Gold/Red		
	1935-39		Type 2, 81 mm.	£300-500	☐
	1939-41		Type 3, 83 mm.	£500-600	☐
28p		'CRAWFORDS'	Red body, 'Crawfords Biscuits' in Gold		
	1935-39		Type 2, 81 mm.	£300-400	☐
	1939-41		Type 3, 83 mm.	£800-1000	☐
28r		'SWAN'	Black body, 'Swan Pens' and logo in Gold		
	1936-39		Type 2, 81 mm.	£300-500	☐
	1939-41		Type 3, 83 mm.	£200-300	☐
28s		'FRYS'	Brown or Cream body, 'Frys Chocolate' in Gold		
	1936-39		Type 2, 81 mm.	£300-500	☐
	1939-41		Type 3, 83 mm.	£300-400	☐
28t		'OVALTINE'	Red body, 'Drink Ovaltine For Health' in Gold/Black		
	1936-39		Type 2, 81 mm.	£300-400	☐
	1939-41		Type 3, 83 mm.	£300-400	☐
28w		'OSRAM'	Yellow body, 'Osram Lamps - a G.E.C. Product' in Gold/Black		
	1936-39		Type 2, 81 mm.	£300-400	☐
	1940-41		Type 3, 83 mm.	£300-500	☐
28x		'HOVIS'	White body, 'Hovis For Tea' in Gold/Black		
	1936-39		Type 2, 81 mm.	£400-600	☐
	1939-41		Type 3, 83 mm.	£300-400	☐
28y		'EXIDE'	Red body, 'Exide Batteries' and 'Drydex Batteries' in Gold/Black		
	1936-39		Type 2, 81 mm.	£300-400	☐
	1939-41		Type 3, 83 mm.	£300-400	☐

Further issues in this series were numbered 280a - 280f

Ref. No.	Year	Name	Description	Market Price Range	
30e	1935-40	Breakdown Car/Crane Lorry	Red, Yellow, Green, Brown or Grey body, Black wings, Black or Blue hubs, rear window, 92 mm.	£70-80	☐
			Blue body, Dark Blue wings, blue hubs, rear window	£100-120	☐
	1946-46		Red or Grey body, Black wings, rear window	£60-70	☐
	1947-48		Red, Grey or Green body and wings, no rear window	£40-50	☐
30j (412)	1950-54	Austin Wagon	Mid-Blue body with hook, Light Blue wheels, 104 mm.	£100-120	☐
			Light, Medium or Dark Maroon body, Maroon or Red wheels	£100-150	☐
			Brown body, Tan wheels	£400-500	☐
			Dark Blue body, Light Blue wheels	NGPP	☐
			Red body, Red wheels	NGPP	☐
30m (414)	1950-54	Rear Tipping Wagon	Maroon or Orange cab, Pale Green rear, 'Dodge' on baseplate, 100 mm.	£60-70	☐
			Blue or Dark Blue cab, Grey rear	£60-70	☐
30n (343)	1950-54	Farm Produce Wagon	Green/Yellow, Yellow/Green or Blue/Red body, hook, 104 mm.	£60-70	☐
30p	1950-54	Petrol Tanker	Based on a Studebaker vehicle, 112 mm.		
30p	1950-51	'PETROL'	Red or Green body, cast in aluminium	£70-80	☐
	1951-52	'PETROL'	Red or Green body, cast in mazak	£70-80	☐
30p (440)	1952-54	'MOBILGAS'	Red body and wheels	£100-120	☐
30pa (441)	1952-54	'CASTROL'	Green body and wheels, some cast in aluminium, most in mazak	£100-120	☐
30pb (442)	1952-54	'ESSO'	Red body and wheels, 'MOTOR OIL - ESSO - PETROL'.	£100-120	☐
30r (422)	1951-54	Fordson Thames Flat Truck	Red or Green body with hook, 112 mm.	£60-70	☐
30s (413)	1950-54	Austin Covered Wagon	Maroon body, Cream cover, Cream wheels, 104 mm.	£100-150	☐
			Dark Blue body, Light Blue cover, Light Blue wheels	£400-500	☐
			Mid-Blue body, Light Blue cover, Light Blue wheels	£100-150	☐
			Red body, Tan cover, Red wheels	£400-500	☐

Dinky Toys — Commercial Vehicles & Vans – continued

Ref. No.					Market Price Range	
30v (491)	1949-54	Electric Dairy Van 'N.C.B.'		Cream body, Red chassis, hubs and logo, 85 mm.	£75-90	☐
				Grey body, Blue chassis, hubs and logo.	£75-90	☐
30v (490)	1949-54	'EXPRESS DAIRY'		Cream body, Red chassis, hubs and logo.	£75-90	☐
				Grey body, Blue chassis, hubs and logo.	£75-90	☐
30w (421)	1952-54	Electric Articulated Vehicle		Maroon body, 'British Railways', hook, trailer uncouples, 135 mm.	£60-70	☐
31	1935-35	Holland Coachcraft Van		Red, Green, Blue or Orange, 'Registered Design', lead body, 88 mm.	£300-350	☐
	1935-36			Diecast body.	£250-300	☐
	1935			Cream body with Red coachline.	£800-1000	☐
				Note: Model owned by Frank Holland, founder of Holland Coachcraft. Sold by Christies in 1994 for £1200 with provenance.		
31a (450)	1951-54	Trojan 15 cwt Van 'ESSO'		Red body and wheels, 85 mm.	£110-125	☐
31b (451)	1952-54	'DUNLOP'		Red body and wheels, 'The Worlds Master Tyre'.	£110-125	☐
31c (452)	1953-54	'CHIVERS'		Green body and wheels, 'CHIVERS JELLIES' and design.	£110-125	☐
31d (453)	1953-54	'OXO'		Dark or Mid-Blue body, Blue wheels, 'Beefy OXO'. (Not boxed)	£200-250	☐
33a	1935-36	Mechanical Horse		Red, Green, Blue or Yellow body, 2.5 mm. trailer step, 65 mm.	£150-175	☐
				N.B. 1st type have long slot and chrome hubs.		
	1936-40			As previous model but trailer step is 9.5 mm. long.	£125-150	☐
	1946-)			As previous model but also in Brown, Grey or Khaki.	£125-150	☐
33b	1935-40	Flat Truck Trailer		Red, Green, Blue or Yellow body, no sides, 61 mm.	£45-55	☐
33c	1935-40	Open Truck Trailer		Red, Green, Blue or Yellow body, with sides, 61 mm.	£45-55	☐
33d	1935-40	Box Van Trailer		Green tinplate body on cast chassis, no advertising, 70 mm.	£100-125	☐
		'HORNBY TRAINS'		Dark Blue body, 'Hornby Trains British and Guaranteed' in Gold.	£125-175	☐
		'HORNBY TRAINS'		Green body, 'Hornby Trains British and Guaranteed' in Gold.	£125-175	☐
		'MECCANO'		Green body, 'Meccano Engineering For Boys' in Red and Black.	£125-175	☐
				N.B. Models 33a & 33d combined and given Ref No 33r.	£200-300	☐
33e	1935-40	Dust Wagon Trailer		Blue or Yellow 33c (Open Trailer) with Blue tinplate top, 61 mm.	£70-90	☐
				Grey or Green 33c (Open Trailer) with Green or Blue tinplate top.	£70-90	☐
	1946-47			Grey or Red body with Blue tinplate top.	£70-90	☐
33f	1935-40	Petrol Tank Trailer		Green (33b) chassis/Red tank, or Red chassis/Green tank, no logo, 61 mm.	£70-90	☐
		'ESSO'		Green chassis/Red tank with 'ESSO' in Gold.	£70-90	☐
		'CASTROL'		Red chassis/Green tank, 'Wakefield Castrol'.	£70-90	☐
33r	1935-40	Railway Mechanical Horse and Trailer Van		33a Mechanical Horse & 33d Box Van Trailer in railway liveries. 112 mm. These were also available separately as 33ra and 33rd (see below).		
33r		'L.N.E.R.'		Blue and Black, 'L.N.E.R. Express Parcels Traffic'.	£200-300	☐
33r		'L.M.S.'		Maroon and Black, 'L.M.S. Express Parcels Traffic'.	£200-300	☐
33r		'G.W.R.'		Brown and Cream, 'G.W.R. Express Cartage Services'.	£200-300	☐
33r		'S.R.'		Green (Cream cab roof) and Black, 'Southern Railway'.	£200-300	☐
33ra	1935-40	Mechanical Horse 'L.N.E.R.'		Blue and Black, 'L.N.E.R. 901', 65 mm.	£200-300	☐
33ra		'L.M.S.'		Maroon and Black, 'L.M.S. 2246'.	£200-300	☐
33ra		'G.W.R.'		Brown and Cream, 'G.W.R. 2742'.	£200-300	☐
33ra		'S.R.'		Green (Cream roof) and Black, '3016 M'.	£200-300	☐
33rd		Railway Trailer 'L.N.E.R.'		Blue and Black, 'L.N.E.R. Express Parcels Traffic'.	£200-300	☐
33rd		'L.M.S.'		Maroon and Black, 'L.M.S. Express Parcels Traffic'.	£200-300	☐
33rd		'G.W.R.'		Brown and Cream, 'G.W.R. Express Cartage Services'.	£200-300	☐
33rd		'S.R.'		Green and Black, 'Southern Railway'.	£200-300	☐
33w (415)	1947-54	Mechanical Horse and Open Wagon		Grey, Fawn, Dark or Mid-Green, Olive, Red, Brown, Blue or Yellow cab, with Maroon, Brown, Light or Mid-Green, Olive or Cream trailer, 102 mm.	£75-95	☐
34a	1935-40	'ROYAL AIR MAIL SERVICE'		Blue car body with Silver lettering and Gold crest, 83 mm.	£200-250	☐
34b	1938-47	'ROYAL MAIL' Van		Red body, Black bonnet/wings/roof/wheels, open rear windows, 83 mm.	£100-150	☐
	1948-51			Red body, Black bonnet/wings/roof, Black or Red hubs, filled-in rear windows.	£80-100	☐
	1952-52			Red body/roof/wheels, Black bonnet/front wings, filled-in rear windows.	£100-125	☐
34c (392)	1948-54	Loudspeaker Van		Green, Brown or Blue body (280 casting) Black loudspeakers, 81 mm.	£60-70	☐
				Brown, Blue or Green body (280 casting) Silver loudspeakers.	£60-70	☐
60y	1938-40	Thompson Aircraft Tender		Red body with 'Shell Aviation Services' in Gold, Black or White solid rubber whheels, 84 mm.	£250-350	☐
151b (25s)	1937-40	6-wheel Covered Wagon		Gloss Green body, tinplate canopy, seat holes, spare wheel, 99 mm.	£60-70	☐
151b (620)	1947-54	6-wheel Covered Wagon		Matt-Green or Greenish-Brown body, (export only from 1950).	£60-70	☐
252 (25v)	1954-60	Bedford Refuse Wagon		Fawn body with Green tinplate shutters, no windows, 107 mm.	£80-90	☐
	1960-62			Fawn body with Green tinplate shutters, with windows.	£80-90	☐
	1962-63			Dark Lime-Green body with Black tinplate shutters, with windows.	£200-300	☐
	1963-63			Orange/Grey body with Green plastic shutters, windows, diecast wheels or Red plastic wheels, Silver radiator.	£150-200	☐
				As previous model with Black radiator.	£200-300	☐
260	1955-61	'ROYAL MAIL' Van		(Morris 'J') Red body, Black roof, Gold 'E II R' crest, 78 mm.	£80-100	☐
261	1955-61	Telephone Service Van		(Morris 'Z') Olive-Green/Black, 'POST OFFICE TELEPHONES', ladder, 73 mm.	£80-110	☐
273	1965-70	Mini Minor Van 'R.A.C.'		Blue body, White roof, Black base, 'ROAD SERVICES', 78 mm.	£100-125	☐
				As previous model but with Silver baseplate and redesigned rear doors.	£75-95	☐
274	1964-73	Mini Minor Van 'A.A.'		Yellow body, White roof, 'PATROL SERVICE', original 'entwined' logo.	£100-125	☐
				Yellow body, Yellow roof, 'PATROL SERVICE', original 'entwined' logo.	£100-125	☐
				Yellow body, White roof, 'AA SERVICE', modern 'simple' logo.	£60-70	☐
				Yellow body, Yellow roof, 'AA SERVICE', modern 'simple' logo.	£60-70	☐

Ref. No.	Year	Name	Description	Market Price Range	
274	1970-70	'JOSEPH MASON PAINTS'....	(Mini Minor Van). Promotional in special Red box with advert card.		☐
			Maroon body, roof sign, 'PAINTS' labels, spun wheels. 650 issued	£250-300	☐
275	1964-66	Brinks Armoured Car	Grey/Blue, *Brinks Security Since 1859'*, 2 figures, 2 crates, plastic wheels	£90-110	☐
	1966-70		Same as previous model but no driver or crates, US packaging	£40-50	☐
			Grey body White roof, Blue base, metal wheels, assembled in USA	NGPP	☐
		Mexican issue:...........	Blue body with Grey doors and Red/White/Blue crests, plastic wheels	£1000-1500	☐
280	1945-47	Delivery Van	Red or Blue body, Type 3, open rear windows	£50-60	☐
	1948-54		Red or Blue body, Type 3, filled-in rear windows, no advertising, 83 mm.	£50-60	☐
280	1966-68	Mobile 'MIDLAND BANK'....	White/Silver, Blue stripe, Gold crest, opening doors, figure, 124 mm.	£70-80	☐

280 series DELIVERY VANS

Delivery Vans numbered 280a   -   280f (plus those shown as 280 ?) are an extension of the 28 series.

Ref. No.	Year	Name	Description	Market Price Range	
280a		'VIYELLA'	Blue body,*'Viyella for the Nursery'* in White & Black		
	1937-39		Type 2, 81 mm.	£250-350	☐
	1939-41		Type 3, 83 mm.	£175-225	☐
280b		'LYONS TEA'	Dark Blue body, *'Lyons Tea Always the Best'* in Red & White		
	1937-39		Type 2, 81mm (only issues as Type 2).	£350-450	☐
280b		'HARTLEYS JAM'	Cream body, *'Hartleys is Real Jam'* in Red/Green		
	1939-39		Type 2, 81 mm.	£800-1000	☐
	1939-40		Type 3, 83 mm.	£300-400	☐
280c		'SHREDDED WHEAT'.....	Cream body, Red stripe, *'Welwyn Garden City, Herts'* in Black		
	1937-39		Type 2, 81 mm.	£250-350	☐
	1939-40		Type 3, 83 mm.	£175-225	☐
280d	1937-40	'BISTO'	Yellow body, *'Ah! Bisto'* with logo, Type 2, 81 mm.	£300-500	☐
280d	1940	'BISTO'	Yellow body, wording altered to *'Bisto'* with logo		
	1938-39		Type 2, with large Bisto Kids transfer, 81 mm.	£300-400	☐
			Type 2, with small Bisto Kids transfer, with pie on table.	£600-800	☐
	1939-40		Type 3, with small Bisto Kids transfer with pie on table, 83 mm.	£300-400	☐
280e	1937-39	'ECKO'	Dark Green body, *'ECKO Radio'* in Gold, Type 2, 81 mm.	£250-350	☐
280e		'YORKSHIRE EVENING POST'	Cream body, *'Yorkshire Evening Post - The Original Buff*		
	1938-39		*Type 2, 81 mm.*	£300-350	☐
	1939-39		Type 3, 83 mm.	£600-800	☐
280f		'MACKINTOSHS'	Red body, *'Mackintosh's Toffee'* in Gold		
	1937-39		Type 2, 81 mm.	£600-800	☐
	1939-40		Type 3, 83 mm.	£300-400	☐
280 ?	1939 ?	'BENTALLS'	Green body, Yellow upper side panels, White roof, Black & Yellow logo *'Bentalls Kingston on Thames', 'Phone Kin: 1001',* promotional, Type 2.	£5000-8000	☐
280 ?	1939 ?	'BONNETERIE'	Dark Red, *'Maison de Bonneterie, Leverancier',* promotional, Type 2	£2000-3000	☐
280 ?	1939 ?	'LIVERPOOL ECHO'......	Promotional, Type 2, no other details available	£2000-3000	☐
280	1939	'FENWICK'......	Apple Green body, White roof, *'Newcastle on Tyne'*, Type 2.	£2000-3000	☐
343 (30n)	1954-64	Farm Produce Wagon	Green cab with Yellow rear, or Yellow cab with Green rear, 104 mm.	£60-70	☐
			Red cab with Blue rear	£100-125	☐
			Late issues with plastic hubs and no bonnet louvres	£70-80	☐

'CONVOY' Series (380-387).   Budget-priced models, having the same cab but with different rear body types.

Ref. No.	Year	Name	Description	Market Price Range	
380	1977-79	Skip Truck......	Yellow and Orange body, 112 mm.	£10-15	☐
381	1977-80	Farm Wagon	Yellow and Brown body, 110 mm.	£10-15	☐
382	1978-80	Dumper Truck	Red body/Grey back, Red body/Black back or Yellow body/Grey back, 118 mm.	£10-15	☐
383	1978-80	'N.C.L.' Truck	Yellow body, *'NATIONAL CARRIERS Ltd'*, 110 mm.	£10-15	☐
384	1977-79	Fire Rescue Wagon......	Red body, White fire escape, 126 mm.	£10-15	☐
385	1977-79	Royal Mail Truck	Red body, 110 mm.	£10-15	☐
386	1979	Truck......	Red body, *'AVIS'.* Catalogued but not issued	NGPP	☐
387	1979	Truck	Red and Blue body, *'PICKFORDS'.* Catalogued but not issued	NGPP	☐
390	1978	Customised Transit Van......	Metallic Blue body with *'VAMPIRE'* & *'FLAME'* design, Type 3	NGPP	☐
400 (14a)	1954-60	B.E.V. Truck	Dark Blue or Mid-Blue (Blue wheels), or Grey with Blue, Grey or Red wheels	£30-35	☐
401 (14c)	1954-64	Coventry Climax Fork Lift	Orange body, Green forks, Tan driver, 108 mm.	£25-30	☐
			Red body, Green forks	£300-400	☐
402	1966-69	Bedford TK Lorry	Red and White body, *'COCA-COLA'*, six trays of crates, 121 mm.	£125-150	☐
404	1967-72	Climax Fork Lift	Red/Yellow body with *'CG4'* rear logo	£25-35	☐
			Red/Yellow front with all red rear, plus stick on *'CG4'* label	£20-25	☐
	1978		Yellow body with *'Climax'* on fork guide and *'TC4'* on engine cover	£20-25	☐
406	1963-66	Commer Articulated Truck	Yellow/Grey, Blue plastic hubs, Supertoy, (424 without accessories), 175 mm.	£80-100	☐
407		Ford Transit Van			
	1966-69	'KENWOOD'	Blue/White, *'KENWOOD'*, Promotional, 122 mm. Type I	£50-60	☐
	1970-71	'TELEFUSION'......	White body, *'Colour TV, Telefusion'.* A promotional never issued	NGPP	☐
	1970-75	'HERTZ'	Yellow body, *'Hertz Truck Rentals'*, Promotional, 122 mm. Type I	£50-60	☐
	1970-73	'AVIS'	Red body, *'Avis Truck Rentals'.* Kit only but not issued	NGPP	☐
408 (922)	1956-63	Big Bedford Lorry	Maroon cab, Fawn truck body, Fawn or Cream wheels, 146 mm.	£90-110	☐
			Blue cab, Yellow truck body, Yellow or Cream wheels	£200-300	☐
			Pink cab, Cream truck body, Cream wheels	£1500-2000	☐
			Blue cab, Orange truck body, Pale Yellow or Cream wheels	£250-350	☐
409 (921)	1956-63	Bedford Articulated Lorry	Yellowish-Orange body, Black wings, Black wheels, 'Dinky Toys' on base	£80-100	☐
			Late issues with windows in lighter Yellow box	£150-200	☐
410 (25m)	1955-62	Bedford Tipper Truck	Red cab, Cream truck body, Red wheels, crank operates tipper, 97 mm.	£80-90	☐
			Yellow cab, Blue truck body, Yellow wheels	£90-110	☐
	1962	Late issues......	With windows, Silver radiator, plastic wheels and in lighter Yellow box	£150-200	☐

128

Ref. No.				Market Price Range	
410		Bedford CF Van			
	1972-72	'SIMPSONS'	Red/Black, 'Simpsons' and logos, Canadian promotional, 90 mm.	£35-45	☐
	1974	'DANISH POST'	Yellow body, 'Danish Post' emblem, Danish promotional, 90 mm.	£35-45	☐
	1974-75	'JOHN MENZIES'	Dark Blue body with 'John Menzies' logo, promotional, 90 mm.	£25-30	☐
	1974-74	'BELACO'	Brown/Black, 'Belaco Brake and Clutch Parts', promotional, 90 mm.	£35-45	☐
	1975-76	'M.J. HIRE'	White body, 'M.J. Hire Service', promotional, 90 mm.	£25-30	☐
	1975-77	'MODELLERS WORLD'	White body, 'Modellers World', 90 mm. This is a Code 2 model	£25-30	☐
	1975-75	'MARLEY TILES'	Red body with 'Marley Building' logo, 90 mm.	£25-30	☐
	1979	'COLLECTORS GAZETTE'	White body, 'Collectors Gazette' logo, 90 mm. A Code 2 model	£25-30	☐
	1972-74	'ROYAL MAIL'	Red body with 'ROYAL MAIL' and 'E II R' crest, 90 mm.	£15-20	☐
	1974-80	'ROYAL MAIL'	As previous model but with raised rectangle on roof	£15-20	☐
411 (25w)	1954-60	Bedford Truck	All-Green body and wheels, 104 mm.	£80-90	☐
412 (30j)	1954-60	Austin Wagon	Powder Blue body, Pale Yellow or Dark Blue wheels, 104 mm.	£350-450	☐
			Dark Red body, Pale Red hubs	£150-200	☐
			Dark Blue body, Blue hubs	£250-350	☐
			Lemon Yellow body, Green or Blue wheels	£350-450	☐
412	1974-80	Bedford CF Van 'AA'	Yellow body, 'AA SERVICE', headboard, plastic wheels, 90 mm.	£15-20	☐
413 (30s)	1954-60	Austin Covered Wagon	Maroon body, Cream cover, Cream hubs, 104 mm.	£100-150	☐
			Dark Blue body, Light Blue cover, Light Blue hubs	£300-400	☐
			Mid-Blue body, Light Blue cover, Light Blue hubs	£100-150	☐
			Red body, Grey cover, Cream or Grey hubs	£300-400	☐
			Red body, Tan cover, Red hubs	£300-400	☐
			Light Blue body, Cream cover, Lemon-Yellow hubs	£275-325	☐
			Red body, Grey cover, Grey hubs	£275-325	☐
414 (30m)	1954-61	'Dodge' Rear Tipping Wagon	Red or Orange cab (with bonnet louvres), Green tipper body, 99 mm.	£60-70	☐
	1961-64		Red or Orange cab (no bonnet louvres), Green tipper body, 99 mm.	£60-70	☐
	1961-64		Blue cab, Grey tipper body.	£60-70	☐
			Royal Blue cab, Grey tipper and wheels	£125-150	☐
415 (33w)	1954-59	Mechanical Horse and Wagon	(Models 33a + 33d), Blue horse/Cream trailer or Red horse/Brown trailer	£125-175	☐
416	1975-78	Ford Transit Van 'FORD'	Yellow body, '1,000,000 TRANSITS', Type 2, promotional, 129 mm.	NGPP	☐
416	1975-78	'MOTORWAY'	Yellow body, 'Motorway Services', special lights, Type 2, 129 mm.	£25-35	☐
417	1978-79	'MOTORWAY'	As previous model but Type 3 casting	£20-30	☐
417 (931)	1956-59	Leyland Comet Lorry with stake body	Blue cab/chassis, Yellow stake body, 'Dinky Toys' on base, 142 mm.	£90-110	☐
			Yellow cab/chassis, Green stake body	£90-110	☐
			Red cab/chassis, Yellow stake body, Yellow wheels	£90-110	☐
418 (932)	1956-59	Leyland Comet with Hinged Tailboard	Green cab, Orange truck body, Cream or Green wheels, 144 mm.	£90-110	☐
			Dark Blue cab, Mid-Blue truck body, Blue, Cream or Red wheels	£100-150	☐
419 (933)	1956-59	Leyland Comet Cement Lorry	Yellow body, 'Portland Blue-Circle Cement', 144 mm.	£100-125	☐
420 (25r)	1954-61	Forward Control Lorry	(Leyland) Red, Grey, Orange, Green or Blue body, hook, 107 mm.	£60-70	☐
421 (30w)	1955-59	Electric Articulated Vehicle	(Hindle-Smart), Maroon body, 'British Railways', hook, 135 mm.	£60-70	☐
422 (30r)	1954-60	Thames Flat Truck	Dark Green or Red body, windows, hook, 112 mm.	£60-70	☐
			Bright Green body and wheels	£100-130	☐
424	1963-66	Commer Convertible Articulated Vehicle	Yellow or Grey cab, 406 plus Blue trailer canopy & 'stake' body fittings, 175 mm.	£130-150	☐
425	1964-69	Bedford TK Coal Wagon	Red body, 'HALL & Co.', windows, 6 coal bags, scales, 121 mm.	£100-125	☐
428 (951)	1955-64	Large Trailer	Grey body with hook, Red wheels, Black front axle mount, Supertoy, 111 mm.	£20-25	☐
	1967-71		Red body with hook, Silver wheels, Silver front axle mount.	£20-25	☐
429 (25g)	1954-64	Trailer	Dark Green or Red, hook, axle pivot is part of main casting, 69 mm.	£20-25	☐
430 (25x)	1954-64	Commer Breakdown Truck	'DINKY SERVICE' logo, operable crane, late issues have windows, 123 mm.		
			Light or Mid-Tan cab, Green back, (in striped box)	£100-120	☐
			Cream cab, Pale Blue back, Red wheels, (in Yellow box)	£300-400	☐
			Dark Stone cab, Ocean Blue back, Red hubs, (in Yellow box)	£300-400	☐
			Red cab, Pale Grey back, Blue or Red metal hubs, (Yellow box)	£300-400	☐
			Red cab, Pale Grey back, Blue plastic hubs, (Yellow box)	£300-400	☐
			Red cab, Pale Grey back, Red plastic hubs (Yellow box)	£500-750	☐
431 (911)	1956-57	Guy 4 ton Lorry	Red 2nd type cab/chassis, Grey body, Red wheels, unpainted hook.	£350-450	☐
			Dark Blue 2nd type cab/chassis, Light Blue body & wheels	£200-300	☐
431	1958-60	Guy Warrior 4 ton Lorry	Beige cab (no windows), Dark Green truck body, painted hook, 136 mm.	£350-450	☐
	1960-64		Beige cab (with windows), Dark Green truck body, painted hook	£350-450	☐
432 (912)	1956-57	Guy Flat Truck	Pale Blue 2nd type cab/chassis/hook, Red flatbed, Pale Blue wheels	£200-300	☐
	1956-57		Red 2nd type cab/chassis/hook, Pale Blue flatbed and wheels	£400-500	☐
432	1958-60	Guy Warrior Flat Truck	Green cab (no windows), Red flatbed, Red wheels 136 mm.	£300-400	☐
	1960-64		Green cab (with windows), Red flatbed, Red wheels	£300-400	☐
432	1976-79	Foden Tipping Lorry	White cab, Red chassis, Yellow rear body, 175 mm.	£30-35	☐
433 (913)	1956-57	Guy Flat Truck with Tailboard	Dark Green 2nd type cab/chassis/hook, Mid-Green flatbed and wheels	£200-300	☐
			Deep Blue 2nd type cab/chassis/hook, Orange body, Light Blue wheels	£200-300	☐

Ref. No.		Name	Description	Market Price Range	
434	1964-66	Bedford TK Crash Truck.........	White body with Green flash, *'TOP RANK Motorway Services'*, 124 mm.......	£55-65	☐
	1966-70		Red or Metallic Red cab Pale Grey back, *'AUTO SERVICES'*.....................	£55-65	☐
435	1964-66	Bedford TK Tipper	Grey cab with Blue roof, Red rear body, 121 mm.................................	£35-40	☐
	1966-68		Yellow cab with Yellow or Black roof, Silver rear body........................	£35-40	☐
	1968-71		White cab and roof, Silver and Blue rear body.................................	£35-40	☐
438	1970-77	Ford D800 Tipper Truck	Metallic Red cab, Yellow tipper, Yellow or Silver wheels....................	£25-35	☐
			Metallic Red cab, Dark Metallic Blue tipper, yellow wheels.................	£25-35	☐
			Orange cab, Orange or Yellow tipper, Silver wheels.........................	£25-35	☐
		promotional issue:	White cab, Blue back, Silver chassis, with cardboard load *'POLCARB'*. Packed in plain White box with folded leaflet..	£200-250	☐
439	1970-76	Ford D800 Snow Plough..........	Dark Metallic Blue cab, Orange tipper, Yellow plough, White wheels.......	£40-50	☐
	1976-78		Dark Metallic Blue cab, Pale Blue tipper, Yellow plough, Silver wheels.....	£40-50	☐
			Light Metallic Blue cab, Orange tipper, dark yellow plough, Silver wheels...	£40-50	☐
			Medium Blue cab, Yellow plough, Powder Blue tipper, Silver wheels.....	£40-50	☐
			Orange cab and tipper, Dark Yellow plough, Silver wheels.................	£40-50	☐
			Orange cab, Dark Yellow tipper and plough, Silver wheels.................	£40-50	☐
440	1977-78	Ford D800 Tipper Truck	Orange cab, Yellow tipper, Silver or Black chassis..........................	£35-40	☐
			Orange cab, Orange or Light Blue tipper, Black chassis....................	£35-40	☐
			Red cab, Red Tipper, chrome wheels.......................................	£35-40	☐
440 (30p)	1954-58	Petrol Tanker 'MOBILGAS'.....	Red body, *'MOBILGAS'* in White letters with Blue borders, 112 mm.	£100-120	☐
	1958-61		Red body, *'MOBILGAS'* in Blue letters on White background, 112 mm. ...	£100-120	☐
441 (30pa)	1954-60	Petrol Tanker 'CASTROL'	Green body, 112 mm..	£100-120	☐
442 (30pb)	1954-60	Petrol Tanker 'ESSO'..............	Red body, *'ESSO MOTOR OIL - PETROL'*, 112 mm.	£100-120	☐
442	1973-79	Land Rover Breakdown Crane	White and Red body, *'Motorway Rescue'*, operable winch, 121 mm........	£15-20	☐
	1974-		White/Red or All-Red body, *'FALCK'*, export model for Denmark............	£15-20	☐
443	1957-58	Petrol Tanker 'NATIONAL'	Yellow body, *'NATIONAL BENZOLE MIXTURE'*, 112 mm.	£120-140	☐
448	1963-68	Chevrolet El Camino Pick-Up with Trailers	Turquoise/White/Red Pick-up & 2 trailers, *'Acme Trailer Hire'*, 256 mm.	£150-230	☐
449	1961-69	Chevrolet El Camino Pick-up ...	Green/White, suspension, fingertip steering, windows, 111 mm.	£150-230	☐
			Red/Yellow, suspension, fingertip steering, windows, 111 mm.	£55-65	☐
		South African issue:	All-Turquoise body	£500-750	☐
		South African issue:	Cream over Chocolate Brown lower body	£500-750	☐
			Turquoise over Cream lower body	£500-750	☐
449	1977-79	Johnston Road Sweeper	Yellow or Lime-Green body, (non-opening doors), 142 mm.	£30-35	☐
			All Yellow body, promotional with *'JOHNSTON'* stickers, normal box......	£40-50	☐
			All Yellow body, promotional with *'JOHNSTON'* stickers, special box	£70-80	☐
			Orange cab, Metallic Green rear...	£40-50	☐
450 (31a)	1954-57	Trojan Van 'ESSO'....................	Red body, White stripe, Red hubs, *'Esso'* logo, 85 mm.......................	£100-125	☐
			Maroon hub version as only issued in U.S.A. trade packs...................	NGPP	☐
450	1965-70	Bedford TK Van 'CASTROL'..	Green/White body, *'CASTROL - The Masterpiece In Oils'*, 143 mm.	£100-125	☐
451 (31b)	1954-57	Trojan Van 'DUNLOP'	Red body with *'Dunlop The Worlds Master Tyre'*, 85 mm.	£100-125	☐
451	1971-77	Johnston Road Sweeper	Orange cab (449 with opening doors), Metallic Green tank, 142 mm.	£30-35	☐
	1971-77		Metallic Green cab (449 with opening doors), Orange tank, 142 mm.	£30-35	☐
452 (31c)	1954-57	Trojan Van 'CHIVERS'...........	Green body with *'Chivers Jellies'* and design, 85 mm.	£80-100	☐
453 (31d)	1954-54	Trojan Van 'OXO'	Blue body and hubs, White *'Beefy OXO'*, Silver trim, (not boxed)........	£250-300	☐
454	1957-59	Trojan Van 'CYDRAX'...........	Light Green body with *'Drink Cydrax'* and design, 85 mm.	£90-110	☐
455	1957-60	Trojan Van 'BROOKE BOND'	Red body, *'Brooke Bond Tea'* and design, 85 mm.	£90-110	☐
		promotional issue:	As previous issue with White label on roof. The Red logo states: *'Since 1924 more than 5,700 Trojan 'Little Red Vans' supplied. Replaced on a long life basis'*. A similar label is attached to its (normal) box..	£400-600	☐
465	1959-59	Morris 10 cwt Van 'CAPSTAN'......................	Light Blue and Dark Blue body with cigarette design *'Have A Capstan'*......	£150-180	☐
470	1954-56	Austin A40 Van 'SHELL-BP'...	Red and Green body with *'SHELL'* and *'BP'* decals, 89 mm.	£80-100	☐
471	1955-60	Austin A40 Van 'NESTLES'	Red body, Yellow wheel hubs, *'Nestles'* logo, 89 mm.	£80-100	☐
472	1954-56	Austin A40 Van 'RALEIGH' ...	Dark Green body with *'Raleigh Cycles'* decals, 89 mm.	£80-100	☐
480	1954-56	Bedford CA Van 'KODAK'	Yellow body, *'Kodak Cameras and Films'* in Red and Black, 83 mm.......	£80-100	☐
481	1955-60	Bedford Van 'OVALTINE'......	Blue body with *'Ovaltine'* on Cream panel, 83 mm.	£70-90	☐
482	1956-60	Bedford Van 'DINKY TOYS'..	Cream and Light Orange body, *'Dinky Toys'* logo in Red, 83 mm.	£100-125	☐
490 (30v)	1954-60	Electric Dairy Van.....................	*'EXPRESS DAIRY'*, Cream body with Red chassis, hubs and logo, 85 mm. ..	£65-75	☐
			'EXPRESS DAIRY', Grey body with Blue chassis, hubs and logo	£65-75	☐
491 (30v)	1954-60	Electric Dairy Van.....................	*'N.C.B.'*, Cream body with Red chassis, hubs and logo, export model......	£65-75	☐
			'N.C.B.', Grey body, Blue chassis, hubs and logo, export model.........	£65-75	☐
491	1960	Electric Dairy Van.....................	*'JOB'S DAIRY'*, Cream/Red. 1176 made for promotional purposes.........	£90-110	☐
492 (34c)	1954-57	Loudspeaker Van	Blue body, Silver loudspeakers, (280 casting, Type 3), 83 mm.	£60-70	☐
492 (34c)	1954-?	Loudspeaker Van	Fawn or Blue body (280 casting), Black loudspeakers, 81 mm.	£60-70	☐
			Blue or Green body (280 casting), Silver loudspeakers	£60-70	☐
492	1964-64	Election Mini Van	White body, Red loudspeakers, *'Vote for Somebody'*, figure, 78 mm.	£60-70	☐
501	1947-48	Foden Diesel 8-Wheel Wagon...	1st type cab (Foden DG) with flash, spare wheel, hook on some, no tank slits in chassis, no chainpost bosses, Black 'herringbone' tyres, Supertoy, 185 mm.		
			Pale Grey cab & body, Red flash & wheels, Black chassis, no hook	£750-1000	☐
			Dark Blue cab & body, Silver flash, Blue wheels, Black chassis, no hook....	£600-700	☐
			Brown cab & body, Silver flash, Brown wheels, Black chassis, no hook	£250-350	☐
			Red cab & body, Silver flash, Red wheels, Black chassis, no hook, (U.S. only issue)..	£4000-5000	☐
			Grey cab & body, Red flash, chassis & wheels, small unpainted hook on some	£400-500	☐

Ref. No.			Description		Market Price Range
501	1948-52	Foden Diesel 8-Wheel Wagon...	Hook & tank-slits in chassis (introduced 1948), Black 'radial' tyres		
			Dark Blue cab/chassis, Light Blue flash/body/wheels, small unpainted hook	**£1000-1200** □	
			Red cab/chassis/wheels, Silver flash, Fawn body, unpainted hook, slits on some	**£400-500** □	
501 (901)	1952-54	Foden Diesel 8-Wheel Wagon...	2nd cab (Foden FG) no flash, large painted hook, Supertoy hubs, 188 mm.		
			Dark Blue cab/chassis, Light Blue body and wheels, Grey tyres................................	**£600-700** □	
			Red cab/chassis, Fawn body, Red wheels, Grey tyres	**£250-350** □	
502	1947-48	Foden Flat Truck	1st type cab (Foden DG) with flash, spare wheel, hook on some, no tank slits in chassis, no chainpost bosses, Black 'herringbone' tyres, Supertoy, 185 mm.		
			Green cab & body, Silver flash, Black chassis, Green wheels, no hook	**£350-450** □	
			Pale Blue cab & body, Dark Blue flash/chassis/wheels, no hook	**£650-750** □	
502	1948-52	Foden Flat Truck	Hook & tank-slits in chassis introduced in 1948, Black 'radial' tyres		
			Blue cab/chassis, Red flash & body, Light Blue wheels, slits on some	**£700-800** □	
			Dull Orange cab/chassis, Green flash & body, Green wheels, slits on some	**£600-700** □	
502	1952-52	Foden Flat Truck	2nd cab (Foden FG) no flash, large painted hook, Supertoy hubs, 188 mm.		
			Blue cab/chassis, Red body, Pale Blue wheels, chainpost bosses	**£2000-2500** □	
502 (902)	1952-54	Foden Flat Truck	Dull Orange cab/chassis, Green body & wheels, chainpost bosses	**£350-450** □	
			Yellow cab/chassis, Green body & wheels, Black or Grey tyres, bosses	**£600-700** □	
503	1947-48	Foden Flat Truck with Tailboard...................	1st type cab (Foden DG) with flash, spare wheel, hook on some, no tank slits in chassis, no chainpost bosses, Black 'herringbone' tyres, Supertoy, 185 mm.		
			Red cab & flatbed, Black flash & chassis, Red wheels, no hook	**£650-750** □	
			Pale Grey cab & flatbed, Blue flash & chassis, Blue wheels, no hook...........................	**£700-800** □	
503	1948-52	Foden Flat Truck with Tailboard...................	Hook & tank-slits in chassis introduced in 1948, Black 'radial' tyres		
			Dark Green cab/chassis, Light Green flash/flatbed/wheels, small hook	**£600-700** □	
			Deep Blue cab/chassis, Dull Orange flatbed, Light Blue wheels, hook, slits	**£600-700** □	
503	1952-52	Foden Flat Truck with Tailboard...................	2nd cab (Foden FG) no flash, large painted hook, Supertoy hubs, 188 mm.		
			Dark Green cab/chassis, Light Green flatbed & wheels, Grey tyres, bosses	**£1500-2000** □	
503 (903)	1952-56		Dark Blue cab/chassis, Orange flatbed, Light Blue wheels, chainpost bosses	**£250-350** □	
503	1952-53		Dull Orange cab/chassis, Yellow flatbed & wheels, Grey tyres, bosses	**£1700-2000** □	
503 (903)	1953-54		Dark Blue cab/chassis, Yellow body, Light Blue wheels, chainpost bosses....................	**£600-700** □	
504	1948-52	Foden 14 ton Tanker	1st type cab (Foden DG) with flash, spare wheel, tinplate tank, hook, no advertising, Black 'fine radial tread' tyres, Supertoy, 185 mm.		
			Dark Blue cab/chassis, Silver flash, Light Blue tank & wheels	**£250-350** □	
			Dark Blue cab/chassis, Light Blue flash, tank and wheels....................................	**£250-350** □	
504	1948-52		Red cab/chassis, Silver flash, Fawn tank, Red wheels	**£450-550** □	
504	1952-57	Foden 14 ton Tanker	2nd cab (Foden FG) no flash, large painted hook, Supertoy hubs, 188 mm.		
504	1952-52		Dark Blue cab/chassis, Light Blue tank and wheels, Grey tyres. In correct 2nd type picture box	**£2000-3000** □	
504	1952-53		Red cab/chassis, Fawn tank, Red wheels, Grey tyres...	**£450-550** □	
504 (941)	1953-54	'MOBILGAS'.....................	Red cab/chassis/tank/wheels, Red filler caps (see 941) Grey tyres	**£450-550** □	
505	1952-52	Foden Flat Truck with Chains	1st type cab (Foden DG) with flash, spare wheel, hook, slits in chassis, 'dimpled' chainpost bosses, Black 'fine radial tread' tyres, Supertoy, housed in Blue covered box showing 1st type cab, 185 mm.		
			Green cab/chassis/flatbed, Light Green flash and wheels....................................	**£1500-2000** □	
			Maroon cab/chassis, Silver flash, Maroon flatbed and wheels..............................	**£2000-2500** □	
505	1952-54	Foden Flat Truck with Chains	2nd cab (Foden FG) no flash, large painted hook, Supertoy hubs, 188 mm.		
			Green cab/chassis/flatbed, Light Green wheels, 'dimpled' chainpost bosses	**£200-300** □	
			Maroon cab/chassis/flatbed/wheels, 'dimpled' chainpost bosses	**£250-350** □	
505 (905)	1954-56		Green cab/chassis/body, Light Green wheels, 'rounded' chainpost bosses....................	**£200-300** □	
			Maroon cab/chassis/body/wheels, 'rounded' chainpost bosses	**£250-350** □	
511	1947-48	Guy 4 ton Lorry......................	1st cab casting, Supertoy, spare wheel, small unpainted hook, 129 mm.		
			Green cab, truck body and wheels, Black chassis and wings.................................	**£200-300** □	
			Brown cab, truck body and wheels, Black chassis and wings.................................	**£250-350** □	
			Grey cab, truck body and wheels, Red chassis and wings	**£200-300** □	
511 (911)	1948-52	Guy 4 ton Lorry......................	1st cab casting, Supertoy, large painted or unpainted hook, 132 mm.		
			Red cab/chassis/wings/'ridged' wheels, Fawn truck body	**£250-350** □	
			Dark Blue cab/chassis/wings, Light Blue truck body & 'ridged' wheels.....................	**£200-300** □	
	1952-54		Red cab/chassis/wings/'grooved' wheels, Fawn truck body	**£250-350** □	
			Dark Blue cab/chassis/wings, Light Blue truck body & 'grooved' wheels.....................	**£200-300** □	
512	1947-48	Guy Flat Truck	1st cab casting, Supertoy, spare wheel, small unpainted hook, 129 mm.		
			Maroon cab, flatbed and wheels, Black chassis and wings...................................	**£300-400** □	
			Dark Brown cab, flatbed and wheels, Black chassis and wings...............................	**£400-500** □	
			Yellow cab and flatbed, Black chassis and wings, Red wheels	**£350-450** □	
			Khaki cab and flatbed, Black chassis and wings, Green wheels	**£550-650** □	
			Grey cab and flatbed, Red chassis and wings, Red wheels..................................	**£550-650** □	
			Grey cab and flatbed, Black chassis, Black wheels	**£500-600** □	
			Red cab and flatbed, Black chassis, Black wheels...	**£700-800** □	
	1948-48		Brown cab/chassis/wings, Green flatbed, Green 'ridged' wheels.............................	**£400-500** □	
512 (912)	1948-54	Guy Flat Truck	1st cab casting, Supertoy, small or large unpainted hook, 129/132 mm.		
			Blue cab/chassis/wings, Red flatbed, Light Blue 'ridged' wheels............................	**£200-300** □	
	1949-54		Orange cab/chassis/wings, Green flatbed, Green 'ridged' wheels...........................	**£400-500** □	
	1952-54		Blue cab/chassis/wings, Red flatbed, Light Blue 'grooved' wheels	**£200-300** □	

131

Ref. No.					Market Price Range
513	1947-48	Guy Flat Truck with Tailboard..................		1st cab casting, Supertoy, spare wheel, small unpainted hook, 129 mm.	
				Dark Yellow cab/flatbed, Black chassis, wings and wheels..............................	£400-500 ☐
				Dark Yellow cab/flatbed, Dark Blue chassis, wings and wheels......................	£450-550 ☐
				Grey cab and flatbed, Black chassis, wings and wheels	£300-400 ☐
				Grey cab and flatbed, Dark Blue chassis, wings and wheels	£750-1000 ☐
513	1948-52	Guy Flat Truck with Tailboard..................		1st cab, 'ridged' wheels, Supertoy, small or large unpainted hook, 129/132 mm.	
				Dark Green cab/chassis/wings, Green body and wheels, small hook	£200-300 ☐
				Deep Blue cab/chassis/wings, Orange body, Light Blue wheels, large hook	£250-350 ☐
513 (913)	1952-54	Guy Flat Truck with Tailboard..................		1st cab, Supertoy, 'grooved' wheels, large unpainted hook, 132 mm.	
				Dark Green cab/chassis/wings, Green body and wheels	£200-300 ☐
				Deep Blue cab/chassis/wings, Orange body, Light Blue wheels....................	£250-350 ☐
				Yellow cab/chassis/wings, Green wheels..	£1000-1200 ☐
514	1950-52	Guy Van 'SLUMBERLAND' ..		Red 1st type cab/chassis/body and 'ridged' wheels, 2 opening rear doors, *'Slumberland Spring Interior Mattresses'*, spare wheel, Supertoy, 134 mm.	£250-350 ☐
514	1952-52	Guy Van 'LYONS'....................		Dark Blue 1st type cab/body, Light Blue 'ridged' wheels, 2 opening rear doors, *'Lyons Swiss Rolls'*, spare wheel, Supertoy, 134 mm.	£800-1000 ☐
				Same model but rear axle in cast mounts..	£800-1000 ☐
514	1952-52	Guy Van 'WEETABIX'		Yellow 1st type cab/body, Yellow 'ridged' wheels, 2 opening rear doors, *'More Than a Breakfast Food'*, spare wheel, Supertoy, 134 mm.	£1500-2000 ☐
514	1952-54	Guy Van 'WEETABIX'		Yellow 1st type cab/body, Yellow 'grooved' wheels, 2 opening rear doors, *'More Than a Breakfast Food'*, spare wheel, Supertoy, 134 mm.	£1500-2000 ☐
514 (917)	1953-54	Guy Van 'SPRATTS'		Red/Cream 1st type cab/body, Red 'grooved' wheels, 2 opening rear doors, *'Bonio Ovals & Dog Cakes'*, spare wheel, Supertoy, 134 mm.	£300-400 ☐
521 (921)	1948-54	Bedford Articulated Lorry		Red body, Black wings, Black wheels, Supertoy, 166 mm.	£150-200 ☐
				Yellow body, Black wings, Black wheels, Supertoy	£200-250 ☐
				Yellowish-Orange body, Black wings, Red wheels, Supertoy	£80-100 ☐
522 (922)	1952-54	Big Bedford Lorry....................		Maroon cab, Fawn truck body, Fawn wheels, Supertoy, 146 mm.	£90-110 ☐
				Blue cab, Yellow truck body, Yellow wheels, Supertoy, 146 mm.	£200-300 ☐
531 (931)	1949-54	Leyland Comet Lorry with stake body.................		Blue cab and chassis, Light Brown stake body, Supertoy, 144 mm.	£300-400 ☐
				Blue cab and chassis, Yellow stake body, Supertoy	£90-120 ☐
				Red cab and chassis, Light Brown stake body, Supertoy	£200-300 ☐
				Red cab and chassis, Yellow stake body, Supertoy	£100-150 ☐

No.581 U.S. issue 'EXPRESS HORSE VAN'. Note the correct box picture of the model.
Picture supplied by Christie's, South Kensington, London.

Ref. No.	Year	Name	Description	Price	
532 (932)	1952-54	Leyland Comet Lorry with Hinged Tailboard	Dark Blue cab, Powder Blue truck body, Supertoy.....................................	£300-350	☐
			Red cab, Blue truck body, Blue wheels...	£500-600	☐
			Dark Blue cab, Mid-Blue truck body; Blue, Cream or Red wheels	£100-150	☐
			Green cab, Red truck body, Cream wheels...	£250-300	☐
			Green cab, Orange truck body, Cream or Green wheels	£90-110	☐
533 (933)	1953-54	Leyland Comet Cement Lorry ..	Yellow body, *'Portland Blue-Circle Cement'*, Supertoy, 142 mm...............	£100-125	☐
551 (951)	1948-54	Trailer	Grey body, Black wheels, hook, Supertoy, 105 mm...............................	£20-30	☐
			Yellow body, Black wheels, hook, Supertoy	£100-125	☐
			Green body, Black wheels, hook, Supertoy	£100-125	☐
	1969-73	Gift Set issue...........................	Red body, Grey front chassis, protruding chromed hubs. Only in GS 339	GSP	☐
561	1962-64	Citroën Delivery Van	Light Blue body, Red/Yellow *'CIBIE'* logo, sliding door, 90 mm. French issue	£60-70	☐
579	1961-63	Simca Glaziers Lorry................	UK issue: Yellow and Green body, mirror/glass load, *'MIROITIER'*...........	£70-80	☐
			French issue: Grey and Green body, mirror/glass load, *'SAINT GOBAIN'*	£80-90	☐
581 (981)	1953-54	Horsebox	Maroon body (cast in aluminium) *'British Railways'*, 175 mm.................	£70-80	☐
581 (980)	1953-54	US issue:	Maroon, *'Hire Service'*, *'Express Horse Van'*, *'Express'*, Blue box with Orange/White labels with picture of US model	£500-700	☐
581	1962-64	Berliet Flat Truck	Red and Grey body, 6 wheels plus spare, hook, 130 mm. French issue.......	£70-80	☐

Note: The French issues listed above have been included because they were sold in the U.K.

Ref. No.	Year	Name	Description	Price	
582 (982)	1953-54	Pullmore Car Transporter	*'DINKY TOYS DELIVERY SERVICE'*, aluminium trailer, 250 mm.		
			Light Blue cab & trailer, Fawn or Dark Grey decks, no windows, Supertoy	£60-70	☐
			Mid-Blue cab and trailer, Fawn decks, no windows, Supertoy	NGPP	☐
			Mid-Blue cab and trailer, Dark Grey decks, Dark Blue print......................	£750-100	☐
591 (991)	1952-54	A.E.C. Tanker	Red/Yellow, *'SHELL CHEMICALS LIMITED'*, Supertoy, 151 mm.	£140-175	☐
620 (151b)	1950-54	6-wheel Covered Wagon............	Matt-Green or Greenish-Brown body, 'Export only' (to USA)	£60-70	☐
893	1962-64	Unic Pipe Line Transporter	Beige articulated body, spare wheel, 6 pipes, 215 mm. French issue	£90-110	☐
894	1962-64	Unic Boilot Car Transporter.....	Grey body, *'Dinky Toys Service Livraison'*, 325 mm. French issue	£100-120	☐
901 (501)	1954-57	Foden 8-wheel Diesel Wagon....	2nd type cab (Foden FG), Supertoy, spare wheel, large hook, 188 mm.		
			Red cab and chassis, Fawn truck body, Red wheels...................................	£230-350	☐
902 (502)	1954-56	Foden Flat Truck	2nd type cab (Foden FG), Supertoy, spare wheel, large hook, 188 mm.		
			Yellow cab and chassis, Green flatbed body, Green wheels	£600-700	☐
	1954-57		Orange cab and chassis, Green flatbed body, Green wheels........................	£250-350	☐
	1957-59		Dark Red cab & chassis, Green flatbed, Green wheels		
			(**NB** Red similar to colour of 919 Guy 'GOLDEN SHRED' van)................	£2000-3000	☐
903 (503)	1954-55	Foden Flat Truck with Tailboard....................	2nd type cab (Foden FG), Supertoy, spare wheel, large hook, 188 mm.		
			Dark Blue cab and chassis, Yellow flatbed, Light Blue wheels....................	£600-700	☐
	1954-57		Dark Blue cab and chassis, Orange flatbed, Light Blue wheels..................	£250-350	☐
	1957-60		Pale Blue cab and chassis, Fawn flatbed, Pale Blue wheels.......................	£600-700	☐
905 (505)	1954-56	Foden Flat Truck with Chains..	2nd type cab (Foden FG), Supertoy, spare wheel, large hook, 188 mm.		
			Maroon cab, chassis and flatbed, Maroon wheels, rounded chainpost bosses	£250-350	☐
	1954-58		Green cab, chassis and flatbed, Light Green wheels, rounded post bosses	£200-300	☐
	1956-57		Maroon cab, chassis and flatbed, Maroon wheels, rounded chainpost bosses	£250-350	☐
	1957-64		Red cab and chassis, Grey flatbed, Red wheels, rounded post bosses........	£250-350	☐
908	1962-66	Mighty Antar and Transformer	Yellow cab, Red/Grey trailer, Supertoy, plastic transformer, 335 mm.......	£400-500	☐
911 (431)	1954-56	Guy 4 ton Lorry......................	2nd type cab casting, Supertoy, 'grooved' wheels, large hook, 132 mm.		
			Red cab and chassis, Grey truck body, Red wheels..................................	£300-400	☐
			Dark Blue cab and chassis, Light Blue truck body and wheels...................	£200-300	☐
912 (432)	1954-56	Guy Flat Truck	2nd type cab casting, Supertoy, 'grooved' wheels, large hook, 132 mm.		
			Orange cab and chassis, Green flatbed body and wheels............................	£400-500	☐
			Blue cab and chassis, Red flatbed body, Light Blue wheels	£150-250	☐
913 (433)	1954-54	Guy Flat Truck with Tailboard....................	2nd type cab casting, Supertoy, 'grooved' wheels, large hook, 132 mm.		
			Yellow cab and chassis, Green body, Green wheels	£1000-1200	☐
	1954-56		Dark Green cab and chassis, Green flatbed body and wheels......................	£200-300	☐
			Deep Blue cab and chassis, Orange flatbed body, Light Blue wheels. Usually in Blue/White striped box with picture of Green lorry	£200-300	☐
			Deep Blue/Orange model in box with correct colours	£1000-1200	☐
914	1965-70	A.E.C. Articulated Lorry	Red cab, Grey trailer, Green tilt *'British Road Services'*, 210 mm............	£110-130	☐
915	1973-74	A.E.C. with Flat Trailer	Orange cab, White trailer, *'Truck Hire Co Liverpool'*, 210 mm................	£45-55	☐
			Orange cab, White trailer, *'Thames Board Mills'*, bubble-packed............	NGPP	☐
917 (514)	1954-56	Guy Van 'SPRATTS'................	Red/Cream 2nd type cab/body, Red 'grooved' wheels, 2 opening rear doors, *'Bonio Ovals & Dog Cakes'*, spare wheel, Supertoy, 134 mm.......	£300-400	☐
917	1968-74	Mercedes Truck and Trailer......	Blue cab/chassis (White roof), Yellow trailers, White tilts, 397 mm.	£45-55	☐
			Blue cab/chassis (White roof), Yellow trailers, Yellow tilts........................	£55-65	☐
			Dark Blue cab/chassis, Yellow trailers, Dark Blue tilts	£65-75	☐
		'MUNSTERLAND'	Dark Green cab & trailers, White tilts, Green logo, promotional................	£250-350	☐

Ref. No.				Market Price Range	
918	1955-58	Guy Van 'EVER READY'	Blue 1st type cab with small square sides to front number plate	NGPP	☐
			Blue 2nd type cab/body, Red 'grooved' wheels, 2 opening rear doors, '*Ever Ready Batteries For Life*', spare wheel, Supertoy 134 mm............................	£200-300	☐
919	1957-58	Guy Van 'GOLDEN SHRED'	Red 2nd type cab/body, Yellow 'grooved' wheels, 2 opening rear doors, '*Robertsons Golden Shred*', spare wheel, 134 mm.	£550-650	☐
920	1960-60	Guy Warrior Van 'HEINZ'	Red cab (no windows), Yellow body, 2 opening rear doors, spare wheel, '*Heinz 57 Varieties*', Tomato Ketchup bottle decal, Supertoy, 137 mm.	£1500-2000	☐
921 (409)	1954-56	Bedford Articulated Vehicle	Yellowish-Orange body, Black wings, Black wheels, Supertoy (521/921/409)..............	£80-100	☐
922 (408)	1954-56	Big Bedford Lorry	Maroon cab, Fawn truck body, Fawn wheels, Supertoy (522/922/408)	£90-110	☐
			Blue cab, Yellow truck body, Yellow wheels	£200-300	☐
923	1955-58	Big Bedford Van 'HEINZ'	Red/Yellow, '*Heinz 57 Varieties*' + Baked Beans can, Supertoy, 146 mm.	£300-400	☐
923	1958-59	Big Bedford Van 'HEINZ'	As previous model but Tomato Ketchup bottle instead of Baked Beans can..............	£700-900	☐
925	1965-69	Leyland Dump Truck (with Tilt Cab)	8-wheeled Supertoy with '*SAND BALLAST GRAVEL*' on tailgate, 192 mm.		
			White cab and chassis, Blue cab roof, Orange diecast tipper	£200-250	☐
			As previous model but with tinplate tipper in Orange, Pale Grey or Red	£200-250	☐
930	1960-64	Bedford Pallet-Jekta Van	Orange and Yellow body, '*Dinky Toys*' & '*Meccano*', Supertoy, 177 mm.	£200-250	☐
931 (417)	1954-56	Leyland Comet Lorry with stake body..................	Blue cab, Brown stake body, Blue or Red wheels, (531/931/417)............................	£300-400	☐
			Blue cab, Yellow stake body..	£90-110	☐
			Red cab, Yellow stake body, Yellow wheels	£90-110	☐
932 (418)	1954-56	Leyland Comet with Hinged Tailboard	Green cab, Orange truck body, Cream or Green wheels, Supertoy, (532/932/418).......	£90-110	☐
933 (419)	1954-56	Leyland Comet Cement Lorry ..	Yellow body, '*Portland Blue-Circle Cement*', Supertoy (533/933/419).....................	£100-125	☐
934	1956-64	Leyland Octopus Wagon...........	Yellow cab and chassis, Green truck body, Green band around cab (but without Yellow band above radiator), Supertoy, 194 mm.	£175-225	☐
			As previous model but with Yellow band immediately above radiator........................	£300-350	☐
			Dark Blue cab/chassis, Yellow truck body, Red metal or plastic hubs........................	£1500-2000	☐
935	1964-66	Leyland Octopus Flat Truck with Chains	6 chain-posts, 8 wheels, flatbed held by rivet, Supertoy, 194 mm.		
			Green cab/chassis, Pale Grey flat-bed body, Red plastic hubs	£1000-1200	☐
			Green cab/chassis, Pale Grey flat-bed body, Grey plastic hubs..................................	£1200-1400	☐
			Blue cab/chassis, Yellow cab flash, Pale Grey flatbed and wheels.............................	£3000-4000	☐
936	1964-69	Leyland 8-wheel Chassis...........	Red/Silver, '*Another Leyland on Test*', three '5-ton' weights, 197 mm.	£70-80	☐
940	1977-80	Mercedes-Benz LP.1920 Truck..	White cab, Pale Grey cover, Red chassis, hubs and interior, 200 mm.	£30-40	☐
			As above but with Black interior and white hubs..	£35-45	☐
		'HENRY JOHNSON'	Dark Green cab, White cover, Green logo, promotional, plain white box	£250-300	☐
		'HALB UND HALB'	'*MAMPE*' & '*BOSCH*' on Blue cab, Elephant design, promotional...........................	£75-100	☐

Sold by Bonhams of Chelsea, London in July 1995.
514 'WEETABIX' Guy Van, 918 'EVER READY' Guy Van, 923 'HEINZ' Big Bedford Van.

Ref. No.			*Dinky Toys — Commercial Vehicles & Vans – continued*	Market Price Range	
941 (504)	1956-56	Foden 14 ton Tanker 'MOBILGAS'	Red body & wheels, Black filler caps (see 504), Black or Grey tyres, Supertoy	£400-500	☐
942	1955-57	Foden 14 ton Tanker 'REGENT'	Dark Blue cab/chassis, Red/White/Blue tank, Black tyres, Supertoy, 188 mm.	£300-400	☐
943	1958-64	Leyland Octopus Tanker	'ESSO PETROLEUM', Red body & tinplate tank with waterslide transfers, metal wheels, spare wheel, hook, Supertoy, 192 mm.	£300-400	☐
			As previous model but with plastic wheels	£300-400	☐
			With plastic wheels, logos on self-adhesive labels	£350-450	☐
944	1963-70	Leyland Octopus Tanker	'SHELL-BP', Yellow/White cab & plastic tank, Grey or White chassis, plastic wheels may be Red, Black or Grey	£175-225	☐
	1963-64	Leyland Octopus Tanker	'CORN PRODUCTS', White body and plastic tank, *'Sweeteners For Industry'* in White on Black labels. Only 500 of these promotionals issued	£1500-2000	☐
945	1966-75	A.E.C. Fuel Tanker	'ESSO PETROLEUM', White body, *'Tiger in Your Tank'* logo on rear, 266 mm.	£70-80	☐
	1975-77		As previous model but without logo at rear, bubble-packed	£60-70	☐
	1977-77	'LUCAS OIL' Tanker	Green cab and tank, White design on labels, promotional, bubble-packed	£70-80	☐
948	1961-67	Tractor Trailer 'McLEAN'	Red cab, Grey trailer (uncouples), *'McLean Winston'*, Supertoy, 290 mm.	£180-230	☐
950	1978-79	Foden S20 Tanker 'BURMAH'	Red cab, Red/White trailer, Black or Grey hatches, Red or Cream wheels, 266 mm.	£40-50	☐
950	1978	Foden Tanker 'SHELL'	Red cab, Red/White trailer, Cream wheels, 266 mm.	£60-70	☐
951 (428)	1954-56	Trailer	Grey body with hook, Red wheels, Black hatches, (551/951/428), 105 mm.	£20-25	☐
			Dark Grey body with hook, Lemon Yellow wheels	£50-70	☐
958	1961-66	Guy Warrior Snow Plough	Yellow/Black body and plough blade, spare wheel, Supertoy, 195 mm.	£150-200	☐
			Yellow/Black body, Silver plough blade	£150-200	☐
			Silver blade version in box with picture showing Silver blade	£250-300	☐
966	1960-64	Marrell Multi-Bucket Unit	Pale Yellow body, Grey skip, Black wheels, 115 mm.	£100-150	☐
967	1959-64	BBC TV Control Room	Dark Green, *'BBC Television Service'*, Green windows, Supertoy, 149 mm.	£100-125	☐
968	1959-64	BBC TV Roving-Eye Vehicle	Dark Green body, BBC crest, camera, windows, Supertoy, 110 mm.	£100-125	☐
969	1959-64	BBC TV Extending Mast	Dark Green body, BBC crest, dish aerial, mast, windows, Supertoy, 195 mm.	£100-125	☐
974	1968-75	A.E.C. Hoynor Transporter	Blue/Yellow/Orange body, *'Silcock & Colling Ltd'*, 322 mm.	£60-70	☐
977	1960-64	Servicing Platform Vehicle	Red and Cream body, operable platform, spare wheel, 197 mm.	£150-200	☐
			N.B. Version seen using 667 Missle Servicing Platform Vehicle chassis in the Red/Cream 977 livery.		☐
978	1964-72	Bedford TK 'Refuse Wagon'	Diecast cab, plastic tipping body, 2 plastic bins, 152 mm.		
			Green cab, Grey tipping body, Red hubs, White plastic roof rack	£50-60	☐
	1973-74		Dark Metallic Green cab, Grey tipping body, White plastic roof rack	£35-45	☐
	1975-77	Bedford TK 'Refuse Wagon'	Lime-Green cab, Black or Brown chassis, plastic or cast roof rack	£35-40	☐
	1978-80		Yellow cab with Brown chassis	£35-40	☐
979	1961-64	Racehorse Transport	Grey/Yellow, 2 horses, 'Newmarket Racehorse Transport Service Ltd', Supertoy	£200-250	☐
980 (581)	1954-60	Horsebox (US issue)	Maroon body (cast in aluminium), *'Hire Service'*, *'Express Horse Van'*, *'Express'*. In Blue/White striped box with picture of model	£400-500	☐
981 (581)	1954-60	Horsebox	Maroon body (cast in aluminium), *'British Railways'*, 175 mm.	£70-80	☐
982 (582)	1954-60	Pullmore Car Transporter	Pale Blue cab & trailer, Fawn decks, no windows, no additional loading ramp, *'Dinky Toys Delivery Service'*, 250 mm. Blue/White striped box	£60-70	☐
	1961-64	1st variation:	Mid-Blue cab (without windows), Pale Blue trailer and decks, supplied with Loading Ramp 794/994. Blue/White striped box	£70-90	☐
		2nd variation:	Mid-Blue cab (with windows), Pale Blue trailer and decks, supplied with Loading Ramp 794/994. Blue/White striped box	£100-120	☐
		3rd variation:	Mid-Blue cab (without windows) and trailer, Brownish-Grey decks and ramp upper surface. Box is fully covered in blue paper with simple label on one end	NGPP	☐
983	1958-63	Car Carrier and Trailer	Red/Grey, *'Dinky Auto Service'*, (Supertoys 984 & 985)	£150-200	☐
984	1958-63	Car Carrier	Red/Grey body, *'Dinky Auto Service'*, Supertoy, 240 mm.	£100-150	☐
985	1958-63	Trailer for Car Carrier	Red/Grey body, *'Dinky Auto Service'*, Supertoy, 196 mm.	£50-60	☐
986	1959-61	Mighty Antar with Propeller	Red cab (windows on some), Grey low-loader with Bronze propeller, 295 mm.	£300-400	☐
987	1962-69	'ABC TV' Control Room	Blue/Grey/Red, *'ABC TELEVISION'*, camera/operator, Supertoy, 149 mm.	£120-140	☐
988	1962-69	TV Transmitter Van 'ABC-TV'	Blue/Grey body, Red stripe, revolving aerial dish, Supertoy, 110 mm.	£150-200	☐
989	1963-65	Car Transporter	'AUTO TRANSPORTERS', Yellow/Light Grey/Blue, Supertoy boxed in all card picture box or Export only Gold 'see through' window box – both rare, 240 mm.	£2000-2500	☐
991 (551)	1954-70	Large Trailer	See 551 for details		☐
991 (591)	1954-55	A.E.C. Tanker	Red/Yellow, 'SHELL CHEMICALS LIMITED', Supertoy, 150 mm.	£90-120	☐
	1955-58		Red/Yellow, 'SHELL CHEMICALS', Supertoy, 150 mm.	£90-120	☐

Dinky Toys - Fire, Police and Ambulance vehicles

NB. Ford Transit casting types are described at the beginning of the Commercial Vehicles section.

Ref. No.	Year(s)	Model Type	Model Features and Size	Market Price Range	
24a	1934-38	Ambulance	Types 1 or 2 criss-cross chassis, types 1, 2 or 3 grille, plated chrome or Black hubs, open windows, 102 mm.		
			Cream body (Red chassis), Cream body (Grey chassis)	£300-500	□
			Grey body (Dark Grey chassis), Grey body (Maroon chassis)	£250-300	□
	1938-40		Type 2 criss-cross chassis, open windows, type 3 grille, 102 mm. See 30f.		
			Cream body (Red chassis), Cream body (Grey chassis)	£200-250	□
			Grey body (Dark Grey chassis), Grey body (Maroon chassis)	£250-300	□
			Black body, Black chassis (thought to be for export only)	£500-750	□
25h	1936-37	Streamlined Fire Engine	Red body, no tinplate chassis, tinplate ladder & bell, White tyres, 101 mm.	£200-250	□
	1937-40		Red body, tinplate baseplate, ladder & bell, Black or White tyres.	£125-150	□
25h (250)	1948-54		Red body, tinplate baseplate, ladder & bell, Black tyres.	£70-80	□
25k	1937-39	Streamline Fire Engine	Red body, tinplate base, 6 firemen, ladder, bell, White tyres, 101 mm.	£400-500	□
30f	1935-38	Ambulance	Grey body, Red wings & criss-cross chassis, plain radiator, open windows	£150-200	□
	1938-40		Grey body, Black moulded chassis, radiator badge, open windows	£50-60	□
	1946-47		Grey body, Black moulded chassis, open windows	£50-60	□
	1947-48		Cream body, Black moulded chassis, filled-in windows	£50-60	□
30h (253)	1950-54	Daimler Ambulance	Cream body, Red crosses and wheels, no window glazing, 96 mm.	£50-60	□
30hm (624)	1950-54	Daimler Military Ambulance	Military-Green body, Red crosses on White backgrounds, (US issue)	£250-350	□
123	1977	Austin Princess 'POLICE' Car	All-White, Bronze/Blue or White/Blue. (This model has not yet been seen)	NPP	□
195	1971-78	Fire-Chief's Range Rover	Red or Metallic Red body, 'Fire Service', Blue roof light, Speedwheels, bubble-packed, 109 mm.		
				£30-35	□
243	1978-79	Volvo 'POLICE' Car	White body, plastic chassis, 141 mm. (Some made in Italy by Polistil)	£15-20	□
244	1978-79	Plymouth Fury Police Car	Black/White, 'POLICE', warning lights, plastic chassis & wheels, 135 mm.	£15-20	□
250 (25h)	1954-62	Fire Engine	Red/Silver body, tinplate ladder and bell, 99 mm.	£75-80	□
250	1968-71	Police Mini Cooper S	White or Off-White, rubber tyres, boot detail on transfer, 75 mm.	£35-40	□
	1971-73		As previous model but cast boot detail, no aerial.	£35-40	□
	1973-75		As previous model but with Speedwheels.	£35-40	□
251	1970-73	U.S.A. 'POLICE' Car	(Pontiac Parisienne), White/Black, beacon, siren, 2 aerials, driver, 132 mm.	£40-45	□
252	1971-74	R.C.M.P. Police Car	(Pontiac Parisienne), Blue/White, driver, Blue light, Speedwheels, 132 mm.	£40-45	□
253 (30h)	1954-58	Daimler Ambulance	Cream body, Red crosses and cast hubs, no window glazing, 96 mm.	£50-60	□
	1958-60		White body, Red crosses and cast hubs, no window glazing	£60-70	□
	1960-62		White body, Red crosses and cast hubs, with window glazing	£60-70	□
	1962-64		White body, Red plastic hubs, with window glazing	£80-100	□
254	1977-79	Police Range Rover	White body, 'Police', opening doors, aerial on some, Speedwheels, 109 mm.	£20-30	□
255	1955-61	Mersey Tunnel Police Van	(Land Rover), Red body, 'Mersey Tunnel' and 'Police', hook, 77 mm.	£60-70	□
255	1967-71	Ford Zodiac 'POLICE' Car	White body, driver, suspension, steering, aerial, warning lights, 114 mm.	£45-55	□
255	1977-79	Police Mini Clubman	Blue/White body, 'POLICE', opening doors & bonnet, plastic wheels, 82 mm.	£25-30	□
256	1960-64	Humber Hawk 'POLICE' Car	Black, no. plate 'PC 49', driver/policeman, suspension/steering, 102 mm.	£65-75	□
257	1960-68	Canadian 'FIRE CHIEF' Car	(Nash Rambler), flashing light, suspension, windows, 102 mm.	£40-50	□
258	1960-61	U.S.A. 'POLICE' Car	(192 DeSoto Fireflite), Black/White body, beacon, windows, 114 mm.	£60-70	□
258	1961-62	U.S.A. 'POLICE' Car	(191 Dodge Royal Sedan), Black body, aerial, windows, 111 mm.	£60-70	□
258	1962-66	U.S.A. 'POLICE' Car	(149 Ford Fairlane), Black/White body, Fingertip steering, 111 mm.	£40-50	□
258	1966-68	U.S.A. 'POLICE' Car	(147 Cadillac 62), Black/White, suspension/steering, 113 mm.	£60-70	□
259	1961-69	Fire Engine (Bedford Miles)	Red body, 'FIRE BRIGADE' & crest, tinplate ladder & bell, 115 mm.	£60-70	□
			As previous model but with 'AIRPORT FIRE TENDER' (from 276)	£60-70	□
261	1967-77	Ford Taunus 'POLIZEI'	White and Green body, (German issue), 110 mm. with label 'Special contract run for Meccano Agent in W. Germany'	£150-200	□
263	1962-68	Superior Criterion Ambulance	Cream, 'AMBULANCE' on windows, stretcher, no beacon, 127 mm.	£50-60	□
263	1978-80	E.R.F. Fire Tender	Yellow body, 'Airport Rescue', flashing light, 177 mm.	£40-50	□
264	1962-66	R.C.M.P. Ford Fairlane	Blue/White body, suspension/steering, beacon, aerial, crest, 111 mm.	£70-80	□
264	1966-68	R.C.M.P. Cadillac	Blue/White body, suspension/steering, beacon, aerial, crest, 113 mm.	£80-90	□
264	1978-80	Rover 3500	White/Yellow, 'POLICE', beacon, opening doors and bonnet, 131 mm.	£10-15	□
266	1976-79	E.R.F. Fire Tender	Red body, 'Fire Service', White wheeled escape ladder, 223 mm.	£40-50	□
	1979-80		As previous model but with Metallic Red body	£40-50	□
	1976-79	Danish issue:	Red body, 'FALCK'.	£60-70	□
267	1967-71	Superior Cadillac Ambulance	White/Red body, 'AMBULANCE' on roof, flashing light, 152 mm.	£40-50	□
267	1978-79	Paramedic Truck	Red, Yellow cylinders, 2 figures, lapel badge, (TV Series 'Emergency').	£15-20	□
268	1973-77	Range Rover Ambulance	White, 'AMBULANCE', stretcher, bubble-packed, 109 mm.	£15-20	□
269	1962-66	Motorway 'POLICE' Car	(Jaguar) White body, suspension/steering, 2 policemen, 95 mm.	£70-80	□
269	1978-79	Ford Transit 'POLICE' Van	White/Red/Blue, figures/lights/signs/cones, Type 3 casting, 129 mm.	£20-25	□
270	1969-72	Ford 'POLICE' Panda Car	Turquoise body, White doors, Blue/White roof sign, cast hubs, 97 mm.	£20-25	□
	1972-77		As previous model but fitted with Speedwheels.	£20-25	□
271	1975-76	Ford Transit 'FIRE'	Red body, hose/axe/bells/plastic ladder, bubble-packed, Type 2, 129 mm.	£40-50	□
		Danish issue:	As previous model but with 'FALCK' logo.	£60-70	□
272	1975-77	'POLICE' Accident Unit	White, radar gun/beacon/aerial/cones/signs, Type 2 casting, 129 mm.	£20-25	□
274	1978-79	Ford Transit Ambulance	White, 'AMBULANCE', Red crosses, beacon, Type 3 casting, 129 mm.	£20-25	□
276	1962-69	Airport Fire Tender	Red body, 'AIRPORT FIRE CONTROL', bell, 115 mm.	£50-60	□
			As previous model but 'FIRE BRIGADE' logo (from 259), no crest.	£50-60	□
276	1976-78	Ford Transit Ambulance	White body, 'AMBULANCE', Type 2 casting	£30-40	□

Ref. No.			*Dinky Toys — Emergency Services – continued*	Market Price Range	
277	1962-68	Superior Criterion Ambulance ..	Metallic Blue, White roof & tyres, driver, roof light, 127 mm.	£50-60	☐
277	1977-80	'POLICE' Land Rover.............	Blue body, White tilt, flashing light, 110 mm.	£15-20	☐
278	1964-69	Vauxhall Victor Ambulance......	White, 'AMBULANCE', suspension/steering, stretcher, 91 mm.	£50-60	☐
282	1973-79	Land Rover Fire Appliance	Red, 'Fire Service', metal ladder, bubble-packed, 119 mm.	£20-25	☐
	1974-78	Danish issue:.............	As previous model but with 'FALCK' logo.	£30-35	☐
285	1969-79	Merryweather Marquis.............	Metallic Dark Red body, escape ladder, working pump with reservoir, black hose, 'FIRE SERVICE', 177 mm.	£40-50	☐
			As previous model but (non-Metallic), Red body	£40-50	☐
		Danish issue:	As previous model but Metallic Dark Red body with 'FALCK' logo	£70-80	☐
286	1968-74	Ford Transit 'FIRE'................	Red, 'Fire Service', hose Type 1 casting, bubble-packed, 122 mm.	£40-50	☐
			As previous model but with Metallic Red body	£40-50	☐
		Danish issue:.............	As previous model but with 'FALCK ZONEN' logo	£70-80	☐
287	1967-71	Police Accident Unit................	Cream/Orange body, roof sign, aerial, Type 1 casting, 122 mm.	£40-50	☐
	1971-74	design change:.............	White/Red body, radar gun, roof rack, Type 1 casting	£40-50	☐
288	1971-79	Superior Cadillac....................	White/Red, 'AMBULANCE', stretcher, no flashing light, 152 mm.	£30-35	☐
		Danish issue:.............	White body with Red mid-section and roof bar, 'FALCK'	£70-85	☐
		Danish issue:.............	Black body/White roof, Blue interior & roof bar, 'FALCK'	£70-85	☐
555 (955)	1952-54	Fire Engine (Commer).............	Red body with Silver trim and ladder, no windows, 2 bells, 140 mm.	£50-60	☐
			As previous issue but with Brown ladder	£80-90	☐
624 (30hm)	1954-?	Daimler Military Ambulance	Military-Green body, Red crosses on White backgrounds, (US issue)	£250-350	☐
954	1961-64	Fire Station.......................	Red, Yellow and 'brick' plastic, base 252 mm. x 203 mm.	£150-200	☐
955 (555)	1954-60	Fire Engine (Commer).............	Red body & diecast hubs, Silver trim & ladder, no windows, 140 mm.	£50-60	☐
	1960-64		Red body & diecast hubs, Silver trim & ladder, with window glazing	£75-90	☐
	1964-70		Red body & plastic hubs, Silver trim & ladder, with windows, in 'picture' box	£90-110	☐
956	1958-60	Turntable Fire Escape Lorry (Bedford cab)	Red body & diecast hubs, no windows, Silver deck & ladder, 200 mm.	£50-60	☐
	1960-64		Red body & diecast hubs, with window glazing	£50-60	☐
	1964-70		Red body & plastic hubs, with window glazing	£60-70	☐
956	1970-74	Turntable Fire Escape Lorry (Berliet cab)	Metallic Red body & hubs, windows, 'ECHELLE INCENDIE', Silver platform	£200-250	☐
			Red body & hubs, windows, 'ECHELLE INCENDIE', Black platform	£170-200	☐
	1974-?	Danish issue:.............	Metallic Red body & hubs, windows, 'FALCK'.	NGPP	☐
2253	1974-76	Ford Capri Police Car..............	White/Orange, 'POLICE', Blue light, suspension, 175 mm. (1/25 scale)	£55-75	☐

Dinky Toys - Farm and Garden models

Ref. No.	Year(s)	Model Type	Model Features and Size	Market Price Range	
22e	1933-40	Farm Tractor............................	'Modelled Miniature' with 'HORNBY SERIES' cast-in, no hook, 70 mm.		
			Yellow/Dark Blue (lead) body, Red or Yellow (lead) wheels	£200-250	☐
			'DINKY TOYS' cast-in, with hook, Red wheels are lead, diecast or both		
			Green/Yellow, Yellow/Blue, Red/Blue, Red/Red	£125-150	☐
			Cream/Blue, Cream/Red, Blue/Cream	£125-150	☐
			'DINKY TOYS' cast-in, with hook, Yellow wheels are lead, diecast or both		
			Green/Yellow, Yellow/Blue, Red/Blue, Red/Red	£150-175	☐
			Cream/Blue, Cream/Red, Blue/Cream	£150-175	☐
27a (300)	1948-54	Massey-Harris Tractor	Red body, Yellow cast wheels, driver, steering wheel, hook, 89 mm.	£60-70	☐
27ak (310)	1952-54	Tractor and Hay Rake	27a Tractor and 27k Hay Rake, 157 mm.	£80-90	☐
27b (320)	1949-54	Halesowen Harvest Trailer.......	Brown body, Red racks, Yellow metal wheels, 133 mm.	£25-35	☐
27d (340)	1950-54	Land Rover	Green or Orange body, tinplate windscreen frame, driver, 90 mm.	£50-60	☐
	1952-53	Gift Set model:	Dark Brown body. Only in Gift Set No.2, Commercial Vehicles Set.	GSP	☐
27c (321)	1949-54	M.H. Manure Spreader	Red body with drawbar, hook, working shredders, 121 mm.	£25-35	☐
27f (344)	1950-53	Estate Car	Pale Brown body, Brown side panels and hubs	£60-70	☐
27g (342)	1949-54	Moto-Cart............................	Brown and Green body, driver, 3 metal wheels/tyres, body tips, 110 mm.	£25-35	☐
27h (322)	1951-54	Disc Harrow	Red/Yellow body, Silver disc blades, tinplate hook, 86 mm.	£25-35	☐
27j (323)	1952-54	Triple Gang Mower.................	Red frame, Yellow blades, Green wheels, cast-in hook, 114 mm.	£25-35	☐
27k (324)	1953-54	Hay Rake	Red frame, Yellow wheels, wire tines, operating lever, 77 mm.	£25-35	☐
27m (341)	1952-54	Land Rover Trailer	Orange or Green body and diecast hubs, drawbar and hook, 79 mm.	£20-25	☐
27n (301)	1953-54	'FIELD MARSHALL' Tractor......................................	Orange body, Silver or Green metal wheels, driver, hook, 76 mm.	£75-90	☐
30n (343)	1950-54	Farm Produce Wagon	Model features stake sides to rear body, Black metal base and hook. 104 mm.		
			Yellow cab and chassis, Green stake body and hubs	£60-70	☐
			Green cab and chassis, Yellow stake body and hubs	£60-70	☐
			Red cab and chassis, Blue stake body and hubs	£60-70	☐
105a (381)	1948-54	Garden Roller.......................	Green handle and Red roller sides, 67 mm.	£15-25	☐
105b (382)	1948-54	Wheelbarrow.......................	Brown and Red body, single metal wheel, 82 mm.	£15-25	☐
105c (383)	1948-54	4 wheeled Hand Truck	Green/Yellow or Blue/Yellow, 126 mm.	£10-15	☐
105e (384)	1948-54	Grass Cutter.........................	Yellow body, Green metal wheels, Red blades, 73 mm.	£15-20	☐
107a (385)	1948-54	Sack Truck..........................	Blue or Pale Green body with two small Black metal wheels, 65 mm.	£10-15	☐
192	1970-74	Range Rover........................	Bronze body, various interior colours, cast detailed or Speedwheels	£15-20	☐
	1973-79		Black or Yellow body, Speedwheels	£15-20	☐
300 (27a)	1954-62	Massey-Harris Tractor	Red body, Yellow cast wheels, 'MASSEY-HARRIS', Tan cast driver, 89 mm.	£60-70	☐
	1962-64		Red, Yellow wheels (cast rear, plastic front, rubber tyres), Tan cast driver	£60-70	☐
	1964-66		Red, Yellow wheels (all plastic), cast-in seat, Blue plastic driver	£60-70	☐

137

Ref. No.			*Dinky Toys — Farm & Garden – continued*	Market Price Range	
300	1966-71	Massey Ferguson Tractor..........	As previous model but name changed to '*MASSEY-FERGUSON*'................................	£60-70	☐
301 (27n)	1954-61	'FIELD MARSHALL' Tractor	Orange body, Green metal wheels, Tan driver, hook, 76 mm.	£75-90	☐
			Orange body, Yellow or unpainted wheels, Tan driver, hook................................	£150-200	☐
	1962-66		Orange body, Green wheels (plastic front, cast rear, rubber tyres)........................	£150-180	☐
			Orange body, Green plastic hubs (front and rear), Black plastic chimney..................	£150-200	☐
	1964-66		Red body, Green plastic hubs, rubber tyres..	£80-90	☐
305	1965-67	David Brown 900 Tractor	Red cowl, Grey engine, Yellow cab/wheels, '*David Brown 990*', 83 mm. Housed in detailed picture box..	£150-200	☐
	1967-74		White cowl/cab, Grey engine, '*David Brown Selectamatic 990*'.	£50-60	☐
	1974-75		White cowl/cab, Red engine/wheels, '*995 David Brown Case*, bubble-packed	£50-60	☐
308	1971-72	Leyland 384 Tractor	Metallic Red body, Cream hubs, '*LEYLAND*', 86 mm. (Bubble-packed)................	£50-75	☐
	1972-77		Blue body, unpainted or Black steering wheel	£40-50	☐
	1977-79		Orange body, unpainted steering wheel	£50-60	☐
310 (27ak)	1954-60	Tractor and Hay Rake	300 Tractor and 324 Hay Rake, 157 mm.	£80-90	☐
319	1961-71	Weeks Tipping Trailer.............	Red/Yellow body, cast or plastic wheels, plain or planked trailer bed, 105 mm.........	£25-30	☐
320 (27b)	1954-60	Halesowen Harvest Trailer.......	Red/Brown body, Red racks, drawbar, hook, cast or plastic wheels, 133 mm.	£25-35	☐
			Red body, Yellow racks, drawbar, hook, cast or plastic wheels, 133 mm.	£25-35	☐
321 (27c)	1954-62	M.H. Manure Spreader.............	Red body, Yellow cast wheels, '*MASSEY-HARRIS*', shredders, 121 mm.	£25-35	☐
321	1962-73		Red body, Red or Yellow plastic hubs, no logo	£25-35	☐
322 (27h)	1954-67	Disc Harrow	Red/Yellow body, Silver disc blades, tinplate hook, 86 mm.	£25-35	☐
322	1967-73		White/Red body, Silver disc blades, no hook, 79 mm.	£25-35	☐
			All White version	NGPP	☐
323	1954-63	Triple Gang Mower...................	Red frame, Yellow blades, Green wheels, cast-in hook, 114 mm.	£25-35	☐
324 (27k)	1954-64	Hayrake	Red frame, Yellow wheels, wire tines, Black or Silver operating lever, 77 mm.	£20-30	☐
325	1967-73	David Brown Tractor and Disc Harrow........................	305 and 322 in White and Red, 152 mm.	£80-90	☐
			305 and 322 in Yellow and Red, 152 mm.	£120-150	☐
340 (27d)	1954-66	Land Rover	Green body, Brown interior and metal wheels, Tan cast driver, 92 mm.	£50-60	☐
340	1966-69		Orange body, Green interior and plastic hubs, Blue cast or plastic driver...............	£50-60	☐
	1969-71		Red body and plastic hubs, Yellow interior, Blue plastic driver	£50-60	☐
	1971		Red body and Green plastic hubs	£70-80	☐
341 (27m)	1954-73	Land Rover Trailer	Orange, Green or Red, drawbar and hook, cast or plastic hubs, 79 mm.................	£20-25	☐
342 (27g)	1954-61	Moto-Cart................................	Tan and Green body, driver, 3 metal wheels/tyres, body tips, 110 mm.	£25-35	☐
343 (30n)	1954-61	Farm Produce Wagon	Red cab and chassis, Blue stake body and cast hubs, 107 mm.	£70-80	☐
			Green cab and chassis, Yellow stake body and cast hubs, 107 mm.	£70-80	☐
343	1961-64		As previous models but no bonnet louvres, cast or plastic hubs	£80-100	☐
344 (27f)	1950-53	Estate Car...............................	Pale Brown body, Brown side panels and hubs	£60-70	☐
344	1970-72	Land Rover Pick-Up.................	Metallic Blue or Red, cast wheels..	£15-20	☐
	1972-78		Metallic Blue or Red, Speedwheels	£15-20	☐
381 (105a)	1954-58	Garden Roller..........................	Green and Red, 67 mm.	£15-25	☐
381	1977-80	Convoy Farm Truck.................	Yellow cab, Brown plastic high-sided truck body, 110 mm.	£15-20	☐
382 (105b)	1954-58	Wheelbarrow	Brown and Red body, single metal wheel, 82 mm.	£15-25	☐
383 (105c)	1954-58	4 wheeled Hand Truck	Green or Blue body, 126 mm...	£10-15	☐
384 (105e)	1954-58	Grass Cutter	Yellow body, Green metal wheels, Red or Green blades, 73 mm.	£15-20	☐
385 (107a)	1954-58	Sack Truck	Blue with 2 small metal wheels, 65 mm.	£10-15	☐
386 (751)	1954-58	Lawn Mower	Green/Red, separate grassbox, 'Dinky Toys' cast-in, 140 mm.........................	£70-80	☐
399	1969-75	Tractor and Trailer...................	300 combined with 428	NGPP	☐
564 (964)	1952-58	Elevator Loader.......................	Yellow with Blue or Dark Blue hubs, hopper and feed chute	£55-70	☐
751 (386)	1949-54	Lawn Mower	Green/Red, separate grassbox, 'Dinky Supertoys' cast-in, 140 mm....................	£70-80	☐

Dinky Toys - Military models

See also Action Kits, Ships, Gift Sets

Ref. No.	Year(s)	Model Type	Model Features and Size	Market Price Range	
22f	1933-34	Army Tank	'Modelled Miniature' with 'HORNBY SERIES' cast-in, 87 mm.		
			Green (lead) body, Orange revolving turret, Red rubber tracks	**£200-250**	☐
			Green (lead) body, Orange revolving turret, Green rubber tracks	**£200-250**	☐
	1935-40		Green/Orange (lead) body, 'DINKY TOYS' cast-in, Red or Green tracks	**£150-200**	☐
			Khaki (lead) body, 'DINKY TOYS' cast-in, Green tracks	**£150-200**	☐
			Grey drab (lead) body, 'DINKY TOYS' cast-in, Green tracks	**£150-200**	☐
22s	1939-40	Searchlight Lorry	Green body, (22c casting), 84 mm.	**£200-300**	☐
25wm (640)	1952-54	Bedford Military Truck	Military-Green body, (made for export to the USA only)	**£250-350**	☐
27m (341)	1952-54	Land Rover Trailer	Military-Green body, (to fit 25wm)	**£250-350**	☐
30hm (624)	1950-54	Daimler Military Ambulance	Military-Green body, Red crosses on White backgrounds, (US issue)	**£250-350**	☐
30sm (625)	1952-54	Austin Covered Wagon	Military-Green body, made for export to USA only), 112 mm.	**£250-350**	☐
37c	1937-40	Signal Dispatch Rider	Green body, Khaki rider, White or Black rubber wheels, 45 mm.	**£100-150**	☐
139am	1950-54	US Army Staff Car	(170m) Ford Fordor in Olive drab with White stars on roof and doors	**£175-250**	☐
150a (600)	1937-40	Royal Tank Corps Officer	Khaki uniformed figure with Black beret, and binoculars in hand	**£25-30**	☐
150b (604)	1938-54	Royal Tank Corps Private	Die-cast figure in Khaki uniform, sitting, 22 mm.	**£25-30**	☐
150c	1937-40	Royal Tank Corps Private	Die-cast figure in Khaki uniform, standing, 30 mm.	**£25-30**	☐
150d	1937-40	Royal Tank Corps Driver	Die-cast figure in Khaki uniform, sitting, 25 mm.	**£25-30**	☐
150e	1937-40	Royal Tank Corps NCO	Die-cast figure in Khaki uniform, walking, 30 mm.	**£10-15**	☐
151a	1937-40	Medium Tank	(Gloss) Green body/base, White markings, chain tracks, aerial, 92 mm.	**£100-125**	☐
			As previous model but with Black rubber wheels instead of tracks	**NGPP**	☐
	1947-49		(Matt) Green body, Black base, no markings, made for export only	**£150-200**	☐
151b	1937-40	6-wheel Covered Wagon	Gloss Green body, tinplate canopy, seat holes, spare wheel, 99 mm.	**£70-80**	☐
151b	1937-40	Lead issue	Gloss Green body, Black ribbed tyres	**£125-150**	☐
151b (620)	1947-54		Matt-Green or Greenish-Brown body, 'Export only' from 1950	**£150-200**	☐
151c	1937-48	Cooker Trailer	Gloss Green trailer, wire stand, hole in seat but no figure, 60 mm.	**£30-40**	☐
151d	1937-48	Water Tank Trailer	Gloss Green, 52 mm.	**£35-40**	☐
152a	1937-40	Light Tank	(Gloss) Green body/base, White markings, chain tracks, aerial, 68 mm.	**£100-125**	☐
			As previous model but with Black rubber wheels instead of tracks	**NGPP**	☐
	1947-50		(Matt) Green body, Black base, no markings, chain tracks, aerial	**£150-200**	☐
152a (650)	1950-54		(Gloss) Green body, Black base, no markings, made for export only	**£150-200**	☐
152b	1937-40	Reconnaissance Car	(Gloss) Green body/base, six wheels, 89 mm.	**£100-125**	☐
	1947-50		(Matt) Green or Brownish-Green body, Black base	**£150-200**	☐
152b (671)	1950-54		(Gloss) Green body, Black base, made for export only	**£100-125**	☐
152c	1937-40	Austin Seven	(Matt) Green body, wire windscreen frame, hole in seat, 50 mm.	**£100-125**	☐
152c	1937-40	Camouflage issue	(Matt) Green camouflage	**£80-100**	☐
153a	1946-47	Jeep	(Matt) Green, White star on flat bonnet, spare wheel at rear, 69 mm.	**£60-70**	☐
	1947-50		(Matt) Green, White star on 'domed' bonnet	**£60-70**	☐
153a (672)	1950-54		(Gloss) Green, White star on 'domed' bonnet, made for export only	**£60-70**	☐
160a	1939-40	Royal Artillery NCO	Khaki uniform, 28 mm.	**£10-15**	☐
160b (608)	1939-54	Royal Artillery Gunner	Khaki uniform, seated, hands on knees, 24 mm.	**£10-15**	☐
160c	1939-40	Royal Artillery Gunlayer	Khaki uniform, seated, hands held out, 24 mm.	**£10-15**	☐
160d	1939-40	Royal Artillery Gunner	Khaki uniform, standing, 28 mm.	**£10-15**	☐
161a	1939-40	Searchlight on Lorry	Gloss Green body, 151b casting plus diecast or lead searchlight	**£200-250**	☐
161b	1939-40	Anti-Aircraft Gun on Trailer	Gloss Green, gun elevates, figure holes, cast drawbar & hook, 115 mm.	**£40-50**	☐
	1946-50		Matt Green or Brownish-Green	**£80-100**	☐
161b (690)	1950-54		Gloss Green, made for export only	**£80-100**	☐
162a	1939-40	Light Dragon Tractor	Gloss Green body, holes in seats, chain tracks, 65 mm.	**£100-125**	☐
			As previous model but Black rubber wheels instead of tracks	**NGPP**	☐
	1946-55		Matt Green or Brownish-Green body (with or without holes) chain tracks	**£150-200**	☐
162b	1939-40	Ammunition Trailer	Gloss Green body and baseplate, drawbar and hook, 54 mm.	**£15-20**	☐
	1946-55		Matt Green or Brownish-Green body, Black baseplate	**£15-20**	☐
162c	1939-40	18 pounder Gun	Gloss Green body, drawbar cast-in, tinplate shield, 78 mm.	**£20-25**	☐
	1946-55	18 pounder Gun	Matt Green or Brownish-Green body and shield	**£20-25**	☐
170m	1954-54	Ford US Army Staff Car	(139am) Military-Green, US issue, renumbered 675	**£175-250**	☐
281	1973-76	Military Hovercraft	Military-Green body, Gunner, aerial, 'Army', 139 mm.	**£20-25**	☐ ·
341 (27m)	1960	Land Rover Trailer	Military-Green body with drawbar and hook, 79 mm.	**£300-400**	☐
600 (150)	194?-4?	Royal Tank Corps Officer	US only re-issue	**£10**	☐
601	1974-76	Austin Paramoke	Military-Green, Tan hood, spun hubs, parachute, 76 mm.	**£40-50**	☐
	1976-78		Military-Green, Tan hood, Speedwheels	**£30-40**	☐
603	1950-68	Army Private (seated)	Diecast figure in Khaki uniform, Black beret, seated, 20 mm.	**£3-4**	☐
	1968-71		Plastic figure in Khaki uniform, Black beret, seated, 20 mm.	**£3-4**	☐
603a	1950-68	Army Personnel Set	Six diecast figures (Khaki uniforms, Black berets, seated)	**£20-30**	☐
	1968-71		Six plastic figures (Khaki uniforms, Black berets, seated)	**£20-30**	☐
604 (150b)	1954-60	Royal Tank Corps Private	Die-cast figure in Khaki uniform, sitting, export only (to USA)	**£10-15**	☐
604	1960-72	Army Personnel	Six army driver figures (Khaki uniforms)	**£20-30**	☐
604	1976-79	Land Rover Bomb Disposal	Military-Green/Orange, 'Explosive Disposal', robot de-fuser, 110 mm.	**£35-45**	☐
608 (160b)	1954-55	Royal Artillery Gunner	Khaki uniform, seated, hands on knees, 24 mm. (Export only)	**£10-15**	☐
609	1974-78	105 mm. Howitzer & Crew	Military-Green body, three soldiers, bubble-packed, 199 mm.	**£20-25**	☐
612	1973-79	Commando Jeep	Army-Green or Camouflage, driver, two guns, jerricans, aerial, 108 mm.	**£20-25**	☐
615	1968-74	US Jeep and 105 mm. Gun	Military-Green body with US Army markings, driver, 108/199 mm.	**£25-30**	☐
616	1968-78	AEC with Chieftain Tank	AEC articulated Transporter 'ARMY' with 683 Tank, 318 mm.	**£40-50**	☐

Ref. No.	Years	Model	Description	Price
617	1967-78	VW KDF and 50 mm. Gun	Grey, German markings, operable anti-tank gun, 115/159 mm.	£30-40
618	1976-79	AEC with Helicopter................	AEC articulated Transporter *'RESCUE'*, 724 Helicopter and net, 318 mm.	£50-60
619	1976-78	Bren Gun Carrier & AT Gun ...	Khaki, plastic tracks, figures, gun/shells, White '57' on red shield	£25-35
			N.B. Two variations exist (i) 20357034 (ii) T2272616 plus star.	
620 (151b)	1954-55	6-wheel Covered Wagon	Matt-Green or Greenish-Brown body, export only (to USA)	NGPP
620	1971-73	Berliet Missile Launcher...........	Military-Green launcher body with White/Red missile, 150 mm.	£80-100
621	1954-60	3 ton Army Wagon	(Bedford 'S') tin tilt, no windows, driver on some, 113 mm.	£50-60
	1960-63	3 ton Army Wagon	(Bedford 'S') tin tilt, with window glazing, driver on some	£50-60
622	1954-63	10 ton Army Truck	(Foden) Military-Green, driver, tin tilt, 137 mm. Supertoys box........................	£60-70
622	1954-63	10 ton Army Truck	(Foden) Military-Green, driver, tin tilt, Dinky Toys box........................	£60-70
622	1975-78	Bren Gun Carrier	Green body, White star, driver, passenger, plastic tracks, 125 mm.	£20-30
623	1954-63	Army Covered Wagon	(Bedford 'QL') Military-Green body with or without driver, 105 mm.	£35-45
624 (30hm)	1954-?	Daimler Military Ambulance	Military-Green body, Red crosses on White backgrounds, (US issue)	£250-350
625 (30sm)	1952-54	Austin Covered Wagon	Military-Green body, made for export only (to USA) 112 mm.	£250-350
625	1975-78	Six-pounder Gun	Green anti-tank gun, 159 mm.	£15-20
626	1956-61	Military Ambulance	Military-Green, Red crosses cast-in, driver on some, no windows, 110 mm.	£40-50
	1961-62		Military-Green, Red crosses cast-in, driver on some, with window glazing	£40-50
630	1973-78	Ferret Armoured Car	Military-Green body, plastic wheels, spare wheel, 80 mm.	£15-20
640 (25wm)	1954-?	Bedford Military Truck	Military-Green body, made for export only (to the USA)	£250-350
641	1954-61	Army 1 ton Cargo Truck	Military-Green, tin tilt, with or without driver, no windows, 79 mm.	£35-40
	1961-64		As previous but with window glazing, with or without driver	£35-40
642	1957-62	R.A.F. Pressure Refueller...........	RAF Blue, French roundel, with or without driver, 142 mm. Supertoys box........	£80-90
	1957-62		RAF Blue, French roundel, with or without driver, Dinky Toys box	£90-110
643	1958-61	Army Water Tanker.............	Military-Green body, no windows, with or without driver, 89 mm.	£30-35
	1961-64		Military-Green body with window glazing, with or without driver	£30-35
650 (152a)	1954-55	Light Tank................	Matt Green body, Black base, no markings, made for export only (to USA)	£100-125
651	1954-70	Centurion Tank	Military-Green, metal or plastic rollers, rubber tracks, Supertoy, 149 mm.	£30-40
			Version housed in U.S. Gold 'see through' box	£75-100
654	1973-79	155 mm. Mobile Gun	Military-Green body with star, operable gun, plastic shells, 151 mm.	£15-20
656	1975-79	88 mm. Gun.................	German Grey, fires plastic shells, 218 mm.	£15-20
660	1956-61	Tank Transporter	Thorneycroft Mighty Antar, Army Green, no windows, driver on some, 335 mm......	£60-70
	1961-64		As previous model but with window glazing, with or without driver	£60-70
660a	1978-80	Anti-Aircraft Gun with Crew....	Military-Green, 3 soldiers, 218 mm. (Bubble-packed model)	£15-20
661	1957-65	Recovery Tractor...................	Army Green, six diecast wheels, driver, operable crane, 134 mm. Supertoy	£60-70
			As previous model but with plastic wheels, packed in Yellow 'picture' box	£125-150
662	1975-77	88 mm. Gun with Crew	German Grey gun (656 without wheels), 3 Germans, shells, bubble-packed	£15-20
665	1964-75	Honest John Missile Erector.....	Army Green, Black/White missile, 10 wheels plus spare, 188 mm...................	£90-100
666	1959-64	Missile Erector Vehicle and Corporal Missile Launcher..	Military-Green, Black/White missile, operable erector, Supertoy, 240 mm.	£150-200
667	1960-64	Missile Servicing Platform........	Military-Green, windows, spare wheel, platform lifts, 197 mm. (Supertoy)	£100-125
667	1976-78	Armoured Patrol Car	Army Green body, aerial, spare wheel, 80 mm.	£15-20
668	1976-79	Foden Army Truck	Military-Green body, windows, plastic tilt and wheels, 197 mm.	£28-33
669	1956-58	U.S.A. Army Jeep	Military-Green body with White star, (US issue) 83 mm. Issued in 'Plain' box	£250-350
670	1954-64	Armoured Car	Military-Green body, turret rotates, diecast wheels, 73 mm.	£15-20
	1964-70		Military-Green body, turret rotates, plastic hubs, 73 mm.	£15-20
671 (152b)	1954-55	Reconnaissance Car.................	(Matt) Green body, Black base, made for export only	£100-125
672 (153a)	1954-55	US Army Jeep	Military-Green, White star on 'domed' bonnet, made for export only	£60-70
673	1953-61	Scout Car	Military-Green body, squadron markings, holes for personnel, 68 mm.	£15-20
674	1954-66	Austin Champ	Military-Green body, driver, tinplate windscreen, diecast hubs, 69 mm.	£20-25
	1966-71		Military-Green body, driver, tinplate windscreen, plastic hubs	£20-25
674	1958-70	'U.N.' Austin Champ	White body, driver, tinplate windscreen. Made for export only	£250-300
675 (170m)	1954-59	Ford US Army Staff Car	Ford Fordor with Olive-drab body, White star, export only (to US)	£200-250
676	1955-62	Armoured Personnel Carrier.....	Military-Green, squadron markings, 6 wheels, revolving turret, 82 mm.	£25-30
676a	1973-76	Daimler Armoured Car............	Army-Green body, Speedwheels, 73 mm. (new version of 670)	£15-20
676a	1973-74	Daimler Armoured Car............	French made version with camouflage net ('Made in England' on base)	NGPP
677	1957-62	Armoured Command Vehicle....	Military-Green body, 6 wheels, (based on an A.E.C. vehicle) 133 mm.	£60-70
680	1972-78	Ferret Armoured Car	Sand or Army-Green, Speedwheels, spare wheel, bubble-packed, 80 mm.	£10-15
681	1972-78	DUKW Amphibious Vehicle	RAF Blue or Army-Green body, Speedwheels, bubble-packed, 127 mm.	£10-15
682	1972-78	Stalwart Load Carrier	Army-Green body, 6 Speedwheels, bubble-packed, 103 mm.	£10-15
683	1972-79	Chieftain Tank.................	Army-Green body, plastic tracks, fires shells, bubble-packed, 217 mm.	£25-35
686	1957-71	25-pounder Field Gun	Military-Green, cast drawbar, (cast hubs, plastic from 1968) 90 mm.	£10-15
687	1957-67	25-pounder Trailer	Military-Green, cast drawbar, (cast hubs, plastic from 1968) 58 mm.	£10-15
687	1978-79	Convoy Army Truck	Green/Black body, 110 mm.	£10-15
688	1957-61	Field Artillery Tractor	Military-Green, driver on some, no windows, cast hubs, 81 mm.	£25-30
	1961-70		Military-Green, driver on some, with windows, (plastic hubs from 1968)	£25-30
689	1957-66	Medium Artillery Tractor	Military-Green, driver on some, holes, 6 wheels, tin tilt, 140 mm. Supertoy	£25-30
690 (161b)	1954-55	Anti-Aircraft Gun on Trailer	Matt Green, 115 mm., made for export only	£40-50
690	1974-79	Scorpion Tank................	Army-Green, camouflage net, working gun, bubble-packed, 120 mm.	£15-20
691	1974-79	Striker Anti-Tank...................	Army-Green, plastic tracks, aerials, 5 firing rockets, 122 mm.	£15-20
692	1955-62	5.5 Medium Gun	Military-Green body, twin cast drawbar, elevating barrel, 131 mm.	£15-20
692	1974-79	Leopard Tank.................	Grey with German markings, plastic tracks, bubble-packed, 198 mm.	£30-35
693	1958-67	7.2 inch Howitzer Gun	Military-Green body, cast drawbar, elevating barrel, 130 mm.	£15-20
694	1974-80	Hanomag Tank Destroyer.........	Grey, German markings, plastic tracks/wheels, bubble-packed, 171 mm.	£25-30
696	1975-79	Leopard Anti-Aircraft Tank	Grey-Green, German markings, plastic tracks, bubble-packed, 152 mm.	£25-30
699	1975-78	Leopard Recovery Tank...........	Grey-Green, German markings, dozer blade/jib, aerial, bubble-packed............	£25-30

Dinky Toys — Military Models – continued

Ref. No.				Market Price Range
815	1962-64	Panhard Armoured Tank	Military-Green with French flag, 104 mm. (French issue)	£75-100 ☐
816	1969-71	Berliet Missile Launcher............	Military-Green body, (French issue)..	£150-200 ☐
817	1962-64	AMX 13-ton Tank	Green body with French flag, 107 mm. (French issue)	£75-100 ☐
822	1962-64	Half-Track M3	Green body, rubber tracks, 121 mm. (French issue)	£75-100 ☐
884	1962-64	Brockway Bridge Truck	Military-Green, 10 wheels, bridge parts, inflatables, 180 mm. French issue	£150-200 ☐

DINKY TOYS & DINKY SUPERTOYS

DINKY TOYS

What is so fascinating about Dinky Toys and why do they appeal so much to boys of all ages?

The answer is that these attractive models are unsurpassed for realism, wealth of detail, rich colouring and sturdy construction.

A small selection is illustrated here . . . the present range consists of more than 120 models—and new ones are being added regularly.

It's fun to be first with the latest Dinky Toys.

982	Pullmore Car Transporter	16/6
964	Elevator Loader	17/6
903	Foden Flat Truck (with tailboard)	7/3
251	Aveling-Barford Diesel Roller	4/4
321	Massey Harris Manure Spreader	4/-
300	Massey Harris Tractor	4/-
342	Motocart	4/3
430	Breakdown Lorry Commer Chassis ..	5/6
962	Muir Hill Dumper Truck	7/-
963	Blaw Knox Heavy Tractor	7/9
401	Coventry Climax Fork Lift Truck ..	6/6
253	Daimler Ambulance	2/11
421	Hindle Smart Electric Articulated Lorry ..	3/11
250	Streamlined Fire Engine	2/11
343	Farm Produce Wagon	3/6
410	Bedford End Tipper	5/3
490	Electric Dairy Van, " Express " ..	3/4
440	Tanker " Mobilgas "	2/10
413	Austin Covered Wagon	3/1
290	Double Deck Bus	4/-
254	Austin Taxi	3/-
231	Maserati Racing Car	2/6
344	Estate Car	2/11
156	Rover 75 Saloon	2/9
154	Hillman Minx Saloon	2/6
405	Universal Jeep	3/3
153	Standard Vanguard Saloon	2/6
235	H.W.M. Racing Car	2/6
151	Triumph 1800 Saloon	2/6
340	Land Rover	4/4

Free delivery in Gamages extensive van area.

Outside this radius, with orders up to £1 in value, please add 1/- to cover postage and packing cost; from £1 to £2 in value, 1/6; from £2 to £3, 2/-. Orders value £3 and over are sent POST & PACKING FREE.

MOST OF THE DINKY TOYS AND DINKY SUPERTOYS CAN BE SEEN ON GAMAGES MAMMOTH LAYOUT

Advertisement in a 1950's Gamages Catalogue.

WHEN REPLYING TO ADVERTISEMENTS PLEASE MENTION JOHN RAMSAY'S CATALOGUE

Dinky Toys - Aircraft

Ref. No.	Year(s)	Model Type	Model Features and Size	Market Price Range	
60a	1934-36	Imperial Airways Liner	(Armstrong-Whitworth Atalanta) cast body, tinplate wings, 4 x 2 PB, Plain or 'Sunray' effect, Silver/Blue, Gold/Blue, Yellow/Blue, Red/Cream, White/Blue/Green, White/Blue, Blue/Yellow, Cream/Green, Cream/Red with no markings ..	£200-250	☐
	1936-39		Blue, Cream, Gold, Red, Silver or White with Black 'G-ABTI' marking....................	£200-250	☐
60a (66a)	1939-41		All-over Gold, Green or Silver, 'G-ABTI', 'Imperial Airways Liner' under wing	£200-250	☐
60b	1934-36	De Havilland 'Leopard Moth' ..	Cast fuselage, tinplate wings, single 2-blade propeller, 76 mm. Green/Yellow or Dark Blue/Orange, Silver/Green, Blue/Yellow, Blue/Red, Gold/Red, no markings, open windows................	£100-150	☐
	1936-39		All-over Green, Gold or Silver, 'Beige, Mid or Pale Blue, Red, G-ACPT', open windows..................	£100-150	☐
60b (66b)	1939-41		As previous model but blank side windows, & 'DH Leopard Moth' under wing..........	£200-250	☐
60c	1934-36	Percival 'Gull' Monoplane	Cast fuselage, tinplate wings, large 2-blade propeller, 76 mm. Blue/Red, Buff/White, Buff/Blue, Buff/Red, Gold/Green, Red/White, Silver/Green, White/Green, open windows with no markings	£100-150	☐
60c (60k)	1936-39		White, Red, Yellow or Light Blue, 'G-ADZO' in Black, open windows	£100-150	☐
60c	1936	"Lewis's" 'Amy Mollinson' Souvenir Issue...........................	Mid Blue with Silver wings and a Blue 'G-ADZO' marking. Sold at 'Lewis's of Liverpool department store in yellow box.........................	NGPP	☐
60c (66c)	1939-41		As previous model but blank or open side windows, & 'Percival Gull' under wing	£200-250	☐
60d	1934-36	Low Wing Monoplane	(Vickers Jockey) Cast body, tinplate wings, 2-blade propeller, 76 mm. Red/Cream, Orange/Cream Blue/Yellow, Silver/Red or Gold/Blue, no markings, no pilot............	£100-150	☐
60d (66d)	1936-41		Red, Orange, Blue, Gold or Silver, 'G-AVYP' in Black, pilot's head cast-in	£100-150	☐
			Red with cream tail and wingtips, no pilot, with 'G-AVPY' marking	NGPP	☐
			As previous but with pilot	NGPP	☐
60e	1934-36	General 'Monospar'	Two-piece diecasting, 2 x 2-blade propellers, 80 mm. Blue/White, Cream/Red, Gold/Red, Red/Cream, Salmon Blue or Silver/Blue, no markings................	£100-150	☐
60e (66e)	1936-41		Silver, Lilac or Gold, 'G-ABVP' in Black	£100-150	☐
			As previous but with 'General Monospar' added, Cream, Gold, Lilac, Silver or Blue..	£100-150	☐
60f	1934-36	Cierva 'Autogiro'......................	Gold body (49 mm.) Blue rotor/propeller, no pilot	£200-300	☐
60f (66f)	1936-40		As previous model but with pilot. (Other colours are French model 60z)	£120-170	☐
60g	1935-36	De Havilland 'Comet'	Cast fuselage & wings, enclosed wheels, 2 x 2-blade propellers, 86 mm. Red/Gold, Gold/Red or Silver/Blue, no markings................	£100-150	☐
			Silver body with black 'G-ACSR' with no 'DH Comet' shown	NGPP	☐
	1936-41		Red, Silver or Gold, 'G-ACSR', 'DH Comet' under wing	£100-150	☐
60g	1945-49	Light Racer (DH 'Comet')........	Yellow, Red or Silver, 'G-RACE', 'Light Racer' under wing, 2 x 3 PB......................	£200-250	☐
60h	1936-36	'Singapore' Flying Boat............	Cast fuselage (126 mm.), tinplate wings, 4 x 2-blade propellers Silver with stencilled RAF roundels, no roller or 'gliding' hole	£150-200	☐
60h (60m)	1936-39		As previous model but with plastic or wooden roller and 'gliding' hole.................	£150-200	☐
60h	1939-40		Silver or Grey with accurate RAF roundel (waterslide transfers)	£150-200	☐
	1940-41		As previous model with gun seat, cutaway bow, no hole, name under wing	£150-200	☐
60k	1936-41	Percival 'Gull' (Amy Mollison)	Blue/Silver version of 60c, 'G-ADZO' in Blue, special box	£150-200	☐
60k	1936-41	Percival 'Gull' (H. L. Brook) ...	Blue/Silver version of 60c, 'G-ADZO' in Black, special box	£150-200	☐
60k (60c)	1945-48	Light Tourer (Percival 'Gull') ...	Red, Silver or Dark or Light Green, 'Light Tourer' or 'Percival Tourer' under wing, no markings, small or large 2-blade propeller, 76 mm............................	£150-200	☐
60m	1936-40	Four Engined Flying Boat	Red, Light Blue, Light Green, Dark Green, Gold, Cream or Silver, 'civilian' version of 60h with 'G-EUTG', 'G-EVCU', 'G-EXGF', 'G-EYCE' or 'G-EYTV' .... N.B. With or without bow hollow, wood or plastic roller or Gliding Game hole	£135-175	☐
60n	1937-40	Fairey 'Battle' Bomber	Silver or Grey, RAF roundels, 1 x 3 PB, undercarriage, 75 mm.	£90-120	☐
60n (60s)	1938-41		Silver or Grey, RAF roundels, 1 x 3 PB, without undercarriage .... N.B. Early issues did not have name of plane cast in.	£120-150	☐
60p	1936-39	Gloucester 'Gladiator'..............	Silver, stencilled roundels, Red 1 x 2 PB, no name under wing, 38 mm.	£100-140	☐
	1939-41		Silver or Grey, transfer roundels, 'Gloucester Gladiator' under wing	£100-140	☐
60r	1937-40	Empire Flying Boat..................	Silver, 4 x 3 PB, plastic roller, hole, own box, 156 mm. Liveries: 'CALEDONIA', ('G-ADHM'), 'CANOPUS', ('G-ADHL'), 'CORSAIR', ('G-ADVB'), 'CHALLENGER', ('G-ADVI') 'CLIO', ('G-AETY'), 'CALYPSO', ('G-AEUA'), 'CENTURION', ('G-ADVE'), 'CAPELLA', ('G-ADUY'), 'CERES', ('G-AETX'), 'CALPURNIA', ('G-AETW'), 'CAMILLA', ('G-AEUB'), 'CORINNA', ('G-AEUC'), 'CAMBRIA', ('G-ADUV'), 'CHEVIOT', ('G-AEUG'), 'CORDELIA', ('G-AEUD')...	£180-230	☐
60r (60x)	1940-49	Empire Flying Boat..................	As previous models but plastic, wood or brass roller, no name. 'CALEDONIA', ('G-ADHM'), or 'CAMBRIA', ('G-ADUV') .... N.B. Camouflage issues: Early issues have Red/White/Blue roundels with a Yellow outer ring. The later (rarer) issues have a darker camouflage with just Blue/Red roundels.	£180-230	☐
60s (60n)	1938-40	Medium Bomber......................	Camouflaged 60n with undercarriage, single roundel has Yellow ring..............	£100-150	☐
60s	1940-41	Fairy 'Battle' Bomber...............	Camouflaged body, two Blue/Red roundels, no undercarriage, 1 x 3 PB .... N.B. Early issues did not have name of plane cast in.	£150-200	☐
60t	1938-41	Douglas DC3 Air Liner	Silver, 'PH-ALI' 2 x 3 PB, hole, tail wheel on some, own box, 132 mm.	£175-225	☐
60v (62t)	1937-41	Armstrong Whitworth Bomber	Silver body, 'gliding' hole in some, RAF roundels, 2 x 3 Red PB. 116 mm.	£150-200	☐
60w	1938-40	Flying Boat 'Clipper III'	Silver, 'USA NC16736', 4 x 3 PB/SBX, plastic roller, hole, 164 mm. (Sikorsky S32)...	£150-200	☐
60w	1945-48	Flying Boat..........................	Silver, Blue or Green, no markings, 4 x 3 PB, brass roller, 164 mm.	£100-130	☐

142

Ref. No.				Market Price Range
60x	1937-41	Atlantic Flying Boat..................	Blue/Cream, *'DAUNTLESS'*, *'G-AZBP'*, 4 x 3 PB, name under wing, 156 mm.	£200-250 ☐
			Green/Cream, *'WHIRLWIND'*, *'G-AZBT'*	£200-250 ☐
			Black/White, *'DREADNOUGHT'*, *'G-AZBV'*	£200-250 ☐
			Orange/Cream *'SWIFTSURE'*, *'G-AZBU'* and Blue/Cream *'ENTERPRISE'*, *'G-AZBR'* and Black/Cream *'ENDEAVOUR'*. *'G-AZBO'*. Red/Cream *'VALORIUS'*, *'G-AZBS'*	£200-250 ☐
62a	1939-40	Vickers-Supermarine 'Spitfire' ...	Silver body (short nose) RAF roundels, 1 x 3 PB. 52 mm.	£100-130 ☐
	1940-41	'Meccano Spitfire Fund'	Model 62a in special souvenir box. Brass ring through fin allows model to be worn as badge or pendant. Sale proceeds went to the Spitfire Fund.	
			Blue, Green, Grey, Magenta, Red, Yellow, or Camouflage (originally 2/6 each.)	£450-500 ☐
			Chromium plated version (originally 10/6).	£1000-1200 ☐
62a	1945-49	'Spitfire'	Silver body (long nose, bubble cockpit) RAF roundels, 1 x 3 PB. 54 mm.	£100-130 ☐
62b	1939-40	Bristol 'Blenheim' Bomber	Silver body, RAF roundels, Red 2 x 3 PB, name under wing, 78 mm.	£100-130 ☐
62b	1945-49	Medium Bomber	Silver body, RAF roundels, Red 2 x 3 PB, name under wing, 78 mm.	£60-80 ☐
62d	1940-41	Bristol 'Blenheim' Bomber	62b with Camouflage/Black/White body, RAF roundels, 2 x 3 PB. 78 mm.	£100-130 ☐
62e	1940-41	Vickers-Supermarine 'Spitfire' ...	62a with Camouflage/Black/White body, RAF roundels, 1 x 3 PB. 52 mm.	£100-130 ☐
62f	1939-40	D.H. Flamingo Airliner.............	Not issued.	NPP
62g	1939-41	Boeing 'Flying Fortress'	Silver, 4 x 3 PB, 'gliding' hole, name under wing, with 'U.S.A.A.C.' markings/stars, own box, 144 mm.	£140-180 ☐
			Pale Grey version	NGPP ☐
62g	1945-48	Long Range Bomber	Silver body, Red 4 x 3 PB, no hole, not boxed	£90-120 ☐
62h	1938-40	Hawker Hurricane Fighter	Camouflaged body, RAF roundels, 1 x 2 PB, with or without undercarriage	£100-130 ☐
62k	1938-41	The King's Aeroplane	Airspeed 'Envoy', Silver/Red/Blue, *'G-AEXX'*, 2 x 2 PB, own box, 91 mm.	£175-225 ☐
62m	1938-41	Airspeed 'Envoy' Monoplane....	Red (*'G-ACVJ'*), Silver (*'G-ADCB'*), Blue (*'G-ADAZ'*), Green (*'G-AENA'*), or Yellow (*'G-ACVJ'*).	£120-150 ☐
62m	1945-48	Light Transport	Red, Yellow, Silver or Blue body, *'G-ATMH'*, 2 x 2 PB, name under wing, 91 mm. ..	£85-115 ☐
62n	1938-41	Junkers 'Ju90' Air Liner...........	Silver, (*'D-AALU'*, *'D-AIVI'*, *'D-AURE'*, or *'D-ADLH'*) 4 x 3 PB, own box	£200-300 ☐
62p	1938-41	'Ensign' Air Liner....................	Silver body, Red 4 x 3 PB, with/without gliding hole, own box, 173 mm. 6 liveries: *'ENSIGN'* (*'G-ADSR'*), *'ELSINORE'* (*'G-ADST'*), *'ECHO'* (*'G-ADTB'*), *'EXPLORER'* (*'G-ADSV'*), *'ETTRICK'* (*'G-ADSX'*), *'ELYSIAN'* (*'G-ADSZ'*)	£150-200 ☐
62p	1945-49	Armstrong Whitworth Air Liner	As previous casting but no hole, name under wing, 4 x 3 PB, no box, Silver, Blue, Green, Silver trim or Grey/Green, 'EXPLORER' or 'ECHO' markings..	£100-150 ☐
62r	1939-41	D.H. 'Albatross' Mail Liner......	Silver, *'G-AEVV'*, Red 4 x 3 PB, hole, name under wing, own box, 145 mm.	£175-225 ☐
62r	1945-49	Four Engined Liner..................	Grey, Light Blue or Silver, no markings, no hole, not boxed, 145 mm.	£100-130 ☐
			Grey, Fawn, Light Blue or Silver, *'G-ATPV'*, Red 4 x 3 PB, 145 mm.	£100-130 ☐
62s	1939-41	Hawker 'Hurricane' Fighter	Silver body, RAF roundels, with or without undercarriage, 1 x 2 or 3 PB, 55 mm.	£90-120 ☐
	1945-49		Silver body, RAF roundels, no undercarriage, 1 x 3 PB, 55 mm.	£60-70 ☐
62t	1939-41	Armstrong Whitworth Bomber	('Whitley') Camouflage/Black/White, RAF roundels, 2 x 3 PB, own box	£160-200 ☐
62w (68b)	1939-41	'Frobisher' Class Air Liner	Silver body (casting as 62r), 4 x 3 PB, hole, own box, 3 liveries: *'FROBISHER'* (*'G-AFDI'*), *'FALCON'* (*'G-AFDJ'*), *'FORTUNA'* (*'G-AFDK'*)	£175-225 ☐
62x (68a)	1939-41	British 40 Seat Airliner.............	Grey/Green, Red/Maroon, TT-Green, Yellow/Maroon, TT-Blue, *'G-AZCA'*, not boxed, with/without gliding hole	£150-190 ☐
62y	1939-40	Giant High Speed Monoplane ..	Blue/Brown, Blue/Silver, Olive/Green, Blue/Cream, Yellow/Maroon, Red/Maroon, TT-Blue or TT-Green, *'D-AZBK'*, hole, not boxed, 160 mm.	£140-180 ☐
	1945-49		Light/Dark Green, Grey/Green or Silver, no hole or box, *'G-ZBK'*	£140-180 ☐
63	1939-41	Mayo Composite Aircraft	Models 63a and 63b together in special box (see below)	£200-300 ☐
63a	1939-41	Flying Boat 'MAIA'	Silver body, *'G-ADHK'*, *'Mayo Composite'* under wing, own box, 156 mm.	£100-150 ☐
63b	1939-41	Seaplane 'MERCURY'	Silver, *'G-ADHJ'*, *'Mercury Seaplane'* under wing, 'hole' in some, 101 mm.	£75-100 ☐
63b (700)	1945-49	Seaplane	Silver body, *'G-AVKW'*, no 'gliding' hole, *'Seaplane'* under wing	£90-120 ☐
66a	1940-41	Heavy Bomber	Camouflaged body, RAF roundels, 4 x 2 PB, no name under wing, 127 mm.	£250-300 ☐
66b	1940-41	Dive Bomber Fighter...............	Camouflaged body, RAF roundels, 1 x 2 PB, 76 mm.	£150-200 ☐
66c	1940-41	Two Seater Fighter..................	Camouflaged body, RAF roundels, 1 x 2 PB, 76 mm.	£150-200 ☐
66d	1940-41	Torpedo Dive Bomber.............	Camouflaged body, RAF roundels, 1 x 2 PB, 76 mm.	£150-200 ☐
66e	1940-41	Medium Bomber......................	Camouflaged body, RAF roundels, 2 x 2 PB, *'General Monospar'* under wing	£150-200 ☐
66f	1940-41	Army Co-operation Autogiro ...	Silver body and blades, Red/White/Blue roundels, (60f casting) 49 mm.	£150-200 ☐
67a	1940-41	Junkers Ju89 Heavy Bomber.....	Black/Pale Blue body, German markings, no hole, own box, 160 mm.	£200-300 ☐
68a	1940-41	'Ensign' Air Liner...................	Camouflaged body, RAF roundels, no 'gliding' hole, 4 x 3 PB, 173 mm.	£200-250 ☐
68b	1940-41	'Frobisher' Class Air Liner	Light or Dark Camouflage, RAF roundels, 4 x 3 PB, 'hole' in some, 145 mm.	£200-250 ☐
70a (704)	1946-49	Avro 'York' Airliner	Silver body, *'G-AGJC'*, Red 4 x 3 PB, 160 mm.	£90-120 ☐
70b (730)	1946-49	Tempest II Fighter	Silver body, RAF roundels, Red 4 blade prop with large spinner, 63 mm.	£35-45 ☐
70c (705)	1947-49	Viking Air Liner	Silver or Grey body, *'G-AGOL'*, Red 2 x 4 PB, large spinners, 140 mm.	£55-65 ☐
70d (731)	1946-49	Twin-Engined Fighter	Silver body, no markings, two Red 3-blade propellers, pointed head spinners, 76 mm.	£25-35 ☐
			As previous model but *'N'* in *'MECCANO'* is reversed.	NGPP ☐
70e (732)	1946-49	Gloster 'Meteor'	Silver body, RAF roundels (with or without Yellow rings), 67 mm.	£25-35 ☐
70f (733)	1947-49	Lockheed 'Shooting Star'	Silver body, US markings on wings (star on port wing only), with *'Made in England by MECCANO Ltd'* underwing, 61 mm.	£25-35 ☐
700 (63b)	1954-57	Seaplane................................	Silver body with *'G-AVKW'* marking	£90-120 ☐
			Silver body, *'G-AVKW'*, no 'gliding' hole, *'Seaplane'* under wing	£90-120 ☐
700	1979	Spitfire Mark II ('Jubilee')	Plated model on plinth, 1 x 3 PB, *'Diamond Jubilee of the RAF'*	£75-95 ☐
701	1947-49	Short 'Shetland' Flying Boat......	Silver body, *'G-AGVD'*, Black 4 x 4 PB, first Supertoys aircraft, own box	£350-450 ☐
702 (999)	1954-55	DH 'Comet' Jet Airliner...........	White/Blue body, Silver wings, *'B.O.A.C.'* livery, 183 mm.	£100-130 ☐
704 (70a)	1954-59	Avro 'York' Airliner	Silver body, *'G-AGJC'*, Red 4 x 3 PB, 160 mm. ('704' beneath wing)	£90-120 ☐
705 (70c)	1952-62	'Viking' Air Liner	Silver body with *'G-AGOL'* marking, flat head spinners	£45-55 ☐
			Silver or Grey body, *'G-AGOL'*, Red 2 x 4 PB, 140 mm.	£45-55 ☐

Ref. No.			*Dinky Toys — Aircraft – continued*	Market Price Range	
706	1956-57	Vickers 'Viscount' Airliner	Silver/Blue/White, *'AIR FRANCE'*, 'F-BGNL', Red 4 x 4 PB, 149 mm.	£80-90	☐
708	1957-65	Vickers 'Viscount' Airliner	Silver/White or Metallic Grey/White, *'B.E.A.'*, 'G-AOJA'	£70-80	☐
710	1965-76	Beechcraft S35 'Bonanza'	Red/White, Bronze/Yellow, or Red/Blue/White body, 1 x 2 PB, 133 mm.	£40-50	☐
		German Promotional	Green/White with *'GLUCK MIT WICKULER'* logo on towing pennant and box flash	£400-500	☐
712	1972-77	US Army T.42A	Military Green (715), Beechcraft plus wing-tip tanks, 2 x 2 PB. 153 mm.	£30-40	☐
715	1956-62	Bristol 173 Helicopter	Turquoise body with Red rotors and stripes, 'G-AUXR', 53 mm.	£25-35	☐
715	1968-76	Beechcraft C55 'Baron'	White/Yellow or Red/Yellow body, Yellow 2 x 2 PB, 150 mm.	£25-35	☐
716	1957-62	Westland Sikorsky S-51	Red and Cream helicopter body, 2 x 3-blade rotors 66 mm.	£35-45	☐
717	1970-75	Boeing '737'	White/Blue body, White or Blue engine pods, *'LUFTHANSA'*, 152 mm.	£35-45	☐
718	1972-75	Hawker 'Hurricane' Mk IIc	Camouflaged body, RAF roundels, Black 1 x 3 PB, guns, 188 mm.	£35-45	☐
719 (741)	1969-77	Spitfire Mk.II	Camouflaged, RAF roundels, Black 1 x 3 PB (battery-operated), 173 mm.	£35-45	☐
721	1969-80	Junkers Ju87b Stuka	Camouflage/Yellow, German markings, 1 x 3 PB, cap-firing bomb, 191 mm.	£30-40	☐
722	1970-80	Hawker 'Harrier'	Metallic Blue/Olive Camouflage, RAF markings, pilot, aerial, 125 mm.	£50-60	☐
723	1970-73	Hawker Siddeley HS 125	Yellow/White/Blue or Metallic Blue/White, drop-down door/steps, 133 mm.	£25-35	☐
724	1971-79	'Sea King' Helicopter	Metallic Blue/White, 5-blade rotors, with 'Apollo' space capsule, 179 mm.	£25-35	☐
725	1972-77	Royal Navy 'Phantom II'	Dark Blue body, Black nose, roundels, decals in bubble-pack, 132 mm.	£40-50	☐
726	1972-74	Messerschmitt Bf-109E	German desert camouflage, 1 x 3 PB, decals in bubble-pack, 165 mm.	£50-60	☐
	1974-76		German Grey/Green camouflage, Brown 1 x 3 PB, decals in bubble-pack	£30-40	☐
727	1974-?	U.S. Air Force Phantom F4 Mark II	Brown/Olive camouflage with U.S. roundels, two figures, (No transfers issued)	£250-500	☐
728	1972-75	R.A.F. 'Dominie'	Metallic Blue and camouflage body, roundels, retractable wheels, bubble-pack	£30-35	☐
729	1974-76	Multi-Role Combat Aircraft	Grey/Camouflage, swing-wings, decals in bubble-pack, 164 mm.	£30-40	☐
730 (70b)	1952-57	Tempest II Fighter	Same as 70b with flat head spinners	£35-45	☐
730	1972-76	US Navy 'Phantom II'	Grey/Red body, 'NAVY', *'USS Saratoga'*, fires missiles, retractable wheels	£40-50	☐
731 (70d)	1954-55	Twin-Engined Fighter	Silver body, no markings, two Red 3-blade propellers, 76 mm.	£25-35	☐
731	1973-76	S.E.P.E.C.A.T. 'Jaguar'	Metallic Blue & camouflage body, Orange pilot, opening cockpit, 106 mm.	£25-35	☐
732 (70e)	1952-62	Gloster 'Meteor'	Same as 70e with '732' beneath wing	£25-35	☐
732	1974-80	Bell Police Helicopter	Orange/Blue/White or Red body, *'POLICE'* sign boards & cones, 211 mm.	£20-25	☐
733 (70f)	1954-62	Lockheed 'Shooting Star'	Silver body, US markings on wings (star on port wing only), 61 mm.	£25-35	☐
			Variant with *'in'* of *'Made in England by Meccano Ltd'* missing	NGPP	☐
733	1973-76	German 'Phantom II'	Grey/Green camouflage body, 'Bundesluftwaffe', (German/Austrian market)	£200-300	☐
733	1976-77	US F-4K 'Phantom II'	Brown camouflage, retractable wheels, fires missiles, (US market only)	£50-60	☐
734	1955-62	Supermarine 'Swift'	Grey/Green camouflaged body, RAF markings, 51 mm.	£30-40	☐
734	1975-78	P47 'Thunderbolt'	Metallic Silver/Black body, Red 1 x 4 PB, retractable wheels, 'U.S.A.A.F.', 190 mm.	£40-50	☐
735	1956-66	Gloster 'Javelin'	Camouflaged 'delta-wing' body, RAF markings. 83 mm.	£35-45	☐
736	1955-63	Hawker 'Hunter'	Camouflaged body, RAF markings, 54 mm.	£30-40	☐
736	1973-78	Bundesmarine 'Sea King'	Grey/Orange helicopter, German markings, decals in bubble-pack, 179 mm.	£25-35	☐
737	1959-68	P.1B 'Lightning' Fighter	Silver (metal wheels) or Metallic Grey (Black plastic wheels) 55 mm.	£30-40	☐
738	1960-65	DH 110 'Sea Vixen' Fighter	Grey/White body, Black nose, RAF roundels, *'ROYAL NAVY'* logo, 80 mm.	£50-60	☐
739	1975-78	A6M5 'Zero Sen'	Metallic Green/Black, Japanese markings, decals in bubble-pack, 184 mm.	£30-40	☐
741	1978-80	Spitfire Mk II	Camouflaged body, (non-motorised version of 719), 173 mm.	£40-50	☐
749 (992)	1955-56	RAF Avro 'Vulcan' Bomber	Silver body (aluminium), only 500 models were made (for Canadian market) 992 is the catalogue (and box) number, '749' is cast into the model. Two castings exist; one has pointed wingtips, the other more rounded	£2000-3000	☐
997	1962-65	Caravelle SE 210 Airliner	Silver/White/Blue, *'AIR FRANCE'*, metal or plastic wheels, 126 mm.	£250-300	☐
998	1959-64	Bristol 'Britannia'	Silver/White body, Red or Blue lines, *'CANADIAN PACIFIC'*, 'CF-CZA', 225 mm.	£250-300	☐
	1964-65		Metallic Grey/White body, Red lines, *'CANADIAN PACIFIC'*, 'CF-CZA', 225 mm.	£250-300	☐
999 (702)	1955-65	DH 'Comet' Jet Airliner	White/Blue body, Silver wings ('G-ALYX' on some) *'B.O.A.C.'*, 183 mm.	£100-130	☐
			As previous but with Silver/Grey wings	£100-130	☐

Recommended Reading:- "Dinky Toy Aeroplanes — A Collection Guide and Checklist". Contact D.C. Barratt, 230 Earlham Road, Norwich, Norfolk NR2 3RH. (Tel: 01603-453650).

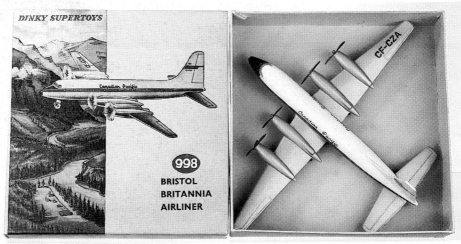

Picture kindly supplied by Christies', South Kensington, London.

*A Dinky Toy factory wooden mock-up
of the Albion 'Milk Marketing Board' Tanker,
circa 1951, with two original Assembly Drawings.*

1994 at Christie's South Kensington was another record year with twelve toy sales generating over £1.8million. Highlights included the celebrated Hemley Collection of Dinky Toys, a Dinky Toy 28 series 'Bentalls' van which realised a world record £12,650, a No. 24 Motor Cars Set which made £14,300 - recent diecast sales in 1995 have regularly totalled over £100,000 each.

We also specialise in selling smaller childhood collections, attaining the best possible prices for the seller and offering collectors a wide variety of fresh material.

Our detailed catalogues give full descriptions and clear condition statements and include, apart from Dinky, diecast toys by Corgi, Matchbox and Spot-On and tinplate toys and railways by Meccano, Minic, Hornby, Märklin and other famous manufacturers.

For further information please contact Hugo Marsh on (0171) 321 3274, Daniel Agnew or Nigel Mynheer on (0171) 321 3335.

Fine Toys & Diecasts

CHRISTIE'S

85 Old Brompton Road, London SW7 3LD
Tel: (0171) 581 7611 Fax: (0171) 321 3321

DINKY TOYS

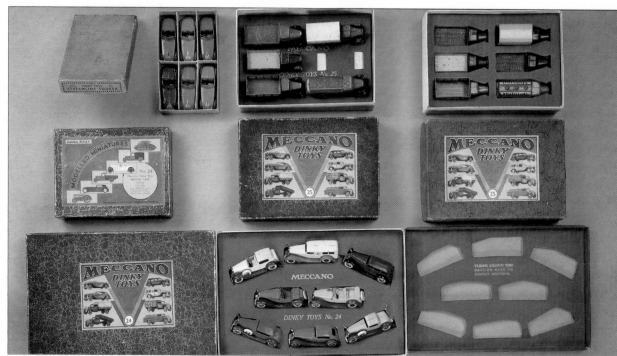

Pre-War Issues. *Top row:* 22g Streamline Tourers (6) in Half Dozen Trade Box. 25 Series Set (missing one model) in early Purple marbled box. 25 Series Set (complete) in later Blue patterned box. 24 Series Modelled Miniatures, 1st Type empty box.
Bottom row: 24 Series Set in 2nd Type Purple box with protective cover. Models have Tootsie Toy style chrome hubs. Sold by Christies, South Kensington, London, 9/94 for £13,000 (World Record for a set).
Picture reproduced by their kind permission.

Pre-War Issues. *Top row:* 35b Racer, 35a Simca (Fiat Topolino), 35a Saloon Car, 35 Small Cars Set (sold for £520), Roadside Accessories (9). *Middle Row:* 35c MG Sports Car, 35d Austin in Lime Green, Maroon and Blue.
Bottom Row: 35a Saloon Car, 35b Racers: Red (White Tyres), Green (Black Tyres), 35c MG Sports Cars - Turquoise (White Tyres), Maroon (Black Tyres), plus 37a Green Civilian Motor Cyclist.
Models sold by Christies South Kensington, London and pictures reproduced by their kind permission

DINKY TOYS

Pre-War Issues. *Top row:* L-R, 29 Motor Bus 29c Double Deck Buses in a range of liveries (5). Rare Cream 31 'Holland' Coachcraft Van (sold for £1200), 34a Royal Mail Air Service Car (sold for £260), 34b, 36g Taxis, Dark Blue (£160), Red (£350), Yellow (£800), 25f, 25d, 25b, 25b with rare 'SPECIAL SEASIDE SERVICE' Logo (£550), 25b 'Meccano' (£600), 25h 1st type, (£240), 25h 2nd type (£320), 25k (with firemen) (£500), 25s (£260).
Models sold by Christies, South Kensington, London and picture reproduced by their kind permission.

Unboxed Post-War Issues. *Top row:* L-R, 27f Estate Car, 29b Streamline Bus, Cream/Dark Blue, smooth hubs (£160), TT Blue 29b Streamline Bus, smooth hubs (£100), 29b Two Tone Green, ridged hubs (£170), 29c Double Deck Bus Type 1 Red/Cream (£80), *2nd Row Down:* 29c DD Bus ridged hubs, Trade Box (6), 2 Red/Grey, Green/Cream, 2 Green/Grey, Red/Cream, (£380), 29c Rare Green and Light Green, ridged hubs (£170), *3rd Row Down:* 29c DD Bus Green/Cream, Leyland (£80), 29c Green/Offwhite Leyland (£70), 29c 3rd Type AEC Red/Cream (£30), 29c Single Deck Bus Cream/Blue (£80), 29c Single Deck bus Trade Box of (6) in TT Green, TT Blue and Cream/Blue (£650), 29f Observation Coach Cream (£50).
Models sold by Christies, South Kensington, London 10/94, picture reproduced by their kind permission.

DINKY TOYS

Top Row: L-R: Early Purple marbled box with Hornby Series 'Modelled Miniatures', 1st Type No 1 Station Staff (£200). Early 'Dinky Toys/Meccano Ltd' 1st Type Set No 5 Train and Hotel Staff in later type Blue patterned box (£350). Early Meccano Dinky Toys 1st Type Set No 4 Engineering Staff in later type Blue patterned box (£180). *Middle Row:-* 2nd Type Set No 3 Railway Passengers, Green box dated 1.39 with pictorial insert (£420). No 12 Postal Set in original box dated 12.38 Code No 2216 (£1700). *Bottom Row:-* Hornby Series 'Modelled Miniatures' No 21 Hornby (Mixed Goods) Train Set in original Purple marbled ladder box c1932 (£800). Meccano/Dinky No 17 Passenger Train Set, Lead and Mazak bodies in later type Blue patterned box with correct Green Spot c1934 (£500). Rare late version No 19 Mixed Goods Train Set in rare 'Landscape' box dated 11.38 with pictorial insert Code No A1045 dated 11.38. Pictorial insert was only ever used in this set (£1200).
Models sold by Christies of South Kensington, London, 9/94. Picture reproduced by their kind permission.

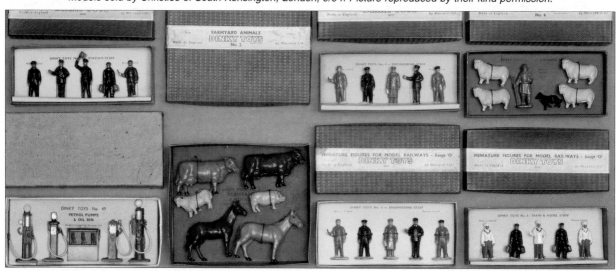

Post-War Accessory Sets: *Top Row:* L-R:- No 1 Station Staff (3rd Type), No 2 Farmyard Animals Set 3rd Type (£400), No 4 Engineering Staff Set 3rd Type, No 6 Shepherd Set 3rd Type (£350). *Bottom Row:-* 49 Petrol Pumps Set in sliding sleeve box (£350), No 4 Engineering Staff Set (£140), No 5 Train and Hotel Staff (£100).
Models sold by Christies, South Kensington, London 9/94. Picture reproduced by their kind permission.

DINKY TOYS

505 Foden Chain Lorry 1st Cab (£600)

505 Foden Chain Lorry 1st Cab.
Rare Maroon (£2200)

501 Foden Diesel 8-Wheel Wagon.
Rare TT Blue 2nd Cab (£3400)

503 Foden Flat Truck with Tailboard
Unboxed (£625)

513 Guy Flat Truck (£620)

431 Guy Warrior (£450)

514 Guy 'Lyons' Van (£850)

919 Guy 'Golden Shred' Van (£450)

923 Big Bedford 'Tomato Ketchup' Van
(£750)

252 Refuse Wagon (£200)

410 Bedford End Tipper (£160)

966 BBC TV Vehicle (£110)

977 Commercial Servicing
Platform Vehicle (£150)

Models sold by Vectis Model Auctions in July, 1995 at their Guildford Saleroom.
The pictures are reproduced by their kind permission. All the models pictured are in excellent condition.

DINKY TOYS

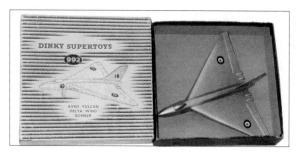

992 Avro Vulcan Bomber(£2800)

Gift Set 201 (£420)

301 Tractor with
green wheels —
plastic at front (£180)

113 Pre-production sample with
'Steed' figure and in rare window box
(£660)

Gift Set No 3 (Good condition)
(£1000)

261 Ford Taunus 'Polizei' Car. Special
Issue for West German Meccano Agent
(£310)

289 RM Bus in Gold (£570). One off
Press Review model with
'Meccano' & 'Dinky Toys' labels on offside

961 Vega Major in special box, for
Swiss Meccano Agent to sell in own
name (£320)

Gift Set 299 (£370)

106 'Prisoner'
Mini Moke
(£190)

342 Pre-production
Austin Mini Moke
with Plastic body
(£500)

23c Speed of the Wind.
Rare Red Post War
Issue (£170)

Trade Box of Sheep
(£250)

296 Post War Streamline Coach —
Dark Green/Stone.
Factory sample with label (£330)

*Models sold by Vectis Model auctions in July 1995 at their Guildford saleroom. The pictures are reproduced by their kind permission.
All the models pictured are in good to excellent condition.*

DINKY TOYS

L-R 154 Hillman Minx (4) i) (£110), ii) (£110), iii) (£110), iv) Cream/Green (£160) and 161 Austin Somerset (2) i) (£150), ii) Yellow/lRed (£210)

L-R 156 Rover 75 Saloons (5) i), ii), iii) TT Green (£180), iv) Blue/Cream (£170), v) Dark Blue and Cream (£330)

165 Humber Hawk Black/Light Green including the roof (£150)

L-R 152 Austin Devon (3) i), ii) Blue/Yellow (£170), iii) Pink/Lime Green (£200)

L-R 151 Triumph 1800 Saloons Mid blue and Light Brown

194 Bentley Coupe (£130)

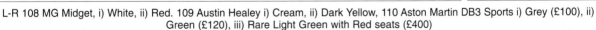

L-R 108 MG Midget, i) White, ii) Red. 109 Austin Healey i) Cream, ii) Dark Yellow, 110 Aston Martin DB3 Sports i) Grey (£100), ii) Green (£120), iii) Rare Light Green with Red seats (£400)

L-R 111 Triumph TR2 Sports i) Turquoise, ii) Salmon Pink, and 114 Triumph Spitfire.

L-R 157 Jaguar XK 120 i) Deep Yellow (£190), ii) White (£150), iii) Greyish-Green (£160)

Models on this page sold by Vectis Model Auctions in at their Guildford saleroom, and the prices realised have been shown where available. At the time of the sale the condition of the models/boxes was excellent. NB Further Dinky Toy pictures in the Miscellaneous Models colour section

Dinky Toys - Buses, Taxis and Trams

1st Type 1938-47
AEC/STL grille
Large 'V' shape
Cutaway wings
No model number
on base
Smooth hubs

2nd Type 1949-53; 1957-59
AEC/Regent grille
Small 'V' shape
Straight across wings
No model number or
29c cast into base
Ridged hubs

3rd Type 1948-49; 1954-63
Leyland grille
Undivided shape
Straight across wings
29c, 290 or 291
on base
Ridged hubs

  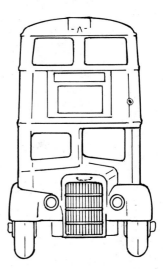

Ref. No.	Year(s)	Model Type	Model Features and Size	Market Price Range	
27	1934-38	Tram Car	Plastic or metal wheels, Red 'OVALTINE' or 'LIPTONS TEA' or no logo, 77 mm. Red, Orange, Green, Yellow or Light or Dark Blue body, Cream upper windows & roof	£200-250	☐
			Light Blue or Dark Blue body, Cream lower/upper windows & roof	£200-250	☐
29 (29a)	1934-38	Motor Bus	Plastic or metal wheels, no logo, or Silver or Red 'MARMITE', 70 mm. Blue, Green, Maroon, Yellow or Red body, Cream or Silver roof	£200-250	☐
29b	1936-46	Streamline Bus	Green/Cream, Orange/Cream, Red/Cream, Black or White tyres, smooth hubs	£125-175	☐
			Two-tone Blue, TT-Green, Yellow/Orange, Red/Maroon, Turquoise/Red, all with smooth Black hubs, open rear window, 88 mm.	£125-175	☐
	1946-47		Cream and Dark Blue, smooth hubs, open windows	£130-160	☐
	1947-50		Two-tone Green or Grey/Blue body, Black tyres, filled-in rear window	£75-100	☐
29c		Double Decker Bus	The different casting types are show in the diagrams above.		
	1938-40	'DUNLOP TYRES'	1st Type AEC/STL, cutaway wings, stairs cast-in, smooth hubs, White tyres, crimped axle ends. Advert in Black on Yellow rectangle, 100 mm.		
		Regular issues	Cream upper deck and roof with Red, Light Blue, Maroon, Green or Orange lower deck	£200-300	☐
	1938	Early Grey roof issues	As previous but with Grey roof	£300-400	☐
		Late issue	Dark Blue lower deck, Cream upper deck and roof	£300-400	☐
	1938-40	no advertising	As above but without advertisement	£200-300	☐
			N.B. Baseplates:- 1st issue 'Made in England' 29 mm x 2 mm 2nd issue As above but 28 mm x 1.5 mm		
	1946	no advertising	1st type AEC/STL grille, cutaway wings, no staircase, six vertical inside body ribs, smooth Black hubs.		
		Colours	Green lower deck with Cream or Grey upper-deck	£100-150	☐
			Red lower deck with Cream or Grey upper deck	£100-150	☐
	1947-48	no advertisement	As previous but with post-war Black ridged hubs	£85-95	☐
		Two tone variant	Two tone Green body	£130-160	☐
	1948-49	no advertising	3rd type Leyland/STL grille, straight across wings, Black ridged hubs. Early issues had six vertical inside body ribs, later issues had five (3 on N/S, 2 on OS)		
		Colours	Red or Green lower deck, Cream upper deck	£85-95	☐
	1949-53	no advertisement	2nd type AEC/Regent grille, straight across wings, lengthwise chassis strengthener with hole in chassis centre, or (1952) eight vertical inside body ribs, ridged hubs, plus in (1953) 29c cast in chassis		
		Colours	Red or Green lower deck, Cream or White upper deck, hubs match the lower deck colour	£85-95	☐
29c (290)	1954-54	'DUNLOP'	3rd type Leyland Titan grille and straight across wings, early issues have recessed stop lights, late issues (1959) protrude. Logo 'DUNLOP -The World's Master Tyre' in Black and Red. Sloping and upright designs exist.		
		Colours	Red or Green lower deck, Cream upper deck, hubs match the lower deck colour	£85-95	☐
29dz	1939-40	Autobus	Green or White body, metal wheels, (French issue sold in UK)	£80-90	☐

Ref. No.				Market Price Range	
29e	1948-52	Single Deck Bus	Blue/Dark Blue, Light Green/Dark Green or Cream/Blue, 113 mm.	£40-50	☐
29f (280)	1950-54	Observation Coach	Grey (Red flashes) or Cream (Red flashes), 112 mm.	£50-60	☐
29g (281)	1951-54	Luxury Coach	Maroon body with Cream flashes	£80-100	☐
			Orange body with Cream flashes	£150-200	☐
			Fawn body with Orange flashes	£100-150	☐
			Blue body with Cream flashes	£150-200	☐
			Cream body with Blue flashes	£150-200	☐
			Cream body with Red flashes	£200-300	☐
			N.B. Model based on the Maudsley Marathon III Coach.		
29h (282)	1952-54	Duple Roadmaster Coach	Red (Silver flashes) or Blue (Silver flashes), 119 mm.	£75-85	☐
36g		Taxi with Driver	'TAXI' cast into Black roof, driver cast into chassis, 72 mm.		
	1936-46		Cream or Red body, Black roof, open rear window	£250-350	☐
	1947-50		Yellow body, Black roof, open rear window	£500-600	☐
			Dark Blue, Green, Light Green, Red, Maroon or Brown body, Black roof on all, rear window filled-in	£80-100	☐
40h (254)	1951-54	Austin Taxi (FX3)	'TAXI' cast into roof, driver cast into chassis, 94 mm.		
			Yellow body (Brown chassis), or Dark Blue body (Black chassis)	£90-120	☐
067	1959-64	'Dublo Dinky' version:	Blue/Cream body, driver & 'TAXI' cast-in, Grey plastic wheels, 59 mm.	£40-50	☐
115	1979-79	United Biscuits Taxi	Yellow/Blue/Black, casting as 120, promotional, 86 mm.	£30-40	☐
120	1979-80	Happy Cab	White/Yellow/Blue, solid wheels, 'flower-power' stickers, 86 mm.	£30-40	☐
241	1977-77	'SILVER JUBILEE TAXI'	Silver body and hubs, Union Jack on bootlid, 284 casting, 112 mm.	£45-55	☐
254 (40h)	1954-56	Austin Taxi (FX3)	'TAXI' cast into roof, driver cast into chassis, 94 mm.		
			Yellow body, Black chassis	£80-90	☐
			Dark Blue (Black chassis, Light Blue hubs)	£90-120	☐
	1956-59		Green and Yellow body	£80-90	☐
	1959-62		Black body, Grey interior, spun aluminium hubs	£90-110	☐
265	1960-64	Plymouth U.S.A. Taxi	Yellow/Red, '25c First 1/5 Mile, 5c Additional', windows, aerial, 108 mm.	£80-90	☐
266	1960-66	Plymouth Canadian Taxi	Yellow/Red body with 'Taxi' and '450 Metro Cab', 108 mm.	£100-150	☐
268	1962-67	Renault Dauphine Mini Cab	Red body with 'Meccano', 'Kenwood', and various other adverts, 92 mm.	£80-90	☐
278	1978-80	Plymouth Yellow Cab	Yellow body, 'Yellow Cab Co', plastic chassis, wheels and aerial, 135 mm.	£15-20	☐
280 (29f)	1954-60	Observation Coach	Grey (Red flashes) or Cream (Red flashes), 112 mm.	£50-60	☐
281 (29g)	1954-59	Luxury Coach	Fawn/Orange, Cream/Orange, Fawn/Cream or Maroon/Cream, 113 mm.	£100-125	☐
			Blue body, Cream flash, Lemon wheels	£200-250	☐
282 (29h)	1954-60	Duple Roadmaster Coach	Red/Silver, Blue/Silver, or Dark Blue/Silver, 119 mm.	£75-85	☐
			Yellow body with Red flashes and hubs	£200-250	☐
			Dark Green lower body with Cream upper body and hubs. (U.S. Export issue)	£200-300	☐
			Same as previous but with Red hubs (U.S. Export issue)	£200-300	☐
			Light Blue body	£75-85	☐
282	1967-69	Austin 1800 Taxi	Blue/White body, Red/White 'TAXI' labels on doors & roof, 101 mm.	£65-75	☐
283	1956-63	B.O.A.C. Coach	Dark Blue/White, 'British Overseas Airways Corporation', 120 mm.	£65-75	☐
			N.B. Model based on Commer Harrington Contender Coach.		
283	1971-77	Single Deck Bus	Red body with White band, operable doors and bell, 'RED ARROW', 167 mm.	£35-40	☐
			As previous model but Metallic Red finish	£40-50	☐
284	1972-79	London Taxi (FX4)	Black (or very Dark Blue) body, driver, Speedwheels, 'TAXI', 112 mm.	£30-40	☐
289		**Routemaster Bus issues**	'London Transport', Route '221', 'KINGS CROSS', driver/conductor, cast hubs, spun hubs or Speedwheels, 121 mm.		
	1964-65	'TERN SHIRTS'	Red body, 'FOR 8am CRISPNESS' transfers	£80-95	☐
	1966-69	'SSSCHWEPPES'	Red body, Blue-Green logo on White transfers	£60-70	☐
	1969-80	'ESSO'	Red body, Red and Blue logo on White paper label 'ESSO SAFETY-GRIP TYRES'	£20-25	☐
			Same as previous issue but with transfers	£100-150	☐
		'ESSO' variant:	Deep Purple body, 'London Transport' and 'ESSO SAFETY-GRIP TYRES' logos, Blue driver and clippie	£400-600	☐
	1968-68	'LONDON STORES'	Red body, Black/Gold logo 'Festival of London Stores', promotional	£100-150	☐
	1970	'INGERSOLL RAND'	Red body, promotional	£75-90	☐
	1974-74	'MECCANO'	Gold body, 'MECCANO - DINKY TOYS'. (Very few issued to the Press only)	NGPP	☐
	1977-79	'MADAME TUSSAUDS'	Red body with White labels, figures in some, promotional	£65-75	☐
		label change:	As previous model but Dark Blue labels	£60-70	☐
		box change:	Red body, with figures, packed in 'SCHWEPPES' picture box	£100-120	☐
	1977-77	'WOOLWORTHS'	Silver body, (Silver Jubilee limited issue) figures in some	£20-25	☐
	1977-77	'EVER READY'	Silver body, (New Zealand Silver Jubilee issue) no figures	NGPP	☐
	1979	'THOLLENBEEK'	Gold body, 'Thollenbeek 1929-79', Belgian promotional	£100-125	☐
290 (29c)		Double Decker Bus	Type 2 (AEC grille), 'DUNLOP - The World's Master Tyre' advert may be upright or sloping, 290 cast on base, diecast hubs match lower deck		
	1954-59	'DUNLOP'	Green lower deck, Cream upper deck	£100-125	☐
			Red lower deck, Cream upper deck	£100-125	☐
	1959-61	'DUNLOP'	Type 3 (Leyland grille), diecast hubs match lower deck colour, roof route box added, Mid Green or Dark Green lower deck, Cream upper deck	£80-100	☐
			Red lower deck, Cream upper deck	£80-100	☐
	1961-63	Spun hubs variant	Same colours as previous with sloping lettering	£100-150	☐
	1963	Plastic hubs variant	Same colours but with Green or Red plastic hubs	£125-175	☐
	1963	'EXIDE BATTERIES'	Red or Green lower deck, Cream upper deck with '290' cast into base	NGPP	☐
291		Double Decker Bus	Type 3 (Leyland grille) with route '73' on roof route box		
	1961-62	'EXIDE BATTERIES'	Red body with Red diecast hubs, logo in Black and Yellow	£80-100	☐
	1962-63	Spun hubs variant	Same body colours as previous model	£100-150	☐
	1963	Plastic hubs variant	Same body colours as previous but with Red plastic hubs	£125-175	☐

Ref. No.				Market Price Range	
291 - 293		**Atlantean City Bus**......................	A Leyland double-decker bus (123 mm. long) available in several versions:		
291	1974-77	'KENNINGS'.........................	Orange body, White engine cover and interior, *'VAN & TRUCK HIRE'*....................	£30-35	☐
			As previous model but with Pale Blue engine cover and interior.................................	£35-40	☐
			As previous model but seen with 'Yellow Pages' stickers	NGPP	☐
	1977	'LONDON & MANCHESTER ASSURANCE'..............	White model on plinth. *'Your Best Man For Life'*. (500 issued to agents)....................	NGPP	☐
292	1962-65	'RIBBLE'..............................	Red and White body with or without 'REGENT' advertisement	£80-100	☐
			Red and Cream body with *'CORPORATION TRANSPORT'* fleetname....................	£80-100	☐
			As previous model but no fleetname or logo	£80-100	☐
292	1977	'LONDON COUNTRY'.......	Green body, shows in 1977 catalogue, but never issues..		
293	1963-65	'BP'..................................	Green & Cream body with Yellow logo and smooth roof, *'BP IS THE KEY'*............	£80-100	☐
			As previous model but with ribbed roof	£110-130	☐
293	1973-78	Swiss Postal Bus 'PTT'.............	Yellow body with Cream roof, clear or tinted windows, (296 casting), 119 mm..........	£20-25	☐
295	1963-69	Atlas Kenebrake Bus.................	Light Blue/Grey body, suspension, windows, 86 mm..	£35-40	☐
			As previous model but all Blue body	£35-40	☐
295	1973-74	Atlantean Bus 'YELLOW PAGES'	Yellow body, *'Let Your Fingers Do The Walking'*, 123 mm.	£35-40	☐
295	1974-76		As previous model but deeper shade of Yellow	£35-40	☐
296	1972-75	Duple Viceroy 37 Coach	Metallic Blue body, clear or tinted windows, bubble-packed, 119 mm.	£15-20	☐
			As previous model but Yellow and Cream body (see also 293)	£20-25	☐
297	1977-77	Silver Jubilee Bus......................	Leyland Atlantean (291) Silver/Black body, *'National'*, 123 mm.	£20-25	☐
	1977-77	'WOOLWORTHS'	Silver Jubilee Bus (Leyland Atlantean) Silver body, promotional	£20-25	☐
949	1961-66	Wayne 'SCHOOL BUS'............	Deep Yellow body, Red body lines & interior, windows, Supertoy, 195 mm.	£200-275	☐
			As previous model but with Black lines on sides	£200-275	☐
952	1964-71	Vega Major Luxury Coach	Pale Grey with Maroon flash, working indicators, 242 mm. Supertoy.......................	£70-85	☐
			As previous model but White body with Maroon flash...	£70-85	☐
953	1963-65	Continental Touring Coach	Blue/White body, *'Dinky Continental Tours'*, windows, 195 mm. Supertoy	£250-325	☐
954	1972-77	Vega Major Luxury Coach	As 952 but without flashing indicators...	£60-70	☐
961	1973-77	Vega Major Coach 'PTT'.........	Orange/Cream body, 'P.T.T.' and emblem, Swiss model (in normal box)	£125-150	☐
		box variant:................	961 in Swiss box (Red/White/Yellow, *'Autocar Postal'*, *'Postauto'*, etc), plus label 'Special contract run 1973 Swiss Post Office Bus – also specially boxed for Swiss Meccano Agent for sale under their name'	£200-250	☐

The Editor wishes to express his thanks to John Gay, 7 Horsham Lane, Upchurch, Sittingbourne, Kent ME9 7AL, Bus specialist dealer for assistance with the 29/290/91 issues.

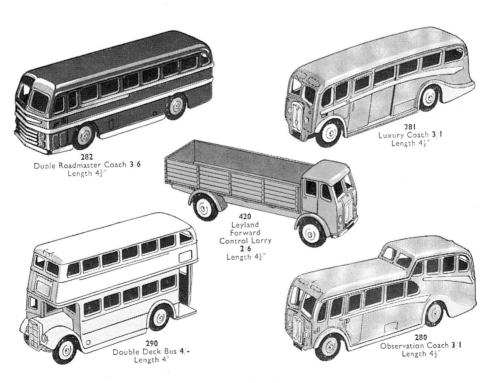

282
Duple Roadmaster Coach 3/6
Length 4¾"

281
Luxury Coach 3/1
Length 4½"

420
Leyland
Forward
Control Lorry
2/6
Length 4½"

290
Double Deck Bus 4/-
Length 4"

280
Observation Coach 3/1
Length 4½"

Page from the 1955 Catalogue.

Dinky Toys - Road-making Equipment and Cranes

Ref. No.	Year(s)	Model Type	Model Features and Size	Market Price Range	
25p (251)	1948-54	Aveling Barford Road Roller....	Mid or Pale Green body with driver and hook, Red wheels, 110 mm.	£30-40	☐
251 (25p)	1954-63	Aveling Barford Road Roller....	Green body with driver and hook, Red wheels, 110 mm.	£30-40	☐
279	1965-71	Aveling Barford Diesel Roller...	Orange body, Grey engine covers, Green wheels, 116 mm.	£25-35	☐
	1971-80		Yellow cab, Black roof, Silver wheels, 116 mm.	£25-35	☐
			Yellow cab, Black roof, Black wheels.	£25-35	☐
			Yellow cab, Blue roof, Yellow square engine covers, Silver wheels.	£25-35	☐
			Yellow cab, Black roof, Yellow square engine covers, Silver wheels.	£25-35	☐
			Yellow cab, Grey Roof, Yellow square engine covers, Silver wheels.	£25-35	☐
430	1977-80	Johnson 2 ton Dumper	Orange/Red body with Blue driver, Black or Orange engine, 106 mm.	£20-25	☐
436	1963-69	'ATLAS COPCO' Lorry	Yellow body, compressor, Fingertip steering, opening engine cover, 89 mm.	£30-40	☐
437	1962-70	Muir Hill 2WL Loader............	Red body with hook, no grille detail, 121 mm.	£20-25	☐
			Yellow body with Red or Silver wheels.	£20-25	☐
	1970-78		Yellow with Red arms with hook, with or without grille detail	£20-25	☐
			Orange body with Orange or Black arms.	£30-40	☐
561 (961)	1949-54	Blaw Knox Bulldozer	Red, Green or Black rubber tracks, driver, lifting blade, Supertoy. Blue box has Red/White label	£40-50	☐
			As previous model but Dark Blue	£100-150	☐
			Yellow body, Grey blade, Green tracks, Beige driver. Blue box has Orange/White label	NGPP	☐
562 (962)	1948-54	Muir Hill Dump Truck	Yellow body, metal wheels/tyres, hook, 105 mm.	£15-20	☐
563 (963)	1948-54	Blaw Knox Heavy Tractor........	Red, Orange or Blue 561 without the dozer blade, 116 mm. Brown cardboard box has Red/White label	£60-70	☐
564 (964)	1952-54	Elevator Loader......................	See 964 for details		☐
571 (971)	1949-54	Coles Mobile Crane..................	Yellow and Black, operable crane, Supertoy, 160 mm.	£30-40	☐
752 (973)	1953-54	Goods Yard Crane	Yellow operable crane on Blue (or Dark Blue) base (steps in some)	£30-40	☐
924	1972-76	Aveling Barford 'CENTAUR' ..	Red/Yellow body, dump truck, 180 mm.	£30-40	☐
959	1961-68	Foden Dump Truck and Bulldozer	Red/Orange body, model number badge, driver, windows, Supertoy, 165 mm.	£50-60	☐
960	1960-68	Albion Lorry Concrete Mixer ...	Orange body, Yellow/Blue rotating drum, spare wheel, Supertoy, 130 mm.	£40-50	☐
			Orange body, Grey rotating drum.	£40-50	☐
961 (561)	1954-62	Blaw-Knox Bulldozer	Red or Yellow body, rubber tracks, Tan driver, Supertoy, 138 mm.	£40-50	☐
	1962-64		Blue body, rubber tracks, Tan driver, Supertoy, 143 mm.	£40-50	☐
	1964-?		Orange plastic body with Silver engine detail, Black plastic blade and exhaust pipe, Blue driver, Light Green or Olive-Green roller wheels N.B. Plastic examples made in 1964.	NGPP	☐
962 (562)	1954-66	Muir Hill Dumper	Yellow body, hook, Supertoy, (rubber tyres from 1962) 105 mm.	£15-20	☐
963 (563)	1954-58	Blaw Knox Heavy Tractor........	961 without blade, Red or Orange body, Green or Black tracks, 116 mm. Packed in Blue/White striped box	£40-50	☐
963	1958-59		As previous model but with Yellow body	£30-40	☐
963	1973-75	Road Grader	Yellow/Red articulated body, Silver blade, Red lower arm, 238 mm.	£20-30	☐
			White or Yellow lower arm	£30-40	☐
964 (564)	1954-68	Elevator Loader......................	Blue/Yellow chutes or Yellow/Blue chutes	£40-50	☐
965	1955-61	'EUCLID' Dump Truck	Yellow, 'STONE - ORE - EARTH', no windows, operable tipper, 142 mm. N.B. 1955-56 Grey backed logo, 1959-61 Red backed logo.	£45-55	☐
	1961-69		As previous model but with window glazing.	£45-55	☐
965	1969-70	'TEREX' Rear Dump Truck	Yellow body (as previous model but 'TEREX' cast under cab) 142 mm.	£75-100	☐
966	1960-64	Marrel Multi-Bucket Unit........	(Albion) Yellow body, Grey buckets, windows, Supertoy, 115 mm.	£50-60	☐
967	1973-78	Muir-Hill Loader/Trencher	Yellow/Red or Orange/Black body, with driver, 163 mm.	£25-35	☐
970	1967-71	Jones Fleetmaster Crane	(Bedford TK) Red and Black body, White folding crane, 178 mm.	£50-60	☐
	1971-77		Metallic Red and Black with White folding crane	£60-70	☐
	1971-77		Yellow and Black with White folding crane	£60-70	☐
971 (571)	1954-64	Coles Mobile Crane..................	Yellow/Black body, Yellow crane & diecast wheels & driver, Supertoy, 160 mm.	£30-40	☐
	1964-66		Yellow/Black body, Silver crane, plastic wheels & driver, Supertoy, 160 mm.	£30-40	☐
972	1955-62	Coles 20 ton Lorry-Mounted Crane	Yellow/Orange (no 'Long Vehicle' signs), 2 drivers, Supertoy, 240 mm.	£30-40	☐
	1962-69		Yellow/Orange (with 'Long Vehicle' signs), 2 drivers, Supertoy.	£30-40	☐
	1967-69		Yellow/Black, Blue metal driver in lorry cab only, Yellow plastic wheels, Black tyres, Black/White diagonal stripes around jib, 'COLES CRANE' in Yellow at rear..	£100-150	☐
973 (752)	1954-59	Goods Yard Crane	Yellow operable crane on Blue base.	£30-40	☐
973	1971-75	Eaton 'YALE' Tractor Shovel ..	Red/Yellow body with Yellow or Silver bucket exterior, 178 mm.	£20-30	☐
			Yellow/Red body, Silver wheels, no engine covers.	£25-35	☐
			All Yellow body, Blue wheels, engine covers	£25-35	☐
975	1963-67	Ruston-Bucyrus Excavator........	Yellow/Red/Grey plastic body, rubber tracks, operable digger, 190 mm.	£175-250	☐
976	1968-76	'MICHIGAN' Tractor Dozer ...	Yellow/Red body, driver, engine covers, Red wheels, 147 mm.	£20-25	☐
977	1973-78	Shovel Dozer	Yellow/Red/Silver, Black or Silver plastic tracks, bubble-packed, 151 mm.	£20-25	☐
980	1972-79	Coles Hydra Truck 150T..........	Lemon Yellow body, triple extension crane, handle at side & rear.	£30-40	☐
			Yellow or Orange body, 2 side handles, no rear handle, 210 mm.	£50-60	☐
		'SPARROWS'......................	Red body, 'SPARROWS CRANE HIRE', (promotional model)	£200-300	☐
984	1974-79	Atlas Digger	Red/Yellow Yellow arm, Yellow cylinders, Silver or Yellow bucket, 'AB 1702'..........	£30-40	☐
			Red/Yellow, Black plastic arm, Black or Yellow cylinders, Silver bucket....................	£30-40	☐

Dinky Toys - Ships, Boats, Hovercraft

Ref. No.	Year(s)	Model Type	Model Features and Size	Market Price Range	
50a	1934-41	Battle Cruiser 'HMS Hood'	Battleship Grey, (without name cast underneath 1939-41) 146 mm.	£25-30	☐
50b	1934-41	Battleship 'Nelson' Class	Battleship Grey, 'HMS Nelson' underneath (no name 1939-41) 117 mm.	£25-30	☐
50b	1934-41	Battleship 'Nelson' Class	Battleship Grey, 'HMS Rodney' underneath (no name 1939-41) 117 mm.	£25-30	☐
50c	1934-41	Cruiser 'HMS Effingham'	Battleship Grey, (without name cast underneath 1939-41) 100 mm.	£15-20	☐
50d	1934-41	Cruiser 'HMS York'	Battleship Grey, (without name cast underneath 1939-41) 98 mm.	£15-20	☐
50e	1934-41	Cruiser 'HMS Delhi'	Battleship Grey, (without name cast underneath 1939-41) 81 mm.	£15-20	☐
50f	1934-41	Destroyer 'Broke' Class	Battleship Grey, no wording underneath, 57 mm.	£5-10	☐
50g	1935-41	Submarine 'K' Class	Battleship Grey, wire mast, no wording underneath, 57 mm.	£5-10	☐
50h	1935-41	Destroyer 'Amazon' Class	Battleship Grey, no wording underneath, 52 mm.	£5-10	☐
50x	1935-41	Submarine 'X' Class	Battleship Grey, wire mast, no wording underneath, 61 mm.	£5-10	☐
51b	1934-40	Norddeutscher-Lloyd 'Europa'	Black hull, White superstructure, Brown funnels, name under, 165 mm.	£35-45	☐
51c	1934-40	Italia Line 'Rex'	Black hull, White decks, Red/White/Green funnels, name under, 152 mm.	£35-45	☐
51d	1934-40	CPR 'Empress of Britain'	Canadian Pacific Railway colours of White hull & Cream funnels, 130 mm.	£30-35	☐
51e	1935-40	P & O 'Strathaird'	White hull, Cream funnels, name underneath, 114 mm.	£30-35	☐
51f	1934-40	'Queen of Bermuda'	Furness-Withy Line, Grey/White hull, Red/Black funnels, 99 mm.	£30-35	☐
51g	1934-40	Cunard 'Britannic'	'White-Star' Liner, Black/White/Brown hull, Black/Tan funnels, 121 mm.	£30-35	☐
52	1934-35	Cunard White-Star Liner 'No. 534'	Black/White/Red, '534' cast underneath, boxed, no rollers, 175 mm.	£70-80	☐
			Same model but '534 Queen Mary' cast underneath	£50-60	☐
52 (52b)	1935-35		As previous model with 'Queen Mary' cast underneath, but without '534'	£50-60	☐
52a	1935-41	Cunard White-Star Liner 'Queen Mary'	Black/White/Red, boxed, with plastic rollers, 175 mm.	£50-60	☐
	1946-49		Black/White/Red, boxed, with brass rollers	£50-60	☐
52b (52)	1935-36	Cunard 'Queen Mary'	Black/White/Red, boxed, without rollers, (renumbered from 52)	£50-60	☐
52c	1935-40	'La Normandie'	Black/White, Red/Black funnels, boxed, made in France, 175 mm.	£40-45	☐
52c		Cunard 'Queen Elizabeth'	Announced in 1939 catalogue but never produced	NPP	
52m	1936-40	Cunard 'Queen Mary'	Renumbered from 52b, without runners, supplied unboxed	£20-30	☐
53az	1938-39	Battleship 'Dunkerque'	Battleship Grey, with or without plastic rollers, boxed French issue	£30-35	☐
281	1973-76	Military Hovercraft	Military-Green body, Gunner, aerial, 'ARMY', 139 mm.	£20-25	☐
290	1970-76	SRN-6 Hovercraft	Red/White/Yellow, Blue or Black skirt, opening door, radar scanner	£10-15	☐
671	1976-78	Mk.1 Corvette	White/Grey/Brown/Black plastic body, fires missiles, 260 mm.	£10-15	☐
672	1976-77	OSA-2 Missile Boat	Grey/Whit/Black, fires missiles, 206 mm.	£10-15	☐
673	1977-78	Submarine Chaser	Grey/White/Black, fires depth charges, 197 mm.	£10-15	☐
674	1977-78	Coastguard Missile Launch	White/Blue/Red/Yellow, 'Coastguard', fires missiles, 155 mm.	£5-10	☐
675	1973-77	Motor Patrol Boat	Grey hull with Cream/Black/Red, 170 mm.	£5-10	☐
678	1974-77	Air-Sea Rescue Launch	Grey/Black/Yellow, Orange dinghy, pilot/launch, 170 mm.	£10-15	☐
796	1960-62	Healey Sports Boat on Trailer	Cream hull with Green, Red or Yellow deck (plastic), Orange cast trailer	£20-25	☐
797	1966	Healey Sports Boat	Sold on its own from trade box of 6	£15-20	☐

Dinky Toys - Trains

For other Meccano produced railway items, see Dinky-Dublo, Accessories, Hornby-Dublo, and Gift Sets sections.

Ref. No.	Year(s)	Model Type	Model Features and Size	Market Price Range	
16	1936-37	Silver Jubilee Set	Locomotive and 2 interlocking coaches, 'LNER' and '2590' cast-in, open windows, smooth hubs with White tyres, special box, 300 mm.		
			Silver loco and coaches, Grey, Mid-Blue, Red or Orange trim	£175-225	☐
			Silver loco and coaches with Dark Blue trim	£200-250	☐
			Cream loco and coaches with Red trim	£250-275	☐
			Blue loco and coaches with Dark Blue trim	£250-275	☐
			Green loco and coaches with Dark Green trim	£250-275	☐
16	1937-40	Streamlined Train Set	As previous models but with a change of name and box	£150-200	☐
16	1946-52	Streamlined Train Set	Blue/Black loco, 'LNER', Brown/Grey coaches, solid windows, Black tyres	£75-100	☐
16 (798)	1952-54	Streamlined Train Set	As previous model but with tinplate base, with or without 'LNER'	£75-100	☐
16z	1935-40	Articulated Train	TT-Blue, or Gold/Red, or Cream with Red, Blue or Orange, French issue sold in UK..	£200-250	☐
17	1935-40	Passenger Train Set	Black/Maroon loco 17a, Maroon tender 17b, Maroon/Cream coaches 20a/20b	£200-250	☐
			Black/Green loco 17a, Green tender 17b, 2 Green/Cream coaches 20a/20b	£200-250	☐
			Lead and Majuk set in 2nd type box with correct colour spot	£300-400	☐
17a	1934-40	Locomotive	Black/Maroon or Black/Green, diecast cab/boiler, lead chassis, 82 mm.	£150-175	☐
17b	1934-40	Tender	Maroon or Green diecast body, 62 mm.	£40-50	☐
18	1935-40	Tank Goods Train Set	Green/Black loco (21a), and 3 Green/Black open wagons (21b)	£200-250	☐
19	1935-40	Mixed Goods Train	Maroon/Black loco (21a), Green/Red open wagon (21b), Red/Blue 'SHELL' tanker wagon (21d), Yellow/Red/Green lumber wagon (21e)	£350-450	☐
			Set in rare 3rd type pictorial landscape box	£800-1000	☐
20	1935-40	Tank Passenger Set	Green/Black loco (21a), 2 Brown/Green coaches (20a), Guard's van (20b)	£200-250	☐
20a	1935-40	Coach	Brown/Cream or Green/White roof, diecast body, lead chassis, 81 mm.	£40-60	☐
20b	1935-40	Guard's Van	Brown/Cream or Green/White roof, diecast body, lead chassis, 81 mm.	£40-60	☐
21	1933-35	Modelled Miniatures Train Set	Blue/Red loco (21a), Green open wagon (21b), Green/Blue crane wagon (21c) Red/Blue 'SHELL' tank wagon (21d), Yellow/Red/Green lumber wagon (21e)	£200-250	☐

Ref. No.		*Dinky Toys — Trains – continued*		Market Price Range	
21a	1932-34	Tank Locomotive	Red/Blue 0-6-0 tank loco, 'HORNBY SERIES' cast into lead body, 82 mm.	**£40-60**	☐
	1934-41		Maroon/Black or Green/Black, 'DINKY TOYS' cast into lead body, 82 mm.	**£40-60**	☐
21b	1932-34	Open Wagon.............................	Green/Red, Green/Blue, Green/Black, Maroon/Black, 'HORNBY SERIES', lead	**£40-60**	☐
	1934-41		Colours as previous model, 'DINKY TOYS' cast into lead body, 58 mm.	**£40-60**	☐
21c	1932-34	Crane Wagon..........................	Green body, Blue chassis, 'HORNBY SERIES' cast-in, lead, 62 mm....................	**£40-60**	☐
21d	1932-34	Tanker Wagon.........................	Red tank, Blue or Black chassis, 'HORNBY SERIES' cast-in, lead, 58 mm.	**£40-60**	☐
	1934-41		Red tank, Blue or Black chassis, 'DINKY TOYS' cast-in, lead, 58 mm....................	**£40-60**	☐
21e	1932-34	Lumber Wagon........................	Brown/Blue, Yellow/Red or Yellow/Black, 'HORNBY SERIES' cast-in, lead	**£40-60**	☐
	1934-41		Brown/Blue, Yellow/Red or Yellow/Black, 'DINKY TOYS', lead, 58 mm.................	**£40-60**	☐
26	1934-40	G.W.R. Rail Car	Cream roof, Brown, Green, Yellow or Red body, plastic rollers, 106 mm.	**£100-125**	☐
			Green body with Red roof	**£100-125**	☐
26z	1937-40	Diesel Road Car	Cream roof, Red, Green, Orange, Yellow or Blue body, 99 mm. (French)	**£100-125**	☐
784	1972-75	Goods Train Set	Blue engine with Yellow 'G.E.R.', Yellow & Red open wagons	**£35-45**	☐
798 (16)	1954-59	Express Passenger Train Set......	Green/Black loco, BR crest, Cream coaches (Grey roofs), Black hubs/tyres	**£100-125**	☐
			Green/Black loco, BR crest, Cream coaches/roofs/hubs, Black tyres.......................	**£80-100**	☐
			Green/Black loco, BR crest, Cream coaches/roofs, Red hubs, White tyres	**£100-125**	☐

Dinky Toys   -   Motor Cycles

Ref. No.	Year(s)	Model Type	Model Features and Size	Market Price Range	

See also Accessories and Gift Sets sections.
SWRW = solid White rubber wheels, SBRW = solid Black rubber wheels, (both are of a larger diameter than those used on the small cars).

Ref. No.	Year(s)	Model Type	Model Features and Size	Market Price Range	
14z	1938-40	Three-wheel Delivery Van	'Triporteur' with Green, Red, Grey, Blue or Yellow body, Black hubs, White tyres, rider is always a different colour from van, French model	NGPP	☐
37a	1937-40	Civilian Motor Cyclist..............	Black cycle, fine paint detail, Blue, Maroon, Green or Black rider, SWRW, 45 mm. ..	**£100-150**	☐
	1946-49		Black cycle, crude paint detail, Green or Grey rider, SBRW	**£50-60**	☐
37a (041)	1950-54		Black cycle, crude paint detail, Green or Grey rider, export only	**£40-50**	☐
37b	1937-40	Police Motor Cyclist.................	Black motor cycle, Silver detail, Blue rider, solid White rubber wheels	**£75-100**	☐
	1946-49		Black motorcycle, no detailing, Blue rider, solid Black rubber wheels........................	**£25-35**	☐
37b (042)	1950-54		Black motorcycle, no detailing, Blue rider, SBRW, export only	**£25-35**	☐
37c	1937-39	Signals Despatch Rider	Green motorcycle, Khaki rider, solid White rubber wheels, 45 mm.	**£100-125**	☐
	1939-41		Green motorcycle, Khaki rider, solid Black rubber wheels, 45 mm.	**£50-60**	☐
42b	1935-40	Police Motorcycle Patrol	Blue cycle, Green sidecar, Blue figures, detailing, SWRW, 47 mm...........................	**£100-125**	☐
	1948-50		Blue cycle, Green sidecar, Blue figures, little detailing, SBRW, 47 mm.	**£50-60**	☐
42b (043)	1950-55		Blue/Green, Blue figures, little detailing, SBRW, export only	**£40-50**	☐
43b	1935-40	R.A.C. Motorcycle Patrol	Black cycle, Blue rider with Red sash, detailing, SWRW, 46 mm.	**£100-125**	☐
	1946-49		Black cycle, Blue rider, little detailing, solid Black rubber wheels............................	**£50-60**	☐
44b	1935-40	A.A. Motorcycle Patrol............	Black/Yellow, Brown rider, good detailing, 5 mm.'AA' badge, SWRW, 45 mm.	**£100-125**	☐
44b (270)	1946-50		Black/Yellow, Tan rider, little detailing, 7 mm.'AA' badge, SBRW, 45 mm.	**£50-60**	☐
44b (045)	1950-55		AS previous model but made for export only	**£50-60**	☐
270 (44b)	1959-62		Black/Yellow, Tan rider, 'AA' sign, solid Grey plastic wheels, 46 mm.	**£40-50**	☐
271	1959-62	T.S. Motorcycle Patrol............	Yellow motorcycle combination, Belgian equivalent of the A.A.	**£150-200**	☐
272	1959-62	A.N.W.B. Motorcycle Patrol	Yellow motorcycle combination, Dutch equivalent of the A.A....................................	**£250-300**	☐

Dinky Toys   -   Caravans

Ref. No.	Year(s)	Model Type	Model Features and Size	Market Price Range	
30g	1936-39	Caravan Trailer	2 wheels, drawbar, body length 81 mm. open roof windows, Blue/Cream, Red/Cream, Green/Cream, Orange/Cream, Two tone-Green....................	**£50-60**	☐
			Chocolate and Beige, Blue hubs	**£100-150**	☐
	1939-40		As previous models but with filled-in roof windows..	**£50-65**	☐
30g	1948-50	Caravan	Orange/Cream body, 'Caravan Club', drawbar, body length 81 mm.	**£45-55**	☐
117	1963-69	Four Berth Caravan	Blue/Cream, clear roof, suspension, detailed interior, 117 mm.	**£25-35**	☐
			Yellow/Cream, clear roof, suspension, detailed interior, 117 mm.	**£25-35**	☐
188	1961-63	Four Berth Caravan	Green/Cream or Blue/Cream, windows, detailed interior, 132 mm.	**£25-35**	☐
	1963-63		As previous model but larger windows, (this model replaced by 117)	**£25-35**	☐
190	1956-62	Caravan	Orange/Cream, or Blue/Cream, drawbar, metal jockey wheel, 118 mm.	**£25-35**	☐
	1962-64		Orange/Cream, or Blue/Cream, drawbar, plastic jockey wheel, 118 mm.	**£25-35**	☐

150

Dinky Toys - Novelty, Space, Film & TV-related models

Ref. No.	Year(s)	Model Type	Model Features and Size	Market Price Range	
100	1967-75	Lady Penelope's 'FAB 1'	Pink body, clear or tinted sliding roof (Pink stripes on some), suspension, rockets/harpoons, Lady Penelope & Parker figures (TV series 'Thunderbirds')	£150-200	□
			As previous model but with Luminous Pink body	£250-300	□
101	1967-73	Thunderbirds II and IV	Gloss Green body with Yellow legs, plastic Thunderbird IV inside, 143 mm.	£250-300	□
	1973-73		Metallic Dark Green, Yellow legs, plastic Thunderbird IV inside	£250-300	□
102	1969-75	Joe's Car	Metallic Green, driver, battery powered, 139 mm. (TV series 'Joe 90')	£100-125	□
103	1968-75	Spectrum Patrol Car	TV series 'Captain Scarlet', shaped hubs, 'screaming motor', 121 mm.		
			Red body with Yellow base, Yellow or Cream plastic interior	£100-125	□
			Metallic Red body with White base, Yellow or Cream plastic interior	£75-100	□
			Metallic Gold body with Blue tinted windows, Yellow or Cream plastic interior	£75-100	□
104	1968-72	Spectrum Pursuit Vehicle	Metallic Blue, 'SPV', separate seat/figure, 160 mm. ('Captain Scarlet')	£100-150	□
	1973-75		As previous model but seat and figure attached to door	£100-125	□
105	1968-75	Maximum Security Vehicle	White/Red, Red or Blue inside, 'RADIOACTIVE' crate, ('Captain Scarlet')	£100-125	□
106	1967-70	'The Prisoner' Mini-Moke	White body, Red/White canopy, 'bicycle' decal on opening bonnet, 73 mm.	£175-225	□
106	1974-77	Thunderbirds II and IV	Metallic Blue body and metal base, Yellow legs, 153 mm.	£75-95	□
			Metallic Blue body, White plastic base, Yellow legs, 153 mm.	£75-95	□
	1977-79		Metallic Blue body, Black plastic base, Red legs, 153 mm.	£50-75	□
107	1967-68	Stripey the Magic Mini	White/Red/Yellow/Blue stripes, with Candy, Andy & the Bearandas, 75 mm.	£200-250	□
108	1969-75	Sam's Car	Keyless motor, 111 mm., separate 'WIN' badge, (TV series 'Joe 90'),		
			Silver plated body, Red or Silver trim, Yellow interior	£75-95	□
			Gold body, Red or Silver trim, Yellow interior	£80-100	□
			Pale Blue body, Red or Silver trim, Yellow interior	£100-130	□
			Metallic Red body, Red or Silver trim, Yellow interior	£75-95	□
			Wine Red body	£80-100	□
109	1969-71	Gabriel Model 'T' Ford	Yellow/Black, 'Gabriel', driver, 83 mm. (TV series 'The Secret Service')	£75-95	□
111	1976-78	Cinderella's Coach	Pink/Gold, plastic figures & horses, 242 mm. ('The Slipper & The Rose')	£25-35	□
112	1978-80	Purdey's TR7	Yellow body, Black 'P' logo, Speedwheels, 98 mm. ('The New Avengers')	£40-50	□
			As previous model but with Yellow 'P' in Black logo on bonnet	NGPP	□
			As previous model but with Silver 'P' logo on bonnet	£35-45	□
113		John Steed's Jaguar XJC	Met. Dark Blue, Gold pinstripes, rubbery 'Steed' inside. Officially not issued	NGPP	□
115	1979-79	United Biscuits Taxi	Yellow/Blue/Black, casting as 120, promotional, 86 mm.	£30-40	□
120	1979-80	Happy Cab	White/Yellow/Blue, solid wheels, 'flower-power' stickers, 86 mm.	£30-40	□
281	1968-70	'PATHE NEWS' Camera Car ..	Black body, Camera and operator, opening doors, (Fiat 2300), 108 mm.	£90-120	□
350	1970-71	Tiny's Mini Moke	Red body, White/Orange striped canopy, 73 mm. ('The Enchanted House')	£90-120	□
351	1971-79	U.F.O. Interceptor	From Gerry Anderson's TV series 'U.F.O', 198 mm., 'S.H.A.D.O.' labels on Light Metallic Green body. Initially packed in card box with pictorial inner mount (prices 10% higher), later bubble-packed.		
			with Black nose, White missile, clear canopy, Red or Orange skids	£90-120	□
			with Black nose, White missile, Blue canopy, Red or Orange skids	£90-120	□
			with Red nose, Yellow missile, clear canopy, Red or Orange skids	£65-85	□
			with Red nose, Yellow missile, Blue canopy, Red or Orange skids	£65-85	□
			N.B. Above Red nose issues are housed in bubble packs.		
352	1971-75	Ed Straker's Car	Gold plated body, Blue interior, Silver trim, keyless motor, (TV series 'U.F.O.')	£890-100	□
			Yellow body, Blue or White interior, Silver trim	£100-125	□
			Red body, Silver trim	£75-95	□
353	1971-79	'SHADO 2' Mobile	Military Green body, operable rocket, 145 mm. (TV series 'U.F.O.')	£65-85	□
			As previous model but later version with Metallic Blue body	£100-125	□
354	1972-77	Pink Panther	Pink car and Panther, flywheel drive, card endflap box, 175 mm	£20-30	□
	1977-79	Pink Panther	Similar to previous model but without flywheel, bubble-packed	£20-30	□
			N.B. A single experimental Green diecast version exists (Christies sale 4/95).		
355	1972-75	Lunar Roving Vehicle	Metallic Blue, White astronauts, front/rear steering, 114 mm.	£30-35	□
357	1977-80	Klingon Battle Cruiser	Metallic Blue, fires photon torpedoes, 220 mm. (from 'Star Trek')	£30-35	□
358	1976-80	'USS Enterprise' ('NCC 1701')	White body, Yellow or White 'photon torpedoes', shuttlecraft, 234 mm.	£40-60	□
359	1975-79	Eagle Transporter	White/Green body, Red cones/landing gear, 222 mm. (from 'Space 1999')	£65-85	□
360	1975-79	Eagle Freighter	White, Red cargo hold, 'RADIOACTIVE' drums, 222 mm. (from 'Space 1999')	£65-85	□
			As previous model but with White cargo hold	£65-85	□
361	1978-80	Galactic (Zygon) War Chariot ..	Metallic Green or Metallic Blue, White spacemen, rockets, 126 mm.	£25-30	□
362	1978-79	Trident Star Fighter	Black/Orange, fires rockets, drop-down stairway, 170 mm.	£25-30	□
363	1979-79	Cosmic Interceptor	Metallic Silver/Blue, 2 pilots, Marks & Spencer model ('St.Michael' box)	NGPP	□
363	1979-80	Zygon Patroller	Metallic Silver/Blue, 2 pilots, ('368' in some catalogues, '363' on box)	£25-30	□
			Yellow/Red/Blue version in 'U.S.S. Enterprise' box	NGPP	□
364	1979	NASA Space Shuttle	White booster, White shuttle, decals, instructions, plastic Orange satellite	£75-100	□
366	1979	Space Shuttle	unboxed version of 364 without booster	£20-30	□
367	1979-80	Space Battle Cruiser	White/Red body, pilot, plastic weapons, 187 mm.	£50-60	□
368	1979-79	Cosmic Cruiser	Blue body, Marks & Spencer model (in 'St.Michael' box)	NGPP	□
368	1979-80	Zygon Marauder	Red/White, 4 spacemen, ('363' in some catalogues, '368' on box)	£30-35	□
371 (801)	1980	Pocket-size 'USS Enterprise'	Small version of 358, bubble-packed, released after factory closure	£45-55	□
372 (802)	1980	Pocket-size Klingon Cruiser	Small version of 357, bubble-packed, released after factory closure	£45-55	□
477	1970-72	Parsley's Car	Green/Black/Yellow, head swivels, 92 mm. ('The Adventures of Parsley').	£80-90	□
485	1964-67	Santa Special Model T Ford	Red/White body, Santa Claus, Xmas tree/toys/decals, 79 mm.	£80-100	□
486	1965-69	'Dinky Beats' Morris Oxford	Pink/Green, 'Da gear', 3 beat-group figures, 92 mm.	£80-100	□
602	1976-77	Armoured Command Car	Military-Green, White star, driver, scanner, 8 plastic wheels, fires sparks	£55-75	□
801 (371)	1980	Pocket-size 'USS Enterprise'	Small version of 358, bubble-packed, released after factory closure	£30-35	□
802 (372)	1980	Pocket-size Klingon Cruiser	Small version of 357, bubble-packed, released after factory closure	£30-35	□

'Dublo Dinky' models

Ref. No.	Year(s)	Model Type	Model Features and Size	Market Price Range	
061	1958-59	Ford Prefect	Fawn or Grey body, Silver trim, Grey smooth wheels, 59 mm.	£40-50	☐
			As previous but with treaded Grey wheels	£60-70	☐
062	1958-60	Singer Roadster	Orange or Fawn body, Red interior, Silver trim, Grey smooth or treaded wheels, 50 mm.	£40-50	☐
			Yellow body, Grey treaded wheels	£125-150	☐
063	1958-60	Commer Van	Blue body, Silver trim, Grey smooth or treaded wheels, 54 mm.	£35-40	☐
064	1957-62	Austin Lorry	Green body, Silver trim, Black treaded or Grey smooth or treaded wheels, 64 mm.	£35-40	☐
065	1957-60	Morris Pick-up	Red body, Silver trim, Grey treaded wheels, 54 mm.	£40-50	☐
066	1959-66	Bedford Flat Truck	Grey body, Silver trim, Grey smooth wheels, with hook, 116 mm.	£40-45	☐
			Grey body, Silver trim, Grey smooth or treaded wheels, without hook	£40-45	☐
067	1959-64	Austin Taxi	Blue lower body, Cream upper body, 'TAXI' sign, Black or Grey treaded wheels, 59 mm.	£40-50	☐
068	1959-64	'ROYAL MAIL' Van	Morris 1000 van with Red body, 'E II R' crest, Silver trim, Grey or Black treaded wheels, 47 mm.	£50-60	☐
069	1959-64	Massey Harris Tractor	Blue body, Silver trim, Grey treaded wheels, hole for driver, 36 mm.	£35-40	☐
			Variation with Grey treaded wheels on front and very Light Tan rear wheels	NGPP	☐
070	1959-64	A.E.C. Mercury Tanker	Green cab, Red tank, Black or Grey treaded wheels, 'SHELL-BP', 91 mm.	£75-85	☐
071	1960-64	Volkswagen Delivery Van	Yellow body with Red 'HORNBY DUBLO' logo, Black treaded wheels, 54 mm.	£60-70	☐
072	1959-64	Bedford Articulated Truck	Yellow cab, Red semi-trailer, Black or Grey smooth wheels, 117 mm.	£40-50	☐
073	1960-64	Land Rover/Trailer/Horse	Green car (Grey wheels), Black treaded wheels, Tan or White horse, 105 mm. Trailers:		
			with Bright Green trailer (Green ramp, smooth Grey wheels)	£40-50	☐
			with Green trailer (Brown ramp, treaded Grey wheels)	NGPP	☐
			with Bright Green trailer (Black ramp, treaded Black wheels)	NGPP	☐
			with Orange trailer (Black wheels and ramp)	£100-125	☐
076	1960-64	Lansing Bagnall (set)	Maroon tractor & trailer, Blue driver/seat, Black smooth or treaded wheels, hooks, 75 mm.	£40-50	☐
078	1960-64	Lansing Bagnall Trailer	Maroon body, Black smooth or treaded wheels, hook, wire drawbar	£20-25	☐

Note: All the 'Dublo Dinky' wheels are made of plastic. Smooth wheels are fairly soft and treaded wheels are hard.

Dinky Action Kits

These Action Kits were issued in the 1970s and have no model numbers on their bases. Paint supplied with the kit is not always the same colour or shade as on the relative model when supplied built and finished.

1001	1971-77	Rolls-Royce Phantom V	Various colours (usually Blue), casting as 152	£20-30	☐
1002	1971-75	Volvo 1800s Coupé	Yellow paint, casting as 116	£20-30	☐
1003	1971-75	Volkswagen 1300	Red and White paint supplied, casting as 129	£20-30	☐
1004	1971-77	Ford Escort Police Car	Blue and White paint with 'POLICE' transfers, casting as model 270	£20-30	☐
1006	1973-77	Ford Escort Mexico	Red paint and 'MEXICO' transfers supplied, casting as model 168	£20-30	☐
1007	1971-75	Jensen FF	Various colours of paint (usually Blue), casting as 188	£20-30	☐
1008	1973-77	Mercedes-Benz 600	Red, Yellow or Green paint supplied, casting as model 128	£20-30	☐
1009	1971-75	Lotus F.1 Racing Car	Green paint and 'Gold leaf' transfers supplied, casting as 225	£20-30	☐
1012	1973-75	Ferrari 312-B2	Red paint and 'SHELL' transfers supplied, casting as 226	£20-30	☐
1013		Matra Sports M530	This item was considered for possible production but was never issued	NPP	
1014	1975-77	Beach Buggy	Blue paint supplied, casting as 227	£20-30	☐
1017	1971-77	Routemaster Bus	Red paint and 'ESSO Safety-Grip Tyres' transfers in kit, casting as 289	£20-30	☐
1018	1974-77	Leyland Atlantean Bus	Various colours (mostly White), usually 'NATIONAL' transfers, model 295	£40-50	☐
1023	1972-77	A.E.C. Single Decker Bus	Green paint and 'GREEN LINE' transfers supplied, casting as 283	£40-50	☐
1025	1971-75	Ford Transit Van	Red paint and 'Avis Truck Rental' transfers supplied, casting as 407	£20-30	☐
1027	1972-75	Lunar Roving Vehicle	Blue/White paint, casting as model 355	£20-30	☐
1029	1971-77	Ford D800 Tipper Truck	Green or Yellow paint supplied, casting as model 438	£20-30	☐
1030	1974-77	Land Rover Breakdown Truck	Red or White paint in kit, casting as 442	£20-30	☐
1032	1975-77	Army Land Rover	Military-Green paint and various 'ARMY' transfers in kit, casting as 344	£20-30	☐
1033	1971-77	U.S.A. Army Jeep	Military-Green paint and military transfers supplied, casting as 615	£20-30	☐
1034	1975-77	Mobile Gun	Military-Green paint in kit, casting as 654	£20-30	☐
1035	1975-77	Striker Anti-Tank Vehicle	Military-Green paint and transfer supplied, casting as 691	£20-30	☐
1036	1975-77	Leopard Tank	Military-Green paint and transfers supplied, casting as 692	£20-30	☐
1037	1974-77	Chieftain Tank	Military-Green paint and transfers, casting as 683	£20-30	☐
1038	1975-77	Scorpion Tank	Military-Green paint and transfers, casting as 690	£20-30	☐
1039		Leopard Recovery Tank	This item was considered for production but was never issued	NPP	
1040	1971-77	Sea King Helicopter	White with Blue or Orange paint plus 'USAF' transfers, casting as 724	£20-30	☐
1041	1973-76	Hawker Hurricane Mk.IIc	Camouflage paints and RAF roundels in kit, casting as 718	£30-35	☐
1042	1971-77	Spitfire Mk.II	Camouflage paints and RAF roundels in kit, casting as 719	£25-35	☐
1043	1974-76	S.E.P.E.C.A.T. Plane	Blue and Green paints and transfers supplied, casting as 731	£20-30	☐
1044	1972-75	Messerschmitt BF-109e	Brown paint and Luftwaffe transfers in kit, casting as 726	£20-30	☐
1045	1975-76	Multi-Role Combat Aircraft	Camouflage paints and transfers supplied, casting as 729	£20-30	☐
1050	1975-77	Motor Patrol Boat	Black/Blue/White paints/stickers, as model 675	£20-30	☐

'Dinky Toys' issued by Airfix Products Ltd

Issued by Airfix as **'DINKY TOYS'**; made in France to 1/43 scale.
Supplied in the last design of Red/Yellow/Blue 'Dinky Toys' window box with header card.

Ref. No.	Year(s)	Model Type	Model Features and Size	Market Price Range	
500	c1980	Citroën 2cv	Red/Orange body or Green body, 'Duck' motif, closed roof	£5-15	☐
501	c1980	Fiat Strada	Blue or Metallic Bronze body, no decals	£5-15	☐
502	c1980	BMW 530	Purple body with 'flame' decal on doors	£5-15	☐
502	c1980	BMW 530	Metallic Green with Black 'cougar' decal	£5-15	☐
503	c1980	Alfetta GTV	Red or Yellow body with Green 'shamrock' on bonnet	£5-15	☐
504	c1980	Citroën Visa	Red body, no decals	£5-15	☐
505	c1980	Peugeot 504	Blue body with 'flame' decal on doors	£5-15	☐
505	c1980	Peugeot 504	Greenish-Gold with Black 'panther' decal on doors	£5-15	☐
506	c1980	Alfa-Sud	Not seen	NGPP	☐
507	c1980	Renault 14	Not seen	NGPP	☐
508	c1980	Ford Fiesta	Not seen	NGPP	☐

COUGAR Model Toys. Many of the 'Airfix Dinky Toys' appeared erratically in the early 1980s (in France then in the UK), under the name of 'Cougar Model Toys' with these common features:
Plastic base marked *'Dinky Toys made in France'* and the code *'1/43 07 80'*.
Presented in a blister-pack on card with *'Metal Cougar'* and *'Fabrique par Solido'*.
Numbers printed on card are 100 less than numbers moulded on base. (TW = tinted windows)

1301-1401		Citroën 2cv6	Orange-Red body with 'ducks' decal, Grey base/interior/open roof	£10-15	☐
			Green body with 'ducks' decal, Grey base, Orange interior, Tan open roof	£10-15	☐
1302-1402		Citroën Visa	Metallic Jade Green, no decal, White plastic base, Dark Cream interior	£10-15	☐
			Metallic Red body, no decal, Grey plastic base and interior	£10-15	☐
1303-1403		Fiat Ritmo	Metallic Orange body, no decal, Dark Cream plastic base and interior	£10-15	☐
			Metallic Blue body, no decal, Yellow plastic base and interior	£10-15	☐
1304-1404		BMW 530	Metallic Green, 'Cougar' decal, Grey base, Black/Grey interior, Green TW	£10-15	☐
			Metallic Purple, 'flames' decal, Grey base, Black & Grey interior, Yellow TW	£10-15	☐
1305-1405		Alfetta GTV	Red body, 'shamrock' decal, Tan base, Black & Tan interior, Yellow TW	£10-15	☐
			Yellow body, 'shamrock' decal, Tan base, Black & Tan interior, Blue TW	£10-15	☐
1306-1406		Peugeot 504 Berline	Metallic Yellow, 'cougar' decal, Brown base & TW, Black/Brown interior	£10-15	☐
			Metallic Blue body, 'flames' decal, Blue base & interior, clear windows	£10-15	☐

AIRFIX - match-box size miniatures made in Hong Kong.
Although announced in 1980, only a few seem to have appeared in the UK.

101	c1980	'56 Corvette	White body with Red flash, bubble-packed, 68 mm.	£10-15	☐
103	c1980	Chevette Hatchback	Yellow body with 'Turbo' decal, bubble-packed, 68 mm.	£10-15	☐
104	c1980	Honda Accord	Lilac body with Orange flash, bubble-packed, 68 mm.	£10-15	☐
105	c1980	Toyota Celica	Red body, bubble-packed, 68 mm.	£10-15	☐
106	c1980	Datsun 280Z	Brown body, bubble-packed, 68 mm.	£10-15	☐
107	c1980	BMW Turbo	Orange body with Black and Yellow flash, bubble-packed, 68 mm.	£10-15	☐
108	c1980	Alfa Romeo	Purple body with Yellow flash, bubble-packed, 68 mm.	£10-15	☐
110	c1980	Stepside Pick-up	Blue and Brown body, bubble-packed, 68 mm.	£10-15	☐
111	c1980	Camper	Yellow and Two-tone Brown body, 68 mm.	£10-15	☐
113	c1980	Pick-up	Red and Black body, '4 x 4' decal, 68 mm.	£10-15	☐
114	c1980	Firebird	Black body, 68 mm.	£10-15	☐
115	c1980	Camaro	Red body with racing-number 'Z28', 68 mm.	£10-15	☐
116	c1980	'63 Corvette	Metallic Blue body, 68 mm.	£10-15	☐
117	c1980	'71 Corvette	Yellow body with 'Vette' decal, 68 mm.	£10-15	☐
119	c1980	Ford Van	Blue body with Orange flash, 68 mm.	£10-15	☐
120	c1980	Renegade Jeep	Yellow body with Green flash	£10-15	☐
121	c1980	Chevy Blazer	Red body, 68 mm.	£10-15	☐
122	c1980	Sun Van	Orange body with 'Sun Van' decal, 68 mm.	£10-15	☐
123	c1980	Yamaha 250 MX	Blue body with 'Yamaha' decal, 82 mm.	£10-15	☐
124	c1980	Honda MT 250	Orange body with 'Honda' decal, 82 mm.	£10-15	☐
125	c1980	Kawasaki FII 250	Red body with 'Kawasaki' decal, 82 mm.	£10-15	☐
126	c1980	Suzuki TM 400	Yellow and Black body with 'CCI' and 'Suzuki' decals, 82 mm.	£10-15	☐
129	c1980	T-Bird Convertible	Red and White body, 68 mm.	£10-15	☐
130	c1980	Chevy Convertible	Metallic Blue and White body	£10-15	☐

Dinky Toys Gift Sets

Ref. No.	Year(s)	Set Name	Contents	Market Price Range

Pre-war sets without 'fatigue' and with pristine boxes attract a premium.
See also Accessories and Dinky Toys Trains sections

Ref. No.	Year(s)	Set Name	Contents	Market Price Range
001 (1)	1954-56	Station Staff ('0' gauge)	1b Guard (flag in right hand), 1c Ticket Collector (right arm extended), 1d Driver, 1e Porter (with oblong bags), 1f Porter (standing)	£90-120 ☐
002 (2)	1954-56	Farmyard Animals (6)	2 x 2a horses, 2 x 2b cows, 1 x 2c pig, 1 x 2d sheep, simplified painting	£200-300 ☐
003 (3)	1954-56	Passengers ('0' gauge)	3a Woman (with child on left), 3b Businessman (Brown suit and case), 3c Male hiker (no stick), 3d Female hiker (Blue shirt), 3e Newsboy (Grey tray), 3f Woman (Light Red coat, round case)	£90-120 ☐
004 (4)	1946-54	Engineering Staff ('0' gauge)	2 x 4b Fitter (all-Blue and all-Brown), 4c Storekeeper (all-Brown), 4d Greaser, 4e Engine-Room attendant	£90-120 ☐
005 (5)	1954-56	Train & Hotel Staff ('0' gauge)	5a Conductor, 2 x 5b waiters, 2 x 5c Porter (both Brown or Blue)	£90-120 ☐
006 (6)	1954-56	Shepherd Set	6a Shepherd (Green hat), 6b sheepdog (all-Black), 4 x 2b sheep	£200-300 ☐
007	1960-67	Petrol Pump Attendants	1 male (White overalls), 1 female (White coat), plastic, 35 mm. tall	£30-40 ☐
008	1961-67	Fire Station Personnel	Set of 6 fire-fighters in Blue uniforms plus hose, plastic, 35 mm. tall	£30-40 ☐
009	1962-66	Service Station Personnel	Set of 8 plastic figures in various colours and stances, 35 mm. tall	£30-40 ☐
010	1962-66	Road Maintenance Personnel	Set of 6 workmen using pick, barrow, shovels, drill etc, plus hut, brazier, barrier, and 4 lamps. Plastic, figures are 35 mm. tall	£60-70 ☐
050	1961-68	Railway Staff ('00' gauge)	Set of 12 Blue plastic figures	£50-60 ☐
051 (1001)	1954-59	Station Staff ('00' gauge)	Set of 6 Blue figures (re-issue of pre-war Hornby-Dublo Set D1)	£45-55 ☐
053 (1003)	1954-59	Passengers ('00' gauge)	Set of 6 Blue figures (re-issue of pre-war Hornby-Dublo Set D2)	£45-55 ☐
054	1962-70	Railway Station Personnel	Set of 12 mostly Blue plastic figures	£50-60 ☐
1	1932-39	Station Staff (6)	1a Station Master, 1b Guard (flag in left hand), 1c Ticket Collector (with open arms), 1d Driver, 1e Porter (round/oblong bags), 1f Porter (walking)	£150-200 ☐
1	1939-41	Station Staff (6)	1a and 1d as above, 1b Guard (flag in right hand), 1c Ticket Collector (right arm extended), 1e Porter (oblong bags), 1f Porter (standing)	£150-200 ☐
1 (001)	1946-54	Station Staff (5)	1b Guard (flag in right hand), 1c Ticket Collector (right arm extended), 1d Driver, 1e Porter (with oblong bags), 1f Porter (standing)	£90-120 ☐
No.1	1934-9	Railway Accessories Set	'Miniature Luggage and Truck'. A Porter's truck and 4 pieces of luggage (tinplate and cast), items not available separately	NGPP ☐
No.1	1946-48	Commercial Vehicles Set	29c Bus, 25b Wagon, 25d Tanker, 25e Tipper and 25f Market Gardeners Lorry, in mottled Greenish-Brown box, Blue/Beige label showing boy and 6 models	£2000-3000 ☐
No.1 (398)	1952-54	Farm Equipment Gift Set	27a Massey-Harris Tractor, 27b Harvest Trailer, 27c Manure Spreader, 27h Disc Harrow, 27k Hay Rake. Blue and White striped box	£1000-1500 ☐
No.1 (699)	1954-55	Military Vehicles Set	621 3-ton Wagon, 641 1-ton Truck, 674 Austin Champ, 676 Armoured Car	£300-400 ☐
2	1934-35	Farmyard Animals	2 x 2a horses, 2 x 2b cows, 1 x 2c pig, 1 x 2d sheep, set presented in 'Modelled Miniatures' box	£750-1000 ☐
2	1935-40	Farmyard Animals	Six items as previous set but displayed in 'Dinky Toys' box	£500-600 ☐
2 (002)	1946-54	Farmyard Animals	Six items as previous set but simplified (less detailed) painting	£200-300 ☐
No.2	1934-?	Railway Accessories Set	'Milk Cans and Truck'. A 4-wheel barrow & 6 milk churns, not available separately	NGPP ☐
No.2	1946-48	Private Automobiles Set	39a Packard, 39b Oldsmobile, 39c Lincoln, 39d Buick, 39e Chrysler	£1250-1750 ☐
No.2	1952-53	Commercials Vehicles Set	25m Bedford End Tipper, 27d Land Rover (Dark Brown), 30n Farm Produce Wagon, 30p 'Mobilgas' Tanker and 30s Austin Covered Wagon	£2500-3500 ☐
3	1932-39	Passengers	3a Woman (with child on right), 3b Businessman (left hand on chest), 3c Male hiker (with stick), 3d Female hiker (White shirt), 3e Newsboy (running), 3f Woman (Red jacket, oblong case)	£150-200 ☐
3	1939-41	Passengers	3a Woman (with child on left), 3b Businessman (case in left hand), 3c Male hiker (no stick), 3d Female hiker (White shirt), 3e Newsboy (standing), 3f Woman (Dark Red coat, round case)	£125-175 ☐
3 (003)	1946-54	Passengers	3a Woman (with child on left), 3b Businessman (Brown suit and case), 3c Male hiker (no stick), 3d Female hiker (with Blue shirt), 3e Newsboy (Grey tray), 3f Woman (Light Red coat, round case)	£90-120 ☐
No.3	1934-?	Railway Accessories Set	'Platform Machines Etc'. A posting box, ticket machine, label machine and two benches, not available separately	NGPP ☐
No.3	1947-52	Private Automobiles Set (i)	30d Vauxhall, 36a Armstrong, 36b Bentley, 38a Frazer-Nash, 39b Oldsmobile	£750-850 ☐
No.3	1947-52	Private Automobiles Set (ii)	30d Vauxhall, 36b Bentley, 36d Rover, 38a Fraser Nash, 38c Lagonda	£750-850 ☐
No.3	1952-54	Passenger Cars Set	27f Estate Car, 30h Daimler Ambulance, 40e Standard Vanguard, 40g Morris Oxford, 40h Austin Taxi, 140b Rover 75	£4000-5000 ☐
4	1932-41	Engineering Staff (6)	4a Electrician, 2 x 4b Fitter (Blue/White and Brown/White), 4c Storekeeper (Brown/Black), 4d Greaser, 4e Engine-Room attendant	£200-300 ☐
4 (004)	1946-54	Engineering Staff (5)	2 x 4b Fitter (all-Blue and all-Brown), 4c Storekeeper (all-Brown), 4d Greaser, 4e Engine-Room attendant	£125-175 ☐
No.4	1934-?	Railway Accessories Set	A combination of No.1 ('Miniature Luggage & Truck'), No.2 ('Milk Cans & Truck'), and No.3 ('Platform Machines Etc'). Individual items from these sets were not available separately	NGPP ☐
No.4 (249)	1953-54	Racing Cars Set	23f Alfa-Romeo, 23g Cooper-Bristol, 23h Ferrari, 23j HWM, 23k Talbot-Lago and 23n Maserati. Blue and White striped box (see 249)	£750-1000 ☐
5	1932-39	Train and Hotel Staff	5a Conductor, 2 x 5b waiters, 2 x 5c Porter (1 Red, 1 Green)	£200-300 ☐
5	1939-41	Train and Hotel Staff	5a Conductor, 2 x 5b waiters, 2 x 5c Porter (both Brown or Blue)	£125-175 ☐
5 (005)	1946-54	Train and Hotel Staff	5a Conductor, 2 x 5b Waiter, 2 x 5c Porter (Brown or Blue) less detail	£90-120 ☐
6	1934-36	Shepherd Set	6a Shepherd (Dark Brown smock, hat and leggings, Black boots, lamb under arm), 6b Collie dog (Black/White), 4 x 2b sheep (Beige, 'Hornby Series' cast-in) set presented in 'Modelled Miniatures' box	£500-750 ☐
6	1936-40	Shepherd Set	As previous but in 'Dinky Toys' box	£400-500 ☐
6 (006)	1946-54	Shepherd Set	6a Shepherd (all Brown below neck, Green hat), 6b Collie dog (all Black), 4 x 2b sheep (without 'Hornby Series')	£150-200 ☐

154

Ref. No.					Market Price Range
No.6	1946-48	Commercial Vehicles Set		29c Bus, 29b Streamline Bus, 25h Fire Engine, 30e Breakdown Car, and 30f Ambulance. Mottled Greenish-Blue box with Beige/Blue label	£1200-1800 ☐
12	1938-40	Postal Set		12a GPO Pillar Box, 12b Air Mail Pillar Box, 12c Telephone Call Box, 12d Telegraph Messenger, 12e Postman, 34b Royal Mail Van	£700-1000 ☐
15	1937-41	Railway Signals Set		1 x 15a 'Home' and 1 x 15a 'Distant' (single-arm signals) 2 x 15b 'Home/Distant' (double-arm signals), 1 x 15c 'Home' and 1 x 15c 'Distant' (double-arm signals)	£100-150 ☐
16-21		See Trains listings			
22	1933-35	Motor Vehicles Set		22a and 22b Cars, 22c Motor Truck, 22d Delivery Van, 22e Tractor, 22f Tank, Purple box lid with full-size full-colour label, 'Modelled Miniatures'	£2000-3000 ☐
23	1936-40	Racing Cars Set		23c Mercedes-Benz, 23d Auto-Union, 23e 'Speed of the Wind'. Blue box	£500-600 ☐
24	1934-40	Motor Cars Set		24a Ambulance, 24b Limousine, 24c Town Sedan, 24d Vogue Saloon, 24e Super Streamlined Saloon, 24f Sportsman's Coup, 24g Sports Tourer (2 seater), 24h Sports Tourer (4 seater). Blue box lid (with colour label), Purple inner (A2205)	£10,000-12,000 ☐
25	1934-37	Commercial Motor Vehicles		25a Wagon, 25b Covered Wagon, 25c Flat Truck, 25d Tank Wagon, 25e Tipper, 25f Market Gardener's Lorry. Mauve 'grained' box lid (colour label) (A1052)	£2000-3000 ☐
28/1	1934-40	Delivery Vans Set in Trade Box		(1st type) 28a Hornby, 28b Pickfords, 28c Manchester Guardian, 28d Oxo, 28e Ensign Lukos, 28f Palethorpes Sausages (A1008)	£6000-9000 ☐
28/1		(Revised Vans Set)		28a Hornby, 28b Pickfords, 28c Manchester Guardian, 28e Firestone, 28f Palethorpes, 28n Atco Mowers	£6000-9000 ☐
28/2	1934-40	Delivery Vans Set in Trade Box		(1st type) 28g Kodak, 28h Sharps Toffees, 28k Marsh's, 28L Crawfords Biscuits, 28m Wakefield Castrol, 28n Meccano (A1008)	£6000-9000 ☐
28/2		(Revised Vans Set)		28d Oxo, 28g Kodak, 28h Dunlop Tyres, 28k Marsh's, 28m Wakefield Castrol, 28h Crawfords	£6000-9000 ☐
28/3	1936-40	Delivery Vans Set in Trade Box		(2nd type) 28r Swan Pens, 28s Frys Chocolate, 28t Ovaltine, 28w Osram Lamps, 28x Hovis, 28y Exide Batteries	£4000-6000 ☐
30	1935-37	Motor Vehicles		30a Chrysler 'Airflow', 30b Rolls-Royce, 30c Daimler, 30d Vauxhall, 30e Breakdown Car (22c 2nd casting), 30f Ambulance	£5000-7000 ☐
30	1937-41	Motor Vehicles		As previous set but 30g Caravan replaces 30f Ambulance	£3000-5000 ☐
33/1	1935-37	Mechanical Horse and Five assorted Trailers		33a Mechanical Horse, 33b Flat Truck, 33c Open Wagon, 33d Box Van, 33e Dust Wagon, 33f Petrol Tank with 'WAKEFIELD CASTROL' logo. Blue 'grained' box lid, large colour label	£500-600 ☐
33/2	1935-37	Mechanical Horse and Four assorted Trailers		with 33a, b, c, e in Green box (A2036) (N.B. Rarer than 5 trailer set 33/1). In Green display box with Yellow inner tray, Box code A2036	£500-600 ☐
35	1935-40	Small Cars Set		35a Saloon Car, 35b Racer and 35c MG Sports Car (A2222). In display type box with tuck in flap and scenic backdrop	£400-500 ☐
36	1936-40	Motor Cars with Drivers, Passengers and Footmen		36a Armstrong-Siddeley, 36b Bentley, 36c Humber, 36d Rover, 36e British Salmson 2-seater, 36f British Salmson 4-seater, all with figures. Set housed in Blue landscape box with Yellow tray with Purple inner and Brown board top packing piece. Box code A2205, dated 6·38.	£8000-10,000 ☐
37a	1937-40	Motor Cycles Set		Six of 37a civilian Motor Cyclists in various colours with hand-painted detail, solid White rubber tyres. Blue box with Green and White pictorial inner	£300-400 ☐
37	1938-40	Motor Cycles Set		Contains 37a (civilian), 37b (Police), 37c (Signals Despatch)	£300-400 ☐
39	1939-41	USA Saloon Cars Set		39a Packard, 39b Oldsmobile, 39c Lincoln, 39d Buick, 39e Chrysler, 39f Studebaker. Mauve box with full colour label on lid	£1250-1750 ☐
42	1935-40	Police Set		42a Police Box, 42b Motor Cycle Patrol, 42c Point-Duty Policeman (White coat), 42d Point-Duty Policeman (Blue uniform), in Blue box with pictorial inner (A2114)	£600-800 ☐
43	1935-40	'R.A.C.' Set		43a RAC Box, 43b RAC Motor Cycle Patrol, 43c RAC Guide directing traffic, 43d RAC Guide saluting. In Blue box with pictorial inner part (A2064)	£750-1000 ☐
44	1935-40	'A.A.' Set		44a AA Box, 44b AA Motor Cycle Patrol, 44c AA Guide directing traffic, 44d AA Guide saluting. The box is Blue with a pictorial inner part (2065)	£750-1000 ☐
46	1937-40	Pavement Set		Dark Grey 'stone' effect (cardboard) pavement pieces in a box	£100-150 ☐
47	1935-40	Road Signs Set		12 road signs, 47e to 47t, (White under base, filled-in triangles) (A2073) Yellow box and inner, Box code A2073	£200-250 ☐
47 (770)	1946-50	Road Signs Set		12 road signs, 47e to 47t, (Black under base, open triangles)	£90-120 ☐
49	1935-40	Petrol Pumps Set		49a, 49b, 49c, 49d, 49e ('Pratts'). White rubber hoses, Blue box	£150-200 ☐
49 (780)	1946-50	Petrol Pumps Set		49a, 49b, 49c, 49d, 49e (plain). Yellow plastic hoses, Yellow box	£80-90 ☐
				49, 49b, 49c, 49d, 49e ('Pratts'). White rubber hoses, Yellow box	£150-200 ☐
				49, 49b, 49c, 49d, 49e (Plain). White plastic hoses, Yellow box	£100-140 ☐
50	1934-42	Ships of the British Navy		50a 'Hood', 50b 'Nelson', 50b 'Rodney', 50c 'Effingham', 50d 'York', 50e 'Delhi', 3 x 50f 'Broke', 50g 'X'-class Submarine, 3 x 50h 'Amazon', 50k 'K'-class Submarine. Blue box with Green/Blue label on lid	£150-200 ☐
51	1934-40	Great Liners Set		51b 'Europa', 51c 'Rex', 51d 'Empress of Britain', 51e 'Strathaird', 51f 'Queen of Bermuda', 51g 'Britannic'	£150-200 ☐
60	1934-39	Aeroplanes Set		60a Imperial Airways, 60b Leopard Moth, 60c Percival Gull, 60d Low-Wing Monoplane, 60e General Monospar, 60f Autogiro. Blue box, colour label	£1000-1500 ☐
60	1939-41	British Aeroplanes Set		As previous set but all planes (except 60f Autogiro) have 'GA-' markings	£900-1200 ☐
60		Box Types	i)	Blue box with Blue/Green/White label and 'Atalanta' drawing	
60			ii)	Blue box with multicoloured label plus '150 varieties' slogan	
			iii) & iv)	Same as previous but with '200' or '300 varieties' slogans	
60p	1938-40	Gloster Gladiator Set		Six planes in Silver livery with RAF roundels	£400-600 ☐
60s	1938-40	'Medium Bomber' Set		Two renumbered 62n Fairey 'Battle' Bombers in Stone-colour box	£150-200 ☐

Ref. No.				Market Price Range	
60z	1937-40	'Avions' Set	French Aeroplanes Set with 60az 'Arc-en-Ciel', Potez 58, Hanriot 180t, 61az DeWetoine 500, Breguet Corsair, 60f Cierva Autogiro. Blue box	£900-1200	☐
61	1937-41	R.A.F. Aeroplanes Set	60h 'Singapore' Flying Boat, 2 x 60n Fairey 'Battle' Bombers, 2 x 60p Gloster 'Gladiator' Biplanes. Contained in Blue box with full colour label on lid	£500-700	☐
61z	1937-40	'Avions' Set	French Aeroplanes Set with DeWoitine D338, Potez 56, Potez 58, 61az DeWetoine 500d, Farman F360, 60f Cierva Autogiro. Blue box	£900-1200	☐
62h	1939	Hawker Hurricane Set	Six planes, camouflaged topsides, Black undersides, mounted on card base with 'DINKY TOYS No.62h HAWKER HURRICANE SINGLE SEATER FIGHTER'. Green box dated 7·39	£400-600	☐
62d	1939	Bristol Blenheim Bomber Set	Six planes, camouflaged, mounted on card base with 'BRISTOL BLENHEIM BOMBER MARK IV - DINKY TOYS 62d'. Green box	£400-600	☐
64	1939-41	Aeroplane Set	60g Light Racer, 62h 'Hurricane' (Camouflaged) 62k 'Kings Aeroplane', 62m Light Transport, 62s 'Hurricane' (Silver) 63b Seaplane 'Mercury'. (In 1940 either 62a 'Spitfire' or 62s were substituted for 62h and 62s)	£500-700	☐
64z	193?-4?	'Avions' Set	French Aeroplanes Set with 61az Dewoitine 'F-ADBF', 64a Amiot 370, 64b Bloch 220 'F-AOHJ', 64c Potez 63, 64d Potez 662 'F-ARAY'. Blue box, Yellow inner.	£2000-2500	☐
65	1939-41	Aeroplane Set	60r Flying Boat, 60t 'DC3', 60v 'Whitely' Bomber, 60w 'Clipper III', 62n Junkers, 62p 'Ensign', 62r 'Albatross', 62w 'Frobisher'. Blue box	£900-1200	☐
66	1940-41	Camouflaged Aeroplanes Set	66a Heavy Bomber, 66b Dive Bomber Fighter, 66c Fighter, 66d Torpedo, 66e Medium Bomber, 66f Army Autogiro (Silver). Yellow-Brown box	£3000-5000	☐
68	1940-41	Camouflaged Aeroplanes Set	2 x 60s 'Battle' Bombers, 2 x 62d 'Blenheim', 3 x 62h 'Hurricane' (Camouflage) 3 x 62s 'Hurricane' (Silver), 62t 'Whitely', 68a 'Ensign', 68b 'Frobisher'. N.B. In Blue or Yellow box, light or dark camouflage	£2000-2500	☐
101	1936-40	Dining-Room Furniture	101a Table, 101b Sideboard, 2 x 101c Carver Chair, 4 x 101d Chair	£300-400	☐
102	1936-40	Bedroom Furniture	102a Bed, 102b Wardrobe, 102c Dressing Table, 102d Dressing Chest, 102e Dressing Table Stool, 102f Chair. Brown or Pink. Green box	£300-400	☐
103	1936-40	Kitchen Furniture	103a Refrigerator, 103b Kitchen Cabinet, 103c Electric Cooker, 103d Table, 103e Chair. Light Blue/White or Light Green/Cream	£300-400	☐
104	1936-40	Bathroom Furniture	104a Bath, 104b Bath Mat, 104c Pedestal Basin, 104d Stool, 104e Linen Basket, 104f Toilet. Brown or Pink. Green box	£300-400	☐
118	1965-69	Towaway Glider Set	135 Triumph 2000 (Cream/Blue), Cream/Red trailer, Yellow glider	£150-200	☐
121	1963-66	Goodwood Racing Set	112 Austin-Healey Sprite, 113 MGB, 120 Jaguar, 182 Porsche, 9 figures	£1200-1500	☐
122	1963-65	Touring Gift Set	188 Caravan, 193 Station Wagon, 195 Jaguar, 270 'AA' Patrol, 295 Atlas Kenebrake, 796 Healey Sports Boat on Trailer.	£1200-1500	☐
123	1963-65	Mayfair Gift Set	142 Jaguar, 150 Rolls-Royce, 186 Mercedes-Benz, 194 Bentley, 198 Rolls-Royce, 199 Austin Mini Countryman, and 4 figures	£1500-2000	☐
124	1964-66	Holiday Gift Set	952 Vega Luxury Coach, 137 Plymouth, 142 Jaguar, 796 Healey Sports Boat	£400-500	☐

Picture supplied by Phillips, West Two, 10 Salem Road, Bayswater, London and reproduced by their kind permission.

Ref. No.	Year	Name	Description	Market Price Range
125	1964-66	Fun Ahoy! Set	130 Ford Corsair with driver, 796 Healey Sports Boat with pilot	£100-150 ☐
126	1967-68	Motor Show Set	127 Rolls-Royce, 133 Cortina, 151 Vauxhall Victor 101, 171 Austin 1800	£1200-1500 ☐
126	1968-69	Motor Show Set	127 Rolls-Royce, 159 Cortina, 151 Vauxhall Victor 101, 171 Austin 1800	£1200-1500 ☐
149	1958-61	Sports Cars Set	107 Sunbeam Alpine, 108 MG Midget, 109 Austin-Healey, 110 Aston-Martin, 111 Triumph TR2, all in 'competition finish'. Blue/White striped box	£1000-1200 ☐
150	1937-41	Royal Tank Corps Personnel	150a Officer, 2 x 150b Private, 2 x 150c Private, 150e N.C.O. Grey/Blue box with Yellow inner Code: A2187	£200-300 ☐
	1946-50	U.S. Export only Set	Post-war issue of pre-war figures in original Green box with Hudson Dobson label	£200-300 ☐
151	1937-41	Medium Tank Set	151a Tank, 151b 6-wheel Wagon, 151c Cooker Trailer, 151d Water Tank Trailer, 150d Royal Tank Corps Driver. Blue box with pictorial inner	£300-400 ☐
152	1937-41	Light Tank Set	152a Tank, 152b Reconnaissance Car, 152c Austin 7 Car with 150d Royal Tank Corps Driver. Blue box with pictorial inner	£300-400 ☐
156	1939-41	Mechanised Army Set	151a Tank, 151b 6-wheel Wagon, 151c Cooker Trailer, 151d Water Tank Trailer, 152a Tank, 152b Reconnaissance Car, 152c Austin 7 Car with 150d Royal Tank Corps Driver, 161a Lorry with Searchlight, 161b A.A. Gun on Trailer, 162a Light Dragon Tractor, 162b Ammunition Trailer, and 162c 18-ponder Gun. Blue box with speckled Beige display inner, with 'Dinky Toys No.156', 'Over 300 Varieties' and '100 per cent British' Code A2308 dated 12·39	£2500-3500 ☐
160 (606)	1939-53	Royal Artillery Personnel	160a N.C.O., 2 x 160b Gunner, 160c Gunlayer, 2 x 160d Gunner (standing) Grey/Blue box Code: A2308 dated 11·39, Yellow box and inner box dated 12·39 Code: A2303 Production of this set continued after the War but only for export (to USA)	£150-200 ☐
161	1939-41	Mobile Anti-Aircraft Unit	161a Lorry with Searchlight and 161b A.A. Gun on Trailer, in Blue box	£600-800 ☐
162	1939-54	18-pounder Field Gun Unit	162a Light Dragon Tractor, 162b Ammunition Trailer, 162c Gun. Blue box	£150-200 ☐
201	1965-68	Racing Cars Set	240 Cooper, 241 Lotus, 242 Ferrari, 243 B.R.M.	£600-800 ☐
237	1978-79	Dinky Way Set	Contains: 178 Mini Clubman, 211 Triumph TR7, 382 Convoy Truck, 412 Bedford 'AA' Van. N.B. Export only version of Set 240.	£80-90 ☐
240	1978-80	Dinky Way Set	211 Triumph TR7, 255 Police Mini, 382 Dump Truck, 412 Bedford Van, 20ft of 'roadway', 20 road signs, decal sheet	£50-60 ☐
245	1969-73	Superfast Gift Set	131 Jaguar 'E'-type, 153 Aston-Martin DB6, 188 Jensen FF	£100-150 ☐
246	1969-73	International Gift Set	187 De Tomaso Mangusta, 215 Ford GT, 216 Ferrari Dino	£100-150 ☐
249	1962-63	World Famous Racing Cars	230 Talbot-Lago, 231 Maserati, 232 Alfa-Romeo, 233 Cooper-Bristol, 234 Ferrari, 239 Vanwall. Bubble-packed onto large display card	£1000-1500 ☐
249 (4)	1955-58	Racing Cars Set	Contains 231, 232, 233, 234, 235	£750-1000 ☐
294	1973-77	Police Vehicles Gift Set	250 Mini-Cooper, 254 Range-Rover, 287 Accident Unit. (Replaces Set 297)	£50-60 ☐
297	1963-73	Police Vehicles Gift Set	250 Mini-Cooper, 255 Ford Zodiac, 287 Accident Unit. (Replaced by Set 294)	£60-70 ☐
298	1963-66	Emergency Services Set	258 Ford Fairlane, 263 Ambulance, 276 Fire Tender, 277 Ambulance, figures	£600-800 ☐
299	1957-59	Post Office Services	260 'Royal Mail' Morris Van, 261 'GPO Telephones' Van, 750 Call Box, 011 Messenger, 012 Postman (blue and white Pillar Box!) Blue and White striped box	£350-450 ☐
299	1963-66	Motorway Services Set	434 Bedford Crash Truck, 269 Motorway Police Car, 257 Fire Chief's Car, 276 Airport Fire Tender, 263 (later 277) Criterion Ambulance	£800-1000 ☐
299	1978-79	Crash Squad Action Set	244 Plymouth Police Car and 732 Bell Helicopter	£35-45 ☐
300	1973-77	London Scene Set	Contains 289 Routemaster Bus 'ESSO' and 284 London Taxi	£30-40 ☐
302	1979-?	Emergency Squad Gift Pack	Paramedic Truck and Plymouth Fire Chief Car plus figures of Gage and DeSoto. Advertised but not issued	NPP ☐
303	1978-80	Commando Squad Gift Set	687 Convoy Army Truck, 667 Armoured Car, 732 Army helicopter	£75-100 ☐
304	1978-79	Fire Rescue Gift Set	195 Fire Chief Range Rover, 282 Land Rover, 384 Convoy Fire Truck	£60-80 ☐
306	1979-?	'Space' Gift Pack	358 'USS Enterprise', 357 Klingon Battle Cruiser, plus Galactic War Chariot. A set advertised but not issued	NPP ☐
307	1979-?	'New Avengers' Gift Pack	Purdey's TR7, John Steed's Special Leyland Jaguar, plus a 'fly-off' assailant!. An intended set advertised but not issued	NPP ☐
309	1978-80	Star Trek Gift Set	357 Klingon Battle Cruiser and 358 'USS Enterprise'	£80-100 ☐
398 (No.1)	1954-64	Farm Equipment Gift Set	300 Massey-Harris Tractor, 320 Harvest Trailer, 321 Manure Spreader, 322 Disc Harrow, 324 Hay Rake. Grey box, Red and Yellow overprinting	£1000-1500 ☐
399	1969-73	Farm Tractor & Trailer	300 Massey-Harris Tractor and 428 Large Trailer (Red/Silver)	£100-125 ☐
399	1977-79	'Convoy' Gift Set	380 Skip Truck, 381 Farm Truck, 382 Dumper Truck. 'Window' box	£20-30 ☐
606 (160)	1954-55	Royal Artillery Personnel	1 x 160a, 2 x 160b, 1 x 160c, 2 x 160d. Export only (to USA)	£150-200 ☐
616	1976-78	AEC Transporter and Tank	Militarised version of 974 with 683 Chieftain Tank and camouflage net	£65-80 ☐
618	1976-79	Transporter and Helicopter	Militarised versions of 974 and 724 with camouflage netting	£50-60 ☐
619	1976-78	Bren-Gun Carrier Set	622 Bren-Gun Carrier and 625 6-pounder Anti-Tank Gun	£20-30 ☐
677	1972-75	Task Force Set	680 Ferret Armoured Car, 681 D.U.K.W., 682 Stalwart Load Carrier	£50-60 ☐
695	1962-66	Howitzer and Tractor	689 Medium Artillery Tractor and 693 7.2in. Howitzer	£250-350 ☐
697	1957-71	Field Gun Set	688 Field Artillery Tractor, 687 Trailer, 686 25-pounder Field Gun	£80-100 ☐
698	1957-65	Tank Transporter Set	660 Mighty Antar Tank Transporter and 651 Centurion Tank	£120-150 ☐
699 (No.1)	1955-58	Military Vehicles Set	621 3-ton Wagon, 641 1-ton Truck, 674 Austin Champ, 676 Armoured Car	£250-350 ☐
754	1958-62	Pavement Set	Twenty various Grey cardboard pieces representing paving	£20-30 ☐
766	1959-64	British Road Signs	Country Set 'A'. Six signs of the times, mostly 55 mm high. Yellow box	£100-125 ☐
767	1959-64	British Road Signs	Country Set 'B'. Six signs of the times, mostly 55 mm high. Yellow box	£100-125 ☐
768	1959-64	British Road Signs	Town Set 'A'. Six signs of the times, mostly 55 mm high. Yellow box	£100-125 ☐
769	1959-64	British Road Signs	Town Set 'B'. Six signs of the times, mostly 55 mm high. Yellow box	£100-125 ☐
770 (47)	1950-54	Road Signs Set	12 road signs, 47e to 47t, (Black under base, open triangles) US export only	£125-175 ☐
771	1953-65	International Road Signs	Set of 12 various road signs with Silver posts and bases, in Yellow box	£100-125 ☐
772	1959-63	British Road Signs	(Sets 766, 767, 768 and 769). 24 various road signs in a Red/Yellow box	£200-250 ☐
780 (49)	1950-54	Petrol Pumps Set	49a, 49b, 49c, 49d, 49e (plain). Yellow plastic hoses, export only	£90-110 ☐
			Version issued in picture box	£100-150 ☐

Ref. No.			*Dinky Toys — Gift Sets – continued*	Market Price Range
784	1972-74	Dinky Goods Train Set.............	Blue loco 'GER', one Red Truck, one Yellow Truck	£30-40 ☐
851	1961-	Sets of vehicle 'Loads'..............	Two each of 846 Oil Drums, 847 Barrels, 849 Packing Cases and 850 Crates.............	£30-40 ☐
900	1964-70	'Site Building' Gift Set	437 Muir-Hill Loader, 960 Albion Concrete Mixer, 961 Blaw-Knox Bulldozer, 962 Muir-Hill Dumper, 965 Euclid Rear Dump Truck. Grey/Red/Yellow box	£900-1200 ☐
950	1969-70	Car Transporter Set..................	974 AEC Car Transporter with 136 Vauxhall Viva, 138 Hillman Imp, 162 Triumph 1300, 168 Ford Escort, 342 Austin Mini-Moke. Not issued	NPP ☐
957	1959-65	Fire Services Gift Set.................	257 Fire Chief's Car, 955 Fire Engine, 956 Turntable Fire Escape	£300-400 ☐
990	1956-58	Car Transporter Set..................	Contains 982 Pullmore Car Transporter and these cars: 154 Hillman Minx (Light Green/Cream), 156 Rover 75 (Cream/Blue), 161 Austin Somerset (Red/Yellow), 162 Ford Zephyr (Green/White)	£1000-1250 ☐
1001 (051)	1952-54	Station Staff ('00' gauge)...........	Set of 6 Blue figures (re-issue of pre-war Hornby-Dublo Set D1)................................	£45-55 ☐
1003 (053)	1952-54	Passengers ('00' gauge)	Set of 6 Blue figures (re-issue of pre-war Hornby-Dublo Set D2)...............................	£45-55 ☐

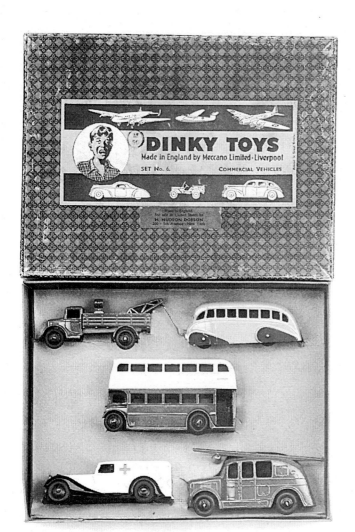

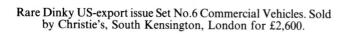

Rare Dinky US-export issue Set No.6 Commercial Vehicles. Sold by Christie's, South Kensington, London for £2,600.

Post-War Issue in Green boxes. No.2 Farmyard Animals and No.6 Shepherd Set. Sold by Christie's, South Kensington, London for £308.

Dinky Toys - Accessories (Pre-War)

See also Gift Sets.

Ref. No.	Year(s)	Accessory	Details	Market Price Range	
1a	1932-41	Station Master	Dark Blue uniform (cap, long coat)	£20-30	☐
1b	1932-39	Guard	Dark Blue uniform (cap, jacket), blowing whistle, flag in left hand	£20-30	☐
1b	1939-41	Guard	Dark Blue uniform (cap, jacket), blowing whistle, flag in right hand	£20-30	☐
1c	1932-41	Ticket Collector	Dark Blue uniform (cap, jacket), slightly open arms	£20-30	☐
1d	1932-39	Driver	Dark Blue uniform (cap, jacket), holding oil-can	£20-30	☐
1e	1932-39	Porter with Bags	Dark Blue uniform, oblong case in right hand, round hat-box in left	£20-30	☐
1e	1939-41	Porter with Bags	Dark Blue uniform, oblong case in each hand	£20-30	☐
1f	1932-39	Porter	Dark Blue uniform, walking, no luggage	£20-30	☐
1f	1939-41	Porter	Dark Blue uniform, standing, no luggage	£20-30	☐
2a	1932-41	Horses	One Light Brown or Dark Brown horse, one White horse	£20-30	☐
2b	1932-41	Cow	3 versions were available; Light Brown, Dark Brown, or Black and White	£10-15	☐
2c	1932-41	Pig	A Pink porker	£10-15	☐
2d	1932-41	Sheep	White sheep with Black hand-painted detail	£10-15	☐
3a	1932-39	Woman and Child	Woman in Green coat, child (in Red) is on woman's right	£20-30	☐
3a	1939-41	Woman and Child	Woman in Green suit with Grey scarf and Red hat, child on woman's left	£20-30	☐
3b	1932-39	Business Man	Dark Blue suit/hat, walking stick in right hand, left hand holds lapels	£20-30	☐
3b	1939-41	Business Man	Grey suit, left hand holds attach case	£20-30	☐
3c	1932-39	Male Hiker	Brown clothing, Khaki rucksack, stick in right hand	£20-30	☐
3c	1939-41	Male Hiker	Brown clothing, Khaki rucksack, no stick	£20-30	☐
3d	1932-41	Female Hiker	Blue skirt, White shirt, stick in right hand	£20-30	☐
3e	1932-39	Newsboy	Brown or Blue clothing, running, papers in right hand and under left arm	£20-30	☐
3e	1939-41	Newsboy	Dark Blue clothing, standing, forms in Cream tray	£20-30	☐
3f	1932-39	Woman	Red jacket, White skirt, coat over left arm, oblong case in right hand	£20-30	☐
3f	1939-41	Woman	Dark Red coat, Black collar, coat over left arm, round case in right hand	£20-30	☐
4a	1932-41	Electrician	Blue overalls, White sleeves, carrying equipment	£10-15	☐
4b	1932-41	Fitter (2 versions)	One in Blue overalls, the other Brown, White sleeves, carrying equipment	£10-15	☐
4c	1932-41	Storekeeper	Brown coat, Black trousers, holding forms in right hand, casting as 1a	£10-15	☐
4d	1932-41	Greaser	Brown overalls, holding oil-can in right hand, casting based on 1d	£10-15	☐
4e	1932-41	Engine-Room Attendant	Blue overalls, with or without White sleeves	£10-15	☐
5a	1932-41	Pullman Car Conductor	White jacket, Blue trousers, slightly open arms, casting as 1c	£20-30	☐
5b	1932-41	Pullman Car Waiter	White jacket, Blue trousers, two slightly different poses were available	£20-30	☐
5c	1932-41	Hotel Porter	Red jacket/Brown trousers, or Green jacket/Blue trousers, casting as 1e	£20-30	☐
6a	1932-41	Shepherd	Brown with Dark Brown hat	£50-75	☐
6b	1932-41	Sheep-dog	Black and White sheep-dog	£20-30	☐
12a	1935-40	G.P.O. Pillar Box 'G.R.'	Red, with or without Red/Yellow 'Post Office' sign on top, White panel, 50 mm.	£25-30	☐
12b	1935-40	Air Mail Pillar Box	Blue body, 'Air Mail', White panel, casting as 12a, 50 mm.	£35-40	☐
12c	1936-40	Telephone Box	Cream with Silver windows, or Red with Black window frames, 58 mm.	£15-20	☐
12d	1938-40	Telegraph Messenger	Dark Blue body, picked out detail in darker Blue, Brown pouch, 35 mm.	£15-20	☐
12e	1938-40	Postman	Dark Blue body, darker Blue detail, Brown post bag and badge, 35 mm.	£15-20	☐
13	1931-40	'HALLS DISTEMPER'	Figures (lead) usually White, Cream (cardboard) panel, Red lettering	£250-300	☐
15a	1937-41	Single Arm Signal	One Red ('Home') signal, or Yellow ('Distant') signal, 65 mm. high	£20-30	☐
15b	1937-41	Double Arm Signal	One Red ('Home') signal and one Yellow ('Distant') signal on single pole	£20-30	☐
15c	1937-41	Junction Signal	Two Red ('Home') signals, OR two Yellow ('Distant') signals on single pole	£20-30	☐
42a	1936-40	Police Box	Dark Blue box, 'POLICE' in Silver, 66 mm. high	£20-25	☐
42c	1936-40	Point Duty Policeman	(cast in lead), White coat, Black helmet, 42 mm. tall	£20-25	☐
42d	1936-40	Point Duty Policeman	(cast in lead), Dark Blue uniform, White gauntlets, 40 mm. tall	£20-25	☐
43a	1935-40	'R.A.C.' Box	Blue and White (tinplate) call-box with 'R.A.C.' emblem, 51 mm.	£100-125	☐
43c	1935-40	'R.A.C.' Guide	(cast in lead), Blue uniform, Red sash, directing traffic, 37 mm. tall	£20-25	☐
43d	1935-40	'R.A.C.' Guide (saluting)	(cast in lead), Blue uniform with Red sash, 36 mm. tall	£20-25	☐
44a	1935-40	'A.A.' Box	Black/Yellow tinplate box with 'A.A.' badge and 3 signs, 81 mm.	£100-125	☐
44c	1935-40	'A.A.' Guide	(cast in lead), Tan uniform, Blue sash, directing traffic, 37 mm. tall	£20-25	☐
44d	1935-40	'A.A.' Guide (saluting)	(cast in lead), Tan uniform, Blue sash, 36 mm. tall	£20-25	☐
45	1935-40	Garage	Cream/Orange (tinplate) garage, Green opening doors, boxed, 127 x 90 mm.	£250-350	☐
46	1937-40	Pavement Set	Dark Grey 'stone' effect (cardboard) pavement pieces in a box	£100-150	☐
47a	1935-40	4-face Traffic Lights	Black on White post, Yellow beacon, White base, 62 mm. high	£20-30	☐
47b	1935-40	3-face Traffic Lights	Black on White post, Yellow beacon, White base, 62 mm. high	£20-30	☐
47c	1935-40	2-face Traffic Lights	Back-to-back lights, Black on White post, Yellow beacon, White base	£20-30	☐
47c	1935-40	2-face Traffic Lights	Lights at 90 degrees, Black on White post, Yellow beacon, White base	£20-30	☐
47d	1935-40	Belisha Beacon	Black on White post, Orange globe, White base, 51 mm. high	£20-30	☐
47e	1935-40	'30 MPH' Limit Sign	Black on White post, Red top '30', 52 mm. high	£20-30	☐
47f	1935-40	De-restriction Sign	Black on White post, diagonal Black bar on White circle, 52 mm. high	£20-30	☐
47g	1935-40	'School' Sign	Black on White post, Red top, Black 'beacon' design, 51 mm. high	£20-30	☐
47h	1935-40	'Steep Hill' Sign	Black on White post, Red top, Black 'incline' design, 51 mm. high	£20-30	☐
47k	1935-40	'S-Bend' Sign	Black on White post, Red top, Black 'S-Bend' design, 51 mm. high	£20-30	☐
47m	1935-40	'Left-Hand Bend' Sign	Black on White post, Red top, Black 'curve' design, 51 mm. high	£20-30	☐
47n	1935-40	'Right-Hand Bend' Sign	Black on White post, Red top, Black 'curve' design, 51 mm. high	£20-30	☐
47p	1935-40	'T-Junction' Sign	Black on White post, Red top, Black 'T' design, 51 mm. high	£20-30	☐
47q	1935-40	'No Entry' Sign	Black on White post, Red 'bar' design, 48 mm. high	£20-30	☐
47r	1935-40	'Major Road Ahead' Sign	Black on White post, Red top, Black lettering, 54 mm. high	£20-30	☐

Ref. No.	Year(s)	Accessory	*Dinky Toys — Accessories (Pre-war)* – *continued*	Market Price Range	
47s	1935-40	'Crossing. No Gates' Sign	Black on White post, Red top, Black 'loco' design, 51 mm. high	£20-30	☐
47t	1935-40	'Roundabout' Sign	Black on White post, Red top, Black 'arrows' design, 51 mm. high	£20-30	☐
			N.B. Pre-war issues have filled in triangles		
48	1935-40	Filling/Service Station	Yellow with Blue or Green base, Green, Brown or Yellow roof, tinplate	£125-175	☐
49a	1935-53	Bowser Petrol Pump	Green pump body, White rubber hose, (Yellow plastic post-war), 46 mm.	£20-25	☐
49b	1935-53	Wayne Petrol Pump	Pale Blue pump, White rubber hose, (Yellow plastic post-war), 39 mm.	£20-25	☐
49c	1935-53	Theo Petrol Pump	Royal Blue or Red pump, White rubber hose, (Yellow plastic post-war), 58 mm.	£20-25	☐
49d	1935-53	'SHELL' Petrol Pump	Red pump body, White rubber hose, (Yellow plastic post-war), 53 mm.	£20-25	☐
49e	1935-40	'Pratts' Oil Bin	Yellow bin body and opening tinplate lid, 'Pratts Motor Oil', 32 mm.		☐
			49e was only available post-war in Set 49 and without 'Pratts' logo	£20-30	☐
101a	1935-40	Dining Table	'Wood' effect dining-room table, 64 mm.	*	☐
101b	1935-40	Sideboard	'Wood' effect sideboard with opening doors, tinplate back, 63 mm.	*	☐
101c	1935-40	Carver chair	'Wood' effect chair with armrests, 33 mm. high	*	☐
101d	1935-40	Dining Chair	'Wood' effect chair without armrests, raised 'leather' cushion	*	☐
102a	1935-40	Bed	Brown or Pink double bed, 74 mm.	*	☐
102b	1935-40	Wardrobe	Brown or Pink wardrobe with opening door, tinplate back, 63 mm.	*	☐
102c	1935-40	Dressing Table	Brown or Pink, opening drawers, tinplate mirror, 51 mm.	*	☐
102d	1935-40	Dressing Chest	Brown or Pink, opening drawer, tinplate back, 40 mm. high	*	☐
102e	1935-40	Dressing Table Stool	Brown or Pink stool, 13 mm. high	*	☐
103a	1935-40	Refrigerator	Light Blue/White or Light Green/Cream, door, tinplate back & food tray	*	☐
103b	1935-40	Kitchen Cabinet	Light Blue/White or Light Green/Cream, opening doors/drawer, tin back	*	☐
103c	1935-40	Electric Cooker	Light Blue/White or Light Green/Cream, opening door, tinplate back	*	☐
103d	1935-40	Kitchen Table	Light Blue/White or Light Green/Cream, 34 mm. high	*	☐
103e	1935-40	Kitchen Chair	Light Blue/White or Light Green/Cream, casting as 102f	*	☐
104a	1935-40	Bath	Pink/White or Light Green/White, Gold taps, 69 mm.	*	☐
104b	1935-40	Bath Mat	Mottled Green (rubber) mat, 50 x 37 mm.	*	☐
104c	1935-40	Pedestal Hand Basin	Pink/White or Light Green/White, Gold taps, tinplate mirror, 63 mm.	*	☐
104d	1935-40	Bathroom Stool	Pink/White or Light Green/White, 15 mm. high	*	☐
104e	1935-40	Linen Basket	Pink/White or Light Green/White, hinged lid, 22 mm. high	*	☐
104f	1935-40	Toilet	Pink/White or Light Green/White, hinged lid, 34 mm. high	*	☐
	1935-40	'Dolly Varden' Dolls House	Not given a reference number, made of 'leather board' (heavy reinforced cardboard), and supplied packed flat. Cream/Brown upper storey, Red brick ground floor, Red roof. 476 x 260 mm. base, 476 mm. high.	NGPP	☐

* Note: It is not really possible to give individual prices for single 'Dolly Varden' items as they are very rarely available in collectable condition. Boxed sets sell for £200-300 for example. See Gift Sets section for more price information.

Dinky Toys   -   Accessories (Post-War)

Sets of accessories may also be found in the Gift Sets section

Ref. No.	Year(s)	Accessory	Details	Market Price Range	
001 (1)	1954-56	Station Staff ('0' gauge)	1b Guard (flag in right hand), 1c Ticket Collector (right arm extended), 1d Driver, 1e Porter (with oblong bags), 1f Porter (standing)	£90-120	☐
002 (2)	1954-56	Farmyard Animals (6)	2 x 2a horses, 2 x 2b cows, 1 x 2c pig, 1 x 2d sheep, simplified painting	£200-300	☐
003 (3)	1954-56	Passengers ('0' gauge)	3a Woman (with child on left), 3b Businessman (Brown suit and case), 3c Male hiker (no stick), 3d Female hiker (Blue shirt), 3e Newsboy (Grey tray), 3f Woman (Light Red coat, round case)	£90-120	☐
004 (4)	1946-54	Engineering Staff ('0' gauge)	2 x 4b Fitter (all-Blue and all-Brown), 4c Storekeeper (all-Brown), 4d Greaser, 4e Engine-Room attendant	£90-120	☐
005 (5)	1954-56	Train & Hotel Staff ('0' gauge)	5a Conductor, 2 x 5b waiters, 2 x 5c Porter (both Brown or Blue)	£90-120	☐
006 (6)	1954-56	Shepherd Set	6a Shepherd (Green hat), 6b sheepdog (all-Black), 4 x 2b sheep	£150-200	☐
007	1960-67	Petrol Pump Attendants	1 male (White overalls), 1 female (White coat), plastic, 35 mm. tall	£15-20	☐
008	1961-67	Fire Station Personnel	Set of 6 fire-fighters in Blue uniforms plus hose, plastic, 35 mm. tall	£30-40	☐
009	1962-66	Service Station Personnel	Set of 8 plastic figures in various colours and stances, 35 mm. tall	£30-40	☐
010	1962-66	Road Maintenance Personnel	Set of 6 workmen using pick, barrow, shovels, drill etc, plus hut, brazier, barrier, and 4 lamps. Plastic, figures are 35 mm. tall	£60-70	☐
011 (12d)	1954-56	Telegraph Messenger	Mid-Blue uniform, detailing in darker Blue, Brown pouch, 35 mm.	£10-15	☐
012 (12e)	1954-56	Postman	Mid-Blue body, darker Blue detail, Brown post bag and badge, 35 mm.	£15-20	☐
013 (13a)	1954-56	Cook's Man	(An Agent for the Thomas Cook travel company), Dark Blue coat, 40 mm. high	£20-30	☐
036		Battery	1.5 volt battery for use with models 276 & 277	NGPP	☐
037		Lamp	Red light-bulb for use with model 277	NGPP	☐
038		Lamp	Blue (or Orange) light-bulb for use with model 276	NGPP	☐
039		Lamp	Clear light-bulb for use with model 952	NGPP	☐
081		Spare tyre	White fine tread tyre, 14 mm. in diameter	NGPP	☐
082		Spare tyre	Black narrow tread tyre, 20 mm. in diameter	NGPP	☐
083		Spare tyre	Grey tyre, 20 mm. in diameter, (also catalogued as 099)	NGPP	☐
084		Spare tyre	Black 'recessed' tyre, 18 mm. in diameter	NGPP	☐
085		Spare tyre	White tyre, 15 mm. in diameter, (also catalogued as 092 and 14095)	NGPP	☐
086		Spare tyre	Black fine tread tyre, 16 mm. in diameter	NGPP	☐

Ref. No.	Year(s)	Accessory		Market Price Range
087		Spare tyre	Black big 'tractor' tyre, 35 mm. in dia., (also catalogued as 60687)	NGPP □
089		Spare tyre	Black 'tractor front tyre', 19 mm. in dia., (also catalogued as 60689)	NGPP □
090		Spare tyre	Black fine tread tyre, 14 mm. in diameter, (also catalogued as 60790)	NGPP □
090		Spare tyre	White fine tread tyre, 14 mm. in diameter, (also catalogued as 60791)	NGPP □
091		Spare tyre	Black block tread tyre, 13 mm. in diameter, (also catalogued as 60036)	NGPP □
092		Spare tyre	Black block tread tyre, 15 mm. in diameter, (also catalogued as 14094)	NGPP □
092		Spare tyre	White block tread tyre, 15 mm. in diameter, (also catalogued as 14095)	NGPP □
093		Spare tyre	Black medium tractor tyre, 27 mm. in dia., (also catalogued as 13978)	NGPP □
094		Spare tyre	Black smooth tyre, 18 mm. in diameter, (also catalogued as 6676)	NGPP □
095		Spare tyre	Black block tread tyre, 18 mm. in diameter, (also catalogued as 6677)	NGPP □
096		Spare tyre	Tyre, 19/32″ (15 mm.) in diameter, (also catalogued as 7067)	NGPP □
097		Spare wheel	Solid rubber wheel, 12 mm. in diameter, (also catalogued as 7383)	NGPP □
098		Spare wheel	Solid rubber wheel, 20 mm. in diameter, (also catalogued as 10118)	NGPP □
099		Spare tyre	Black block tread tyre, 20 mm. in diameter, (also catalogued as 10253)	NGPP □
099		Spare tyre	Grey block tread tyre, 20 mm. in diameter, (also catalogued as 10253)	NGPP □
1a	1946-54	Station Master	Dark Blue uniform (cap, long coat), (in Set 001 till 1956)	£20-25 □
1b	1946-54	Guard	Dark Blue uniform, blowing whistle, flag in right hand (see Set 001)	£20-25 □
1c	1946-54	Ticket Collector	Blue uniform, only right arm is extended (in Set 001 till 1956)	£20-25 □
1e	1946-54	Porter with Bags	Blue uniform, oblong case in each hand (in Set 001 till 1956)	£20-25 □
1f	1946-54	Porter	Dark Blue uniform, standing, no luggage (in Set 001 till 1956)	£20-25 □
2a	1946-54	Horses	3 versions; Dark Brown horse (Black tail and mane), Light Brown horse (Light Brown tail and mane), White horse. (2 in Set 002 till 1956)	£20-25 □
2b	1946-54	Cows	3 versions; Light Brown, Dark Brown, or Black and White. (2 in Set 002 till 1956)	£20-25 □
2c	1946-54	Pig	Cream body (in Set 002 till 1956)	£20-25 □
2d	1946-54	Sheep	White body with Black hand-painted detail (in Set 002 till 1956)	£20-25 □
3a	1946-54	Woman and Child	Woman in Green suit & hat (Brown scarf), child on left (see Set 003)	£20-25 □
3b	1946-54	Business Man	Brown suit, left hand holds attach case (in Set 003 till 1956)	£20-25 □
3c	1946-54	Male Hiker	Brown clothing, Khaki rucksack, no stick (in Set 003 till 1956)	£20-25 □
3d	1946-54	Female Hiker	Blue or Dark Blue skirt and shirt, stick in right hand (see Set 003)	£20-25 □
3e	1946-54	Newsboy	Dark Blue clothing, standing, papers in Grey tray (in Set 003 till 1956)	£20-25 □
3f	1946-54	Woman	Light Red coat, round case in right hand (in Set 003 till 1956)	£20-25 □
4a	1946-54	Electrician	Blue overalls, White sleeves, carrying equipment (in Set 004 till 1956)	£10-15 □
4b	1946-56	Fitters	2 versions; one in Blue, the other Brown, carrying equipment (Set 004)	£10-15 □
4c	1946-56	Storekeeper	Brown coat, Black trousers, holding forms in right hand	£10-15 □
4d	1946-56	Greaser	Brown overalls, holding oil-can in right hand	£10-15 □
4e	1946-56	Engine-Room Attendant	Blue overalls, Blue sleeves	£10-15 □
5a	1946-56	Pullman Car Conductor	White jacket, Blue trousers, slightly open arms, casting as 1c	£20-25 □
5b	1946-56	Pullman Car Waiter	White jacket, Blue trousers, two slightly different poses were available	£20-25 □
5c	1946-56	Hotel Porter	Red jacket/Brown trousers, or Green jacket/Blue trousers, casting as 1e	£20-25 □
6a	1946-56	Shepherd	Brown with Green hat	£40-50 □
6b	1946-56	Sheep-dog	All-Black sheep-dog	£20-30 □
12c (750)	1946-54	Telephone Box	Red call-box with Silver windows, 58 mm. high	£10-15 □
12d (011)	1946-54	Telegraph Messenger	Dark Blue body, picked out detail in darker Blue, Brown pouch, 35 mm.	£15-20 □
12e (012)	1946-54	Postman	Mid-Blue body, darker Blue detail, Brown post bag and badge, 35 mm.	£15-20 □
13a (013)	1952-54	Cook's Man	(An Agent for the Thomas Cook travel company), Blue coat, 40 mm. high	£20-30 □
42a (751)	1954-60	Police Hut	Dark Blue hut, 'POLICE' in Silver, 66 mm. high	£20-30 □
502	1961-63	Garage	Blue/Grey plastic garage, opening door, 272 mm. (French issue)	£90-110 □
750 (12c)	1954-62	Telephone Box	Red call-box with Silver windows, 58 mm. high	£20-30 □
751 (42a)	1954-60	Police Hut	Dark Blue hut, 'POLICE' in Silver, 66 mm. high	£20-30 □
752 (973)	1953-54	Goods Yard Crane	Yellow with Blue or Dark Blue, mazak or cast-iron base (100 x 100 mm.)	£40-50 □
753	1962-67	Police Crossing	Black/White box on traffic island with policeman directing traffic	£35-45 □
754	1958-62	Pavement Set	Grey cardboard paving slabs (20 items in box)	£20-30 □
755	1960-64	Lamp Standard (Single)	Grey/Fawn/Orange, plastic single-arm lamp on metal base, 145 mm. high	£10-15 □
756	1960-64	Lamp Standard (Double)	Grey/Fawn/Orange, plastic double-arm lamp on metal base, 145 mm. high	£10-15 □
760	1954-60	Pillar Box	Red and Black pillar box with 'E II R' cast-in, 42 mm. high	£10-15 □
763	1959-64	Posters for Hoarding	Six different coloured poster advertisements (on paper)	£10-15 □
764	1959-64	Posters for Hoarding	Six different coloured poster advertisements (on paper)	£10-15 □
765	1959-64	Road Hoardings (6 Posters)	Green plastic hoarding, 'David Allen and Sons Ltd', 205 mm.	£10-15 □

N.B. For Road sign sets 766-772 see Gift Sets.

Ref. No.	Year(s)	Accessory		Market Price Range
773	1958-63	4 face Traffic Lights	Black/White, Black base, similar to 47a but without beacon, 62 mm.	£10-15 □
777	1958-63	Belisha Beacon	Black/White post on Black base, Orange globe, casting as 47d, 51 mm.	£5-8 □
778	1962-66	Road Repair Boards	Green and Red plastic warning signs, 6 different, 30-40 mm.	£75-100 □
781	1955-62	'ESSO' Petrol Station	'ESSO' sign, no kiosk, 2 pumps ('ESSO' and 'ESSO EXTRA'), 114 mm.	£50-60 □
782	1960-70	'SHELL' Petrol Station	'SHELL' sign, Green/Cream kiosk, 4 Red/Yellow 'SHELL' pumps, 203 mm.	£35-45 □
783	1960-70	'BP' Petrol Station	'BP' sign, Green/Cream kiosk, 4 Green/White 'BP' pumps, 203 mm.	£35-45 □
785	1960-64	'SERVICE STATION'	Fawn and Red plastic, with 'BP' sign, 335 x 185 mm. (unbuilt kit, boxed)	£125-175 □
786	1960-66	Tyre Rack with tyres	Green tyre rack with 21 assorted tyres and *'DUNLOP'* on board, 52 mm.	£20-25 □
787	1960-64	Lighting Kit	Bulb and wire lighting kit for model buildings	£20-25 □
788	1960-68	Spare Bucket for 966	Grey bucket for use with 966 Marrel Multi-Bucket Unit	£5-7 □
790	1960-64	Granite Chippings	Plastic bag of imitation granite chippings (50790)	£5-7 □
791	1960-64	Imitation Coal	in a plastic bag	£5-7 □
792	1960-64	Packing Cases (3)	White/Cream plastic packing cases, *'Hornby Dublo'*, 38 x 28 x 19 mm.	£5-7 □

Ref. No.	Year(s)	Accessory		Market Price Range	
793	1960-64	Pallets..	Orange pallets for 930 Bedford Pallet-Jekta Van and 404 Conveyancer	£5-7	☐
794 (994)	1954-64	Loading Ramp...........................	Blue loading ramp for use with 582/982 Carrimore Transporter, 233 mm.	£15-20	☐
846	1961-	Oil Drums.................................	Pack of 6 oil drums. French issue	£5-7	☐
847	1961-	Barrels......................................	Pack of 6 barrels. French issue.	£5-7	☐
849	1961-	Packing Cases...........................	Pack of 6 packing cases. French issue..	£5-7	☐
850	1961-	Crates of Bottles......................	Pack of 6 crates. French issue...	£5-7	☐
851	1961-	Sets of vehicle 'Loads'.............	Two each of 846 Oil Drums, 847 Barrels, 849 Packing Cases and 850 Crates...............	£20-25	☐
954		Fire Station Plastic Kit............	Red doors, Cream roof, Grey floor with clear roof. 'DINKY TOYS' 'FIRE STATION' 'DINKY TOYS' in Red	£150-200	☐
994 (794)	1954-55	Loading Ramp...........................	Renumbered from 794 to 994 then back to 794 after only a year!...............................	£15-20	☐
973 (752)	1954-59	Goods Yard Crane	Yellow with Blue or Dark Blue, 1st issues have steps, mazak or cast-iron base..........	£40-50	☐

Dinky Toys   -   Catalogues (U.K. issues)

The compiler of this Catalogue is indebted to Mr David Salisbury of the Vintage Toy & Train Museum, Sidmouth, Devon for providing in-depth information on catalogues and leaflets. In addition, much information has been drawn from the catalogue collection of Dr Cecil Gibson for which due acknowledgment is given.

Pre-War Catalogues, booklets, leaflets and listings

Hornby 'Modelled Miniatures' were introduced in 1931 as model railway accessories and the first issues were of Station Staff etc. The first catalogue listings to be published appeared in Hornby Train catalogues, Meccano catalogues and the 'Meccano Magazine'.

Ref. No.	Year(s)	Publication	Cover Features & Details	Market Price Range	
-	1932-33	Hornby 'Book of Trains'........	First 'Modelled Miniatures' listed as 'Railway Accessories'	£40-50	☐
-	1932	Meccano trade catalogue...........	First 'Modelled Miniatures' listed as 'Railway Accessories'	£40-50	☐
-	1933	'Meccano Magazine'.................	42 Hornby 'Modelled Miniatures' listed in December issue	£20-25	☐
-	1933-34	Hornby 'Book of Trains'........	Accessories are depicted in full colour.	£40-50	☐
-	1934	Meccano trade catalogue...........	'Modelled Miniatures' briefly renamed 'Meccano Miniatures'................................	NGPP	☐
-	1934	'Meccano Magazine'.................	February issue contained the last published 'Modelled Miniatures' listing	£30-40	☐
-	1934	'Meccano Magazine'.................	April issue contained the first 'Meccano Dinky Toys' listing	£30-40	☐
-	1934	'Meccano Magazine'.................	The May, June, July, August, September and November issues each reflected increasing number of varieties of 'Dinky Toys'.	£15-20	☐
-	1934	'Meccano Magazine'.................	'150 varieties of Dinky Toys' on double pages in October & December issues	£15-20	☐
-	1934-35	Hornby 'Book of Trains'..........	Catalogue shows 150 'Dinky Toys' in full colour on a double page	£50-75	☐
13/834/900	1934-35	Meccano Catalogue.................	Boat plane and model plus boy on cover, 3 pages of Dinky Toys	NGPP	☐
16/934/100	1934-35	'Hornby Trains/Meccano' Catalogue	Blue cover, full colour design of 'The World', lists 150 models of Dinky Toys...........	£70-90	☐
-	1934-35	Meccano Book........................	Cover depicts viaduct over river, complete Dinky Toys range is listed	NGPP	☐
-	1935	Meccano Magazine...................	January to November issues have various Dinky Toys listings	£15-20	☐
-	1935	Meccano Magazine...................	December issue shows 200 varieties of Dinky Toys in Black & White	£15-20	☐
7/835/65	1935-36	Hornby 'Book of Trains'........	Catalogue features 200 varieties of Dinky Toys in full colour	£40-50	☐
-	1935-36	Hornby/Meccano Catalogue	Has the same cover as the 1934-35 issue	£70-90	☐
-	1936	Meccano Magazines	The February and August issues featured a road layout and a competition; the May issue introduced the 'Queen Mary' model.	£15-20	☐
-	1936-37	Hornby 'Book of Trains'..........	The catalogue features full colour pictures of the Dinky Toys range.......................	£40-50	☐
-	1937	Hornby/Meccano Catalogue	The 1934-35 'World' cover again. Contains 7 pages of listings	£50-70	☐
-	1937	Meccano Magazines	Details given in the monthly listings of the superb new 'Army' range.....................	£15-20	☐
13/638/1150	1938	Hornby/Meccano Catalogue	74 pages with full Dinky Toys listings and numerous Black/White pictures...............	£30-40	☐
13/638/1150/ UK	1938	'Wonder Book of Toys'............	Two boys with Meccano models plus 11 pages with Dinky Toys	NGPP	☐
8/1238/25	1938	'DINKY TOYS' Catalogue.......	Small booklet - cover features boy and 6 models including 29c Bus, 151a Tank, and 63 Mayo Composite Aircraft. Printed in brown on pale-yellow paper	£75-100	☐
-	1938	Meccano Magazine...................	Details of the full range (with pictures] are published each month	£15-20	☐
1/439/10	1939	'DINKY TOYS' leaflet	'New Products' leaflet detailing items such as the Presentation Aeroplane Sets Nos 64 and 65. Black printing on pinkish paper	£20-30	☐
-	1939	MECCANO booklets...............	with complete Dinky Toys listings:		
13/639/1 13/639/	1939	Hornby/Meccano Catalogue	74 pages with full Dinky Toys listings and Black/White pictures.............................	£30-40	☐
11500 UK	1939	'A Wonder Book Of Toys'........	Green and Yellow cover depicts two boys with their Meccano models. The booklet includes 13 pages of Dinky Toys information	£30-40	☐
2/739/10(1P)	1939	'DINKY TOYS' Catalogue.......	Famous Red/Yellow cover picture of schoolboy with outstretched arm and 17 models. Contains 14 black and white pages	£200-250	☐
-		'Toys Of Quality'....................	Maroon Express train features on cover plus 'The Hornby Railway Co' logo. 13 pages of Dinky Toys are included	£30-40	☐
-	1939	Trade catalogue	Cover depicts boy with Dinky Toys and Hornby pictures with 'MECCANO TOYS OF QUALITY' logo.	£30-40	☐
2/1139/ 20(3P)UK	1939	'DINKY TOYS' Catalogue.......	Superb Red and Yellow cover picture of schoolboy with outstretched arm and 17 models. Catalogue contains 10 Black/White pages of listings & pictures................	£100-150	☐
-	1939	Meccano Magazine...................	Each month contained Dinky Toys listings...	£15-20	☐

Ref. No.	Year(s)	Publication		Market Price Range	
16/1040/100	1940	Meccano Price List....................	All products listed but no pictures	NGPP	☐
16/1040/200	1940	'DINKY TOYS' leaflet	Listing of models with pictures	£15-20	☐
-	1940	Meccano Magazine...................	Wartime Dinky aircraft and the Meccano 'Spitfire Fund' are featured	£15-20	☐
16/541/25 UK	1941	'DINKY TOYS' leaflet	Wartime camouflaged aircraft feature in this leaflet	£15-20	☐
16/641/20 UK	1941	'DINKY TOYS' leaflet	Similar to previous leaflet, military models listed..	£15-20	☐
16/1141/20 UK	1941	'DINKY TOYS' leaflet	Listing of models and retail prices...	£15-20	☐

Full Dinky Toys listings also appeared in the toy catalogues of major retailers such as Gamages and Bentalls. These catalogues are themselves highly collectable, difficult to find, and are in the region of £30-40.

Post-War UK Catalogues, booklets, leaflets and listings
Early Post-War period, 1945 - 1954

There were at least two editions per annum so the following listings are not complete. The 'leaflet' approach reflects the shortage of paper in early post-war years.

Ref. No.	Year(s)	Publication	Cover Features & Details	Market Price Range	
16/1145/75UK	1945	Meccano leaflet..........................	leaflet lists the models to be reintroduced after the War and features pictures of 23e, 29c, 39a, 62s, 62p. Sepia print on cream paper	£10-15	☐
16/546/30 UK	1946	Meccano leaflet..........................	Sepia printed listing on cream paper featuring pictures of models 70a, 38c, 29c, 23e	£10-15	☐
16/1146/65UK	1946	Meccano leaflet..........................	Blue/Black print on cream paper, featuring models 70a, 38c, 70b, 38e........................	£10-15	☐
16/347/50UK	1947	Meccano leaflet..........................	Brown print on light cream paper. Models depicted are 70a, 70b, 70c, 70e, 38c, 38e, 38f, and 153a Jeep..	£10-15	☐
16/448/30	1948	Meccano General Products	Booklet with green printing on light cream paper	£10-15	☐
16/948/200	1948	....	Same as previous issue but with mauve print on light cream paper............................	£10-15	☐
16/1248/5	1948	'Dinky Toys Tyre Sizes'	Simple Leaflet giving information on Dinky Toys spare tyres....................................	£10-15	☐
16/449/100	1949	Meccano General Products	booklet with brown printing on light cream paper	£10-15	☐
	1949	Independent shop listings	Full Dinky Toys listings and pictures featured in the catalogues published by the larger toy shops such as Bentalls, Gamages, etc.....................	£15-20	☐
16/450/150	1950	Meccano General Products	booklet with pale Blue/Black printing on light cream paper	£10-15	☐
	1950	Independent shop listings	Full Dinky Toys listings & pictures featured in the catalogues of larger toy shops such as Gamages, Bentalls, etc.......................................	£15-20	☐
16/251/33	1951	Meccano General Products	booklet with brown printing on light cream paper	£10-15	☐
	1951	Independent shop listings	Full Dinky Toys listings and pictures featured in the catalogues of larger toy shops such as Bentalls, Gamages, etc.......................................	£15-20	☐
13/952/250	1952	Price List..................................	Beige leaflet with pictures and prices..	£10-15	☐
13/953/678	1953	Meccano Catalogue..................	Includes Dinky Toys, Meccano & Hornby Dublo	£15-20	☐
16/85/25	1953	Price List..................................	Beige leaflet with pictures and prices..	£15-20	☐
16/854/25	1954	Price List..................................	Beige leaflet with pictures and prices..	£10-15	☐

Meccano Magazines, 1942 - 1952

During the latter part of the war and especially during the early post-war years when Dinky Toys catalogues were not issued, the Meccano Magazine was the main source of new information for collectors. It advised on the reintroduction of models after the war and of the forthcoming new releases. Consequently the Magazines of this period are highly collectable in their own right.

1942 - September 1943 No Dinky Toys adverts or listings appeared
September 1943 - December 1944 Back page adverts for Meccano incorporated listing and pictures of De Havilland Flamingo Aircraft and Buick 'Viceroy' Saloon.
January - November 1945 Back page adverts said 'Sorry, not available but will be ready after the war'.
December 1945 Advert on back page announced 'Ready during December'.
1946 Virtually every month a new model was added to the listing printed on the inside front cover. A picture of each model was shown.
January - September 1947 new models added regularly each month.
October 1947 First advert appears of Dinky Supertoys with pictures of 501 Foden Diesel Wagon, 502 Foden Flat Truck, 503 Foden Flat Truck with Tailboard, 511 Guy 4 ton Lorry, 512 Guy Flat Truck, 513 Guy Flat Truck with Tailboard, and 701 Short 'Shetland' Flying Boat.
1948 Single page advert every month, new models continually introduced
1949, 1950, 1951 Double page advert each month listing new models.
1952 Double page adverts each month. The December issue shows Gift Sets No.1 Farm Gear and No.2 Commercial Vehicles

Prices for Meccano Magazines of this period range between £10-15

UK Catalogue editions, 1952 - 1965

The series included fourteen editions although not all issues were given an edition number. More than one catalogue was issued in some years. It was common for catalogues to be overprinted with the name and address of the toy retailer. In addition to issuing Dinky Toys catalogues, Meccano Ltd continued to issue 'Meccano Toys Of Quality' leaflets which provided a full listing of Dinky Toys with their retail prices plus details of their 'Hornby', 'Hornby-Dublo' and 'Meccano' products. As many as five printings per annum were produced using green, pink, blue or buff paper. When in perfect condition these leaflets sell for £5-8 each.

Ref. No.	Year(s)	Publication	Cover Features & Details	Market Price Range	
16/152/50	1952	(February) 16 pages......................	Cover features unknown 'C6321'....................................	£40-50	☐
15/852/165	1952	(September) 16 pages.................	Cover shows hands holding 27f Estate Car, 'Dinky Toys' logo	£40-50	☐
	1953	24 page catalogue	Cover shows boy wearing green sweater, 'Dinky Toys' & 'Price 3d'....	£40-50	☐
7/953/360	1953	(1st October) 24 pages..............	Cover features 555 Fire Engine, 522 Big Bedford Lorry and 25x Breakdown Lorry, price '2d'..................................	£40-50	☐
13/953/678	1953	(1st October) (i)	Cover shows 'Meccano Magic Carpet', two boys plus globe with flag	£40-50	☐
7/754/600	1954	(1st September) 24 pages...........	Cover features 157 Jaguar, 480 'Kodak' Van, 641 Army Truck, 'Dinky Toys' logo, price '2d'.............................	£30-40	☐
7/455/250	1955	(May) 8 page leaflet................	Cover shows 251, 641, 170 & 401, 'Dinky Toys' & 'Dinky Supertoys'.....	£15-20	☐
7/755/945	1955	24 page catalogue	'Dinky Toys','Supertoys', 481 'Ovaltine' Van on cover, ('2d')..........	£30-40	☐
7/456/800	1956	(June) 32 pages	Cover shows 942 'REGENT' Tanker, 255 Mersey Tunnel 'Police' Land Rover, 157 Jaguar XK120, 'Dinky Toys' & 'Dinky Supertoys', price '2d'..	£30-40	☐
7/657/820	1957	(August) 28 pages	Cover shows 290 'DUNLOP' Double Decker Bus etc, 'Dinky Toys', and 'Dinky Supertoys', price '2d UK'	£30-40	☐
7/458/856	1958	28 page catalogue	Houses of Parliament shown on front cover with 'Dinky Toys' and 'Dinky Supertoys', price '2d UK'	£30-40	☐
7/559/900	1959	28 page catalogue	Red Jaguar XK120 Coupé (157) on front cover with 'Dinky Toys' and 'UK Seventh Edition', price '3d'.................	£20-25	☐
7/3/800	1960	32 page catalogue	Motorway bridge on cover, 'Dinky Toys' & 'UK Eighth Edition'.........	£20-25	☐
7/561/700	1961	32 page catalogue	Black/Yellow cover with 6 models, 'Dinky Toys', 'UK 9th Edition'	£20-25	☐
72537/02	1962	32 page catalogue	Cover features 120 Jaguar 'E' type, 'Dinky Toys', price '2d'	£15-20	☐
7/263/400	1963	?	No details available.............................	NGPP	☐
13/163/200	1963	32 page catalogue	Motor Show stands featured on cover, '11th Edition', 'UK', '2d'	£15-20	☐
13/763/400	1963	32 page catalogue	11th Edition, 2nd impression	NGPP	☐
7/164/450	1964	16 page catalogue	A large catalogue with 'Widest Range & Best Value In The World' and 'Dinky Toys' logos. Price '3d'	£15-20	☐
7/265/200	1965	16 page catalogue	Rolls Royce (127) on cover with 'Dinky Toys by Meccano'. Price '3d'....	£15-20	☐
72557/02	1965	16 page catalogue	Cover features cars 127, 128, 133, 151 and 178	£15-20	☐

UK Catalogue editions, 1966 - 1978

Ref. No.	Year(s)	Publication	Cover Features & Details	Market Price Range	
72561/2	1966	106 page catalogue	'1st Edition', '6d', 'Always Something New From Dinky' on the cover. Accompanied by separate (pink) price list............	£25-30	☐
72561/2	1966	(after 21st July)........................	2nd edition, same cover as 1st, 104 pages plus (buff) price list............	£20-25	☐
72571	1967	104 page catalogue	'No.3', '6d'. Cover features 12 models and has same logo as 72561/2. Price list (on green paper) included...................	£20-25	☐
72580	1968	104 page catalogue	'No.4', '6d', Spectrum Pursuit Vehicle (104) on cover. Same logo as 72561/2. Accompanied by (buff) price list..............	£20-25	☐
72585	1969	(1st Sept)...................	'No.5', '3d', (2nd printing). Cover features 102 'Joe's Car' and has same logo as 72561/2. There are 24 pages.............	£15-20	☐
165000	1970	24 page catalogue	'No.6', '3d', many models on cover. Same logo as 72561/2.............	£15-20	☐
100103	1971	24 page catalogue	'No.7', '2p', '1971 Meccano Tri-ang Ltd' on rear cover. Same logo as on 72561/2. (Note the change to Decimal Currency in 1971) ...	£10-15	☐
100107	1972	(1st November) 28 pages.........	'No.8', '2p', 2nd printing, shows 683 Chieftain Tank, 'Dinky Toys'....	£10-15	☐
100108	1972	28 pages	No.8, 725 Phantom, 784 Goods Train etc on cover.............	£10-15	☐
100109	1973	(October) 40 pages..................	'No.9', '3p', 2nd printing, shows 924 'Centaur', 'Dinky Toys'..........	£10-15	☐
100113	1974	(May) 48 pages	'No.10', '4p', cover shows 731 S.E.P.E.C.A.T. & 'Dinky Toys'........	£10-15	☐
100115 UK	1975	(June) 48 pages	'No.11', '5p', 'Dinky Toys' & 675 Motor Patrol Boat on cover.......	£10-15	☐
100118 UK	1976	48 page catalogue	'No.12', '5p', 'Dinky Toys' & 358 'USS Enterprise' on cover.	£10-15	☐
100122 (UK)	1977	44 page catalogue	'No.13' & '5p'. Cover features 357 Klingon Battle Cruiser.	£5-10	☐
100100	1978	44 page catalogue	'No.14', '5p', 'AIRFIX GROUP' & 180 Rover 3500 on cover.	£5-10	☐

Leaflets and Price Lists, 1954 - 1978

Ref. No.	Year(s)	Publication	Cover Features & Details	Market Price Range	
no ref. DT/CF/5	1957	Booklet	Yellow cover, Red lettering 'A NEW SERIES' and 'DUBLO DINKY TOYS'..........	£20-30	☐
16/159/100 DT/CF/7 16/160/	1959	Illustrated price list........	Colour cover showing 983 Transporter and cars, etc......................	£10-15	☐
100(3P) DT/CF/8 16/160/	1960	Illustrated price list........	Colour cover with 666 Missile Vehicle and 785 Service Station, etc	£10-15	☐

Ref. No.	Year(s)	Publication	*Dinky Toys — Leaflets – continued*	Market Price Range	
100(4P) DT/CF/11	1960	Illustrated price list............	Colour cover with 930 Pallet-Jekta plus GS 951 Fire Service, etc...............................	**£10-15**	☐
8/561/100	1961	Illustrated price list............	(72535/02) Colour cover with 4 cars, 'Purchase Tax Surcharges 26th July 1961'	**£10-15**	☐
72557/02	1965	Leaflet................	Cover with 133, 127, 128, 151, 171, with price list...	**£10-15**	☐
72579	1967	Leaflet................	Trade Fair leaflet, 'THUNDERBIRDS'..	**£10-15**	☐
72569	1968	Leaflet................	Features 103-105 'Captain Scarlet' vehicles...	**£10-15**	☐
100482	1971	Adhesive shop poster................	'No. 451 Road Sweeper'..	**£20-25**	☐
100362	1972	Single sheet..................................	'All Action Fighting Vehicles'..	**£10-15**	☐
100367	1973	Singe Sheet..................................	'Highway Action Models'..	**£10-15**	☐
	1979	Trade Catalogue 1979	'Fifty New Models', 11½" x 8¼"..	**£20-30**	☐

Further information. It is known that other leaflets, sales literature and price lists were published.
The Editor would welcome further information to add to these listings.

Meccano Trade Catalogues listing Dinky Toys

These were issued for many years but little information has been recorded (please send any information that you may have). For example:
Ref.100126, 1978 Trade Catalogue with 'Todays World', 'Todays Meccano', Todays Dinky Toys' on the cover plus colour design of late 1970s models on Motorway with 'Meccano' buildings in background.
Ref.100102, 1979 Trade Catalogue 'Today's Meccano & Dinky'.

Overseas Catalogues

Catalogues were often adapted so that they could be switched for use in most countries in the world irrespective of the language or the currency used.
An example of this is the 1965 catalogue:

72257/02UK	1965	UK catalogue	16 pages. Cover depicts 5 cars namely Nos.127, 128, 133 and 171 plus a description of various model features...	**£15-20**	☐
72557	1965	Overseas edition...........	16 pages. The cover is the same but replacing the features listing is a panel with 'Precision Diecast Scale Models' printed in English, German, French, Spanish, Italian and Swedish. The catalogue pages contain only the basic English model name and number - all the English text having been removed. The models are the same as 72257/02..	**£20-25**	☐
72559	1965	Overseas edition...........	24 pages. Whilst the cover is the same as 72557, the listings are entirely different for they feature both English and French Dinky Toys, including the French issues sold in the UK	**£40-50**	☐

Price lists. Prior to the overseas editions being despatched, price lists in the correct language and currency would be inserted.
The Editor would like to express his thanks to the many collectors around the world who have contributed to this listing. New information would be welcomed.

Dinky Toys Overseas Catalogue editions recorded to date

Ref. No.	Year(s)	Publication	Cover Features & Details	Market Price Range	
NETHERLANDS/HOLLAND		Agents: Hausemann & H tte NV, Kromboomsloot 57-61, Amsterdam.			
Pre-War Editions					
1/736/5	1936	....	Yellow paper with Black ink	**£75-100**	☐
13/637/7.5	1937	....	Yellow paper with Black ink	**£75-100**	☐
13/738/22	1938	....	Yellow paper with Black ink	**£75-100**	☐
Post-War Editions - Some black/white, later coloured as per UK issues					
16/954/108	1954	Illustrated price list........	Printed in French	**£15-20**	☐
8/1255/50	1955	(DT/L/7)................................		**£30-35**	☐
16/256/30n	1956	(DT/CL/2)		**£20-25**	☐
16/256/30n	1956	(DT/L/9)................................		**£20-25**	☐
16/1158/20	1958		'Nederland Frs 3-'. Cover same as 1958 UK issue..................................	**£30-35**	☐
16/256/30	1962	(72538/29).............................		**£20-25**	☐
72571	1967	Catalogue..............................	3rd Edition, price list in Dutch, florins, 162 pages..................................	**£40-50**	☐
no ref.	1970	Catalogue..............................	6th Edition includes 8 pages of French Dinky, 32 pages................................	**£20-30**	☐
BELGIUM and LUXEMBOURG (French printing). Agents: P. FREMINEUR et Fils, Rue des Bogards 1, Bruxelles 1					
Pre-War Edition					
13/736/26.5	1936	Meccano Catalogue		**£75-100**	☐
Post-War Editions - Mostly same covers as equivalent UK issues					
16/1053/10	1954	Catalogue..............................	Same cover as 1953 UK issue..	**£30-40**	☐
16/1054/2	1954	Catalogue..............................	Same cover as 1954 UK issue..	**£30-40**	☐
16/656/156	1956	Catalogue..............................	(DT/CL/5) Same cover as 1956 UK issue..	**£30-40**	☐
7/539/-	1959	Catalogue..............................	with Red Jaguar XK140 on cover...	**£30-40**	☐
no ref.	1960	48 page catalogue	English and French models in one catalogue. Printed and issued only in Belgium/Luxembourg. Cover depicts Land Rover plus two French Dinky Toys cars. Frs 3-....	**£75-100**	☐
BELGIUM (Flemish printing).					
16/1054/2	1954	Illustrated price list........		**£15-20**	☐
72551	1966	1st Edition price list	in French & Flemish, 164 pages..	**£40-50**	☐

ITALY Agents: Alfredo Parodi, Piazza 8, Marcellino 6, Genova.

Post-War Editions

Ref. No.	Year(s)	Accessory	Description	Market Price Range	
16/657/5	1957	Leaflet	with 101-105	£10-15	☐
16/3/57/5	1957	Leaflet	677 & 472 Raleigh	£10-15	☐
16/357/5	1957	Leaflet	642 & 455 Brook Bond Tea	£10-15	☐
16/857/5	1957	Leaflet	237 Mercedes front, 136, 236, 238 back	£10-15	☐
16/457/5	1957	Leaflet	697 Military Set	£10-15	☐
16/457/5	1957	Leaflet	661 & 919 Golden Shred	£10-15	☐
no ref.	1957	Leaflet	with 163, 236 and 238 on racing circuit	£20-25	☐
no ref.	1957	Leaflet	with 237, 661, and 919 'Golden Shred'	£20-25	☐
16/357/5	1957	Illustrated price list	with 'Italy' printed after the reference number	£20-25	☐
12/757/50	1957	Leaflet	(DT/CL/15) 642 and 455 'Brooke Bond' shown	£20-25	☐
7/857/50	1957	Catalogue	Same cover as UK issue 7/657/820	£30-40	☐
DT/CL/12	1957	Leaflet	with 677 and 472 on cover	£20-25	☐
7/758/50	1958	Catalogue	Same cover as UK issue 7/458/856	£30-40	☐
7/364/40 72250/37	1964	Catalogue	12th 8″x11″, includes 4 pages of French Dinky, 12 pages	£20-30	☐

U.S.A. Agents: H. Hudson Dobson, PO Box 254, 26th St. and Jefferson Avenue, Kenilworth, NJ. From 1957 the address changed to 627 Boulevard, Kenilworth. New York showroom: 200, Fifth Avenue, PO Box 255. Models sold by this distributor will often be found with an 'H.Hudson Dobson' label. From 1963? Lines Bros. Inc., 1107 Broadway, New York. From ? A.V.A. International, Box 7611, Waco, Texas 76710.

War-Time Issue

Ref. No.	Year(s)	Accessory	Description	Market Price Range	
no ref.	1941	Large leaflet	No details available	NGPP	☐

Post-War Editions

Ref. No.	Year(s)	Accessory	Description	Market Price Range	
no ref.	1950	Catalogue	Boy's side face, 5 models, black & white, green printing, 16 pages	£50-75	☐
7/753/150	1953	Catalogue	Same cover as 1953 UK issue 7/953/360	£50-75	☐
7/954/150	1954	Catalogue	Same cover as 1954 UK issue 7/754/600	£50-75	☐
7/753/150	1954	Catalogue	157 Jaguar, 480 Kodak, 641 Army, Separate price list, 28 pages	£50-75	☐
no ref.	1955		Yellow/Red cover has Red lined sections displaying English and French models. Red panel with US address of H.Hudson Dobson. 36 black/white pages of English and French models	£75-100	☐
no ref.	1956	Catalogue	20 models on cover, 5 French, black & white, prices $, 32 pages	£50-75	☐
no ref.	1957	Catalogue	Yellow, Red lines, black/white, 9-30-57, prices in $, 36 pages	£50-75	☐
no ref.	1957	Catalogue	'Ever Ready' + 11 others, Feb 57, black/white, prices $, 32 pages	£50-75	☐
7/958/250	1958	Catalogue	House of Parliament in colour, prices in $, 32 pages	£50-75	☐
7/7/125	1959	Leaflet	Colour, English & French, prices in $	£20-30	☐
7/559/250	1959	USA Catalogue	Cover depicts Red Jaguar XK140 etc. 26 pages English models, 6 pages French	£50-75	☐
7/8/125	1959	Leaflet	3 pages of colour pictures plus price list. Cover shows English and French models, eg. 195 Jaguar 3.4, 265 Plymouth Taxi	NGPP	☐
no ref.	1960	Leaflet	6 pages introducing 'Mini-Dinky' models with pictures of complete range	£40-45	☐
14/561/200	1961	Catalogue	Black with 7 models, USA 1961, 16 pages, French & UK, 48 pages	£50-75	☐
9/762/50	1962	Leaflet	72542/22 & D.T./CL 14	£10-15	☐
725377/22	1962	Catalogue	10th Edition, 48 pages, same as UK 7253702 plus French Dinky	£20-30	☐
72537/22	1962	Catalogue	120 Jaguar E Type, 10th Edn 5c, 16 pages, French Dinky, 48 pages	£50-75	☐
13/763/60 16/163/50	1963	Catalogue	11th Edition, 48 pages, same as UK 13/763/400 plus French Dinky	NGPP	☐
72547/22 13/763/10	1963	Leaflet	Illustrated Flyer price list, black & white	£20-30	☐
72545/22	1963	Catalogue	Motor Show 11th USA, 16 pages French Dinky, 48 pages	£25-35	☐
no ref.	1965	Leaflet	Lines Bros. Flyer 8½″x11″, Hong Kong on cover	£20-30	☐
no ref.	1965	'Lines Bros' leaflet	4 pages, Yellow/Red cover with 113 MGB	£30-35	☐
72577/3	1967	Leaflet	10″x12¼″ includes 5 Hong Kong Dinky	£15-20	☐
100103	1971	Catalogue	7th Edition, same as UK, 24 pages	£10-15	☐
100108	1972	Catalogue	8th Edition, same as UK, 28 pages	£10-15	☐
100110	1973	Catalogue	9th Edition, same as UK, 40 pages	£10-15	☐
100265	1973	Leaflet	4 pages Dinky Kits Catalogue	£10-15	☐
100114	1974	Catalogue	10th Edition, same as UK, 48 pages	£10-15	☐
100/117	1975	Catalogue	11th Edition, 40 pages, same as UK 100115	£10-15	☐
100/120	1976	Catalogue	12th Edition, 40 pages, same as UK 100118	£10-15	☐
100/135	1977	13th Edition, 40 pages, same as UK 100122 but background on cover is Blue not Red		£10-15	☐
100/101	1978	Catalogue	14th Edition, 64 pages, same as UK 100/100	£10-15	☐

CANADA Agents: Meccano Limited, 675, King Street West, Toronto.

Post-War Editions

Ref. No.	Year(s)	Accessory	Description	Market Price Range	
16/351/25	1951	Catalogue	Boy with 3 models, pictures in blue, 16 pages	£50-60	☐
7/953/150	1953	Catalogue	555 F/E, 522 Big Bedford, 25x Breakdown Truck, 28 pages	£40-50	☐
16/355/90	1955	Illustrated price list	Printed on Off-White leaflet	£30-35	☐
7/556/90	1956	Catalogue	Regent Tanker/Tunnel, 1st June 1956 in colour, 32 pages	£40-50	☐
16/656/18c	1956	Illustrated price leaflet	(DT/CL/4) in colour, featuring 131 Cadillac and 660 Tank Transporter	£15-20	☐
16/756/18	1956	Illustrated price leaflet	in colour, featuring 706 Vickers 'Air France' Airliner	£15-20	☐
7/757/90	1957	Catalogue	Piccadilly Circus, vertical, with prices, 28 pages	£40-50	☐
7/559/90 3/41/25	1959	Catalogue	Red Jaguar + 6 models on cover, in colour, 28 pages	£40-50	☐
72523/42 13/163/100	1961	Catalogue	Black with 7 models, Cover 9th Canada/English, 32 pages	£30-40	☐
72542/42 13/1063/50	1963	Catalogue	Motor Show 11th, Canada/English, 32 pages	£30-40	☐
72548/42 7/464/150	1963	Catalogue	Flyer 8″x10¼″ Cover, 10 models, Canada 1963, 8 pages	£10-15	☐

Ref. No.	Year(s)	Publication	*Dinky Toys — Catalogues – continued*	Market Price Range	
72550/42	1964	Catalogue	12th 8″x11″, Canada/English, 8 pages	**£10-15**	☐
None	1964	Catalogue	Flyer, 5½″x3½″, shows 6 Hong Kong models, 12 pages	**£10-15**	☐
None	1965	Catalogue	1st Edn. 8½″x5½″, 5 models on cover, 16 pages	**£20-25**	☐
72561	1966	Catalogue	1st Edition, 108 pages	**£30-40**	☐
72561	1966	Catalogue	2nd Edition, 106 pages	**£30-40**	☐
72571	1967	Catalogue	3rd edition, 106 pages	**£30-40**	☐
72580	1968	Catalogue	4th Edition, 106 pages	**£30-40**	☐
72585	1969	Catalogue	5th Edition, 24 pages	**£20-30**	☐

MALAYA & SINGAPORE Agents: King & Co., Singapore.

Ref. No.	Year(s)	Publication		Market Price Range	
16/557/ 2.5(IP)	1957	Catalogue	Cover depicts 170, 626, 716, 955, 8 pages, includes other pictures and price list in $ (Ref DT/CF/3)	**£40-50**	☐
7/958/10	1958	Catalogue	Same cover as UK, 4 pages with prices in $	**£40-50**	☐

AUSTRALIA Agents:

Ref. No.	Year(s)	Publication		Market Price Range	
7/757/30	1957	Catalogue	Piccadilly Circus, colour, vertical, no prices, 28 pages	**£75-100**	☐

SOUTH AFRICA Agents:

Ref. No.	Year(s)	Publication		Market Price Range	
7/655/20	1955	Catalogue	Ovaltine Van + 7 others, prices in shillings/pence, 24 pages	**£50-75**	☐

SWITZERLAND Agents: Riva & Kunzmann S.A. Basel 2, Switzerland. From 1965 address changed to Prattela, Switzerland.

Ref. No.	Year(s)	Publication		Market Price Range	
7/356/20	1956	Catalogue	Ovaltine Van + 7 others, prices in francs, 24 pages	**£40-50**	☐
72537/25	1962	Catalogue	10th Edition, 48 pages, same as UK issue 72537/02 plus French Dinky	**£40-50**	☐
13/163/175	1963	Catalogue	11th Edition, 48 pages, same as UK issue 13/163/20 plus French Dinky	**£40-50**	☐
72559	1965	Catalogue	24 pages, same cover as UK issue 72557 plus French Dinky	**£40-50**	☐

WEST GERMANY Agents: Biengngraeber of Hamburg.

Ref. No.	Year(s)	Publication		Market Price Range	
72585	1969	Catalogue	32 pages, No.5 features 'Joe's Car' on cover, Catalogue in English, price list in German	**£20-25**	☐

SWEDEN Agents: Ludvig Wigart & Cos, AB Helsingborg.

Ref. No.	Year(s)	Publication		Market Price Range	
7/654/14	1954	4 pages	3 pages colour pictures plus price list in kroner with Swedish text	**£30-40**	☐
16/357/15	1957	Leaflet	Leaflet depicts 455 'Brooke Bond' Trojan plus 642 R.A.F. Tanker and price list in Kroner with Swedish text	**£15-20**	☐
14/561/60	1961	Catalogue	Same as 1961 U.K. issue, text in Swedish	**£20-30**	☐
72580	1968	162 page Catalogue	Same as U.K. 1968 edition, but in Swedish	**£20-30**	☐

EIRE & CHANNEL ISLANDS Agents: S.J.Gearey, 1, St.Stephens Green, Dublin. (Ceased trading 1968).
Agents from 1969: Kilroy Bros. Ltd., Shanowen Road, Whitehall, Dublin 9.

Ref. No.	Year(s)	Publication		Market Price Range	
7/755/20	1955	Catalogue	'Eire' and 'C.I.' on cover	**£20-25**	☐
7/659/75	1959	Catalogue	'Eire' on cover	**£20-25**	☐
7/364/7	1964	Catalogue	'Eire' on cover	**£20-25**	☐
No.5	1969	Catalogue	'Irish' on cover. Distributed by Kilroy Bros Ltd	**£20-25**	☐

HONG KONG Representatives: W.R.Loxley & Co Ltd, Jardine House, 11th Floor, 20, Pedder Street, Hong Kong.

Ref. No.	Year(s)	Publication		Market Price Range	
DT/CF/5	1959	Illustrated price list	Same cover as 1959 UK issue DT/CF/5	**£20-25**	☐

CYPRUS (Distributor Unknown)

Ref. No.	Year(s)	Publication		Market Price Range	
No Ref	1969	Catalogue	Same as U.K. issue	**£20-25**	☐

Meccano Magazines 1952 - 1975

With the introduction of yearly Dinky Toys catalogues from 1952 the Meccano Magazine lost its somewhat unique role as a combined magazine/catalogue. However, with the help of 'The Toyman' and his monthly articles plus superb colour advertising of new models, the Magazine continued to provide a valuable service for collectors.
Meccano Magazines of this period are in the price range of £5-10

Meccano Catalogues 1954 - 1958 with colour 'Dinky Toys' & 'Hornby-Dublo' listings

These contained sections with listings and pictures of 'Dinky Toys' and 'Hornby-Dublo' products. Details known to the compiler relate solely to issues in the mid-1950's period. 'MECCANO TOYS OF QUALITY' logo on each cover.

Ref. No.	Years(s)	Publication	Cover Features & Details	Market Price Range	
13/654/ 995UK	1954-55	24 pages, price '2d'	Cover depicts 4 boys on a desert island. Black/White pictures	**£20-25**	☐
13/655/ 797UK	1955-56	28 pages, price '2d'	Cover shows boys looking in toyshop window. Black/White pictures	**£20-25**	☐
13/756/ 525UK	1956	32 pages, price '4d'	Cover depicts Dinky Toys, Hornby-Dublo, and a Meccano helicopter. This is a large catalogue with colour printing	**£30-35**	☐
13/757/ 500UK	1957	32 pages, price '4d'	Famous cover showing Meccano Tower, Hornby-Dublo train crossing viaduct and Dinky Toys passing beneath. Large, with colour pictures	**£50-75**	☐
13/758/ 450UK	1958	20 pages, price '4d'	Cover depicts boy, Hornby-Dublo train, 8 Dinky Toys and a Meccano model. Includes some superb engine pictures.	**£30-35**	☐

Trade Boxes

Virtually all Dinky Toys models were supplied in their own individual boxes from around 1954. Before then most small models were supplied to shopkeepers in 'Trade Boxes' containing 3, 4, 6 or 12 identical models separated by strips of card. (Some aircraft and ship models were an exception to this general rule). A single item would be sold without further packaging except perhaps for a paper bag. The Trade Boxes have become collectors items in their own right whether full or empty (the latter selling for between £20 and £50 depending on its rarity and that of its original contents. Most of these boxes that come to auction are full and the listing below derives from a recent survey of such items. It is known that others exist and the Editor would welcome any information regarding Trade Boxes.

YB = Yellow box,   GB = Green box
N.B. Early boxes are Fawn with only the end sticker Yellow.

No.	Description	Price		No.	Description	Price
078	Lansing Bagnall Trailers, Box of 6	£140-170 ☐		35b	Racer (Silver/Red) YB x 6	£280-330 ☐
12c	Telephone Box, YB x 6	£150-200 ☐		36a	Armstrong-Siddeley, YB x 6	£400-500 ☐
12d	Telegraph Messenger (post-war) GB x 6	£60-70 ☐		37c	Signals Despatch Rider, YB x 6	£150-200 ☐
12e	Postman (post-war) GB x 6	£80-90 ☐		38b	Sunbeam Talbots, YB x 6	£400-500 ☐
13a	Cook's Man, box of 6 (50174)	£30-40 ☐		38e	Armstrong-Siddeley, YB x 6	£450-550 ☐
22g	Streamline Tourer, YB x 6 Code A2018	£1500-1750 ☐		40a	Riley, YB x 6	£350-450 ☐
23b	Small Closed Racing Car, YB x 6	£200-300 ☐		40b	Triumph 1800, YB x 6	£350-450 ☐
23c	Racing Car, YB x 6	£300-400 ☐		40e	Standard Vanguard, YB x 6	£350-450 ☐
23e	Speed of the Wind, YB x 6	£200-300 ☐		40d	Austin Devon, YB x 6	£350-450 ☐
23f	Alfa Romeo, YB x 6	£250-300 ☐		40f	Hillman Minx, YB x 6	£250-350 ☐
24g	Sports Tourer, A1017, YB x 6	£1500-2000 ☐		40g	Morris Oxford, YB x 6	£350-450 ☐
25d	Petrol Wagon, (common colours) YB x 6	£300-400 ☐		40h	Austin Taxi, YB x 6	£350-450 ☐
25e	Tipping Wagon, YB x 6	£250-350 ☐		40j	Austin Somerset, YB x 6	£350-450 ☐
25f	Market Gardeners, YB x 6	£300-400 ☐		42a	Police Box, YB x 6	£140-170 ☐
25h	Fire Engine, YB x 6	£300-400 ☐		44b	'AA' Motorcycle Patrol, YB x 6	£200-300 ☐
25m	Bedford Truck (common colours), YB x 6	£300-400 ☐		47c	Two-face Traffic Lights, YB x 12	£40-70 ☐
25p	Aveling Barford, YB x 6	£150-200 ☐		70d	Twin Engined Fighter, YB x 6	£80-120 ☐
25p	Aveling Barford Diesel Roller, YB x 3	£150-200 ☐		70e	Gloster Meteor, YB x 6	£40-60 ☐
25g (405)	Jeep, YB x 3	£150-200 ☐		70f	Shooting Star, YB x 6	£100-150 ☐
25v	Refuse Truck (common colours), YB x 4	£200-300 ☐		105a	Garden Roller, YB x 6	£100-125 ☐
25w	Bedford Truck (common colours), YB x 6	£300-400 ☐		105b	Wheelbarrow, YB x 6	£150-200 ☐
25y	Universal Jeep, YB x 6	£150-225 ☐		105c	Hand Truck, YB x 6	£40-60 ☐
27	Tram Car (pre-war) YB x 6	£900-1200 ☐		105e	Grass Cutter, YB x 6	£120-150 ☐
27a	Massey-Harris Tractor, YB x 3	£150-200 ☐		107a	Sack Truck, YB x 6	£130-170 ☐
27b	Harvest Trailer, YB x 6	£75-85 ☐		139a	Ford Fordor, YB x 6	£350-450 ☐
27c	M.H. Manure Spreader, YB x 3	£85-100 ☐		139b	Hudson Commodore, YB x 6	£500-700 ☐
27d	Land Rover, YB x 6	£275-325 ☐		140a	Austin Atlantic, YB x 6	£500-700 ☐
27e	Estate Car, YB x 6	£275-325 ☐		140b	Rover 75, YB x 6	£350-450 ☐
27g	Moto-Cart, YB x 3	£100-140 ☐		152b	Reconnaisance Car, YB x 6	£400-500 ☐
27h	Disc Harrow, YB x 4	£60-80 ☐		152c	R.T.C. Austin 7, YB x 6	£400-500 ☐
27j	Triple-Gang Mower, YB x 6	£150-200 ☐		160b	Royal Artillery Gunners, YB x 12	£200-250 ☐
27m	Land Rover Trailer, YB x 3	£70-90 ☐		161b	Mobile A.A. Gun, YB x 6	£200-250 ☐
28/1	Delivery Vans, 1st Type, A1008, YB x 6	£6000-9000 ☐		253	Daimler Ambulance, YB x 6	£150-200 ☐
29a	'Q' type Bus, YB x 6	£1000-1200 ☐		270	AA Motor Cycle (post-war), YB x 6	£200-300 ☐
29c	AEC Bus (post-war) YB x 6	£300-400 ☐		551	Trailer (Grey/Red), YB x 3	£45-65 ☐
29f	Observation Coach, YB x 6	£400-500 ☐		551	Trailer (various colours), Blue box x 3	£65-85 ☐
29g	Luxury Coach, YB x 6	£500-600 ☐		603a	Army Personnel (metal), YB x 12	£80-110 ☐
29h	Duple Roadmaster, YB x 6	£400-500 ☐			N.B. Early Y/B long, later issues square	
30b	Rolls Royce, YB x 6	£400-500 ☐		603a	Army Personnel (plastic), YB x 12	£85-120 ☐
30d	Vauxhall, YB x 6	£400-500 ☐		687	Field Gun Trailer, YB x 6	£65-85 ☐
30e	Breakdown Lorry, YB x 6	£150-200 ☐		705	Viking Airliner, YB x 6	£200-300 ☐
30f	Ambulance, YB x 6	£400-500 ☐		750	Telephone Call Box, YB x 6	£200-300 ☐
30h	Daimler Ambulance, YB x 4	£200-300 ☐		751	Police Hut, YB x 6	£240-280 ☐
30m	Rear Tipping Wagon, YB x 6	£150-200 ☐		760	Pillar Box, YB x 6	£150-200 ☐
30p	'Mobilgas' Tankers, YB x 6	£500-600 ☐		768	Racks with Tyres, YB x 6	£75-100 ☐
30pa	'Castrol' Tanker, YB x 6	£500-700 ☐		773	Traffic Lights, YB x 12	£150-175 ☐
30pb	'Esso' Tanker, YB x 6	£500-700 ☐		777	Belisha Beacon, YB x 12	£65-90 ☐
30j	Austin Wagon, YB x 6	£150-200 ☐		786	Tyre Rack, YB x 6	£120-160 ☐
30m	Dodge Tipping Wagon, YB x 6	£150-180 ☐		788	Spare Bucket for 966, YB x 6	£175-225 ☐
30r	Thames Flat Truck, YB x 6	£130-160 ☐		797	Healey Raceboats, YB x 6	£150-200 ☐
30s	Austin Covered Wagon, YB x 6	£150-200 ☐		994	Loading Ramp, Plain box x 3	£55-80 ☐
30v (490)	Electric Milk Float, YB x 6	£300-400 ☐		14095	Tyres, YB x 12	£5-10 ☐
30v (491)	N.C.B. Milk Float, YB x 6	£300-400 ☐				
30w	Electric Articulated Vehicle, YB x	£300-400 ☐				
31a	Trojan 'Esso' Van, YB x 6	£600-800 ☐				
31b	Trojan 'Dunlop' Van, YB x 6	£600-800 ☐				
31c	Trojan 'Chivers' Van, YB x 6	£600-800 ☐				
33w	Horse and Wagon, Grey box x 3	£110-150 ☐				
34b	Royal Mail Van, YB x 6	£300-400 ☐				
34c	Loudspeaker Van, YB x 6	£150-180 ☐				
35a	Saloon Car, YB x 6	£290-330 ☐				

Trade Packs of BOXED models

No.	Description	Price
106	'The Prisoner' Mini-Moke, (6)	£600-800 ☐
159	Morris Oxford (3 Green, 3 Tan)	£250-350 ☐
161	(40j) Austin Somerset, (6)	£600-800 ☐
195	Jaguar 3.4 Saloon, (6)	£400-500 ☐
471	Austin Vans 'NESTLE', (6)	£300-400 ☐
491	Electric Dairy Van 'N.C.B.' (6)	£300-400 ☐

N.B. Expect Trade Boxes containing rare colour variations to attract a corresponding premium.
N.B. See also Gift Sets for 62h & 62d Pre-War Aeroplane Trade Box items.

Dinky Toys Trade Accessories

Trade Display Unit packed in plain cardboard box. Black wooden case with 'Property of Meccano Ltd Liverpool' in black on gold; three shelves in light blue/white/yellow; four gold supports with two yellow and two red supports; four red tin flags 'DINKY TOYS'; three tin flags 'ASK FOR BOOKLET', 'OVER 200 MODELS', and 'ALWAYS SOMETHING NEW'; plus two red and two yellow balls. .... £400–500 ☐

Glass Display Case. Oak frame with three glass shelves. Size approximately 32″ (80 cm.) wide, 24″ (60 cm.) high, 9″ (22 cm.) deep. With 'DINKY TOYS' in green lettering on glass front .... £300–400 ☐

Trade Display Stand Large yellow folding cardboard stand which non-erected measures approximately 28″ (70 cm.) x 14″ (35 cm.); three display levels with 'DINKY TOYS' logo in green plus 'MECCANO PRODUCT' in red on top header board. Outer corrugated cardboard packing has green printed instruction leaflet .... £200–300 ☐

Trade Display Stand Small yellow and red folding cardboard stand which non-erected measures approximately 12″ (31 cm.) x 7½″ (15 cm.); with one 'DINKY TOYS' and two 'DINKY SUPERTOYS' logos in red plus yellow 'MASTERPIECES IN MINIATURE' logo on red background.... £75–100 ☐

Display Stand (circa 1950 - 1960) Large metal stand which measures approximately 36″ x 21″ x 22″ (91.5 x 53 x 56 cm.); with nine display shelves covered in black plastic track. Metal advertisement affixed to top states in yellow/red/black 'A MOTOR SHOW FOR GIRLS AND BOYS', 'PRECISION DIE-CAST MODELS BY MECCANO'. 'BEST RANGE'. and 'BEST VALUE IN THE WORLD'. Lower large transfer also in yellow/red/black repeats the message .... £400–500 ☐

Window Sign (plastic), Top half is dark blue with white 'MECCANO' logo, bottom half is yellow with red 'Dinky Toys' logo. Approximately 18″ x 6″ .... £70–80 ☐

Counter Display (cardboard), Small display stand suitable for a single new model, 'ALWAYS NEW MODELS' logo in white on red background, header states 'DINKY TOYS' in red on yellow .... £70–80 ☐

Counter Display (cardboard) 'BATTLE OF BRITAIN' Blue/yellow displaying 719 Spitfire MkII and 721 Junkens JU 87b Stuka .... £100–150 ☐

Illuminated Shop Display Sign with 'DINKY TOYS' in large wooden letters above a glass panel lettered either 'Made by Meccano Ltd' or 'British and Guaranteed' .... £300–400 ☐

Shop Display Carousel with tripod base supporting four stacks of clear plastic.. £200–300 ☐

Illuminated Counter or Window display unit 13″ x 9½″ with perspex front 'DINKY TOYS' and 'NEW MODELS EVERY MONTH' logo.............. £100–1500 ☐

Counter Carousel Unit with 'Always Something New from Dinky' around its edge. Red/Yellow 'DINKY TOYS BY MECCANO' sign on top, 26″ high overall .... £200–250 ☐

Metal Counter Display Sign, triangular in shape with red 'DINKY TOYS' on yellow background, approximately 8″ x 1″ x 1″................................ £30–40 ☐

Electric Revolving 'Meccano' Wooden Display Stand 'DINKY TOYS – LOOK FOR THE NAME ON THE BASE' logo, (28″ square and 10″ high).. £250–350 ☐

Note: This section is far from complete and the Editor would welcome details of other trade stands, posters, display cards, promotional material and advertising signs, for example:

Acknowledgements

The Editor would like to express his appreciation to the following traders and collectors for supplying new Dinky Toy information:

Bob Ewers, Berkshire; John Kinchen, Hampshire; Ray Pearson, Cheshire; John Marshall, California, U.S.A.; David Ranford, Worcester; John Hughes, Wales; Michael Butcher, Western Australia; Andy Thompson, Suffolk; Mr Alistair Grahame, Scotland; Michael Watts, Devon; F Vanden Eynde, Belgium; Ray Holcroft, Lancashire; Mr A Wilson, Middlesex; Paul Ottaway, Wiltshire; Tim Roberts, Shropshire; Mr T.P. Versey, Suffolk; John Humperson, Wales; John Westcombe, Herts; Mr R.D. Jones, Staffs; Mr Bernard Ivinson, Berkshire; Mr David Cooke, Norfolk; Mr Andrew Hind, Surrey; Mike Mastin, Victoria, Canada; Peter Naylor, Staffs.; Peter Clawson, Lincs.; Greg Reilly, Texas, U.S.A.; Mr Hugo Marsh, Christies; Mr Roger Mazillius, Vectis Model Auctions; Mr John Anderson, Anderson & Garland, Newcastle (Auctioneers); Mr George Beevis, Lacy Scott Auctions; Mr Barry Potter, Barry Potter Auctions; Mr Rob Butler, Wallis & Wallis Auctions; Mr Leigh Gotch, Bonhams Auctioneers; Mr Kegan Harrison, Phillips Auctioneers; Ms Susan Duffield, Sotheby's Auctions; Mrs Joyce Peterzell, Los Angeles; Mike Mastin, British Columbia; Peter Winterbone, Essex; R. Hoeksema, Denhaag, Holland; Luciano Luppi, Italy; Vaughan Holcombe, Connecticut U.S.A; P.D. Searle, Surrey; Gary McDonald, North Humberside; Brian Lee, Romsey Auctions.

Dinky Toys Auction Results

Christies Auction Results

Condition abbreviations:- (P) Poor, (F) Fair, (G) Good, (E) Excellent, (M) Mint, (NPA) No price available

Auction Sale, 14th October 1994. 'The Hemley Collection'
Pre-war 24 Series Motor Cars
Grey and red 24a Ambulance, 2nd Type chassis and 3rd Type Bentley grille with badge and over-riders **£187**
Dark blue and black 24c Town Sedan, 2nd Type chassis and body without spare wheel, 3rd Type Bentley grille with badge and over-riders, black hubs, (slight fatigue to body and chassis, grille repainted) **£264**
Pink and green 24d Vogue Saloon, with black hubs, 2nd Type chassis, 3rd Type grille (G, pink faded, slight fatigue to hubs, radiator grille silver painted)**£308**
Green 25b 'Carter Paterson' Covered Van, with blue hubs (G-E, grille repainted, a few scratches to tilt) **£440**
Green 25b 'Meccano Engineering for Boys' Covered Van, '20 mph' disc on tailboard (G-E, chassis fractured, one chip mising from side member, lacks tow hook) **£418**
Green 25f Market Gardener's Van with tinplate radiator, with black chassis and plated hubs, 1934-1935 (a few retouches to front wings) **£264**
Red 25d 'Texaco' Petrol Tank Wagon, with black hubs **£418**
Green 25d 'Wakefield Castrol' Petrol Tank Wagon, with black hubs and '20 mph' disc on back **£308**
Blue 25d 'Redline-Glico' Petrol Tank Wagon, with black hubs, overall E **£264**
Rare wartime grey 25d 'Pool' Petrol Tank Wagon with white chassis, with black hubs and '20 mph' disc on back, 1940 .... **£440**
Yellow 28a 2nd Type 'Hornby Trains' Delivery Van, 1935-1936 .... **£308**
Cream 28a 2nd Type 'Golden Shred Marmalade' Delivery Van, 1935-1939 (G) **£1045**
Blue 28b 2nd Type 'Seccotine' Delivery Van, with blue hubs, 1935-1939 . **£396**
Rare blue 28b 3rd Type 'Seccotine' Delivery Van, 1940-1941 .... **£990**
Rare 28d 3rd Type 'Oxo' Delivery Van, 1939-1941 .... **£715**
Blue 28e 2nd Type 'Firestone Tyres' Delivery Van, 1935-1939 .... **£528**
Rare blue 28e 3rd Type 'Firestone' Delivery Van, 1940-1941 (G) **£715**
Grey 28f 2nd Type 'Palethorpe's' Sausages Delivery Van, with blue hubs, 1935-1938 (P-F) **£143**
Yellow 28f 2nd Type 'Virol' Delivery Van, 1938-1939 .... **£990**
Yellow 28g 2nd Type 'Kodak' Delivery Van, 1935-1939 (overall G) **£220**
Rare yellow 28g 3rd Type 'Kodak' Delivery Van, 1940-1941 (G-E) **£825**
Rare red 28h 3rd Type 'Dunlop Tyres' Delivery Van, 1940-1941 (G) **£440**
Rare green 28k 3rd Type 'Marsh and Baxter's' Delivery Van, 1940-1941 (E)**£715**
Green 28m 2nd Type 'Wakefield's Castrol' Delivery Van, 1935-1939 .... **£242**
Rare green 28m 3rd Type 'Wakefield's Castrol Motor Oil' Delivery Van, 1940-1941 .... **£1210**
Rare red 28p 3rd Type 'Crawfords' Delivery Van, 1940-1941 .... **£1210**
Black 28r 2nd Type 'Swan Pens' Delivery Van, with blue hubs, 1936-1939 (F) **£262**
Brown 28s 2nd Type 'Fry's Chocolate' Delivery Van, with brown hubs, 1936-1939 (G-E) **£385**
Red 28t 2nd Type 'Ovaltine' Delivery Van, with blue hubs, 1936-1939 .... **£660**
Rare yellow 28w 3rd Type 'Osram' Delivery Van, 1940-1941 (G-E) **£528**
White 28x 2nd Type 'Hovis' Delivery Van, 1936-1939 .... **£715**
Red 28y 2nd Type 'Exide and Drydex Batteries' Delivery Van, 1936-1939**£352**
Rare blue 280a 2nd Type 'Viyella' Delivery Van, 1937-1939 (G) **£352**
Dark blue 280b 2nd Type 'Lyons'Tea' Delivery Van, 1937-1939 (overall G-E) Only issues as 2nd Type **£495**
Rare cream 280b 2nd Type 'Hartley's Jam' Delivery Van, 1939 .... **£1320**
Cream 280c 2nd Type 'Shredded Wheat' Delivery Van, 1937-1939 (F) **£244**
Rare yellow 280d 2nd Type 'Bisto' Delivery Van, 2nd Variant with 'Bisto' and small Bisto Kids transfers with pie dish on table, 1940 (G-E) **£825**
Rare cream 280e 3rd Type 'Yorkshire Evening Post' Delivery Van, 1940-1941 (G) **£990**
Red 280f 2nd Type 'Mackintosh's Toffee' Delivery Van, 1937-1939 (overall G-E) **£990**
Very rare green 28 Series 2nd Type 'Bentall's' Department Store Promotional Delivery Van with yellow upper side panels and white roof, (G-E) **£12,650**
A rare Dinky US-export issue Set No.6 Commercial Vehicles, (G-E) **£2600**
A rare Dinky US export-issue two-tone blue 39bu Oldsmobile 6 Sedan, with 'solid' baseplate without towing aperature and smooth tyres, circa 1950-1952 .. **£280**
A rare Dinky US export-issue two-tone green 39eu Chrysler Royal Sedan, blued steel axles and smooth tyres, circa 1950-1952 (P-F) **£280**
A rare Dinky US export-issue 581 'Express Horse Van Hire Service' Horsebox, with special US market transfers, white, brown and grey cast metal horses and packing pieces, in original box with special US market label (E) **£350**

Auction Sale, 21st April 1994, 'The Rayleigh and Yorkshire Collections'
Pre-war 62g Boeing 'Flying Fortress' Bomber, with instructions, in original box dated 6-39 .... **£143**
Rare 998 Canadian Pacific Bristol 'Britannia' Airliner, finished in metallic grey and white, in original picture box, circa 1964 .... **£242**
Grey 30b Rolls-Royce minor retouching **£30**
Blue 36b Bentley **£99**
Red 36e British Salmson Two-Seater **£132**
Yellow 38b Sunbeam-Talbot Sports Car, with fawn tonneau and interior**£198**
Brown 39a Packard Super Touring Sedan **£110**
Grey 39d Buick Viceroy with white tyres, one very minor retouch to bonnet**£121**
Tan 40e Standard Vanguard, with red hubs and open rear wheel arches, rear axle retained by clip, no name inside roof, 1948-1950 .... **£242**
Light blue 106 Austin Atlantic with red seats, in original box (box G-E) **£143**
Two-tone yellow and grey Jaguar XK120, in original box **£286**
Rare US-issue all yellow 57-003 Chevrolet Impala, in original box **£143**
Blue 57-005 Ford Thunderbird with white roof, in original box **£143**
Red 521 Bedford Articulated Lorry, with black wheels, in original box... **£176**
Blue and yellow 922 Big Bedford Lorry, in original box dated 1954 .... **£286**
Rare powder blue 412 Austin Wagon, with pale yellow wheels, in original 412/30j box with blue spot **£264**
Rare yellow 412 Austin Wagon, with green hubs, in original box (minor retouching) **£264**
Dark blue 413 Austin Covered Wagon with pale blue tilt and hubs, in original box **£385**
Light blue 413 Austin Covered wagon with cream tilt and yellow hubs, with treated tyres, in original box **£308**
Red 413 Austin Covered Wagon with grey tilt and hubs in original box... **£396**
Light grey 501 Foden Diesel 8-Wheel Wagon, grey cab, red flashes, grey back, black chassis, red hubs, no hook, in original box **£660**
Blue 501 Foden Diesel 8-Wheel Wagon, blue cab, silver flashes, blue back, black chassis, blue hubs, no hook, in original box (G-E) **£715**
Grey 501 Foden Diesel 8-Wheel Wagon, grey cab, red flashes, back, chassis and hubs, no hook, in original box **£550**
Red and grey 501 Foden Diesel 8-Wheel Wagon, red cab, silver flashes, grey back, red chassis with tank-fitting slots, red hubs, with hool, in original box .. **£440**
Brown 501 Foden Diesel 8-Wheel Wagon, brown cab, silver flashes, brown back, black chassis, brown hubs, no hook, in original box **£352**
Rare blue and red 502 Foden Flat Truck, blue cab, red flashes, red back, blue chassis, light blue hubs, with hook, without tank-fitting slots, in original box **£880**
Green 502 Foden Flat Truck, green cab, silver flashes, green back, black chassis, green hubs, no hook, in original box (one small area of restoration to lid label) **£286**
Red and grey 901 Foden Diesel 8-Wheel Wagon, red cab, grey back, red chassis, herring-bone tyres, in original box **£242**
Rare yellow and green 902 Foden Flat Truck, yellow cab, green back, yellow chassis, light green hubs, grey herring-bone tyres, in original box **£1595**
Orange and green 902 Foden Flat Truck, orange cab, green back, orange chassis, green hubs, grey herring-bone tyres, in original box dated 1956 .... **£308**
Blue and orange 903 Foden Flat Truck with Tailboard, blue cab, orange back, blue chassis, light blue hubs, grey treaded tyres, in original box dated 1956**£330**
Blue and yellow 903 Foden Flat Truck with Tailboard, blue cab, yellow back, blue chassis, light blue hubs, black treaded tyres, in original box dated 1956 **£880**
Light blue and fawn 903 Foden Flat Truck with Tailboard, light blue cab, fawn back, light blue chassis, light blue hubs, black treaded tyres, in original box**£550**
Blue and yellow 417 Leyland Comet Lorry, in original box with US-export 'Hudson-Dobson' sticker on lid **£264**
Blue and fawn 531 Leyland Comet Lorry, in original box **£418**
Rare blue and yellow 934 Leyland Octopus Wagon, in original box, US-export 'Hudson-Dobson' sticker on lid side **£2640**
Yellow and green 934 Leyland Octopus Wagon, in original box dated 1959**£308**
Rare green and grey 935 Leyland Octopus Flat Truck with Chains, with red plastic hubs, in original box **£1210**
Red and grey 511 Guy 4-Ton Lorry, 1st Type cab, in original box **£715**
Grey 511 Guy 4-Ton Lorry, 1st Type cab, in original box **£242**
Brown 511 Guy 4-Ton Lorry, 1st Type cab, in original box **£605**
Dark blue and red 432 Guy Flat Truck, 2nd Type cab, in original yellow box dated 1956 (box G) **£264**
Maroon 512 Guy Flat Truck, 1st Type cab, in original box **£660**
Brown and green 512 Guy Flat Truck, 1st Type cab, in original box (very minor retouching to back) **£572**
Yellow 512 Guy Flat Truck, 1st Type, in original box **£440**
Blue and orange 433 Guy Flat Truck with Tailboard, 2nd Type cab, in original yellow box, US-export 'Hudson-Dobson' sticker on lid **£242**
Green and light green 513 Guy Flat Truck with Tailboard, 1st Type cab, in original box **£242**
514 Guy 'Weetabix' Van, 2nd Type, in original box **£2640**
Rare No.1 Farm Gear Gift Set, in original box with plain brown insert card, circa 1952 .... **£1760**
Rare Gift Set No.2 Commercial Vehicles, in original box, circa 1952 .... **£3200**

No.4 Racing Cars Gift Set in original box also with small '249' number **£825**
Rare No.123 'Mayfair' Gift Set, in original display box, circa 1964....**£2860**
Rare No.149 Sports Car Gift Set, with printed insert card, in original box dated 1957................**£1760**
Trade box of six 270 AA Motorcycle Patrols, five with grey smooth plastic wheels and one with grey treaded plastic wheels.....**£242**
No. 299 Post Office Services Gift Set, in original box............**£418**
No. 771 Twelve International Road Signs Set, with instructions, in original box dated 1960................**£121**
No. 957 Fire Services Gift Set, 955 and 956 with plastic hubs, with internal packing piece, in original box, circa 1964....**£528**
943 'Esso Petroleum Company Ltd' Leyland Octopus Tanker, with plastic hubs and paper labels instead of transfers on tank sides (G) chip to one hub, mark to roof................**£154**
A rare fluorescent pink Dinky 100 Lady Penelope's F.A.B.1, in original box (E, minor chips, box F-G, inner card slightly torn)....**£320**

Auction Sale, 15th September 1994, 'The Barnes Collection'
Blue 2nd Type 23a Racing Car with white 'humbug' stripes and driver, racing number 11 (F-G, slight fatigue)....**£550**
Yellow 23b Hotchkiss Racing Car with blue upper body flash, racing number '9'....**£420**
Silver 23m 'Thunderbolt' Racing Car, with shiny silver-coloured baseplate, in original box dated 2·38, code no. A2247 (E-M, baseplate loose, box G-E)**£170**
Green 23p 'Gardner's M.G. Record Car', in original box dated 1·9·1939, code no. A2298 (G, some fatigue, box G)....**£240**
Rare blue 23s Streamlined Racing Car with silver detailing, cast in lead rather than mazak, 1939 (G) Unrecorded colour variant....**£550**
Rare No. 24 Motor Cars Set, all vehicles with Tootsie Toy style chromed wheels, 1st Type bodies, radiator grilles and bumpers, and 2nd Type chassis except where indicated, comprising yellow and red 24a Ambulance (G), maroon and black 24b Limousine, rare 1st Type unpainted chassis (F), cream and blue 24c Town Sedan, (E, roof retouched), light and medium blue 24d Vogue Saloon (G, nearside windscreen pillar missing, slight fatigue to bonnet), green and brown 24e Streamlined Saloon (E, beige and brown 24f Sportsman's Coupé (E), yellow and brown 24g Sports Tourer (Four Seater) open windscreen, steering wheel spokes at 90° (G, one blister on bonnet, chassis slightly bowed), green and medium green 243h Sports Tourer (Two Seater), open windscreen, steering wheel spokes at 60° (G, slight fatigue, nearside wing repaired), in original early purple marbled box, code no. DT24, with packing piece and insert, circa 1935 (G-E, three tears to insert, one lid corner repaired) ...**£13,000 (World Record)**
Blue 24c Town Sedan with blue wings, 1st Type body, 2nd Type chassis and chrome Tootsie Toy style hubs (E-M)....**£700**
Cream and blue 24d Vogue Saloon, 1st Type body and 2nd Type chassis chrome Tootsie Toy style hubs, (E, a few chips, repaired blister to bonnet, nearside windscreen pillar missing)....**£260**
Pink and green 24d Vogue Saloon, 2nd Type body, 2nd Type chassis, 3rd Type radiator with Bentley grille and black hubs (G)....**£400**
Green 25d 'Castrol' Petrol Tank Wagon, tinplate radiator, black chassis and blue hubs, 1935 (E, one fatigue blister to offside wing)....**£800**
Green 25b 'Meccano' Covered Wagon with cream tilt, cast radiator, chrome smooth convex hubs, 'Carter Paterson Express Carriers London' on tilt, circa 1935 (G-E, some wear to transfer)....**£380**
Rare green 25b 'Carter Paterson Special Seaside Service' Covered Wagon with cream tilt, cast radiator, 'Carter Paterson Express Carriers Special Service To The Seaside' transfers on tilt (G-E, one headlamp missing)....**£550**
No.25 Commercial Vehicle Set, 2nd Type cast radiators and black hubs, comprising green 25a wagon (F, slight period retouching to chassis and wings), green and deep yellow 25b Covered Wagon, dark blue 25c Flat Truck, chrome hubs, (E, slight fatigue to load bed), red 25d 'Mobiloil' Petrol Tank Wagon (F), maroon and yellow 25e Tipping Wagon (G, slight period retouching to chassis and wings) and green and black 25f Market Gardener's Van (E), in original later blue patterned box with insert and packing piece, code no. A1052 (G)....**£3000**
Red 25h Streamlined Fire Engine, 1st Type without tinplate baseplate, 1936 (E)....**£240**
Rare red 25h Streamline Fire Engine, 2nd Type, with tinplate baseplate, circa 1938 (E)....**£320**
Red 25k Streamlined Fire Engine with tinplate Firemen, circa 1938 (E, hubs G)....**£500**
Royal blue 25s Six-Wheeled Wagon, white tyres (E)....**£260**
Rare set of six 28/1 1st Type lead Delivery Vans, comprising yellow 28a 'Hornby Trains', 'Dinky Toys' inside roof, green wheels (E), blue 28b 'Pickfords', green wheels (G-E, wings slightly bent), black and red 28c 'Manchester Guardian', 'Dinky Toys' inside roof, blue wheels (G, one worn patch to roof, wings bent), blue 28d 'Oxo' Van, 'Meccano' inside roof, pink wheels (G, some rusting to radiator), orange 28e 'Ensign', blue wheels (E, wing bent and chipped) and grey 28f 'Palethorpe's', 'Dinky Toys' inside roof, green wheels (E, left-hand transfer askew, slight bending to wings), in rare original Half-Dozen Trade Box, code no. A1008, 1934 (E)....**£7000**
Rare orange 28a 1st Type lead 'Hornby Trains' Delivery Van, (F) Unrecorded colour variant....**£950**

Rare blue late-version 28b 1st Type 'Pickfords' Delivery Van with diecast hubs and white rubber tyres, circa June 1935 (G, front wings chipped and bent) Unrecorded version....**£950**
Green 28m 2nd Type 'Atco' Delivery Van, (E)....**£750**
Green and cream 29 Motor Bus with 'Marmite' advertisements, metal wheels (M)....**£320**
Light blue and cream 29c Double Decker bus with green roof (G-E)....**£420**
Dark blue and cream 29c Double Decker Bus with grey roof (G, some chipping to roof)....**£300**
Red and cream 29c Double Decker Bus with grey roof (G-E, slight fatigue to base)....**£240**
Lime green and cream 29c Double Decker Bus with grey roof (G-E, some chipping to roof)....**£380**
Dark blue and cream late version 29c Double Decker Bus without grey roof, with black hubs and tyres (G-E, slight fatigue)....**£450**
Turquoise 30a Chrysler 'Airflow' Saloon, with chrome hubs (G)....**£380**
Red and dark red 30b Rolls-Royce (G, small fatigue split in offside window)**£450**
Rare light green and black 30d Daimler (E) Unrecorded colour variant ..**£350**
Green and black 30d Vauxhall, with Vauxhall radiator, spare wheel (E)....**£280**
Rare cream 31 Holland Coachcraft Van with red coachline, with 'Holland Coachcraft Registered Design' transfers, circa 1935 (E, a few chips). This model was used for advertising purposes by Frank Holland, the founder of Holland Coachcraft, and was probably commissioned by him from Frank Hornby. It was bought by the present owner from one of his children. Sold with provenance....**£1200**
Maroon 32 Chrysler 'Airflow' Saloon, with blue hubs circa 1935 (E)....**£500**
No.33 Mechanical Horse and Four Assorted Trailers, with black hubs and white tyres, comprising red 33a Mechanical Horse (G), green 33b Flat Truck (G, slight fatigue), yellow 33e Dust Wagon with blue tinplate top (E) and green 33f 'Castrol' Petrol Tank Wagon (E, one fatigue crack), in original green box, code no. A2036, circa 1937 (G) Four Trailer Set rarer than Five Trailer Set....**£750**
Green and red 33r Mechanical Horse and 'Meccano' Box Van Trailer, 1st Type Horse with long slot and chrome hubs (E)....**£320**
Maroon and black 33r Railway Mechanical Horse and LMS Trailer Van, 2nd Type Horse, with black hubs (E, one axle lug repaired)....**£150**
Blue and black 33r Railway Mechanical Horse and LNER Trailer Van, 2nd Type Horse, with black hubs (E)....**£350**
Brown and cream 33r Railway Mechanical Horse and SR Trailer Van, 2nd Type Horse, green hubs (Horse P-F, Trailer Van G)....**£100**
Red and black 34b Royal Mail Van, with open rear windows (G)....**£85**
Green 35b Racer with driver, with black tyres, circa 1940 (G, some fatigue). Unrecorded colour variant....**£140**
Rare No.36 Motor Cars (with Drivers, Passengers, Footmen) Set, comprising maroon 36a Armstrong Siddeley Limousine with maroon chassis (E, missing one headlight), cream and black 36b Bentley Two-Seater Sports Coupé (F-G), blue and dark blue 36e British Salmson Two-Seater Sports (E, one blister to rear), red and maroon 36f British Salmson Four Seater Sports (G-E), light green and dark green 36d Rover Streamline Saloon (G-E, windscreen uprights repaired), in original box dated 6·38, code no. A2205, with insert and brown board packing piece, 1938 (G, two splits to lid)....**£11,000**
Red 36g Taxi (G, some chips)....**£350**
Rare yellow 36g Taxi (E, a few chips, very slight fatigue over rear wheel arches)....**£800**
37a Civilian Motor Cyclist, with rider in green outfit (E-M)....**£200**
No. 42 Police Set, comprising 42a Police Box, 42b Police Motor Cycle Patrol, 42c Point Duty Policeman in white coat and 42d Point Duty Policeman, in original box, code no. A2114 (E-M, box E)....**£800**
No. 43 RAC Set, comprising 43a RAC Box, 43b RAC Motor Cycle Patrol, 43c RAC Guide and 43d RAC Guide Saluting, in original box, code no. A2064 (E, box E, original '1/9' label in insert)....**£1400**
No.44 AA Set, comprising 44a AA Box, 44b AA Motor Cycle Patrol, 44c Guide directing traffic and 44d AA Guide saluting, in original box, code no. A2065 (E, box E)....**£1600**
No.47 Twelve Road Signs Set, filled in warning triangles, in original yellow box, code no. A2073 (E, 'No Entry' roundel oxidised, box E)....**£260**
Pre-war French Factory Vehicles
Red 14z Triporteur, (E)....**£220**
Rare white and blue 16z Streamlined Train, in original box (E, centre car fatigued and repaired, box E)....**£350**
Blue 24kz Peugeot (E-M)....**£520**
Green and yellow 26z Autocar (E)....**£130**
Green and cream 29dz Parisien Bus, with floor, metal wheels (E-M)....**£280**
Blue 35az Simca Cinq (Fiat Topolino), with white wheels (F)....**£160**
Rare light blue 30B Rolls Royce, 1st Type baseplate, smooth hubs (G). Unrecorded colour variant....**£480**
Rare sand 30C Diamler, 1st Type baseplate, smooth hubs, circa 1946 (G)**£480**
Green 30A Airflow, (G)....**£190**
Dark blue 30B Rolls Royce (E)....**£260**
Rare grey 36A Armstrong Siddeley, moulded chassis with slots, smooth hubs....**£140**

Light green 36B Bentley, moulded chassis with slots, smooth hubs (E)... **£300**
Saxe blue 36B Bentley, moulded chassis without slots, smooth hubs, black tyres (E) ... **£320**
Rare brown 36E British Salmson (two-seater), (overall E) ... **£380**
Red 36E British Salmson (two-seater), (E) ... **£320**
Dark blue and light blue 38A Fraser-Nash, pre-war gold baseplate made from Hornby Series Signal Cabin lithographed tinplate sheet, solid steering wheel, smooth hubs, spread spigot not rivet, 1946 (G-E) ... **£240**
Grey and fawn 38B Sunbeam Talbot, solid steering wheel, silver-edged windscreen, smooth hubs, spread spigot not rivet, 1946 (E) ... **£420**
Blue and putty 38A Fraser-Nash, silver-edged windscreen (G-E) ... **£85**
Light blue and putty 38F Jaguar (E) ... **£160**
Yellow and green 38B Sunbeam Talbot yellow hubs (E) ... **£220**
Grey 39B Oldsmobile, pre-war gold baseplate, smooth hubs (G) ... **£160**
Green 39E Chrysler, pre-war gold baseplate, smooth hubs (F-G) ... **£70**
Rare US issue tan 39B Oldsmobile, tan hubs, blued axles, oval studs,closed baseplate to rear, circa 1952 (E). Unrecorded colour variant. ... **£650**
Rare two-tone blue U.S. issue 39BU Oldsmobile, blue hubs, blued axles, oval studs, closed baseplate to rear, circa 1952 (G, wings F, chipping) ... **£700**
Rare U.S. issue two-tone yellow and red 39EU Chrysler, yellow hubs, blued axles, circa 1952 (F-G, some chipping to roof and wings) ... **£656**

Vectis Auction Results

The letters A-E describes the conditions of each lot as follows:- A+ = As near mint or pristine condition; A = Virtually mint boxed; B+ = Model is near mint, box has very slight faults; B = Slight model or box faults; C = More obvious model chips and box faults inc. tears, but still complete; D = Same as C but box has one or more end flaps missing and model may have faded paint as well as chips; E = Model and box both have considerable faults.

UNBOXED CARS

38E Armstrong Siddeley Sports Grey body and wheels/dark green interior, B+ to A ... **£125**
165 Humber Hawk rare Black lower & all green upper body (no black roof) with front number plate, B+ apart from two small roof chips ... **£140**
157 Jaguar XK120 deep yellow/yellow wheels, brilliant A to A+, rare trade box of six ... **£140**
262 VW 'PTT' yellow body & wheels/black wings, lovely B+ (some touching in to roof) rare ... **£200**
39B Oldsmobile mid blue ... **£230**
40F Hillman Minx dark tan/grey wheels, rare combination, A ... **£160**
40J Austin Somerset dark blue/blue wheels B+ to A ... **£160**

BOXED CARS

103 Austin Healey 100 Sports Touring finish, cream/red int. & wheels/Driver, B+ to A scarce ... **£125**
105 Triumph TR2 Sports Touring finish, lemon/light green interior/driver/spun wheels, B+ in A Correct late light yellow box with yellow spot ... **£120**
206 Maserati Red/white flash & driver/9/yellow plastic wheels (one of which has been fitted inside out!!). A to A+ in B sealed bubble card, scarce late production ... **£240**
102 MG Midget orange/red seats & wheels/'civilian' driver, A to A+ in B+ to A correct box ... **£250**
104 Aston Martin DB3S light pink/red seats & wheels/'civilian' driver, A to A+ in B correct box ... **£170**
155 Ford Anglia turquoise/pale blue interior instead of normal red, A in B+ to A box, scarce ... **£150**
189 Triumph Herald all red, brilliant A to A+ in 'plain' print box, red spot ... **£1700**
405 Universal Jeep orange/red plastic wheels, very rare late production (usual colours are red or dark green), B+ to A in late lighter yellow box C ... **£340**
102 MG Midget Sports orange/red interior & wheels/'civilian' driver, lovely A ... **£160**
105 Triumph TR2 Sports grey/red interior & wheels/'civilian' driver, lovely A (one wheel is B+) in B box ... **£120**
105 Triumph TR2 Sports lemon/light green interior/green wheels/'civilian' driver, B+ to A ... **£160**
152 Austin Devon yellow/blue upper half & wheels, A (tiny touched in spot on O/S front door) in C 'bi-colour' box but spot is pink/green ... **£160**
194 Bentley Coupe gold/cream seat/driver/blue tonneau/SP, A in B+ box **£150**
274 Mini Van 'Joseph Mason's Paints' maroon with leaflet in Special maroon box, all A to A+ ... **£600**
135 Triumph 2000 black/cactus roof/red interior/spun wheels, C in B+ box with luggage, rare colour ... **£160**
145 Singer Vogue rare yellow, B+ ... **£800**
164 Ford Zodiac Mark IV met. bronze/red interior/cast wheels, A rigid perspex cased, scarce colour ... **£110**
197 Morris Mini Traveller rare luminous green/red interior/spun wheels, A in B+ box ... **£80**
197 Morris Mini Traveller dark green body, brown woodwork, yellow interior, spun wheels, A in B box ... **£480**

405 Universal Jeep rare orange/red plastic wheels, B in B box ... **£130**

SMALL COMMERCIALS

465 Morris Van 'Capstan' Navy blue/light blue/blue wheels, A ... **£180**
482 Bedford Van 'Dinky Toys' Orange/yellow upper half & wheels, A to A+ in B+ box ... **£140**
Gift Set 299 Post Office Services with 260 Royal Mail Van B+ to A; **P.O. Telephone Van** A, plus **Telephone Box** B+ & two figures B+, Inner lining is B+, box lid is B ... **£290**
273 'RAC' Mini Van Blue/white/spun wheels, A to A+ in A box ... **£160**
274 'AA' Mini Van Yellow/white/block printed logo, A to A+ in A box **£180**
25D Petrol Tank Wagon grey/open chassis/smooth wheels but early post-war production 'pool', B+ to A ... **£410**
25D Petrol Tank Wagon orange/moulded chassis, B+ to A ... **£380**
412 Austin Wagon lemon/green wheels, brilliant A to A+ in B+ box shows correct spot, rare ... **£400**
413 Austin Covered Wagon light blue/cream/lemon wheels, lovely A in C box, rare ... **£200**
25D Petrol Tank Wagon orange/black/moulded chassis, scarce colour, B unboxed ... **£90**

LARGER COMMERCIALS
(All original boxed unless stated)
GUY

919 'Golden Shred' Red/yellow wheels, lovely A (adverts A to A+) in A striped picture box apart from repaired corner seam ... **£610**
511 4 Ton Lorry first type, two tone blue, B+ to A in B+ to A striped pic box showing correct col. ... **£140**
513 Flat Truck with tailboard, grey/navy blue wings, wheels & chassis, B+ in A early type uncovered box, rare ... **£1100**
513 Flat Truck with tailboard, black wings, wheels & chassis, A ... **£460**
514 'Lyons Swiss Rolls' Van B+ to A in B blue covered box ... **£680**
514 Guy Van 'Weetabix' brilliant A to A+ in B+ box, rare so good .. **£2200**
918 'Ever Ready' Van brilliant A to A+ in B+ striped picture box ... **£180**

FODEN

501 8W Wagon Red cab, back & wheels/black wings & chassis/no hook/silver cab flash, brilliant A to A+ in B early type box with correct Red Dot **£5200**
501 8W Wagon Grey/black/red wheels & cab flash, A to A+ in B+ early box with correct grey spot, rare ... **£1200**
501 8W Wagon Standard tread tyres, B to B+ in C box with late blue covered bottom half ... **£200**
501 Flat Truck Dark green, cab, back & wheels/black wings & chassis/no hook/silver cab flash/'herringbone' tyres, lovely A to A+ in A early type box ... **£460**
502 Flat Truck Blue cab & back/navy blue wings, chassis, wheels & cab flash, A apart from not too noticeable rubs (three places) on cab roof & touching in to N/S Edge of flat bed, in C early type box ... **£700**
503 Flat Truck with tailboard dark green cab, wings & chassis/light green back, wheels & dab flash/hook/standard tread tyres, A part from slight rubs to cab roof, in B+ early box with correct green spot ... **£680**
505 Flat Truck with chains Dark green with light green cab flash & green wheels, B (cab roof & flat bed edges are C), in C blue covered box showing First Cab picture ... **£950**
905 Flat Truck with chains but dark green/green wheels/grey tyres, lovely B+ to A in B box ... **£130**
502 Flat Truck 2nd Cab/red Cab, chassis & wheels/green back/grey tyres in scarce correct early blue covered box showing 2nd Cab picture ... **£600**
504 14 Ton Tanker first cab, two tone blue/silver flash, brilliant A in B+ early type box ... **£260**
504 14 Ton Tanker second cab, red/brown grey tank, scarce B+ in B to C green covered box showing 1st cab picture ... **£350**
903 Flat Truck with Tailboard 2nd cab, violetish blue/orange back/blue wheels, lovely A to A+ in B+ striped picture box ... **£190**
905 Chain Lorry maroon/grey tyres, lovely A in B+ box ... **£200**

BEDFORD

923 Big Bedford Van 'Heinz' sauce bottle, red/yellow B+ (adverts virtually A) box shows correct picture, very scarce ... **£920**
450 TK Box Van 'Castrol' met. bright green/red plastic wheels, B to B+ in A yellow pic box ... **£100**
522 Big Bedford Lorry blue/deep yellow back/yellow wheels, B+ to A in B blue covered box stamped '13 DE 1953' on lid apart from two circular holes at each end of box base, scarce ... **£110**
923 Big Bedford Van 'Heinz Baked Beans' brilliant A to A+ in B+ striped picture box ... **£350**
252 Refuse Wagon light brown/windows/green shutters/red wheels, A in C later type card box, scarce ... **£75**
252 Refuse Wagon orange/grey/green plastic shutters/red plastic wheels/silver grill/windows, another lovely A in B to C late type box, very scarce ... **£220**
923 'Heinz Baked Beans' Van red/yellow, lovely A in B box ... **£200**
930 Pallet Jekta Van yellow/orange/3 pallets/instructions, lovely B+ to A, scarce ... **£190**

LEYLAND

944 Octopus Tanker 'Shell' 'BP', grey chassis & wheels, brilliant A to A+ in B 'end flap' detailed picture box, scarce **£210**

417 Comet Lorry violetish blue/dark yellow/red wheels, lovely brilliant colours, B+ to A in B yellow picture box, scarce **£170**

OTHER COMMERCIALS

975 Ruston Bucyrus Excavator Lemon/red/green/grey rollers, A to A+, A special box **£230**

980 'Express' Horse Van Maroon/red wheels, very scarce, USA issue, A in B+ correct box **£470**

983 Car Carrier & Trailer Red/grey/'Dinky Auto Service' B (rear ramp is B) with top inner shaped lining in B long striped picture box **£220**

965 'Terex' Rear Dump Truck light yellow B+ to A in B 'lift off' lid detailed pic box, scarce **£180**

968 BBC TV Roving Eye inner lining A **£100**

979 Racehorse Transporter 'Newmarket' lemon/grey with two horses & packing ends, A to A+ **£260**

Gift Set 900 'Site Building' content minimum B+ **£1400**

988 ABC TV Transmitter Van with cupola A, box is B+ to A **£160**

FARM

305 David Brown Tractor red/yellow, lovely A in B+, detailed picture box, rare **£220**

BUSES & COACHES

29G Luxury Coach Rare cream/red flashes & wheels, B+ unboxed **£220**

291 London Bus 'Exide' red body & wheels, A apart from rear roof edge chips, in C picture box **£75**

291 London Bus 'Exide' spun wheels, A in B box **£160**

29E Single Deck Bus cream/blue/black wheels, lovely A, unboxed, scarce **£140**

282 Duple Roadmaster Coach rare US export issue, dark green/cream B+ to A unboxed **£150**

ACCESSORIES

785 Service Station Kit appears complete & unmade, A to A+ in B+ box, scarce **£100**

750 Telephone Call Box yellow trade box of 6 with dividers, two are B+, two are B, and two are C (wear to roofs), box is A, rare box **£230**

772 British Road Signs set of 24, all B+ to A+ in A box **£150**

44B 'AA' Motorcycle Patrol yellow trade box of six, all black rubber tyres, B+ to A **£260**

DUBLO DINKY

065 Morris Pick Up Red B **£65**

067 Austin Taxi Blue/cream, A in B+ box **£50**

068 Royal Mail Van B in B+ to A box **£50**

EMERGENCY SERVICES

288 Superior Cadillac Ambulance - 'Falck' black/white/stretcher, A to A+ in bubble pack with broken perspex, scarce Danish issue **£100**

956 Turntable Fire Escape with large Berliet cab, red/black, A box **£160**

MILITARY

25WM(640) Bedford Military Truck B+ unboxed, scarce USA export issue **£180**

341 Military Trailer A to A+ unboxed, very rare **£460**

651 Centurion Tank A to A+ in scarce US issue, gold 'see through' box good B+ **£100**

661 Recovery Tractor windows & plastic wheels, A to A+ **£200**

Wallis & Wallis Auction Results

908 Scarce Supertoys Mighty Antar with transformer, yellow truck with light grey trailer, red ramps and wheels, complete with Alsthom plastic transformer in dark grey, original box, VGC **£400**

25D Pre-war Petrol Tank Wagon 2nd Type, 'Mobiloil' red with black open chassis, 'Mobiloil' to sides, smooth wheels, QGC **£120**

152 War Time Royal Tank Corps Light Tank Set containing light tank (152a), reconnaissance car (152b) and an Austin 7 (152c) all in olive green, original first type grey display box, GC **£170**

151 War Time Royal Tank Corps Medium Tank Set comprising medium tank (151a), 6 wheeled transport wagon (151b) cooker trailer (151c) and water tank trailer (151d) all in olive green, original display box, VGC **£210**

162 War Time 18 Pounder Quick Firing Field Gun Unit comprising light dragon tractor (162a) trailer (162b) all in olive green, original display box, GC. **£140**

28B Pre War 1st Type Van 'Pickfords' two piece van, dark blue, 'Pickfords Removals and Storage, over 100 Branches' to sides, smooth wheels with white rubber tyres, GC to VGC **£600**

28F Pre War 1st Type Van 'Palethorpes' two piece van in grey, 'Palethorpes Royal Cambridge' to sides, solid metal wheels, QGC **£300**

60B Pre War DH Leopard Moth Aeroplane green with yellow wing tips and tailplane, GC **£75**

60k Pre War Percival Gull Aeroplane Amy Mollinson light blue and silver with light blue registration letters G-ADZO, GC **£140**

920 Guy Warrior Heinz Van 'Heinz 57 Varieties' and a tomato ketchup bottle decals to sides. Boxed, VGC **£2200**

162A Military Light Dragon Tractor fitted with solid wheels and white rubber tyres in thin axles, mid olive green, semi gloss finish, GC **£50**

289 Six Routemaster Buses unopened pack of six, cellophane wrapped boxes, showing 'Ssschweppes' decals to side. Mint **£95**

949 Supertoys Wayne School Bus orange with black lines 'School Bus' etc to bodywork, original box, VGC **£190**

953 Supertoys Continental Touring Coach turquoise with white roof, 'Dinky Continental Tours' to roof sides, original box, VGC **£190**

38D Sunbeam Talbot Sports Car brown with blue tonneau; and a **38C Lagonda Sports Coupe** dark green with a deep green interior, GC to VGC **£230**

126 Motor Show Presentation Set comprising Austin 1800 in metallic blue, a Ford Cortina in pale yellow, a Vauxhall 101 in metallic maroon and a Ford Zodiac in silver. QGC to VGC **£350**

Camouflaged Aeroplanes Set No.68: containing Frobisher airliner (68B) (wing tips missing), Fairey battle bomber (60S) (one missing) 3 x Spitfire fighter (62E) 3 x Hawker Hurricane fighter (62H) Armstrong Whitworth Whitley bomber (62T) Armstrong Whitworth Ensign liner (68A), also missing from the set are two Bristol Blenheim bomber (62D), the aircraft are contained in an original box in VGC for age. Most aircraft are suffering from fatigue. AF-QGC**£1500**

988 Supertoys ABC TV Transmitter Van light blue/light grey livery, complete with detachable dish, original box, VGC-Mint **£145**

Set 47 Road Signs comprising 12 various types mounted on yellow card insert, contained in early type original box, VGC **£120**

120 Jaguar E Type metallic blue, cream interior, black plastic detachable roof, original box, GC **£975**

923 Supertoys Big Bedford Van 'Heinz' red cab and chassis, yellow box with Baked Bean can 'Heinz 57 Varieties' to sides, yellow wheels and grey rubber tyres, original box. VGC **£350**

923 Supertoys Big Bedford Van 'Heinz' tomato ketchup bottle version, cab and chassis red, yellow body, original box. GC-VGC **£500**

157 Jaguar XK 120 Coupe white, fawn wheels, black tyres, original associated box, VGC-Mint **£160**

103 Austin Healey 100 Sports red with grey interior and wheels, black tyres, driver, original box, VGC **£110**

104 Aston Martin DB3S light blue, dark blue interior, mid blue wheels, black tyres, driver, original box. VGC-Mint **£130**

Sotheby's, Billinghurst, Sussex Auction Sale – June 1995

A rare Dinky Toys No.28C Delivery Van 'Manchester Guardian' finished in red and black with gold lettering **£943**

A rare green and grey Dinky Supertoy No.935 Leyland Octopus Flat Truck with chains, in original box, excellent condition, minute chip to fuel tank, rub mark to cab roof **£977**

Dinky Toys Sports Car Gift Set No.149 comprising Nos. 108, 109, 107, 110 and 111, in original blue and white striped box, paint chip on one driver's helmet, cardboard insert missing, pen lines on base, one box corner damaged ... **£460**

Dinky Toys No.919 Guy Van 'Golden Shred', in original blue striped box, some scratches and paint chipping, box slightly worn **£207**

Vectis Model Auctions July 1995 Sale RW – Ridged Wheels

No.110 Aston Martin DB3 Sports, rare light green/red interior & RW/22, A (shade as is No. 236 Connaught RC) **£400**

No.156 Rover 75 cream lower body, dark blue upper body, B+ in C to D box with blue spot, rare **£330**

No.159 Morris Oxford rare pale brown (sand) body & RW, B+ in C box with brown spot, at least as rare as the mid-blue version **£1700**

No.167 AC Aceca Coupe, all light cream body, spun wheels, lighter yellow box, rare **£320**

No.189 Triumph Herald very dark, nearly navy blue/very pale blue/SP, B to B+ in C box with fawn spot, rare promotional colour **£380**

No.505 Foden Chain Lorry, 1st cab, dark green/light green cab flash/green RW/tank slits, C blue covered box with correct picture, rare **£600**

No.505 Another First Cab as previous lot but exceptionally rare, maroon/silver flash, cab is B, flat bed is A, edges of wings and flat bed are C, box is C**£2200**

No.342 Austin Mini-Moke, rare pre-production sample in yellow plastic with light grey canopy/military green bonnet and speedwheels, A unboxed, an outstanding and interesting Dinky rarity **£500**

Oak Shop Display Cabinet 'Dinky Toys' with four glass shelves and two rear opaque sliding doors, lovely A, scarce so good **£700**

No.301 Field Marshall Tractor, orange/tan driver/green wheels (plastic at front), black rubber tyres, rare late issue with inner lining in B lighter yellow box**£180**

No.289 RM Bus "Meccano Multi Kit' gold body, advert labels are "Meccano", "DINKY Toys" and "Plastic Meccano", exceptionally rare issue, A in standard bubble pack but with typed label, "Special hand-made model to commemorate the press preview of the London Bus Advertising Meccano – Nov. 1973"**£570**

Wallis & Wallis, Lewes, Sussex
Late July 1995

A scarce original Dinky shop display from the 1968 epic film "Battle of Britain", card construction in blue and yellow livery "Dinky Toys" headings in red, made to display DT No.719 Spitfire MkII and DT No.721 Junkers JU 87B Stuka. VGC to Mint (very minor wear)...**£160**

A scarce pre-war Dinky 33 series mechanical horse and trailer No.33r, "LMS Express Parcels Traffic" livery, VGC for age (some chipping, no fatigue)**£180**

A scarce pre-war Dinky 33 series mechanical horse and trailer No.33d, in dark green "Meccano Engineering For Boys" livery, GC to VGC for age **£205**

A pre-war Dinky medium tank (151a) in matt olive green and gloss baseplate, complete with aerial and tracs. GC to VGC **£160**

A scarce Dinky US export model Austin Military covered wagon (625 30SM) in olive green, complete with rear tilt. GC...**£260**

A scarce Dinky US export model Ford Sedan staff car (139am) in olive green with US star markings to roof and sides, VGC..**£160**

A scarce Dinky US export model Daimler military ambulance (624 30hm) in olive green. **£150**

A Dinky "Tiny's Mini Moke" from the TV series The Enchanted House (350) moke in original display box, mint **£100**

A Dinky Superfast gift set No.245 in original display box, VGC to Mint**£110**

A Dinky Supertoys military 10 ton Foden army truck (622) in olive green, complete with tilt, in original box, VGC (minor wear to box) **£120**

A rare Dinky Leyland Comet wagon (532) dark blue cab and chassis with mid blue loadbed and sides, red wheel hubs, in original display box, VGC...**£260**

A Dinky Supertoys Foden 14 ton tanker, "Regent" (942) in dark blue, red and white livery, in original box, VGC to mint (minor wear) **£200**

A scarce pre-war Dinky Royal Tank Corps medium tank set No.151 in original display box, QGC for age **£320**

Lacy Scott, Bury St. Edmunds
July 1995 Sale

A Foden flat truck with tailboard, red cab & flat bed (no hook), (503), wrong photo on box, BDG **£240**

A Foden 8 wheel wagon 1st series, brown cab/chassis, (501), BM **£250**

A Foden 14 ton tanker, 1st series, red cab/chassis, fawn tank (504), BM **£360**

A missle erector vehicle with launching platform (666), BM **£150**

A trade box of six 4 berth caravans, (3 blue, 3 green) (188), BM.............**£160**

A trade box of 6 caravans, blue & cream (190), BM-BDM....................**£130**

A trade box of 6 grass cutters (green blades), (105E), BM **£90**

Bonhams of Chelsea, London
Auction Sale – July 1995

A Dinky 930 Bedford Van, English, 1960-1964. The Pallet Jekta van finished in yellow and orange with Dinky Toys logo, pallets and instructions, boxed (E, box E), few minor chips **£110**

A rare Dinky 513 'Weetabix' Guy Van English, 1952. The 1st type van finished in yellow with yellow ridged wheels, boxed (E, box E), Weetabix logo has a few minor flakes **£950**

A Dinky 918 'Ever Ready' Guy Van, English, 1955-1958. The 2nd type cab/body finished in blue, with Ever Ready logo and red grooved wheels, boxed (E, box G-E), one logo has a small scratch **£160**

A Dinky 923 'Heinz' Big Bedford Van, English, 1955-1958. Red and yellow with Heinz 57 varieties and Baked Bean can logo, boxed (E, box E).............**£220**

A rare Dinky 920 'Heinz' Guy Van English, 1960, the red and yellow van with 'Heinz 57 Varieties' and Tomato Ketchup bottle logo (G–E), few minor chips, unboxed **£550**

A rare Dinky No.149 gift set English, 1958-1961. Set comprising a 107 Sunbeam Alpine, 108 M.G. Midget, 109 Austin Healey, 110 Aston Martin, and a Triumph TR2, in original box with printed insert card (F-G, box G) **£520**

Factory Pre-Production, Sample Models & Original Drawings
Vectis Model Auction – July 1995

1. 'New Super Value Champs'. Large chunky diecast vehicles. Plastic mock-ups of the five models shown in the 1980 catalogue 59011/2/3 and 59050/1. i) Tipper Truck, ii) 'YORKIE' Container Truck, iii) 'CRASH' Breakdown Truck, iv) DISCO Roadshow Van, v) 'SAFARI PARK' Van plus artwork used at the 1979 Earls Court Toy Show. **£300.**

2. 'New Starchasers'. Six-wheeled surface and flying space vehicles. 811 Command Vehicle, 813 Radar Scanner Vehicle, 814 Solar Camera Vehicle, 825 Grekon Invader, 826 Star Freighter, 827 Stella Interceptor, 828 Flying Saucer. Diecast with 'DINKY TOYS – STAR CHASERS – Made in England' cast into base. Blister packed. **£300.**
N.B. Additional models pictured in the 1980 catalogue but never seen.

3. 950 Foden Tanker 'BURMAH'. Pre-production sample used at the 1977 Earls Court Toy Fair in Bright Red livery. **£210.**

4. Gift Set 302 'Emergency Squad'. Set shown in the 1979 catalogue but never released. Production sample 288 Yellow/White Superior Cadillac Ambulance. Plus Two Transit Vans with resin extended bonnets, based on 269 'POLICE' & 417 'MOTORWAY SERVICES' plus 263 Airport Fire Rescue Tender, Yellow body with White ladder and shown on the 1979 catalogue. **£140.**

5. Convoy Series of Trucks. 383 'NATIONAL CARRIERS' in new pictorial blister card pack, plus 388 Cement Mixer Truck, Orange, pre-production sample and 389 'TEXACO' Tanker with resin tank. Plus 386 'GODFREY DAVIS' Hire Truck in Dark Blue, plus 387 'PICKFORDS' Truck in Dark Blue/White with Red advert – see the 1979 catalogue. **£120.**

6. 449 Johnston Road Sweepers. Promotional Mock up made for 'TUBES – Part of the Dimec Group' in Light Blue/Orange, plus all Yellow sample for 'JOHNSTONS' but without their logo. **£230.**

7. Racing Jaguar XJC (No number). Pre-production sample in Red and Yellow with body stripe and RN '24'. Black interior with 'STEED' figure in drivers seat. 'DINKY TOYS – Made in Hong Kong' on base. **£640.**

8. 113 'STEEDS' Jaguar XJC No 219 from 'THE NEW AVENGERS'. Resin model in Metallic Blue with Yellow stripe as shown on the 1979 catalogue. It is known that a few diecast samples were issued to salesmen. **£570.**

9. 219 THE BIG CAT JAGUAR XJC. Sample model in exceptionally rare window box with 'STEED' figure in drivers seat. **£660.**

10. 170 Ford Granada Ghia. Pre-production sample in Metallic Silver with Red plastic interior, Speed wheels, bare metal baseplate inscribed 'DINKY TOY – FORD GRANADA – MADE IN ENGLAND'. Model displayed at the 1979 Earls Court Toy Show. **£800.**

11. 248 'LIVERPOOL FOOTBALL CLUB'. Single Decker Coach, see picture on page 15 1979 catalogue with White resin mock up body and plastic roof with Red club crest. **£530.**

12. 115 Taxi. Pre-production sample in 'UNITED BISCUITS' colours but with 'KRAZY CAB' logo and Keystone Kops type figures. **£300.**

13. 285 London Taxi. A production sample with Maroon body with Grey interior. **£300.**

Factory Prototypes and Samples.

291 Rare Orange Dinky Atlantean Bus – Factory sample **£101.**

432 Foden 6-wheel Tipper, Prototype 1st shot casting in White and Yellow with plastic bumper, plus original drawings **£168.**

211 Triumph TR7 Colour samples:- i) Red with Grey interior, ii) Blue with Black interior; iii) Metallic Green with Grey interior, iv) Metallic Green with Black interior **£78.**

192 Range Rover Sample, Metallic Turquoise, plus 227 Beach Buggy sample with Grey hood & *'FIRE'* logo **£157.**

289 Rare Silver 'SILVER JUBILEE' Routemaster Bus used as promotional by Meccano Ltd at Trade Fairs **£135.**

295 'YELLOW PAGES' Atlantean Bus – Factory approval model with trial labels, plastic wheels and Yellow driver **£506.**

352 Shado 2 Mobile with factory substituted small Olive Green wheels.

940 Mercedes-Benz Covered Truck, unassembled sample with Yellow cab and Dark Blue canopy **£146.**

181 Volkswagen Sedan (Beetle) Colour samples:- i) Pale Blue body with baseplate, ii) Pale Blue with spun alloy hubs, iii) Metallic Blue, iv) Metallic Turquoise. (All unfinished castings) **£393.**

190 Monteverdis – unissued colour samples:- i) Copper with White interior, ii) Metallic Blue with White interior (both of these have no wing mirror holes) and iii) Metallic Red (standard colour) but with unissued Black interior **£472.**

No Ref. 'Scarlet Arrow' Delivery Lorry, prototype based on 22c Motor Truck, Yellow body, Red hubs and grille, Red arrow to cab roof, c.1946 **540.**

38f Jaguar Sports Prototype, Red with Maroon interior with unpressed baseplate, c.1946 **£472.**

39d Buick Viceroy Saloon with 'COLOUR SCHEME' and '2 APR 1946' on cream tie on label. Stone body colour sample **£731.**

29h Duple Roadmaster Coach 'First Shot' Colour sample, two tone Red lower body and Cream upper body, C.1952-54 **247.**

107 Sunbeam Alpine Sports Car 'First Shot' unfinished castings:- i) Maroon body, Grey interior **£50.**

110 Aston Martin DB 3S Sports Car 'First Shot' unfinished casting. Grey body, Blue interior, no silver detailing **£50.**

111 Triumph TR2 Sports Car 'First Shot' unfinished casting. Pink body, Blue interior and windscreen, no silver detailing **£61.**

No Ref: An important Dinky Factory wooden mock-up model of the unissued Green 'Albion' 'MILK MARKETING BOARD' Tanker. (See the Christie's advertisement for picture), c.1980. Lot included original drawings **£2475.**

Original Dinky Toy Factory Drawings

Christie's Model Auction – September 1995

These may be identified by the Job Number, signature and date — examples from sale:-

Job 13946 261 Telephone Service Van, (G), dates 27.8.57, signed 'B.A.B.' **£101.**

Job 13980 260 'ROYAL MAIL' Van, (F), dated 26.1.54 and dates up to 27.8.57, signed 'N.B.' **£101.**

Job 14729 Morris 'CAPSTAN' Van, (G), signed 'R.N.' and dated 10.8.56 and 27.8.57 **£225.**

Job 13879 480 Bedford 'KODAK', (G) and Job 13879A 481 Bedford 'OVALTINE' Van (G), signed 'J.W.' and dated 4.2.53 and 28.7.57 **£168.**

Job 13890 482 Bedford 'DINKY TOYS' Van, (G), signed 'G.L.', and dated 18.4.56 **£157.**

Job 13964A 923 Big Bedford 'HEINZ' Van (G), 'TOMATO KETCHUP' adverts, signed 'R.V.', undated, memo dated 18.6.56 **£337.**

Job 13009 919 Guy 'GOLDEN SHRED' Van, (G), signed 'F.G.' dated 28.12.56 **£900*.**

Job 13010/D 514 Guy 'SPRATTS' Van, (G), signed 'J.C.', dated 7.7.52 **£315.**

Job 13010/E 918 Guy 'EVER READY' Van, (G-E), signed 'V.R.', dated 26.10.54 and 19.10.55 **£180.**

Job 13018 920 Guy Warrior 'HEINZ' Van, (G-E), 'TOMATO KETCHUP' adverts, signed 'C.B.', dated 29.10.60 **£292*.**

Job 14791 Unissued Guy Warrior Flat Truck with Tailboard, (G), signed 'F.G.', dated 22.11.56 & 14.1.60 etc. **£270*.**

Job 14794 Unissued Guy Warrior 'GOLDEN SHRED' Van, (F-G), signed 'H.R.B.', dated 26.3.57 & 14.1.60 etc. **£562*.**

Job 10896 29c Double Deck Bus 'DUNLOP', signature indistinct, dated 22.7.37 plus dates up to 3.11.61 (G) **£360*.**

Job 7876 943 Leyland Octopus 'ESSO' Tanker (G-E), signed 'E.R', dated 19.2.57 & 10.4.63 **£236.**

Job 13120 417 Leyland 'Comet' (F-G), signed 'D.L.M.', dated 26.8.48 and 8.4.58 etc. **£131.**

Job 12162 501 (1st Type) Foden Diesel 8-wheel Wagon, signed 'H.J.H.', dated 26.4.46 etc. (F-G) **£213.**

Job 12174 503 (1st Type) Foden Flat Platform with Tailboard, signed 'H.J.H', dated 11.2.47 etc. (G) **£168.**

Job 12821 504 (1st Type) Foden 8-wheel Tanker, (G), signed 'H.J.H.', dated 31.3.48 etc. (G) **£180.**

Job 12821B 941 (2nd Type) Foden 'MOBILGAS' Tanker, (G), dated 6.11.52 and 3.7.57, signed 'N.B.', **£393.**

Job 12821C 942 (2nd Type) Foden 'REGENT' Tanker, (G), signed 'F.J.R.', dated 15.10.53 and 2.5.57 **£180*.**

Original Dinky Toy Factory Drawings

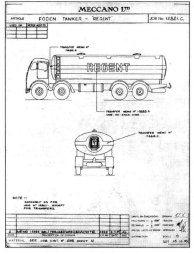

942 Foden Tanker

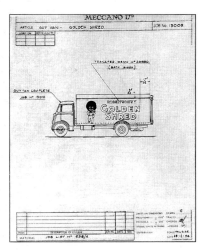

919 Guy Van

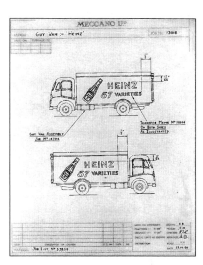

920 Guy Warrior Van

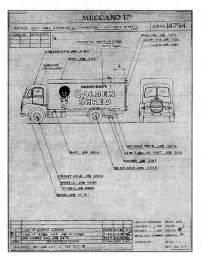

Unissued Guy Warrior Van

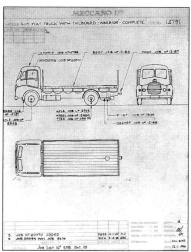

Unissued Guy Warrior Flat Truck
with Tailboard

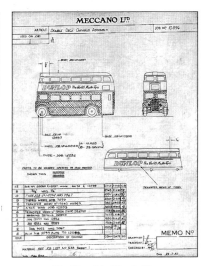

29c Double Deck Bus

Sold by Christies, South Kensington, London in September 1995 and pictures reproduced by their kind permission.

EXCLUSIVE FIRST EDITIONS — E.F.E.

Leyland Atlantean (Park Royal) — 18102 'London Transport'

A.E.C. Regent III (Orion body) — 19701 'Sheffield City'

Leyland PD2 Highbridge — 16107 'Stratford Blue'

Daimler CVG6 (Orion body) — 19803 'Dundee Corporation'

A.E.C. Routemaster — 15616 'London Transport'

A.E.C. Regent V (Orion body)— 19703 'St Helens'

A.E.C. Routemaster Provincial — 15615 'United Counties'

Leyland Atlantean — 16509 'Birmingham City'

i

EXCLUSIVE FIRST EDITIONS — E.F.E.

A.E.C. Routemaster Open Top — 1780 'London Coaches'

Daimler CVG6 Orion — 19801 'City of Manchester'

Bristol Lodekka — 14202 'Midland General'

Leyland PD2 Lowbridge — 16004 'Devon General'

Leyland National Short 2 Door — 16603 'Ensign Bus'

Leyland National Long, Volvo — 17301

Harrington Cavalier — 12109 'Robin Hood'

Bristol LS Bus — 16301 'United'

EXCLUSIVE FIRST EDITIONS — E.F.E.

Bristol MW Coach — 16205 'Wilts & Dorset'

Harrington Cavalier — 12101 'Southdown'

Plaxton Panorama De-Luxe — 15706DL 'Bristol Greyhound'

Bristol CS with MW style body — 16209 'United'

Bedford SB Duple Vega — 18706 'Barton Transport'

Bedford SB Duple Vega Coach — 18704 'Southern Vectis'

Leyland TS8 Tiger — 18301 'Yorkshire Woollen'

Leyland Tiger TS8 — 18405 'Lincolnshire'

EXCLUSIVE FIRST EDITIONS — E.F.E.

A.E.C. Artic Semi-Trailer Box Van — 19501 'Hoover'

A.E.C. Semi-Trailer Flat Bed — 19601 'British Road Services'

Leeds Tramcar with Bow Collector — 13404 W.W. II Livery

Atkinsons Semi-Trailer Flat Bed — 19302

Atkinson Semi-Trailer Boxvan — 19401 'Flowers Brewery'

L-R Triumph Roadster, Vitesse, MGB & Austin Healey Sprite

LLEDO 'MODELS OF DAYS GONE'

Rupert Bear Limited Edition Set RUL 1003 L-R Bottom Up:-
DG59 015a Bedford 30 cwt Truck, DG63 008a,
Bedford 13 cwt Delivery Van, DG43 019a 1931 Morris Van

Rupert Bear Issues L-R Top down:- DG11 026a, Horse Drawn Removal Van; DG16 039a, 1934 Dennis Parcels Van;
DG21 045a 1934 Chevrolet Van; DG51 010a, 1934 Chevrolet Boxvan; DG52 013a, 1935 Morris Parcels Van; DG44 015a,
1937 Scammell 6-wheeler

LLEDO 'MODELS OF DAYS GONE'

Golden Age of Steam Limited Edition Models:- Top down L-R DG6 126a 'Caledonian Railway', 127a 'Great Eastern Railway', 128a 'North British Railway', 129a 'Great Western Railway'

Top Down L-R DG74 Mini, DG71 Morris LD150 Van, DG72 VW Beetle, DG73 VW Transporter

LLEDO 'MODELS OF DAYS GONE'

L-R Top down: '7-Up' Issues, DG26 017a, 1934 Chevrolet Bottle Delivery Truck, DG30 018a, 1939 Chevrolet Panel Van, DG 58 012a, Morris 'Z' Van, DG59 016a, Bedford 30cwt Truck

L-R Top Down:- 'Pepsi' Issues DG6 122a, Model '"T" Ford Van, DG28 033a, 1934 Mack Canvas-Back Truck, DG50 010a, 1926 Bull-Nose Morris Van, DG58 006a, 1950 Morris 'Z' Van, DG59 007a, 1950 Bedford 30cwt Truck, DG61 004a, 1953 Pontiac Delivery Van

LLEDO 'MODELS OF DAYS GONE'

DG75 Bristol Lodekka Double Deck Buses 1/87 Scale

DG71 Morris LD 150 Vans 1/50 Scale

DG74 Austin 7 Mini 1/43 Scale

DG69 Morris Minor Vans 1/43 Scale

E.F.E. MODELS
Exclusive First Editions

In 1989 a range of models called 'Exclusive First Editions' was introduced with the intention of satisfying a number of requirements that collectors were beginning to express at the time. Initially only commercial vehicles and buses were planned though cars have also made an appearance. The models are collectable as a growing range of vehicles, colours and liveries, a particular strength being the introduction of various bus types not tackled by other model manufacturers. The decision to produce the models to a constant scale of 1:76 ('00' gauge) means that not only do the various vehicles look right together but they can also be used by model railway enthusiasts.

To maintain compatibility with other publications, this listing is divided into three main areas of interest:
1. Buses, Coaches and Trams,   2. Cars,   3. Commercial Vehicles.

Some of the early issues carried no reference numbers. These have been listed first and subsequent issues of the same models which were given references follow in number order. Models enhanced by the addition of 'loads' or extra detail were marketed by EFE as 'Deluxe'. These versions of the original model are listed together following the numbered models in each section.
Gift Sets are listed separately and it should be noted that some liveries and logos only exist in certain sets, the particular model not being available in that form as an individual item.

The listings provide sufficient detail to identify the models for pricing purposes and a 'Market Price Range' is quoted where this information is helpful. Current models still available in shops are generally shown as 'NRP' (the current normal retail price). If a model is listed separately but is only available in a set then 'GSP' (Gift Set Price) is shown and reference to that section will give the price for the set. Collectors wishing for further details (of casting modifications, colour variations, promotional or special productions, etc) are recommended to read:

'EFE - A Collectors Guide', by Ken Benham

This and other publications are available from the EFE Official Collectors Club. The address is at the end of these listings.

Buses, Coaches and Trams

Ref. No.	Year(s)	Model Type	Model Features and Size	Market Price Range	

AEC Regent Double-Deck Bus, (closed top)

Base A is smooth with 'AEC REGENT' in raised lettering,
Base B is textured with 'AEC REGENT' in raised lettering,
Base C is textured with 'RT/RTL' in raised lettering.

'London Transport' fleetname

Ref. No.	Year(s)	Model Type	Model Features and Size	Market Price Range	
-	1989	'STAR GROUP'	Red body, Cream stripe, 'RTW 75', supplied with additional labels and numbered certificate 001 - 288	£100-125	☐
-	1989	'STAR GROUP'	Red body, Cream stripe, 'RTW 75', supplied with additional labels and numbered certificate 289 - 1008	£75-85	☐
-	1989	'STAR GROUP'	Red body, Yellow stripe, 'RTW 75'	£40-50	☐
10101	1989	'DURACELL'	Red body, Cream stripe, 'RT 981', base A	£17-19	☐
10101	1989	'DURACELL'	Red body, Cream stripe, 'RT 206', base A	£17-19	☐
10101	1989	'DURACELL'	Red body, Cream stripe, 'RT 206', base B. Also in Gift Set 99901	£17-19	☐
-	1989	'RT 50 YEARS'	Red body, Cream stripe, 'RT 3254', base A	£50-60	☐
-	1989	'RT 50 YEARS'	Dark Green body, Cream stripe, 'RT 3254', base A	£60-70	☐
-	1989	'RT 50 YEARS'	Dark Green body, Yellow stripe, 'RT 3254', base A	£350-400	☐
-	1989	'FISHERMANS FRIEND'	Red body, Cream stripe, 'RT 3254', base A, special box	£22-28	☐
10104	1990	'SCHWEPPES'	Red body, 'RT 858', base B, also in Gift Set 99901	£14-16	☐
10105	1990	'TATE & LYLE'	Red body, 'RT 4093', base B, part of Gift Set 99901	GSP	☐
10106	1990	'RANK HOVIS'	Red body, 'RT 206', base B, part of Gift Set 99902	GSP	☐
10106 DL	1993	'RANK HOVIS'	'deluxe' version of previous model, with registration plates	£15-20	☐
10107	1990	'DULUX'	Red body, 'RT 33', base C	£38-43	☐
10108	1990	'FISHERMANS FRIEND'	Re-issue of 1989 model, base B, in Gift Set 99902	GSP	☐
10109	1990	'BIRDS CUSTARD'	Red body, 'RT 4572', base C	£24-27	☐
10110	1991	'TAYLOR WOODROW'	Red body, 'RT 4331', base C, part of Gift Set 19904	GSP	☐
10111	1991	'BARCLAYS'	Red body, 'RT 4245', base C	£19-22	☐
10112	1991	'VERNONS'	Red body, 'RT 2861', base C	£23-26	☐
10116	1992	'AIR FRANCE'	Red body, 'RT 3402', base C	£19-22	☐
10127	1995	'DULUX'	Green body, 'RT 3148', base C (Green)	£14-16	☐
10121A	1995	'DULUX/ALLSORTS'	Green body, 'RT 3148', base C (Green)	£14-16	☐
10121B	1995	'DULUX/ST ALBANS '95'	Green body, 'RT 3148', base C (Green)	£14-16	☐
10121C	1995	'DULUX/BAXTERS'	Green body, 'RT3148', base C (Kidney machine appeal bus)	£23-26	☐
—	1995	'ALLSORTS'	Green body, 'RT 3254', base A (Black)	£175-200	☐
16402	1994	'PREMIUM BONDS'	Green body, Cream windows, 'RT602', base C	£18-22	☐
16402A	1994	'ST ALBANS '94'	Green body, Cream windows, 'RT 602', base C	£27-32	☐
16401	1994	'NATIONAL SAVINGS'	Red body, Cream windows, 'RT ???', base C	GSP	☐
16403	1994	'PEARL ASSURANCE'	Red body, 'RT ???', base C	£15-20	☐
10110DL	1994	'TAYLOR WOODROW'	Red body, 'RT 4331', base C	£14-17	☐

'London Country' fleetname

Ref. No.	Year(s)	Model Type		Market Price Range	
101005	1989	'BEATTIES'	Green body, 'RT 1044', base A	£28-32	☐
10103	1990	'BIRDS EYE'	Green body, 'RT 4050', base B, singly and in Gift Set 99901	£14-16	☐

'Greenline' fleetname

-	1990	'PEARL ASSURANCE'	Green body, 'RT 3639', base B	£25-35	☐
10102	1989	'BUXTED CHICKENS'	Green body, 'RT 981', base A	£17-19	☐
10102	1990	'BUXTED CHICKENS'	Green body, 'RT 981', base B	£17-19	☐
10117	1992	'EFE CLUB 1992'	Green, 'RT 3254', base B, 'Bullseye' motif	£45-55	☐

Provincial operators and fleetnames

-	1989	'EVENING DESPATCH'	'Midland Red', Red body, base A, numbered certificate	£35-45	☐
-	1990	'EFE 1'	'Midland Red', Red body, base B, numbered certificate	£14-17	☐
-	1990	'EFE FENCE CLUB'	'Midland Red', Red body, base B, 350 only, numbered certificates	£150-175	☐
			Without a certificate	£100-120	☐
-	1989	'ATKINSONS'	'Coventry', Maroon body, base A, with certificate	£65-80	☐
-	1989	'PAIGNTON ZOO'	'Devon General', Maroon body, base A, with certificate	£125-145	☐
-	1990	'SMITHS BEER'	'Birmingham', Blue/Ivory body, base A	£45-50	☐
-	1990	'DULUX'	'Glasgow', Yellow/Green body, base A	£45-50	☐
-	1990	'GARDEN FESTIVAL'	'Northern', Red body, base C, 5,000 only, numbered certificates	£12-15	☐
10113	1991	'COURIER ADVERTISER'	'Dundee', Green/White body, base C	£40-50	☐
10114	1992	'LONDON/MANCHESTER'	'Bradford', Blue/White body, base C	£15-20	☐
10118	1993	(no advert)	'St.Helens Corporation', Red/Cream, route '6'	£11-13	☐
10119	1994	'HULL'	Blue and White body, base C	£11-13	☐
10120	1994	'ENSIGN BUS'	Blue and Silver body, base C	£11-13	☐

AEC Regent Double-Deck Bus, (open top)

-	1990	'EFE 2'	'Birmingham', Blue/Ivory body, base A, with numbered certificate	£12-14	☐
-	1990	'COLMANS'	'London', Red body, base B	£30-35	☐
-	1990	'See The Island'	'Southern Vectis', Cream body, base B	£140-165	☐
10201	1989	'BEACHY HEAD'	'Eastbourne', Ivory/Blue body, base A	£8-10	☐
10201	1990	'BEACHY HEAD'	'East Bourne', Ivory/Blue body, base B	£8-10	☐
10202	1989	'COLMANS'	'Great Yarmouth', Dark Blue body, base A	£8-10	☐
10202	1990	'COLMANS'	'Great Yarmouth', Dark Blue body, base B	£8-10	☐
10203	1990	'CORONATION'	'Great Yarmouth', Cream body, base C	£15-20	☐
10204	1991	'TYPHOO'	'London', Red body, base C	£25-30	☐

AEC Routemaster Double-Deck Bus

'London Transport' fleetname

15601	1993	'B.O.A.C.'	Red body, 'RM 2110', route '8A'	£9-11	☐
15601b	1993	'B.O.A.C.'	Red body, 'RM 1910', route '15'	£9-11	☐
15602	1993	'OVALTINE'	Red body, 'RM 2103', route '3'	£9-11	☐
15602 b	1993	'OVALTINE'	Red body, 'RM 1818', route '76'	£9-11	☐
15605	1993	'EVENING STANDARD'	Red body, *TYPHOO*, 'RM 1018', route '16'	£9-11	☐
15605 b	1993	'EVENING STANDARD'	Red body, *TYPHOO*, 'RM 1277', route '73'	£9-11	☐
15608	1993	'PICKFORDS'	Red body, *WILKINSON SWORD*, 'RM 1768', route '7'	£9-11	☐
15608 b	1993	'PICKFORDS'	Red body, *WILKINSON SWORD*, 'RM 966', route '141'	£9-11	☐
-	1993	'BRITISH DIECAST MODEL TOYS CATALOGUE'	Promotional only available with 5th Catalogue. Red body, Yellow side posters with Red/Black design, plus 'Exclusive Fifth Edition' logo at rear	£11-13	☐
15602	1993	'BEATTIES'	Red body, 'RM 1818'	£11-13	☐
15612	1993	'FARES FAIR'	Red body, 'RM 84'	GSP	☐
15610	1994	'DALTONS'	Red body, 'RM 1992'	£11-13	☐
15616	1995	'TRUMANS'	Red body, 'RM 291'	£11-13	☐
15605	1994	'BROMLEY PAGEANT'	Red body, 'RM 1018'	£18-20	☐
15614	1994	'BEA'	Red body, 'RM 996'	£10-12	☐
15614	1994	'RM 40 YEARS'	Red body	£18-22	☐
15608HW	1994	'TYPHOO TEA' (USA)	Red body, 'RM 1768'	£40-60	☐
15602	1995	'BROMLEY PAGEANT'	Red body, 'RM 2103'	£12-15	☐
15617	1995	'EAST LONGON'	Red body, *STAGE COACH*	£10-12	☐
15610	1995	'BRITISH AIRWAYS'	Red body, 'RM 1992'	NGPP	☐
C15608		'ASTON MANOR TPT. MUSEUM'	Red body, 'RM ???'	£15-25	☐

Provincial operators and fleetnames

15603	1993	'BLACK PRINCE'	Red/Yellow body (no advert) route 'X 51'	£9-11	☐
15604	1993	'SOUTHEND TRANSPORT'	Blue/White body, 'ESSEX RADIO', route '29'	£9-11	☐
15606	1993	'EAST YORKSHIRE'	Dark Blue/Primrose body (no adverts)	£9-11	☐
15607	1993	'CLYDESIDE'	Red/Yellow body, 'THE SCOTSMAN'	£9-11	☐
15609	1993	'MANSFIELD & DISTRICT'	Green/Cream body (no adverts)	£9-11	☐
15611	1993	'BURNLEY & PENDLE'	Red & Cream body	£9-11	☐
15613	1994	'BLACKPOOL'	Red & White body	£9-11	☐
15604	1944	'SOUTHEND'	Blue & White body	£9-11	☐
15609DL	1994	'MANSFIELD'	Green & White body, GS 99910	GSP	☐
15611DL	1994	'BURNLEY & PENDLE'	Red & Cream body, GS 99910	GSP	☐
15615DL	1995	'UNITED COUNTIES'	Green body	£11-13	☐
15607DL	1994	'CLYDESIDE'	Red and Yellow body, special advertisement for *MODEL & COLLECTORS MART*	£12-15	☐
15606B	1995	'E. YORKS'	Dark Blue/Primrose *BEATTIES*	£10-15	☐

AEC Routemaster Double-Deck Bus, (open-top)

17901	1994	'LONDON RM 94'	Red body, *SIGHTSEEING TOUR*	£10-12	☐
17902	1994	'LONDON RM 644'	Red body, *METRO LINE*	£10-12	☐
17801	1995	'LONDON COACHES'	Red & White body	£10-12	☐
17802	1995	'LONDON COACHES'	Red & White body, *LONDON PLUS*	£10-12	☐

Leyland RTL Double-Deck Bus

11101	1990	'BOAT SHOW'	'London', Red body, 'RTL 815', base C, part of Gift Set 19903	GSP	☐
11102	1990	'WILKINSON SWORD'	'London', Green body, 'RTL 1245', base C, part of Gift Set 19903	GSP	☐
11103	1990	'T. F. BOTT'	'Contractus', Green body, base C, part of Gift Set 19903	GSP	☐
11104	1990	'LOCKEYS'	Black body (no advertising) base C	£20-25	☐
11105	1991	'BRYLCREEM'	'London', Red body, 'RTL 2', base C	£20-25	☐
11106	1991	'FISHERMANS FRIEND'	'London', Red body, 'RTL 285', base C, special box	£12-15	☐
11106 DL	1993	'FISHERMANS FRIEND'	'London Transport', Red body, route '145', extra detail	£17-20	☐
11107	1992	'BARTONS'	Multi-coloured, in Set 99905	GSP	☐
11108	1992	'A1 SERVICES'	Multi-coloured body	£12-15	☐
11102	1994	'BOAT SHOW'	Red body, base C (deluxe)	£10-12	☐
11109	1995	'OK MOTOR SERVICES'	Maroon and Cream body	£10-12	☐

Orion Bodied Double Deck Bus

19701	1995	'SHEFFIELD'	White & Blue body (AEC)	£11-13	☐
19702	1995	'DEVON'	Maroon & White body (AEC)	£11-13	☐
19703	1995	'ST HELENS'	Red & Cream body	£11-13	☐
19801	1995	'POTTERIES'	Red & White body (Daimler CVG 6)	£11-13	☐
19802	1995	'MANCHESTER'	Red body (Daimler CVG 6)	£11-13	☐
19803	1995	'DUNDEE'	Green & Cream body (Daimler CVG 6)	£11-13	☐
19804	1995	'COVENTRY'	Maroon & Cream body (Daimler CVG 6)	£11-13	☐
20001	1995	'RIBBLE'	Maroon body (Leyland PD2)	£11-13	☐
20002	1995	'MAIDSTONE & DISTRICT'	Green & Cream body (Leyland PD2)	£11-13	☐

STOP PRESS – NEW DOUBLE DECK MODEL
Look out for an exciting addition to the Double Deck Bus range late in 1995. Full details in the 1996 MODEL PRICE REVIEW.

Bristol Lodekka FLF

13901	1992	'BRISTOL'	Green/Black, late radiator, no heating vents	£14-16	☐
13902	1992	'BRISTOL'	As previous model but with *BEATTIES* adverts	£11-13	☐
14001	1992	'BRIGHTON'	Red and Cream body, late radiator, heating vents	£11-13	☐
14002	1993	'EASTERN NATIONAL'	Green/Cream/Black, late radiator, heating vents	£10-12	☐
14003	1993	'CROSVILLE COACH'	Cream body (no adverts) Silver detail, Black wheels	£10-12	☐
14004	1993	'CHELTENHAM'	Red/Cream body, *GLOUCESTERSHIRE ECHO*, Red wheels	£10-12	☐
14005	1993	'SOUTHDOWN'	Green/Cream body, *THE BURNLEY*, part of Gift Set 99907	GSP	☐
14006	1993	'LINCOLNSHIRE'	Green/Cream body, *TRUSTEE SAVINGS BANK*, Black wings and wheels	£25-30	☐
14007	1993	'THAMES VALLEY'	Red/Cream body, *MAIDENHEAD AUTOS*	NRP	☐
14101	1992	'UNITED'	Red body & wheels, early radiator, no heating vents	£10-12	☐
14102	1992	'UNITED'	As previous model but with *BEATTIES* adverts	£11-13	☐
14201	1992	'ALEXANDER'	Blue body, White wheels, early radiator, no heating vents	£12-14	☐
14202	1993	'MIDLAND GENERAL'	Blue/Cream body, *FARMER & STOCKBREEDER*	£10-12	☐
14006	1994	'BATH SERVICES'	Green body	£24-28	☐
14005	1993	'SOUTHDOWN BH & D'	Green and Cream body, part GS 99907	GSP	☐
13905	1994	'EASTERN COUNTIES'	Red body	£10-12	☐
13906	1994	'SOUTHERN VECTIS'	Green body	£12-14	☐
13907	1995	'CUMBERLAND'	Red body	£10-12	☐
14202	1994	'MIDLAND GENERAL'	Blue and White body	£10-12	☐
13908	1995	'NOTTS & DERBY'	Blue and Cream body	£10-12	☐

Leyland National Mk.I and Mk.II Single Deck Bus

There are two versions of this model:
1 - a **short** version having a single pair of doors, and 2 - a **long** version with two pairs of doors, plus long, short, or no, roof pod.

14401	1992	'GREENLINE'	Green/White body, Green wheels, short, single pair of doors	£10-12	☐
14402	1992	'MANCHESTER'	Orange/White/Brown body, Brown wheels, short, single pair of doors	£10-12	☐
14403	1993	'UNITED'	Red/White/Blue body, Black wheels, short, single pair of doors	£10-12	☐
14403	1994	'UNITED'	Red, Blue & White body	£11-12	☐
14701	1993	McGILLS'	Red/Grey, *McGILLS BUS SERVICE LTD BARRHEAD*, Cream wheels, short, two pairs of doors	£10-12	☐
15101	1992	'HANTS & DORSET'	Red body, Grey wheels, long, two pairs of doors	£10-12	☐
15101	1993	'BEATTIES'	Red body	£25-30	☐
15102	1993	'CROSVILLE'	Green body, Grey wheels, long, two pairs of doors	£10-12	☐
15102	1993	'BEATTIES'	Green body	£14-16	☐
15102	1993	'EFE CLUB'	Green body	£18-22	☐
15103	1993	'NORTHERN'	Yellow body, Grey wheels, long, two pairs of doors	£10-12	☐
15103	1993	'NORTHERN'	Yellow body (deluxe)	£10-12	☐
15104	1993	'BRISTOL CITY'	Green/White body, Grey wheels, long, two pairs of doors	£10-12	☐
16901	1993	'LONDON LS 487'	Red, White & Grey body, Mk 2 short, 2 door	GSP	☐
16701	1994	'LONDON LS 6'	Red body	£11-12	☐
14601	1994	'RIBBLE'	Red body	£10-11	☐
17201	1994	'TRENT'	Red, Cream & Black body	£11-12	☐
17202	1994	'THAMESWAY'	Yellow & Maroon body	£11-12	☐

179

Ref. No.	Year(s)	Model Type	*E.F.E. Models – continued*	Market Price Range
16602	1994	'EASTBOURNE'	Blue & Cream body	**£11-12** ☐
16603	1995	'ENSIGN BUS'	Blue & Silver body	**£11-12** ☐
17301	1995	'READING'	Red & Cream, single door, large pod	**£10-12** ☐
17203	1995	'YORKSHIRE TERRIER'	Yellow & Green body	**£10-12** ☐

LEYLAND TITAN 'RTL'

11101	1990	'CONTRACTUS'	Light Green, part GS 19903	GSP ☐
11102	1990	'WILKINSON'	Dark Green (LT), part GS 19903	GSP ☐
11103	1990	'BOAT SHOW'	Red (LT), part GS 19903	GSP ☐
11103DL	1990	'BOAT SHOW'	Red (LT), only from LT Museum	**£12-15** ☐
11104	1990		Black (Lockeys)	**£40-45** ☐
11105	1990	'BRYLCREAM'	Red (LT)	**£35-40** ☐
11106	1992	'FISHERMANS FRIEND'	Red (LT), Cream windows	**£18-22** ☐
11106DL	1993	'FISHERMANS FRIEND'	Red (LT), Cream windows	**£22-26** ☐
11107	1992	'BARTON'	Red/Maroon, part GS 99905	GSP ☐
11108	1992	'A1 SERVICE'	Blue Maroon	**£18-22** ☐
11109	1995	'OK MOTOR SERVICES'	Red/Cream/Maroon	**£11-13** ☐

AEC Reliance Coach - Harrington Cavalier

11902	1991	'YELLOWAYS'	Dark Cream & Orange body with front roof box, Orange wheels, Gold logo	**£30-35** ☐
11903	1992	'GREY-GREEN'	Green and Grey body with front roof box, Green wheels	**£10-12** ☐
12101	1991	'SOUTHDOWN'	Two-tone Green body (no front roof box), Dark Green wheels, Gold logo	**£35-40** ☐
12102	1992	'EAST YORKS'	Cream/Blue, Blue wheels	**£9-11** ☐
12103	1992	'HEBBLE'	Cream/Red, Red wheels	**£9–11** ☐
12103	1993	'HEBBLE'	Cream & Red body	**£9-11** ☐
12103	1993	'PENNINE RALLY'	Cream & Red body	**£9-11** ☐
12104	1992	'SURREY'	Yellow/Brown, in Gift Set 99906	GSP ☐
12105	1992	'NEATH & CARDIFF'	Brown/Red, Red wheels	**£9-11** ☐
12106	1993	'VALIANT'	Red/White, Silver detail, White wheels, Standard & Deluxe issues	**£10-12** ☐
12107	1993	'SOUTHDOWN'	Green & Cream body, part of GS 99907	GSP ☐
12108	1994	'RIBBLE'	Cream & Red body	**£10-12** ☐
12109	1994	'ROBIN HOOD'	Cream & Red body	**£10-12** ☐

AEC Reliance Coach - Harrington Grenadier

12201	1991	'BLACK & WHITE'	Black and White body with front roof box, White wheels, Black logo	**£14-16** ☐
12202	1992	'PREMIER'	Grey-Green & Navy body with front roof box, Navy wheels	**£9-11** ☐
12203	1992	'BARTONS'	Red/Maroon/Cream, roof box, in Set 99905	GSP ☐
12204	1992	'ORANGE LUXURY'	Cream/Grey/Orange body with front roof box, *'ESSEX EXPRESS'*	**£9-11** ☐
12204 DL	1992	'ORANGE LUXURY'	As previous model but with added detail	**£12-14** ☐
12301	1991	'MAIDSTONE'	Cream & Green body (no front roof box), Green wheels, Black logo	**£24-26** ☐
12302	1992	'GREY CARS'	Grey and Maroon body (no front roof box), Maroon wheels	**£9-11** ☐
12303	1992	'TIMPSONS'	Ivory and Maroon body, in Gift Set 99906	GSP ☐
12304	1992	'SOUTHDOWN'	Two-tone Green body Dark Green wheels	**£9-11** ☐
12305	1993	'ELLEN SMITH'	White and Maroon body, Maroon wheels, Standard & Deluxe issues	**£10-12** ☐
12305	1993	'BLACKPOOL RALLY'	White and Red body	**£12-14** ☐
12306	1993	'B.O.A.C.'	White, Grey and Blue body	**£10-12** ☐
12306	1994	'B.O.A.C.'	Grey and White body	**£10-11** ☐

Bedford OB Duple Vista Coach

20101	1995	'SOUTHERN VECTIS'	Cream and Green body	**£11-13** ☐
20102	1995	'ROYAL BLUE'	Royal Blue and Cream	**£11-13** ☐

Bedford SB Duple Vega Coach

18701	1995	'ORANGE LUXURY'	Orange body	**£11-13** ☐
18702	1995	'GURWOODS'	Green & Cream body	**£11-13** ☐
18703	1995	'GREY GREEN'	Grey & Green body	**£11-13** ☐
18704	1995	'SOUTHERN VECTIS'	Cream & Green body	**£11-13** ☐
18705	1995	'B.O.A.C.'	Blue & White body	**£11-13** ☐
18706	1995	'BARTONS'	Red, Cream & Maroon body	**£11-13** ☐
18707	1995	'STEVENSONS'	Yellow & Black body	**£11-13** ☐

Bristol MW Coach

16201	1993	'BRISTOL GREYHOUSE'	Cream & Red body	**£18-22** ☐
16202	1993	'CROSVILLE'	Cream & Black body	**£18-22** ☐
16203	1994	'ROYAL BLUE'	Navy & Ivory body	**£22-26** ☐
16204	1994	'SOUTH MIDLAND'	Red & Ivory body	**£10-12** ☐
16205	1994	'WILTS & DORSET'	Red & Cream body	**£10-12** ☐
16206	1994	'LINCOLNSHIRE'	Cream & Green body	**£10-12** ☐
16207	1995	'EASTERN COUNTIES'	White & Red body	**£10-12** ☐
16208	1995	'SOUTHERN VECTIS'	Cream & Green body	**£11-13** ☐
16209	1995	'UNITED'	Cream & Sage Green body	**£11-13** ☐

Bristol LS Single Deck Coach

16301	1993	'UNITED'	Red body	£16-20	☐
16302	1993	'EASTERN NATIONAL'	Green body	£10-12	☐
16303	1994	'THAMES VALLEY'	Red body	£10-12	☐
16304	1994	'WESTERN NATIONAL'	Green body	£10-12	☐
16307	1994	'WILTS & DORSET'	Red body	£10-12	☐
16308	1994	'LINCOLNSHIRE'	Green body	£10-12	☐
16309	1994	'GREENLINE'	Green body	£10-12	☐
16310	1994	'EASTERN COUNTIES'	Red body	£10-12	☐
16311	1995	'BRISTOL OMNIBUS'	Cream & Green body	£10-12	☐

Leyland Tiger Duple Bodied Coach

18301	1994	'YKS WOLLEN'	Maroon & Cream body	£16-22	☐
18302	1994	'SUNDERLAND'	Blue, Ivory & Grey body	£11-13	☐
18303	1995	'BARTONS'	Red, Maroon & Cream body	£11-13	☐
18401	1994	'WEST RIDING'	Green & Cream body	£11-13	☐
18402	1995	'LANCASHIRE'	Red, Cream & Grey body	£11-13	☐
18403	1995	'COUNTY MOTORS'	Blue & White body	£11-13	☐
18404	1995	'DONCASTER'	Maroon, Ivory & Grey	£11-13	☐
18304	1995	'YKS WOOLLEN'	Grey body	£11-13	☐
18405	1995	'LINCOLNSHIRE'	Green & Grey body	£11-13	☐
18406	1995	'OK MOTORS'	Red & Cream body	£11-13	☐

Plaxton Panorama Elite Coach

15701	1993	'SOUTH WEST NBC'	White body, 'NATIONAL EXPRESS', Grey wheels	£10-12	☐
15702	1993	'RIBBLE NBC'	White body, 'NATIONAL', Grey wheels	£10-12	☐
15703	1993	'EAST KENT'	Red/Beige body	£10-12	☐
15704	1993	'ABBOTTS of BLACKPOOL'	Red and Grey body	£10-12	☐
15704	1994	'ABBOTTS'	Red & Grey body	£10-12	☐
15705	1993	'SHEFFIELD UNITED'	Red and Off-White body	£10-12	☐
15705	1994	'SHEFFIELD TOURS'	Red & White body	£10-12	☐
15706	1993	'BRISTOL GREYHOUND'	Red and White body	£10-12	☐
15707	1993	'GREY GREEN'	Green & White body	£10-12	☐
15707	1994	'GREY GREEN'	Green & White body	£10-12	☐
15708	1994	'BARTONS'	Red, Cream & Maroon body	£12-14	☐
15709	1994	'SOUTHDOWN'	Green body	£15-20	☐
15701/2DL	1994	'UNITED'	White body (deluxe)	£18-22	☐
15706	1995	'BRISTOL'	White & Red (deluxe)	£10-12	☐

Leyland Titan PD1 Lowbridge Bus

15801	1993	'WIGAN CORPORATION'	Red/White body	£10-12	☐
15802	1993	'EAST KENT'	Red/White body	£10-12	☐
15801	1995	'WIGAN'	Maroon & Ivory body, Collector Club Model	£14-16	☐

Leyland Titan PD1 Highbridge Bus

15901	1993	'LEICESTER CITY'	Red/White body, 'C.W.S.', Standard & Deluxe issues	£10-12	☐
15902	1994	'RIBBLE'	Maroon body	£15-18	☐
15903	1994	'LEDGARD'	Blue and White body	£10-12	☐
15904	1994	'CITY COACH'	Brown and Ivory body	£10-12	☐

Leyland Titan PD2 Lowbridge Bus

16001	1993	'TODMORDEN'	Dark Green/White body, 'LMS RAILWAY', side blind 'SUMMIT'	£40-50	☐
			As previous but with 'HEPDEN BRIDGE' on side blind	NGPP	☐
16002	1993	'TODMORDEN'	Dark Green/White body, 'BRITISH RAILWAYS'	£11-13	☐
16003	1994	'EAST KENT'	Red and White body, 'LITTLEWOODS'	£11-13	☐
16004	1994	'DEVON'	Maroon and Ivory body	£11-13	☐
16005	1994	'MIDLAND'	Red body	£11-13	☐
16006	1994	'WEST RIDING'	Green and Cream body	£11-13	☐
16007	1995	'NORTH WESTERN'	Red and Cream body	£11-13	☐

Leyland Titan PD2 Highbridge Bus

16101	1993	'WIGAN CORPORATION'	Red and White body	£11-13	☐
16102	1993	'LEICESTER CITY'	Cream and Red body, 'LEICESTER MERCURY'	£11-13	☐
16103	1994	'CROSVILLE'	Green body	£15-18	☐
16104	1994	'LEEDS'	Blue & Silver body	£11-13	☐
16105	1994	'SHEFFIELD'	Ivory & Blue body	£11-13	☐
16101	1995	'WIGAN'	Maroon & Ivory (Collectors Club Model)	£14-16	☐
16107	1995	'STRATFORD'	Blue & Cream body	£11-13	☐

Leyland Atlantean/Daimler Fleetline Double-Deck Bus

16501	1994	'RIBBLE'	Maroon body	£28-32	☐
16502	1994	'WALLASEY'	Green & Cream body	£16-18	☐
16503	1994	'DEVON'	Maroon & Cream body	£28-32	☐

Ref. No.	Year(s)	Model Type	E.F.E. Models – continued	Market Price Range	
16504	1994	'MAIDSTONE'	Green & Cream body	£28-32	☐
16505	1994	'PLYMOUTH'	Red body	£10-12	☐
16506	1994	'SHEFFIELD'	Ivory & Blue body	£10-12	☐
16507	1994	'GATESHEAD'	Green & Cream body	£12-14	☐
16508	1994	'NORTHERN'	Yellow body	£10-12	☐
16509	1995	'LEICESTER'	Cream & Maroon body	£10-12	☐
16510	1994	'BIRMINGHAM'	Blue, Cream & Navy body	£10-12	☐
16511	1995	'HULL'	Blue & White body	£10-12	☐
16513	1995	'SALFORD'	Green body	£10-12	☐
18001	1994	'BIRMINGHAM'	Navy, Cream & Buff body	£13-16	☐
18002	1995	'MANCHESTER'	Red body	£10-12	☐
18101	1994	'LONDON XA13'	Red body	£32-38	☐
18201	1994	'LONDON COUNTRY'	Green body	£10-12	☐
18202	1994	'LONDON XF2'	Green body, Part of GS 99909	GSP	☐
18102	1995	'LONDON XA9'	Red body	£10-12	☐
16515	1995	'TRENT'	Red & Ivory body	£10-12	☐
16514	1995	'STEVENSONS'	Yellow & Black body	£10-12	☐

Leeds Horsfield Double-Deck Tram

13402	1991	'CO-OPERATIVE'	'Leeds City', Red/White body, bow type current collector	£9-11	☐
13403	1992	'JACOBS'	'Leeds City', Red/White body, bow type current collector	£9-11	☐
14301	1992	'YORKSHIRE POST'	'Leeds City', Blue/White body, pole type current collector	£9-11	☐
14302	1993	'WHITBREADS'	'Leeds City', Blue/White body, pole type current collector	£9-11	☐
14303	1994	'YORKS EVE POST'	'Leeds City', Grey, Navy, Ivory & Brown body	£9-11	☐
13404	1995	'LEEDS'	'Leeds City', World War II Khaki livery	£11-13	☐

Open Touring Cars

Ref. No.	Year(s)	Model Type	Model Features and Size	Market Price Range	

These models were given individual reference numbers but issued as pairs in a single box and it is to this 'twin-pack' that the price range refers.

11401	1991	Triumph Roadster	Red body, Red wheels, packed with 11601 Triumph Vitesse	£10-12	☐
11402	1991	Triumph Roadster	Black body, Silver wheels, packed with 11602 Triumph Vitesse	£5-8	☐
11403	1992	Triumph Roadster	Blue body, Silver wheels, packed with 11603 Triumph Vitesse	£5-8	☐
11404	1992	Triumph Roadster	Dark Green body, Green wheels, packed with 11604 Triumph Vitesse	£5-8	☐
11501	1991	MG MGB	Dark Green body and wheels, packed with 11701 Austin-Healey Sprite	£12-16	☐
11502	1991	MG MGB	Red body and wheels packed with 11702 Austin-Healey Sprite	£5-8	☐
11503	1992	MG MGB	Orange body and wheels, packed with 11703 Austin-Healey Sprite	£5-8	☐
11504	1992	MG MGB	Black body, Silver wheels, packed with 11704 Austin-Healey Sprite	£5-8	☐
11601	1991	Triumph Vitesse	White body, White wheels, packed with 11401 Triumph Roadster	£10-12	☐
11602	1991	Triumph Vitesse	Light Blue body and wheels, packed with 11402 Triumph Roadster	£5-8	☐
11603	1992	Triumph Vitesse	Red body and wheels, packed with 11403 Triumph Roadster	£5-8	☐
11604	1992	Triumph Vitesse	Dark Blue body and wheels, packed with 11404 Triumph Roadster	£5-8	☐
11701	1991	Austin-Healey Sprite	Yellow body and wheels, packed with 11501 MGB	£12-16	☐
11702	1991	Austin-Healey Sprite	White body and wheels, packed with 11502 MGB	£5-8	☐
11703	1992	Austin-Healey Sprite	Green body and wheels, packed with 11503 MGB	£5-8	☐
11704	1992	Austin-Healey Sprite	Red body and wheels, packed with 11504 MGB	£5-8	☐

Commercial Vehicles

Ref. No.	Year(s)	Model Type	Model Features and Size	Market Price Range	

AEC Mammoth Major Articulated Truck

19501	1994	'HOOVER'	Maroon and Blue body (Box Van)	£11-13	☐
19502	1995	'PICKFORDS'	dark Blue & White body (Box Van)	£11-13	☐
19601	1995	'B.R.S.'	Red and Black body (Flatbed)	£11-13	☐

AEC Mammoth Major 6-wheel Box Vans

-	1989	'FISHERMANS FRIEND'	White body, Red chassis and wheels, special box	£8-10	☐
10201	1989	'LONDON CARRIERS'	Dark Green body and wheels, Black chassis	£6-7	☐
10501	1989	'LONDON CARRIERS'	Re-run of 10201 with darker shade of Dark Green body	£6-7	☐
10502	1989	'START-RITE'	Cream body, Red chassis and wheels	£6-7	☐
10503	1990	'BRS'	Red body and wheels, 'Huddersfield' depot	£6-7	☐
-	1991	'BRS EFE CLUB'	Same model but 'Lincoln' depot, and 'EFE Collectors Club 1991'	£12-14	☐
10504	1990	'PEK PORK'	Blue body and wheels, Black chassis	£6-7	☐
10505	1990	'OXYDOL'	Blue body and wheels, Black chassis	£6-7	☐
10506	1991	'HOOVER'	Blue body, Burgundy wheels and chassis	£4-6	☐

Ref. No.	Year(s)	Model Type	E.F.E. Models – continued	Market Price Range	
10507	1990	'FISHERMANS FRIEND'	Re-run of 1989 model, singly and in Set 99902..	NGPP	☐
10507 DL	1993	'LORD RAYLEIGH's'............	Mid-Blue chassis, Pale Blue cab, White/Blue box	£8-10	☐
Deluxe	1991	'LONDON CARRIERS'	Re-run of 10501 with additional printing. In Set 99903	GSP	☐
Deluxe	1991	'BRS'...	Re-run of 10503 with additional printing. In Set 99903	GSP	☐
Deluxe	1992	'WELCHS'.................................	Turquoise body and wheels	£8-10	☐

AEC Mammoth Major 8-wheel Box Vans

Ref. No.	Year(s)	Model Type		Market Price Range	
11001	1989	'CROFT SHERRY'	White body, Black wheels and chassis..	£6-7	☐
11002	1989	'PICKFORDS'..........................	Blue body and wheels, Black chassis	£9-10	☐
11003	1990	'TATE & LYLE'	White body, Green wheels and chassis, in Set 19901	GSP	☐
11004	1990	'RANK HOVIS'	Cream body, Brown wheels, in Gift Set 19902	GSP	☐
11005	1990	'LACONS'.................................	Yellow body, Red wheels, Black chassis	£6-7	☐
11006	1991	'ROSES LIME JUICE'............	Green body and wheels, Black chassis	£6-7	☐
Deluxe	1991	'PICKFORDS'..........................	Model 11002 with additional printing. In Set 99903...	GSP	☐
11004	1993	'HOVIS'....................................	Brown and Cream body (deluxe)...	£9-10	☐

AEC Mammoth Major 6-wheel Dropside Wagon

Ref. No.	Year(s)	Model Type		Market Price Range	
-	1989	'FISHERMANS FRIEND'	White body, Red wheels and chassis, special box	£25-30	☐
10301	1990	'FENLAND AGGREGATES'	Orange body and wheels, Black chassis..	£6-7	☐
10302	1990	'CYRIL RIDGEON'.................	Turquoise body, Black wheels and chassis	£6-7	☐
10303	1990	'J. D. LOWN'...........................	Green body and wheels, Black chassis	£6-7	☐
Deluxe	1991	'FENLAND AGGREGATES'	Model 10301 but with plastic 'load'	£7-8	☐
Deluxe	1991	'CYRIL RIDGEON'.................	Model 10302 but with plastic 'load'	£7-9	☐
Deluxe	1991	'J. D. LOWN'...........................	Model 10303 but with plastic 'load'	£7-8	☐

AEC Mammoth Major 8-wheel Dropside Wagon

Ref. No.	Year(s)	Model Type		Market Price Range	
10801	1989	'BRITISH STEEL'...................	Dark Blue body and wheels, Black chassis	£6-7	☐
10802	1989	'WHITBREAD'.........................	Brown body and wheels, Black chassis	£6-7	☐
10803	1990	'MARLEY TILES'...................	Red body and wheels, Black chassis	£9-11	☐
10804	1991	'MACREADYS'........................	Orange body and wheels, Black chassis..	£6-7	☐
10805	1990	'FISHERMANS FRIEND'	White body, Red wheels/chassis, special box (? in Set 99902)	NGPP	☐
10806	1991	'TAYLOR WOODROW'	Yellow/Green body and wheels, Black chassis. In Set 19904.................................	GSP	☐
10806 DL	1993	'TAYLOR WOODROW'	Yellow body and wheels, Black chassis, additional 'covered load'	£8-9	☐
Deluxe	1992	'BRITISH STEEL'...................	Model 10801 but with plastic 'load'	£8-9	☐
Deluxe	1991	'WHITBREAD'.........................	As model 10802 but with plastic 'load'	£8-9	☐
Deluxe	1992	'LACONS'.................................	Mustard Yellow body with plastic 'load', Red wheels	£8-9	☐
Deluxe	1992	'MOBILOIL'............................	Dark Blue body with plastic 'load', Red wheels	£8-9	☐
Deluxe	1992	'MACREADYS'........................	As model 10804 but with plastic 'load'	£8-9	☐
Deluxe	1993	'ROSES LIME'	Green body...	£8-9	☐

AEC Mammoth Major 6-wheel Flatbed Truck

Ref. No.	Year(s)	Model Type		Market Price Range	
10701	1989	'FURLONG Bros.'	Cream body and wheels, Black chassis...	£6-7	☐
10702	1989	'BLUE CIRCLE'......................	Yellow body and wheels, Black chassis	£6-7	☐
10703	1990	'WIMPEY'	Yellow body and wheels, Black chassis	£6-7	☐
10703	1990	'WIMPEY'	Orange body and wheels, Black chassis..	£7-8	☐
Deluxe	1991	'FURLONG Bros.'	Model 10701 with plastic 'load'	£7-8	☐
Deluxe	1991	'BLUE CIRCLE'......................	As model 10702 but with plastic 'load'	£7-8	☐
Deluxe	1992	'WIMPEY'	As 10703 (Orange body) with plastic 'load' added	£8-9	☐
Deluxe	1992	'BRS'...	Red body and wheels, plastic 'load'	£8-9	☐
Deluxe	1993	'RANK HOVIS'.......................	Cream body..	£8-9	☐
Deluxe	1994	'J.D. LOWN'............................	Green body..	£10-12	☐

AEC Mammoth Major 8-wheel Flatbed Truck

Ref. No.	Year(s)	Model Type		Market Price Range	
10401	1989	'BATH & PORTLAND'	Dark Blue body and wheels, Black chassis	£6-7	☐
Deluxe	1991	'BATH & PORTLAND'	Same model but with plastic 'load'...	£7-8	☐
10402	1989	'LONDON BRICK'	Orange body and wheels, Black chassis..	£6-7	☐
Deluxe	1991	'LONDON BRICK'	Same model but with plastic 'load'...	£7-8	☐

AEC Mammoth Major 6-wheel Tanker

Ref. No.	Year(s)	Model Type		Market Price Range	
10901	1989	'HEYGATES'............................	White body, Burgundy cab and wheels, Black chassis..	£6-7	☐
10902	1989	'RAYLEIGHS'..........................	White body, Blue cab, Black wheels, Blue chassis	£6-7	☐
10903	1990	'L.P.G.'	White round tank, Yellow cab and wheels...	£6-7	☐
10903 DL	1993	'L.P.G.'	As 10903 but 3rd type (oval) tank in Silver, additional detail	£9-10	☐
10904	1990	'RANK HOVIS'	Cream body & cab, Orange wheels & chassis. In Set 19902	GSP	☐
10905	1990	'WELCHS'.................................	Turquoise body, cab and wheels, Black chassis	£6-7	☐
Deluxe	1991	'L.P.G.'	Model 10903 but additional detail. In Set 19904...	GSP	☐

AEC Mammoth Major 8-wheel Tanker

Ref. No.	Year(s)	Model Type		Market Price Range	
10601	1989	'CENTURY OIL'	Black body, cab, wheels and chassis..	£6-7	☐
10602	1989	'J. & H. BUNN'	Cream body, cab and chassis, Black wheels..	£6-7	☐
10603	1990	'TATE & LYLE'	Dark Blue body, cab & wheels, Black chassis. In Set 19901	GSP	☐
10604	1990	'MOBILGAS'	White body, Dark Blue cab & chassis, Red wheels	£6-7	☐
10605	1990	'REGENT'.................................	Red body and cab, Black chassis, White wheels	£12-16	☐

Ref. No.	Year(s)	Model Type	E.F.E. Models – continued	Market Price Range	
10606 DL	1993	'WHITBREAD'	Brown body and cab, Black wheels. With ladder	£9-10	☐
Deluxe	1991	'CENTURY OIL'	As model 10601 but additional detail. In Set 99904	GSP	☐
Deluxe	1991	'MOBILGAS'	As model 10604 but additional detail. In Set 99904	GSP	☐

AEC Mammoth Major 8-wheel Tipping Wagon

12001	1990	'WIMPEY'	Yellow body, cab and wheels, Black chassis	£9-10	☐
12002	1990	'TARMAC'	Green body and cab, Black wheels and chassis	£9-10	☐
12003	1991	'TAYLOR WOODROW'	Yellow/Green body and wheels, Black chassis. In Set 19904	GSP	☐
12004	1991	'KETTON'	Cream body and cab, Red wheels and chassis	£9-10	☐
Deluxe	1992	'TARMAC'	As model 12002 but plastic 'load' added	£12-14	☐
Deluxe	1992	'TAYLOR WOODROW'	As model 12003 but with 'load' and available singly	£9-10	☐

Atkinson Silver Knight Articulated Vehicles

13001	1991	'TSL RECOVERY'	Light Blue body and wheels, Car transporter	£15-18	☐
13002	1991	'SWIFTS'	Yellow body, Blue wheels, Car transporter	£11-13	☐
13003	1992	'MIDLAND CAR'	Maroon/Green/Silver, Car transporter	£11-13	☐
13004	1993	'CLASSIC'	Blue/Maroon body, Maroon wheels, Car transporter	£11-13	☐
19301	1995	'SUTTONS'	Red body (Flatbed)	£11-13	☐
19302	1995	'BOWKERS'	Navy and Red body (Flatbed)	£11-13	☐
19401	1995	'FLOWERS'	Yellow and Silver body (Box Van)	£11-13	☐
19402	1995	'TATE & LYLE'	Dark Blue with Gold logo (Box Van)	£11-13	☐

Atkinson Silver Knight 6-wheel Rigid Vehicles

12501	1992	'WELLS DRINKS'	White/Red body, Red chassis and wheels. (Box Van)	£6-7	☐
12601	1991	'McNICHOLAS'	Brown body, chassis and wheels. (Dropside Wagon)	£6-7	☐
12601 DL	1991	'McNICHOLAS'	As previous model but with 'timber and crate load' and extra detail	£7-8	☐
12701	1991	'CHARRINGTONS'	Dark Blue body and chassis, Red wheels. (Tanker)	£11-13	☐

Atkinson Silver Knight 8-wheel Rigid Vehicles

12801	1992	'McPHEES'	Dark Green body, chassis and wheels. (Flatbed Truck)	£35-40	☐
12901	1991	'FYFFES'	Yellow/Blue. (Box Van with AEC pattern wheels)	£10-12	☐
13301	1991	'St.ALBANS'	Silver body, Orange cab and wheels. (Tipping Wagon)	£16-18	☐
13301 DL	1993	'St.ALBANS'	As previous model but with 'load' and extra detail, (deluxe)	£10-12	☐
13701	1992	'FINA'	Blue body, Black wheels. (Tanker, 2 type tank)	£14-18	☐
12802	1994	'SUTTONS'	Red body (Flatbed Truck)	£11-13	☐
13201	1994	'SUTTONS'	Red and Silver body (Tanker)	£11-13	☐

E.F.E. Gift Sets

Ref. No.	Year(s)	Set Name	Contents	Market Price Range	
19901	1990	'TATE & LYLE'	10105 AEC Bus, 11003 8-wheel Van, 10603 8-wheel Tanker	£22-26	☐
19902	1990	'RANK HOVIS'	10106 AEC Bus, 11004 8-wheel Van, 10904 6-wheel Tanker	£22-26	☐
19903	1990	'The RTL Story'	11101 'Boat Show', 11102 'Wilkinson', 11103 'Bott'	£30-40	☐
19904	1991	'TAYLOR WOODROW'	10110 AEC Bus, 10806 8-wheel Dropside, 12003 8-wheel Tipper	£22-26	☐
19905	1994	Routemaster Set	15609 & 15611 AEC Routemasters	£24-28	☐
19906	1995	World War II Set	13404 Tram & 18304 Leyland Tiger	£20-24	☐
19907	1995	Liverpool Set	16512 Atlantean & 16106 Leyland PD, only available from Ian Allen	£20-24	☐
99901	1990	'London Buses'	10101 'Duracell', 10103 'Birdseye', 10104 'Schweppes'	£40-50	☐
99902	1990	'FISHERMANS FRIEND'	10108 AEC Bus, 10507 6-wheel Van, 6 or 8 wheel Dropside Wagon.		
		1st run	in separate boxes (smooth base RT Bus and 6 wheel Dropside Wagon)	£40-50	☐
		2nd run	in separate boxes (textured base RT Bus and 8 wheel Dropside Wagon)	£20-25	☐
		3rd run	in one box, (textured base RT Bus and 8 wheel Dropside Wagon)	£15-18	☐
99903	1991	'Deluxe Boxvans Set'	10501 'London Carriers', plus 10503 'B.R.S.' & 11002 'Pickfords'	£24-28	☐
99904	1991	'Tankers'	(Deluxe) 'L.P.G.', 'CENTURY OIL', 'MOBILGAS'	£24-28	☐
99905	1992	'BARTONS'	Leyland RTL and Harrington Grenadier	£16-20	☐
99906	1992	'Harrington Coaches'	Cavalier 'Surrey' and Grenadier 'Timpsons'	£25-30	☐
99907	1993	'SOUTHDOWN'	Bristol Lodekka and Harrington Cavalier, both in Green/Cream	£25-30	☐
99908	1993	London Transport Museum Set	16401 A.E.C. Regent, plus 16901 Leyland National & 15612 AEC Routemaster	£30-35	☐
99909	1994	London Transport Museum Set	18202 Leyland Atlantean plus 16310 Bristol LS Coach	£24-28	☐
C99906	1995	Harrington's Set	12104 Cavalier plus 12303 Grenadier (Commissioned Set) 'FOOTBALL SPECIAL'	£45-60	☐

E.F.E. packaging and presentation

Standard issues of single models were packed in rigid card window boxes coloured in two shades of grey, with black and red printing. The contents were secured by a moulded clear plastic inner shell.

Special boxes were made for certain models used for promotional purposes. The models were the 'BRS' Box Van, the 'HEYGATES' Tanker and the 'J.D.LOWN' Dropside Wagon. Their boxes were white with 'COMMERCIAL MOTOR' and 'DAF - LEYLAND' printed on them.
White boxes (with black printing) were used initially for the 'FISHERMANS FRIEND' issues that were part of an 'on-pack offer' promotion, and a subsequent RT bus promotion presented in a pale blue customised box.
The 'Road Transport' Gift Set was issued in a dark blue window box with the three models encased in a flock-covered vac-form with a clear lid.
Certain of the models were designated 'Deluxe' by acquiring additional detail or plastic 'loads' of various kinds. They were packed in a double blister-pack that folded to enclose the model, and was designed to hang on display stand pegs though they could also stand (untidily) on a shelf.
The first of the Gift Sets ('Tate & Lyle') was designed to look like a book (even having 'Volume One' printed on its blue card covering). The inner container was plain white expanded polystyrene - good for insulation but not the nicest form of presentation! Subsequently the 'Rank Hovis' set (designated 'Volume Two') had an inner container of improved appearance with a flock base and clear plastic covering. Standard issues are currently presented a little more assertively in black window boxes with light red printing, with a similar box in royal blue used for the De Luxe range.

The E.F.E. Official Collectors Club

Formed in January 1991, the Club aims to assist its members by way of monthly bulletins and a telephone help-line, to form a complete and as comprehensive collection as possible of all the EFE product range.
Included in this service are the following:

Monthly advice of all new issues,
Bi-monthly updates to the Collectors Guide,
4-monthly colour photo-packs showing selected models from the EFE range,
Telephone help-line (available 12 hours per day)
Sales and promotional material (brochures and badges)
Standing order scheme for the supply of all new issues.

If you are interested in joining then please write to the following address for details:
The EFE Official Collectors Club, 'Farmside', Witham Bank, Martin Dales, Woodhall Spa, Lincolnshire, LN10 6XS.
Please remember to enclose a stamped self-addressed envelope with your initial enquiry. Thank you.

British Diecast Catalogue Promotional Bus Issue

5th EDITION 'BRITISH DIECAST MODEL TOYS CATALOGUE' AEC Routemaster Bus (De-Luxe) as advertised in the 5th Edition. A limited number are available price £9.95 (UK only). Please send to: Mark Sole, EFE – Gilbrow (Holdings) Ltd, PO Box 560, Hemel Hempstead, Herts. Please make all cheques payable to Exclusive First Editions, credit cards not accepted.

Mobil Midget Fun Ho! Series

Manufactured and distributed by the Underwood Engineering Co. Ltd, Mamaku Street, Inglewood, New Zealand.

Market Price Range. Small cars and trucks etc. £20-30. Exceptions:- No 7 B.O.A.C. Observation Coach £40-50; No 9 VW Beetle £40-50; No 11 Morris Mini Minor £80-90; No 12 Vauxhall Velox £30-40; No ? Morris 1100 £40-50; No 17 Austin Mini £80-90; No 23 Mark 10 Jaguar £80-90; No 25 MG Sports £80-100; No 43 E Type Jaguar £80-90.

Larger Commercials/Emergency vehicles etc. Nos. 18, 21, 22, 27, 31, 35, 36, 40 £30-40.

Technical Information. Models from No 10 are 1/80 scale. Early models 1-32 1963-66 were all either chrome or copper plated. Painted finishes were introduced in 1966. Boxed models 1-18 include a folded leaflet in black and white giving details of the first 18 models and all have Black plastic wheels. Similarly the later issues contained leaflets showing the complete 1-46 model range as per the above leaflet.

1. MF 35 Tractor
2. Holden Car
3. Austin Truck
4. Mobil Tanker
5. VW Combi Bus
6. Mercedes Benz Racer
7. BOAC Bus
8. Austin Tip Truck
9. VW Car
10. Ford Falcon
11. Morris Mini-Minor
12. Vauxhall Velox
13. Morris 1100
14. Cortina Estate Car
15. Hillman Imp
16. Fordson Super Major Tractor
17. Austin-Mini
18. Austin Articulated Truck
19. Land Rover
20. Thames Freighter Van
21. Fire Engine
22. Bedford Articulated Truck
23. Mark 10 Jaguar
24. Chevrolet Bel Air
25. M.G. Sports
26. Thames Freighter Pick Up
27. Mobil Articulated Tanker
28. Morris Pick Up

Look for these models in the **Mobil MIDGET "Fun Ho!" SERIES**

Models from No. 10 onwards are 1/80 scale.

The Mobil Midget Fun Ho! Series is manufactured and distributed by **The Underwood Engineering Co. Ltd.,** Mamaku St., Inglewood, New Zealand.

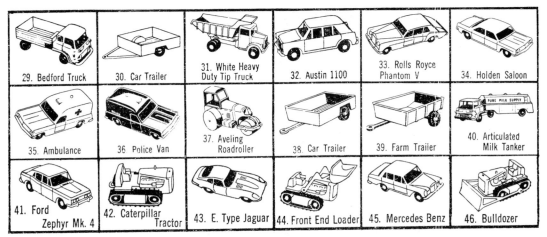

29. Bedford Truck	30. Car Trailer	31. White Heavy Duty Tip Truck	32. Austin 1100	33. Rolls Royce Phantom V	34. Holden Saloon
35. Ambulance	36. Police Van	37. Aveling Roadroller	38. Car Trailer	39. Farm Trailer	40. Articulated Milk Tanker
41. Ford Zephyr Mk. 4	42. Caterpillar Tractor	43. E. Type Jaguar	44. Front End Loader	45. Mercedes Benz	46. Bulldozer

N.B. Early Issues shown on facing page.

Later issues (c.1965?) Window Boxes.
48 Ford Brown/Green, Two-tone Green or Maroon White body £10-15
49 Ford Sand Dumper, Red/Blue body £10-15

50 Ford Dumper £10-15
51 Ford Articulated Truck £15-20
52 Sand Dumper Trailer £5-10

'Fun Ho!' Mighty Mover Sets

Ref. No.	Model Type	Model Features	Market Price Range	
1	Army Construction Battalion Kit Set......	Contains six Military models, Bulldozer, Cement Mixer, Road Roller, Earth Mover, JCB, Land Rover, Brown display box	£50-60	☐
2	Civilian Road Construction Set	Yellow/Silver Bulldozer, Red/Silver Bedford Lorry, Green Aveling Road Roller, Blue Earth Mover, Red/Blue Ford Sand Dumper, Yellow JCB, Red window display box	£50-60	☐
3	Fire Service Kit Set	Contains six Red models, 21 Fire Engine, Jeep, Pick Up, Artic Lorry, Rescue Truck, Fire Van with Blue light, Red window display box	£50-60	☐

Auction Results — Vectis Model Auctions

June 1994

All Models Boxed Mint

No.4 Mobil Tanker chrome/copper tank/'Mobil' decal on back £35
No.5 VW Combi Bus chrome £35
No.9 VW Beetle copper/chrome baseplate...£50
No.10 Ford Falcon copper/chrome baseplate, plus No.24 Chevrolet Bel Air, turquoise £40
No.11 Morris Mini Minor copper/chrome baseplate £85
No.13 Morris 1100 copper/chrome baseplate, plus No.32 Austin 1100 orange £55
No.14 Ford Cortina Estate copper/chrome £30
No.15 Hillman Imp chrome £30
No.16 Fordson Super Major Tractor copper/metal wheels.................£35
No.17 Austin Mini copper/chrome baseplate £90

No.19 Landrover green/chrome driver...£35
No.20 Thames Freighter Van copper/chrome baseplate, plus No.26 Thames Freighter Pick-up chrome/green back/interior..£70
No.21 Fire Engine (Merryweather Marquis type) copper/metal ladder, extremely rare in plated finish £45
No.22 Bedford Artic. Truck green/met. grey back, plus No.29 Bedford Truck greyish blue/pale grey back/chrome chassis...£50
No.23 Mark 10 Jaguar metallic brown £100
No.25 MG Sports chrome, rare £100
No.27 Mobil Artic. Tanker copper/chrome tank with two 'Mobil' decals in sides, extremely rare in plated finish...£40

187

LLEDO

'Models of Days Gone'

Introduction

One of the founders of Matchbox Toys, Jack Odell OBE formed the Lledo toy company in 1982 and the first 6 models made their appearance at Easter 1983. Successful 'Sunday magazine' type marketing raised public awareness of these delightful new collectables and the number of dedicated collectors grew rapidly.

Lledo introduced the 'Premier Collection' and the 'Military Collection' in 1991 to offer greater choice, more detailed finish and improved appearance of certain models. Both these ranges have their own attractive packaging.

With increasing interest the range has expanded to around sixty models and has generally represented only vehicles made up to the 1930s. 'Days Gone Vanguards' introduced in 1993 enhances and extends the range of interest into the 1950s and 1960s. Rationalisation of output means that some earlier models are now being discontinued and are likely to increase in price.

Part of the success of the Lledo company is due to the demand for use of certain models for promotional purposes. A review of this aspect of Lledo collecting follows the main 'Days Gone' listing.

The Compiler of this Catalogue is indebted to RDP Publications for supplying information on which these lists are based. Details of Club membership and other specialist services to Lledo collectors are given at the end of this chapter.

1   2   3   4

5   6   7   8

9   10   11   12

13   14   15   16

17   18   19   20

Lledo - Models of Days Gone

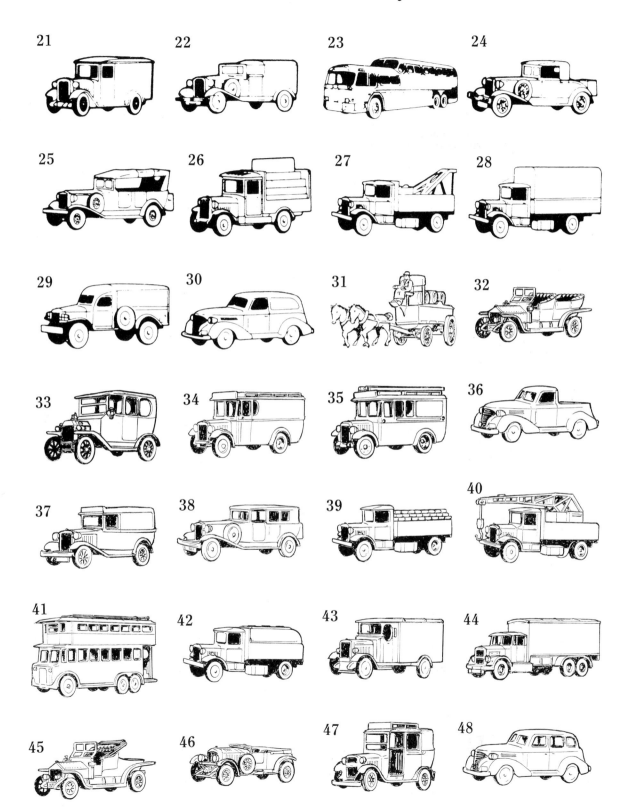

21 22 23 24

25 26 27 28

29 30 31 32

33 34 35 36

37 38 39 40

41 42 43 44

45 46 47 48

Lledo - Models of Days Gone

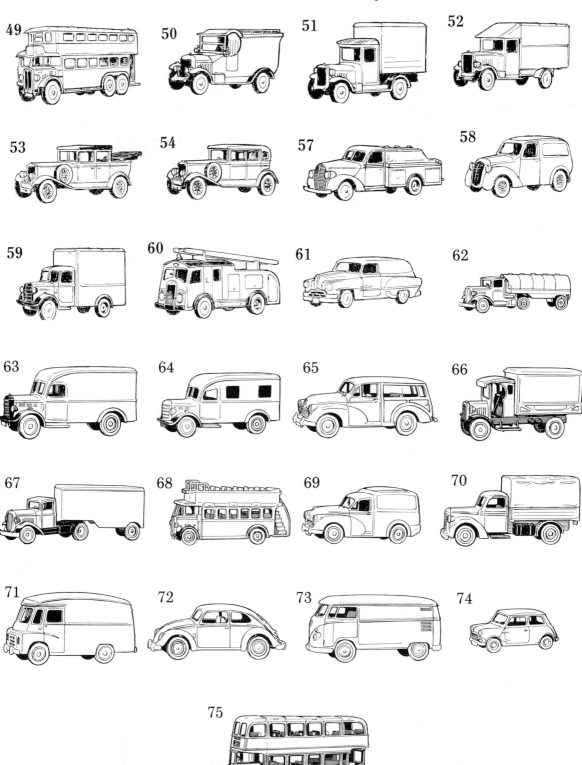

49

50

51

52

53

54

57

58

59

60

61

62

63

64

65

66

67

68

69

70

71

72

73

74

75

'Days Gone' Model Numbers & Types

DG 1	Horse-Drawn Tram
DG 2	Horse-Drawn Milk Float
DG 3	Horse-Drawn Delivery Van
DG 4	Horse-Drawn Omnibus
DG 5	Shand Mason Horse-Drawn Fire Engine
DG 6	1920 Ford Model 'T' Van
DG 7	1934 Ford Model 'A', Woody-Wagon
DG 8	1920 Ford Model 'T' Tanker
DG 9	1934 Ford Model 'A' Car (open)
DG 10	1935 Dennis Single-Deck Coach
DG 11	Horse-Drawn Removal Van
DG 12	1934 Dennis Fire Engine
DG 13	1934 Ford Model 'A' Van
DG 14	1934 Ford Model 'A' Car (with hood)
DG 15	1932 AEC Regent Double-Deck Bus
DG 16	1934 Dennis Parcels Van
DG 17	1932 AEC Regal Single-Deck Bus
DG 18	1936 Packard Van
DG 19	1931 Rolls-Royce Phantom II (Brewster)
DG 20	1936 Ford Stake Truck
DG 21	1934 Chevrolet Van
DG 22	1933 Packard Town Van
DG 23	1954 Scenicruiser
DG 24	1934 Rolls-Royce Playboy (Brewster)
DG 25	1925 Rolls-Royce Silver Ghost (Barker)
DG 26	1934 Chevrolet Bottle Delivery Truck
DG 27	1934 Mack Breakdown Truck
DG 28	1934 Mack Canvas-Back Truck
DG 29	1942 Dodge 4 x 4
DG 30	1939 Chevrolet Panel Van
DG 31	Horse-Drawn Brewers Dray
DG 32	1907 Rolls-Royce Silver Ghost
DG 33	1920 Ford Model 'T' Car
DG 34	1932 Dennis Delivery Van
DG 35	1932 Dennis Limousine
DG 36	1939 Chevrolet Pick-Up
DG 37	1932 Ford Model 'A' Van Panel Van
DG 38	1925 Rolls-Royce Silver Ghost Saloon
DG 39	1934 Mack Truck
DG 40	1934 Mack Crane Truck
DG 41	1928 Karrier E6 Trolley-Bus
DG 42	1934 Mack Tanker
DG 43	1931 Morris Van
DG 44	1937 Scammell 6-Wheeler
DG 45	1908 Rolls-Royce Silver Ghost Coupé
DG 46	1930 Bentley 4.5 Litre
DG 47	1933 Austin Taxi
DG 48	1939 Chevrolet Car
DG 49	1931 AEC Renown Double-Deck Bus
DG 50	1926 'Bull-Nose' Morris Van
DG 51	1934 Chevrolet Box Van
DG 52	1935 Morris Parcels Van
DG 53	1926 Rolls Royce Landaulet
DG 54	1929 Rolls Royce 'D' Back
* DG 55	Horse-Drawn Tanker
DG 56	1934 Ford Model 'A' Van (Raised Roof)
DG 57	1939 Ford Tanker
DG 58	1950 Morris 'Z' Van
DG 59	1950 Bedford 30cwt Truck
DG 60	1955 Dennis F8 Fire Engine
DG 61	1953 Pontiac Delivery Van
DG 62	1935 Ford Articulated Tanker
DG 63	1950 Bedford 13cwt Delivery Van
DG 64	1950 Bedford Ambulance
DG 65	1960 Morris Traveller
DG 66	1926 Dennis Delivery Van
DG 67	1935 Ford Articulated Truck
DG 68	AEC Open-top Double-decker Bus
DG 69	Morris 5cwt Van
DG 70	Ford Lorry
DG 71	Morris LD Van
DG 72	Volkswagen Beetle
DG 73	Volkswagen Van
DG 74	Mini Saloon
DG 75	Bristol Lodekka Bus

* Not issued as a 'Model of Days Gone' — only issued as a promotional to date.

Pictures kindly supplied by Lledo Plc.

'Models of Days Gone'

DG 1 HORSE-DRAWN TRAM. Model features a metal body with plastic horse & seats. It has brass trim and includes a set of figures: 2 lady passengers, a male passenger, a girl and the driver.

000a	1983	'WESTMINSTER'		
		Green chassis, Orange seats, Yellow crest.....	£15-25	☐
000b	1983	Green chassis, Orange seats, Cream crest	£10-15	☐
000c	1983	Green chassis, Orange seats, White crest.......	£4-6	☐
		(a,b,c) with no strengtheners on end panel		
		or shafts..	£100-120	☐
		(a,b,c) with strengtheners on shafts but not		
		end panels..	£20-30	☐
000d	1987	Green chassis, Red seats, White crest...........	£3-5	☐
001a	1984	'MAIN STREET', Green/Grey	£4-6	☐
002a	1984	'MAIN STREET', Brown/Cream	£4-6	☐
003		Not allocated		
004a	1984	'CRICH', Blue chassis, Cream roof	£4-6	☐
005a	1984	'DOWNTOWN', Cream, Green seats	£4-6	☐
005b	1987	Cream chassis, Dark Green seats	£3-5	☐
005c	1988	Dark Green seats, no Gold in crest	£3-5	☐
005d	1992	Dark Green seats, reversed crest	NRP	☐
006a	1990	'HERSHEY', Dark Brown & Green	£3-5	☐
	1990	Model withdrawn (but re-run for DG1-005d)		

DG 2 HORSE-DRAWN MILK FLOAT. Model features a metal body with a plastic roof section, horse & 3 milk crates. It has 'brass' 12-spoke wheels and a set of Cream plastic figures including a woman, a man, the driver and a dog.

000a	1983	'EXPRESS DAIRY', Blue/White	£4-6	☐
001a	1984	'CHAMBOURCY', Cream/Blue	£4-6	☐
002		Not allocated		
003a	1984	'CLIFFORD DAIRY', Red/Yellow/White...	£4-6	☐
004a	1984	'CELTIC DAIRY', Cream/Red	£4-6	☐
	1990	Model withdrawn from production		

DG 3 HORSE-DRAWN DELIVERY VAN. Model has a metal body with a plastic horse and roof section. Until 1985 a set of Cream plastic figures was included - a woman, a boy and a driver.

000a	1983	'WINDMILL BAKERY',		
		Yellow body, Cream shafts	£4-6	☐
000b	1984	Yellow body, Beige shafts	£4-6	☐
001a	1985	'COCA-COLA', Yellow/Black	£4-6	☐
002a	1984	'FINE LADY BAKERIES', Beige	£4-6	☐
003a	1984	'ROBERTSONS', Green/Yellow	£4-6	☐
003a	1987	re-run, darker Green 'leaves'	£4-6	☐
004a	1984	'PEPPERIDGE FARM', White/Tan	£4-6	☐
005a	1984	'STAFFS COUNTY SHOW', Pale Green	£4-6	☐
005b	1984	'STAFFS COUNTY SHOW', Mint Green...	£5-7	☐
006a	1984	'MATTHEW NORMAN', Green	£4-6	☐
007a	1985	'ROYAL MAIL', solid Red wheels, SBX	£4-6	☐
008a	1984	'LSWR', Dull Pink/Brown............................	£4-6	☐
009a	1984	'HAMLEY'S TOYS', (special box)	£4-6	☐
010a	1985	'TRI-SUM POTATO CHIPS', Red	£4-6	☐
011a	1987	'LLEDO WORLDWIDE CC', SBX	£5-7	☐
012a	1988	'J.SPRATT', Blue, (special box)	£3-5	☐
013a	1990	'ROYAL MAIL', (special box)	£3-5	☐
014a	1992	'HARRODS', (Set HD1004)...........................	GSP	☐
015a	1992	'GREAT EASTERN', (Set RSL4003)..........	GSP	☐
	1990	Model withdrawn from standard production but casting remains available for use in sets.		

DG 4 HORSE-DRAWN OMNIBUS. Model consists of metal omnibus body, plastic seats & horses. Cream plastic figures included: 2 ladies, a man, the driver & conductor, (No.'4' moulded-in the surround).

000a	1983	'VICTORIA-KINGS CROSS',		
		Red body, Green seats,		
		Green 'LIPTONS' on Off-White panel......	£10-20	☐
000b		As 000a but pure White panel	£4-6	☐
000c		As 000a but White logo, Green panel	£4-6	☐
000d	1984	As 000c but Brown seats	£4-6	☐
001a	1984	'BOWERY to BROADWAY'		
		Red body, Black wheels................................	£4-6	☐
002a	1984	'BOWERY to BROADWAY'		
		Green body, Brown seats & wheels...............	£4-6	☐
002b	1984	Green body & seats, Brown wheels...............	£4-6	☐
002c	1984	Dark Green, Brown seats, Gold wheels	£4-6	☐

002d	1988	Mid-Green, Brown seats, Gold wheels..........	£3-5	☐
003a	1984	'PUTNEY', White body, Red seats................	£4-6	☐
004a	1985	'MASONS PANTRY', Dark Brown body....	£4-6	☐
004b	1985	with 'Mrs Beaton' on wrong sides.................	£18-22	☐
005a	1984	'PEARS', Beige body, Red wheels.................	£4-6	☐
005b	1987	'PEARS', Beige body, Black wheels	£3-5	☐
006a	1984	'MADAME TUSSAUDS'		
		Yellow body, Red seats and wheels...............	£4-6	☐
006b	1987	Yellow body, Red seats, Black wheels	£4-6	☐
007a	1986	'HIGH CHAPARRAL', Beige body............	£4-6	☐
008a	1984	'HAMLEYS TOYS', Red, SBX....................	£4-6	☐
009a	1987	'BALMORAL TOURS', Yellow, SBX	£3-5	☐
010a	1988	'RADIO TIMES' ('A Million Copies')		
		in special box	£75-100	☐
010b	1988	'RADIO TIMES' ('Thomas Tilling') SBX ..	£3-5	☐
011a	1988	'NEWS of the WORLD', SBX......................	£3-5	☐
012a	1989	'COLMANS MUSTARD', Yellow/Red	£3-5	☐
013a	1991	'STONES GINGER WINE', Cream.............	NRP	☐
014a	1992	'OXO', Red body, Black seats......................	NRP	☐
015a	1993	'CO-OP TEA'..	NRP	☐
016a	1993	'FURNESS RAILWAY', (set RSL4003)......	GSP	☐
017a	1994	'MADAME TUSSAUDS'	£3-5	☐
018a	1994	'HARRODS' (set HR 2002)...........................	GSP	☐
019a	1995	'MANN'S BEER'	£3-5	☐

DG 5 SHAND MASON HORSE-DRAWN FIRE ENGINE. The model features a metal main body with plastic horses. A set of 3 (Dark Blue) plastic firemen figures was included up to 1985 (and re-introduced in 1989 partially painted and affixed).

000a	1983	'LONDON', Red body, Black wheels	£4-6	☐
000c	1987	Red body, Gold wheels..................................	£65-80	☐
001a	1983	'CHICAGO', Red body,		
		Black wheels, Black horses...........................	£4-6	☐
001b	1985	Gold wheels, Cream horses. (72 only)..........	£65-80	☐
002a	1983	'GUILDFORD', Green body, Gold		
		wheels, Black boiler (288 made).................	£100-150	☐
002b	1983	Green body, Gold boiler................................	£4-6	☐
002c	1984	Dark Green body, Gold boiler	£4-6	☐
003a	1984	'HONG KONG', White body,		
		Red wheels, Red boiler (288 issued)	£100-150	☐
003b	1984	'HONG KONG', Gold boiler	£4-6	☐
004a	1984	'GWR', Brown body/wheels, Cream horses..	£4-6	☐
004b	1985	Gold wheels, wood plinth, special box	£7-10	☐
004c	1985	Gold wheels, Black horses............................	£4-6	☐
005a	1985	'LAKE CITY', Yellow body, Red wheels.....	£4-6	☐
005b	1987	Yellow body, Black wheels...........................	£3-5	☐
006a	1984	'PHILADELPHIA', Red body......................	£4-6	☐
007a	1984	'BIFBAC 2', Maroon body............................	£4-6	☐
008a	1988	'LONDON EAST HAM', Red, SBX............	£3-5	☐
009a	1989	'CARROW WORKS', Red body	£3-5	☐
010a	1994	'LONDON FB'	£3-5	☐
	1991	Model withdrawn from standard production (but re-run for DG 5-010a)		

DG 6 1920 FORD Model 'T' VAN. A 'Brass' radiator features on this model (except where 'Chrome' noted), along with metal main body and plastic roof section. Later issues cast without cab door imprint. Models 000-035 came with Blue plastic figures: a policeman, man with starting-handle & dog, girl with teddy. There are 4 variations of baseplates: 1st (metal) 'DG6-DG', 2nd (metal) 'DG6-DG8', 3rd (metal 'DG6-8', 4th (plastic) 'DG6-8-33'.

000a	1983	'OVALTINE', Orange body,		
		with 1st baseplate...	£8-10	☐
		with 2nd or 3rd baseplate	£4-6	☐
001a	1983	'YORKSHIRE POST',		
		(1st Lledo Code 1 Trade Special)................	NGPP	☐
002a	1984	'COOKIE COACH Co', Yellow logo	£4-6	☐
002b	1984	'COOKIE COACH Co', White logo	£4-6	☐
003a	1984	'BRITISH MEAT', Cream body,		
		Brown chassis, Brown roof...........................	£7-10	☐
003b	1984	Black chassis, Black roof	£10-15	☐
004a	1984	'AEROPLANE JELLY', Blue body..............	£4-6	☐
005a	1984	'BRITISH MEAT', Cream, rear doors	£4-6	☐
006a	1984	'MARCOL', Beige/Maroon/Black		
		with Maroon 'Red Dragon'...........................	£4-6	☐
006b		'MARCOL', no 'Red Dragon'	£4-6	☐
007a	1984	'POLICE AMBULANCE', CLE of 5000	£30-40	☐
008a	1984	'I.P.M.S.', Cream and Blue...........................	£7-10	☐
009a	1984	'LIVERPOOL GARDEN FESTIVAL'	£4-6	☐
010a	1984	'ILLINOIS TOYFAIR', Lemon/Tan............	£4-6	☐
011a	1984	'STRETTON', Blue chassis, Black roof........	£4-6	☐

012a	1984	'YORKSHIRE EVENING POST'	£4-6	☐
013a	1984	'DAYS GONE C.C.' Black	£7-10	☐
014a	1984	'BRITISH BACON', Blue/Black	£4-6	☐
015a	1984	'HARRY RAMSDEN', Cream and Red	£4-6	☐
016a	1985	'OVALTINE 75th', Stone roof, SBX	£5-7	☐
016b	1990	Tan roof, (000a re-run error)	£5-7	☐
017a	1984	'DAILY EXPRESS' (in CP1 Pack)	GSP	☐
018a	1985	'PERRIER JOUET', Cream and Black	£4-6	☐
019a	1985	'HOME ALES', Green and Black	£4-6	☐
020a	1984	'COCA-COLA' 'At Soda Fountains'	£4-6	☐
021a	1984	'COCA-COLA' 'Every Bottle Sterilized'	£4-6	☐
022a	1984	'WONDERBREAD', White/Dark Blue	£4-6	☐
023a	1984	'RAILWAY EXPRESS' ('84 USA Pack)	GSP	☐
024a	1984	'KODAK', Yellow and Black	£4-6	☐
025a	1984	'MARKS & SPENCER', Green/Black	£4-6	☐
026a	1984	'MARCOL 2', Yellow body, printed rear doors	£4-6	☐
027a	1984	'PHILADELPHIA', Cream/Black	£4-6	☐
028a	1984	'PHILADELPHIA', Red/Black	£4-6	☐
029a	1984	'YORKSHIRE BISCUITS', Brown/Black	£4-6	☐
030a	1984	'AUTOMODEL EXCHANGE', Maroon and Black	£4-6	☐
031a	1984	'ECHO 100', Cream and Blue	£4-6	☐
032a	1985	'STRETTON', Green chassis & roof	£7-10	☐
033a	1985	'BARCLAYS', Light Blue body, Cream chassis, Blue headboard letters	£18-20	☐
033b	1985	with Cream headboard letters	£4-6	☐
033c	1990	with Black chassis and tyres	£500-800	☐
034a	1984	'MAGASIN Du NORD', Dark Green, with White headboard lettering	£30-40	☐
034b	1984	with Gold headboard lettering	£4-6	☐
035a	1984	'HAMLEYS', Dark Green/Red, SBX	£4-6	☐
036a	1985	'AUSTRALIAN Collectors Club', Dark Beige body, Dark Brown chassis, Tan roof	£7-10	☐
036b		with Dark Brown roof	£7-10	☐
036c		Beige body, '85 Convention' (36 only)	£750-1000	☐
037a	1984	'MURPHYS CRISPS', Yellow/Red	£4-6	☐
038a	1985	'WELLS DRINKS', Lemon/Dark Brown	£4-6	☐
039a	1985	'WOODWARDS', Dark Blue body	£4-6	☐
040a	1985	'LINDT', Pale Blue body, Blue roof	NRP	☐
040b		Pale Blue body, Pale Blue roof	£30-40	☐
041a	1985	'EVENING CHRONICLE', Red/Black	£4-6	☐
042a	1986	'CWM DALE', White, Blue chassis	£4-6	☐
042b		'CWM DALE', White, Red chassis	£7-10	☐
043a	1985	'ROYAL MAIL', Red/Black, SBX	£4-6	☐
044a	1985	'ALTON TOWERS', Dark Brown/Cream, special box	£4-6	☐
045a	1985	'NORTHERN DAILY', Green/Black	£4-6	☐
046a	1986	'CADBURYS BOURNVILLE', Red and Cream	£4-6	☐
047a	1986	'JOHN SMITHS', Green/Black	£4-6	☐
048a	1986	'BAY to BIRDWOOD RUN', SBX	£4-6	☐
049a	1986	'HARDWARE JOURNAL', Blue, SBX	£40-50	☐
050		'TOY FAIR'. Trade-only models, Red/Cream, in White promotional box:		
050a	1986	'TOY FAIR '86, Harrogate'	£10-15	☐
050b	1986	'TOY FAIR '86, Harrowgate', (with 'w')	£60-75	☐
050c	1987	'TOY FAIR '87, Harrogate'	£10-15	☐
050d	1988	'TOY FAIR '88, Harrogate'	£10-15	☐
050e	1989	'TOY FAIR '89, Harrogate'	£10-15	☐
051a	1986	'CADBURYS DRINKING CHOCOLATE', special box	£4-6	☐
052		Not allocated		
053a	1986	'TIZER', Yellow and Black	£4-6	☐
054a	1986	'COCA-COLA', Green model, SBX	£4-6	☐
055a	1986	'HERSHEYS', Orange/Brown, in SBX	NRP	☐
056a	1987	'HEDGES & BUTLER', Green/Cream	£3-5	☐
057a	1986	'CANADIAN TRAVEL & GIFT', 500	£60-75	☐
058a	1986	'COCA-COLA', Red/Black van, Red hubs, Chrome radiator, special box	£4-6	☐
058b	1987	with Brass hubs & radiator	£3-5	☐
059a	1986	'CRAFT & HOBBY', 500, Canadian	£60-75	☐
060a	1987	'BLACK VELVIT', Pink and Black	£3-5	☐
061a	1987	'FAIRY SOAP', White and Dark Green	£3-5	☐
062a	1987	'ROSE & CROWN', Green and White	£3-5	☐
063a	1987	'ROYAL FLYING CORPS', (RFC/RAF set)	GSP	☐
064a	1988	'HAMLEYS', Green and Black	£3-5	☐
065a	1988	'BUDWEISER', Cream/Brown, SBX	£3-5	☐
066a	1988	'LLEDO WORLDWIDE CC', Green/ Black	£4-6	☐
067a		Not Allocated		
068a	1988	'GOLDEN SHRED', Red/Green/White	£3-5	☐
069a	1988	'CHARRINGTONS', Red and Brown	£3-5	☐
070a	1988	'MILLBANK BOOKS', Black	£3-5	☐
071a	1990	'HMV', Burgundy/Black/Cream	NRP	☐

072a	1989	'SHELL PUMP SERVICE', Red/Black	£3-5	☐
073a	1989	'WALLS ICES', Black/Cream, Chrome radiator	£3-5	☐
074-	1986	13 Canadian models, each in 'maple-leaf' box, as a set, later available singly:	£40-45	☐
074a	1988	'ONTARIO', White/Red	£3-4	☐
075a	1988	'YUKON', White/Blue/Green	£3-4	☐
076a	1988	'N.W.TERRITORIES', White/Red/Blue	£3-4	☐
077a	1988	'PRINCE EDWARD ISLE', White/Green/Red, wrong date ('1870')	£75-100	☐
077b	1990	with correct date ('1873')	£3-4	☐
078a	1988	'NEWFOUNDLAND', White/Blue/Red	£3-4	☐
079a	1988	'QUEBEC', White/Red/Blue	£3-4	☐
080a	1988	'NOVA SCOTIA', White/Blue/Red	£3-4	☐
081a	1988	'MANITOBA', White/Red	£3-4	☐
082a	1988	'ALBERTA', White/Blue	£3-4	☐
083a	1988	'NEW BRUNSWICK', White/Yellow	£3-4	☐
084a	1988	'BRITISH COLUMBIA', White/Yellow/ Blue	£3-4	☐
085a	1988	'SASKATCHEWAN', White/Yellow/Green	£3-4	☐
086a	1988	'CANADA', White/Red	£3-4	☐
087a	1989	'SELFRIDGES' (in Set LS1004)	GSP	☐
088a	1989	'AU BON MARCHE', Yellow/Black	£3-5	☐
089a	1989	'SCHNEIDERS', Orange and Blue	£3-5	☐
090a	1989	'WINCHESTER CLUB', Green/Black	£3-5	☐
091a	1989	'BRITANNIA FILM' (in 'Gold Set')	GSP	☐
092a	1989	'NESTLES', Pale Red/Black/White	£3-5	☐
093a	1989	'NORTH YORKS MOORS' (in Set)	GSP	☐
094a	1989	'HAMLEYS '89', Blue/Black/Cream, special box	£3-5	☐
095a	1990	'4711', Cyan body, Black chassis & roof	NRP	☐
096a	1990	'ROWNTREES COCOA', Red/Black	NRP	☐
097a	1990	'JAEGER', (in Set LS2004)	GSP	☐
098a	1990	'ROYAL MAIL TELEGRAMS', Red and Black	NRP	☐
099a	1990	'HERSHEY', issued in USA	NGPP	☐
100a	1990	'DAYS GONE' Club Model, Burgundy and Black	£4-6	☐
101a	1990	'ARNOTTS' (in Set ABL1003)	GSP	☐
102a	1991	'DAYS GONE' Club Model, Blue/Green	£4-6	☐
103a	1991	'JOSEPH LUCAS', Dark Green/Grey	NRP	☐
104a	1991	'BLACKPOOL VAN TRANSPORT'	NRP	☐
105a	1991	'ZEBRA GRATE POLISH'	NRP	☐
106a	1992	'DAYS GONE' Club Model, Pale Metallic Green/Black	NRP	☐
107a	1992	'JAMESONS', Cream/Green/Burgundy	NRP	☐
108a	1992	'HOTEL COLUMBIA', (in Set HLL1003)	NRP	☐
109a	1993	'HUNTLEY & PALMERS', Green body	NRP	☐
110a	1993	'MIDLAND', ('Golden Age of Steam')	NRP	☐
111a	1993	'LANCS & YORKS', ('Golden Age of Steam')	NRP	☐
112a	1993	'Nth EASTERN', ('Golden Age of Steam')	NRP	☐
113a	1993	'LMS', ('Golden Age of Steam')	NRP	☐
114a	1993	'DAYS GONE' Club Model	NRP	☐
115a	1994	'Days Gone Club' 1994	£3-5	☐
116a	1994	'FLORIS TOILETRIES'	£3-5	☐
117a	1994	'LONDON N.W.'	£3-5	☐
118a	1994	'LONDON S.W.'	£3-5	☐
119a	1994	'CAMBRIAN'	£3-5	☐
120a	1994	'SOMERSET & DORSET'	£3-5	☐
121a	1994	'RUPERT BEAR'	£3-5	☐
122a	1995	'PEPSI-COLA'	£3-5	☐
123a	1994	'NORMAN ROCKWELL', SBX	£3-5	☐
124a	1994	'AUSTRALIAN POST' (Australia)	NGPP	☐
125a	1995	'ANTON BERG'	£3-5	☐

DG 6 'Golden Age of Steam' Limited Edition models:

126a	1995	'Caledonian Railway'	£3-5	☐
127a	1995	'Great Eastern Railway'	£3-5	☐
128a	1995	'North British Railway'	£3-5	☐
129a	1995	'Great Western Railway'	£3-5	☐
130a		not yet allocated.		
131a		not yet allocated.		
132a		not yet allocated.		
133a	1995	'DAYS-GONE CLUB, 1995'	£3-5	☐

DG 7 1934 FORD Model 'A' WOODY WAGON. The model has metal body, plastic roof, seats, radiator & bumper. Cream plastic figures of a woman with 3 poodles were discontinued after 005.

000a	1984	'PATS POODLE PARLOUR', Yellow/Red, with headboard	£4-6	□
001a	1984	'COCA-COLA', Yellow/Black, headboard ...	£4-6	□
002a	1984	'FORD', headboard, (set GS1)	GSP	□
002b	1985	no headboard, available singly	£4-6	□
003a	1984	'WEST POINT TOY SHOW'	£4-6	□
004a	1984	'HAMLEYS', Pale Cream/Red, Chrome radiator, headboard, SBX	£4-6	□
004b	1985	Brass radiator, headboard, SBX	£4-6	□
005a	1985	'GODFREY DAVIS', White/Blue	£4-6	□
006a	1986	'DELLA', Cream body	NRP	□
007a	1986	'COMMONWEALTH GAMES' (in set)	GSP	□
008a	1988	'CASTROL OIL', White/Green	£3-5	□
009a	1990	'PASCALL SWEETS', White/Green	NRP	□
	1990	New baseplate introduced ('7-9-13-14-37')		
	1991	Model withdrawn from production		

DG 8   1920 FORD Model 'T' TANKER'. A metal body and plastic tank are the main features of this model. The same Blue plastic figures included with DG 6 were provided with 000 to 004 inclusive.

000a	1984	'ESSO', 'Inflamable' (only 1 'm')	£5-7	□
000b	1984	'Inflammable' (correct spelling)	£4-6	□
001a	1984	'COCA-COLA', Dark Yellow/Black	£4-6	□
002a	1985	'CASTROL', Dark Green/Black/White...	£4-6	□
003a	1984	'PHILADELPHIA', Red, Black roof	£4-6	□
003b	1985	'PHILADELPHIA', Red, White roof	£10-15	□
004a	1985	'PENNZOIL', Red/Black/Yellow	£4-6	□
005a	1985	'HOFMEISTER', Yellow/Brown	£4-6	□
006a	1986	'BLUE MOUNTAIN', All Red body	£3-5	□
007a	1987	'CROW CARRYING', Yellow/Black	£3-5	□
008a	1986	'HERSHEYS', White/Brown, special box.....	£4-6	□
009a	1987	'WATER WORKS', Blue/Black	£3-5	□
010a	1987	'ZEROLENE', (Dealer promotional, 3,000)	£15-18	□
011a	1988	'SHELL FUEL OIL', Red/Black/White	£4-6	□
012a	1988	'HOMEPRIDE', White/Red/Blue	£3-5	□
013a	1988	'DUCKHAMS OILS', Grey/Black/Green ...	£3-5	□
014a	1989	'SHELL FRANCE', Red/Black/White	£4-6	□
015a	1989	'BP MOTOR SPIRIT', Green/Black	NRP	□
016a	1989	'TEXACO', Red and Black	NRP	□
017a	1989	'ARMY WATER' (part of Army set)	GSP	□
018a	1990	'PRATTS', Green and Black	NRP	□
019a	1991	'MOBILGAS', Red and Black	NRP	□
020a	1993	'RUSSIAN OIL', Grey/Red	NRP	□
	1994	Model withdrawn from production.		

DG 9   1934 FORD Model 'A' CAR. This model has a metal open car body with DG 7 baseplate & chassis. White plastic figures (2 bank robbers & seated policeman with gun) included with 001a & b. The same figures (but Black plastic), were with 001c and 002 to 004.

000a	1984	'POLICE' Car, Mid Blue/Dark Blue	£20-30	□
000b	1984	All Dark Blue body, Cream seats	£4-6	□
000c	1984	All Dark Blue body, Black seats	£4-6	□
001a	1984	'NEW YORK - RIO', (in Set GS1)	GSP	□
002a	1984	'PHILADELPHIA FIRE', Red body	£4-6	□
003a	1985	'15 MILLIONTH FORD', Black body......	£4-6	□
	1991	Model withdrawn from production		

DG 10   1935 DENNIS SINGLE-DECK COACH. This was the first Lledo model to have twin rear wheels. Other features are metal body castings and plastic roof/window section, seats & baseplate. Cream plastic figures included (1984-85) were of: man leaning on bus-stop, man & woman with boy, young woman with dog.

000a	1984	'BRIGHTON BELLE', Maroon body, Beige roof, Chrome radiator	£15-20	□
000b		Beige roof, Brass radiator	£4-6	□
000c		Cream roof, Brass radiator	£4-6	□
001a	1984	'TILLINGBOURNE', Maroon/Black......	£4-6	□
002a	1987	'SILVER SERVICE', Silver/Red, Silver 'Matlock'	£3-5	□
002b	1987	Silver/Red, White 'Matlock'	£3-5	□
003a	1984	'SOUTHERN VECTIS', Green/Cream, with Yellow logo	£4-6	□
		with White logo	£12-15	□
004a	1984	'SCHOOL BUS', Yellow/Black, with Chrome radiator	£7-10	□
004b	1984	with Brass radiator	£4-6	□
004c	1987	'OAKRIDGE SCHOOL', Yellow/Black	£3-5	□
005a	1984	'POTTERIES', Red/Black, Cream roof	£4-6	□

005b	1986	with Red roof	£14-16	□
006a	1985	'GWR', Dark Brown and Cream '150th Anniversary' model, SBX......	£8-12	□
007a	1985	'BARTON', Red/Maroon/Cream	£4-6	□
008a	1986	'LONDON COUNTRY', Green, with Brass radiator	£3-5	□
008b	1986	with Chrome radiator.	£3-5	□
008c	1988	Green body, Black chassis	£75-100	□
009a	1984	'HAMLEYS', Dark Brown/Cream, SBX	£5-7	□
010		Not allocated		
011		Not allocated		
012a	1985	'TARTAN', Red and Cream	£4-6	□
013a	1985	'TRAILWAYS', (part of 3-bus Set)	GSP	□
014a	1985	'IMPERIAL AIRWAYS', Blue roof	£4-6	□
014b	1987	'IMPERIAL AIRWAYS', Red roof	£12-15	□
015a	1986	'REDBURNS', Red/Cream	£3-5	□
016a	1986	'COMMONWEALTH GAMES', (in set)	GSP	□
017a	1986	'HERSHEYS', Brown/Cream	£4-6	□
018a	1988	'E.B.TAYLOR', Red/Black	£3-5	□
	1989	New baseplate text ('DG10-12-34-35')		
019a	1989	'CITY of COVENTRY', Crimson/Cream.....	£3-5	□
020a	1990	'BOAC', Dark Blue and Cream......	NRP	□
021a	1991	'BEA', Grey and Cream	NRP	□
	1992	Model withdrawn from production		

DG 11   HORSE-DRAWN REMOVAL VAN. Large metal body, plastic roof, metal base. Cream plastic figures (not included after 1985) were: driver, woman with hoop, girl with hoop, boy with bag & bulldog. In 1989 a driver figure was re-introduced along with a change in design of horses.

000a	1984	'TURNBULL & Co', White/Red/Green.......	£4-6	□
001a	1985	'ABELS', Pale Blue/Red/Blue......	£4-6	□
002a	1985	'BIG TOP CIRCUS', Cream/Red/Blue......	£4-6	□
003a	1985	'Staffs COUNTY SHOW', Buff/Brown......	£4-6	□
004a	1985	'ROYAL MAIL', Red/Black, SBX	£4-6	□
005a	1985	'WILLIAMS GRIFFIN', Green/Red/Beige, Gold wheels	£4-6	□
006a	1986	'MacCOSHAMS', Yellow, Black wheels	£3-5	□
007a	1986	'COCA-COLA', White/Red, Hartoy Set.......	GSP	□
008a	1986	'BUDWEISER', White/Red, special box	£3-5	□
009a	1989	'LLEDO WORLDWIDE CC', Blue/White...	£4-6	□
010a	1988	'R.P.COOPER', White/Black	£3-5	□
011a		Not allocated		
012a	1989	'JAMES BROWN & SON', Cream/Green ...	£3-5	□
013a	1989	'ALBERT DALEY & Co', Yellow body	£3-5	□
014a	1990	'MARKS & SPENCER', Red/Black, SBX ...	NRP	□
015a	1990	'ROYAL MAIL', Red/Black, SBX	NRP	□
016a	1990	'ARNOTTS', Red, (Set ABL1003)......	GSP	□
017a	1991	'ROBERT HEATON & SON', Black	NRP	□
018a	1991	'DG CLUB SUMMER '91'	NRP	□
019a	1991	'SAINSBURYS', Blue/Black	NRP	□
020a	1992	'HARRODS', (in Set HD1002)	GSP	□
021a	1992	'HAMLEYS', (in Set HAL1004)	GSP	□
022a	1993	'SCHWEPPES', Green/Black/Red......	NRP	□
023a	1993	'PEPSI-COLA', White, SBX......	NRP	□
024a	1993	'GREAT NORTHERN', (Set RSL4003)	GSP	□
025a	1994	'OXO TRENCH HEATER'.	£3-5	□
026a	1995	'RUPERT' (SBX)	£3-5	□

DG 12   1934 DENNIS FIRE ENGINE. This model uses the same chassis/baseplate/wheels/radiator as DG 10 with plastic windscreen/ladder mount & ladder. Escape wheels not fitted to 000a, 001a, 003a. 3 Blue plastic firemen included up to 1985.

000a	1984	'LUCKHURST', Red/Green	£4-6	□
000b	1989	Red body, Red chassis	£4-6	□
001a	1985	'CARDIFF CITY', Red/White	£4-6	□
002		Not allocated		
003a	1985	'BERMUDA', Blue body, Cream floor......	£4-6	□
003b	1985	'BERMUDA', Blue body, White floor......	£4-6	□
004a	1986	'LCC', Red body, Black chassis	£3-5	□
005a	1986	'CHELMSFORD', Red/Black, Brass radiator	£3-5	□
005b	1987	Red/Black, Chrome radiator	£3-5	□
006a	1987	'AUXILIARY', Green body/chassis	£3-5	□
007a	1987	'ESSEX COUNTY', Red/White......	£3-5	□
007b	1990	same but White 'ESSEX'	£5-8	□
008a	1987	'WARE FIRE SERVICE', All Red	£3-5	□
009a	1987	'WINDSOR', All Red, special box	£3-5	□
010a	1988	'GLASGOW', All Red......	£3-5	□
011a	1988	'BOSTON', Red body......	£3-5	□
012a	1989	'BIRMINGHAM', Red and Black......	£3-5	□

	1989	Baseplate with 'DG10-12-34-35' introduced		
013a	1990	'BRADFORD', Red and Black	NRP	☐
014a	1990	'HERSHEY', Red/White, SBX	NRP	☐
015a	1991	'MANCHESTER', Red and Black	NRP	☐
016a	1992	'WEST HAM', Red and Black	NRP	☐
017a	1993	'VALLETTA', (Set MG1003)	GSP	☐
018a	1994	'HAMLEYS 1994'	£3-5	☐
019a	1994	'LONDON FB'	£3-5	☐

DG 13 1934 FORD Model 'A' VAN. Model features metal body and plastic fluted roof with advertising board on some. Cream plastic figures included up to 011 included: a newsboy, a deliveryman, man reading paper.

000a	1986	'CAMP COFFEE', Cream/Brown, SBX	£3-5	☐
001a	1984	'EVENING NEWS', Yellow body	£4-6	☐
002a	1985	'TUCHER BEERS', Cyan/Black, SBX	£4-6	☐
003a	1986	'MITRE 10', Caramel/Black, SBX	£20-25	☐
004a	1984	'HAMLEYS', Yellow body, SBX	£4-6	☐
005a	1985	'MICHELIN', Yellow/Blue (also in Set)	£4-6	☐
006a	1985	'JERSEY EVENING POST', White/Pink	£10-15	☐
007a	1985	'MARY ANN BREWERY', Blue body	£10-15	☐
008a	1984	'ROYAL MAIL', Red and Black	£4-6	☐
008b	1992	'ROYAL MAIL', new longer body	£3-4	☐
009a	1985	'COCA-COLA', Yellow and Black	£4-6	☐
010a	1985	'BASILDON BOND', White/Blue with matt finish	£6-8	☐
010b	1985	with gloss finish	£4-6	☐
011a	1986	'RYDER', Yellow body	£3-5	☐
012a	1985	'COCA-COLA', All Yellow	£3-5	☐
013a	1985	'EVENING SENTINEL', Blue and Black (with figures)	£4-6	☐
014a	1985	'STROH'S', Red body, Black roof	£4-6	☐
015a	1985	'ROYAL MAIL 350', Red/Black, SBX	£4-6	☐
016a	1985	'FESTIVAL GARDENS LIVERPOOL'	£4-6	☐
017a	1986	'ROBINSONS', Cream and Green	£3-5	☐
018a	1988	'EVER READY', Blue and White	£3-5	☐
019a	1987	'HP SAUCE', Maroon and White	£3-5	☐
020a	1986	'FDB' (Danish), Grey and Blue	£20-25	☐
021a	1986	'COCA-COLA', Black chassis	£3-5	☐
021b		'COCA-COLA', Yellow chassis	£100-150	☐
022a	1988	'J. LYONS', Blue and White	£3-5	☐
023a	1986	'HERSHEYS KISSES', Brown/Cream	£3-5	☐
024a	1986	'HERSHEYS', Cream/Brown	£3-5	☐
025a	?	'ROYAL MAIL', Red and Black, SBX	£3-5	☐
026a	1988	'HEINZ TOMATO SOUP', Red/Cream	£3-5	☐
027a	1988	'CHARLES TATE', Brown and Black	£3-5	☐
028a	1988	'EXCHANGE & MART', White/Black	£3-5	☐
029a	1988	'ELIZABETH SHAW', Cream/Blue	£3-5	☐
030a	1989	'OXYDOL', Light and Dark Blue	£3-5	☐
031a	1989	'AQUASCUTUM', (in Set LS1004)	GSP	☐
032		Not allocated		
033a	1989	'ALLENBURYS', Maroon /Cream	£3-5	☐
034a	1989	'EMPIRE', (part of 'Gold Set')	GSP	☐
035a	1989	'KLEENEX', White and Blue	£3-5	☐
036a	1991	'AUSTIN REED', (in Set LS2004)	GSP	☐
037a	1989	'BBC', Green and Black	£3-5	☐
038a	1989	'ARMY RECRUITMENT', (BA1003)	GSP	☐
039a	1990	'PERSIL', Green and Black	NRP	☐
040a	1990	'MADAME TUSSAUDS', Blue/White	NRP	☐
041a	1990	'MARKS & SPENCER', White and Green, special box	NRP	☐
042a	1990	'ROYAL MAIL', Red and Black	NRP	☐
043a	1990	'HERSHEYS', Silver/Brown, (US issue)	NGPP	☐
044a	1990	'Nth YORKS MOORS', (NYM Set 2)	GSP	☐
045a	1990	'ARNOTTS', (Set ABL1003)	GSP	☐
	1990	Baseplate with '7-9-13-14-37' introduced		
046a	1991	'ROSELLA', Yellow and Green	NRP	☐
047a	1991	'CASTROL', Red and Black	NRP	☐
	1991	Steering wheel and seats added		
048a	1992	'HAMLEYS', White and Blue	NRP	☐
	1992	Longer body introduced		
049a	1992	'RINSO', Two-tone Blue	NRP	☐
050a	1992	'SOUTHERN RAILWAY', (RSL2003)	GSP	☐
051a	1992	'HARRODS', (HD1004)	GSP	☐
052a	1992	'QANTAS', (in Set QA1002)	GSP	☐
053a	1992	'GODE', (for German market)	£25-30	☐
054a	1992	'RAMA', (for German market)	£20-25	☐
055a	1993	'GOLDEN SHRED', Red/White	£3-4	☐
056a	1993	'PEPSI-COLA', White, SBX	£3-4	☐
057a	1993	'MARKS & SPENCER', (MS2004)	GSP	☐
058a	1993	'Grand Hotel Peking', (HLL2003)	GSP	☐
059a	1994	'CARLSBERG'	£3-5	☐
060a	1994	'KODAK' (Mexico)	£30-40	☐
061a	1994	'RUPERT BEAR' (SBX)	£3-5	☐
062a	1994	'DR. PEPPER', (SBX)	£3-5	☐
063a	1994	'NORMAN ROCKWELL', (SBX)	£3-5	☐
064a	1994	'RITTER SCHOKOLADE'	£3-5	☐
	1995	'DAILY HERALD' (Set VE 1003)	GSP	☐

DG 14 1934 FORD Model 'A' CAR with HOOD. Model has metal body and raised plastic hood. Cream plastic figures (1 US policeman & 2 firemen), were only issued with 000a/b and 001a.

000a	1985	'SAN DIEGO', 'Fire Chief' in Gold with Black surround	£150-200	☐
000b		'Fire Chief' not in Gold with Black surround	£4-6	☐
001a	1985	'TAXI', Yellow and Black	£3-5	☐
002a	1985	'ACME CLEANERS', White body	£4-6	☐
003a	1986	'HAMLEYS', Red and Black, SBX	£3-5	☐
004a	1986	'GRAND HOTEL', Brown/Cream	£3-5	☐
004b	1987	'GRAND HOTEL', Brown/Beige	£3-5	☐
005		Not allocated		
006a	1987	'STATE PENITENTIARY', Light Grey	£4-6	☐
007a	1988	'SAN DIEGO', (US version)	NGPP	☐
	1990	Baseplate with '7-9-13-14-37' introduced		
008a	1990	'RALEIGH CYCLES', Green/Black	NRP	☐
	1991	Model withdrawn from production		

DG 15 1932 AEC REGENT DOUBLE-DECK BUS. The first 'Days Gone' model to be issued without the plastic figures. Components include metal main body, roof, staircase and baseplate; plastic windows, radiator, wheels and upper seats. Lower seats were absent till 1989.

000a	1985	'HALLS WINE', Red/Black, Silver roof, Chrome radiator	£4-6	☐
000b	1985	Silver roof, Brass radiator	£4-6	☐
001a	1985	'COCA-COLA', Red and Black	£4-6	☐
002a	1985	'CASTLEMAINE XXXX', (in 3-bus Set)	GSP	☐
003a	1985	'HAMLEYS', Red and Black, SBX	£4-6	☐
004a	1985	'LIVERPOOL GARDENS', Cream/Brown	£4-6	☐
005a	1986	'CINZANO', Cream seats, Chrome radiator	£4-6	☐
005b	1988	Ivory seats, Brass radiator	£3-5	☐
006a	1986	'EVENING ARGUS', Red/Black/Cream	£3-5	☐
007a	1986	'HALLS WINE', Pale Brown body	£30-35	☐
007b	1986	'HALLS WINE', bare metal body	£15-20	☐
007	1986	(a & b) in display case with components	£100-125	☐
008a	1986	'ROYAL WEDDING', Blue/Red, SBX	£10-13	☐
009a	1987	'MADAME TUSSAUDS', with Chrome radiator	£3-5	☐
009b	1987	with Brass radiator	£3-5	☐
010a	1986	'SWAN VESTAS', with Cream seats, Chrome radiator	£3-5	☐
010b	1987	with Ivory seats, Brass radiator	£3-5	☐
011a	1986	'COMMONWEALTH GAMES', White, Chrome radiator, (in 3-model Set)	GSP	☐
011b	1987	with Brass radiator	£3-5	☐
012a	1987	'HEINZ', Red and Black	£3-5	☐
013a	1987	'STRATFORD BLUE', Blue/Silver, SBX	£3-5	☐
014a	1987	'TV TIMES', Red and Black	£3-5	☐
015a	1988	'HAMLEYS', All Red	£3-5	☐
016a	1988	'BIRMINGHAM MAIL', Blue/Cream	NRP	☐
017a	1988	'GOLDEN WONDER', Blue/Silver	£3-5	☐
018a	1988	'LLEDO COLLECTORS CLUB'	£10-15	☐
019a	1989	'MAPLES', All Red	£3-5	☐
020a	1989	'TERRY'S GYM', Blue/Cream/Silver	£3-5	☐
021a	1989	'St.IVEL CHEESE', Red and Cream	£3-5	☐
022a	1989	'HAMLEYS', Red and Black, SBX	£3-5	☐
023a	1990	'PALMOLIVE', Red and Black	NRP	☐
024a	1990	'RAC', Blue and Cream	NRP	☐
025a	1990	'POST EARLY FOR XMAS', Red body, Red seats, special box	NRP	☐
025b	1990	Red body, Cream seats, special box	NRP	☐
026a	1990	'HERSHEYS', Beige/Brown, (US issue)	NGPP	☐
027a	1990	'Nth.YORKS MOORS', (NYM Set 2)	GSP	☐
028a	1992	'HARRODS', (Set HD1002)	GSP	☐
029a	1993	'Mazawattee Tea', Green/Cream	NRP	☐
030a	1993	'Van HOUTENS COCOA', Blue/Cream	NRP	☐
031a	1993	'DG CLUB' Autumn '93	£3-5	☐
032a	1994	'LIBBYS PINEAPPLE'	£3-5	☐
033a	1994	'HAMLEYS' (Set HA 2002)	GSP	☐
034a	1994	'GODE' (German market)	£15-20	☐
035a	1995	'PEARS SOAP'	£3-5	☐
036a	1994	'HARRODS', (Set HR 2004)	GSP	☐

DG 16 1934 DENNIS PARCELS VAN. The model features a single metal body casting, plastic roof and baseplate. The plastic seats and steering wheel did not appear until 1991. Either separate wheel/tyre units or composite wheels can be found.

000a	1985	'MAYFLOWER', Yellow/Black/Green........	£4-6	☐
001a	1985	'ROYAL MAIL', Red and Black, SBX	£4-6	☐
002a	1985	'CROFT ORIGINAL', Cream body............	£4-6	☐
003a	1986	'HAMLEYS', All Black, special box.........	£3-5	☐
004a	1986	'TREBOR', Green/Black/White	£3-5	☐
005a	1986	'L.N.E.R.', Dark Blue.............................	£3-5	☐
006a	1986	'KIWI', Black hubs, Brass radiator............	£3-5	☐
006b	1987	'KIWI', Cream hubs, Chrome radiator	£3-5	☐
007a	1985	'BUSHELLS', Dark Blue and Black..........	£4-6	☐
008		Not allocated		
009a	1987	'CADBURYS', Purple and White	£3-5	☐
010a	1987	'FYFFES', Yellow/Blue/White	£3-5	☐
011a	1986	'COCA-COLA', Red and Black, SBX	£3-5	☐
012a	1986	'HERSHEYS GOODBAR', Yellow, SBX	£3-5	☐
013a	1986	'HERSHEYS KRACKEL', Red body		
		with Brass radiator, special box............	£4-6	☐
013b	1987	with Chrome radiator, special box	£4-6	☐
014a	1988	'PICKFORDS', Blue body	£3-5	☐
014b	1989	'PICKFORDS', Dark Blue body................	£3-5	☐
015a	1987	'LLEDO WORLDWIDE CC',		
		Black body, special box........................	£4-6	☐
016a	1988	'HAMLEYS', All Black.............................	£3-5	☐
017a	1989	'ABELS', Pale Blue and Black	£3-5	☐
018a	1990	'MADAME TUSSAUDS', Red/Black	NRP	☐
019a	1989	'ALLIED', Orange/Black/White	£3-5	☐
020a	1989	'COSMOS', White and Black	£3-5	☐
021a	1989	'GOODYEAR', Blue/Black/White	£3-5	☐
021b	1990	same model but White 'Goodyear'	£4-6	☐
022a	1990	'HAMLEYS', Maroon/Black/Cream..........	£3-5	☐
023a	1990	'OXO', Black body, Chrome radiator	NRP	☐
024a	1990	'ROYAL MAIL', Red and Black................	NRP	☐
025a	1990	'Nth.YORKS MOORS', (NYM Set 3)	GSP	☐
026a	1991	'SCHWEPPES', Dark Blue body	NRP	☐
	1991	Steering wheel and seats added		
027a	1991	'ATORA FOR XMAS', Green/Black	NRP	☐
028a	1991	'LNER East Coast, (Set TPL1003)	GSP	☐
029a	1991	'LNER Skegness', (Set RSL1003).............	GSP	☐
030a	1991	'Y.M.C.A.', (Set HF1003)........................	GSP	☐
031a	1992	'HUDSONS SOAP', Blue/Black	NRP	☐
032a	1993	'TUNNOCKS', Red/Black	NRP	☐
033a	1993	'NAAFI', (Set DM1003)...........................	GSP	☐
034a	1993	'RAF Runway Control' (Set DML1003)	GSP	☐
035a	1994	'KODAK'...	£3-5	☐
036a	1994	'BOVRIL'...	£3-5	☐
037a	1994	'RUPERT BEAR'.....................................	£3-5	☐
038a	1994	'DG CLUB' Autumn '94	£3-5	☐
039a	1995	'RUPERT BEAR'.....................................	£3-5	☐

DG 17 1932 AEC REGAL SINGLE DECK BUS. The model features metal body, chassis & roof castings with plastic baseplate, and composite window and seat section.

000a	1985	'SOUTHEND', Blue body, Cream wings,		
		with filler cap casting	£60-75	☐
000b		without filler cap casting	£4-6	☐
000c	1986	with Red roof, (1,000 only)......................	£25-35	☐
001a	1985	'EUROTOURS', Green/Cream, (in Set)	GSP	☐
002a	1985	'CORPORATION TRANSPORT',		
		Yellow/Grey	£4-6	☐
003a	1986	'HAMLEYS', Green/Cream, SBX..............	£25-35	☐
004a	1985	'LONDON TRANSPORT', Red/Black........	£4-6	☐
005a	1986	'OXFORD (MORRELL'S)',		
		Red/Black/Maroon	£3-5	☐
006a	1986	'COMMONWEALTH GAMES', White,		
		SBX..	£4-6	☐
007a	1986	'STRATFORD BLUE', Chrome radiator......	£3-5	☐
007b	1987	'STRATFORD BLUE', Brass radiator........	£6-9	☐
008a	1987	'BURNLEY CORPORATION', Blue/		
		White	£3-5	☐
009a	1986	'BIG TOP CIRCUS', Cream/Blue	£3-5	☐
010a	1987	'PENNINE', Orange and Black	£3-5	☐
011a	1987	'ROYAL FLYING CORPS', (in Set)	GSP	☐
012a	1988	'HAMLEYS', Two-tone Blue	£3-5	☐
	1988	New roof (with 2 hoardings) introduced.		
013a	1988	'HANTS & DORSET', Green/Black.............	NRP	☐
014a	1988	'SUTTONS', Red and Grey	£3-5	☐
015a	1989	'ROYAL BLUE', Blue and Black	£3-5	☐
015b	1989	'ROYAL BLUE', as 015a but with White		
		background to headboard decal...............	£3-5	☐
016a	1989	'COLCHESTER', Maroon, no hoardings.....	£3-5	☐

017a	1988	'ROYAL NAVY', (in Set RN1003)	GSP	☐
018a	1989	'Nth.YORKS MOORS', (NYM Set)	GSP	☐
019a	1990	'RED & WHITE', Cream/Black/Red............	NRP	☐
020a	1991	'BUCKLAND OMNIBUS Co', Red	NRP	☐
021a	1992	'SOUTHERN VECTIS', Green...................	NRP	☐
022a	1992	'GREEN LINE', Green/Black/Silver	NRP	☐
022b	1993	No fleet number on bonnet.......................	£3-5	☐
022c	1994	Silver print on side boards	£3-5	☐
023a	1995	'SUNDERLAND'....................................	£3-5	☐
	1995	'US RED CROSS', (Set VE 1003)	GSP	☐

DG 18 1936 PACKARD VAN. This model has metal body & chassis castings, plastic roof and baseplate. Steering wheel & seats appeared in 1991.

000a	1985	'AMBULANCE', Chrome radiator..............	£4-6	☐
000b	1987	'AMBULANCE', Brass radiator.................	£3-5	☐
001a	1985	'AMERICAN AMBULANCE', as		
		000a but Red cross in circle....................	£4-6	☐
002a	1986	'COMMONWEALTH GAMES',		
		with Chrome radiator, special box...........	£5-7	☐
002b	1987	with Brass radiator, normal box	£3-5	☐
003a	1986	'RAPID CASH', Blue/Black/Cream...........	£3-5	☐
004a	1986	'FIRESTONE', with Chrome radiator..........	£4-6	☐
004b	1987	'FIRESTONE', with Brass radiator	£3-5	☐
005		Not allocated		
006a	1987	'WHITE STAR', Chrome radiator..............	£3-5	☐
006b	1987	'WHITE STAR', Brass radiator.................	£3-5	☐
007a	1987	'COLMANS', Yellow and Black	£3-5	☐
008a	1987	'ROYAL FLYING CORPS', (in Set)	GSP	☐
009a	1988	'PERRONI BIRRA', White and Blue.........	£3-5	☐
010a	1988	'NATIONAL WESTMINSTER', Silver/		
		White	£10-15	☐
011a	1988	'FOTORAMA', Chrome radiator	£3-5	☐
011b	1989	'FOTORAMA', Brass radiator	£3-5	☐
012a	1990	'St.IVEL', Yellow/Black/Green	NRP	☐
013a	1989	'FORTNUM & MASON', (in Set LS1004)..	GSP	☐
014a	1989	'B & C FILMS', (in 'Gold' Set)................	GSP	☐
015a	1988	'St.MARY'S HOSPITAL',		
		(Canadian charity model).......................	£20-25	☐
016a	1989	'LEYLAND PAINTS', Blue/Maroon	£3-5	☐
017a	1989	'HAMLEYS', Cream and Blue, SBX..........	£3-5	☐
018a	1990	'ASPREY', (in Set LS2004)	GSP	☐
019a	1990	'DAYS GONE CLUB' Autumn model........	NRP	☐
020a	1991	'McVITIE & PRICE', Burgundy...............	NRP	☐
021a	1992	'CAMP COFFEE', Cream/Brown..............	NRP	☐
022a	1992	'St.JOHN AMBULANCE', in Set MG1003	GSP	☐
023a	1993	'FERODO', Green/Black..........................	NRP	☐
024a	1993	'IMPERIAL HOTEL' (Set HLL2003)	GSP	☐
TBA	1986	'CAMPERDOWN HOSPITAL',		
		(Australian charity)	£75-90	☐
025a	1994	'NORMAN ROCKWELL', (SBX)	£3-5	☐

DG 19 1931 ROLLS-ROYCE PHANTOM II (BREWSTER). The model has a one-piece metal body and incorporates the DG 18 baseplate. Plastic seats, roof, trunk and radiator. It acquired a steering wheel in 1989.

000a	1985	Burgundy/Black, ('TV Times' offer).........	£4-6	☐
001a	1986	Yellow/Tan, Chrome radiator	£3-5	☐
001b	1986	Yellow/Tan, Brass radiator......................	£3-5	☐
002a	1986	'Basketweave', Beige/Cream,		
		Grey tyres, Brass radiator	£4-6	☐
002b	1987	Grey tyres, Chrome radiator	£3-5	☐
002c	1987	Beige tyres, Brass radiator	£3-5	☐
003a	1988	Metallic Grey/Black, (in 3-car Set)	GSP	☐
003b	1988	Not mounted or drilled, (unofficial)	£7-10	☐
004a	1987	Gold and White	£3-5	☐
005a	1987	'Ruby Wedding', Maroon body, SBX	£4-6	☐
006a	1989	Dark Green/ Black/Beige........................	£3-5	☐
007a	1988	'Minder', Gold/White	£3-5	☐
008a	1989	'Lledo Worldwide C.C.', Silver/Black........	£3-5	☐
009a	1989	'Army Staff Car', in Set BA1003	GSP	☐
010a	1992	Black/Ivory, Chrome radiator	NRP	☐
011a	1992	Silver/Black (for German market).............	£20-25	☐
TBA	1985	All Cream, Chrome radiator, (108 only).......	£30-35	☐
	1993	Model withdrawn from the standard range		

DG 20 1936 FORD STAKE TRUCK. Model features one-piece metal cab and cast stake body, plastic baseplate and load (barrels, tyres, cylinders or sacks). The steering wheel and seats appeared in 1991.

000a	1986	'EAGLE ALES', Yellow and Brown	£3-5	☐

001a	1986	'COCA-COLA', Yellow/Black, SBX	£3-5	☐
001b	1987	same but with Red barrels	£3-5	☐
002a	1987	'STROH'S', Red/Black, Brass radiator	£3-5	☐
002b		same but with Chrome radiator	£3-5	☐
003a	1986	'WHITBREAD', Brown/Black, Brass radiator	£3-5	☐
003b	1987	Brown/Black, Chrome radiator	£3-5	☐
004a	1986	'GOODRICH', Cream and Blue	NRP	☐
005a	1988	'AULD SCOTCH GINGER', Blue	£3-5	☐
006a	1987	'UNIROYAL', Red and Black	£3-5	☐
007a	1988	'BUDWEISER', White body, SBX	£4-6	☐
008a	1988	'IND COOPE', All Green	£3-5	☐
009a	1989	'WATNEYS', Green and Black	£3-5	☐
010a	1989	'CALOR GAS', Orange/Green/White	£3-5	☐
011a	1988	'ROYAL NAVY', (in Set RN1003)	GSP	☐
012a	1990	'PIRELLI', Yellow and Black	NRP	☐
013a	1990	'BRITISH OXYGEN', Maroon/Black	NRP	☐
014a	1990	'HERSHEYS', US issue in SBX	NGPP	☐
015a	1990	'RAF', (in RAF Set BB1003)	GSP	☐
016a	1990	'WINN DIXIE', Black/Cream	£3-4	☐
017a	1991	'DUNLOP TYRES', White/Blue	NRP	☐
	1993	'DUNLOP TYRES', 'Brooklands Collection'	NRP	☐
018a	1991	'GOODYEAR TYRES', Blue body	NRP	☐
019a	1993	'McDOUGALLS', Grey/Blue	NRP	☐
020a	1994	'NESTLES MILK'	£3-5	☐
021a	1994	'Dr. PEPPER', SBX	£3-5	☐
022a	1995	'PENNZOIL'	£3-5	☐

DG 21 1934 CHEVROLET VAN. Model has one-piece cast body plus metal chassis mounted on a plastic baseplate. The plastic roof may have front headboard, front & lengthways headboard, or no headboard at all. Seats & steering wheel added in 1991. Baseplate updated in 1992.

000a	1986	'SHARPS', Cream, Chrome radiator	£3-5	☐
000b	1987	'SHARPS', Yellow, Brass radiator	£3-5	☐
001a	1986	'LLEDO WORLDWIDE CLUB', SBX	£3-5	☐
001b	1986	Maroon hubs, Black prototype logo	£3-5	☐
002a	1986	'LEICESTER MERCURY', Blue/Black	£3-5	☐
003a	1986	'HOSTESS CAKE', White and Red	£3-5	☐
004a	1987	'Dr.PEPPER', Red and Black	£3-5	☐
005a	1986	'COCA-COLA', Cream and Red, SBX	£3-5	☐
006		Not allocated		
007a	1988	'HAMLEYS', Red and Cream	£3-5	☐
008a	1988	'BUDWEISER', Green/Black, SBX	£3-5	☐
009a	1988	'BIRDS CUSTARD', Yellow/Blue	£3-5	☐
010a	1988	'FARRAH'S TOFFEE', Purple/White	£3-5	☐
011a	1988	'VITA-WHEAT', Beige and Brown	£3-5	☐
012a	1989	'SIMPSONS', (in Set LS1004)	GSP	☐
013a	1989	'BENETTONS', Cream and Green	£3-5	☐
014a	1989	'HERSHEYS KISSES', Brown/Cream	£3-5	☐
015a	1989	'CHERRY BLOSSOM', Blue/White	£3-5	☐
016a	1989	'MAJESTIC FILMS', (in 'Gold' Set)	GSP	☐
017a	1990	'TOYFAIR '90', Cream and Green	£8-11	☐
018a	1990	'RECKITTS BLUE', Blue/Black	NRP	☐
019a	1990	'MARKS & SPENCER', Cream/Green	NRP	☐
020a	1990	'LIBERTY'S', (in Set LS2004)	GSP	☐
021a	1990	'CLUB SUMMER '90', Blue/Cream	NRP	☐
022a	1990	'SCOTTISH BLUEBELL', in Set BM1004	GSP	☐
023a	1990	'BRYANT & MAY', in Set BM1004	GSP	☐
024a	1990	'SWAN VESTAS', in Set BM1004	GSP	☐
025a	1990	'ENGLANDS GLORY', set BM1004	GSP	☐
026a	1991	'HAMLEYS', Two-tone Blue	NRP	☐
027a	1991	'EXIDE ', Cream and Green	NRP	☐
028a	1991	'FAIRY SOAP', White and Green	NRP	☐
029a	1991	'BUSHELLS COFFEE', Cream/Blue	NRP	☐
030a	1991	'U.S. MARINES', (in Set PH1003)	GSP	☐
031a	1992	'ELLIMANS', Red/Black	NRP	☐
032a	1992	'MAGGI'S SOUP', Blue/Black	NRP	☐
033a	1991	'SCRIBBANS', (Trade special)	NGPP	☐
034a	1992	'LMS & LNER', in Set RSL2003	GSP	☐
035a	1992	'GRAND HOTEL', in Set HLL1003	GSP	☐
036a	1992	'LNER Country', in Set RSL3003	GSP	☐
037a	1992	'HAMLEYS', in Set HAL1004	GSP	☐
038a	1993	'PEPSI-COLA', Blue, SBX	NRP	☐
039a	1994	'ROSES LIME JUICE'	£3-5	☐
040a	1994	'SPRENGEL' (German)	£20-25	☐
041a	1994	'HENDERSON' (Set MCL 1003)	GSP	☐
042a	1994	'USA WORLD CUP'	£3-5	☐
043a	1994	'NORMAN ROCKWELL', SBX	£3-5	☐
044a	1995	'NIVEA CREAM'	£3-5	☐
045a	1995	'RUPERT BEAR'	£3-5	☐

DG 22 1933 PACKARD TOWN VAN. The model features a metal box body (with plastic roof) behind a roofless cab. Spare wheels in front wings.

000a	1986	'STAG WHISKY', Cream and Red	£3-5	☐
001a	1986	'LORD TED', Black body	£3-5	☐
002a	1987	'FLORISTS', Brass radiator	£3-5	☐
002b	1987	'FLORISTS', Chrome radiator	£3-5	☐
003a	1987	'WHITMANS', Yellow/Brown/Red	£3-5	☐
004a	1987	'LLEDO WORLDWIDE C.C.', SBX	£5-7	☐
005a	1988	'HAMLEYS', Cream and Black	£3-5	☐
006a	1988	'PIZZA EXPRESS', White/Red	£3-5	☐
007a	1988	'BUDWEISER', Black/Red, SBX	£3-5	☐
008a	1988	'TESCO', White and Red	£20-25	☐
009a	1989	'SOHO DAIRIES', Black body	£3-5	☐
009b	1990	'SOHO DAIRIES', Dark Brown body	£3-5	☐
010a	1990	'HEINZ 57', Cream and Blue	NRP	☐
011a	1991	'SHARPS TOFFEE', Beige body	NRP	☐
012a	1992	'PUNCH', Green/Black	NRP	☐
	1993	Model withdrawn from the standard range		

DG 23 1954 SCENICRUISER. This is the only 'Days Gone' model to feature window glazing. The body is a single metal casting and the baseplate is plastic.

000a	1987	'GREYHOUND', Silver body, pale windows, bare metal chassis	£8-12	☐
000b	1987	dark windows, Silver chassis	£4-6	☐
000c	1987	dark windows, Black chassis	£4-6	☐
001a	1987	'GOLDEN WEST', Gold body	£3-5	☐
002a	1987	'BUFFALO', Red body	£3-5	☐
	1991	Model withdrawn from production		

DG 24 ROLLS-ROYCE PLAYBOY (BREWSTER). A single cast 2-door body and windscreen feature on this model which was fitted with a steering wheel from its introduction. The radiator is that used on the DG 19.

000a	1987	Yellow body, (TV Times offer)	£3-5	☐
001a	1987	Lilac body, Mauve chassis	£3-5	☐
001b	1987	Dark Lilac body, Mauve chassis	£3-5	☐
002a	1988	Metallic Grey body, (in 3-car Set)	GSP	☐
002b	1988	Not mounted or drilled, (unofficial)	£7-10	☐
003a	1987	Red and White, special box	£3-5	☐
004a	1988	Metallic Green body	£3-5	☐
005a	1989	Dark Green body	£3-5	☐
-	1989	24k Gold plated, on plinth, (110 made)	NGPP	☐
	1991	Model withdrawn from production		

DG 25 1925 ROLLS-ROYCE SILVER GHOST (BARKER). The 4-door body on this model is a single casting with wing-mounted spare wheels and plastic roof. Newly introduced with DG 25 was the one-piece plastic seats/ steering wheel moulding.

000a	1987	Dark Blue/Black, ('TV Times' offer)	£3-5	☐
001a	1987	Silver and Blue	£3-5	☐
002a	1988	Metallic Grey, (in 3-car Set)	GSP	☐
002b	1988	Not mounted or drilled, (unofficial)	£7-10	☐
003a	1987	White and Black, (Cream seats)	£3-5	☐
003b	1988	All White body, (White seats)	£3-5	☐
004a	1989	Blue/Black/Tan	£3-5	☐
005a	1989	Dark Green body	£3-5	☐
	1991	Model withdrawn from production		

DG 26 1934 CHEVROLET BOTTLE DELIVERY TRUCK. This model uses the same baseplate, chassis & radiator as the DG 21. The plastic crate load is mounted in a metal truck body. Steering wheel and seats added in 1991.

000a	1987	'SCHWEPPES', Lemon, Red chassis	£12-16	☐
000b	1987	Yellow body, Red chassis	£3-5	☐
000c	1988	Yellow body, Black chassis	£80-100	☐
001a	1987	'LLEDO WORLDWIDE C.C.', White/ Black	£4-6	☐
002a	1987	'COCA-COLA', Brass radiator	£3-5	☐
002b	1989	'COCA-COLA', Chrome radiator	£3-5	☐
003a	1988	'BUDWEISER', in SBX	£3-5	☐
004a	1988	'BARR'S', Red and Black	£3-5	☐
005a	1988	'CORONA', Green and Black	£3-5	☐
006a	1988	'TIZER', Red and Blue	£3-5	☐
007a	1989	'CANADA DRY', (illegible artwork)	£3-5	☐
007b	1989	Legible rear, illegible side	£3-5	☐

007c	1990	Legible rear & side	£3-5	☐
008a	1990	'SCHWEPPES', Red and Black	NRP	☐
009a	1991	'TENNENTS', Green/Black	NRP	☐
010a	1992	'BASS', Blue/Black	NRP	☐
011a	1992	'FYFFES', fleet no. '6' at rear....................	NRP	☐
011b	1992	'FYFFES', fleet no. '6' at front	NRP	☐
012a	1993	'PEPSI-COLA', Blue, SBX	NRP	☐
013a	1993	'PERRIER', Green/Black	NRP	☐
014a	1993	'BROOKE BOND', Red/Black	NRP	☐
015a	1994	'Dr. PEPPER' SBX......................................	£3-5	☐
016a	1995	'BECK'S BEER'	£3-5	☐
017a	1995	'7-UP'	£3-5	☐

DG 27 1934 MACK BREAKDOWN TRUCK. A metal crane jib features on this model which has metal cab, body and chassis surmounting a plastic baseplate. The steering wheel appeared in 1991.

000a	1987	'A1 RECOVERY', Orange/Black	£3-5	☐
001a	1988	'HANKS AUTO', Green body.....................	£3-5	☐
002		Not allocated		
003a	1988	'MOBILOIL', White and Blue	£3-5	☐
004a	1989	'MOBILOIL', (French issue)	£5-7	☐
005a	1989	'ARTHUR DALEY', Red and Black	£4-6	☐
006a	1991	'US ARMY', (in Set US1003)	GSP	☐
007a	1992	'LONDON CC', Green/Black	NRP	☐
	1993	'BROOKLANDS AUTOMOBILE RACING CLUB', Yellow/Green, (in 'Brooklands Collection')......................	NRP	☐
	1993	Model withdrawn from standard production.		

DG 28 1934 MACK CANVAS-BACK TRUCK. This model is distinguished by the addition of a large plastic 'tilt' (canvas cover) on the metal truck body. The chassis and the plastic baseplate & radiator are those shared by DG 27. From 1991 the model was fitted with a steering wheel.

000a	1988	'TYPHOO', Red/Black/Cream	£3-5	☐
000b	1988	same but 'leaf' outline in Black	£3-5	☐
001a	1988	'TATE & LYLE', Blue/Cream	£3-5	☐
002a	1988	'LLEDO WORLDWIDE CLUB', SBX........	£4-6	☐
003a	1988	'HEINZ BEANS', Chrome radiator..............	£3-5	☐
003b	1989	'HEINZ BEANS', Brass radiator	£3-5	☐
004a	1989	'DUNLOP', Blue/Black/White	£3-5	☐
005		Not allocated		
006a	1989	'ROYAL NAVY', in Set RN1003.................	GSP	☐
007a	1990	'STROH'S', Dark Blue and Black	NRP	☐
008a	1989	'NORTH YORKS MOORS', (NYM Set)	NRP	☐
009a	1989	'COCA-COLA', (few released)	£600+	☐
010a	1991	'GREENE KING', Dark Green/Black	NRP	☐
011a	1990	'ROYAL AIR FORCE', (in RAF Set)	GSP	☐
012a	1990	'WINN DIXIE', (US issue)	NGPP	☐
013a	1991	'HAMLEYS', Dark Blue, SBX	NRP	☐
014a	1991	'LNER', in Set TPL1003	GSP	☐
015a	1991	'LMS', in Set RSL1003	GSP	☐
016a	1991	'8th ARMY', in 'Military' box	NRP	☐
017a	1991	'Quartermasters Corps', in Set USA1003	GSP	☐
018a	1991	'REVELL '91', US Trade special	NGPP	☐
019a	1991	'Corps Truck', in Set PH1003....................	GSP	☐
020a	1992	'GWR', in Set RSL2003	GSP	☐
021a	1992	'HAMLEYS', in SBX	NRP	☐
022a	1991	'Motor Torpedo', in Set PH1003................	GSP	☐
023a	1992	'WINCARNIS', Maroon/Black	NRP	☐
024a	1992	'DG Club 91-92', Crimson/Black	NRP	☐
025a	1992	'TOYFAIR '92', Trade Fair model	NGPP	☐
026a	1992	'ROYAL NAVY', in Set MG1003	GSP	☐
027a	1992	'US Marines', in Set GU1003	GSP	☐
028a	1992	'SR Express', in Set RSL3003.....................	GSP	☐
029a	1993	'KAFFEE HAG', Red/Black	NRP	☐
030a	1993	'RAF', in Set DML1003...............................	GSP	☐
031a	1993	'LLEDO SHOW' 1993.................................	£3-5	☐
032a	1994	'SAINSBURY'S LAMB'	£3-5	☐
033a	1995	'PEPSI-COLA'...	£3-5	☐
034a	1994	'Dr. PEPPER', SBX.....................................	£3-5	☐
035a	1995	'PERSIL'...	£3-5	☐

DG 29 1942 DODGE 4x4. This unusual choice of model required new components throughout. The plastic baseplate is surmounted by a metal chassis and a one-piece metal body casting incorporating front bumper & radiator.

000a	1988	'US Field Ambulance', Military-Green	£3-5	☐
001a	1989	'RAF Aircrew', Pale Blue...........................	£3-5	☐
002a	1991	'TEXACO', Red body, Black wings.............	NRP	☐
003a	1991	'US Army Ambulance', in Set USAL1003	GSP	☐
004a	1992	'Bomb Disposal', 'Military' box	£3-5	☐
005a	1992	'Marines Corps', in Set GU1003	GSP	☐
006a	1993	'Police Emergency'	NRP	☐
007a	1994	'SAN JOSE FIRE DEPT.'	£3-5	☐
008a	1994	'Canadian Army', (Set DDL 1003)..............	GSP	☐
009a	1994	'US Army Signals', (Set DDU 1003)...........	GSP	☐

DG 30 1939 CHEVROLET PANEL VAN. Completely new components were required again with the introduction of this model. They include a one-piece metal body, metal chassis, plastic baseplate, radiator, lights, interior and bumpers.

000a	1988	'JOHN BULL TYRES', Red/Black	£3-5	☐
001a	1989	'FRY'S COCOA', Black body......................	£3-5	☐
002a	1989	'LIPTONS', Green body...............................	£3-5	☐
002b	1990	'LIPTONS', Dark Yellow print....................	£3-5	☐
003a	1989	'LLEDO WORLDWIDE CLUB', SBX........	£4-6	☐
004a	1989	'HAMLEYS', Maroon body, SBX	£3-5	☐
005a	1990	'SPRATTS', Cream body	NRP	☐
006a	1990	'BROOKE BOND', Red body	NRP	☐
007a	1990	'HERSHEY', (US issue, SBX)	NGPP	☐
008a	1990	'ROYAL AIR FORCE', in Set BBL1004	GSP	☐
009a	1991	'NESTLES', Dark Red body.........................	NRP	☐
010a	1991	'GOLDEN STREAM TEA', Gold/Black	NRP	☐
011a	1991	'Polish Army Ambulance', SBX	NRP	☐
012a	1991	'Army Surgical Unit', Set USA1003............	GSP	☐
013a	1991	'US Navy', in Set PHL1003.........................	GSP	☐
014a	1992	'STEPHENS INKS', Blue	NRP	☐
015a	1993	'SHELL-BP', Yellow...................................	NRP	☐
016a	1994	'RANSOMES LAWNMOWERS'.................	£3-5	☐
017a	1994	'INDIAN', (Set MCL 1003)	GSP	☐
018a	1995	'7-UP'	£3-5	☐

DG 31 HORSE-DRAWN BREWERS DRAY. The large/small wheels from DG 4, 5 & 11 came back into use for this model, the first to have a dedicated driver figure and painted detail on the horses. Plastic drivers seat, headboard and barrels.

000a	1988	'WHITBREAD', Brown body........................	£3-5	☐
001a	1988	'EVERARDS', Red body, (Dealer Promotion)...	£12-16	☐
002a	1989	'TAUNTON CIDER', Red body	£3-5	☐
002b	1990	same but tampo on wrong side	£3-5	☐
003a	1989	'GREENE KING', (reversed tampo)............	£3-5	☐
003b	1989	'GREENE KING', (correct tampo)...............	£3-5	☐
004a	1989	'TRUMANS', Red body	£3-5	☐
005a	1991	'COURAGE ALES', Blue body.....................	NRP	☐
006a	1992	'WORTHINGTON', Dark Blue.....................	NRP	☐
007a	1993	'BASS', Dark Blue	NRP	☐
008a	1994	'FULLERS ALES' (red bar)	£3-5	☐
008b	1994	'FULLERS ALES' (green bar)......................	£3-5	☐

DG 32 1907 ROLLS-ROYCE SILVER GHOST. This model echoes the Odell design of the Lesney Y15-1 version of 1960 with its cast metal body, bonnet, chassis and windscreen. The seats, steering wheel, radiator and headlights assembly are in plastic.

000a	1988	Silver body, Maroon seats	£3-5	☐
001a	1989	Dark Green body, Beige seats	£3-5	☐
002a	1990	Metallic Green body, Black seats	NRP	☐
003a	1990	'Gold-plate' effect......................................	NGPP	☐
004a	1991	Dark Red, Black seats	NRP	☐
005a	1992	Dark Blue, Black seats................................	NRP	☐
006a	1992	Bronze body, (German market)...................	£20-25	☐
007a	1992	'Gold' effect, (German market)	£20-25	☐
008a	1995	Gold-plated, (Set RPL 1003)	GSP	☐

DG 33 1920 FORD Model 'T' CAR. Existing DG6 & 8 radiator, chassis, baseplate & wheels were used on this model. A new metal body casting was designed with new plastic windscreen, roof, seats & spare wheel mounting.

000a	1989	Black body, chassis and roof......................	£3-5	☐
001a	1989	'SINGER', Green, Maroon seats	NRP	☐
001b	1989	'SINGER', Green, Black seats	NRP	☐
002		Not allocated		
003a	1990	'HERSHEYS', (US issue, SBX)	NGPP	☐
004a	1991	'GRAND HOTEL', Red/Black	NRP	☐

005a	1992	'HOTEL PARIS', in Set HLL1003	GSP	☐
006a		Gold	NGPP	☐
007a	1993	'PFAFF', Cream body................................	NRP	☐
008a	1994	Black 'Exchange & Mart' model	£3-5	☐
009a	1994	'Huis Ten Bosch', Maroon (Japan)	NGPP	☐
010a	1994	'Huis Ten Bosch', Green (Japan).............	NGPP	☐
011a	1994	'Huis Ten Bosch', Blue (Japan)	NGPP	☐
012a	1994	'Huis Ten Bosch' Cream (Japan).............	NGPP	☐

DG 34   1932 DENNIS DELIVERY VAN. This model is a modification of DG 10 with the addition of a roof-rack and with reduced seating section. It has 'D' shaped side windows behind cab.

000a	1989	'HOVIS', Cream body	£3-5	☐
001a	1989	'SMEDLEYS', Dark Green body	£3-5	☐
002a	1989	'HAMLEYS', Dark Green/Black	£3-5	☐
003a	1990	'CHEDDAR CHEESE', Yellow/Green.........	NRP	☐
004a	1990	'ROYAL AIR FORCE', Set BBL1003	GSP	☐
005a	1991	'DAYS GONE CLUB, Spring'	£4-6	☐
006a	1992	'Wartime Library', Dark Green..................	£3-4	☐
007a	1994	'HARRODS', (Set HR 2004)	GSP	☐
	1993	Model withdrawn from production		

DG 35   1932 DENNIS LIMOUSINE. Another modification of DG 10, this time a utility vehicle using the ladder component from DG 12. The main differences are in the upper body/roof moulding which has a smaller roof-rack than DG 34 and rectangular side windows.

000a	1989	'EDINBURGH Fire Brigade'........................	£3-5	☐
001a	1990	'POST OFFICE TELEPHONES'	NRP	☐
002a	1990	'ROYAL AIR FORCE', Set BB1003...........	GSP	☐
003a	1991	'1st Div. SIGNALS HQ', SBX	NRP	☐
004a	1991	'NFS', in Set HF1003	GSP	☐
005a	1992	'BBC Wartime Outside Broadcasts'...............	NRP	☐
	1994	Model withdrawn from standard production.		

DG 36   1939 CHEVROLET PICK-UP. Based on the DG30 Panel Van, the major new component in this model is the one-piece cast metal pick-up body. Oil-drums load introduced in 1992.

000a	1989	'BUCK & HICKMAN', Dark Green/Black	£3-5	☐
001a	1990	'CAKEBREAD & ROBEY', Red body........	NRP	☐
002a	1991	'AVON TYRES', Dark Blue body	NRP	☐
003a	1991	'US Army Explosives', Set USAL1003..........	GSP	☐
004a	1992	'DUCKHAMS', White/Black	NRP	☐
005a	1993	'REDEX', Red/Black	NRP	☐
	1993	'CASTROL', Green/Black, oil drums, (in 'Brooklands Collection'	NRP	☐
006a	1994	'GODE'..	£15-20	☐
007a	1994	'PENNZOIL'..	£3-5	☐
008a	1994	Service Truck, (Set DDB 1003)	GSP	☐
009a	1994	'Dr. PEPPER', SBX....................................	£3-5	☐

DG 37   1932 FORD Model 'A' PANEL VAN. The model has a modified DG 9 body with the addition of a plastic van upper body & roof section.

000a	1990	'CANADIAN CLUB', Brown body	NRP	☐
001a	1990	'Mr THERM', Dark Green body.................	NRP	☐
002a	1991	'USA POLICE', Dark Blue	NRP	☐
003a	1992	'DAYS GONE CLUB '92', Cream	NRP	☐
	1993	'EXIDE', Cream, in 'Brooklands Collection'	NRP	☐
	1992	Model withdrawn from standard production.		

DG 38   1925 ROLLS-ROYCE SILVER GHOST SALOON. Basically a DG 25 with a new plastic roof moulding.

000a	1989	Dark Green body, Gold lining	£3-5	☐
	1991	Model withdrawn from production		

DG 39   1934 MACK TRUCK. The DG 28 with canvas tilt replaced by plastic sack load. The steering wheel appeared in 1991.

000a	1990	'BLUE CIRCLE', Yellow/Blue	NRP	☐
001a	1991	'KETTON CEMENT', White/Black	NRP	☐
002a	1989	'GAS LIGHT & COKE', Black	£3-5	☐
003a	1992	'PORTLAND CEMENT', Yellow/Blue.......	£3-4	☐
004a	1992	Military Sand-Bag Truck, SBX	£3-4	☐
	1994	Model withdrawn from standard production.		

DG 40   1934 MACK CRANE TRUCK. The model is basically DG 27 Breakdown Truck but with a new forward-facing crane assembly.

000a	1990	'TARMAC', Black body, Red chassis..........	NRP	☐
001a	1991	'RICHARD COSTAIN', Grey body..............	NRP	☐
002a	1991	Ammunition Crane, in Set PH1003.............	GSP	☐
003a	1992	'US NAVY', in Set GU1003	GSP	☐
004a	1993	'RAF', in Set DM1003	GSP	☐
	1993	Model withdrawn from standard production		

DG 41   1928 KARRIER E6 TROLLEY BUS. The model features six wheels, new metal body castings, upper & lower plastic seat mouldings. Plastic trolley poles surmount the metal roof. This was the first model in the new **'Premier Collection'** range.

000a	1990	'ROBIN STARCH', Maroon body	NRP	☐
001a	1990	'MARKS & SPENCER', SBX	NRP	☐
002a	1991	'HAMLEYS', Red body, SBX	NRP	☐
003a	1991	'BISTO', Red body	NRP	☐
004a	1991	'BOVRIL', Red body	NRP	☐
005a	1991	'NORTH YORKS MOORS', in NYM Set ..	GSP	☐
006a	1992	'SAXA SALT', Red body.............................	NRP	☐
007a	1992	'SCHWEPPES', Dark Green	NRP	☐
008a	1992	'HAMLEYS', in Set HAL1004....................	GSP	☐
009a	1992	'SUNMAID RAISINS', Red........................	NRP	☐
010a	1994	'CROSSE & BLACKWELL'........................	£4-5	☐
011a	1994	'ROWNTREE'..	£4-5	☐
012a	1994	'HUIS TEN BOSCH' (Japan)	NGPP	☐

DG 42   1934 MACK TANKER. DG 27 again, this time with a plastic tank replacing the original crane assembly. It acquired a steering wheel in 1991.

000a	1990	'NATIONAL BENZOLE', Yellow body	£3-5	☐
001a	1990	'ROYAL AIR FORCE', Set BB1003...........	GSP	☐
002a	1991	'REGENT PETROL', Blue/Red	NRP	☐
003a	1991	'US Air Corps', in Set USAL1003	GSP	☐
004a	1991	'US Navy', in Set PHL1003.......................	GSP	☐
005a	1992	Army Water Tanker, in Set EAL1003..........	GSP	☐
006a	1992	'SHELL FUEL OIL', (German market).......	NGPP	☐
	1994	'SHELL FUEL OIL' (Brooklands)...............	£3-5	☐
007a	1993	'PENNZOIL', Yellow/Black	NRP	☐
008a	1994	'TEXACO'	£3-5	☐

DG 43   1931 MORRIS VAN. Another in the **'Premier Collection'** range. Apart from the use of DG 30 wheels, this model has all-new components: cast metal body, chassis & roof, with plastic baseplate, interior & radiator.

000a	1990	'WEETABIX', All Yellow	£3-5	☐
001a	1990	'CHIVERS JAMS', All Cream......................	£3-5	☐
002a	1991	'HAMLEYS', Green/Black, SBX	NRP	☐
003a	1991	'DG CLUB Winter 90/91'............................	NRP	☐
004a	1991	'AC SPARK PLUGS', Yellow/Blue.............	NRP	☐
005a	1991	'LNER', (in Set TPL1003)..........................	GSP	☐
006a	1991	'METROPOLITAN Rly', (Set RSL1003).....	GSP	☐
007a	1991	'BIRDS CUSTARD', Blue/White	NRP	☐
008a	1991	'8th Army Ambulance', SBX	£8-10	☐
009a	1991	'91 Toyfair', Dealer PRM/SBX	NRP	☐
009b	1991	no locations printed on door	NGPP	☐
010a	1991	'Cornwall Home Guard', (Set HF1003)	GSP	☐
011a	1991	'HAMLEYS', Cream, SBX...........................	NRP	☐
012a	1992	'AMBROSIA', Dark Green	NRP	☐
013a	1992	'ARNOTTS', Red body................................	NRP	☐
014a	1992	'GWR', in Set RSL3003	GSP	☐
015a	1992	'HARRODS', in Set HD1004......................	GSP	☐
016a	1992	'SUNLICHT SEIFE', (German market).......	NGPP	☐
017a	1993	'TATE SUGARS'	NRP	☐
018a	1994	'BRANDS'...	£4-5	☐
019a	1994	'RUPERT BEAR' (SBX)..............................	£4-5	☐
020a	1995	'BRASSO'...	£4-5	☐
021a	1995	'RUPERT BEAR' (Set RUL 1003)...............	GSP	☐

DG 44 1937 SCAMMELL 6-WHEELER. Realistic 'heavy-duty' wheels distinguish this all-new model in the **'Premier Collection'** range.

000a	1990	'BISTO', (matt and gloss versions)	**£3-5**	☐
001a	1990	'TOBLERONE', Cream/Green	**£3-5**	☐
002a	1991	'MARMITE', Green body	NRP	☐
003a	1991	'FOX's GLACIER MINTS', Dark Blue	NRP	☐
004a	1991	'NORTH YORKS MOORS', NYM Set	GSP	☐
005a	1992	'ROWNTREES', Grey body	NRP	☐
006a	1992	'McMULLEN', Dark Brown	NRP	☐
007a	1992	'DG CLUB Spring '92'	NRP	☐
008a	1992	'British Army', Set EAL1003	GSP	☐
009a	1993	'BERLINER KINDL', German market	NGPP	☐
010a	1993	'TETLEYS FINE ALES'	NRP	☐
011a	1994	'HEINZ PICKLES'	**£4-5**	☐
012a	1994	'CARNATION'	**£4-5**	☐
013a	1994	'Command Caravan', (DDB 1003)	GSP	☐
014a	1995	'KRONENBOURG'	**£4-5**	☐
015a	1995	'RUPERT BEAR'	**£4-5**	☐
	1995	'VICTORY ALE'	**£4-5**	☐

DG 45 1908 ROLLS-ROYCE SILVER GHOST COUPE. Lledo ingenuity applied to the DG 32 resulted in this rather sporty 2-seater.

000a	1992	Metallic Green	**£3-4**	☐
001a	1991	Crimson body, Black seats	NRP	☐
002a	1993	White body	NRP	☐
003a	1994	'DG Journal' 'Gold' model	NGPP	☐

DG 46 1930 BENTLEY 4.5 Litre. Another echo of the past (Lesney Y5-1) in this delightful model with separate wing mouldings and side-mounted spare wheel.

000a	1991	British Racing Green	NRP	☐
001a	1991	Dark Blue body, No.'1'	NRP	☐
002a	1991	'Gold-plate' effect	NGPP	☐
003a	1992	British Racing Green, No.'2'	NRP	☐
004a	1992	Cream body, No.'18'	NRP	☐
005a	1993	Maroon body, No.'10'	NRP	☐
	1993	British Racing Green body, No.'85' (in 'The Spirit of Brooklands' Collection)	**£4-5**	☐
006a	1994	Black	**£3-5**	☐
007a	1995	Dark Green	**£3-5**	☐

DG 47 1933 AUSTIN TAXI. Introduced at the end of 1991 in the **'Premier Collection'**, the usual Lledo mix of metal and plastic components producing an attractive model taxi.

000a	1991	Dark Blue body	**£3-4**	☐
001a	1992	Black body	**£3-4**	☐
002a	1992	'HAMLEYS', (in Set HA1002)	GSP	☐
003a	1992	'HAMLEYS', (in Set HAL1004)	GSP	☐
004a	1993	Maroon body	**£3-4**	☐

DG 48 1939 CHEVROLET CAR. To broaden their range of model cars Lledo developed the DG 48 from DG 30 & 36 and released it in July 1991.

000a	1991	Cream and Dark Green	**£3-4**	☐
001a	1991	'DG CLUB Autumn '91', Gold	**£3-4**	☐
002a	1992	Cream and Maroon	**£3-4**	☐
003a	1992	'British Army', in Set EAL1003	GSP	☐
004a	1993	'YELLOW CABS', Yellow taxi	**£3-4**	☐
005a	1993	'RAF', in Set DML1003	GSP	☐
006a	1994	'HIGHWAY PATROL'	**£3-5**	☐
007a	1994	'SHAEF' Staff Car, (Set DDL 1003)	GSP	☐
008a	1994	'GHQ' Staff Car, (Set DDU 1003)	GSP	☐
009a	1995	'BOOMERANG TAXIS'	**£3-5**	☐

DG 49 1931 AEC RENOWN DOUBLE DECK BUS. The AEC radiator used on DG 15 and 17 came into use again on this 6-wheeled bus introduced in October 1991 in the **'Premier Collection'** range.

000a	1991	'BOURN-VITA', Red	NRP	☐
001a	1991	'ROSES LIME JUICE', Red	NRP	☐
002a	1992	'HAMLEYS', Black chassis, SBX	NRP	☐
002b	1992	'HAMLEYS', Red chassis, SBX	NRP	☐

003a	1992	'MARTINI', Red	NRP	☐
004a	1992	'JANTZEN', Red	NRP	☐
005a	1992	'HAMLEYS', in Set HA1002	GSP	☐
006a	1992	'DG CLUB 1992', Red	NRP	☐
007a	1992	'HARRODS', in Set HD 1004	GSP	☐
008a	1992	'QANTAS', in Set QA1002	GSP	☐
009a	1993	'PEPSI-COLA', Red, SBX	NRP	☐
010a	1993	'HAMLEYS', Grey advert, SBX	NRP	☐
011a	1993	'LITTLEWOODS'	NRP	☐
012a	1993	'St.MICHAEL', Set MS2004	GSP	☐
013a	1994	'HEINZ SPAGHETTI'	**£4-5**	☐
014a	1994	'SWAN VESTAS'	**£4-5**	☐
015a	1994	'HUIS TEN BOSCH' (Japan)	NGPP	☐
016a	1995	'SHREDDED WHEAT'	**£4-5**	☐
017a	1995	'VICTORY-MARS', (Set VE 1003)	GSP	☐

DG 50 1926 'BULL-NOSE' MORRIS VAN. This vintage van model was introduced to the standard range in June 1992. It has a cast metal body and plastic roof with goods rack.

000a	1992	'LYONS TEA', Dark Blue	NRP	☐
001a	1992	'BRYANT & MAY', Maroon	NRP	☐
002a	1993	'HAMLEYS'	NRP	☐
003a	1993	'H.M.V. - MILLERS'	NRP	☐
004a	1993	'DAYS GONE CLUB'	NRP	☐
005a	1993	'MARKS & SPENCER', Set MS2004	GSP	☐
006a	1993	'RAFFLES Hotel', Set HLL2003	GSP	☐
007a	1994	'KODAK' (Mexico)	**£30-40**	☐
008a	1994	'KIWI BOOT POLISH'	**£3-5**	☐
009a	1994	'RUPERT BEAR'	**£3-5**	☐
010a	1995	'PEPSI-COLA'	**£3-5**	☐
011a	1994	'HARRODS', (Set HR 3002)	GSP	☐
012a	1994	'NORMAN ROCKWELL', SBX	**£3-5**	☐
013a	1994	'AUSTRALIAN POST', (Australia)	NGPP	☐
014a	1995	'SILVER KING GOLF BALLS'	**£3-5**	☐

DG 51 1934 CHEVROLET BOX VAN. Another vintage van model in the standard range (introduced April 1992). It has a tall cast metal box body and plastic roof.

000a	1992	'MADAME TUSSAUDS', Black	NRP	☐
001a	1992	'STARTRITE', White	NRP	☐
002a	1993	'HOVIS', Cream/Black	NRP	☐
003a	1993	'DAYS GONE CLUB'	NRP	☐
004a	1993	'MARKS & SPENCER', Set MS2004	GSP	☐
005a	1994	'BUSHELL'S TEA'	**£3-5**	☐
006a	1994	'ERDAL', SBX (German)	**£15-20**	☐
007a	1994	Army Wireless Truck (DDB 1003)	GSP	☐
008a	1994	'NORMAN ROCKWELL', SBX	**£3-5**	☐
009a	1995	'HAMLEYS'	**£3-5**	☐
010a	1995	'RUPERT BEAR'	**£3-5**	☐

DG 52 1935 MORRIS PARCELS VAN. This new van model in the **'Premier Range'** was introduced in October 1992. Although the radiator, baseplate and wheels are of plastic, it is a heavy model with relatively large die-castings.

000a	1992	'ROYAL MAIL', Red/Black	NRP	☐
001a	1992	'PICKFORDS', Dark Blue	NRP	☐
002a	1993	'PEPSI-COLA', White, SBX	NRP	☐
003a	1993	'LNER PARCELS'	NRP	☐
004a	1993	'43rd Division'	NRP	☐
005a	1993	'DAYS GONE CLUB'	NRP	☐
006a	1993	'1993 TOYFAIR'	NRP	☐
007a	1993	'RAF Ambulance', Set DM1003	GSP	☐
008a	1994	'NEW YORK TOY FAIR'	**£4-5**	☐
009a	1994	'KODAK FILMS' (Mexico)	**£30-40**	☐
009b	1994	'KODAK FILMS' (general release)	**£3-5**	☐
010a	1995	'HARRODS' (HR 2002)	GSP	☐
011a	1995	'HAMLEYS'	**£4-5**	☐
012a	1995	'SAROTTI SCHOKOLADE'	**£4-5**	☐
013a	1995	'RUPERT BEAR' (SBX)	**£4-5**	☐
	1995	'ARP London Ambulance' (VEL 1003)	GSP	☐

DG 53 1926 ROLLS ROYCE LANDAULET. The first appearance of this model was early in 1992 as a Promotional. It was issued as a standard model in October of that year.

000a	1992	'Days Gone Collector', 'Gold-plate' effect	NRP	☐

001a	1993	'Gold-plate' effect, 'Promotional' base	NGPP	☐
002a	1995	Gold plated, in Set RPL 1003	GSP	☐

DG 54 1929 ROLLS ROYCE 'D' BACK. This version appeared first as a Promotional (in May 1992). The spare wheel in the wing, the rear truck and the coachlining add a touch of class to this attractive model car.

000a	1993	Blue body, Tan roof	NRP	☐
001a	1994	'Days Gone Collector' Vol.4.....................	£3-5	☐
002a	1995	Gold plated, in Set RPL 1003	GSP	☐

DG 55 HORSE-DRAWN TANKER. Though given a Days Gone number this model has only been used for Promotional purposes, and there are no plans to issue it in the standard range.

DG 56 1934 MODEL 'A' FORD VAN (Raised Roof). Initially introduced only for Promotional use, this large van now features in this Days-Gone version.

000a	1994	'Days Gone Club', Winter 94	£3-5	☐

DG 57 1939 FORD TANKER. A new 'late pre-war' model introduced in April 1993.

000a	1993	'SHELL-BP Aviation'	NRP	☐
001a	1994	'ESSO PETROLEUM'	£3-5	☐
003a	1994	'US AIRFORCE' (Set DDU 1003)..............	GSP	☐
002a	1995	'ROYAL NAVY' (Set DDL 1003)................	GSP	☐
004a	1995	'GULF GASOLINE'	£3-5	☐

DG 58 1950 MORRIS 'Z' VAN. This was the first in a new range of 1950s and 1960s model vehicles called 'Days Gone Vanguards' for which new colourful packaging was designed.

000a	1993	'P.O. TELEPHONES'	£4-6	☐
001a	1993	'MALVERN WATER'	£4-6	☐
002a	1993	'MACKESONS STOUT'	£4-6	☐
002b	1993	Word 'Glasgow' in forward position............	£4-6	☐
003a	1994	'ROYAL MAIL'	£4-6	☐
004a	1994	'GILLETTE'	£4-6	☐
005a	1994	'HAMLEYS'	£4-6	☐
006a	1994	'PEPSI COLA'	£4-6	☐
007a	1994	'DG CLUB', Spring 1994	£4-6	☐
008a	1994	'DG GOLD CLUB' (Gold finish)	NGPP	☐
009a	1995	'SINGER'	£4-6	☐
010a	1995	'BRITISH RAILWAYS' (BRL 1003)	GSP	☐
011a		not yet allocated.		
012a	1995	'7-UP'	£4-6	☐
013a	1994	'HARRODS' (Set HR 2004)	GSP	☐

DG 59 1950 BEDFORD 30cwt TRUCK. A popular subject with collectors and the second of the 'Days Gone Vanguards'. This model has separate cab and box body castings of diecast metal and runs on plastic disc wheels.

000a	1993	'BIRDS CUSTARD'	£4-6	☐
001a	1993	'CANADA DRY'	£4-6	☐
002a	1993	'DUNLOPILLO'	£4-6	☐
003a	1994	'PEPSI-COLA XMAS', SBX	£4-6	☐
004a	1994	'LUCOZADE'	£4-6	☐
005a	1994	'BE-RO FLOUR'	£4-6	☐
006a	1994	'HAMLEYS 1994'	£4-6	☐
007a	1994	'PEPSI-COLA'	£4-6	☐
008a	1994	'WEET-BIX'	£4-6	☐
009a	1994	'1994 TOYFAIR'	£10-15	☐
010a	1994	'NEW YORK TOYFAIR', USA	£120-140	☐
011a	1995	'ARNOTTS BISCUITS'	£4-6	☐
012a	1995	'OXYDOL'	£4-6	☐
013a	1995	'BRITISH RAILWAYS' (BRL 1003)	GSP	☐
014a		not yet allocated.		
015a	1995	'RUPERT BEAR' (Set RUL 1003)	GSP	☐
016a	1995	'7-UP'	£4-6	☐
	1995	'DG CLUB', Autumn 95	£3-5	☐

DG 60 1955 DENNIS F8 FIRE ENGINE. A long awaited addition to the Lledo range of fire appliances, this model was the third in the Days Gone 'Vanguards' range.

000a	1993	'ESSEX'..	£4-6	☐
001a	1993	'DERBYSHIRE'...................................	£4-6	☐
002a	1993	'WESTERN AREA - OBAN'	£4-6	☐
003a	1994	'WEST SUSSEX F.B.'............................	£4-6	☐
004a	1994	'NEW ZEALAND F.B.'...........................	£4-6	☐
005a	1994	'LONDON F.B., Set FB 1003	GSP	☐
006a	1994	'Special Fire Service' (Set HR 3002).........	GSP	☐
007a	1995	'LONDON F.B.'..................................	£4-6	☐
008a	1995	'CIVIL DEFENCE'..............................	£4-6	☐

DG 61 1953 PONTIAC DELIVERY VAN. This stylish American 'panel van' was the fourth in the Days Gone 'Vanguards' range. It has a single-piece cast metal body and plastic disc wheels.

000a	1993	'Dr. PEPPER'...................................	£4-6	☐
001a	1993	'DETROIT POLICE'	£4-6	☐
002a	1993	'MILWAUKEE' Ambulance.....................	£4-6	☐
003a	1994	'TRANS-WORLD AIRLINES'	£4-6	☐
004a	1994	'PEPSI COLA', Special box	£4-6	☐
005a	1994	'EXCELSIOR', Set MCL 1003	GSP	☐
006a	1994	'Dr. PEPPER', SBX	£4-6	☐
007a	1995	'AGFA FILMS'..................................	£4-6	☐

DG 62 1935 FORD ARTICULATED TANKER. Articulated vehicles were a long-awaited subject among Lledo collectors. This model features a four-wheel cab/tractor unit and a two-wheel semi-trailer tank.

000a	1994	'REGENT PETROLEUM'	£3-5	☐
001a		not yet allocated.		
002a	1995	'FINA PETROL'	£3-5	☐

DG 63 1950 BEDFORD 13cwt DELIVERY VAN. Very reminiscent of the early 1950s period, this chunky model has a one-piece cast van body and plastic disc wheels. It is another in the Days Gone 'Vanguards' range.

000a	1994	'SAINSBURYS'	£4-6	☐
001a	1994	'PENGUIN BOOKS'.............................	£4-6	☐
002a	1994	'OXO'	£4-6	☐
003a	1994	'DG Club', Summer 1994	£4-6	☐
004a	1995	'HAMLEYS'	£4-6	☐
005a	1995	'CEREBOS SALT'...............................	£4-6	☐
006a	1995	'WALL'S SAUSAGES'..........................	£4-6	☐
007a		not yet allocated.		
008a	1995	'RUPERT BEAR' (Set RUL 1003)............	GSP	☐
	1995	'1995 TOYFAIR'	£10-15	☐
	1995	'NEW YORK TOYFAIR'	£120-140	☐

DG 64 1950 BEDFORD AMBULANCE. A development from the DG 63 casting, this model is also in the Days Gone 'Vanguards' range.

000a	1994	'KENT COUNTY'	£4-6	☐
001a	1994	'DURHAM COUNTY'...........................	£4-6	☐
002a	1995	'LCC AMBULANCE'............................	£4-6	☐
003a	1995	'FAMAGUSTA'	£4-6	☐
004a	1995	'BRITISH RAILWAYS' (BRL 1003)..........	GSP	☐

DG 65 1960 MORRIS 1000 TRAVELLER. The first car model in the 'Vanguards' range and also the first Lledo model to be made to a quoted scale of 1:43.

000a	1994	Green..	£4-6	☐
001a	1994	White..	£4-6	☐
002a	1995	Trafalgar Blue	£4-6	☐
003a	1995	Smoke-Grey.....................................	£4-6	☐

DG 66 1926 DENNIS DELIVERY VAN. A model of a robust four-wheel truck with a box body and open cab.

000a	1994	'CASTROL'	£3-5	☐
001a	1994	'AUSTRALIAN POST', (Australia)............	NGPP	☐
002a	1994	'PEPSI COLA XMAS', SBX	£3-5	☐
003a	1995	'CAMPBELL'S SOUPS'.........................	£3-5	☐
004a	1995	'HARRODS' (Set HR 2004)	GSP	☐
005a	1995	'DG CLUB, Winter 94-95', SBX...............	£4-6	☐

DG 67 1935 FORD ARTICULATED TRUCK. The same cab unit as DG 62 is here teamed up with a box van semi-trailer.

000a	1994	'DUNLOP'..	£3-5	☐
001a	1994	'ROBERT BROS. CIRCUS'........................	£3-5	☐
002a	1995	'LYONS SWISS ROLLS'............................	£3-5	☐
003a	1995	'DG CLUB' Summer '95, SBX	£4-6	☐

DG 68 1932 AEC OPEN-TOP DOUBLE-DECKER BUS. The DG 15 lower section casting with a new open upper deck.

000a	1994	'RAF DUXFORD' (Lledo Show LE)..........	£6-8	☐
001a	1994	'DG CLUB', Summer '94............................	£3-5	☐
002a	1995	'LONDON TRANSPORT'	£3-5	☐
003a	1995	'CROSVILLE'..	£3-5	☐
	1995	'Victory in Europe' (Set VEL 1003)	GSP	☐

DG 69 1960 MORRIS 1000 VAN. A very popular subject from the early 1960s and one that is sure to be featured for promotional use. (1:43 scale).

000a	1995	'EVER-READY'...	£3-5	☐
001a	1995	'CURRYS'..	£3-5	☐
002a	1995	'DG CLUB' Spring'95, SBX	£4-6	☐

DG 70 1939 FORD CANVAS BACK TRUCK. A small 4-wheel truck model from the late pre-war period with cast metal body and plastic tilt and wheels.

000a	1995	'ANCHOR BEER'......................................	£3-5	☐

DG 71 1959 MORRIS LD150 VAN. A 1:50 scale 'Days Gone Vanguards' model of a van that was a common sight on our roads in the early 1960s.

000a	1995	'KODAK'..	£4-6	☐
001a	1995	'WORMWOOD SCRUBS'.........................	£4-6	☐
002a	1995	'HP SAUCE'..	£4-6	☐

DG 72 1952 VOLKSWAGEN BEETLE. The 'Days Gone Vanguards' version of a much-modelled car in 1:43 scale.

000a	1995	Blue	£4-6	☐
001a	1995	Pale Green	£4-6	☐

DG 73 1955 VOLKSWAGEN KOMBI VAN. A one-piece body casting is used for this 'Days-Gone Vanguards' model in 1:50 scale.

000a	1995	'CINZANO'	£4-6	☐
001a	1995	'BOSCH'	£4-6	☐

DG 74 1959 AUSTIN '7' MINI SALOON. This most British of small cars is modelled at 1:43 scale in the 'Days Gone Vanguards' range.

000a	1995	Pale Blue	£4-6	☐
001a	1995	Red	£4-6	☐
002a	1995	'Police'..	£4-6	☐

DG 75 BRISTOL LODEKKA BUS. Another 'Days Gone Vanguards' bus model in the 'HO' scale of 1:87.

000a	1995	'DULUX'..	£4-6	☐
001a	1995	'WESTONS'..	£4-6	☐

Miscellaneous models by Lledo

Marathons

These models were introduced in 1987 to balance the vintage feel of 'Days Gone' vehicles with something having a more modern appeal. Although some were used as promotional models (particularly the buses), they did not attract sufficient interest among collectors to warrant continuing the range after 1988.

Ref. No.	Year(s)	Model Type	Model Features and Size	Market Price Range	
M1a 01a	1987	Leyland Olympian Bus.............	'LONDON PRIDE SIGHTSEEING', 'PINDISPORTS', Blue body	£2-3	☐
M1a 01b	1987		same model but 'PINDISPORTS' address printed in Red	£2-4	☐
M1a 02a	1987		'LONDON TRANSPORT' & 'LONDON ZOO', Red body	£2-3	☐
M1a 03a	1987		'CORPORATION TRANSPORT' & 'PAN AM', White/Blue	£2-3	☐
M2a 01a	1987	Setra Coach	'PAN AM', White body, Blue roof	£2-3	☐
M2a 02a	1987		'AIR CANADA', White body, Red roof	£2-3	☐
M2a 03a	1987		'GHANA AIRWAYS', Yellow body and roof	£2-3	☐
M3a 01a	1987	Neoplan Spaceliner..................	'ISLAND TOURS', Yellow body and roof	£2-3	☐
M3a 02a	1987		'SPEEDLINK', White body and roof	£2-3	☐
M3a 03a	1987		'GATWICK FLIGHTLINE', Yellow body, White roof	£2-3	☐
M4a 01a	1988	Leyland Rigid Truck	'FEDERAL EXPRESS', White cab, chassis & body	£2-3	☐
M5a 01a	1988	Leyland Tipper	'LECCA ARC', Yellow cab & chassis, Silver tipper......................	£2-3	☐
M6a 01a	1988	Leyland Tanker	'SHELL', Yellow cab, Black chassis, Silver tank.........................	£2-3	☐

'Fantastic Set-O-Wheels' models

A series of models introduced in 1985 for the US toy market and distributed by Hartoy Inc of Florida. They were blister-packed on card with the legend 'Made in England by Lledo (London) Ltd' on most of the baseplates.

Ref. No.	DG Model	Model Name	Features	Market Price Range	
F1a	DG 6	'MALIBU OR BUST'..............	Yellow/Dark Brown/Tan, 'Made In England by Lledo' on baseplate...........................	£10-15	☐
F1b			same model but with 'Days Gone' on baseplate...	£10-15	☐
F2a	DG 7	'TRI-STATE DEALER'	White/Blue with Yellow wheels, 'Made In England' baseplate.................................	£10-15	☐
F2b			As previous model but Black wheels, 'Days Gone' baseplate...................................	£10-15	☐

F3a	DG 15	'LIQUID BUBBLE'	Blue/Pink/White body, 20-spoke Red wheels with Cream tyres	£10-15	☐
F4a	DG 10	'OAKRIDGE SCHOOL'	Yellow/Black body, Cream tyres on Black wheels	£10-15	☐
F5a	DG 12	'BOSTON FIRE Dept'	Red body and wheels, Cream floor and tyres, 'Made In England' baseplate	£10-15	☐
F5b			As previous model but with 'Days Gone' on the baseplate	£10-15	☐
F6a	DG 13	'JOLLY TIME'	Cream/Pink, 'Made In England' baseplate, Red wheels, Cream tyres	£10-15	☐
F6b			same model but with 'Days Gone' baseplate	£10-15	☐
F7a	DG 14	'POLICE' Car	Black body, Cream tyres on Black 12-spoke wheels, 'Made In England' base	£10-15	☐
F7b			As previous model but 'Days Gone' baseplate	£10-15	☐
F7c			As F7a but with 20-spoke wheels	£10-15	☐
F8a	DG 14	'SAN-DIEGO FIRE'	Red body, Black roof and wheels, Cream tyres, Chrome grille	£10-15	☐
F8b			As previous model but with Brass grille	£10-15	☐

Edocar ('Old-Timer' Series)

A range of eight models made in 1986 for Edor BV (Fred Beheer BV), in the Netherlands and sold there under the name 'EDOCAR'. The baseplates all have the wording 'EDOCAR - Made in England by Lledo' plus the model number. Some models have original Days Gone colours but have been left unprinted (without logos). All but A7 have only Black tyres. The 'double window' boxes were made and printed in Holland.

Ref. No.	DG Model	Model Name	Features	Market Price Range	
A1a	DG 8	Tanker (unprinted)	Red body, Black chassis & roof, Yellow tank, Brass wheels	£10-15	☐
A1b		'ESSO BLUE'	Blue body, White roof, (produced for ESSO garages in Holland)	£10-15	☐
A2a	DG 12	Dennis Fire Engine	Red body and wheels, White floor, Brass grille	£10-15	☐
A2b			As previous model but with Black floor	£10-15	☐
A3	DG 14	Taxi	Yellow body, Black roof, Yellow 20-spoke wheels, Chrome grille	£10-15	☐
A4a	DG 16	'HUMBROL'	Green/White with Chrome grille, White wheels	£10-15	☐
A4b			As previous model but with Brass grille	£10-15	☐
A5	DG 17	AEC Single Deck Bus	White body, Blue seats, (box states 'AEC Double Decker Bus')	£10-15	☐
A6a	DG 18	Packard 'AMBULANCE'	White body, White wheels, Chrome grille	£10-15	☐
A6b			same model but with Brass grille	£10-15	☐
A7	DG 19	Rolls Royce Phantom	Silver body, Black chassis and wheels, Black or Cream tyres	£10-15	☐
A8	DG 21	'EDOCAR'	Blue/Black/White Chevrolet van with Brass grille	£12-18	☐

The 'Grey' Series

Finished in neutral Grey and left unprinted for use as samples of promotionals by sales representatives (mainly in the USA). Only 144 sets of models were produced (in 1986) and all except DG7, DG11 and DG14 have 'Days Gone' baseplates.

Ref. No.	Year(s)	Model Type	Model Features and Size	Market Price Range	
DG 2	1986	Horse-Drawn Milk Float	Cream 20-spoke wheels, Black horse, Pale Blue milk crates	£12-18	☐
DG 3	1986	Horse-Drawn Delivery Van	Cream 20-spoke wheels, Black horse and roof	£12-18	☐
DG 4	1986	Horse-Drawn Omnibus	Cream horses, Red seats	£12-18	☐
DG 5	1986	Horse-Drawn Fire Engine	Cream horses, Black wheels, Bronze boiler	£12-18	☐
DG 5	1986		same model but with Gold wheels	£12-18	☐
DG 6	1986	Ford Model 'T' Van	Cream 20-spoke wheels, Black tyres, White roof	£12-18	☐
DG 7	1986	Ford Woody Wagon	Cream 20-spoke wheels with Black tyres, 'Lledo' and 'DG' baseplates	£15-20	☐
DG 8	1986	Ford Model 'T' Tanker	Cream 20-spoke wheels with Black tyres, Green plastic tank	£12-18	☐
DG 10	1986	Dennis Single Deck Bus	Red body, Brown hubs, Cream tyres & seats	£15-20	☐
DG 10	1986		same model but with Yellow roof	£15-20	☐
DG 11	1986	Horse-Drawn Large Van	Cream horses, Blue roof, 'Lledo' & 'DG' baseplates	£12-18	☐
DG 12	1986	Fire Engine	Brown wheels with Cream tyres, Brass radiator, Tan ladder	£12-18	☐
DG 13	1986	Ford Model 'A' Van	Cream 20-spoke wheels, White roof, Chrome radiator	£12-18	☐
DG 14	1986	Ford Model 'A' Car	Cream 20-spoke wheels, roof & seats, 'Lledo' & 'DG' baseplates	£12-18	☐
DG 15	1986	AEC Double Deck Bus	Yellow wheels and windows	£15-20	☐
DG 16	1986	Dennis Parcels Van	Brown wheels, Cream tyres & roof	£12-18	☐
DG 17	1986	AEC Single Deck Bus	Pale Blue wheels, White windows	£15-20	☐
DG 18	1986	Packard Van	Brown roof, Cream wheels & tyres	£12-18	☐
DG 19	1986	Rolls-Royce Phantom II	Cream hubs and tyres, Black roof, Tan boot and seats	£12-18	☐

American Days Gone models   -   the '500' series

To generate more interest in the USA a range of six Days Gone models were marketed which were in plain colour finishes having no printed logos or liveries. In each case the standard reference number carried the suffix '500'.

Ref. No.	Year(s)	Model Type	Model Features and Size	Market Price Range	
DG14-500		Ford Model 'A'	Yellow body/chassis and 20-spoke wheels, Black roof, Brass radiator	£20-25	☐
DG22-500		Packard Town Van	Black body/roof, Red chassis, Brass radiator and 12-spoke wheels	£20-25	☐
DG30-500		Chevrolet Van	Red body, Black chassis and wheels, Chrome radiator	£20-25	☐
DG33-500		Ford Model 'T'	Black body/chassis/wheels/tyres, Chrome radiator	£20-25	☐
DG36-500		Chevy Pick-Up	Green body, Black chassis, wheels and tyres, Chrome radiator	£20-25	☐
DG37-500		Ford Model 'A' Van	Blue body/chassis/roof, Brass wheels, Chrome radiator	£20-25	☐

'Days Gone' Gift Sets

The individual models that make up these sets are listed separately in the 'Days Gone' listings. The following list indicates the content of specific sets and prices where available.

Ref. No.	Year(s)	Set Name	Contents	Market Price Range	
AB 1003	1990	Arnotts Biscuits Set	DG6-101a Ford T Van, DG11-016a Horse Drawn, DG13-045a Ford A Van	£20-25	☐
BA 1003	1989	British Army Collection	DG8-017a Tanker, DG13-038a Recruitment, DG19-009a Staff Car	£20-25	☐
BB 1003	1990	RAF Ground Crew Support	DG20-015a Balloon Tender, DG35-002a RAF Riggers, DG42-001a Fuel Tanker	£15-20	☐
BBL 1003	1990	RAF Personnel Transport	DG28-011a Truck, DG30-008a Ambulance, DG34 004a Office. (12,500)	£15-20	☐
BM 1004	1990	Bryant & May Set	Four DG21 vans: 022a Scottish Bluebell, 023a Bryant & May, 024a Swan Vestas, 025a Englands Glory (Limited Edition of 12,500)	£20-25	☐
	1986	Commonwealth Games Set	DG7-007a Woody Wagon, DG10-016a Dennis Coach, DG15-011a AEC Bus	£10-12	☐
BRL 1003	1995	'BRITISH RAILWAYS' Ltd. Ed. Set	DG58-010a, DG59-013a, DG64-004a	£12-15	☐
CC 1003	1986	Coca-Cola Set	DG6-058a Ford T Van, DG11-007a Horse Drawn, DG13-021a Ford A Van	£20-25	☐
CC 2003	1987	Coca-Cola Set	DG6-054a Ford T Van, DG21-005a Chevrolet, DG26-002a Chevrolet	£20-25	☐
CP 1	1984	Collector Pack	DG3-003a Robertsons, DG4-005a Pears Soap, DG6-017a Daily Express	£10-15	☐
DDB 1003	1994	British D-Day Set	DG36 Service Truck, DG51 Wireless Truck, and DG44 Command Caravan	£12-15	☐
DDL 1003	1994	'D-DAY' Ltd. Ed. Set	DG29-008a, DG48-007a, DG57-002a	£12-15	☐
DDU 1003	1994	American D-Day Set	DG29 Signals Truck, DG48 GHQ Staff Car, DG57 Flight Refueller	£12-15	☐
DML 1003	1993	Dambusters Set	DG16-034a Control, DG28-030a RAF, DG48-005a RAF, (7,500)	£12-15	☐
DM 1003	1993	Dambusters Set	DG16-033a NAAFI, DG40-004a RAF, DG52-007a RAF	£10-13	☐
EAL 1003	1992	El Alamein Set	DG42-005a Water, DG44-008a Army, DG48-003a Army, (12,500)	£10-13	☐
FB 1003	1994	London Fire Brigade	DG5-010a, DG12-019a, DG60-005a	£12-15	☐
GS 1	1984	Gift Set	DG6-023a Railway Express, DG7-002a Ford Sales, DG9-001a New York-Rio	£10-15	☐
GS 2	1985	Gift Set	DG6-033a Barclays, DG11-001a Abels, DG13-005a Michelin	£15-20	☐
GS 3	1985	Bus Gift Set	DG10-013a Trailways, DG15-002a Castlemaine, DG17 001a Eurotour	£10-15	☐
GS 4	1986	Coca-Cola Set	DG6-058a Ford T Van, DG11-007a Woody Wagon, DG13-021a Ford A Van	£20-25	☐
GS 5	1986	Hersheys Set	DG6-055a Ford T Van, DG13-023a Ford A Van, DG16-012a Dennis Van	£20-25	☐
GS 1004	1989	Golden Days Of Film	Early Film Industry vans in 'gold-plate': DG6-091a Britannia, DG13-034a Empire, DG18-014a B & C Films, DG21-016a Majestic. (10,000)	£60-65	☐
GU 1003	1992	Guadalcanal Set	DG28-027a Marines, DG29-005a Marines, DG40-003a Navy	£10-13	☐
	1984	Hamleys Set	DG3-009a, DG4-008a, DG6-035a, DG7-004a, DG10-009a, DG13-004a	£35-40	☐
HA 1002	1992	Hamleys London Set	DG47-002a Austin Taxi, DG49-005a AEC Bus	£8-10	☐
HA 2002	1994	Hamleys London Set	DG12-018a and DG15-033a	£8-12	☐
HAL 1004	1992	Hamleys Ltd Ed Set	DG11-021a, DG21-037a, DG41-008a, DG47-003a, (5,000)	£15-20	☐
HD 1002	1992	Harrods Set	DG11-020a Horse Drawn Removals Van and DG15-028a AEC Bus	£8-10	☐
HD 1004	1992	Harrods Set	DG3-014a, DG13-051a, DG43-015a, DG49-007a	£12-16	☐
HF 1003	1991	The Home Front Set	DG16-030a YMCA, DG35-004a NFS, DG43-010a Cornwall	£10-13	☐
HLL 1003	1992	Hotel Labels Set	DG6-108a Colombia, DG21-035a de Paix, DG33-005a de Paris, (12,500)	£10-13	☐
HLL 2003	1993	Hotel Labels Set	DG13-058a Grand, DG18-024a Imperial, DG50-006a Raffles, (7,500)	£12-15	☐
HR 2002	1994	Harrods Set	DG4-018a, DG52-010a	£8-12	☐
HR 3002	1994	Harrods Set	DG50-011a, DG60-006a	£8-12	☐
HR 2004	1994	Harrods Set	DG15-036a, DG34-007a, DG58-013a, DG66-004a	£15-20	☐
LOS 8002	1995	'Souvenir of London' Set	(Fire + Ambulance)	£8-12	☐
LOS 9002	1995	'Souvenir of London' Set	(Bus + Taxi)	£8-12	☐
LOS 10002	1995	'Souvenir of London' Set	(Bus + Van)	£8-12	☐
LP 1553	1991	Charles & Diana Set	Two Rolls Royce models in special Purple box (not limited)	£7-10	☐
LS 1004	1989	London Stores Set No.1	Four different vans: DG6-087a Selfridges, DG13-031a Aquascutum, DG18-013a Fortnum & Mason, DG21-012a DAKS Simpson. (Not limited)	£12-17	☐
LS 2004	1990	London Stores Set No.2	DG6-097a Jaeger, DG13-036a Austin Reed, DG18-018a Asprey, DG21-020a Liberty. (Not limited)	£12-17	☐
MCL 1003	1994	Motorcycle Vans Set	DG21-041a, DG30-017a, DG61-005a	£12-15	☐
MG 1003	1992	Malta George Cross Set	DG12-017a Valletta, DG18-022a St.John, DG28-026a Royal Navy	£10-13	☐
MS 1004	1990	Marks & Spencer Set	DG11-014a, DG13-014a, DG21-019a, DG41-001a. (Also available singly)	£10-15	☐
MS 2004	1993	Marks & Spencer Set	DG13-057a, DG49-012a, DG50-005a, DG51-004a	£12-16	☐
NYMR1003	1989	Nth Yorks Moors Set 1	DG6-093a Cartage, DG17-018a NYM Railway, DG28-008a Parcels (7,500)	£12-16	☐
NYMR2003	1990	Nth Yorks Moors Set 2	DG13-044a, DG15-027a, DG16-025a (6,500)	£12-16	☐
NYMR1002	1991	Nth Yorks Moors Set 3	DG41-005a Scarborough and DG44-004a NYMR, (6,500)	£9-12	☐
PHL 1003	1991	Pearl Harbor Set 1	DG28-019a Corps, DG30-013a Navy, DG42-004a Navy, (12,500)	£11-14	☐
PH 1003	1991	Pearl Harbor Set 2	DG21-030a Marines, DG28-022a Torpedo, DG40-002a Crane	£10-13	☐
QA 1002	1992	Qantas Set	DG13-052a Ford A Van, and DG49-008a AEC Bus	£7-10	☐
	1987	Royal Flying Corps/RAF Set	DG6-063a and DG-011a '216 Squadron', DG18-008a Ambulance	£35-45	☐
RN 1003	1988	Royal Navy Set	DG17-017a Britannia, DG20-011a Rooke, DG28-006a Devonport (10,000)	£25-35	☐
RPL 1003	1995	3 Gold Rolls-Royces Ltd.Ed. Set	DG43-021a, DG59-015a, DG63-008a	£12-15	☐
RR 1003	1988	Rolls Royce Set	DG19-003a, DG24-002a & DG25-002a on wooden plinth, (7,500)	£30-35	☐
RSL 1003	1991	Railway Express Parcels 1	DG16-029a LNER, DG28-015a LMS & DG43-006a Metropolitan, (12,500)	£9-12	☐
RSL 2003	1991	Railway Express Parcels 2	DG13-050a Southern, DG21-034a LMS/LNER & DG28-020a GWR, (10,000)	£10-13	☐
RSL 3003	1991	Railway Express Parcels 3	DG21-036a LNER, DG28-028a Southern & DG43-014a GWR, (10,000)	£10-13	☐
RSL 4003	1993	Railway Road Vehicles 1900s	DG3-015a GER, DG4-016a Furness & DG11-024a Gt.Northern, (7,500)	£12-16	☐
RUL 1003	1995	'RUPERT 75th' Ltd.Ed. Set	DG43-021a, DG59-015a, DG63-008a	£12-15	☐
TPL 1003	1991	LNER Express Parcels Vans	DG16-028a Dennis, DG28-014a Mack & DG43-005a Morris, (12,500)	£9-12	☐
USA 1003	1991	US Army Set 1	DG27-006a Mack, DG28-017a Quartermaster & DG30-012a Surgical	£9-12	☐
USAL1003	1991	US Army Set 2	DG29-003a Ambulance, DG36-003a Pick-Up, DG42-003a Air Corps, (12,500)	£9-12	☐
VE 1003	1995	'VE-DAY' Set	DG13, DG17, DG49	£12-15	☐
VEL 1003	1995	'VE-DAY' Ltd.Ed. Set	DG44, DG52, DG68	£12-15	☐

Lledo Promotional models

In 1985, in response to customer demand, Lledo began to provide models for promotional purposes using their standard range of castings. The models were originally produced in runs of as few as 500 and went direct to clients, making them unavailable through normal retail outlets.

Some of the earlier models were supplied with the 'Days Gone' logo on the baseplate although this was soon modified to read 'Lledo Promotional'. Production runs of up to 1000 units were finished with printed adhesive labels, but runs of 1000 or more warranted direct tampo printing (as on normal 'Days Gone' models).

The majority of Lledo Promotionals tend to be priced in the range **£5 - £10**. The examples that follow are those that have attained notable rarity or extra desirability for various reasons.

Ref. No.	Year(s)	Model Type	Model Features and Size	Market Price Range	
LP1 001a	1988	Horse-Drawn Tram	'MANX TELECOM', (tampo) Red/White, 'DG' base	£10-15	☐
LP2 001a	1989	Horse-Drawn Milk Float	'MILK INDUSTRY' on label, Red/White, 'DG' base	£50-75	☐
LP3 001a	1985	Horse-Drawn Delivery Van	'PHOENIX STEAM-DRY LAUNDRY', Blue/Black with tampo, USA model	£35-45	☐
LP4 001a	1985	Horse-Drawn Omnibus	'BRIDLINGTON' logo on label, Red, 'Lledo' base	£35-45	☐
LP5 004x	1986	Horse-Drawn Fire Engine	'METROPOLITAN Fire Brigade', tampo print, 'DG' baseplate	£20-30	☐
LP6 004a	1985	Ford Model 'T' Van	'OVERDRIVE MANPOWER', White/Green label, 'DG' baseplate	£300-400	☐
LP6 012a	1986	Ford Model 'T' Van	'SALVATION ARMY', Black, tampo, 'Promotional' base, (US issue)	£100-150	☐
LP6 022a	1986	Ford Model 'T' Van	'TERRY PRINTING GROUP' on label, Black, 'Promotional' base	£300-400	☐
LP6 023a	1986	Ford Model 'T' Van	'CHANNEL 4' on label, Royal Blue, 'Promotional' baseplate	£45-55	☐
LP6 030a	1985	Ford Model 'T' Van	'SERVICE OFFSET SUPPLIES' on label, Beige, 'Promotional'	£300-400	☐
LP6 038a	1987	Ford Model 'T' Van	'NATIONAL COAL BOARD', tampo print, Blue, 'Promotional' base	£100-150	☐
LP6 060a	1987	Ford Model 'T' Van	'KIT KAT', tampo print, Red/White, 'Promotional' base	£50-70	☐
LP6 192a	1989	Ford Model 'T' Van	'MAXWELL HOUSE', tampo print, White/Red body	£500+	☐
LP6 248a	1990	Ford Model 'T' Van	'BILLON 1920-90', tampo print, Blue/White, French issue	£150-200	☐
LP6 541a	1990	Ford Model 'T' Van	'A. BOLTON & SON', Green/White, 500 only	£400+	☐
LP6 542a	1990	Ford Model 'T' Van	'PEARSON CANDY', Red, USA issue	£400+	☐
LP6 543a	1990	Ford Model 'T' Van	'BOOTS 150 PHOTO', Blue/White, 150 only	£400+	☐
LP6 544a	1990	Ford Model 'T' Van	'ALCA', Blue/White, 1,000, French issue	£400+	☐
LP7 001a	1986	Ford Woody Wagon	'FERGUSONS', White/Blue, 'DG' & 'Promotional' bases	£40-50	☐
LP8 006a	1986	Ford Model 'T' Tanker	'BONDY', Blue/Silver, 'Promotional' base, US issue	£75-100	☐
LP8 017a	1988	Ford Model 'T' Tanker	'BOEHMERS', Yellow/Green, 'Promotional' base, Canadian	£50-75	☐
LP8 020a	1990	Ford Model 'T' Tanker	'WYNNS', Blue/White, Dutch issue	£40-50	☐
LP9 001a	1986	Ford Model 'A' Car	'CAVE PHOTOGRAPHIC', Silver body with tampo print	£40-50	☐
LP10 001a	1985	Dennis Single Deck Bus	'THORPE HALL SCHOOL', Green/Yellow, 'Days Gone' baseplate	£20-30	☐
LP11 001c	1985	Horse-Drawn Removal Van	'LONDON POLICE' label, Mustard-Brown body, 'Promotional' base	£25-35	☐
LP13 060a	1986	Ford Model 'A' Van	'TIMEX CPGA' tampo print, White/Blue, Canadian issue	£40-50	☐
LP13 081a	1987	Ford Model 'A' Van	'KELLOGGS CORN FLAKES' tampo, White/Red, South African issue	£80-100	☐
LP13 092a	1987	Ford Model 'A' Van	'Le CRUNCH BUNCH' tampo print, Cream/Green body	£185-220	☐
LP15 007a	1985	AEC Double Deck Bus	'HASTINGS & Dist', ('HALLS WINE') tampo print, Maroon/Silver	£50-60	☐
LP15 008a	1985	AEC Double Deck Bus	'CITY Of COVENTRY' on label, Maroon/Cream	£90-110	☐
LP15 032a	1986	AEC Double Deck Bus	'CITY Of LINCOLN', ('LINCS ECHO') Green body	£40-50	☐
LP15 035a	1986	AEC Double Deck Bus	'FLEETWOOD 150' on label, 'DG' & 'Promotional' bases	£50-60	☐
LP15 079a	1987	AEC Double Deck Bus	'LONDON TRANSPORT', ('SRA') label, Red, 350 issued	£195-225	☐
LP15....	1990	AEC Double Deck Bus	'SUBBUTEO', 'ROME 1990', Green/White body	£20-25	☐
LP16 008a	1985	Dennis Parcels Van	'MODEL CARS 1985' tampo print, Yellow body, Japanese issue	£135-160	☐
LP16 020a	1986	Dennis Parcels Van	'RELIANCE ELECTRICAL' on label, Cream/Brown body	£85-100	☐
LP16 028a	1986	Dennis Parcels Van	'GRIMLEY & SON' on label, Red/White body	£90-100	☐
LP16 036a	1986	Dennis Parcels Van	'ALFRED QUAIFE', Black body with tampo print	£60-75	☐
LP17 001a	1985	AEC Single Deck Bus	'HEDINGHAM & Dist' on label, Blue/Cream, 'Days Gone' base	£85-100	☐
LP17 003a	1985	AEC Single Deck Bus	'MAIDSTONE & Dist' with 'RYE' destination, (label)	£40-50	☐
LP17 006b	1986	AEC Single Deck Bus	'SOUTHDOWN' with 'BRIGHTON destination, (label)	£40-50	☐
LP17 009a	1986	AEC Single Deck Bus	'STEVENSONS' tampo print on Yellow/Black body	£30-40	☐
LP17 015a	1986	AEC Single Deck Bus	'RIBBLE' with 'PRESTON' destination, (label)	£75-100	☐
LP18 003a	1986	1936 Packard Van	'MILK MARKETING BOARD' on label, Dark Green body	£60-75	☐
LP19 002a	1986	1931 Rolls-Royce	'ROYAL WEDDING', Blue/Red body	£20-25	☐
LP20 008a	1987	1934 Ford Stake Truck	'1905' livery, 1,000 issued	£30-40	☐
LP21 064a	1987	1934 Chevrolet Van	'BROOKE BOND PG TIPS', White/Red body	£50-60	☐
LP22 001a	1986	1933 Packard Town Van	'JUST CONTINENTAL 5th ANNIVERSARY', Blue body, 75 only	£70-80	☐
LP23 001a	1987	1954 Scenicruiser	'B & A TOP MARKS', Pink body, artwork on label	£15-20	☐
LP24 001a	1987	1934 Rolls-Royce	'FRANKLIN DIECAST', Black body, Red hubs, (Canadian)	£15-20	☐
LP25 001a	1987	1925 Rolls-Royce	'FRANKLIN DIECAST', Black body, Red hubs, (Canadian)	£15-20	☐
LP26 002a	1988	Chevrolet Crate Truck	'LOWCOCKS LEMONADE', Maroon body, 1,500 issued	£10-15	☐
LP27 002a	1988	Mack Breakdown Truck	'BOURNEMOUTH BUS MUSEUM', Yellow/Black, 500 issued	£10-15	☐
LP28 021a	1989	Mack Canvas-Back Truck	'LOCKHEED HYDRAULIC BRAKES', Brown/Black, 1,000 issued	£30-40	☐
LP29 002a	1990	1942 Dodge 4 x 4	'CROYDON LETTERS', Red body, 1,000 issued	£10-15	☐
LP30 003a	1989	1939 Chevrolet Van	'FAMILY REUNION', Red/Black body, artwork on label	£15-20	☐
LP31 002a	1988	Horsedrawn Brewers Dray	'EVERARDS', Green/Gold	£15-20	☐
LP33 006a	1991	Ford Model 'T' Car	'SUN CHEMICAL', Dark Green/Black	£10-15	☐
LP34 005a	1989	1932 Dennis Van	'3M FINESSE-IT', Red body	£10-15	☐
LP35 001a	1989	1932 Dennis Limousine	'ISLE of WIGHT FIRE BRIGADE', White/Red, 1,000	£10-15	☐
LP36 002a	1992	1939 Chevy Pick-up	'TYRE SERVICES', White/Blue	£15-20	☐
LP37 002a	1990	1932 Ford Panel Van	'HARTLEPOOL MAIL', Red/White	£15-20	☐
LP38 004a	1991	1925 Rolls-Royce	'SHARON and PAUL', Green/Cream	£30-40	☐
LP39 002a	1990	1934 Mack Truck	'STAUFFER CHEMICALS', Black body	£15-20	☐
LP41 027a	1991	Karrier Trolley Bus	'ANADIN 1931-1991', Yellow/Green, 1,300	£35-40	☐
LP42 002a	1990	1934 Mack Tanker	'RED CROWN', Red body, (USA model)	£10-15	☐
LP43 014a	1991	1931 Morris Van	'PROJECT CONWAY', Cream/Dark Blue, 1,000	£25-30	☐
LP44 006a	1991	1937 Scammell	'LOVE REUNION', White, 1,000, (Romanian model)	£10-15	☐
LP46 001a	1991	1930 Bentley	'SARAH and MARK', British Racing Green	£20-25	☐
LP49 025a	1992	1931 AEC Renown Bus	'LIVERPOOL FOOTBALL CLUB', Red/Silver, 1,100	£40-50	☐

Ref. No.	Year(s)	Model Type	*Lledo Promotional Models – continued*	Market Price Range	
LP50 010a	1992	1926 Morris Van	'CANNES 1992', White/Black, French	£100+	☐
LP51 001a	1992	Chevrolet Box Van	'SWAN VESTAS', Yellow/Green, 1,000	£20-25	☐
LP59 012a	1993	Bedford 30cwt Truck	'BRITISH DIECAST MODEL TOYS CATALOGUE' 5th Edition	£8-12	☐
LP69	1995	Morris 1000 Van	'PICTURE PRIDE DISPLAYS' Dark Blue with Red logo. Limited Edition Certificated – Only available to purchasers of Display Cabinets	NGPP	☐

'BRITISH DIECAST MODEL TOYS CATALOGUE'. '5th EDITION'

LP59 012a Bedford 30cwt Truck. Promotional. A few of these models are available, price £7.95 including postage (UK only). Please send to:- Swapmeet Publications, P.O. Box 47, Felixstowe, Suffolk IP11 7LP.

View Vans & Souvenir Buses

These are a variation on the Promotional theme and include LP6, LP13, LP15, LP17, LP21. They are printed with a standard 'camera' logo and supplied in a choice of three colours for each type. They are finished with adhesive photographic labels featuring various subjects including tourist areas, stately homes, football teams, etc. They are completed by a company independent of Lledo and are packed in distinctive 'dark gold' boxes. Values have yet to exceed the normal retail price of these souvenirs. A detailed Guide is available, see below.

Lledo Reference Material

The intention of this Catalogue is to provide collectors with a useful guide to current prices of this highly collectable range of die-cast models. However, the listings must of necessity be simplified for ease of use. Collectors seeking full details of all the variations of Lledo products are admirably catered for by RDP Publications who provide the books, reference material and services in the following list.

'Days Gone Collector'

This is the official full-colour Journal for 'Models Of Days Gone' collectors. Published quarterly, it contains regular features and up to date information to get the best from Lledo collecting. It includes a pull-out section of high quality photographs depicting 'Models of Days Gone' and will eventually build to a comprehensive full-colour photographic library of the entire 'Days Gone' range.

In recent years subscribers have received special and exclusive models such as a DG 32 Rolls-Royce Silver Ghost in Gold vacuum-metallized finish and a similarly finished DG 46 Bentley and DG 65 Morris 1000 Traveller.

Lledo Information Service

This is an information club for Lledo enthusiasts, mainly with emphasis on Lledo Promotional Models (although ALL new issues are fully featured). Members receive five high-quality magazines per year packed with Lledo information.

Lledo Days Gone Guide
Lledo Promotional Model Guide
View Vans & Souvenir Bus Guide

The Guides are packed with listings, data, production information, colour variations, etc, and include many photographs. The books are hard-wearing and pocket-size for easy reference.

For further details of these specialist publications and other services offered to Lledo collectors, please send a stamped, self-addressed envelope to:
RDP Publications, Dept BD4, PO Box 1946, Halesowen, West Midlands, B63 3TS.

Model listing information

Only Code 1 models are listed (that is models wholly produced by Lledo PLC and sold through normal retail outlets or by mail-order at normal retail prices).

LONE STAR

Robert Newson has provided the following information on Lone Star models.

'Lone Star' was the trade name of Die Casting Machine Tools Ltd (DCMT) who started in 1939 as manufacturers of diecasting machines, based at Palmers Green in North London. After the war they started making diecast toys which were distributed by The Crescent Toy Co Ltd. In the Crescent Toys section of this catalogue, the items listed as 'early post-war models' were all made by DCMT with the exception of the Locomotive and the Racing Car. From 1950 DCMT arranged their own distribution direct to wholesalers.

Over the next four decades DCMT Lone Star made several ranges of diecast vehicles including 'Slikka Toys' (early 1950s), 'Modern Army Series' (mainly 1960s), 'Roadmaster Majors' (1960s and 1970s), the miniature 'Tuf-Tots' (1970s) 'Farmer's Boy' (1980s) and the well known 'Lone Star Locos' miniature railway system (later called 'Treble-O-Lectric' or 'Treble-O-Trains'). The three ranges of most interest to collectors are listed here - the original DCMT 'Roadmasters' of 1956, the 1:50 scale 'Roadmasters' (1960s) and the 'Impy' and 'Flyers' series made in various forms from 1966 to the mid 1980s.

DCMT Lone Star Roadmasters

This was a short-lived series introduced in 1956, consisting of three sports cars and four veteran cars, all around 1:35 to 1:40 scale. The models had diecast bodies but all other components were plastic. Plastic drivers and passengers were included with the models. Nowadays the models are hard to find hence NGPP shown below.

Ref. No.	Year(s)	Model Type	Model Features and Size	Market Price Range	
....		1904 Darracq 'Genevieve'	Black or Red body, Yellow plastic chassis; Metallic Blue body, Black chassis............	NGPP	☐
....		1904 Daimler 'Windsor' Phaeton........................	Red body, Yellow plastic chassis........................	NGPP	☐
....		1912 Ford Model 'T'	Silver body, Black plastic chassis........................	NGPP	☐
....		1912 Morris Oxford 'Bullnose'..	Metallic Blue body, Black plastic chassis	NGPP	☐
....		Daimler Conquest Roadster......	Red, Metallic Light Blue, Pale Yellow, Pale Green or Pale Blue............	NGPP	☐
....		Ford Thunderbird	Pale Green, Pale Blue, Red or Metallic Light Blue........................	NGPP	☐
....		MG Midget TF	Metallic Light Blue or Red	NGPP	☐

Lone Star Roadmasters - 1:50 scale

In 1960 Lone Star produced four American cars on behalf of the US firm of Tootsietoy. These were the first four models listed below and they had 'Tootsietoy Classic Series' cast underneath. This arrangement only lasted for a couple of years, as by 1962 there were eight models available, all now marked 'Lone Star Roadmasters'. The models featured plated grilles, bumpers and wheels, and had windows but no interior detail. Around 1964 the plated parts were replaced by less attractive painted or self-coloured plastic, and vacuum-formed interiors were fitted. Five further numbers were added to the range before they were withdrawn around 1966.

Ref. No.	Year(s)	Model Type	Model Features and Size	Market Price Range	
1470	....	Chevrolet Corvair......................	Red	NGPP	☐
1471	....	Rambler Rebel Station Wagon	Green with Cream roof, Metallic Brown with White roof or all Green............	NGPP	☐
1472	....	Cadillac 62	Blue with Cream roof or all Blue	NGPP	☐
1473	....	Ford Sunliner Convertible........	White or Light Blue	NGPP	☐
1474	....	Chevrolet El Camino Pick-Up ..	Orange or Yellow	NGPP	☐
1475	....	Dodge Dart Phoenix.................	Metallic Dark Blue or Mid Blue........................	NGPP	☐
1476	....	Rolls-Royce Silver Cloud II......	Grey with Black roof or Metallic Blue........................	NGPP	☐
1477	....	Dodge Dart Police Car.............	Black	NGPP	☐
1478	....	Rambler Ambulance.................	White	NGPP	☐
1479	....	Chevrolet Corvair......................	'FIRE CHIEF' in Black on Red body	NGPP	☐
1480	....	Chevrolet Corvair......................	Army Staff Car (continued after 1966 as no.1273 in 'Modern Army' series), Olive Green	NGPP	☐
1481	....	Rambler Military Ambulance ...	(continued after 1966 as no.1274 in 'Modern Army' series), Olive Green................	NGPP	☐
1482	....	Citroën DS19........................	Turquoise	NGPP	☐

Lone Star Impy and Flyers

In the following listing the year shown is the date of introduction. Most models remained in production until 1976.

Ref. No.	Year(s)	Model Type	Model Features and Size	Market Price Range	
7	1971 -	Vauxhall Firenza	Flyers wheels, right and left hand drive versions	£10-20	☐
8		Ford Capri	Not issued	NPP	☐
9	1970 -	Maserati Mistral	Flyers wheels	£10-20	☐
10	1966 -	Jaguar Mk.X	Impy or Flyers wheels	£10-20	☐
11	1966 -	Chevrolet Corvette Stingray	'Gran Turismo', Impy or Flyers wheels	£10-20	☐
12	1966 -	Chysler Imperial	Impy or Flyers wheels	£10-20	☐
13		Ford Thunderbird	Not issued	NPP	☐
13	1971 -	Toyota 2000 GT	Flyers wheels	£10-20	☐
14	1966 -	Ford Zodiac Mk.III Estate	Impy or Flyers wheels	£10-20	☐
15	1966 -	Volkswagen Microbus	Impy or Flyers wheels	£10-20	☐
16	1966 -	Ford Zodiac Mk.III Estate	'POLICE' Car, Impy or Flyers wheels	£10-20	☐
16		Chrysler Imperial	'POLICE' Car, Impy wheels	£10-20	☐
16 M		Mercedes-Benz 220 SE	'POLIZEI' Car, Impy wheels	£10-20	☐
17	1966 -	Mercedes-Benz 220 SE	Impy or Flyers wheels	£10-20	☐
18	1966 -	Ford Corsair	Impy or Flyers wheels	£10-20	☐
19	1967 -	Volvo 1800 S	Impy or Flyers wheels	£10-20	☐
20	1967 -	Volkswagen Ambulance	Impy or Flyers wheels	£10-20	☐
21	1967 -	Fiat 2300 S Coupé	Impy or Flyers wheels	£10-20	☐
22	1967 -	Rolls-Royce Silver Cloud III	Convertible, Impy or Flyers wheels	£10-20	☐
23	1967 -	Alfa Romeo Giulia 1600 Spider	Impy or Flyers wheels	£10-20	☐
24	1967 -	Foden Tilt-cab 8w Tipper	Black plastic or Hi-Speed wheels	£10-20	☐
25	1967 -	Tractor Shovel	International Harvester	£10-20	☐
26	1967 -	Foden Petrol Tanker	Tilt-cab, 8 wheels, 'MOBIL' labels, Black plastic or Hi-Speed wheels	£10-20	☐
27	1967 -	Ford Taunus 12M	Impy or Flyers wheels	£10-20	☐
28	1967 -	Peugeot 404 Saloon	Impy or Flyers wheels	£10-20	☐
29		Cement Mixer Lorry	Not issued	NPP	☐
29	1971	Foden Tilt-cab 8w Box Van	'LUCAS BATTERIES' labels, Black plastic or Hi-Speed wheels	£10-20	☐
29	1972	Foden Tilt-cab 8w Box Van	'EXPRESS FREIGHT' labels, Black plastic or Hi-Speed wheels	£10-20	☐
30	1967 -	AEC Merryweather Fire Engine	Black plastic or Hi-Speed wheels	£10-20	☐
31	1967 -	Breakdown Lorry	Ford Transit, with towing cradle, 'ESSO' labels, Black plastic or Hi-Speed wheels	£10-20	☐
32	1968 -	'FIRE CHIEF' Car	Ford Corsair, Red body, roof light, Impy or Flyers wheels	£10-20	☐
32		'FEUERWEHR' Car	Ford Corsair, Red body, roof light, Impy wheels	£10-20	☐
33	1968 -	Austin-Western Mobile Crane	Elevating jib	£10-20	☐
34	1968 -	Euclid Crawler Tractor	Rubber tracks	£10-20	☐
35		Articulated Flat Truck	Not issued	NPP	☐
36	1969 -	Lotus Europa	Flyers wheels	£10-20	☐
37		Ford GT	Not issued	NPP	☐
38	1971 -	Chevrolet Corvette Stingray	Flyers wheels	£10-20	☐
39	1971 -	Ford Mustang	Flyers wheels	£10-20	☐
40	1973 -	Cadillac Eldorado	Flyers wheels	£10-20	☐
41	1972 -	Builders Supply Lorry	Leyland 8 wheel flat lorry, 4 girders, Hi-Speed wheels	£10-20	☐
41	1973 -	Builders Supply Lorry	Leyland 6 wheel flat lorry, 4 girders, Hi-Speed wheels	£10-20	☐
41	1973 -	Builders Supply Lorry	Foden half-cab 6 wheel flat lorry, 4 girders, Hi-Speed wheels	£10-20	☐
42	1972 -	Foden Half-cab 8w Tipper	'TILCON' labels, Hi-Speed wheels	£10-20	☐
43	1973 -	Flat Lorry with Pipes	Leyland 6 wheel flat lorry, Hi-Speed wheels	£10-20	☐
43	1973 -	Flat Lorry with Pipes	Foden half-cab 6 wheel flat lorry, Hi-Speed wheels	£10-20	☐
44	1972 -	Marine Transport Lorry	Leyland 8w flat lorry, Speedboat, Hi-Speed wheels	£10-20	☐
44	1973 -	Marine Transport Lorry	Leyland 6w flat lorry, Speedboat, Hi-Speed wheels	£10-20	☐
44	1973 -	Marine Transport Lorry	Foden half-cab 6w flat lorry, Speedboat, Hi-Speed wheels	£10-20	☐
46	1973 -	Leyland 6w Dropside Lorry	Hi-Speed wheels	£10-20	☐
47	1973 -	Leyland High-Side Lorry	6 wheel lorry, Hi-Speed wheels	£10-20	☐
47	1973 -	Foden High-Side Lorry	Half-cab, 6 wheel lorry, Hi-Speed wheels	£10-20	☐
48	1973 -	Hopper Lorry	Leyland 6 wheel chassis, Hi-Speed wheels	£10-20	☐
48	1973 -	Hopper Lorry	Foden half-cab 6 wheel chassis, Hi-Speed wheels	£10-20	☐
49	1973 -	Foden Tipper	Half-cab 6 wheel chassis, Hi-Speed wheels	£10-20	☐

GIFT SETS

All are scarce, hence NGPP

301	1967 Six-piece Gift Set	NGPP	☐
302	1967 Six-piece Gift Set	NGPP	☐
303	1968 'MOBIL' Gift Set	NGPP	☐
304	1968 Five-piece Commercial Vehicle Gift Set	NGPP	☐
309	1968 Twelve-piece Gift Set	NGPP	☐

IMPY ACCESSORIES

401	1967 Car Lifting Ramp	£5-10	☐
402	1967 Lock-Up Garage (plastic)	£5-10	☐
403	Service Station (not issued)	NGPP	☐
404	1968 'MOBIL' Petrol Pump Island with Canopy and Forecourt Sign	£5-10	☐
406	Fire House (not issued)	NGPP	☐

IMPY TWO-PACKS

422	VW Ambulance (no.20) and Mercedes-Benz 'Polizei' (no.16M)	£15-20	☐
423	Fiat 2300s (no.21) and Breakdown Lorry (no.31)	£15-20	☐
424	Foden Tanker (no.26) and Ford Taunus (no.27)	£15-20	☐
425	Ford Zodiac (no.14) and Tractor (no.25)	£15-20	☐
427	Alfa Romeo (no.23) and 'MOBIL' Petrol Pumps (no.404)	£15-20	☐
431	Chevrolet Corvette (no.11) and Fiat 2300s (no.21)	£15-20	☐
432	Fire Engine (no.30) and Ford Corsair 'FEUERWEHR' (no.32)	£15-20	☐

IMPY series, post-1976

The Market Price Range is shown as £5 - £10 but as yet there is little collectors' interest in these recent models.

50	Six-wheel Tipper	£5-10	☐	81	Volvo Coupé	£5-10	☐
51	Six-wheel High Side Lorry	£5-10	☐	82	Mercedes-Benz	£5-10	☐
52	Six-wheel Flat Lorry with Crane	£5-10	☐	181	Articulated Flat Lorry with Crane	£5-10	☐
53	Six-wheel Flat Lorry with Speedboat	£5-10	☐	182	Articulated Petrol Tanker	£5-10	☐
54	Six-wheel Cement Mixer	£5-10	☐	183	Articulated Low Loader with Tuf-Tots car	£5-10	☐
55	Six-wheel Luton Van	£5-10	☐	184	Articulated Flat Lorry with Pipes and water tank	£5-10	☐
56	Six-wheel Dropside Lorry	£5-10	☐	185	Cadillac Eldorado with Tuf-Tots Speedboat on		
57	Six-wheel Flat Lorry with Water Tank	£5-10	☐		trailer	£5-10	☐
58	Six-wheel Hopper Lorry	£5-10	☐	185	Range Rover with Tuf-Tots Speedboat on trailer	£5-10	☐
59	Six-wheel Flat Lorry with Pipes	£5-10	☐	185	Range Rover 'RNLI' with boat on trailer	£5-10	☐
60	Six-wheel Flat Lorry with Planks	£5-10	☐	185	Jaguar Mk.X with Cabin Cruiser on trailer	£5-10	☐
61	Six-wheel Petrol Tanker	£5-10	☐	186	Crane Lorry (no.52) with Impy car	£5-10	☐
71	Range Rover	£5-10	☐	187	Luton Van (no.55) with Trailer	£5-10	☐
72	Cadillac Eldorado	£5-10	☐	188	Articulated Low Loader with Cabin Cruiser	£5-10	☐
73	Chevrolet Corvette Stingray	£5-10	☐	189	Articulated Flat Lorry with Planks	£5-10	☐
74	Toyota 2000 GT	£5-10	☐	190	Petrol Tanker (no.61) with Trailer	£5-10	☐
75	Range Rover Police Car	£5-10	☐	191	High Side Lorry (no.51) with Trailer	£5-10	☐
76	Chevrolet Corvette Stingray 'GT Rally'	£5-10	☐	192	Cement Mixer (no.54) with Flat Trailer	£5-10	☐
77	Jaguar Mk.X	£5-10	☐	1251	Articulated Car Transporter	£5-10	☐
78	Maserati Mistral	£5-10	☐	1252	AEC Merryweather HTTL Fire Engine (re-		
79	Ford Mustang	£5-10	☐		packaging of no.30)	£5-10	☐
80	Lotus Europa	£5-10	☐	1256	Car Transporter (no.1251) with four Impy cars	£30-40	☐

Lone Star Set

International Peace Force Vehicles Set (made 1974) contains:

1271	Small Tank, Blue body	1275	Ack-Ack Gun
1272	Searchlight on Trailer	1276	Silver Small Canon
1273	Mortar Launcher	1277	All Blue Military Jeep
1274	Radar Detector Unit		

Model Price Range NGPP.

Lone Star Routemaster Bus

Made from two castings which include seats and stair details. Colour is Red with Silver trim, paper adverts on sides *SEE LONDON BY BUS* and *'BUY LONE STAR'* Route is *'29 VICTORIA'*, Black plastic tyres, cast into base 'LONE STAR' & 'MADE IN ENGLAND', No. 1259, made 1972-1989 ....**£5-10**

ACKNOWLEDGEMENT Thanks to Les Percy of Rochdale and Bob Ewers of Maidenhead for supplying new Lone Star Model information.

LONE STAR

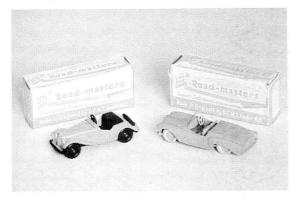

MG 'TF' & Daimler Conquest Roadster

Darracq 1904 'Genevieve' Film Car

The models shown form part of the David Kerr collection and are shown by his kind permission.

(Swapmeet photos)

MATCHBOX TOYS

INTRODUCTION

The company was founded in 1947 by the unrelated Leslie and Rodney Smith who combined their names to form 'Lesney' Products Ltd. They were soon joined by Jack Odell a recognised die-casting expert. The most famous of the various early products was the 'Coronation Coach'. During the 1950s the company developed the highly successful Matchbox '1-75' and 'Models of Yesteryear' ranges.

Following a difficult trading period Lesney Products Ltd was bought in 1982 by the Universal Toy Co. of Hong Kong.

On the 7th May 1992 it was announced in the 'New York Times' that 'Tyco Toys Inc.' had acquired by merger the 'Universal Matchbox Group'. Since this merger Matchbox is now referred to as 'Tyco-Matchbox' although the products are still marketed under the famous Matchbox brand name. Late in 1992 Tyco Toys announced the formation of a new division called Matchbox Collectibles which will be responsible for the future sales and marketing of Matchbox 'Models of Yesteryear'.

The Editor is indebted to Hardy Ristau of Berlin who has totally revised the Regular wheel issues. As a result the listings are now far more specific and accurate with a separate grading for each wheel variation.

'MoKo' Products

'MoKo' Products was a toy distribution firm founded by Moses Kohnstam who came to Britain from Nuremburg, Germany at the turn of the century. 'MoKo' provided the distribution and storage facilities and, irrespective of the supplier, all toys were marketed as 'MoKo' products. The early issues after the Second World War were housed in plain cardboard boxes with 'tuck in' ends, usually with single colour printing and no model picture. During the early 1950s the packaging became much more attractive with colour boxes displaying a picture of the model inside. 'MoKo' will best be remembered for their distribution of the early Matchbox '1-75' Toys under the name of 'MoKo-Lesney'. Moses Kohnstam was succeeded by Richard Kohnstam in 1953.

The following listing of 'MoKo' items constitutes all the information available to publish at present. Additional information would be welcomed by the Editor.

Ref. No.	Year(s)	Model Type	Model Features and Size	Market Price Range	
i)	c1948-53	Mechanical Tractor	Probably early Lesney. Orange body, Green rubber tracks, Black wheels, Green/Black driver. (Early issue in plain box - see picture in colour section).........................	£125-150	☐
	1950-55	Mechanical Tractor	As previous model but with Orange wheels, (later issue in picture box)......................	£125-150	☐
ii)	1947-50	Excavator (with open cab)	Orange body and jib, Black digger and chassis, Green rubber tracks, Orange crank handle. Early card box has *'MoKo TOYS OF DISTINCTION'* logo (see colour section picture)	£160-200	☐
iii)	1950-55	'RUSTON BUCYRUS' Excavator	Yellow over Red body with Black '10 RB' logo. Black or Dark Grey chassis, jib, digger, crank wheel and rubber tracks. Later box with full colour picture....................	£160-200	☐
iv)	1950-55	Builders Crane	All Blue crane base and jib with unpainted metal hook. Later card box with full colour picture (see colour section)	£160-200	☐
v)	1950-55	Drummer Boy (Mechanical)......................	Red body with Gold trim and wearing a Black busby. Cream/Yellow drum with Gold trim and drumsticks...	£500-750	☐
vi)	1947-50	Crawler Bulldozer......................	Red body and dozer blade (possibly early Lesney). Early plain card box	£125-150	☐
vii)	1947-50	Hayrick....................................	Yellow/Green body..	£160-200	☐
viii)	1947-50	Fairground Carousel	Blue/Red base and centre column, Maroon/Blue roof, 2 Red and 2 Blue seated figures. Plain card box (see picture in colour section)..	£160-200	☐
ix)	1947-50	Mechanical Mouse....................	Grey body with Red eyes plus curling tail. Early plain card box............................	£100-150	☐
x)	1950-55	Model Motor Scooter...............	Dark Red scooter with Black seat. Female figure has blonde hair, blue sweater, red trousers. Later box with full colour picture	£250-350	☐

MoKo 'Farmette Series' (circa 1950 - 1953)

Miniature size models packed in end-flap type boxes with colour picture of the model. The horses are die-cast with dark brown bodies and white feet.

Ref. No.	Year(s)	Model Type	Model Features and Size	Market Price Range	
No.1	1950-53	Timber Trailer with two Horses.....................	Green body, four Red wheels, Timber load	£125-150	☐
No.2	1950-53	Farm Cart with two Horses	Mid or Dark Blue cart body with Red raves, four Red 12-spoke wheels	£125-150	☐
No.3	1950-53	Bull Wagon with two Horses	Green wagon body, two horses in tandem, Brown metal bull, four Red 12-spoke wheels	£125-150	☐

'Treasure Chest' Series

Packed in Brown 'Chests' with Yellow 'Strapping'.

No.10	1950-53	Hay Cart (1 Horse)	Orange body, Two Green raves, Two Green wheels	£50-75	☐
No.11	1950-53	Millers Cart (1 Horse)	Blue body, Two Red wheels, 3 White sacks	£50-75	☐
No.12	1950-53	Water Cart (1 Horse)	Green/Red cart, two Red wheels	£50-75	☐

The early 'Lesney' toys

Lesney Products first produced diecast toys in 1948. Whilst production ceased during the Korean war period (1950-52), the models produced formed the basis from which the 1-75 series was launched in 1953 and were sold in boxes under the name of 'MOKO' who were ultimately to also market all the early 1-75 series models.

Ref. No.	Year(s)	Model Type	Model Features and Size	Market Price Range	
i)	....	Road Roller	All Green body and flywheel, unpainted wheels	£250-300	☐
			As previous model but with Red roller wheels and Yellow flywheel	£250-300	☐
		casting change:	With a driver but without a flywheel	£175-200	☐
		casting change:	Without a driver and without flywheel	£150-175	☐
ii)	....	Cement Mixer	All Green body, Red wheels	£150-175	☐
			Pale Green body, Red mixer and wheels	£125-150	☐
			Dark Green body, Red mixer and wheels	£100-150	☐
			Red body, Green mixer and wheels	£125-150	☐
iii)	....	Caterpillar Tractor	Orange or Yellow body, Red roller wheels, Black rubber tracks, driver	£125-150	☐
iv)	....	Caterpillar Bulldozer	Green, Orange or Red body, driver, Black rubber tracks	£125-150	☐
			Yellow body, Red dozer blade and wheels	£125-150	☐
v)	....	Prime Mover	Orange tractor (Green engine on some), Beige or Blue trailer, Red/Yellow dozer, 'BRITISH ROAD SERVICES'	£800-1000	☐
			As previous model but with Beige trailer	£500-600	☐
vi)	....	'MASSEY HARRIS' Tractor	Red body, Cream hubs, Black rubber tyres	£300-400	☐
vii)	....	Milk Cart	Orange body, White driver and 6 crates, Black or Brown horse, Black or Grey wheels, 'PASTEURISED MILK' cast into cart sides	£400-500	☐
			As previous model but with Blue body	£600-700	☐
viii)	....	Breadbait Press	1st type: Red body, unpainted 'butterfly' press	£40-50	☐
			2nd type: As 1st type but with Green press	£50-60	☐
			3rd type: As 2nd type with 'MILBRO' cast onto Red body	£60-70	☐
ix)	....	Quarry Truck	Yellow body, Black tyres, 'LAING'. Only one example known to exist	NGPP	☐
x)	....	Covered Wagon with Barrels	Green body, White cover, 2 Red barrels, 6 Mid-Brown horses (with White tails), with postilion rider and wagon driver	£200-250	☐
xi)	....	Covered Wagon without Barrels	As previous model but with Chocolate Brown horses and no barrels	£200-250	☐
xii)	....	'RAG & BONE MERCHANTS' Cart	Yellow body, Red wheels, Black horse, Brown driver, with 7 pieces of 'junk': mangle-wheel, bike frame, bedhead, bath, bucket, box, cistern	£750-1000	☐
			As previous model but Green body, Red wheels	NGPP	☐

Picture kindly supplied by Phillips West Two, 10 Salem Road, Bayswater, London and reproduced by their kind permission.

Ref. No.	Year(s)	Model Type	Matchbox – Early 'Lesney' toys – continued	Market Price Range
xiii)	....	Soap-Box Racer.........................	Brown box, Grey spoked wheels (16 and 9), Dark Blue boy with Pink face	NGPP ☐
xiv)	....	Coronation Coach (large)..........	Gold coach with King & Queen, eight White horses, Gold/Red trappings, 4 Red riders. 200 issued	£750-850 ☐
xv)	....	Coronation Coach (large)..........	Gold, Silver or Gilt coach with just the Queen inside. Horses and riders as for previous model	£150-200 ☐
xvi)	....	Coronation Coach (small)........	Silver or Gold coach, 8 White horses, Red/Gold trappings, 4 Red riders, 'A MOKO TOY BY LESNEY' cast into horsebar (1,000,000 sold).......	£85-100 ☐
xvii)	....	'Muffin The Mule'	White body, Red/Gold harness, Black trim	£175-200 ☐
xv111)	....	Excavator...................................	Digger and chassis are Dark Brown...	£100-125 ☐
xix)	....	Motor Scooter	Blue Scooter	NGPP ☐

Other early Lesney toys. Collectors should be aware that in addition to die-cast models some tin-plate items were also produced, namely: a clockwork 'JUMBO' elephant, 'PEREGRINE' puppet, and a Red drummer-boy.

Matchbox Model identification

Many models have common identifying features and these are shown below to avoid any unnecessary repetition.

Model Number is always cast into the base, chassis or body. Obvious exceptions are the early models which were not numbered.

'Lesney' is cast into the base, chassis or body of all issues between 1953 and 1982.

'Matchbox' or 'Matchbox Series' is shown on the base or chassis of all issues after 1965.

Model name. All issues after 1957 had the model name on the base or chassis. Exceptions include those without a base (No.24 Excavator for example).

Suspension and windows. All car models were fitted with windows after 1961 and with suspension after 1965.

Windscreen, seats and steering wheels are usually made of plastic (though some earlier open cars, dump trucks, etc have metal seats).

Length of models is shown in mm. and is taken from Matchbox publications or from actual models.

Boxes often have differing designs for the same model and provide additional collecting interest.

Baseplates are metal castings until the late 1970s when plastic bases introduced. From 1983 they are marked 'Made in Macau' and from 1986 'Made in China'.

Wheels were metal castings on early models gradually changed to grey, silver or black plastic. Superfast wheels introduced in late 1960s and issues from 1968-69 may be found with either type. Novelties such as 'Laser Wheels' introduced in the late 1980s.

Rolamatics were introduced in the 1970s having working parts that were operated by pushing.

Model descriptions. This Catalogue tries to give original makers description of model names and colours but early matchbox listings are known to be inaccurate graphically. Makers catalogue photographs are often taken of mock-ups months before production starts and model designs are changed before release.

Matchbox Miniatures (1-75 Series)

Ref. No.	Year(s)	Model Type	Model Features and Size	Market Price Range

MB 1

Ref. No.	Year(s)	Model Type	Model Features and Size	Market Price Range
1a	1953	Diesel Road Roller (Aveling Barford)..................	Type 1: curved lower canopy ends & thin braces above canopy supports, Type 2: straight ends & thick braces above supports, brace extension. Dark Green body, Type 1 or 2, Red metal roller wheels, Gold trim, Tan driver cast-in, no number, crimped axles, tow hook, 49 mm.	£40-50 ☐
		colour change:............	As previous model but Type 2 with Light Green body	£80-100 ☐
1b	1956	Diesel Road Roller (Aveling Barford)..................	Light Green body, Red metal roller wheels, Light or Dark Tan driver, high peaked canopy, no number, crimped axles, hook, 57 mm.	£30-40 ☐
1c	1958	Diesel Road Roller (Aveling Barford)..................	Light Green body and driver, Red metal roller wheels, number cast-in, high peaked canopy, hook, 62 mm.	£60-80 ☐
			Dark Green body	£30-40 ☐
1d	1962	Diesel Road Roller (Aveling Barford)..................	Green body and driver, Red plastic rollers, 67 mm.	£15-20 ☐
1e	1967	Mercedes Truck	Turquoise body, Orange canopy, Black plastic wheels, 75 mm.	£8-12 ☐
		Superfast wheels:	Metallic Gold body, Orange-Yellow canopy	£6-10 ☐
			Red body, Yellow canopy, *'Transcontinental'*	£6-10 ☐
			Blue body, Yellow canopy, 'IMS'	£8-12 ☐
			Military Olive body, Tan canopy, *'USA'*	£6-10 ☐
			Olive Drab body, Tan canopy, *'USA'*	£12-15 ☐

212

Ref. No.	Year(s)	Model Type	*Matchbox Miniatures – continued*	Market Price Range	
1f	1972	'Mod Rod'........................	Yellow body, Silver exposed rear engine, Superfast wheels, 73 mm.	**£4-6**	☐
		colour change:........	Same as previous model but with 'flower' label	**£10-15**	☐
		colour change:..........	As previous model but with Red interior or wheels..	**£8-11**	☐
		note:........................	Other variations exist		
		'Silver Streak'	US issued version of model 1f	**£8-11**	☐
1g	1976	Dodge Challenger	Red body, White roof, Red or Silver interior, Superfast, 74 mm.	**£8-11**	☐
		colour change:..........	Blue body with Red interior	**£8-11**	☐
		colour change:..........	Dark Blue body with Red interior..	**£5-8**	☐
	1982	design change:..........	Blue or Orange body, 'Revin Rebel', clear windows, Superfast, 74 mm.	**£2-4**	☐
	1983	design change:..........	Yellow body, Black roof, 'Toyman', clear windows, Superfast	**£2-4**	☐
1h	1988	Jaguar XJ6	Red body, Silver trim, authentic radiator..	**£2-4**	☐
	1989		White body	**£2-4**	☐
	1988	Promotional:.............	Green body, 'REDOXON' on bonnet, Superfast, (Hong Kong model)	**£1-3**	☐
	1988	Promotional:.............	'WHYTE & MACKAY', Black body, Gold bonnet design	**£1-3**	☐
	1991	Jaguar XJ6 (Police)	White body, Yellow 'Police' logo on Blue background, 2 Blue rooflights	**£1-3**	☐
	1992	design change:..........	Same but 'Police' crests on doors & bonnet, Red band on sides........................	**£1-3**	☐

MB 2

2a	1953	Muir Hill Site Dumper	Dark Green body, Red dumper, Green painted metal wheels, 42 mm.	**£60-80**	☐
		colour change:..........	As previous model but with unpainted metal wheels..	**£30-35**	☐
2b	1957	Muir Hill Site Dumper	Same but Tan driver, metal wheels, 46 mm.	**£25-30**	☐
		wheel change:........	As previous model but with Grey plastic wheels..	**£30-40**	☐
2c	1962	Muir Hill Dumper Truck	Red body, Green dumper, 'LAING' logo, Black plastic wheels, 54 mm.	**£15-20**	☐
		decal change:..........	With 'MUIR HILL' logo & picture-box (72 only known to exist)............................	**£50-70**	☐
2d	1967	Mercedes Trailer	Turquoise body, Orange canopy.	**£8-10**	☐
		Superfast Wheels:	Metallic Gold body, Orange-Yellow canopy..	**£5-8**	☐
			Red body, Yellow canopy, 'Transcontinental'	**£4-7**	☐
			Blue body, Yellow canopy, 'IMS'	**£6-10**	☐
			Military Olive body, Tan canopy, 'USA'	**£4-7**	☐
			Olive Drab body, Tan canopy, 'USA'	**£8-12**	☐
2e	1972	Jeep Hot Rod	Pink with Green base, Cream seats, Superfast wheels	**£5-8**	☐
		variants:	Pink with White base	**£25-30**	☐
			Red with Green base..	**£25-30**	☐
			Red with White Base	**£5-8**	☐
		note:	Other variations exist		
2f	1977	Rescue Hovercraft	Green/Fawn body, 'Rescue', Superfast wheels, 77 mm.	**£4-7**	☐
		colour change:..........	Metallic Green/Tan body, Chrome/Red top, 'Rescue', Superfast, 77 mm.	**£5-8**	☐
		colour change:..........	Pale Green/Black body, Chrome/Red top, '2000'	**£5-£8**	☐
		Note:	Many other variations exist		
2g	1980	Mazda RX7	Yellow or Green body, Japanese issued model	**£5-8**	☐
2h	1981	S-2 Jet	Black/Yellow body, Red or Yellow cockpit, folding wing-tips, 76 mm.	**£3-5**	☐
		colour change:..........	Black/Red body, Red flash, 'VIPER'	**£3-5**	☐
		colour change:..........	Blue/White body, Silver wings	**£3-5**	☐
	1989	colour change:..........	Camouflage paintwork	**£1-3**	☐
2i	1985	Pontiac Firebird........................	Black body, *Halleys Comet'*, US issued model..	**£3-5**	☐
2j	1985	Pontiac Fiero	White/Blue/Orange body, racing number '85'	**£3-5**	☐
	1986	colour change:..........	Blue body, Yellow/Red panels..	**£1-3**	☐
	1987	colour change:..........	White/Red body	**£2-4**	☐
2k	1987	Rover Sterling..........................	Maroon body, Black chassis, Superfast wheels	**£1-3**	☐
	1987	Laser Wheels issue:....	Silver body	**£1-3**	☐
	1992	design change:..........	Silver body, Black chassis, 'ROVER STERLING' logo	**£1-3**	☐
2L	1993	BMW 850	All Silver body	**£1-3**	☐

MB 3

3a	1953	Cement Mixer	Orange metal wheels, Blue main body	**£25-35**	☐
			Grey plastic wheels, crimped axles..	**£70-80**	☐
			Grey plastic wheels, rounded axles..	**£40-50**	☐
3b	1961	Bedford Tipper Truck	Maroon dump, Grey plastic wheels with 24 treads	**£60-80**	☐
			Maroon dump, Grey plastic wheels with 45 treads	**£100-120**	☐
			Maroon dump, black plastic wheels..	**£20-30**	☐
			Red dump, Grey plastic wheels	**£50-75**	☐
			Red dump, Black plastic wheels	**£25-35**	☐
3c	1967	Mercedes Ambulance	Cream body, 'Red Cross'	**£12-16**	☐
			Off-White body, 'Red Cross'	**£10-14**	☐
		Superfast wheels	Off-white body, 'Red Cross'	**£8-12**	☐
			Military Olive body, 'Red Cross'	**£7-10**	☐
3d	1973	Monteverdi Hai	Orange body, RN '3', tinted windows, opening doors, Superfast, 74 mm.	**£5-8**	☐
		label change:	Red body, racing number '16'	**£5-8**	☐
3e	1979	Porsche Turbo	Brown or Silver body, opening doors, Superfast, 74 mm.	**£3-5**	☐
	1981	colour change:..........	Green body, Yellow interior, opening doors, Superfast	**£3-5**	☐
		colour change:..........	As previous model but with Red interior	**£6-9**	☐
	1982	colour change:..........	Red body, White RN '90' and 'Porsche', opening doors, Superfast....................	**£3-5**	☐
	1985	colour change:..........	Black body, Red 'Turbo', racing number '90'	**£2-4**	☐
	1987	colour change:..........	White body	**£1-3**	☐
	1989	colour change:..........	Metallic Blue body, Yellow design	**£1-3**	☐
	1990	colour change:..........	Red body	**£1-3**	☐
	1992	colour change:..........	Red body, '911' on doors, large crest on bonnet	**£1-3**	☐
		note:..........................	Other variations exist		
	1994	'Hummer'............................	....	**£1-2**	☐

MB 4

Ref. No.	Year(s)	Model Type	Description	Price	
4a	1954	Massey Harris Tractor	(with mudguards over rear wheels), Red body, Tan driver	**£40-50**	☐
4b	1957	Massey Harris Tractor	(without mudguards over rear wheels)		
			Metal wheels..	**£30-35**	☐
			Grey plastic wheels..............................	**£45-55**	☐
4c	1960	Triumph T110 Motor Cycle.....	Steel Blue bike/sidecar, 11 mm. Silver wheels, Black plastic tyres, 54 mm.	**£35-45**	☐
		colour variant:	As previous model but Copper body, 9.5 mm.	**£1500-1700**	☐
4d	1966	Stake Truck	Blue stake body...............................	**£50-60**	☐
			Green stake body...............................	**£8-12**	☐
		Superfast wheels	Orange-Yellow body, Green stake body....................	**£8-12**	☐
			Bright yellow body, Green stake body...................	**£20-25**	☐
4e	1972	'Gruesome Twosome'	Gold body, Pink roof, Silver exposed engine, Superfast, 73 mm.	**£5-8**	☐
4f	1976	Pontiac Firebird......................	Metallic Blue body, Silver trim, Orange tinted windows, Superfast, 73 mm.	**£5-8**	☐
4g	1981	'57' Chevy	Metallic Mauve body, Silver trim and engine, opening doors, Superfast, 75 mm.	**£3-5**	☐
	1982	colour change:	All Red body, 'Cherry Bomb' labels, Superfast, 75 mm.	**£3-5**	☐
	1983	colour change:.............	Black/Red/Yellow, 'flames' effect, Superfast, 75 mm.	**£3-5**	☐
	1989	US issue:	'HEINZ' promotional model	**£2-4**	☐
4h	1985	Chrysler Daytona	White body, (US issued model)	**£3-5**	☐
4i	1988	FX4-R Taxi	Black body, Silver trim	**£1-3**	☐
	1989	Australian issue:........	Black body, 'LONDON TO SYDNEY', promotional model......................	**£6-8**	☐

MB 5

No. 5 London Bus

Ref. No.	Year(s)	Model Type	Description	Price	
5a	1954	London Bus (52 mm.)	'Buy Matchbox Series' paper label.	**£45-55**	☐
5b	1957	1957 London Bus (57 mm.)	'Buy Matchbox Series' decal, metal wheels	**£40-50**	☐
			'Buy Matchbox Series' decal, Grey plastic wheels...............	**£60-70**	☐
			'Players Please' decal, Grey plastic wheels............	**£90-110**	☐
			'BP Visco-Static' decal, Grey plastic wheels...............	**£180-200**	☐
5c	1960	Routemaster (66 mm.)	'Players Please decal, Grey plastic wheels	**£75-90**	☐
			'Peardrax' decal, Grey or Black plastic wheels...........	**£200-230**	☐
			'BP Visco-Static' decal, Grey or Black plastic wheels........	**£25-35**	☐
			'Baron of Beef' decal, Grey or Black plastic wheels........	**£250-300**	☐
5d	1965	Routemaster (70 mm.)	'BP Longlife' decal	**£15-20**	☐
			'BP Visco-Static' decal or label	**£12-16**	☐
			'Baron of Beef' decal	**£250-300**	☐
			'Pegram' label	**£300-350**	☐
5e	1970	Lotus Europa............................	Dark Metallic Blue body, no 'Superfast' cast on base	**£120-150**	☐
			Dark Metallic Blue body, with 'Superfast' on base	**£10-15**	☐
			Pink body, unpainted base	**£7-10**	☐
			Pink body, Silver-Grey base	**£12-15**	☐
			Pink body, '20' labels	**£12-15**	☐
			Black body, 'JPS' tempa (Japan)	**£15-20**	☐
			Many other (Bulgarian) variantions exist	**£5-20**	☐
5f	1976	Seafire Motor Boat....................	All models with 'Seafire' label, some came with trailer		
			White and Blue body	**£3-6**	☐
			White and Brown body.............................	**£55-75**	☐
			Red and White body	**£7-10**	☐
			Red and Blue body	**£15-20**	☐
			Red and Yellow body	**£8-12**	☐
			Black and Yellow body	**£15-20**	☐
5g		Nissan Fair Lady 2802X	Red or Metallic Red body (Japanese issued model)	**£6-8**	☐
		Police Car variant:.....	White/Black body...................................	**£5-8**	☐
5h	1980	U.S. Mail Truck	Blue body, White roof, 'U.S. Mail' logo, Superfast, 59 mm.	**£3-5**	☐
		variants:	Pale blue, sleet and snow base, US issue, 'No. 38 Jeep'	**£7-9**	☐
			Yellow body, 'GLIDING CLUB' logo	**£7-9**	☐
5i	1982	4 x 4 Jeep................................	Bronze body, large wheels, Black roll-bar and bumpers...........	**£2-4**	☐
	1989	colour change:............	Camouflage paintwork	**£2-4**	☐
5j	1984	**Peterbilt Tanker**			
		'SHELL'.............................	White/Grey body, Yellow/Red design	**£3-5**	☐
		'AMOCO'	Black body, Black exhaust pipes, etc..............	**£3-5**	☐
	1985	'AMOCO'	Black body, Chrome exhausts, etc...................	**£12-15**	☐
		'AMPOL'	Australian issued model	**£8-11**	☐
		'SUPERGAS'.............................	Black/Yellow (US issued model).....................	**£3-5**	☐
		'GETTY'	Red/Chrome (US issued model)	**£3-5**	☐
	1988	'SHELL'.............................	White/Chrome body, Yellow/Red design	**£2-4**	☐

MB 6

Ref. No.	Year(s)	Model Type	Description	Price	
6a	1954	Quarry Truck...........................	Orange body, Grey tipper with 6 ribs, metal wheels, 55 mm...........	**£25-30**	☐
		wheel change:...............	With Grey plastic wheels, domed/crimped axles	**£450-500**	☐
6b	1959	Euclid Quarry Truck	Yellow body, 4 ribs, decals, 6 Black plastic wheels, 'Euclid' decal, 63 mm.	**£20-30**	☐
		wheel change:...............	With Grey plastic wheels, rivetted axles	**£300-350**	☐
6c	1963	Euclid Dump Truck	6 Black wheels (rear double wheels are one piece)	**£15-18**	☐
			10 Black wheels (rear wheels are normal double wheels)........	**£12-15**	☐
6d	1968	Ford Pick Up	Red body, White canopy, White or chrome grill	**£8-12**	☐
		Superfast wheels:	Red body, White canopy, unpainted or Metallic Green base	**£20-25**	☐
			Same but with Black, Grey or Green base	**£6-12**	☐

Ref. No.	Year(s)	Model Type	Description	Market Price Range	
6e	1974	Mercedes 350SL	Orange/Black body, Yellow interior, Superfast, 75 mm.	£3-5	☐
	1976	colour change:	Yellow/Black body, Superfast	£2-4	☐
	1978	G15 Gift Set model:	Metallic Silver/Black body, 'Rennservice'	£15-20	☐
	1978	colour change:	Metallic Bronze body, Black roof	£1-2	☐
	1980	colour change:	Red body, White roof	£1-2	☐
6f	1982	Mercedes 350SL Open Top	Metallic Blue body, White interior, Superfast, 75 mm.	£2-4	☐
	1982	colour change:	Maroon body, White interior	£2-4	☐
6g	1986	F1 Racer	Red body, racing number '3', Superfast	£1-2	☐
	1987	colour change:	Blue body, racing number '20', (US issue)	£2-4	☐
	1988	colour change:	Yellow body, racing number '5'	£1-3	☐
	1989	colour change:	White body, 'MR JUICY' design	£1-3	☐
6h	1991	Alfa Romeo SZ	Red body, Black roof, 'ALFA ROMEO' logo	£1-3	☐
	1995	Plymouth Prowler		£1-2	☐

MB 7

Ref. No.	Year(s)	Model Type	Description	Market Price Range	
7a	1954	Horse Drawn Milk Float	Orange body, White man, crates & logo, metal wheels	£45-60	☐
			As previous but with Grey plastic wheels	£75-95	☐
			Pale Orange body, metal wheels	£50-65	☐
			Pale Orange body, White hat and crates only, Grey plastic wheels	£70-85	☐
			Variation with Silver driver and milk bottles	£400-600	☐
7b	1961	Ford Anglia	Light Blue, Green windows, Grey plastic wheels, 67 mm.	£56-60	☐
		wheel change:	With Silver plastic wheels	£35-50	☐
		wheel change:	With Black plastic wheels	£25-35	☐
7c	1967	Refuse Truck	Orange-Red body, Grey and Silver dumper	£8-12	☐
		Superfast wheels:	Orange-Red body (shades), Grey and Silver dumper	£7-12	☐
7d	1973	'Hairy Hustler'	Metallic Orange body, RN'5', clover-leaf wheels, Purple or Yellow windows	£3-5	☐
		colour change:	White body, Amber windows, 'streaker' design	£3-5	☐
		colour change:	Yellow body, 'flame' design	£3-5	☐
		note:	Many other variations exist.		☐
7e	1977	VW Golf with Surfboards	Light or Dark Green body, 2 Black surfboards, hook, Superfast	£3-5	☐
	1979	colour change:	Red body	£2-4	☐
	1981	colour change:	Yellow body, Red seats, Black base, hook, Superfast	£2-4	☐
	1982	colour change:	Silver body, Green flash 'Golf', Red interior, Superfast	£2-4	☐
		colour change:	With Tan interior	£20-25	☐
		Export issues:	'ADAC' German and Japanese issued models	£15-20	☐
7f	1983	IMSA Mazda	Blue body, Orange/White flash, 'Mazda', 76 mm.	£2-4	☐
7g	1986	Porsche 959	Silver body, 'Porsche' logo	£1-3	☐
	1988	colour change:	Metallic Dark Grey body, Red interior	£1-3	☐
	1991	design change:	Silver body, Red design, Yellow 'Porsche' logo on doors	£1-3	☐
	1992	design change:	As previous model but Yellow 'Porsche 959' logo on doors	£1-3	☐
7h		'Rompin' Rabbit'	US issued model	£5-8	☐
7i		'Ruff Rabbit'	Yellow/Black body, 'VW rabbits' tampo print design, US issued model	£5-8	☐
7j		London Bus	'Nice to Meet You'. Japanese issued model	£5-8	☐
	1984	logo change:	'1984 Yokohama'. Japanese issued promotional	£35-45	☐

MB 8

Ref. No.	Year(s)	Model Type	Description	Market Price Range	
8a	1955	Caterpillar Tractor (42 mm.)	Yellow body and rollers, Red driver, Green tracks, 41 mm.	£130-150	☐
			As previous but with unpainted rollers	£40-45	☐
		colour change:	Orange body and driver, Gold grille	£55-65	☐
		colour change:	Same but Yellow body and driver, Silver or Yellow grille, Green or Grey tracks	£30-35	☐
8b	1958	Caterpillar Tractor (42 mm.)	Yellow body and driver, no. '8' cast-in, Green rubber tracks, 42 mm.	£45-55	☐
8c	1961	Caterpillar Tractor (48 mm.)	Yellow body, metal rollers, Green tracks	£18-22	☐
			As previous, but with Silver rollers	£55-70	☐
			As previous, but with Black rollers	£20-25	☐
8d	1964	Caterpillar Tractor (51 mm.)	Yellow body, No driver, Green rubber tracks, Black rollers, 51 mm.	£12-15	☐
8e	1966	Ford Mustang	White body, Black wheels with Silver hubcaps	£15-20	☐
			White body, Silver wheels with Black tyres	£12-15	☐
			Orange body, Silver wheels	£120-150	☐
		Superfast wheels	White body	£40-50	☐
			Orange body, Ivory interior	£15-20	☐
			Orange body, Red interior	£45-55	☐
			Red body, Ivory interior	£25-30	☐
			Red body, Red interior	£55-70	☐
8f	1970	Wildcat Dragster	Orange or Pink, base in various colours, 'Wild-Cat', Superfast, 74 mm.	£8-11	☐
8g	1975	De Tomaso Pantera	White or Blue body, Red seats, racing number '8' and 'Pantera'	£3-5	☐
		colour change:	As previous model but with Orange interior	£5-7	☐
		label change:	As previous model but with 'SUN' label	£7-10	☐
8h	1981	Rover 3500	Red body, Cream seats, Black base, Superfast, 73 mm.	£4-6	☐
8i	1983	Rover 3500 'POLICE' Car	White body, Yellow/Black decal, 2 Blue flashing lights, 73 mm.	£4-6	☐
	1984	variant:	As previous model but with the addition of a rooflight bar	£4-6	☐
		variant:	As previous model but with Red/Black stripes	£4-6	☐
8j	1986	'Greased Lightnin''	Red body, racing number '31', US issued model	£4-6	☐
8k	1986	1962 Corvette	Orange body	£3-5	☐
	1988	colour change:	Metallic Green body	£3-5	☐
8L	1988	Astra Police	White body, Red/Blue side stripes, Blue light bar on roof	£1-2	☐
	1992	design change:	As previous model but Yellow/Blue side stripes	£1-2	☐

MB 9

Ref. No.	Year(s)	Model Type	Description	Price	
9a	1955	Fire Escape (Dennis)	Red body, Gold trim on some, metal wheels on crimped axles, 57 mm.	£30-35	☐
9b	1958	Fire Escape (Dennis)	Red body, Gold trim, metal wheels, fully cast front bumper with number cast on the underside, 58 mm.	£40-45	☐
		wheel change:	As previous model but with Grey plastic wheels	£180-220	☐
9c	1959	Merryweather Marquis Series III Fire Engine	Red body with Tan ladder, Grey plastic wheels, crimped axles, 64 mm.	£45-55	☐
		axle change:	Grey wheels, Tan ladder, rounded axles	£30-40	☐
		ladder change:	As previous model but with Gold ladder	£35-45	☐
		wheel change:	With Gold ladder and Black plastic wheels	£15-20	☐
		ladder change:	With Silver ladder, Black plastic wheels	£60-70	☐
		ladder change:	With Tan ladder, Black plastic wheels	£50-60	☐
9d	1966	Boat and Trailer	Blue/White boat (76 mm.), with Blue trailer (77 mm.), Black plastic wheels	£10-12	☐
	1970	wheel change:	As previous model but fitted with Superfast wheels	£5-8	☐
9e	1972	AMX Javelin	Metallic Lime Green body, Yellow interior, Superfast, 77 mm.	£5-8	☐
		interior change:	With Cream or Orange interior	£5-8	☐
	1980	colour change:	Blue body, Yellow interior, 'Cam Cracker', RN '1', Superfast	£4-6	☐
9f	1978	Ford Escort RS2000	White body, 'Shell' and 'Ford' decals, Superfast, 74 mm.	£6-10	☐
	1981	colour change:	Metallic Green, White grille, 'Seagull', Superfast, 74 mm.	£6-10	☐
		rare variant:	As previous model but with Red interior	£75-85	☐
9g		'Cam Cracker'	Blue body, (US issued model)	£4-6	☐
9h	1990	Caterpillar Bulldozer	Dark Red body, 'Dr.PEPPER' design	£1-3	☐
		colour change:	Yellow body, Black cab roof	£1-3	☐
	1992	colour change:	Yellow body, Red cab and stripes on blade	£1-2	☐

MB 10

Ref. No.	Year(s)	Model Type	Description	Price	
10a	1957	Scammell Mechanical Horse	Red cab, Gold trim, Grey trailer, crimped axles, metal wheels, 56 mm.	£35-45	☐
10b	1957	Scammell Mechanical Horse	Red Cab, Brown trailer, crimped axles, metal wheels, 75 mm.	£35-45	☐
			Red cab, Light Brown Trailer, Grey plastic wheels	£50-60	☐
10c	1960	Foden 8-wheel Truck Sugar Container	Dark Blue body, Grey wheels, with crown on rear decal	£65-75	☐
			without crown at rear, Grey wheels	£30-40	☐
			as previous, but with Silver wheels	£70-80	☐
			as previous, but with Black wheels	£35-45	☐
10d	1966	Leyland Pipe Truck	Red body, 6 or 7 Grey pipes, Silver base & grille	£10-15	☐
			as previous, but with White base & grille	£40-50	☐
		Superfast wheels	Red body, Grey pipes	£25-35	☐
			Orange body, Grey or Yellow pipes, chrome base & grille	£8-120	☐
			Orange body, Yellow pipes, Grey base & grille	£35-45	☐
10e	1973	'Piston Popper'	Metallic Blue, Silver exposed engine, Rolamatic, Superfast, 75 mm.	£5-8	☐
		colour change:	White body (German 5 Pack Release)	£50-60	☐
		'Hot Popper'	US issued model. No details available	£7-10	☐
10f	1979	Plymouth Gran Fury	White body, Black 'POLICE' logo, 2 warning lights, Superfast, 75 mm.	£2-4	☐
	1981	logo change:	White body, Black 'METRO POLICE' logo, Superfast	£1-3	☐
	1983	colour change:	White body, Blue Police shield, Superfast	£1-3	☐
	1985	new logo:	White body, 'SFPD' logo, Superfast, (US issue)	£1-3	☐
	1987	new logo:	White body, Red logo, 'SHERIFF', Superfast, (US issue)	£1-3	☐
10g	1988	Buick Le Sabre	Black body, racing number '4', '355 CID'.	£1-2	☐
	1989	colour change:	Yellow body, Red skirt, racing number '10', Superfast wheels	£1-3	☐
	1989	Laser Wheels issue:	Metallic Red body, 'KEN WELLS' logo	£1-3	☐
10h	1993	Chevy Van	Yellow body, Blue and Red design	£1-3	☐

MB 11

Ref. No.	Year(s)	Model Type	Description	Price	
11a	1955	E.R.F. Road Tanker	All models with metal wheels		
			Green body, Gold trim	£450-500	☐
			Dark Yellow body, Silver trim	£90-120	☐
			Light Yellow body, Silver trim	£65-80	☐
			Red body, Gold trim, small 'ESSO' decal on rear of tank	£80-90	☐
			Red body, Gold trim, large 'ESSO' decal on rear of tank	£45-60	☐
			Red body, Gold trim, small 'ESSO' decals on tank sides	£220-250	☐
			Red body, Gold trim, large 'ESSO' decal in tank sides	£150-180	☐
11b	1958	'ESSO' Petrol Tanker (E.R.F.)	All models with red body and 'ESSO' decal at rear		
			Metal wheels, Gold trim	£150-180	☐
			Metal wheels, Silver trim	£30-40	☐
			Grey plastic wheels	£25-35	☐
			Silver plastic wheels	£400-500	☐
			Black plastic wheels	£45-55	☐
11c	1965	Jumbo Crane	Yellow body, and weight box	£12-15	☐
			Yellow body, Red weight box	£8-12	☐
11d	1969	Mercedes Scaffolding Truck	Silver body, Yellow plastic scaffolds	£8-12	☐
		Superfast wheels	as previous	£7-10	☐
11e	1973	'Flying Bug'	Red/Yellow body, Silver helmet, Superfast, 73 mm.	£3-5	☐
11f	1977	Car Transporter	Orange/Cream body, 3 cars, Superfast, 75 mm.	£3-5	☐
	1980	colour change:	Red/Cream body	£2-4	☐
	1983	colour change:	Orange/Grey body, Silver grille	£2-4	☐
11g		Cobra Mustang	Orange body, US issued model	£4-6	☐
11h		IMSA Mustang	Green/White US issued model	£4-6	☐

216

Ref. No.	Year(s)	Model Type	*Matchbox Miniatures – continued*	Market Price Range	
11i		Ferrari 308 GTB......................	Yellow body, US issued model	£4-6	☐
11j	1985	Lamborghini Countach	Red body, Yellow seats	£1-3	☐
	1986	colour change:	Black/Orange body, Red racing number '5'	£1-3	☐
	1988	colour change:	Yellow body, *'COUNTACH'* in Black	£1-2	☐
	1987	Laser Wheels issue:.....	Silver body, *'LP 5005'* logo	£1-2	☐

MB 12

Ref. No.	Year(s)	Model Type		Market Price Range	
12a	1955	Land Rover	Green body, Silver trim on some, Tan driver, metal wheels, 43 mm......	£25-35	☐
12b	1959	Land Rover Series II	Green body, Black plastic wheels, crimped axles	£35-45	☐
			Black plastic wheels, rounded axles	£25-35	☐
			Grey plastic wheels	£200-250	☐
12c	1965	Land Rover Safari....................	Green body, Brown luggage, Black plastic wheels	£12-15	☐
			Blue body, Brown or Red-Brown luggage, Black plastic wheels	£10-14	☐
			Metallic Gold body, Red-Brown luggage, Black plastic wheels	£330-380	☐
		Superfast wheels	Blue body	£500-600	☐
			Metallic Gold body	£10-15	☐
12d	1971	Setra Coach	Gold body with Grey roof, Red lights, clear windows, Superfast, 76 mm.	£9-12	☐
		colour change:..........	Gold body, White roof, Superfast	£8-11	☐
		colour change:..........	Gold body, Light Brown roof, Superfast	£8-11	☐
	1972	colour change:..........	Yellow body, White roof, Superfast	£8-11	☐
	1973	colour change:..........	Maroon body, White roof, Green tinted or clear windows, Superfast	£5-8	☐
	1973	colour change:..........	Green body, White roof	£5-8	☐
12e	1975	'Big Bull'...............................	Orange body, Green dashboard, Red Superfast wheels, 63 mm.	£3-5	☐
		wheel change:.............	As previous model but with Black wheels	£30-40	☐
		wheel change:.............	Same but with Orange wheels, shiny metal dashboard, Black wheels	£3-5	☐
12f	1979	Citroën CX	Metallic Blue body, Yellow interior, hook, Superfast, 77 mm.	£2-4	☐
	1980	interior change:.........	With Red interior	£50-60	☐
	1980	colour change:..........	Metallic Light Blue, Superfast	£1-3	☐
	1982	'TEAM MATCHBOX'	Yellow body, Black or Blue logo, Superfast	£2-4	☐
	1983	'AMBULANCE'	White body, Black/White cross, Superfast	£1-3	☐
12g	1986	Pontiac Firebird Racer.............	Yellow body, Blue chassis, racing number '55' or '56' (US issue model)......	£4-6	☐
	1987	colour change:..........	Blue body, racing number '10', (US issue model)	£1-3	☐
	1987	colour change:..........	White body, Blue chassis, racing number '15', Superfast	£1-3	☐
	1987	Laser Wheels issue:....	Metallic Blue, racing number '10'.......................................	£1-3	☐
12h	1986	Chevy Prostocker	White body (US issued model)	£4-6	☐

Late 1950's Advert in the Gamages Catalogue aimed at model railway enthusiasts.

Ref. No.	Year(s)	Model Type	*Matchbox Miniatures – continued*	Market Price Range
12i	1988	Modified Racer............	Orange body, Red racing number '12'	**£1-3** ☐
	1990	design change:............	White body, *'TOMY'* or *'JAMIE'* logo, racing number '1'	**£1-3** ☐
		design change:............	Red body, *'MIKE'* logo, racing number '15'	**£1-3** ☐
		design change:............	Yellow body, *'REGGIE'*, racing number '44'	**£1-3** ☐
	1991	colour change:............	Orange body, *'GOODYEAR'*, racing number '12'	**£1-3** ☐
12j	1992	Cattle Truck............	Green cab, Yellow stake rear body, 2 Black plastic cows	**£1-3** ☐
	1994	Dodge Viper............		**£1-2** ☐

MB 13

13a	1955	Wreck Truck (Bedford)............	Tan body, Red crane and hook, metal wheels on crimped axles, 51 mm.	**£30-40** ☐
13b	1958	Wreck Truck (Bedford)............	Tan, Red crane and hook, '13' cast-in, metal or Grey plastic wheels, 53 mm.	**£35-45** ☐
			As previous but with Grey plastic wheels	**£60-70** ☐
13c	1960	Thames Trader Wreck Truck....	All models with Red body & crane, Yellow side decals	
			Knobbly Grey wheels (24 treads), Red hook	**£40-50** ☐
			Fine Grey wheels (45 treads), Grey hook	**£65-80** ☐
			Black wheels, Silver or Grey hook	**£30-40** ☐
13d	1965	Dodge Wreck Truck............	Green cab, Yellow body, Grey hook, 'BP' decal	**£1000-1200** ☐
			Fakes from 1970 are with red hooks, 'BP' labels, crimped axles and the thick crane casting. Only the original Green cab version has a thin crane. But these fakes (only 24 are produced) are now sought after from many collectors and are also very valuable (300-400)!	
			Yellow cab, Green body, Grey hook	**£15-20** ☐
			As previous but with Red hook	**£10-14** ☐
		Superfast wheels........	Yellow cab, Green body, Red hook	**£8-12** ☐
13e	1972	Baja Buggy............	Green body with Black/Red trim, Silver engine, Superfast wheels, 66 mm.	**£7-9** ☐
		design change:............	As previous but with 'Police' shield label	**£10-12** ☐
13f	1978	Snorkel Fire Engine............	Red body, Yellow or White hoist, Superfast, 78 mm.	**£3-5** ☐
	1982	new version:............	Merryweather (35) casting with altered cab	**£1-2** ☐
	1982	'METRO FIRE DEPT'	Red body, White hoist, Superfast	**£1-2** ☐
	1982	'LOS ANGELES FIRE'........	Red body, White hoist, Superfast	**£1-2** ☐
	1986	'FIRE DEPT'........	Red body, White hoist, Superfast	**£1-2** ☐
13h	1985	Volvo Container............	Blue body, White container *'COLDFRESH'*	**£2-3** ☐
	1994	'Rhino'............		**£1-2** ☐

MB 14

14a	1955	Ambulance (Daimler)............	Cream body, Silver trim, Red cross on roof, metal wheels on crimped or domed/crimped axles, no number, 'Ambulance' cast onto sides, 49 mm.	**£30-35** ☐
14b	1958	Daimler Ambulance (59 mm.)....	All models with 'Red Cross' on roof	
			Cream body, metal wheels	**£35-45** ☐
			Cream body, Grey plastic wheels	**£50-60** ☐
			Off-White body, metal wheels	**£50-60** ☐
			Off-White body, Grey plastic wheels	**£35-45** ☐
			Off-White body, Silver plastic wheels	**£100-130** ☐
14c	1962	Bedford Lomas Ambulance.......	All models with 'Red Cross' & 'LCC Ambulance' on sides	
			White body, Black wheels	**£70-80** ☐
			White body, Silver wheels	**£90-100** ☐
			Off-White body, Silver wheels	**£50-60** ☐
			Off-White body, Grey wheels	**£150-180** ☐
			Off-White body, Black wheels	**£15-20** ☐
14d	1968	Iso Grifo............	Metallic Blue body, Blue interior	**£20-25** ☐
			Dark Metallic Blue body, Blue interior	**£8-12** ☐
		Superfast wheels........	Dark Blue body, Dark Blue interior	**£18-22** ☐
			Dark Blue body, Light Blue interior	**£12-18** ☐
			Dark Blue body, White interior	**£8-12** ☐
			Light or Mid-Blue body, White interior	**£5-10** ☐
			Powder Blue body	**£8-12** ☐
14e	1977	'Mini-Ha-Ha'............	Red body, Blue seats, Silver trim, driver, 60 mm.	**£3-5** ☐
14f		Rallye Royale............	Silver or White body (US issue model)	**£4-6** ☐
14g	1982	Leyland Petrol Tanker............	Red/White body, Blue or Turquoise *'ELF'* logo, Superfast, 77 mm.	**£3-5** ☐
	1989	colour change:........	Same but military version in camouflage paintwork	**£1-3** ☐
14h	1985	Jeep Laredo............	Black body, White roof (US issue model 20)	**£4-6** ☐
	1986	colour change:........	Red body, White roof, Grey seats & bonnet	**£1-2** ☐
14i	1986	BMW Cabriolet............	White body (US issue model)	**£4-6** ☐
14j	1988	Grand Prix Racing Car............	Blue/White body, Red driver	**£1-2** ☐
	1990	colour change:........	Red Ferrari, *'FIAT'*, White driver, no racing number	**£1-3** ☐
		colour change:............	Red Ferrari, racing number '27', no logo	**£1-3** ☐

MB 15

15a	1955	Diamond T Prime Mover.........	Yellow body, 6 metal wheels, hook, no number, 55 mm.	**£900-1100** ☐
		colour change:........	Orange body, 6 metal wheels	**£25-30** ☐
			As previous model but with ten Grey plastic wheels	**£150-200** ☐
15b	1959	Super Atlantic Tractor............	Orange body, Black base, hook, Black plastic wheels, 67 mm.	**£15-20** ☐
			Orange body, Grey plastic wheels	**£150-180** ☐
15c	1963	Tippax Refuse Collector............	All models with Blue body, Grey container and Black wheels	
			Knobbly wheels (24 treads), decal	**£60-70** ☐
			Fine wheels, *'Cleansing Service'* decal or label	**£12-16** ☐
15d	1968	Volkswagen 1300 Saloon............	Off-White or Cream body, '137' decals on doors	**£20-25** ☐
			As previous, but with '137' labels on doors	**£15-20** ☐
	1969	wheel change:............	As previous model but with Superfast wheels	**£10-15** ☐
	1970	colour change:............	Red body, Superfast	**£10-15** ☐

Ref. No.	Year(s)	Model Type	*Matchbox Miniatures – continued*	Market Price Range	
15e	1973	'LANSING BAGNALL' Fork Lift Truck	Red body, Yellow forks, horse design faces front...	**£2-4**	□
		label design change:	With horse design facing rear	**£1-3**	□
		colour change:..........	Red body, Black/Grey forks..	**£2-4**	□
		colour change:..........	Red body with White forks, *'Hi-Lift'*	**£1-3**	□
15f	1985	Peugeot 205 Turbo 16	White body with racing number '205'	**£1-2**	□
	1986	design change:..........	Blue/Red print, *'SHELL'* advert on lifting rear section	**£1-2**	□
15g	1988	UK (69) Corvette	Yellow body	**£1-2**	□
	1990	colour change:..........	Metallic Blue, White band on roof/bonnet, RN '15' on doors/boot/bonnet	**£1-2**	□
	1992	design change:..........	As previous model but with *'CORVETTE'* on doors, (no racing number).........	**£1-2**	□
	1993	colour change:..........	White body with central Red stripe	**£1-2**	□

MB 16

16a	1955	Transporter Trailer..................	Tan body, 6 metal wheels (crimped or domed & crimped axles), 80 mm.........	**£24-28**	□
16b	1960	Super Atlantic Trailer..............	Tan body, Grey plastic wheels..	**£60-75**	□
			Orange body; Grey plastic wheels	**£300-400**	□
			Orange body, Black plastic wheels, Black drawbar.......................................	**£25-30**	□
			as previous, but with Orange drawbar	**£30-40**	□
16c	1963	Scammell Snow Plough	Grey body, Orange tipper, Red/White or Orange/White decal		
			Grey plastic wheels	**£60-70**	□
			Black plastic wheels	**£75-100**	□
16d	1969	Case Bulldozer Tractor	Red/Yellow body, Green rubber tracks, hook, 64 mm.	**£7-9**	□
16e	1974	Badger Truck...........................	Red body; White, Cream or Silver Radar, 6 Black plastic wheels, Rolamatic......	**£5-8**	□
		colour change:..........	As previous model but Metallic Red body...	**£5-8**	□
		colour change:..........	As previous model but Military Green issue...	**£15-18**	□
16f	1980	Pontiac Saloon........................	Metallic Gold body with 'eagle' design, Superfast wheels, 77 mm.	**£2-4**	□
	1982		Metallic Bronze or White body, 'eagle' design...	**£2-4**	□
	1983	open top 'T' issue:	Black body, *'Turbo'* logo, Superfast	**£2-4**	□
	1985	colour change:..........	Silver body, Red/Orange design, Superfast	**£1-3**	□
	1986	colour change:..........	Black body, Orange striped design, Superfast	**£1-3**	□
16g	1988	Land Rover Ninety	Blue body, White roof, Orange flash...	**£1-3**	□
	1989	colour change:..........	Red/white body, Yellow bonnet emblem..	**£1-3**	□
	1989	colour change:..........	Camouflage paintwork..	**£1-3**	□
	1990	colour change:..........	Yellow body, White roof, Green *'PARK RANGERS'* logo	**£1-3**	□
	1992	colour change:..........	Yellow body, Grey roof, Black *'PARK RANGERS'* logo	**£1-3**	□

MB 17

17a	1955	Bedford Removals Van	All models with *'MATCHBOX REMOVALS SERVICE'* decals and metal wheels		
			Light Blue body, Silver trim	**£120-160**	□
			Maroon body, Silver trim	**£200-230**	□
			Maroon body, Gold trim	**£140-180**	□
			Green body, Silver trim	**£40-50**	□
17b	1958	Bedford Removals Van	Green body, metal wheels, decal with or without Black outline......................	**£35-45**	□
			Green body, Grey plastic wheels, decal with outline	**£55-70**	□
			Dark Green body, Grey plastic wheels, decal with outline	**£100-120**	□
17c	1960	Austin FX3 Taxi	Maroon body, Mid-Grey interior, Tan driver, Grey plastic wheels, 60 mm.	**£45-55**	□
		wheel change:.............	As previous model but with Silver plastic wheels, Mid-Grey interior	**£75-90**	□
		US issue:	With Pale Grey interior & Silver plastic wheels	**NGPP**	□
17d	1964	Foden Tipper...........................	Red chassis, Orange tipper, *'HOVERINGHAM'*, Black base..........................	**£14-18**	□
			as previous, but with Red base...	**£10-14**	□
17e	1969	AEC Horse Box........................	Red body, Dark Green box, Grey door, Silver base & grille	**£9-12**	□
17f	1972	**LONDONER BUS (1st type)....**	**DAIMLER FLEETLINE Double Decker.** Unless otherwise shown each has a Red body, White interior, painted metal base or plastic base, one set double opening doors, 2 open rear windows, 5-spoked Superfast wheels, 78 mm.		
	1972	'SWINGING LONDON'	Red body with multi-coloured label *'CARNABY ST'*	**£10-15**	□
			Silver or Gold plated versions	**£30-40**	□
		'THE BARON OF BEEF'	Red body, White logo...	**£75-85**	□
		'PRESTON M.G.'	Red body, Green label, *'MERCHANT GUILD'*...	**£60-70**	□
		'BUSCH GARDENS'	Red/White body, *'BRITISH AIRWAYS'*...	**£60-70**	□
		'SELLOTAPE'....................	Red body, 2 different labels	**£60-70**	□
		'SELLOTAPE	Red body, *'SELBESTKLEBEBANDER'*, German issue	**£60-70**	□
		'TYPHOO'.........................	White and Black decals, metal baseplate, 'VJ' emblem.................................	**£60-70**	□
		'CHAMBOURCEY'.............	Multicoloured decal with countryside scene	**£60-70**	□
		'IMPEL 73'	Red/White body, Red/Black logo	**£10-15**	□
		'IMPEL 76'	Off-White body, Brown upper deck, White label..	**£10-15**	□
		'ESSO EXTRA'	Red, White and Blue decals, metal baseplate	**£25-30**	□
		'AIM BUILDING'	Black and White decal. Metal baseplate..	**£30-35**	□
		'JACOBS BISCUITS'	Orange or Red body, Black/White decals	**£10-15**	□
		'SILVER JUBILEE'	Silver or Red body	**£10-15**	□
		'MATCHBOX 1953-78'........	Red, Blue or Brown body, Red/Yellow/Orange/Black decals, metal base	**£5-10**	□
		'KENSINGTON HILTON' ..	Red body, Black logo on White label..	**£25-35**	□
		colour variation:	Silver body, Black logo on White label...	**NGPP**	□
		'LONDON HILTON'	Red body, Black logo on White label..	**£50-60**	□
		'BISTO'	Red body, *'BISTO KIDS'* on Yellow labels..	**£10-15**	□
		'AVIEMORE CENTRE'.......	Red body, Blue logo/emblem..	**£65-75**	□
		'SELFRIDGES'	Red body, White label, Black logo..	**£10-15**	□

		'BARCLAYS BANK'	Red body, Blue/White label..	**£40-50** ☐
		'ILFORD HPS'	Red body, Black/White label	**£50-60** ☐
		'AMCEL'	Red body, White label, Orange logo	**£40-50** ☐
		'LONDON MUSEUM'........	Red body, Black/White label with *'new'* logo	**£30-35** ☐
		'ARAL'	Blue body, White/Blue label *'DEUTSCHLANDS AUTO PARTNER'*...	**£35-45** ☐

LONDONER BUS (1st type) – continued

		'BERGER PAINTS'.............	Red body, Purple/Orange/Gold lower body	**£5-8** ☐
			Silver body	**£20-25** ☐
			Gold body	**£20-25** ☐
			Coffee/Cream body	**£15-20** ☐
			Red/Yellow body (this version made in Brazil)................	**£30-35** ☐
			Red/White body (this version made in Brazil	**£30-35** ☐
			Blue/White body (this version made in Brazil).................	**£30-35** ☐
		note:...........................	'Paint brushes' may be either end of label.	
		'KEDDIES' 'No. 1 in ESSEX'	Blue body, White interior, White paper (round end) labels, sold in Blue box (900).....	**£35-40** ☐
		note:...........................	Beware fakes with square cut label ends, sold in white boxes.	
	1982	**LONDONER BUS (2nd type)...**	**(new casting), LEYLAND 'TITAN' Double Decker.** The model is Red with 2 sets double opening doors and 3 open rear windows unless differently described.	
		'LAKER SKY TRAIN'	Red, White and Blue label	**£5-8** ☐
		'CHESTERFIELD'	Green body, Green and White label	**£5-8** ☐
		'YORK FESTIVAL'	Red body, Purple lower body, 'MYSTERY PLAYS'	**£4-7** ☐
		'RAPPORT'	Maroon body, Yellow lower body, 'SALES FROM WALES'	**£4-7** ☐
		'JAPAN 84'	Red body, *'NICE TO MEET YOU'*, Japanese issue model	**£15-20** ☐
		'NESTLES'	Red body, *'MILKY BAR'* label	**£4-7** ☐
		colour change:........	As previous model but with Blue body	**£10-15** ☐
		'ROWNTREES'	Red body, *'FRUIT GUMS'* label	**£4-7** ☐
		colour change:........	As previous model but with Cream body	**£10-15** ☐
		'KEDDIES'	Blue body, White label, Red logo *'No. 1 in ESSEX'*	**£35-40** ☐
		'MB' London Bus	Red body, Red/Yellow/White/Blue label.	**£4-7** ☐
		'YOU'LL LOVE NEW YORK'	Red body, White label, 'USA' and 'TWA'	**£4-7** ☐
		colour change:........	Blue/White body, White label	**£10-15** ☐
		'MATCHBOX No. 1'...........	As previous model but with Red body	**£10-15** ☐
		'YOKOHAMA FAIR'	Red body, Yellow label, Japanese issue model	**£15-18** ☐
		'STAFFS POLICE'	White/Blue body, *'CHARITY APPEAL'* logo	**£15-18** ☐
		'CITYRAMA'	All Blue body, multicoloured labels depicting flags	**£5-7** ☐
		'MIDLAND MUSEUM'	Brown/White body, *'Bus & Transport - Wythall'*	**£5-7** ☐
		'TRAMWAY MUSEUM'....	All Blue body, Red logo, *'THE NATIONAL CRICH'*	**£5-7** ☐
		'BAND AID'	Red body, White label *'Playbus'*.	**£5-7** ☐
		'W. H. SMITH & SONS......	Orange/White body	**£10-14** ☐
		'WEST MIDLANDS TRAVEL'.........................	Blue/Cream body, White label, Blue logo	**£5-8** ☐
		'AROUND LONDON'........	Red body, *'TOUR BUS'* label	**£3-5** ☐
		'MICA' Commemorative......	All White body, Red/White/Blue/Yellow label, (Promotional in special box), Logo reads *'M.I.C.A. 1st Convention'* (250 only)........................	**NGPP** ☐
		'DENNY'............................	White body, Red/Blue labels, Blue tampo print...............	**£3-5** ☐
	1993	'MARKFIELD PROJECT' ..	Code 1 model	**£1-3** ☐
	1989	'TOUR BUS'	Red body, Red/White/Blue design	**£1-3** ☐
	1989	'COKE'	Yellow body, *'ITS THE REAL THING'*	**£1-3** ☐
	1990	'CORNING GLASS'............	US issue	**£1-3** ☐
	1992	'TOUR BUS'	Red bus, *'London Guide Tour Bus'* on Black/Yellow background	**£1-3** ☐

MB 18

18a	1955	Caterpillar Bulldozer (46 mm.)..	Yellow body, Red blade, Green tracks	**£30-35** ☐
18b	1958	Caterpillar Bulldozer (50 mm.)..	Yellow body & blade, Green tracks	**£50-60** ☐
			as previous, but with Grey tracks	**£80-100** ☐
18c	1961	Caterpillar Bulldozer (58 mm.)..	Yellow body & blade, Green tracks; metal rollers	**£15-20** ☐
			same but with Silver plastic rollers	**£70-80** ☐
			same but with Black plastic rollers	**£18-22** ☐
18d	1964	Caterpillar Bulldozer (62 mm.)..	Yellow body & blade, no driver cast, Green tracks	
			Silver plastic rollers	**£70-80** ☐
			Black plastic rollers	**£10-15** ☐
18e	1969	Field Car..............................	Yellow body, Red-Brown roof, Red wheels	**£10-15** ☐
			as previous but unpainted base, Red wheels	**£7-10** ☐
			as previous but with Green wheels	**£220-250** ☐
	1970	wheel change:	As previous model but with Superfast wheels	**£5-8** ☐
		colour change:............	Military Green issue, with or without star	**£12-15** ☐
			White body, Checker label, Silver or Black hubs, Superfast wheels............	**£30-40** ☐
		note:...........................	Several variations were issued in the 'Twin-Pack' series	
18f	1975	'Hondarora'	Red body, Black seat, Silver trim, *'Honda'*, spoked wheels, 63 mm.	**£5-8** ☐
		colour change:............	As previous model but with White seat.	**£45-55** ☐
		colour change:............	Same but Black front forks, seat and handlebars	**NGPP** ☐
		colour change:............	Yellow body, Silver engine, Black seat, forks & handlebars	**NGPP** ☐
		colour change:............	Dark Military Green	**£14-18** ☐
		colour change:............	Orange body, *'Honda'*	**£12-16** ☐
		colour change:............	Metallic Green, Black handlebars, *'Honda'*	**£4-6** ☐
18g	1984	Fire Engine	Red body, White ladder, flashing light bar on roof	**£4-6** ☐
	1987	design change:............	*'FIRE DEPT'* livery	**£4-6** ☐

MB 19

Ref. No.	Year(s)	Model Type	Description	Market Price Range	
19a	1956	MG Midget TD......	Cream body, Brown driver, Red seats, metal wheels, no number, 51 mm.	£65-75	☐
		colour change:...........	Off-White body, metal wheels............	£80-110	☐
19b	1958	MG 'MGA' Sports Car...........	All models with Off-White body, Red seats and Brown driver		
			Metal wheels, Gold trim.....	£150-200	☐
			Metal wheels, Silver trim	£55-75	☐
			Grey plastic wheels, Silver trim	£60-75	☐
			Silver plastic wheels.....	£90-110	☐
19c	1962	Aston Martin DBR5	All models body, Yellow wheels, White driver,		
			Number 19	£20-30	☐
			Number 41 or 52.....	£70-80	☐
			Number 3 or 5.....	£55-70	☐
19d	1965	Lotus Racing Car	Dark Green body, Yellow wheels, White driver,		
			Racing number 3 as decal or label	£9-12	☐
			Orange body, RN3.....	£30-40	☐
		Superfast wheels	Purple body, RN3.....	£12-18	☐
19e	1971	Road Dragster..........	Red body, Silver exposed engine, clear windows, Superfast, 76 mm.	£5-8	☐
		design change:...........	With 'Scorpion' labels.....	£30-35	☐
		design change:...........	Pink with 'WYNNS' labels.....	£30-35	☐
19f	1976	Cement Truck............	Red body, Orange barrel, Red or Black stripes, Superfast, 75 mm.	£3-5	☐
	1978	barrel change:	Red body, Grey barrel, Red stripes, Superfast.....	£3-5	☐
	1981	barrel change:	Red body, Yellow barrel, Red stripes, Superfast	£6-9	☐
19g	1982	Peterbilt Cement Truck	Metallic Green/Orange/Blue, 'BIG PETE', Green door design	£1-3	☐
	1984	colour change:...........	As previous model but with Yellow door design.....	£1-3	☐
	1985	'CEMENT COMPANY'.........	Blue body, Yellow mixer drum.....	£1-3	☐
	1988	colour change:............	Yellow body, Silver mixer drum	NRP	☐
	1990	'READYMIX'...........	Pink/grey body. Australian issue.	£4-6	☐
	1991	design change:...........	Blue cab, Red circular designs on roof/doors, Yellow/Black drum, various logos	£2-3	☐
	1992	colour change:............	Yellow cab, Red design, Red drum & logos on doors/bonnet	£2-3	☐

MB 20

Ref. No.	Year(s)	Model Type	Description	Market Price Range	
20a	1956	E.R.F. Stake Truck	Light Green body, Silver trim, metal wheels.....	£1500-1700	☐
			Maroon body, Gold trim, metal wheels	£120-150	☐
			Maroon body, Silver trim, metal wheels	£25-35	☐
			Maroon body, Silver trim, Grey plastic wheels.....	£200-220	☐
			Dark Red body, metal wheels.....	£40-50	☐
			Dark Red body, Grey plastic wheels.....	£220-250	☐
20b	1959	E.R.F. 68G Truck	All models with Dark Blue body and 'EVER READY' decals on sides		
			Early decals are with Orange outline, later with red outline.		
			Grey plastic wheels, crimped axles.....	£65-75	☐
			Grey plastic wheels, rounded axles.....	£45-65	☐
			Silver plastic wheels.....	£100-150	☐
			Black plastic wheels.....	£55-75	☐
20c	1965	Chevrolet Impala Taxi	Orange-Yellow body, Cream interior, Grey wheels, Taxi decal.....	£250-300	☐
			Orange-Yellow body, Cream interior, Black wheels, Silver base, Taxi decal	£30-40	☐
			as previous, but with unpainted base	£10-12	☐
			as previous, but with red interior	£12-18	☐
			Yellow body, Cream interior, Taxi label.....	£80-100	☐
			Yellow body, Red interior, Taxi label.....	£18-22	☐
20d	1969	Lamborghini Marzal	Metallic Dark Red, White seats, Silver trim, Superfast, 70 mm.	£8-11	☐
		colour change:...........	Pink body.....	£8-11	☐
		colour change:...........	Yellow body.....	£14-18	☐
	1971	colour change:...........	Orange body.....	£5-8	☐
20e	1975	Police Range Rover...........	White body, Orange flash, 'Police', flashing light, 82 mm.	£3-5	☐
	1981	colour change:...........	White body, Red/Yellow/Black flash.....	£2-4	☐
	1983	colour change:...........	Gold body, 'Securit Rallye Paris Dakar 83'.....	£6-8	☐
	1984		As previous model but no design on bonnet, unpainted chassis	£4-6	☐
		colour change:...........	Military Green body, 'AMBULANCE' and Red crosses	£20-25	☐
		colour change:...........	Military Green body, 'POLICE'.....	£20-25	☐
		colour change:...........	White body with 'SHERIFF', US issue model	£4-6	☐
		colour change:...........	Orange body, 'SITE ENGINEER'.....	£10-12	☐
		note:...........	There are many other variations		
20f		'Desert Dawg'...........	White body, Red roof, 'JEEP' logo	£4-6	☐
20g		**Volvo Container Truck**			
	1985	'COLD FRESH'...........	Blue body, White box.....	£1-3	☐
	1986	'FEDERAL EXPRESS'...........	White cab and container, (US issue model).....	£3-5	☐
	1987	MATCHBOX 'MB 75'............	Blue body, Red/Yellow design, 'No. 1 Selling Toy 86-5-4-3'.....	£30-35	☐
	1987	'SCOTCH CORNER'...........	White cab and container.....	£1-3	☐
	1987	'CROOKES HEALTHCARE'..	Dark Blue body, Red/White design.....	£1-3	☐
	1987	'SUPERSAVE DRUGSTORES'...........	Grey cab and container.....	£1-3	☐
	1988	'ALLDERS'...........	Dark Blue body, Gold tampo, promotional.....	£1-3	☐
	1989	'COMMA OIL COMPANY'....	Dark Blue body, promotional.....	£1-3	☐
	1990	'YORKIE'...........	White body, Blue panel, Yellow logo.....	£1-3	☐
		'BIG TOP CIRCUS'...........	Red/White body, Yellow/Red design.....	£1-3	☐
		'KIT KAT'...........	White body, Red/White design.....	£1-3	☐
20h	1988	VW Transporter...........	White body, Orange stripe and cross.....	£1-3	☐
	1989	colour change:...........	Camouflage paintwork.....	£1-3	☐
	1989	'AMBULANCE'...........	White body, Red stripe & cross, Blue dome light on roof.....	£1-3	☐

MB 21

21a	1956	Bedford Coach (57 mm.)	Green body & base, Red/Yellow *'LONDON-GLASGOW'*, metal wheels	£35-45	☐
21b	1958	Bedford Coach (68 mm.)	All models with Black base and *'LONDON TO GLASGOW'* decals		
			Green body, metal wheels	£45-55	☐
			Green body, Grey plastic wheels	£55-70	☐
			Dark Green body, Grey plastic wheels	£80-100	☐
21c	1961	Commer Bottle Float	All models with Pale Green body and Black base. On early models the bottle are Cream, later are White		
			Bottle on door, Silver wheels, clear windows	£90-120	☐
			Bottle on door, Silver wheels, Green windows	£50-60	☐
			Cow on door, Silver wheels	£40-50	☐
			Cow on door, Grey wheels	£80-100	☐
			Cow on door, Black wheels	£18-25	☐
21d	1968	Foden Concrete Truck	Yellow body, Red chassis, Black wheels	£8-12	☐
		Superfast wheels	Yellow body, Red chassis, Superfast wheels	£10-15	☐
21e	1973	Road Roller	Yellow body, Green or Black base, Black plastic roller wheels, 70 mm.	£5-7	☐
21f	1978	Renault 5TL	Blue body, Silver trim, Tan seats, Superfast wheels, 65 mm.	£5-7	☐
		colour change:	With Red interior and Silver or Black base	£12-16	☐
	1980	colour change:	Yellow body, *'Le Car'* decals, opening tailgate	£2-4	☐
	1981	colour change:	Silver body with Orange flash, *'Le Car'*, opening tailgate....	£2-4	☐
	1982	colour change:	White body with Green labels, *'MICHELIN'* decals, etc	£2-4	☐
	1983	colour change:	White body, *'RADIO MONTE CARLO'* design	£2-4	☐
	1984	colour change:	Black body, Red/Yellow design *'ROLOIL'*.	£1-3	☐
21g	1986	Chevy Breakdown Van.............	Red body, White hoist *'24hr SERVICE'*	£1-3	☐
	1989	colour change:	Yellow body, Black hoist, *'24 HOURS'* logo........................	NRP	☐
21h		Corvette Pace Car	US issued model	£3-5	☐
21i	1991	Nissan Prairie	Two-tone Blue and Grey body	NRP	☐
	1992	colour change:	Metallic Silver body with *'NISSAN'* logos on sides.............	NRP	☐

MB 22

22a	1956	Vauxhall Cresta	Body colours from Dark Red to Maroon, roof from White to Cream	£35-40	☐
22b	1958	Vauxhall Cresta	Pale Pink or Cream body, without windows, metal wheels	£350-400	☐
			as previous, but with Grey plastic wheels............................	£65-85	☐
			as previous, but with windows..	£100-130	☐
			Pale Pink body, Blue-Green side panels...............................	£900-1000	☐
			Light Metallic Brown body, Blue-Green side panels............	£100-130	☐
			Light Grey body, Lilac side panels, Grey or Silver plastic wheels...	£80-110	☐
			Light Gold body, Grey or Silver wheels	£90-120	☐
			Dark Gold body, Silver wheels..	£70-90	☐
			Metallic Copper body, Grey, Silver or Black wheels	£55-80	☐
22c	1965	Pontiac GP Sports Coup..........	Red body, Grey interior, Black plastic wheels, 76 mm.	£10-15	☐
	1970	wheel change:	Red body, Superfast wheels	£500-600	☐
		colour change:	Metallic Purple body, Superfast wheels	£12-18	☐
22d	1971	Freeman Inter City...................	Maroon or Purple body, White seats, *'Arrow'* motif, Superfast, 76 mm. ...	£5-8	☐
		colour change:	As previous model but Metallic Gold body, Off-White interior, *'arrow'* motif ...	£4-6	☐
22e	1976	'Blaze Buster'	Red body, *'Fire'*, Yellow ladder, Silver or White seats, 77 mm.	£3-5	☐
		ladder change:	With Black ladder	£7-9	☐
			With White ladder	£30-40	☐
22f		'BIG FOOT'	Grey body, White roof, '26', US issued model	£4-6	☐
22g	1984	Jaguar XK120..........................	Green body, Red seats, windscreen	£3-5	☐
	1986	colour change:	White body, racing number '414', Red seats........................	£1-3	☐
	1993	colour change:	Cream body, Red seats	£1-3	☐
22h	1988	Saab 9000 Turbo	Red body, opening doors	NRP	☐
	1990	colour change:	White body, Red/Yellow design, *'SAAB'* and *'No.22'* logos......	NRP	☐
	1995	Mitsubishi Spyder......................	....	£1-2	☐

MB 23

23a	1956	Berkeley Cavalier Caravan........	Pale Blue, *'On Tow MBS 23'*, metal wheels, slight body outlines, 65 mm.	£30-40	☐
23b	1957	Berkeley Cavalier Caravan........	All models with *'ON TOW'* rear decal		
			Pale Blue, metal wheels	£25-35	☐
			Lime-Green, metal wheels...	£75-90	☐
			Lime-Green, Grey plastic wheels	£55-70	☐
			Metallic Lime-Green, Grey plastic wheels............................	£600-800	☐
23c	1960	Bluebird Dauphine Caravan	All models without windows and with *'ON TOW'* rear decal		
			Metallic Lime-Green body, Grey plastic wheels...................	£300-400	☐
			Metallic Mauve, Grey plastic wheels	£25-35	☐
			as previous, but with Silver wheels	£30-40	☐
			as previous, but with Black wheels	£200-300	☐
23d	1965	Trailer Caravan	Yellow body	£10-15	☐
			Pink body	£7-11	☐
23e	1970	Volkswagen Camper.................	Blue body, with gas tank on left side	£50-60	☐
			Blue body, without gas tan, with or without 'Yacht' labels	£8-12	☐
			Orange body, Orange interior	£45-55	☐
			Orange body, White interior	£8-12	☐
	1973	colour change:	Orange body with 'yacht' labels, Superfast	£5-8	☐
	1980	US issue:	White body, *'PIZZA VAN'* logo	£5-8	☐
23g	1976	Atlas Dump Truck	Metallic Blue/Orange, Silver or Grey seats, Superfast, 71 mm.	£4-6	☐
	1981	colour change:	Red cab and chassis, Silver dumper, Superfast	£2-4	☐

Ref. No.	Year(s)	Model Type	*Matchbox Miniatures – continued*	Market Price Range	
23h	1983	Peterbilt Quarry Truck	Yellow/Grey body, '*DIRTY DUMPER*', Superfast	£2-4	☐
	1985	design change:............	As previous model plus Blue/White '*PACE*' design	£1-3	☐
	1992	colour change:	Yellow cab with Red design, Red rear tipper	NRP	☐
23i	1986	GT350 Wildcat Dragster	White/Grey body, US issued model	£4-6	☐
23j	1987	Honda ATC 250R	US issued model	£4-6	☐

MB 24

Ref. No.	Year(s)	Model Type		Market Price Range	
24a	1956	'Hydraulic' Excavator...............	Orange-Yellow body, metal wheels, "*WEATHERILL*", 58 mm.	£25-35	☐
		colour change:	Same but Yellow body, metal wheels, '*WEATHERILL*'.	£35-50	☐
24b	1959	'Hydraulic' Excavator...............	Yellow body, Grey plastic wheels, crimped axles	£35-40	☐
			Yellow body, Grey plastic wheels, rounded axles	£25-30	☐
			Yellow body, Black palstic wheels	£15-20	☐
24c	1967	Rolls-Royce Silver Shadow	All models with Metallic Red body and Black base		
			Black wheels with Silver hubcaps	£12-18	☐
			Silver wheels with Black tyres	£10-15	☐
		Superfast wheels	Metallic Red body, Black base	£7-10	☐
			Metallic Red body, Silver-Grey, Metallic Green or Pink base	£15-20	☐
			Metallic Gold body	£20-25	☐
24d	1973	'TEAM MATCHBOX'	Metallic Blue body	£200-220	☐
			Yellow body	£150-180	☐
			Metallic Green body	£20-25	☐
			Metallic Red body, RN '8'	£5-8	☐
			Metallic Dark Red body, RN '44'	£6-9	☐
			Orange body	£8-12	☐
24e	1979	Diesel Shunter	Green or Yellow body, '*Railfreight*' or '*D1496RF*'...	£2-4	☐
24f	1983	Datsun 280 ZX	Black body, Gold flashes, opening doors, clear windows, Superfast. 74 mm.	£2-4	☐
	1984	logo change:.............	As previous model plus gold '*TURBO ZX*' on bonnet	£1-3	☐
24g	1986	Nissan 3002X...........................	Silver body with Black/Yellow stripes	£1-3	☐
	1987	design change:...........	'*FUJI FILM*' design	£1-3	☐
	1987	US issue:..................	Red body, Orange/Yellow design	£4-6	☐
	1987	Laser Wheels issue:.....	Metallic Purple body, Orange/Yellow design	£1-3	☐
24h	1989	Lincoln Town Car	White body	£1-3	☐
24i	1992	Fire Tender	Red body, Blue design with '*FIRE*' and '*No.5*' logos........	£1-3	☐

MB 25

Ref. No.	Year(s)	Model Type		Market Price Range	
25a	1956	Bedford 12 cwt Van	Dark Blue body, Black base, '*DUNLOP*' decals on sides		
			metal wheels	£25-35	☐
			Grey plastic wheels......................................	£30-40	☐
			Black plastic wheels.....................................	£300-400	☐
25b	1960	Volkswagen 1200	Silver Blue body, Grey plastic wheels, 62 mm.	£35-45	☐
		window change:	As previous model but with Green tinted windows, Grey plastic wheels....	£25-35	☐
		wheel change:	As previous but with Silver plastic wheels.	£40-50	☐
25c	1964	Bedford Petrol Tanker	Yellow cab, Green chassis, White tank, '*BP*', Black plastic wheels.	£12-18	☐
			As previous with Grey plastic wheels	£200-250	☐
	1964	German issue:	Dark Blue cab and chassis, White tank, '*ARAL*', Black plastic wheels	£70-90	☐
25d	1968	Ford Cortina Mk.II.................	Metallic Light Brown body, Black plastic wheels	£10-15	☐
		Gift Set issue:...........	As previous with Yellow roof rack.......................	£30-40	☐
	1970	Superfast wheels:	Metallic Brown body.....................................	£40-50	☐
			Dark Metallic Blue body.	£20-25	☐
			Metallic Light Blue body	£10-15	☐
		Bulgarian issues:	Various Bulgarian variations exist	£5-30	☐
25e	1972	Mod Tractor........................	Purple body, Yellow seat, with headlights on rear fenders	£25-30	☐
			As previous, but without headlights	£4-8	☐
			Purple body, Red seat (Two-Pack)	£75-90	☐
			Red body, Yellow seat (Two-Pack)	£7-11	☐
25f	1979	Flat Car and Container............	Black chassis, Red/Beige container, '*NYK*' and '*USL*', 72.5 mm.	£4-6	☐
25g		Toyota Celica	US issued model...	£4-6	☐
25h		'Yellow Fever'	US issued model	£4-6	☐
25i	1982	Audi Sport	White body, Brown/Red panels, racing number, '*AUDI SPORT*', 76 mm.	£1-3	☐
	1985	colour change:...........	Black body, Gold '*TURBO*' design	£1-3	☐
	1986	colour change:...........	Maroon body, White '*QUATTRO*' design	£1-3	☐
	1989	colour change:...........	Metallic Grey body, '*AUDI QUATTRO*' logo	£1-3	☐
25j	1987	'Paramedics' Ambulance	US issued model...	£4-6	☐
25k	1991	Peugeot 205 Turbo 16	Red body, Blue/White racing number '*48*'	£1-3	☐
	1992	colour change:...........	Yellow body, Blue logos '*PEUGEOT*' and number '*48*' ..	£1-3	☐
25L	1993	Model 'A' Ford	White body, Red chassis/wings, 'flame' design.	£1-3	☐

MB 26

Ref. No.	Year(s)	Model Type		Market Price Range	
26a	1956	E.R.F. Cement Mixer	Orange body, Gold trim, metal wheels, crimped axles, 45 mm.	£150-180	☐
		trim colour change:.....	As previous model but with Silver trim, metal wheels....	£30-35	☐
		wheel change:............	With Grey plastic wheels, Silver trim...................	£55-75	☐
		wheel change:............	With Silver plastic wheels, Silver trim	£250-300	☐
26b	1961	Foden Cement Mixer	Orange body, Dark Grey barrel, Grey plastic wheels, 66 mm.	£230-280	☐
		colour change:...........	As previous model but with Light Grey barrel, Grey plastic wheels. 66 mm.	£230-280	☐
		colour change:...........	Orange body, Orange barrel, Grey or Black plastic wheels.	£18-25	☐
		wheel change:............	Orange body, Orange barrel, Silver plastic wheels.	£250-300	☐
26c	1968	G.M.C. Tipper Truck..............	Red cab, Green chassis, Silver tipper, Black plastic wheels, 67 mm.	£6-9	☐
	1970	wheel change:.............	As previous model but with Superfast wheels.	£8-12	☐

Ref. No.	Year(s)	Model Type	Matchbox Miniatures – continued	Market Price Range
26d	1972	'BIG BANGER'	Red or Brown body, Silver exposed engine and trim, Superfast, 76 mm.	£5-8 ☐
26e		'Brown Sugar'	US issued model	£7-10 ☐
26e	1976	Site Dumper	Yellow body, Black base, Superfast, 64 mm.	£3-5 ☐
	1981	colour change:	Red body, Silver dumper, Superfast, 64 mm. Many other variations exist	£2-4 ☐
26f	1982	Cable Truck	Yellow body, Black/Grey cable drums, tinted windows, Superfast, 77 mm.	£1-3 ☐
	1984	colour change:	Yellow/Red body	£1-3 ☐
26g		'Cosmic Blues'	White body, Blue 'stars' design, US issue model	£4-6 ☐
26h		**Volvo Tilt Truck**		
	1985	'FRESH FRUIT'	Blue body, Yellow tilt	£1-3 ☐
	1986	'FERRYMASTERS'	Yellow body, White cab & side panel, contains Collector Card	£2-4 ☐
	1986	'HI BRAN'	White/Green body, Red design	£1-3 ☐
	1986	'TT86 ISLE OF MAN'	Two-tone Blue body with Red roof	£1-3 ☐
	1987	'FEDERAL EXPRESS'	All White body, Dark Blue design	£1-3 ☐
	1988	'PIRELLI'	White body, 'GRIPPING STUFF' logo	£1-3 ☐
	1989	'MICHELIN'	Blue/Yellow body	£1-3 ☐
		Military version	With Camouflage paintwork	£1-3 ☐
	1990	'PIRELLI'	White body	£1-3 ☐
26i	1993	Jaguar XJ-220	Deep Blue body	£1-3 ☐

MB 27

Ref. No.	Year(s)	Model Type		Market Price Range
27a	1956	Bedford Low Loader	Pale Blue cab, Dark Blue trailer, 6 metal wheels, crimped axles, 78 mm.	£400-500 ☐
		colour change:	Pale Green cab, Light Brown trailer	£40-50 ☐
27b	1958	Bedford Low Loader	Pale Green cab, Light Brown trailer, metal wheels, 95 mm.	£80-90 ☐
			As previous but with Grey plastic wheels	£95-110 ☐
		colour change:	Dark Green cab, Light Brown trailer, Grey plastic wheels	£100-130 ☐
27c	1960	Cadillac Sixty Special	Metallic Pale Green/White, Crimson base, Silver plastic wheels, 69 mm.	£250-300 ☐
		colour change:	Silver Grey body, Off-White roof, Silver plastic wheels	£90-110 ☐
		colour change:	Metallic Lilac/Pink, Crimson base, Grey or Silver plastic wheels	£25-35 ☐
		base colour change:	Same model but with Black base; Grey or Silver plastic wheels	£35-45 ☐
		wheel change:	Same model but with Black plastic wheels	£90-110 ☐
27d	1966	Mercedes 230 SL	White body, Red interior	£10-15 ☐
	1970	Superfast wheels:	White body, Red interior	£20-25 ☐
			White body, Black interior	£180-200 ☐
			Yellow body, Red interior	£15-20 ☐
			Yellow body, Black interior	£10-15 ☐
27e	1973	Lamborghini Countach	Yellow or Orange/Red main body, RN '3' or '8', Superfast, 74 mm.	£3-5 ☐
27f	1981	Swing Wing Jet	Red/White main body, retractable wings, 'JET', 76 mm.	£1-3 ☐
		design change:	White body with 'Jet Set' in Red on wings	£1-3 ☐
27g	1986	Jeep Cherokee	White body, multi-coloured side panels, contains Collector Card	£1-2 ☐
		'FOREST RANGER'	Yellow/Green body	£1-3 ☐
	1988	'Mr FIXER'	Yellow body, logo in Red	£1-3 ☐
		'BP'	Yellow body, Dutch promotional model	NRP ☐
		'HOLIDAY CLUB'	Beige body	£1-3 ☐
27h	1990	Mercedes Benz Tractor	Lime Green & Dark Green body	£1-3 ☐
	1994	'Tailgater'		£1-2 ☐

MB 28

Ref. No.	Year(s)	Model Type		Market Price Range
28a	1956	Bedford Compressor	Orange/Yellow body, Silver trim, metal wheels, 47 mm.	£25-30 ☐
		colour change:	Yellow body, Silver trim, metal wheels, domed/crimped axles	£40-50 ☐
28b	1959	Ford Thames Compressor Truck	Yellow body, Black wheels, crimped axles	£40-50 ☐
			Yellow body, Black wheels, rounded axles	£20-25 ☐
			Yellow body, Grey wheels	£300-400 ☐
28c	1964	Jaguar Mk.10	Pale Metallic Brown, Cream seats, Black plastic wheels, 74 mm.	£15-20 ☐
		rare variant:	With Grey plastic wheels and without 'Matchbox Series' on base	£400-500 ☐
28d	1968	Mack Dump Truck	Orange body, Red wheels	£10-12 ☐
			Orange body, Yellow wheels	£12-15 ☐
	1970	Superfast wheels:	Lime-Green body, open steeps	£8-12 ☐
			Lime-Green body, closed steps	£6-10 ☐
			Military Olive body	£8-12 ☐
28e	1974	Stoat	Gold body, driver rotates, Rolomatic, Superfast, 67 mm.	£4-6 ☐
		colour change:	Olive Green body, Chrome hubs	£10-15 ☐
		colour change:	Olive-Drab (Military Matt-Green) body	£45-55 ☐
		note:	Base may plastic and metal or all plastic. Many other variations exist.	
28f	1979	Lincoln Continental	Red body, White roof, Tan seats, Superfast, 72 mm.	£2-4 ☐
28g	1982	Formula Racing Car	Gold and Black, RN '8', White driver, Superfast, 75 mm.	£2-4 ☐
	1983	colour change:	Metallic Green and Black body	£1-3 ☐
28h	1985	Dodge Daytona	Brown/Grey body, opening bonnet	£1-2 ☐
	1986	colour change:	Silver/Red/Black body	£1-3 ☐
	1988	colour change:	Red body, Blue/Yellow design	£1-3 ☐
28i	1989	1987 Corvette	Yellow body, Red/Black design	£1-3 ☐
28j	1991	BMW 323i Cabriolet	Red body, Brown interior, Black trim	£1-3 ☐
28k	1992	Thunderbird Coupé	Dark Metallic Blue with Red body design	£1-3 ☐
	1994	Mustang Mach III		£1-2 ☐

MB 29

Ref. No.	Year(s)	Model Type		Market Price Range
29a	1956	Bedford Milk Delivery Van	Light Brown body, White bottle load, metal wheels, 57 mm.	£25-30 ☐
		wheel change:	Same but Grey plastic wheels, White or Cream bottles	£30-35 ☐

CLASSIC TOYS

The newest

and many say the best full colour magazine covering antique toys, new and old diecast models, trains and new releases.

Issue 8 available now

from all good newsagents and hobby shops or by subscription.

MATCHBOX TOYS — MOKO LESNEY SERIES

'Farmette' and 'Treasure Chest' Series
Picture kindly supplied by Christies, South Kensington, London and reproduced by their kind permission

Moko 'Farmette' Series models including the rare 'Bull Cart'.
Picture kindly supplied by John Clarke

MATCHBOX TOYS — 1-75 SERIES

No 43a Hillman Minx in the rare Green livery

5a London Bus with paper labels. 17a Bedford Removal Van in Light Blue livery

L-R 27a Bedford Low Loader in the rare Two-Tone Blue livery, 4a Massey Harris Tractor, 11a E.R.F. Road Tanker with side 'Esso' labels

MODELS OF YESTERYEAR SERIES

Y16-1 1904 Spyker in Maroon livery with Gold radiator shell, headlamps and sidelights, Black knobbly tyres.
Sold by Wallis & Wallis (£1200)

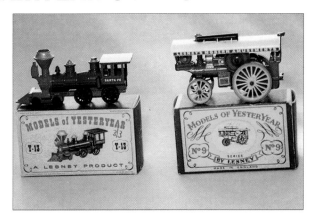

Y13-1 1862 Sante Fe Locomotive in Light Green livery.
Y9-1 1924 Fowlers Showman's engine with Gold cylinder block

Pictures kindly supplied by John clarke and reproduced by his kind permission

MATCHBOX TOYS — MODELS OF YESTERYEAR

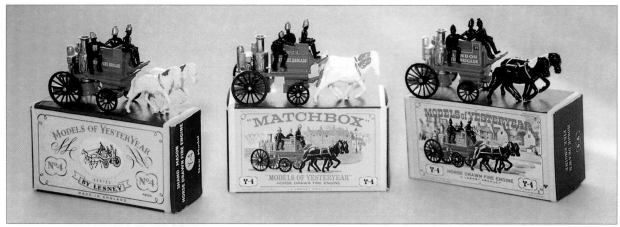

Y4-2 Shand Mason Fire Engines — Note the different box types and horses.

The rare Australian Art Set (code 2).
The above pictures kindly supplied by John Clarke

KING SIZE SERIES

K1 Hoveringham Tipper with the rare outer box
used by the company.
Picture kindly supplied by Mark Sciniele of Emerson, N.J. USA

K15 Merryweather Fire Engine. Note the model has a different
door emblem to the box picture which also has firemen
in the cab!

MATCHBOX TOYS — 1-75 SERIES

No 10 Foden Truck 'Tate & Lyle' with crown

No 26 Foden Cement Mixer with rare Grey barrel.

No 71a Water Truck with the often missing collector badge

No 32a Jaguar XK 140 — Rare Red version

No 33a Ford Zodiac. Note the different box types

No 22a Vauxhall Cresta in the Metallic Brown and Blue Green
lower body livery

Pictures kindly supplied by Gerry Savage of Model & Collectors Mart

MATCHBOX COLLECTIBLES — FIRE ENGINE SERIES

1920 Mack Fire Engine

1952 Land Rover Auxiliary

1939 Bedford Tanker Truck

1932 Mercedes Benz Ladder Truck

1933 Cadillac V16 Fire Wagon

1932 Ford AA Fire Engine

Picture taken from Matchbox Collectibles Catalogue and reproduced by their kind permission

MATCHBOX COLLECTIBLES —
'HERITAGE HORSE DRAWN CARRIAGE' SERIES

THE 1875
WELLS FARGO STAGECOACH

Wells Fargo Stagecoaches played a vital role in the opening up of America's West. For nearly 70 years, they carried the mail and travellers across a new and rapidly expanding nation.

Model shown much smaller than actual size of 200mm x 45mm x 70mm

The original stagecoaches used by Wells Fargo were built in Concord, New Hampshire and seated nine passengers in somewhat cramped circumstances.

THE 1900
GYPSY CARAVAN

This authentically decorated Gypsy Caravan captures the spirit of the Gypsies – those mysterious people who travelled the highways and byways of England and the Continent in horse drawn carriages at the turn of the century!

Model shown much smaller than actual size of 180mm x 53mm x 95mm

This particular model is a reproduction of the classic Reading wagon – or "Kite" as it was also known because of its flared sides. The large rear wheels made for better clearance and the gargoyles in each top corner served to disperse rainwater.

THE 1886
LONDON OMNIBUS

The original London Omnibus was often caught up in the hustle and bustle of London rush hour traffic in the late 1800s. This particular model, faithfully captures the look and feel of the first double decker buses of the era, from the wooden two-seater benches on the top deck, the outside staircase with the conductor and a glimpse of the advertising of the time.

Model shown much smaller than actual size of 160mm x 50mm x 90mm

Picture taken from Matchbox Collectibles Catalogue and reproduced by their kind permission

MATCHBOX COLLECTIBLES —
THE GRAND MARQUES COLLECTION

The 1938 Hispano-Suiza
Hispano-Suiza modified its six-cylinder World War I aeroplane powerplant to create exceptionally fast motor cars, including this V-12 luxury car. The year 1938 marked the end of this classic sedan.

The 1931 Stutz Bearcat
With its powerful engine, Roots supercharger and vacuum-servo brakes, the 1931 Bearcat revived the legendary Stutz name before falling victim to the Depression.

The 1937 Cord 812 Supercharged Viton
The proudest achievement of legendary automotive designer Gordon Buehrig, this Cord was among the last ever produced by one of history's greatest automakers.

The 1928 Bugatti Type 44
As powerful as it was luxurious, this masterpiece featured custom coachwork that epitomized the Bugatti passion for regal elegance.

The 1939 Lincoln-Zephyr
The Zephyr was restyled inside and out for 1939. Model number H74750 was custom-designed for Mr Ford and became the forerunner of the Lincoln Continental

The 1935 Mercedes-Benz 500 K
Pronounced a classic the day it was unveiled, this Special Roadster was a radical departure for Mercedes. It was a fast sports car and a comfortable touring car.

Picture taken from Matchbox Collectibles Catalogue and reproduced by their kind permission

Ref. No.	Year(s)	Model Type	*Matchbox Miniatures – continued*	Market Price Range	
29b	1961	Austin A55 Cambridge............	Two-tone Green body, Green tinted windows, Grey plastic wheels, 68 mm.	£30-35	☐
		wheel change:.............	Same but Silver plastic wheels, clear or tinted windows	£22-25	☐
		wheel change:.............	As previous but with Black plastic wheels...	£18-24	☐
29c	1966	Fire Pumper Truck	Red body, with or without *'Denver'* decal	£8-12	☐
	1970	Superfast wheels:	Red body, no decal	£20-25	☐
29d	1971	Racing Mini	Metallic Bronze body, racing number '29' on Yellow label, 57 mm.	£9-12	☐
		colour change:.............	Deep Orange body with Cream interior and racing number '29'	£5-8	☐
		colour change:.............	Pale Orange body, racing number '29'	£5-8	☐
		label change:	Orange models issued with RN '29' on Yellow labels with Green border	£5-8	☐
		colour change:.............	Red body, racing number '29'	£5-8	☐
29e	1977	Shovel-Nose Tractor................	Yellow body, Red shovel, Black trim, 72 mm.	£2-4	☐
	1981	colour change:.............	Orange body, Black shovel, Grey trim	£1-3	☐
	1982	colour change:.............	Yellow body, Black shovel	£1-3	☐
	1989	German issue:	Lemon Yellow body, *'THOMAS MUCOSLVAN'*, promotional	£4-6	☐
	1992	colour change:.............	Yellow body with Red shovel and design	£1-3	☐
	?	colour change:.............	Lime Green body	NGPP	☐

MB 30

Ref. No.	Year(s)	Model Type		Market Price Range	
30a	1956	Ford Prefect............................	Grey Brown body, Red & Silver trim, metal plastic wheels, 58 mm.	£25-35	☐
			As previous but with Grey plastic wheels...	£30-40	☐
		colour change:.............	As previous model but Light Blue body, Grey plastic wheels, 58 mm.	£150-180	☐
30b	1961	Magirus-Deutz Crane Lorry	Light Brown body, Red or Orange crane..	£1500-1800	☐
			Silver body, Orange jib & hook, Grey or Silver wheels..	£30-40	☐
			Silver body, Orange jib, Grey or Silver hook, Grey or Black wheels......................	£25-30	☐
30c	1965	8 Wheel Crane Truck	Green body, Orange jib	£10-13	☐
			Turquoise body, Orange jib	£250-300	☐
		Superfast wheels:	Red body, Orange jib	£220-250	☐
			Red body, Gold jib	£10-15	☐
30d	1970	Beach Buggy	Metallic Mauve or Yellow, 'Clover' motif on some, Superfast, 65 mm.	£4-7	☐
30e	1976	'SWAMP RAT'	Olive Green body, Superfast, 77 mm.	£2-4	☐
	1989	colour change:.............	Camouflage paintwork	£1-3	☐
30f	1981	Leyland Articulated Truck	Blue cab, Silver trailer, 'Leyland' on front, Superfast, 77 mm.	£2-4	☐
30g	1983	colour change:.............	Blue cab, Yellow trailer, *'International'*.	£2-4	☐
	1984	logo change:..................	Blue body, White radiator grille, flashing light, *'PAULS'*	£25-30	☐
			As previous but Special Pack version	£35-45	☐
30h	1985	Mercedes-Benz 280GE Truck...	Red body with White roof, 3 warning lights, *'RESERVE'*	£1-3	☐
	1988	Police version:.............	Green/White body, 3 Blue beacons, *'POLIZEI'*	£4-6	☐
	1990	Fire Set issue:.............	Red body, *'FIRE RESCUE'* livery (MC 15)	GSP	☐

MB 31

Ref. No.	Year(s)	Model Type		Market Price Range	
31a	1957	Ford Station Wagon.................	Yellow body, metal wheels, hook, 66 mm.	£30-35	☐
			Yellow body, Grey plastic wheels	£40-50	☐
31b	1960	Ford Station Wagon.................	Yellow body, Black base, Grey wheels	£220-250	☐
			Yellow body, Black base, Silver wheels	£200-230	☐
			Yellow body, Crimson base, clear or Green windows..	£180-210	☐
			Metallic Green body, Pink roof, Crimson base; Grey, Silver wheels......................	£25-35	☐
			as previous, but with Black base	£30-40	☐
			as previous, but with Grey wheels	£40-50	☐
			as previous, but with Black wheels	£70-90	☐
31c	1964	Lincoln Continental..................	Metallic Blue body, Black plastic wheels...	£12-15	☐
			Sea Green body	£10-13	☐
			Metallic Lime Green body	£500-600	☐
		Superfast wheels:	Sea Green body	£600-700	☐
			Metallic Lime-Green body	£10-15	☐
31d	1972	'Volks-dragon'	Red body, Silver exposed engine, 'eyes' decal, 66 mm.	£5-8	☐
31e	1977	Caravan	White, Yellow door and windows, opening door, 70 mm.	£4-6	☐
	1981	colour change:.............	White with Blue door, Orange tinted windows	£2-4	☐
		with logo:..................	White with Blue door, *'MOBILE 500'*	£1-3	☐
31f	1983	'MAZDA RX7'...........................	Metallic Gold and Black, Red seats, opening doors, Superfast wheels, 76 mm.	£1-3	☐
		colour change:.............	Black body, Gold shape, US issued model..	£5-7	☐
31g		'Lady Bug'	US issued model...	£4-6	☐
31h	1985	Rolls-Royce Silver Cloud ('James Bond' model)........	Silver or Cream body, (linked to the film 'View To A Kill'), special box	£4-6	☐
31i	1989	BMW 5 series	Dark Blue body	NRP	☐
	1991	rally version:	White body, Red/Blue design, *'BMW TEAM'* logo, rally number '31'	NRP	☐
	1995	Audi Avus...............................	....	£1-2	☐

MB 32

Ref. No.	Year(s)	Model Type		Market Price Range	
32a	1957	Jaguar XK-140	Off-White body, Black base, metal wheels, 60 mm.	£35-40	☐
		wheel change:.............	As previous but with Grey plastic wheels...	£40-50	☐
		colour change:.............	Red body, Black base, Grey plastic wheels	£130-160	☐
32b	1962	Jaguar 'E'-type.........................	Metallic Red body, Green windows, Grey tyres, 66 mm.	£80-100	☐
			Metallic Red body, clear windows, grey tyres	£34-45	☐
			Metallic Red body, clear windows, Black tyres...	£30-35	☐
32c	1968	Leyland Tanker	Green chassis, White tank, Silver base & grille, 'BP' decal	£30-40	☐
			Green chassis, White tank, Silver base & grille, 'BP' label	£8-12	☐
			Green chassis, White tank, White base & grille, 'BP' label	£40-50	☐
			Blue chassis, White tank, Silver base & grille, 'ARAL' label	£75-90	☐

Ref. No.	Year(s)	Model Type	*Matchbox Miniatures – continued*	Market Price Range	
		Superfast wheels:	Green chassis, White tank, Silver base & grille, 'BP' label	**£7-10**	☐
			Green chassis, White tank, Grey base & grille, 'BP' label	**£30-40**	☐
			Blue chassis, White tank, Silver base & grille, 'ARAL' label	**£45-55**	☐
			Metallic Purple, Silver tank, 'NAMC' labels	**NGPP**	☐
			Red, White tank, 'NAMC' labels	**NGPP**	☐
			Purple cab, Silver/Grey tank, 'NATIONAL ASSOCIATION OF MATCHBOX COLLECTORS' (Code 2 labels)	**NGPP**	☐
32d	1972	Maserati Bora..........................	Metallic Pink body, Yellow interior, RN '8', Superfast wheels, 76 mm.	**£5-8**	☐
		design change:...........	As previous model but with racing number '3'	**£10-15**	☐
32e	1977	Field Gun and Diorama...........	Military Green and Black, 2 figures, 4 shells, 77 mm.	**£2-4**	☐
32f	1981	Atlas Excavator	Orange cab, Black base and grab, 80 mm.	**£2-4**	☐
	1982	colour change:............	Yellow cab, Black base and grab.	**£1-3**	☐
	1992	colour change:............	Yellow cab, Black base and arm with Red grab	**£1-3**	☐

MB 33

Ref. No.	Year(s)	Model Type		Market Price Range	
33a	1957	Ford Zodiac.............................	Dark Green body, hook, no windows, metal wheels, 68 mm.	**£30-40**	☐
	1958	colour change:............	Dark Blue body, hook, no windows, metal wheels	**£400-500**	☐
	1958	colour change:............	Sea-Green body, hook, no windows, metal wheels	**£80-90**	☐
			As previous, but with Grey plastic wheels...	**£60-75**	☐
	1959	colour change:............	Metallic Mauve body, Orange panels, no windows, Grey plastic wheels	**£80-100**	☐
	1960	window change:..........	Same but with Green tinted windows, Grey or Silver plastic wheels	**£60-80**	☐
33b	1963	Ford Zephyr 6	Sea-Green body, Grey plastic wheels, 67 mm.	**£30-35**	☐
			same, but with Silver plastic wheels...	**£20-30**	☐
			same, but with Black plastic wheels..	**£15-20**	☐
33c	1968	Lamborghini Miura..................	Yellow body, Red interior, 71 mm. Black plastic wheels	**£12-15**	☐
			Yellow body, Cream interior	**£200-250**	☐
			Metallic Gold body, Cream interior	**£200-220**	☐
		Superfast wheels:	Yellow body, Red interior	**£75-90**	☐
			Yellow body, Cream interior	**£350-400**	☐
			Bronze body, Red interior	**£45-55**	☐
			Dark Gold body, Red interior	**£12-18**	☐
			Gold body, Cream interior, Dark or Light Red base	**£10-15**	☐
			Gold body, Cream interior, unpainted base	**£8-12**	☐
33e	1973	Datsun 126X............................	Yellow body, with or without flame design, 76 mm.	**£2-4**	☐
		US issue:	Gold body, 'Golden X' on base.	**£4-6**	☐
		note:..........................	Datsun 126X reissued as a 'Super GT' in 1986		
33f	1977	Honda 'POLICE' Motor Cycle	White body, Green or White seat, wire wheels, 74 mm.	**£2-4**	☐
	1980	wheel change:.............	As previous model but with Black plastic wheels	**£1-3**	☐
		US Issue:.....................	Black body, White seat, 'Los Angeles Police Department' decal	**£5-7**	☐
	1982	colour change:............	White body with Black seat, or vice versa	**£1-3**	☐
	1984	colour change:............	Black body, White panniers, Yellow stripes	**£1-3**	☐
33g	1989	Renault 11................................	Dark blue body, Silver stripe, 'TURBO'	**£1-3**	☐
33h	1989	Mercury Sable Wagon.............	White body	**£1-3**	☐
33i	1990	Mercedes-Benz 500 SKL	Silver body, Blue interior	**£1-3**	☐
	1992	colour change:............	White body, Green base, White '500 SL' logo	**£1-3**	☐
	1995	Ford Mondeo	....	**£1-2**	☐

MB 34

Ref. No.	Year(s)	Model Type		Market Price Range	
34a	1957	Volkswagen 15cwt Van	All models with Blue body and 'MATCHBOX' side decals		
			Metal wheels...	**£30-35**	☐
			Grey plastic wheels..	**£30-40**	☐
			Silver plastic wheels..	**£80-100**	☐
34b	1962	Volkswagen Caravette	All models with Pale Green body and Green interior		
			Silver wheels	**£150-200**	☐
			Knobbly Grey wheels (24 treads)	**£25-35**	☐
			Fine Grey wheels (45 treads)	**£50-60**	☐
			Black wheels	**£20-30**	☐
34c	1967	Volkswagen Camper.................	Silver body, with high roof (7 windows)	**£20-25**	☐
			same, but with lower roof (1 window)...	**£15-20**	☐
34d	1971	Formula 1 Racing Car	Metallic Pink or Orange body, RN '16' on Yellow design, Superfast...............	**£5-8**	☐
		Promotional issue:	As previous model but with 'WYNNS' logo	**£7-9**	☐
	1974	colour change:............	Yellow body, racing number '16' on 'arrow' design, Superfast...........................	**£3-5**	☐
		colour change:............	Metallic Blue body, racing number '15' on 'arrow' design, Superfast	**£3-5**	☐
34e	1976	'Vantastic'	Orange body, White baseplate and interior, RN '34', Superfast........................	**£3-5**	☐
34f	1981	Pro-Stocker..............................	White/Blue body, RN '34' on some, 'Lightning' , Superfast, 76 mm.	**£2-4**	☐
	1983	design change:............	Yellow body, Orange/Black stripes, RN '4', 'Chevy', 76 mm.	**£2-4**	☐
	1984	'PEPSI'	Red/White body, racing number '14'..	**£1-3**	☐
	1986	'7 UP'	Green/White body..	**£1-3**	☐
	1987	Laser Wheels issue:.....	White body, racing number '21'	**£1-3**	☐
34g	1988	Ford RS 2000	White body, Blue design, racing number '7'..	**£1-3**	☐
	1989	colour change:............	Camouflage paintwork..	**£1-3**	☐
	1991	design change:............	White body, Red design, racing number '7'...	**£1-3**	☐
34h	1990	Dodge Challenger	Yellow/Black, Red design & interior, 'TOYMAN' & 'D/174 PRO'	**£1-3**	☐

MB 35

Ref. No.	Year(s)	Model Type		Market Price Range	
35a	1957	E.R.F. Marshall Horse Box	Red cab, Light Brown box, metal wheels, 52 mm...	**£25-35**	☐
		wheel change:.............	Same but with Grey plastic wheels..	**£30-40**	☐
		wheel change:.............	With Silver plastic wheels	**£90-110**	☐
		wheel change:.............	With Black plastic wheels	**£75-90**	☐

Ref. No.	Year(s)	Model Type	*Matchbox Miniatures – continued*	Market Price Range	
35b	1964	Snow-Trac	Red body, Silver base, White tracks, *'Snow Trac'* cast on sides	£20-25	☐
			same but with *'Snow Trac'* decals in sides	£15-20	☐
			same without *'Snow Trac'* on sides	£12-15	☐
35c	1969	Merryweather Fire Engine	Metallic Red body, *'London Fire Service'*	£8-11	☐
		colour change:	With Cream base	£10-12	☐
	1975	Promotional issue:	Red body, *'FLAME-PROOF WOOL'* logo	£35-40	☐
	1981	US issue:	*'Los Angeles City Fire Department'*	£5-8	☐
35d	1975	'Fandango'	White or Red body, racing number '35', Superfast, 75 mm.	£2-4	☐
	1977	label change:	White body, RN '6', Red base, clear windows, Superfast	£10-12	☐
	1979	window change:	Red body, Purple windows, racing number '35'	£4-6	☐
35e	1982	Zoo Truck	Red body, Blue cage, Yellow lions, tinted windows, Superfast, 77 mm.	£1-3	☐
	1985	Pick Up Camper	Red/White body, *'Aspen Ski Holidays'*	£1-2	☐
	1988	'SLD Pumps'	Promotional model with White body	£1-2	☐
35f	1986	Pontiac T.Roof	Black body, US issued model	£3-5	☐
35g	1988	Ford Bronco II	White/Orange body, big wheels	£1-3	☐
	1990	colour change:	White body, *'COASTGUARD'*	£1-3	☐
	1992	colour change:	Dark Blue body, Red *'BRONCO'* & *'4x4'* logos	£1-3	☐

MB 36

Ref. No.	Year(s)	Model Type		Market Price Range	
36a	1957	Austin A50 Cambridge	Blue-Green body, Black base, metal wheels, 60 mm.	£20-25	☐
		wheel change:	As previous model but with Grey plastic wheels	£25-30	☐
		colour change:	Pale Blue body, Grey plastic wheels	£30-35	☐
36b	1961	Lambretta & Sidecar	Pale Metallic Green Scooter and side-car, Black plastic wheels, 49 mm.	£35-45	☐
36c	1966	Opel Diplomat	Metallic Gold body, Silver engine, 74 mm.	£10-15	☐
			Metallic Gold body, Grey engine	£35-45	☐
		Superfast wheels	Metallic Gold body, Silver engine	£12-18	☐
36d	1970	Hot Rod 'Draguar'	Metallic Red or Pink body, Silver engine, *'Draguar'*, Superfast, 72 mm.	£5-8	☐
36e	1976	Formula 5000	Orange body, Blue driver, RN '3', *'Formula 5000'*, Superfast, 74 mm.	£3-5	☐
		colour change:	As previous model but Red body, racing number '3' and '5000'	£3-5	☐
	1977	colour change:	Red body, racing number '11', *'MARLBORO'*, Superfast	£3-5	☐
	1978	label change:	Red body, racing number '11', *'CHAMPION'*, Superfast	£3-5	☐
36f	1980	Refuse Truck	Metallic Red and Yellow body, *'Collectomatic'*	£2-4	☐
		design change:	As previous model but without *'Collectomatic'*	£20-25	☐
		colour change:	Metallic Blue/Yellow body, with *'Collectomatic'*	£1-3	☐
	1982	colour change:	Blue and Orange body	£1-3	☐
	1983	colour change:	Blue and Cream body	£1-3	☐
	1984	colour change:	Blue/Grey body with *'Collectomatic'*	£1-3	☐
	1987	colour change:	Green/Yellow body	£1-3	☐
	1989	colour change:	Orange body, Silver tipper, Blue logo	£1-3	☐
	1992	colour change:	Green body, Yellow tipper, Green wastebin/person design	£1-3	☐
	1993	design change:	Orange-Yellow cab, White rear, *'DISPOSAL'* logo	£1-3	☐

MB 37

Ref. No.	Year(s)	Model Type		Market Price Range	
37a	1957	Karrier Bantam Lorry	All models with *'COCA-COLA'* side and rear decals		
			Orange-Yellow body, uneven load, metal wheels	£80-100	☐
			Yellow body, uneven load, metal wheels	£110-140	☐
			Orange-Yellow body, even load, metal wheels	£35-45	☐
			Orange-Yellow body, even load, grey plastic wheels	£150-180	☐
			Yellow body, even load, metal wheels	£40-50	☐
			Yellow body, even load, Grey plastic wheels	£200-220	☐
37b	1960	Karrier Bantam Lorry	All models with *'COCA-COLA'* side and rear decals		
			Grey plastic wheels, crimped axles	£45-55	☐
			Grey plastic wheels, rounded axles	£35-45	☐
			Silver plastic wheels	£400-500	☐
			Black plastic wheels	£45-55	☐
37c	1966	(Dodge) Cattle Truck	Yellow body, Grey cattle box, 2 White bulls		
			Silver plastic base	£15-18	☐
			Unpainted metal base	£8-12	☐
	1970	wheel change:	As previous models but with Superfast wheels	£4-6	☐
37d	1973	'Soopa Coopa'	Metallic Pink, Blue or Purple body, flower decal, Superfast, 74 mm.	£5-8	☐
		colour change:	Orange body, *'JAFFA-MOBILE'* (Mail Offer model)	£60-75	☐
37e	1977	Skip Truck	Red Cab and chassis, Yellow skip, Silver trim, 69 mm.	£2-4	☐
		colour change:	Red with Blue skip	NGPP	☐
	1981	colour change:	Blue/Yellow body, Black or Silver base	£2-4	☐
37f	1982	Matra Rancho	Blue or Yellow body, hook, opening tailgate, Superfast, 74 mm.	£2-4	☐
37g	1985	Ford Escort Cabriolet XR3i	White or Blue body with *'XR3i'* logo, Superfast	£1-3	☐
	1986	colour change:	Red body, Black seats, *'FORD'* logo, Superfast	£1-3	☐
	1987	Laser Wheels issue:	Blue body, racing number '3', Superfast	£1-3	☐
		US issue:	White body, racing number '3', Superfast	£1-3	☐
37h	1990	Nissan 300 ZX	Yellow body, Black *'300 ZX'* logos, White interior, clear windows	£2-4	☐

MB 38

Ref. No.	Year(s)	Model Type		Market Price Range	
38a	1957	Karrier Refuse Collector	All models with *'Cleansing Department'* side decals		
			Grey/Brown body, metal wheels	£250-300	☐
			Grey body, metal wheels	£25-30	☐
			Grey body, Grey plastic wheels	£30-40	☐
			Silver body, Grey plastic wheels	£40-50	☐
			Silver body, Silver plastic wheels	£220-250	☐

Ref. No.	Year(s)	Model Type	Description	Market Price Range	
38b	1963	Vauxhall Victor Estate	Red interior, Grey wheels	£80-100	☐
			same but with Silver wheels	£18-25	☐
			same but with Black wheels	£15-18	☐
			Green interior, Grey wheels	£40-50	☐
			same but with Silver wheels	£20-30	☐
			same but with Black wheels	£15-18	☐
38c		Honda Motorcycle & Trailer	Orange trailer without decals, Metallic Green bike	£20-30	☐
			Yellow trailer with 'HONDA' decals or labels	£8-12	☐
	1971	colour change:............	Metallic Purple or Pink body, 'HONDA' labels, Superfast	£10-15	☐
38d	1973	'Stingeroo'.................................	Metallic Pink with Purple, Blue handlebars, Superfast, 78 mm.	£4-7	☐
			As previous but with Silver handlebars	NGPP	☐
38e	1977	Jeep	Military-Green body, with 'star' label, Black gun, 61 mm........	£2-3	☐
			Red body (TP-7 release with Red glider)	NGPP	☐
38f	1981	Camper	Red and Cream body, tinted windows, Superfast, 76 mm.	£2-3	☐

38g   Ford Model 'A' Van

Year(s)	Model	Price		Year(s)	Model	Price	
1982	'CHAMPION'	£5-7	☐	1989	'MICA 2nd N.A. CONVENTION'........	£7-9	☐
1984	'KELLOGGS'	£3-5	☐	1989	'SOUVENIR of CHESTER'	£5-7	☐
1984	'TOY FAIR 84' (US)			1989	'CHEESES'	£4-6	☐
	with roof label	£80-100	☐	1989	'ISLE of MAN TT 89'	£3-5	☐
	without roof label	£50-70	☐	1989	'JORDANS'	£4-6	☐
1984	'PEPSI COLA'			1989	'JUNIOR MATCHBOX CLUB'............	£5-7	☐
	'COME ALIVE'	£7-10	☐	1989	'RIBENA'	£3-5	☐
	Without 'COME ALIVE'...................	£10-15	☐	1989	'BARRATT SHERBET FOUNTAIN'		
	'PEPSI COLA', 'Matchmates'	£8-12	☐		Black base, normal box	£3-5	☐
1984	'BEN FRANKLIN'	£300-400	☐		Red base, Woolworths box	£5-7	☐
1984	'MATCHBOX USA'	£20-25	☐	1989	'MOORLAND CENTRE'	£3-5	☐
1984	'ARNOTTS'	£6-8	☐	1989	'LIGHTWATER VALLEY'..................	£3-5	☐
1984	'LARK LANE'	£3-5	☐	1989	'TANDY ELECTRONICS' (Aus).........	£3-5	☐
1984	'TITTENSOR FIRST SCHOOL'..........	£3-5	☐	1989	'YORK FAIR' (US)	£4-6	☐
				1989	'BALTIMORE ORIOLES' (US)............	£4-6	☐
1985	'BASS MUSEUM'	£4-6	☐	1989	'ASDA BAKED BEANS'	£3-5	☐
1985	'COLLECTORS GUIDE'	£4-6	☐	1989	'LION WHOLESALERS'	£3-5	☐
1985	'The AUSTRALIAN'	£4-6	☐	1989	'MATCHBOX USA COLLECTORS CLUB'	£20-25	☐
1986	'BBC 1925'	£7-9	☐	1989	'JACKY MAEDER' (Swiss).................	£4-6	☐
1986	'WEET-BIX'/'SANITARIUM'	£6-9	☐	1989	'JOHNSONS SEEDS'........................	£4-6	☐
1986	'H.H. BRAIN'	£7-10	☐	1989	'SWARFEGA'	£10-12	☐
1986	'MATCHBOX SPEED SHOP'	£2-4	☐	1989	'CAMPERDOWN' (Aus)	NGPP	☐
1986	'ISLE of MAN TT 86'	£3-5	☐				
1986	'SMITHS POTATO CRISPS'	£4-6	☐	1990	'PAVA RUSTPROOFING' (Danish)	£3-5	☐
				1990	'MATCHBOX 40th' (US)...................	£10-15	☐
1987	'W.H.SMITH & SON Ltd', Red	£8-12	☐	1990	'CARMELLE' (Saudi-Arabia)............	£10-12	☐
1987	'MICA' 2nd CONVENTION	£200-300	☐	1990	'FRESH DAIRY CREAM'	£3-5	☐
1987	'JUNIOR MATCHBOX CLUB'...........	£5-7	☐	1990	'LYCEUM THEATRE'......................	£3-5	☐
1987	'ISLE of MAN TT 87'	£3-5	☐	1990	'RICE KRISPIES', Dark Blue (US)......	£7-10	☐
1987	'SILVO 1912-1987'	£10-12	☐	1990	'COCA-COLA'	£5-7	☐
1987	'CHESTY BONDS'	£4-6	☐	1990	'ISLE of MAN TT 90'	£3-5	☐
1987	'DEWHURST'	£4-6	☐	1990	'MATCHBOX USA 9th CONVENTION'	£8-10	☐
1987	'ISLE of MAN POST OFFICE'	£4-6	☐	1990	'CANADA DRY'	£12-15	☐
1987	'JOHN WEST SALMON'.....................	£3-5	☐	1990	'YORK FAIR 1990'	£4-6	☐
1987	'THIS VAN DELIVERS',			1990	'PENN STATE' (US)	£5-7	☐
	with phone number	£10-12	☐	1990	'COLLECTORS CLUB 90' (US)...........	£35-45	☐
	without phone no.	£100-150	☐	1990	'JOHNNY WALKER'	£18-22	☐
1987	'RICE KRISPIES', Mid-Blue (UK).......	£3-5	☐	1990	'TYNE BRAND'	£8-12	☐
1987	'RICE KRISPIES', Dark Blue, (US)......	£9-11	☐	1990	'LYONS TEA'	£7-10	☐
				1990	'PG TIPS'	£10-12	☐
1988	'MICA 3rd CONVENTION'	£8-10	☐	1990	'MITRE 10'	£4-6	☐
1988	'MICA 1st N.A. CONVENTION'	£5-7	☐	1990	'WILLIAM LUSTY'	£3-5	☐
1988	'JAMES NEALE & Sons'	£4-6	☐	1990	'RUTTER Bros.' (US)	£6-8	☐
1988	'ISLE of MAN TT 88'	£3-5	☐	1990	'USA BASEBALL TEAMS', each	£4-6	☐
1988	'ISLE of MAN POST OFFICE', as '87 model but Black 'island'	£3-5	☐		Set of 26	£100-130	☐
1988	'ROYAL MAIL'	£4-6	☐				
1988	'MANX CATTERY'	£4-6	☐	1991	'DAIRYLEA CHEESE'	£7-10	☐
1988	'MERVYN WYNN', gold 'island'	£4-6	☐	1991	'COLLECTORS CLUB 91' (US)...........	£45-55	☐
	with black 'island'.	£20-25	☐	1991	NATIONAL FOOTBALL LEAGUE (USA),		
1988	'P.M.G. 252' (Australia)	£3-5	☐		(28 different), each...........................	£4-6	☐
1988	'ALEX MUNRO'	£3-5	☐		Set of 28	£100-130	☐
1988	'CHESTER HERALDRY CENTRE'....	£3-5	☐	—	'MATCHBOX USA CLUB 15th'	£45-55	☐
1988	'W.H. SMITH & SON Ltd', Yellow	£8-12	☐	—	'MATCHBOX COLLECTORS CLUB',		
1988	'TOY MUSEUM, CHESTER'.............	£4-6	☐		Silver body	£75-100	☐
1988	'COBB of KNIGHTSBRIDGE'............	£4-6	☐		Green/Orange	£35-45	☐
1988	'ROWNTREES JELLY'.....................	£3-5	☐				
1988	'BARRATT SHERBERT FOUNTAIN'	£3-5	☐	1992	'COLLECTORS CLUB 92 (US)	£25-30	☐
1988	'GUERNSEY POST OFFICE'	£4-6	☐	1992	'NATIONAL HOCKEY LEAGUE'		
1988	'RAYNERS CRUSHA'	£3-5	☐		Set of 6 pairs	£50-60	☐
1988	'HISTORICAL COLLECTION'............	£4-6	☐	1992	'NATIONAL HOCKEY LEAGUE 92'		
1988	'BIG SISTER' (Australia)...................	£4-6	☐		Set of 6	£25-30	☐
1988	'UNIROYAL' (Canada)	£10-12	☐	1992	'FLAVOURS of AUSTRALIA'		
1988	'NATWEST BANK'	£3-5	☐		Set of 6	£20-25	☐
1988	'GREENS SPONGE MIXTURE'..........	£4-6	☐				
1989	'MATCHBOX SERIES'	£4-6	☐	1993	'WINES of AUSTRALIA'		
1989	'MICA 4th CONVENTION'................	£7-9	☐		Set of 6	£25-30	☐

38g cont.

	1994	'PILLS , POTIONS AND POWDERS' series: 'Milk of Magnesia', 'Vicks Vapour Rub', 'Aspirin', 'Alka-Seltzer', 'Tiger Balm', 'Cod Liver Oil'	NGPP ☐	

	1995	'The CIRCUS COMES TO TOWN' series: 'Circus Oz', Circus Krone', 'Gerry Cottle's Circus', 'Big Apple Circus', 'Circus Barum', 'Chipperfields Circus'....	NGPP ☐
	1995	'INTERNATIONAL POSTAL TRUCKS' series: 'US Mail', 'Canada Post', 'Guernsey', 'Australia Post', 'Reichpost', 'De Post' ..	NGPP ☐

Ref. No.	Year(s)	Model Type	Description	Price	
38h	1986	Flareside Pick-Up	Red body, White interior	£2-4	☐
	1987	colour change:.............	Yellow body, Blue design	£2-4	☐
38i	1992	Ford Courier Van 'MATCHBOX'	Dark Blue body, *'The Ideal Premium'*. 1000 only. (German issue)	NGPP	☐
	1992	'MILKA'	Purple body, White *'MILKA'* logo	£1-2	☐
	1992	'COURIER'	White body, Yellow/Green/Purple side flash. Ford garages Limited Edition..............	NGPP	☐
	1994	Corvette Stingray III		£1-2	☐

MB 39

Ref. No.	Year(s)	Model Type	Description	Price	
39a	1957	Zodiac Convertible	Pale Peach body, Light Brown base/interior/driver, metal wheels, 68 mm.	£180-220	☐
		colour change:.............	Same but with Light Green base and interior, metal wheels	£30-40	☐
		wheel change:.............	Light Green base, Grey plastic wheels.	£35-45	☐
		colour change:.............	Dark Peach body, Blue-Green base & interior, Grey plastic wheels.	£35-45	☐
		wheel change:.............	As previous model but with Silver plastic wheels................................	£60-70	☐
		base change:.............	Dark Peach body with Sea-Green base, Grey plastic wheels	£50-60	☐
39b	1962	Pontiac Convertible	Metallic Violet body, Crimson base, Silver wheels................................	£70-80	☐
			same but with Grey wheels................................	£220-250	☐
			Yellow body, Crimson base, Red steering wheel, Silver or Grey wheels...........	£45-55	☐
			same but with Cream steering wheel	£25-35	☐
			Yellow body, Black base, Silver wheels...............................	£25-35	☐
			same but with Grey wheels	£30-40	☐
			same but with Black wheels	£15-20	☐
39c	1967	Ford Tractor............................	Blue body, Yellow engine cover, Black plastic tyres, 55 mm.	£8-10	☐
			Blue body & engine cover	£12-15	☐
			Orange body & engine cover	£40-50	☐
39d	1973	Clipper	Metallic Pink, Yellow interior, Rolamatic feature, 77 mm.	£4-7	☐
39e	1979	R.R. Silver Shadow Mk.II	Metallic Silver body, Red seats, opening doors, Superfast, 75 mm.	£2-4	☐
	1981	colour change:.............	Metallic Red body, Cream seats	£2-4	☐
	1982	colour change:.............	Metallic Gold body, White seats	£2-4	☐
	1984	colour change:.............	Metallic Maroon body, Silver base	£1-3	☐
39f	1985	BMW 323i Cabriolet	Metallic Blue body	£1-2	☐
	1986	colour change:.............	All Red body	£1-2	☐
	1987	colour change:.............	White body, *'323i'* logo, Superfast	£1-3	☐
	1987	Laser Wheels issue:....	White body, *'ALPINA'* logo	£1-3	☐
	1989		Green body, flame design *'BP'* (Dutch promotional).........................	£1-3	☐
39g	1990	Mach CH 600 Tractor............	White body, Red/Blue stripes	£1-3	☐
39h	1992	Mercedes-Benz 600 SEL...........	Metallic Silver body. (Catalogue picture not seen)	£1-3	☐

MB 40

Ref. No.	Year(s)	Model Type	Description	Price	
40a	1957	Bedford 7 Ton Tipper	Red body, Brown tipper, metal wheels, 53 mm..............................	£25-35	☐
		wheel change:.............	Same but with Grey plastic wheels, domed crimped axles	£25-30	☐
		axle change:	As previous model with Grey plastic wheels on rivetted axles	£15- 20	☐
40b	1961	Leyland Tiger Coach	Steel Blue body,		☐
			Grey plastic wheels	£45-55	☐
			Silver plastic wheels	£20-25	☐
			Black plastic wheels	£12-18	☐
40c	1967	Hay Trailer	Blue body, Yellow plastic hay racks and wheels, Black plastic tyres, 86 mm.	£5-10	☐
		note:	Model deleted in 1972 but appeared in Two-Packs between 1976-1981:		
		Twin-Pack model:......	Red body..............................	£8-10	☐
		Twin-Pack model:......	Lemon body..............................	£4-6	☐
		Twin-Pack model:......	Pale Blue body..............................	£5-7	☐
		scarce colour:	Tan body with Black racks..............................	£50-60	☐
40d	1972	Vauxhall Guildsman.................	Pink body, Green windows, Cream interior, hook	£5-8	☐
		colour change:............	Red body, Green windows, racing number '40'	£5-8	☐
		colour change:............	Gold body (Bulgarian issue)	£25-30	☐
		note:.......................	Many other variations exist		
40e	1976	Horse Box	Orange and Cream body, Tan ramp, 2 White horses, Superfast, 72 mm.	£3-5	☐
	1981	colour change:............	Green and Cream body, Brown drop-down ramp	£2-4	☐
	1983	colour change:............	Orange and Brown body, White drop-down ramp	£2-4	☐
		colour change:............	Brown and Yellow body, White drop-down ramp	£1-3	☐
		colour change:............	Cream and Black body, Brown drop-down ramp	£1-3	☐
40f	1982	Corvette 'T' Roof	White body	£1-3	☐
40g	1985	Rocket Transporter	White body, Red logo *'NASA'*	£1-3	☐
	1989	colour change:............	As previous model but in Camouflage finish	£1-3	☐

MB 41

Ref. No.	Year(s)	Model Type		Price	
41a	1957	Jaguar 'D'-Type (55 mm.)	Green body, metal wheels, No 41...	**£30–40**	☐
			Green body, metal wheels, No 52...	**£70–80**	☐
			Green body, Grey plastic wheels, No 41................................	**£80–100**	☐
41b	1960	Jaguar 'D'-Type (62 mm.)	All models with Green body and Black base		
			Grey plastic wheels, crimped axles, No 41............................	**£50–60**	☐
			same but with rounded axles	**£40–50**	☐
			Wire wheels with Black tyres, No 41.....................................	**£35–40**	☐
			same but with No 5 or 6..	**£75–90**	☐
			Red wheels with Black tyres..	**£150–180**	☐
41c	1965	Ford GT	All models with RN 6		
			White body, Red hubs, Black, 67 mm.	**£100–120**	☐
			White body, Yellow hubs, Black tyres	**£10–15**	☐
			Yellow body, Yellow hubs, black tyres (Italian 5 Pack set)	**£100–120**	☐
			White body, Superfast wheels..	**£8–12**	☐
			Metallic Red body, Black or Green base, Superfast wheels..	**£8–12**	☐
			same but with Cream or Yellow base.....................................	**£12–18**	☐
41d	1973	Siva Spyder................................	Metallic Red, Black or Silver band on roof, Superfast	**£4–7**	☐
		colour change:............	Blue body, 'GOODYEAR'	**£3–5**	☐
		colour change:............	Blue body, stars on bonnet, Red/White stripe, 'S'	**£3–5**	☐
		colour change:............	Blue body, spider-web print, 'Black Widow' on base, Superfast..	**£3–5**	☐
41e	1979	'AMBULANCE'	White body, Red/Yellow/Black decal, opening rear door, Superfast, 75 mm.	**£2–4**	☐
	1981		White body, Blue/Yellow decal...	**£2–4**	☐
		colour change:............	Silver body, White doors	**£25–30**	☐
		colour change:............	Red 'NOTARTZ', German model	**£10–15**	☐
		logo change:.............	Small 'Ambulance' on labels...	**£8–11**	☐
41f	1982	Kenworth Aerodyne	Orange, Black or Green body (issued with Convoy sets).......	**£1–3**	☐
41g	1983	Racing Porsche..........................	Two-tone Blue body, 'Team Porsche', 'Elf', etc, Superfast ...	**£2–4**	☐
	1986	colour change:............	White body, Red RN '10', 'PORSCHE', (box also contains Collector Card)	**£1–3**	☐
	1987	Laser Wheels issue:....	Metallic Red body, racing number '35'..................................	**£1–3**	☐
	1989	colour change:............	Red body, White design, Red racing number '4'	**£1–3**	☐
41g	1990	Vauxhall Cavalier Gsi 2000......	Metallic Dark Pink body	**£1–3**	☐
41h	1991	'Sunburner'	Yellow body with Black seats, Orange/Red 'fire' design........	**£1–3**	☐
	1993	colour change:............	Blue body with double White stripe	**£1–3**	☐
	1994	Ferrari 456GT	....	**£1–2**	☐

MB 42

Ref. No.	Year(s)	Model Type		Price	
42a	1957	Evening News Van	Yellow body, 'EVENING NEWS' decals		
			Metal wheels, 57 mm..	**£35–40**	☐
			Grey plastic wheels with 24 treads..	**£35–45**	☐
			Grey plastic wheels with 45 treads..	**£55–65**	☐
			Black plastic wheels with 24 treads.......................................	**£55–70**	☐
			Black plastic wheels with 45 treads.......................................	**£70–90**	☐
42b	1965	Studebaker Lark Wagonaire	(With hunter & dog figures)		
			Blue body, sliding rear roof painted as body	**£35–45**	☐
			same but rear roof painted light Blue....................................	**£12–15**	☐
42c	1969	Iron Fairy Crane	Red body, Yellow boom, Black plastic wheels.......................	**£10–15**	☐
		Superfast wheels:	Red body, Yellow boom	**£18–25**	☐
			Red body, Gold boom	**£60–70**	☐
			Orange-Red body, Gold boom	**£15–20**	☐
			Orange body, Gold boom	**£20–30**	☐
42d	1972	'Tyre Fryer'...............................	Metallic Blue body, Yellow interior, Superfast, 76 mm.	**£5–8**	☐
		colour change:............	Orange body, 'Jaffa Mobile' logo (Mail Offer model)............	**£45–55**	☐
42e	1978	**Mercedes Container Truck**	'MATCHBOX', Red body, Cream or White container, Superfast ...	**£3–5**	☐
		'MAYFLOWER'	Metallic Dark Green body and container	**£3–5**	☐
		'SEALAND'	Red body, Cream container	**£3–5**	☐
		'KARSTADT'..........................	Blue body, Blue container. (German issue model)	**£10–15**	☐
		'DEUTSCHE BUNDESPOST'	Yellow body and container. (German issue model)	**£10–15**	☐
		'CONFERN'............................	Red body, Cream/Red container. (German issue model)	**£10–15**	☐
		'NYK'	Red body, Cream container	**£3–5**	☐
		'OCL'	Red body, Cream container	**£3–5**	☐
		'MODEL TRANSPORTSBETRIEBE'...	Red/White body, (German issue)	**£4–6**	☐
		'TRUST FORTE HOUSE' ...	All Blue body (German promotional)	**£35–45**	☐
42f	1983	'57 'T-Bird'	Red and White body, Red seats	**£2–4**	☐
		US issue:	Black body	**£4–6**	☐
42g	1984	Mobile Crane............................	Yellow body, Black crane, Red logo 'REYNOLDS CRANE HIRE' ...	**£1–3**	☐
	1992	colour change:............	Yellow body, Red cab with Yellow design..............................	**£1–3**	☐

MB 43

Ref. No.	Year(s)	Model Type		Price	
43a	1958	Hillman Minx	Light Green body, Silver/Red trim, metal wheels, hook, 66 mm........	**£300–350**	☐
			As previous but with Grey plastic wheels...............................	**£60–70**	☐
		colour change:............	Blue/Grey body, Pale Grey roof, metal wheels	**£30–35**	☐
		colour change:............	Turquoise body, Cream roof, Grey plastic wheels	**£35–45**	☐

Ref. No.	Year(s)	Model Type	*Matchbox Miniatures – continued*	Market Price Range	
43b	1962	A.B. Tractor Shovel	Yellow body, driver & shovel, 65 mm.	£75-90	☐
			Yellow body & shovel, Red driver & base	£15-22	☐
			Yellow body, driver & base, Red shovel	£20-30	☐
			Yellow body, Red driver, base & shovel	£200-250	☐
43c	1968	Pony Trailer............................	Yellow body, Grey ramp, Light Brown base, Black plastic wheels, 67 mm.	£12-18	☐
			same but with Dark Green base	£8-12	☐
	1970	Superfast wheels:	Yellow body, Grey ramp, Light Green base	£15-20	☐
			same but with Dark Green base	£8-12	☐
			Many other colours exist (Two-Pack Range) i.e. Orange or Light Brown	£5-12	☐
43d	1973	'Dragon Wheels'	Green main body, Red decal, Silver engine, Superfast wheels, 72 mm.	£3-5	☐
43e	1979	**Steam Locomotive**	Red/Black body, Yellow number '4345', 0-4-0, hook, 68 mm.	£1-3	☐
	1989	'NORTH YORKSHIRE MOORS'.	Red body, Promotional.	£2-4	☐
	1989	'WEST SOMERSET RAILWAY'	Green body, Promotional .	£2-4	☐
	1989	'ISLE of MAN RAILWAY'	Blue body, 'HUTCHINSON', Promotional.	£2-4	☐
	1989	'BLUE TRAIN'	A Promotional model commissioned by M/s K.H.Norton of Leicester	£2-4	☐
	1990	'BRITISH RAIL'	Black body with 'lion' emblem. Promotional.	£2-4	☐
	1990	'G.W.R.'	Matt Green/Black body, Gold design, Promotional.	£2-4	☐
	1990	'KELLOGGS'	Green/Black body, White design, Promotional.	£2-4	☐
43f	1982	Peterbilt Conventional.............	Black body (US issue).	£2-4	☐
	1984	Convoy Set issues:	Red, Black, White or Yellow. Various logos	£2-4	☐
43g	1984	Mercedes 500 SEC AMG........	All White body.	£1-3	☐
	1985	colour change:............	All Red body.	£1-3	☐
	1987	colour change:............	Black body.	£1-3	☐
	1987	Laser Wheels issue:....	Red body, 'AMG 500 SEC' logo.	£1-3	☐
	1988	colour change:............	White body, Silver stripe, (German issue).	£1-3	☐
	1989	colour change:............	Black body, 'REDOXON' on bonnet. Hong Kong promotional issue	£4-6	☐
43h	1990	'57 Chevy	Blue body, White logo 'MILKY WAY', (Mars on-pack offer).	£1-2	☐
	1990	design change:............	Black body with Red/Yellow 'fire' design covering front, 'CHEVY' on boot.	£1-3	☐
	1993	design change:............	Red body with 'flame' effect .	£1-3	☐

MB 44

Ref. No.	Year(s)	Model Type		Market Price Range	
44a	1958	Rolls-Royce Silver Cloud	Metallic Blue body, Red trim, metal wheels, 67 mm.	£25-35	☐
	1960		As previous but with Grey plastic wheels.	£30-40	☐
			As previous model but with Silver plastic wheels.	£30-35	☐
44b	1964	Rolls-Royce Phantom V...........	Metallic Mauve body, Black wheels .	£20-25	☐
			same but with Grey wheels .	£50-60	☐
			same but with Silver wheels .	£75-90	☐
			Silver-Grey body, Black wheels .	£60-70	☐
			same but with Silver wheels .	£220-250	☐
44c	1967	GMC Refrigerator Truck.........	Red body, Sea-Green container, Black wheels, 76 mm.	£8-12	☐
	1970	Superfast wheels:	Red body, Sea-Green container .	£30-40	☐
			Yellow body, Sea-Green container .	£300-400	☐
			Yellow body, Red container .	£6-10	☐
44d	1972	Boss Mustang	Yellow/Black or Green body, Superfast wheels, 75 mm.	£5-8	☐
44e	1979	Passenger Coach	Red/Black body, Green tinted windows, '431-432', 73 mm.	£2-4	☐
44f	1983	Citroën 15cv	Black body, Tan seats, Silver trim, Superfast.	£1-3	☐
	1986	colour change:............	Deep Blue body.	£2-4	☐
44g	1988	Skoda 130LR	White body, Blue 'SKODA' on roof, racing number '44'	£2-4	☐
44h	1982	4 x 4 Chevy Van.....................	Green body and windows, 'RIDIN' HIGH' decal	£2-4	☐
44i		**1921 Ford Model 'T' Van**	Promotional issues introduced in 1990.		
44i	1990	'5th MICA UK CONVENTION'	White/Blue body with UK and E.E.C. flags design	£5-7	☐
	1990	'3rd MICA USA CONVENTION'	White/Blue body with US and UK flags design.	£5-7	☐
	1990	'BIRDS CUSTARD'................	Yellow/Red/Blue body, 'ORIGINAL FLAVOUR' logo.	£1-3	☐
	1994	Ford Probe GT.........................		£1-2	☐

MB 45

Ref. No.	Year(s)	Model Type		Market Price Range	
45a	1958	Vauxhall Victor	Red body, metal wheels, 61 mm.	£750-900	☐
		colour change:............	Yellow body, metal wheels.	£30-35	☐
			Yellow body, Grey plastic wheels, no windows.	£30-35	☐
			same but with clear windows.	£50-60	☐
			same but with Green windows.	£25-35	☐
			Yellow body, Silver plastic wheels.	£40-50	☐
			Yellow body, Black plastic wheels.	£45-55	☐
45b	1965	Ford Corsair with Boat............	Cream body, Red interior, Black wheels, Silver painted base, 68 mm.	£25-30	☐
			Same but with unpainted base.	£10-15	☐
			Same but with Grey wheels.	£50-60	☐
			Models with white interior are pre-productions.	£500-600	☐
45c	1970	Ford Group Six	Dark Green body (no metallic), 75 mm.	£220-250	☐
			Dark Metallic Green body, RN 7 .	£12-18	☐
			same but with RN 45 .	£8-12	☐
			Lime-Green body.	£6-10	☐
			Red body.	£8-12	☐

Ref. No.	Year(s)	Model Type	*Matchbox Miniatures – continued*	Market Price Range	
45d	1976	BMW 3.0 CSL..........................	Red body, Yellow interior, *'BMW'*, opening doors, Superfast, 74 mm.	**£2-4**	☐
	1979	colour change:.............	Orange body, White interior, *'BMW'*	**£2-4**	☐
	1977	colour change:.............	White body, *'POLIZEI'* and *'123'* logos, Superfast	**£2-4**	☐
		colour change:.............	White body, *'MANHAULTER'*.	**£20-25**	☐
		colour change:.............	Red body, Dark Green windows, (U.S. Gift Set)	**NGPP**	☐
45e	1982	Kenworth Cabover	White/Blue body, Amber tinted windows, Superfast, 71 mm.	**£2-4**	☐
	1984	colour change:.............	Silver Grey body, '45' design..	**£1-3**	☐
			Silver Grey and Blue handpainted cab from CY-8 Showliner issue	**NGPP**	☐
	1985	colour change:.............	Black body	**£1-3**	☐
	1986	colour change:.............	Red body, Yellow/White/Orange design, (with Collector Card)................	**£1-3**	☐
		US Issue:........................	*'Chef Boyardee'*.	**£12-15**	☐
45f	1988	Skip Truck	Yellow body, Grey/Orange skip	**£1-3**	☐
	1992	colour change:.............	Yellow body/chassis, Red skip...	**£1-3**	☐

MB 46

46a	1958	Morris Minor 1000...................	Pale Brown body, no windows, metal wheels, 53 mm...........................	**£800-1000**	☐
		colour change:.............	Dark Green body, Black base, metal wheels, domed crimped axles........	**£50-60**	☐
		colour change:.............	Dark Blue/Green body, metal wheels	**£70-80**	☐
			As previous but with Grey plastic wheels...	**£120-150**	☐
		colour change:.............	Blue body, Grey plastic wheels	**£150-180**	☐
46b	1960	Pickford Removal Van.............	Dark Blue body, Grey wheels, three line decal	**£60-80**	☐
			Dark Blue body, Silver wheels, three line decal	**£90-120**	☐
			Dark Blue body, Grey wheels, two line decal	**£100-130**	☐
			Dark Blue body, Silver wheels, two line decal	**£180-200**	☐
			Green body, Grey wheels	**£55-65**	☐
			Green body, Silver wheels	**£55-70**	☐
			Green body, Black wheels	**£35-45**	☐
			Light Brown body, *'Beales Bealesons'* decal, without box	**£280-330**	☐
			same model in special White box with *'Sun'* & *'It's A Pleasure'* decal ...	**£400-450**	☐
46c	1968	Mercedes-Benz 300 SE	Green body	**£12-15**	☐
	1969		Metallic Blue body	**£9-12**	☐
		Superfast wheels:	Metallic Blue body	**£80-100**	☐
			Metallic Dark Gold body, opening doors	**£25-35**	☐
			Metallic Gold body, cast doors	**£6-10**	☐
			Silver body (Multipack)	**£50-60**	☐
			Various Bulgarian colour variations exist	**£10-30**	☐
46d	1973	'Stretcha Fetcha'......................	White body, Red baseplate and cross, Blue tinted windows and beacons, 70 mm.......	**£3-5**	☐
		window change:.............	With Amber windows	**£3-5**	☐
		design change:.............	With small Red cross label	**£12-15**	☐
		German issue:.............	Red body	**£12-15**	☐
		note:.............	Other variations exist.		
46e		'Viper' Van	No details	**£2-4**	☐
46f	1979	Ford Tractor and Harrow.........	Blue body, Silver engine, Yellow harrow and seat, hook, 52 mm.	**£2-4**	☐
		colour change:.............	Metallic Green body, with or without 'FORD' on engine cover, US issue ..	**£1-3**	☐
46g	1984	Sauber Group 'C' Racer	Red body, *'BASF'*, (with Collector Card)...	**£1-3**	☐
	1986	colour change:.............	White body, Black racing number '61'	**£1-3**	☐
	1988	colour change:.............	White/Blue body, racing number '46', *'SHELL'*, Superfast....................	**£1-3**	☐
	1989	colour change:.............	Two-tone Blue body, racing number '46'..	**£1-3**	☐
	1989	colour change:.............	White body..	**£1-3**	☐
	1991	colour change:.............	White/Blue body, *'Grand Prix'* & *'Sauber'* logos, racing number '46'.......	**£1-3**	☐
46h	1987	'Hot Chocolate'	US issue..	**£4-6**	☐
46i	1987	'Big Blue'	Metallic Blue lift-up Volkswagen body, racing number '39'	**£4-6**	☐

MB 47

47a	1958	Trojan Van	Red body, *'BROOKE BOND TEA'*, metal wheels, 58 mm.	**£30-40**	☐
			As previous but with Grey plastic wheels...	**£35-45**	☐
47b	1963	Commer Ice Cream Van	Metallic Blue body, Black wheels, *'LYONS MAID'*, 58 mm.	**£75-100**	☐
			Blue body, Black wheels, *'LYONS MAID'*	**£25-35**	☐
			Blue body, Grey wheels, *'LYONS MAID'*.	**£120-150**	☐
			Blue body, Black wheels, White side decals	**£35-45**	☐
			Cream body, *'LYONS MAID'* side decals	**£180-220**	☐
			Cream body, White side decals..	**£50-60**	☐
		design change:.............	Cream body, Red/White side labels *'LORD NIELSENS ICE CREAM VAN'*..........	**£50-60**	☐
47c	1968	DAF Container Truck	Sea Green body, Grey roof, Yellow container, Black plastic wheels, 77 mm............	**£45-55**	☐
		colour change:.............	Silver body, Grey or Silver roof, Yellow container, Black plastic wheels ...	**£10-12**	☐
	1970	wheel change:.............	Same but Superfast wheels, 'Patent app. for' on base of some...............	**£10-15**	☐
47c	1974	Beach Hopper	Metallic Blue body, Yellow design, Rolomatic, Superfast, 66 mm.	**£3-5**	☐
47e	1980	'G.W.R.' Pannier Locomotive...	Green/Black body, Gold decals, 0-6-0, hook, 77 mm.	**£2-4**	☐
47f	1982	Jaguar SS100	Red body, Silver trim, Beige seats & steering wheel, Superfast, 76 mm. ...	**£2-4**	☐
	1986	colour change:.............	Blue body, Grey bonnet, White seats, (includes Collector Card)	**£2-4**	☐
	1990	colour change:.............	Green/Red body, (Brooke Bond promotional model)	**£1-3**	☐
47g	1988	School Bus.............................	Yellow body, US issue model, *'School District'*	**£4-6**	☐
	1988	Army version:	Olive Green bus celebrating U.S.A. Matchbox Club's 7th Anniversary.......	**£4-6**	☐
	1995	'Rotwheeler'............................	....	**£1-2**	☐

MB 48

Ref. No.	Year(s)	Model Type	Description	Price
48a	1958	Meteor Sports Boat & Trailer...	Black trailer, Light Brown boat, Blue hull	
			Metal wheels..	£25-30 ☐
			Grey plastic wheels..	£28-35 ☐
			Silver plastic wheels..	£120-150 ☐
48b	1961	Sports Boat & Trailer...............	Boat with Cream or White deck and Red hull or with Red deck and Cream or white hull	
			Dark Blue trailer, Black wheels..................................	£15-20 ☐
			Dark Blue trailer, Grey wheels...................................	£80-120 ☐
			Light Blue trailer, Black wheels.................................	£20-30 ☐
48c	1966	(Dodge) Dumper Truck	Red body, Silver trim, wide or narrow Black plastic wheels, 76 mm.	£8-10 ☐
	1970	colour change:.............	Blue cab and chassis, Yellow tipper, Superfast wheels.	£5-8 ☐
48d	1973	'Pie-Eyed Piper'	Metallic Blue, Silver engine, tinted windows, Superfast wheels.	£3-5 ☐
	1981	US issue:	Red body, 'RED RIDER' logo	£5-8 ☐
			Red body, 'BIG BANGER' labels, No 48 base	£30-40 ☐
	1983	US issue:	White body, racing number '48'	£5-8 ☐
48e	1978	'White Lightning'......................	US issued model...	£4-6 ☐
48f	1978	Sambron Jacklift.......................	Yellow/Black or Yellow/Orange body, 78 mm.	£2-4 ☐
			Yellow body, 'SAMBRON' in Red on side door	£30-40 ☐
48g	1983	(Mercedes) Unimog	Yellow/White/Black body, Red 'Rescue', snowplough, Superfast, 64 mm....	£2-3 ☐
		variant:..................	With White blade	£9-11 ☐
	1987	colour change:..............	White body, Yellow blade, 'ROAD RAIDER' logo......	£1-3 ☐
48h	1986	Vauxhall Astra GTE	Red body, opening doors, (includes Collector Card).....	£2-3 ☐
	1987	design change:.............	With 'A.C. Delco' tampo print	£2-3 ☐
	1987	colour change:.............	White body, racing number '48'	£1-3 ☐
	1988	design change:.............	White/Blue/Red/Yellow body with 'STP' logo, racing number '7'.............	£1-3 ☐

MB 49

Ref. No.	Year(s)	Model Type	Description	Price
49a	1958	M3 Personnel Carrier...............	Military Green, White 'Star' decal on bonnet	
			Metal wheels & rollers, 62 mm.	£20-30 ☐
			Grey plastic wheels, metal rollers	£20-30 ☐
			Grey plastic wheels & rollers	£350-400 ☐
			Grey plastic wheels, Silver rollers	£60-80 ☐
			Black plastic wheels and rollers, Grey tracks	£25-35 ☐
		track change:..............	Black plastic wheels and rollers, Green tracks	£35-45 ☐
49b	1967	(Mercedes) Unimog	Light Brown body, Sea-Green base, 61 mm..................	£12-15 ☐
			Light Brown body, Red base	£700-800 ☐
			Light Blue body, Red base	£8-12 ☐
		Superfast wheels:	Light or Mid-Blue body, Red base	£7-10 ☐
			Metallic Blue body, Red base	£8-12 ☐
49c	1973	'Chop Suey'	Metallic Red body, Silver engine and handlebars, 72 mm.	£35-45 ☐
	1974	colour change:.............	Metallic Red body, Red handlebars	£3-5 ☐
49d	1977	Crane Truck	Yellow/Black body, Purple windscreen, 76 mm.	£2-4 ☐
		colour change:.............	Yellow/Black body, 'SAFETY FIRST' decal	£2-4 ☐
		colour change:.............	Red/Yellow body	£2-4 ☐
		colour change:.............	All Yellow body, Orange jib, Red hook, Green tinted windows, Superfast	£2-4 ☐
49e	1983	'SAND DIGGER'......................	Green body, exposed engine, Yellow logo....................	£2-4 ☐
	1985	'DUNE MAN'	Red body, Yellow design on bonnet............................	£2-4 ☐
49f	1987	Peugeot Quasar	White body, Chrome interior, (with Collector Card).....	£2-4 ☐
	1987	Laser Wheels issue:......	Metallic Blue body...	£2-4 ☐
	1988	colour change:.............	Maroon body, Yellow design, exposed engine	£2-4 ☐
49g	1992	Lamborghini Diablo	Yellow body with Red 'DIABLO' on doors.................	£2-4 ☐

MB 50

Ref. No.	Year(s)	Model Type	Description	Price
50a	1958	Commer Pick-Up......................	Pale Brown body, metal wheels, 64 mm.	£25-35 ☐
			Pale or Light Brown body, Grey plastic wheels............	£35-45 ☐
			Light Brown body, Silver wheels................................	£80-120 ☐
			Red and White body, Silver wheels............................	£400-500 ☐
			Red and Grey body, Silver wheels..............................	£80-100 ☐
			Red and Grey body, Grey wheels................................	£60-70 ☐
			Red and Grey body, Black wheels...............................	£50-60 ☐
50b	1964	John Deere Lanz Tractor	Green body, Yellow hubs, Grey tyres, 50 mm.	£15-20 ☐
			Green body, Yellow hubs, Black tyres.........................	£10-15 ☐
			Green body, Green hubs, Black tyres..........................	£500-600 ☐
50c	1969	Ford Kennel Truck	Metallic Green body, White grille, smooth kennel floor, 71 mm.	£15-20 ☐
			Metallic Green body, White grille, textured kennel floor.	£8-12 ☐
			same but with Silver grillr..	£12-15 ☐
	1971	Superfast wheels:	Metallic Green body, Black base................................	£7-19 ☐
			same with Yellow base..	£15-20 ☐
			Lime-Green body, Black or Grey base.........................	£8-12 ☐
			same with unpainted base...	£20-25 ☐
50d	1974	Articulated Truck	Yellow cab, Blue trailer, tinted windows, Superfast wheels	£4-6 ☐
	1974	colour change:.............	As previous model but with Blue/Yellow labels...........	£2-4 ☐
50e	1981	Harley Davidson Motor Cycle..	Metallic Bronze body, Silver engine, Black seat and handlebars, 70 mm.	£2-4 ☐
	1982	colour change:.............	Metallic Plum body, Brown rider, Black seat & forks..	£2-4 ☐
50f	1985	Chevy Blazer............................	Red/White body, 'SHERIFF' crest, 'ISP7'.................	£2-4 ☐
50g	1988	Dodge Dakota	Red pick-up, side stripes, 2 spotlights	£1-3 ☐
50h	1991	Auxiliary Power Truck	Yellow/White body, 'Floodlight Heavy Rescue' logo...	£1-3 ☐
	1992	Auxiliary Power Truck	Red/White body, Blue 'No.2', 'Fire', 'Rescue Dept.' logos....	£1-3 ☐

MB 51

Ref. No.	Year(s)	Model Type	Description	Market Price Range	
51a	1958	Albion Chieftain	All models with Yellow body, Light Brown load		
			'PORTLAND CEMENT' decals, metal wheels	£40-50	☐
			'BLUE CIRCLE PORTLAND CEMENT' decals, metal wheels	£33-38	☐
			same with Grey plastic wheels	£35-45	☐
			same with Silver plastic wheels	£80-120	☐
			same with Black plastic wheels	£180-220	☐
51b	1964	Tipping Trailer	Green body, 3 Yellow barrels, Yellow hubs, Grey tyres	£10-15	☐
			same with Yellow hubs, Black tyres	£5-10	☐
			same with Green hubs, black tyres	£250-300	☐
51c	1969	AEC Mammoth Major 8 Wheel Tipper	Orange body, Silver tipper, 'DOUGLAS', White base & grille	£50-60	☐
			same with chrome base & grille	£20-25	☐
			Yellow body, Silver tipper, 'DOUGLAS'	£40-50	☐
			Yellow body, Silver tipper, 'POINTER'	£12-18	☐
51d	1973	Citroën SM	Metallic Red body, Cream seats, clear windows, Superfast, 78 mm	£3-5	☐
		colour change:	Metallic Orange body	£3-5	☐
		colour change:	Metallic Blue body	£3-5	☐
		Bulgarian issues:	Green, Gold or Blue body	£10-15	☐
	1977	colour change:	Blue body, Red flash, racing number '8'	£2-4	☐
51e	1978	Combine Harvester	Red body, Yellow moving parts. Superfast or ordinary plastic wheels.	£2-4	☐
51f	1982	'Midnight Magic'	Black/Silver, Chrome interior, US issued model	£4-6	☐
51g	1983	Pontiac Firebird	Red body, White decals, Tan seats, Superfast, 76 mm.	£2-4	☐
	1983	design change:	Red or Black body, 'Firebird' design	£2-4	☐
	1986	US issue:	Black body, 'HALLEYS COMET' logo	£2-4	☐
	1987	Laser Wheels issue:	Metallic Blue body	£2-4	☐
	1987	Matchbox/Dinky issue:	Blue body, racing number '18'	£2-4	☐
51h	1988	Ford Police Car	White body, Black tampo, Red 'PD-21'	£2-4	☐

MB 52

Ref. No.	Year(s)	Model Type	Description	Market Price Range	
52a	1958	1948 Maserati 4 CLT	Red body, Cream driver, no decal, Black plastic wheels, 61 mm.	£30-40	☐
			As previous but with 'RN 52' decal	£35-45	☐
		wheel change:	Red body, racing number '52', wire wheels, Black plastic tyres	£220-250	☐
			Yellow body, wire wheels, RN 52	£35-45	☐
			same but with RN 3 or 5	£70-100	☐
52b	1965	B.R.M. Racing Car	Blue body, Yellow wheels with Black tyres, RN 5	£8-12	☐
			same but with RN 3	£60-75	☐
			Red body, Yellow wheels with Black tyres (Giftset)	£60-80	☐
52c	1970	Dodge Charger Mk.III	Red body, Black/Yellow flash on some, Superfast, 76 mm.	£7-9	☐
		colour change:	Green body, 'CASTROL' label on bonnet	NGPP	☐
	1973	colour change:	Purple body, racing number '5' on some, Superfast	£5-8	☐
	1974	colour change:	Lime Green body, decal on some, Red base, Superfast	£5-8	☐
52d	1977	'POLICE' Launch	Blue and White boat, Blue tinted windows, 2 policemen, 77 mm	£2-4	☐
	1989	colour change:	Military version with Camouflage paint finish	£2-4	☐
52e	1981	BMW MI	Silver body, Black racing number '52', Red seats, Superfast, 75 mm.	£2-4	☐
	1983	colour change:	White body, Black RN '52', Red 'BMW MI', Superfast wheels	£2-4	☐
	1984	design change:	Red/Yellow body, racing number '5'	£2-4	☐
	1985	design change:	Black body, racing number '59'	£2-4	☐
	1986	design change:	Yellow/White body, Red racing number '11'	£2-4	☐
	1988	design change:	Red body, Blue/Red/White design	£2-4	☐
52f	1991	Isuzu Amigo	Blue body, spare wheel on rear, 'ISUZU' logo	£1-3	☐
	1992	colour change:	Red body, slanting side designs on Blue/Orange	£1-3	☐
	1994	Escort Cosworth		£1-2	☐

MB 53

Ref. No.	Year(s)	Model Type	Description	Market Price Range	
53a	1958	Aston Martin DB2-4 Mk.I	Metallic Green body, metal wheels, 65 mm.	£30-40	☐
			As previous but with Grey plastic wheels	£35-45	☐
		colour change:	Metallic Red body, Grey plastic wheels	£180-220	☐
		wheel change:	Metallic Red body, Black plastic wheels	£120-150	☐
53b	1963	Mercedes-Benz 220SE	Maroon body, Silver wheels, 69 mm.	£15-20	☐
			Maroon body, Grey wheels	£30-40	☐
			Maroon body, Black wheels	£20-30	☐
			Dark Red body, Grey wheels	£20-25	☐
			Dark Red body, Black wheels	£12-18	☐
53c	1968	Ford Zodiac Mk.IV	Light Metallic Blue body, Black, 71 mm.	£8-12	☐
			Light Metallic Green body, Black wheels	£400-500	☐
		Superfast wheels:	Light Metallic Blue body	£300-400	☐
			Light Metallic Green body	£8-12	☐
			Metallic Green body	£10-13	☐
			Dark Metallic Green body	£12-18	☐
			Lime Green body	£20-30	☐
53d	1973	'Tanzara'	Orange body, 'Clover-leaf' decal on some, Superfast, 76 mm.	£3-5	☐
	1976	colour change:	White body, Blue/Red stripes, racing number '53', Superfast	£3-5	☐
	1981	US issue:	Black body, Silver design, 'MIDNIGHT MAGIC'	£6-8	☐

Ref. No.	Year(s)	Model Type	*Matchbox Miniatures – continued*	Market Price Range	
53e	1977	CJ6 Jeep..................................	Red body, Fawn seats and roof, Superfast, 75 mm.	£2-4	☐
		seat change:................	With Black seats	£7-9	☐
		colour change:............	Green body, with Black seats	£7-9	☐
		colour change:............	Yellow body, with Brown roof	£5-7	☐
	1981	colour change:............	Green body, Yellow seats, Fawn roof	£2-4	☐
53f	1982	Flareside Pick-Up.....................	Blue or Orange body, *'Baja Bouncer'* logo, Superfast..........................	£2-4	☐
	1986	design change:............	Yellow/Blue body, *'FORD'*	£2-4	☐
	1987	colour change:............	Military-Green body, *'STICK-UP PICK-UP'* logo	£2-4	☐
53g	1989	Dump Truck..............................	Yellow body, Grey tipper, Red stripes	£1-3	☐
	1992	colour change:............	Yellow cab and chassis, Red tipper	£1-3	☐

MB 54

Ref. No.	Year(s)	Model Type		Market Price Range	
54a	1958	Saracen Personnel Carrier	Olive Green body, 6 Black plastic wheels, crimped axles, 57 mm.	£25-35	☐
			Same as previous but with rounded axles	£18-25	☐
54b	1965	Cadillac Ambulance	White, Red cross label or decal & roof lights, Black plastic wheels, 72 mm.	£8-12	☐
	1970	wheel change:.............	As previous model but with Superfast wheels..................................	£12-18	☐
54c	1971	Ford Capri...............................	Red body, Red or Black bonnet, Cream or White seats, Superfast, 77 mm.	£2-4	☐
		colour change:............	As previous model but Orange body...	£2-4	☐
	1974	colour change:............	Metallic Purple body, Cream or White seats	£2-4	☐
	1985	colour change:............	Pink body with Pink or Black bonnet	NRP	☐
54d	1977	Personnel Carrier	Green body, Brown figures, Superfast wheels, 76 mm.	£2-4	☐
54e	1980	Mobile Home............................	Cream or White body, Orange interior, Superfast, 76 mm.	£2-4	☐
54f	1982	'NASA' Tracking Vehicle..........	White body, Blue/Red decal, with or without *'Space Shuttle'* logo....	£2-4	☐
54g	1984	Airport Unit	Red/White body, Black/White design	£2-4	☐
	1985	design change:............	Red/Yellow body, *'METRO'*, 2 Blue warning lights............................	£2-4	☐
	1989	colour change:............	Red body, *'AIRPORT FOAM PUMPER'*...	£2-4	☐
	1989	colour change:............	Yellow body, Red tampo *'FOAM'*	£2-4	☐
	1989	colour change:............	Military version in Camouflage paintwork	£2-4	☐
54h	1990	Chevrolet Lumina......................	Blue body, *'MATCHBOX MOTORSPORTS'*, Yellow racing number '35'....	£1-3	☐
	1992	colour change:............	Green body, Yellow *'MATCHBOX MOTORSPORTS'*, and RN '35'..............	£1-3	☐
	1993	design change:............	Red body, racing number '12', Yellow *'Performance'* logo	£1-3	☐
	1994	Mazda RX-7..............................		£1-2	☐

MB 55

Ref. No.	Year(s)	Model Type		Market Price Range	
55a	1958	DUKW Amphibian....................	Olive Green body, metal wheels, 71 mm.	£15-20	☐
			same but with Grey plastic wheels..	£18-25	☐
			same but with Black plastic wheels...	£20-30	☐
55b	1963	Ford Fairlane 'POLICE' Car....	Dark Blue body (non metallic) and crests, Black plastic wheels, 66 mm.	£150-180	☐
		colour change:............	Metallic Blue body, Black plastic wheels	£18-22	☐
		wheel change:.............	With Grey plastic wheels..	£120-150	☐
			With Silver plastic wheels	£200-250	☐
55c	1966	Ford Galaxy 'POLICE' Car.....	White body, *'Police & Shield'* decal, Blue roof light	£60-80	☐
			same but with Red roof light	£12-15	☐
	1970	wheel change:.............	As previous model but with Superfast wheels..................................	£8-12	☐
55d	1968	Mercury 'POLICE' Car............	White body, *'Police & Shield'* labels, Red roof light	£50-60	☐
			same but with Blue roof light	£12-15	☐
		Superfast wheels:	Superfast wheels, Red roof light	£15-20	☐
			same but with Blue roof light	£20-25	☐
	1987	Laser Wheels issue:....	White body, *'R-15'* logo..	£2-4	☐
55e	1971	Mercury 'POLICE' Estate Car..	White body, Police crest, Superfast wheels, 77 mm...........................	£6-9	☐
55f	1976	'Hell Raiser'.............................	White body, Silver exposed engine, Red seats, 75 mm........................	£3-5	☐
	1978	colour change:............	Metallic Blue body, stars and stripes decal	£2-4	☐
55g	1980	Ford Cortina 1600 GL	Metallic Green body, Red seats, opening doors, Superfast wheels, 75 mm....	£2-4	☐
	1981		Metallic Red body, Yellow seats, opening doors, Superfast	£2-4	☐
	1982	colour change:............	Metallic Bronze and White body, Yellow seats, (many other variations)	£2-4	☐
	1983	colour change:............	Metallic Tan body with Dark Blue racing stripes...............................	£2-4	☐
55h	1983	Ford Sierra XR4i	Metallic Silver & Black body, Red seats, Superfast wheels, 76 mm. ...	£2-4	☐
	1984	colour change:............	Silver/Grey body, Red/Black design	£2-4	☐
	1985	colour change:............	Silver/Red body, Red *'XR4i'* design	£2-4	☐
	1987	colour change:............	Cream body, racing number '55', Superfast	£2-4	☐
	1987	colour change:............	White body, *'VIRGIN'* logo, Superfast	£2-4	☐
	1987	Laser Wheels issue:....	Metallic Green, racing number '85' logo	£2-4	☐
	1989	design change:............	Black body, *'TEXACO'* logo, racing number '46'	£2-4	☐
55i	1986	Ford Sierra XR44	Yellow body, Black chassis, spoiler, tampo-print design	£2-4	☐
		design change:............	Yellow body, Red interior	£2-4	☐
	1989	design change:............	Yellow body, Black bonnet stripes	£2-4	☐
	1991	design change:............	Black body, White/Red *'TEXACO'* and star logos, RN '6'	£1-3	☐
	1992	design change:............	White body, Red racing number '1', plus various Blue logos	£1-3	☐

MB 56

Ref. No.	Year(s)	Model Type		Market Price Range	
56a	1958	London Trolley Bus	All models with Red body, *'DRINK PEARDRAX'* and destination decals		
			Black poles, metal wheels...	£100-130	☐
			Black poles, Grey plastic wheels...	£220-250	☐
			Red poles, metal wheels..	£40-50	☐
			Red poles, Grey or Black plastic wheels	£35-45	☐
			Red poles, Silver wheels...	£90-120	☐

Ref. No.	Year(s)	Model Type	*Matchbox Miniatures – continued*	Market Price Range	
56b	1965	Fiat 1500	Sea-Green body, Brown luggage, 65 mm.	£12-18	☐
			Sea-Green body, Red-Brown luggage	£8-12	☐
			Red body, Red-Brown luggage (Giftset)	£60-80	☐
56c	1969	B.M.C. 1800 Pininfarina	Gold body, White seats, opening doors, Superfast wheels, 70 mm.	£8-11	☐
	1970	colour change:	Orange body, White seats, wide or narrow Superfast wheels	£5-8	☐
	1971	colour change:	Bronze body, White seats, Superfast	£5-8	☐
			Off-White body and seats, metal base, wide or narrow Superfast	£5-8	☐
56d	1975	Hi-Tailer	White body, Blue/Orange driver, racing number '5', *'TEAM MATCHBOX'*	£3-5	☐
		logo change:	As previous model but with Red base, *'MARTINI RACING'*	£3-5	☐
56e	1980	Mercedes 450 SEL	Metallic Blue body, Tan or Red interior, clear windows.	£2-4	☐
	1981	Taxi version:	Cream body, Red *'Taxi'* on roof	£2-4	☐
	1983	Police Car version:	Green and White body, *'Polizei'*, 2 Blue warning lights, Superfast	£2-4	☐
	1981	colour change:	White body	£2-4	☐
	1992	Taxi version:	Yellow body, Red *'Taxi'* on White roof sign, Black '56' on bonnet	£2-4	☐
56f	1982	Peterbilt Tanker	Blue/White body, *'MILKS THE ONE'*	£2-4	☐
	1989	colour change:	Camouflage paint	£2-4	☐
56g	1985	VW Golf Gti	Red body, opening bonnet	£2-4	☐
	1986	design change:	as previous models but White body with *'GTI'* design	£2-4	☐
	1987	design change:	Blue/White body, *'QUANTUM'*, racing number '66', promotional	£2-4	☐
	1987	design change:	White body, *'FEDERAL EXPRESS'* or *'QUANTUM'* logo	£2-4	☐
	1989	colour change:	Two-tone Metallic Grey body	£2-4	☐
56h	1989	4 x 4 Jeep	Red body and seats, *'GOLDEN EAGLE'* logo in Yellow	£2-4	☐
	1994	Camaro Z-28		£1-2	☐

MB 57

57a	1958	Wolseley 1500	Pale Green body, Grey plastic wheels, Gold trim, 55 mm.	£100-120	☐
			As previous but with Silver trim	£30-40	☐
57b	1961	Chevrolet Impala	All models with Metallic Blue body and pale Blue roof		
			Clear windows, Black base, Silver wheels	£60-75	☐
			Clear windows, Dark Blue base, Silver wheels	£30-40	☐
			Green windows, Dark Blue base, Silver wheels	£20-25	☐
			same but with Grey wheels	£30-40	☐
			Green windows, Pale or Light Blue base, Silver wheels	£40-50	☐
			Black base, Grey wheels	£40-50	☐
			Black base, Silver wheels	£35-45	☐
			Black base, Black wheels	£25-35	☐
57c	1966	Land Rover Fire Truck	Red body, *'KENT FIRE BRIGADE'*, Black plastic wheels, 64 mm.	£12-16	☐
	1970	wheel change:	As previous model but with Grey plastic wheels	£200-250	☐
	1970	wheel change:	As previous model but with Superfast wheels	£25-35	☐
57d	1970	Eccles Caravan	Pale Yellow body, Orange roof, Maroon stripe, Superfast, 75 mm.	£7-10	☐
		colour change:	Same but Brown stripe, White interior, 'flower' decal on some	£5-8	☐
	1971	colour change:	Off-White body, with or without 'flower' decal	£5-7	☐
	1973	colour change:	Cream body, Brown stripe and 'flower' decal on some, Green interior	£3-5	☐
57e	1974	Wild Life Truck	Yellow body, *'Ranger* decal, clear cover, Rolamatic, 70 mm.	£2-4	☐
	1981	colour change:	White body, Black stripes	£2-4	☐
57f	1982	Carmichael Police Vehicle	White body, Black roof, *'Police Rescue'*.	£2-4	☐
57g	1983	Carmichael Fire Vehicle	Red/White body, *'FIRE'*, Black plastic ladder	£2-4	☐
		'Mountain Man'	Blue body, *'CIBIE'*, 4 x 4, US issued model	£4-6	☐
57h	1986	Mission Helicopter	Blue body, White rotor and tail	£2-4	☐
	1987	colour change:	Red body, *'SHERIFF'* tampo-print	£2-4	☐
	1989	colour change:	Camouflage paint finish	£2-4	☐
	1992	Police version:	White with Dark Blue side panels, White *'POLICE'* logo, Red trim	£1-3	☐
	1995	Jeep Cherokee		£1-2	☐

MB 58

58a	1958	AEC 'BEA' Coach	Dark Blue body, White letters, Grey wheels, 65 mm.	£40-50	☐
			Dark Blue body, Black letters on White ground, Grey wheels	£35-45	☐
			same but with Silver wheels	£80-100	☐
			same but with Black wheels	£75-90	☐
58b	1962	Drott Excavator	Red body, Silver base, Black rollers, Green tracks, 65 mm.	£12-18	☐
			same but with Silver rollers	£70-90	☐
			Orange body, Silver base, Black rollers	£18-25	☐
			Orange body & base, Black rollers	£15-20	☐
58c	1968	DAF Girder Truck	White body, Red base & 12 girders, 6 Black plastic wheels, 75 mm.	£8-12	☐
	1970	wheel change:	as previous model but with Superfast wheels	£20-30	☐
		colour change:	Same but Metallic Lime Green body, Red plastic base	£8-12	☐
58d	1973	'Woosh-N-Push'	Yellow body, racing number '2', Superfast wheels, 77 mm.	£2-3	☐
		design change:	Yellow body with 'flower' label	£10-12	☐
		design change:	Purple body with '8' label	£3-5	☐
		design change:	Metallic Dark Red body, Pale Yellow interior, metal base, RN '2'	£4-6	☐
58e	1977	Faun Dumper	Yellow body, *'Cat'* logo on some, Superfast wheels, 71 mm.	£1-3	☐
58f	1983	'RUFF TREK' (Pick Up)	Gold/Brown body, Red trim, Black load, spare wheel, 74 mm.	£2-4	☐
	1985	design change:	White body, Red/Yellow tampo-print design, racing number '217'	£2-4	☐
	1989	colour change:	White body, 'flame' design, (James Bond Set)	£2-4	☐
	1987	colour change:	Brown body, *'CAR POW'* logo, Superfast wheels	£2-4	☐
58g	1988	Mercedes 300e	Metallic Blue body with Silver trim	£1-3	☐
	1991	'POLIZEI' version:	White and Green body with Black logo	£1-3	☐

MB 59

Ref. No.	Year(s)	Model Type	Description	Price	
59a	1958	Ford Thames Van 'SINGER' ...	Pale Green body, Red Seats and logo, Grey plastic wheels, 56 mm.	£35-45	☐
		wheel change:	As previous model but with Silver plastic wheels, rivetted axles	£70-80	☐
		colour change:	Mid-Green body and Grey plastic wheels, rivetted axles	£150-180	☐
		wheel change:	Mid-Green body and Silver plastic wheels, rivetted axles	£180-220	☐
59b	1963	Ford Fairlane Fire Chief	All models with Red body and 'FIRE CHIEF' decals on doors and bonnet		
			Black wheels	£20-25	☐
			Grey wheels	£50-75	☐
			Silver wheels	£150-180	☐
			With 'SHIELD' decals on doors	£200-250	☐
59c	1966	Ford Galaxie Fire Chief	Red body, Blue dome light, 'FIRE CHIEF & SHIELD'	£10-15	☐
			same but with Red dome light	£200-220	☐
			With Superfast wheels (blue dome light)	£12-18	☐
59d	1970	'FIRE CHIEF' Car	Red body, Yellow logo, driver and passenger, Superfast wheels, 73 mm.	£8-11	☐
59e	1976	Planet Scout	Two-tone Green body, tinted windows, 2 warning lights, 70 mm.	£3-5	☐
	1979	colour change:	Red body, Cream chassis	£2-4	☐
	1981	colour change:	Green/Black body, Purple windows	£6-8	☐
	1983	colour change:	Metallic Blue with Purple windows	£15-18	☐
59f	1980	Porsche 928	Metallic Brown body, 'PORSCHE', opening doors, Superfast wheels, 75 mm.	£2-4	☐
	1981	colour change:	Blue body	£2-4	☐
	1982	colour change:	Black body, White stripes, crest on bonnet	£2-4	☐
	1984	colour change:	Grey/Blue body, 'PORSCHE'	£1-3	☐
	1985	colour change:	Black with Tan interior	£1-3	☐
	1986	colour change:	Silver/Blue body, Blue 'PORSCHE'	£1-3	☐
59g	1988	Porsche '944 Turbo'	All Red body, Yellow design	£1-3	☐
	1989	colour change:	Red body, Black print 'CREDIT CHARGE'	£1-3	☐
	1989	colour change:	Black body, bonnet design	£1-3	☐
	1990	colour change:	White body, 'DUCKHAMS OIL'.	£1-3	☐
	1991	colour change:	White body & interior, Yellow '944' on doors, 'PORSCHE' bonnet crest	£1-3	☐
	1995	Vauxhall Frontera		£1-2	☐

MB 60

Ref. No.	Year(s)	Model Type	Description	Price	
60a	1958	Morris J2 Pick Up	All models with Light Blue body and 'BUILDERS SUPPLY COMPANY' decals		
			Two line in decal Black, Grey wheels	£45-55	☐
			Two line in decal White, with rear windows, Grey or Black wheels	£25-35	☐
			same but with Silver wheels	£30-40	☐
			Without rear window, Grey wheels	£70-90	☐
			Without rear window, Black wheels	£35-45	☐
60b	1966	Site Hut Truck	Blue body, Yellow and Green plastic building, Black wheels	£8-12	☐
	1970	Superfast wheels:	Same with Superfast wheels, two rivets on base	£18-22	☐
			Same but with one rivet on base	£10-15	☐
60c	1972	Lotus Super Seven	Light Brown body, Black seats, Black plastic wheels, 74 mm.	£6-9	☐
	1976	colour change:	Yellow body, Red stripes racing number '60'	£4-6	☐
		design change:	Orange body, Black seats, metal base, 'devil' logo	£5-8	☐
60d	1977	Holden Motorcycle Pick-Up	Metallic Red body, 2 Yellow motorcycles, '500', Superfast wheels	£5-8	☐
	1978	colour change:	Orange body, 2 Yellow motorcycles, '500', Superfast	£3-5	☐
	1981	colour change:	Red body, 2 Green or Yellow motorcycles, '500', Superfast	£2-4	☐
	1982	colour change:	Cream body, 2 Red motor-bikes, 'SUPERBIKE' logo	£3-5	☐
60e	1983	'TOYOTA RACING'	White/Black body, racing number '41' in Red, Superfast wheels, 76 mm.	£2-4	☐
	1985	logo change:	As previous model but without racing number, with 'SUPRA' logo	£2-4	☐
	1987	Matchbox/Dinky issue:	White body, Blue/Red/Yellow design, bubble packed	£2-4	☐
60f	1986	**Ford Transit Van**			
	1986	'MOTORSPORT'	Red body with Blue design, promotional	£2-4	☐
	1987	'AMBULANCE'	White body, promotional	£2-4	☐
	1987	'UNICHEM'	White body	£2-4	☐
	1987	'FEDERAL EXPRESS'	White body	£2-4	☐
	1987	'AUSTRALIA POST'	Red body, Australian issue	£2-4	☐
	1987	'XP'	White body	£2-4	☐
	1988	'GREAT ORMOND St HOSPITAL'	White body, 'WISHING WELL APPEAL'	£4-6	☐
	1988	'WELLA'	White body, Brown/Red design, German promotional model	£4-6	☐
	1988	'FORD MOTOR Co.'	All Green body, Ford box, Dutch issue model	£4-6	☐
	1988	'AUSTRALIAN POST'	Bright Orange/White body, 'WE DELIVER', promotional	£4-6	☐
	1989	'PETER COX'	White body, Blue/Red stripe (K.H.Norton promotional)	£2-4	☐
	1990	'D.C.S.'	White body, 'TECHNICAL SERVICES COMPANY'.	£1-3	☐
	1990	'RYDER TRUCK RENTALS'	Yellow body with Black logo	£1-3	☐
	1992	'CADBURYS FLAKE'	Yellow body with Purple logo	£1-3	☐
	1995	Toyota Supra		£1-2	☐

MB 61

Ref. No.	Year(s)	Model Type	Description	Price	
61a	1959	Ferret Scout Car	Olive Green body, Tan driver Silver or Black plastic wheels, 57 mm.	£20-25	☐
61b	1966	Alvis Stalwart 'BP'	White body, Green wheels with Black tyres, smooth carried bed	£25-30	☐
			same but with ribbed carried bed	£10-15	☐
			White body, Yellow wheels with Black tyres	£35-45	☐
			Olive Green body, Black wheels (Two-Pack)	£15-20	☐

Ref. No.	Year(s)	Model Type	*Matchbox Miniatures – continued*	Market Price Range
61c	1972	'Blue Shark'	Metallic Blue body, White driver, racing number '86' Superfast, 77 mm.	£2-4
		design change:	With 'SCORPION' label	£12-16
		design change:	With '69' label	£12-16
		design change:	With '86' label and Silver/Grey base	£6-9
61d	1978	Ford Wreck Truck	Red body with Red or White jibs, Superfast wheels	£2-4
	1981	colour change:	Yellow body with Red or Green jibs	£2-4
	1982	colour change:	Red body, White jibs, '24 HOUR TOWING' logo	£2-4
61e	1982	Peterbilt Wreck Truck	Red body, 2 Black jibs, 'Eddies Wrecker', Superfast	£2-4
	1982	colour change:	White body, Black jibs, 'DIAL 911'	£2-4
	1984	colour change:	White body, Blue jibs, 'DIAL 911'	£2-4
	1985	colour change:	Orange jibs and 'SFPD' logo	£2-4
	1987	colour change:	Orange body, Green jibs, 'TOWNAILER' logo	£2-4
	1989	colour change:	Camouflage paint finish	£2-4
			Blue body (Pre-production but reported on Gift Sets)	NGPP
61f	1991	Fork Lift Truck	Yellow/Black body and forks	£1-3
	1991	colour change:	Lime or Mid-Green body, Red/White stripes, Black chassis & forks	£1-3
61g	1988	T-Bird Turbo	All Red body, Black band	£1-3
	1995	Abrams M1 Tank		£1-2

MB 62

Ref. No.	Year(s)	Model Type		Market Price Range
62a	1959	AEC General Service Lorry	Olive Green body, tow hook, 6 Black plastic wheels, 68 mm.	£24-30
62b	1963	Commer TV Service Van	All models with Cream body and Red plastic ladder, aerial & 3 TVs	
			'RENTASET', knobbly Grey wheels (24 treads)	£120-150
			'RENTASET', Black wheels	£40-50
			'RENTASET', Fine Grey wheels (45 treads)	£180-200
			'RADIO RENTALS', Black wheels	£50-60
			'RADIO RENTALS', Fine Grey wheels	£250-300
62c	1968	Mercury Cougar	Cream body, White interior	£800-1000
			Metallic Lime Green body, Red interior	£10-15
	1969	wheel change:	Metallic Lime-Green body, Superfast wheels	£12-16
			Metallic Yellow-Green body, Superfast wheels	£15-20
62d	1970	Rat Rod Dragster	Lime Green body, 'RAT ROD' labels, unpainted base	£5-10
			same but with Silver-Grey base	£10-15
		design change:	Lime-Greem body, 'WILD CAT' labels	£15-20
62e	1974	Renault 17 TL	Red body, White seats, Blue tinted windows, RN '9', Superfast, 76 mm.	£4-6
		window change:	As previous model but with Green tinted windows	£4-6
62f	1980	Chevrolet Corvette	Metallic Red body, White stripe, Superfast wheels, 74 mm.	£4-6
	1981	colour change:	Black body, Orange stripe or '54' logo	£2-4
	1983	US issue:	Silver body, 'PACE CAR' logo	£4-6
	1986	Laser Wheels issue:	Black body, 'TURBOVETTE' logo	£2-4
62g	1982	Chevrolet Corvette T Roof	White body, Orange/Black stripes, racing number '09', Superfast	£2-4
	1985	colour change:	Blue body, Red interior, Red/White/Yellow design, Superfast	£2-4
	1987	colour change:	Yellow body, 'CORVETTE' logo, Superfast	£2-4
62h	1989	Volvo Container Truck	White body, Purple/Red print 'FEDERAL EXPRESS'	£2-4
	1991	design change:	Red body, White container with 'BIG TOP CIRCUS' design	£1-3
62i	1986	Volvo 760	Silver body, opening doors	£1-3
	1988	colour change:	Red body	£1-3

MB 63

Ref. No.	Year(s)	Model Type		Market Price Range
63a	1959	Service Ambulance (Ford)	Olive Green body, Red crosses, Black plastic wheels, crimped axles, 63 mm.	£30-35
			As previous but with rounded axles	£25-30
63b	1963	Alvis Foamite Crash Tender	Red body, Silver hose nozzle, 6 Black plastic wheels, 63 mm.	£50-60
		hose change:	With Gold hose nozzle	£22-28
63c	1968	Dodge Crane Truck	Yellow body, Red hook, 76 mm.	£8-12
			Yellow body, Yellow hook	£10-15
	1970	Superfast wheels:	Yellow body, Red hook, Superfast wheels	£10-15
63d	1973	Freeway Gas Tanker	78 mm. long with Red cab, White/Red tank unless otherwise stated:	
		'BURMAH'	Black logo, Red/Blue company motif, Superfast wheels	£4-6
		'ARAL'	Blue cab, Blue and White logo, Superfast, German issue	£30-35
		'SHELL'	White/Yellow body, Red logo, Superfast	£4-6
		'CHEVRON'	Red cab, Red/White/Blue logo, Superfast	£4-6
		'BP SUPER'	White cab, White/Green tank, Yellow logo, Superfast	£4-6
		'EXXON'	US issued model	£4-6
		Army issue	Dark Military Green body with French Flag	£30-40
		Army issue	Military Green, '95 High Octane'	£4-6
		'CASTROL'	Red/White body	£25-35
63e	1980	Dodge Challenger	Metallic Green, 'SPEEDSTICKS', (US issued model)	£4-6
	1981	logo change:	Metallic Green, 'HOT POINTS' logo, (US issued model)	£4-6
63f	1982	4 x 4 Pick-Up Truck	Orange body, racing number '24' with '4 x 4' or 'FWD' logo, 71 mm.	£2-4
	1984	colour change:	Yellow body, Orange panels, racing number '24'	£2-4
	1986	colour change:	White/Blue body, racing number '63' logo	£2-4
63g	1988	Volvo 480 ES	All White body, '480 ES'	£2-4
	1988	Laser Wheels issue:	Silver body, '480' logo	£2-4
	1989	colour change:	White body, with or without 'VOLVO' on bonnet	£2-4
63h	1991	Volkswagen Golf GT	White body with 'flower' design, 'ABSTRACT'	£1-3
63i	1992	Steam Locomotive	Green body with Black tank and chassis, with 'British Railways' crest	£1-3
	1994	Aston-Martin DB7		£1-2

MB 64

Ref. No.	Year(s)	Model Type	Description	Market Price Range	
64a	1959	Scammell Breakdown Truck	Olive Green body, metal or plastic hook, Black plastic wheels, 64 mm.	£25-35	☐
64b	1966	MG 1100...................................	Green body, White seats, driver, dog, Black plastic wheels, 67 mm......................	£8-12	☐
		wheel change:.............	Green body, Superfast wheels...	£100-120	☐
	1970	colour change:..........	Metallic Blue body, Superfast wheels...................................	£7-9	☐
64c	1972	'Slingshot' Dragster	Pink body, racing number '9', driver, Superfast, 76 mm.	£6-9	☐
	1974	colour change:.............	Metallic Green body, Silver/Red exposed engine, Black base, RN '9'	£6-9	☐
			same with unpainted base	£20-25	☐
		colour change:.............	Metallic Green body, racing number '3' or 'Flame' label	£15-20	☐
		colour change:.............	Orange body, RN '9'	£75-90	☐
	1975	colour change:.............	Blue body, Silver/Red exposed engine	£2-4	☐
64d	1976	Fire Chief Car	Red body, Yellow/Black 'Fire, Blue tinted windows, 77 mm.	£2-4	☐
64e	1979	Caterpillar D8H Bulldozer	Yellow body & dozer blade, Brown canopy............................	£2-4	☐
	1982	colour change:	Yellow body & blade, Black canopy	£2-4	☐
		colour change:	As previous but with Bright Red canopy	NGPP	☐
	1983	colour change:.............	Yellow body, Black blade & canopy, 'C' or 'CAT' logo	£2-4	☐
64f	1984	Dodge Caravan......................	Silver body, Black stripes, Red interior, chrome trim, sliding door	£2-4	☐
		colour change:.............	Black body, Silver stripes.......................................	£2-4	☐
		colour change:.............	Red body, Black stripe..	£2-4	☐
	1985	colour change:.............	Black body, Silver/Gold design.................................	£2-4	☐
	1987	colour change:..........	White with 'CARAVAN', 'PAN-AM' or 'VIRGIN' logo	£2-4	☐
64g	1989	Oldsmobile Aerotech	All Silver or Red body..	£2-4	☐

MB 65

Ref. No.	Year(s)	Model Type	Description	Market Price Range	
65a	1959	Jaguar 3.4 litre..........................	Dark Blue body, Silver rear number-plate, Grey plastic wheels, 62 mm.	£45-55	☐
			As previous but with Blue rear number plate	£35-45	☐
		colour change:.............	Metallic Blue body and number-plate, Grey plastic wheels	£100-130	☐
65b	1962	Jaguar 3.8 Sedan..................	Metallic Red body, Silver base, Silver wheels, 68 mm.	£70-80	☐
		colour change:.............	Red body, Silver wheels	£30-40	☐
			Red body, Grey wheels	£35-45	☐
			Red body, Black wheels	£20-25	☐
65c	1967	Claas Combine Harvester.........	Red body, Yellow blades and front hubs, No hole in base, 76 mm.	£80-100	☐
			As previous but with hole in base	£6-10	☐
65d	1973	Saab Sonnet......................	Metallic Blue body, Orange seats, Superfast wheels, 73 mm.	£4-6	☐
			White body, Orange seats (Multi-pack)..........................	£80-120	☐
65e	1978	**Airport Coach**	Model has painted lower body (colour as listed), White plastic upper body, Amber or clear windows, Yellow or Ivory interior, Superfast wheels, 78 mm.		
		'BRITISH AIRWAYS'...............	Metallic Blue lower body, Red/White/Blue labels..................	£5-7	☐
		'AMERICAN AIRWAYS' ...	Metallic Blue lower body, Red/White/Blue labels..................	£5-7	☐
		'LUFTHANSA'....................	Metallic Blue body, Black/Blue/Orange/White labels...............	£5-7	☐
	1980	'TWA'	Metallic Red/White, Yellow interior, Amber windows................	£5-7	☐
		'QUANTAS'....................	Metallic Red, Yellow interior, Amber windows...................	£5-7	☐
	1982	'ALITALIA'	Green/Red/Black body...	£5-7	☐
		'SCHULBUS'	Orange lower body, White upper body, German issue model	£5-7	☐
		'PAN AM'	White body...	£5-7	☐
		'GIROBANK'....................	Blue/White body, 'SIMPLY MORE CONVENIENT'	£5-7	☐
		'STORK SB'	White/Blue body, Australian issue..................................	£5-7	☐
		'VIRGIN'....................	Red body	£2-3	☐
65f		Kenworth 'Tyrone Malone'			
	1982	US issue:	Black body, 'Bandag Bandit' logo................................	£4-6	☐
	1987	colour change:.............	Tan body, 'Barrel Bomber' logo.................................	£4-6	☐
65g		Indy Racer	Yellow body, (US issue model).................................	£2-4	☐
65h	1985	Plane Transporter....................	Yellow body, Red/White plane, 'RESCUE', (includes Collector Card)	£2-4	☐
	1989	colour change:.............	Camouflage paint finish	£2-4	☐
65i	1987	Cadillac Allante..................	Silver body, Red seats, opening doors.............................	£2-4	☐
	1987	Laser Wheels issue:...	Black body	£1-3	☐
	1989	colour change:.............	All Pink body, White interior	£1-3	☐
	1989	US issue:	Silver body	£4-6	☐
	1991	design change:.............	Pink body, White interior, Yellow side stripe, Black design	£1-3	☐
	1995	Ford F-150 Pick-Up	....	£1-2	☐

MB 66

Ref. No.	Year(s)	Model Type	Description	Market Price Range	
66a	1959	Citroën DS 19..........................	Yellow body, Silver trim, Grey plastic wheels, 64 mm.................	£35-45	☐
		wheel change:.............	Same but with Silver plastic wheels, rivetted axles................	£55-75	☐
66b	1962	Harley Davidson Motor Cycle..	Metallic Bronze bike & sidecar, 3 spoked wheels, Black plastic tyres, 66 mm. .	£50-60	☐
66c	1966	'GREYHOUND' Coach	Silver-Grey body, clear windows, 'GREYHOUND' decal...............	£50-60	☐
		window change:	Silver-Grey body, Amber windows, 'GREYHOUND' decal or label......	£10-12	☐
	1970	Superfast wheels:	Silver-Grey body, Black base...................................	£10-12	☐
			Siver-Grey body, Yellow or Pink base	£20-30	☐
66d	1972	'Mazda' RX500	Orange body, Amber windows.....................................	£60-75	☐
			Orange body, Purple windows, White base........................	£4-6	☐
			Same but with unpainted base	£8-10	☐
			Red body, White base, no tempa................................	£50-60	☐
			Red body, White base, 'CASTROL'...............................	£150-200	☐
			Red body, White base, '77' tempa..............................	£5-8	☐
			Same but with unpainted base	£10-12	☐
			Green body, '66' tempa (US)..................................	£10-12	☐
			Various Bulgarian issues exist................................	£5-20	☐

Ref. No.	Year(s)	Model Type	Matchbox Miniatures – continued	Market Price Range	
66e	1978	Ford Transit Pick Up................	Orange body, Yellow or Green interior, Green tinted windows, Tan crate	£5-7	☐
		window change:	As previous model but with Amber tinted windows	£2-4	☐
66f	1983	Tyrone Malone........................	White body, Red & Blue design 'SUPERBOSS', Superfast	£2-4	☐
66g		Rolls-Royce Silver Spirit	Brown body and interior, opening doors, Superfast	£2-4	☐
	1988	colour change:.............	Metallic Greenish-Gold body	£2-4	☐
	1990	colour change:.............	Metallic Red body................	£2-4	☐

MB 67

Ref. No.	Year(s)	Model Type		Market Price Range	
67a	1959	Saladin Armoured Car	Olive Green body, 6 Black plastic wheels, crimped axles, 61 mm.	£25-35	☐
			As previous but with rounded axles	£24-30	☐
67b	1967	Volkswagen 1600 TL................	Red body, Black wheels with Silver hubcaps	£15-20	☐
			Red body, Silver wheels with black tyres	£10-15	☐
			Red body with Maroon plastic roof rack (Giftset)................	£50-60	☐
			Metallic Purple body, Silver wheels with Black tyres................	£220-250	☐
		Superfast wheels:	Red body................	£40-50	☐
			Metallic Dark Purple body	£18-22	☐
			Metallic Purple or Metallic Pink body (many shades)	£8-10	☐
67c	1974	'Hot Rocker'.........................	Metallic Green body, White seats, Rolamatic, Superfast wheels, 77 mm.	£2-4	☐
	1976	colour change:.............	Red body................	£2-4	☐
	1981	US issue:	Yellow body, 'MAXI TAXI'................	£4-6	☐
67d	1979	Datsun 260 Z........................	Metallic Purple body, Yellow interior, hook, Superfast wheels, 75 mm.	£2-4	☐
	1981	colour change:.............	Metallic Silver, Red stripes & '2 x 2' on some, Superfast	£2-4	☐
	1982	colour change:.............	Black body, with or without '2 x 2' logo	£2-4	☐
	1983	colour change:.............	Metallic or plain Blue body, Pale Yellow interior	£2-4	☐
67e	1983	IMSA 'FORD MUSTANG'.....	Black body, Red/White/Blue stripes tinted windows, Superfast	£2-4	☐
	1985	window change:.........	As previous model but with luminous 'Glo' windows	NRP	☐
67f	1986	'IKARUS' Coach	White body, 'GIBRALTAR' (Spanish issue)	£4-6	☐
	1986	design change:.............	White body, Orange roof, 'VOYAGER', (with Collector Card)	£2-4	☐
	1988	design change:.............	White with Green stripes, 'TOURIST CITY LINE'	£2-4	☐
	1988	design change:.............	White body, 'I LOVE CANARY ISLAND', promotional	£1-3	☐
	1992	design change:.............	White body, 'ESPANA' logo	£1-3	☐

MB 68

Ref. No.	Year(s)	Model Type		Market Price Range	
68a	1959	Austin Radio Truck Mk.II.......	Olive Green body and base, Black plastic wheels, crimped axles, 62 mm.	£30-35	☐
			As previous but with rounded axles	£25-30	☐
68b	1965	Mercedes Coach	Turquoise/White body, Black plastic wheels, 73 mm.	£175-200	☐
		colour change:.............	Orange/White body, Black plastic wheels................	£8-12	☐
68c	1970	Porsche 910.........................	Metallic Red, White seats racing number '68', Superfast, 76 mm.	£5-8	☐
		design change:.............	With '68' and 'Porsche' labels on sides (Giftset)	£12-18	☐
		colour change:.............	White body (Brrromstick)	£20-30	☐
68d	1976	'Cosmobile'	Metallic Blue and Yellow or Metallic Red and Light Brown body................	£4-8	☐
			Avocado body, Black chassis, Amber windows	£35-45	☐
			Avocado body, Black chassis, Purple windows	£12-18	☐
			Metallic Blue body, Black chassis	£40-50	☐
68e	1980	Chevrolet Van........................	Orange body, Red and Black flashes, Superfast wheels, 77 mm.	£2-4	☐
	1981	colour change:.............	Green body, Orange flash, 'Chev.', ...	£2-4	☐
	1982	colour change:.............	Silver body, Black/Blue/Red flashes 'Vanpire', Superfast	£2-4	☐
	1983	colour change:.............	White body, Orange flashes, 'Matchbox Racing'................	£2-4	☐
		colour change:.............	Orange body, 'Matchbox Collectors Club'................	£10-15	☐
		colour change:.............	White body, 'Adidas', (German issued model)	£10-15	☐
		logo change:.............	White body with 'USA' logo	£5-7	☐
	1985	logo change:.............	White body with 'Dr. PEPPER' logo	£1-3	☐
		logo change:.............	Yellow body with 'PEPSI' logo	£1-3	☐
68h	1991	Road Roller...........................	Orange body, Black roller wheels	£1-3	☐
	1992	colour change:.............	Yellow body with Red body design	£1-3	☐
68f	1982	Chevy 4 x 4 Van.....................	Metallic Green body with 'RIDIN' HIGH' logo	£1-3	☐
	1983	colour change:.............	White body, 'RACING' logo	£1-3	☐
	1984	Japanese issues:..........	White body with 8 various designs	£1-3	☐
	1985	Australian issue:........	White body with 'CASTROL' logo	£1-3	☐
68g	1987	Camero Iroc-Z........................	Blue or Pale Green body, (with Collector Card)	£1-3	☐
	1987	Laser Wheels issue:.....	Red body, 'GOODYEAR' logo	£1-3	☐
	1988	design change:.............	Yellow body, Blue/Red design	£1-3	☐
	1988	design change:.............	Blue body, Yellow 'BP' print, Dutch promotional	£1-3	☐
	1988	Laser Wheels issue:.....	Metallic Bronze body, racing number '12'	£1-3	☐
	1989	design change:.............	Yellow body, Blue or Green stripes	£1-3	☐
	1995	'Stinger'........................	....	£1-2	☐

MB 69

Ref. No.	Year(s)	Model Type		Market Price Range	
69a	1959	Commer Van 'NESTLES'........	Maroon body, driver, Yellow logo, Grey plastic wheels, 56 mm.	£35-40	☐
		colour change:.............	Red body, Grey plastic wheels with 20 treads................	£55-70	☐
		wheel change:.............	Red body, Grey plastic wheels with 36 treads................	£70-80	☐
69b	1965	Hatra Tractor Shovel	Orange body; Orange wheels, Grey tyres, 78 mm.	£60-75	☐
			Orange body, Red wheels, Grey tyres	£25-35	☐
			Orange body, Red wheels, Black tyres	£15-20	☐
			Orange body, Yellow wheels, Black tyres	£10-15	☐
			Yellow body, Yellow wheels	£10-15	☐
			Yellow body, Red wheels	£70-90	☐
			Orange body, Yellow shovel	£250-300	☐

Ref. No.	Year(s)	Model Type	*Matchbox Miniatures – continued*	Market Price Range	
69c	1970	Rolls-Royce Silver Shadow	Blue body, Black base..	£8-10	☐
			Blue body, Yellow base...	£20-30	☐
			Metallic Gold body, Yellow or Tan base........................	£15-20	☐
			Metallic Gold body, Silver or Grey base........................	£10-22	☐
			Metallic Gold body, Black base.....................................	£6-10	☐
69d	1974	Turbo Fury.............................	Red body with flash, RN '69', White driver, Rolamatic, Superfast	£2-4	☐
		decal change:............	As previous model but with '86' label...........................	£10-12	☐
69e		Security Truck	Metal body, plastic roof, Superfast wheels, 73 mm.		
	1979	'WELLS FARGO'	Red body, White roof & logo, special lights, Superfast........	£2-4	☐
	1980	'DRESDNER BANK'......	Green body, White roof, German issue model..................	£5-8	☐
69f	1982	Willys Street Rod	White or Blue body, '313' logo. (US issue).....................	£4-6	☐
69g	1983	'83 Corvette	Silver body, Red bands, '83 Vette'logo.........................	£2-4	☐
	1984	colour change:............	Red/Grey body, 'Vette'..	£2-4	☐
	1986		White body, racing number '7' or 'BOYARDEE' logo.......	£4-6	☐
	1987	colour change:............	Grey/Blue body, 'THUNDER GUNNER' logo.................	£2-4	☐
	1987	Matchbox/Dinky issue: ..	Red/Silver body, bubble packed.....................................	£2-4	☐
69h	1990	Snow Plough...........................	Yellow body, Black/Yellow plough, '45' in Blue............	£2-4	☐
	1992	Maintenance Truck	Yellow body, Red tipper and plough. (This is 69h Snow Plough renamed 'Maintenance Truck' in the 1992 Matchbox catalogue)........	£1-3	☐

MB 70

Ref. No.	Year(s)	Model Type		Market Price Range	
70a	1959	Ford Thames Estate Car...........	Turquoise and Yellow body		
			Grey wheels, no windows...	£25-30	☐
			Grey wheels, clear windows	£35-40	☐
			Grey wheels, Green windows	£22-28	☐
			Silver wheels, clear windows	£35-40	☐
			Silver or Black wheels, Green windows	£25-30	☐
70b	1966	Ford Grit Spreader..................	Red body, Pale Lemon container, Black plastic wheels, 68 mm.	£8-12	☐
		colour change:............	Red body, Dark Yellow container, Black or Grey slide, Black plastic wheels............	£25-35	☐
	1971	wheel change:............	As previous model but with Superfast wheels................	£8-12	☐
70c	1972	Dodge Dragster	Pink body, 'snake' decal, Superfast, 78 mm.	£3-5	☐
	1978	US issue:	Yellow body, 'HOT SMOKER'.......................................	£4-6	☐
	1980	US issue:	White body, 'ORANGE PEEL'..	£4-6	☐
		US issue:	Pink body, 'CASTROL' label on bonnet	NGPP	☐
70d	1977	SP Gun	Olive Green body, Black gun, Tan tracks, 68 mm.	£1-3	☐
	1989	colour change:............	Camouflage paint finish	NRP	☐
70e	1981	Ferrari 308 GTB......................	Orange body, Black flash, Black interior, Superfast wheels, 75 mm.	£2-4	☐
	1982	colour change:............	Same colours with 'Ferrari' decal, Superfast	£2-4	☐
	1983	colour change:............	Red body, White chassis, Superfast	£1-3	☐
	1985	colour change:............	Red/Blue body, racing number '39', 'Pioneer'	£1-3	☐
	1987	Laser Wheels issue:.....	Yellow body, 'FERRARI'	£1-3	☐
70f	1989	Ferrari F40	All Red body, Ferrari badges front & sides....................	£1-3	☐

MB 71

Ref. No.	Year(s)	Model Type		Market Price Range	
71a	1959	200 gallon Water Truck	Olive Green, Black plastic wheels, 61 mm. With first 'Matchbox Collectors' badge	£50-60	☐
		alternative version:......	Same model but without badge	£22-28	☐
71b	1964	Jeep Gladiator Pick-UP...........	Red body, Green interior, Black plastic wheels, 66 mm.	£40-50	☐
		colour change:............	As previous model but with White interior	£10-15	☐
71c	1969	Ford Heavy Wreck Truck	Red and White body, Amber windows, Black, 75 mm.	£120-150	☐
			Red and White body, Green windows, Black wheelsMilitary Green, Black wheels......	£8-12	☐
		Superfast wheels:	Red and White body, Green windows..............................	£10-13	☐
			Military Olive Green body, Black hubs...........................	£7-10	☐
			Military Olive Green body, chrome hubs.........................	£15-20	☐
			Blue body, chrome or Black hubs (U.K. 5 Pack issue)......	£75-90	☐
71d	1973	Jumbo Jet Motor Cycle............	Metallic Blue body, Light or Dark Blue handlebars..........	£3-5	☐
71e	1977	Dodge Cattle Truck.................	Bronze cab, Yellow cage, 2 Black cows..........................	£2-4	☐
	1979	colour change:............	Red cab, Yellow or Ivory cage, 2 Black cows	£2-4	☐
	1981	colour change:............	Red cab, White cage, 2 Black cows	£20-25	☐
	1982	colour change:............	Yellow cab, Brown cage, 2 Brown cows	£3-5	☐
		colour change:............	Metallic Orange cab, Yellow cage, 2 Brown cows	£8-11	☐
		colour change:............	Non-Metallic Green cab, Brown cage, 2 Brown cows	£15-20	☐
		colour change:............	Metallic Lime Green, Cream cage, 2 Brown cows	£3-5	☐
	1983	colour change:............	Green and White body, 2 Brown cows, Superfast	£2-4	☐
		note:...........................	Many other variations exist, for example with either Amber, Orange, Red, Blue, Purple or Green windows!		
71f	1987	Corvette	Blue, Red or White body (USA issued model)	£4-6	☐
	1987	Laser Wheels issue:.....	Orange or Metallic Green body, racing number '11'	£2-4	☐
71g	1985	Scania T142	White/Blue body, Black bumper	£2-4	☐
	1987	colour change:............	Blue body	£2-4	☐

Note: 71g was reissued many times as part of the 'Convoy' series. Logos include 'Amoco', 'Duckhams', 'Readymix', 'Varta', 'Sealink', 'Kit Kat', 'Tizer', 'Weetabix', 'Walls', 'Heinz', 'Signal', 'Shell', '7 Up', 'Beefeater', 'Golden Wonder' and 'Michelin'.

Ref. No.	Year(s)	Model Type		Market Price Range	
71h	1987	'Blue Flame 'Vette'	White body (USA issued model)	£4-6	☐
71i	1988	GMC Wrecker........................	White Red body, 'FRANKS'..	£2-4	☐

MB 72

Ref. No.	Year(s)	Model Type		Market Price Range	
72a	1959	Fordson Major Tractor............	All models with Blue body		
			Grey front wheels, Orange rear wheels with Grey tyres, 50 mm.	£35-40	☐
		wheel change:............	Black front wheels, Orange rear wheels with Black tyres	£33-38	☐
		wheel variant:............	Orange wheels front & rear, Grey tyres	£38-42	☐
			Orange wheels front & rear, Black tyres	£28-35	☐
			Yellow wheels front & rear, Grey or Black tyres	£150-180	☐

Ref. No.	Year(s)	Model Type	*Matchbox Miniatures – continued*	Market Price Range	
72b	1966	Jeep CJ5...............	Orange-Yellow body, Yellow wheels, White seats, 61 mm...........	£450-500	☐
			Yellow body, Yellow wheels, Red seats................	£8-12	☐
		Superfast wheels:	Yellow body, Red seats..............	£10-15	☐
72c	1972	'SRN6' Hovercraft	White/Red/Black body with Union Jack, 77 mm...........	£2-4	☐
72d	1979	Bomag Road Roller	Yellow body, Red engine and interior, Superfast wheels, 71 mm...........	£2-4	☐
		wheel change:..........	With Silver rear hubs	£9-12	☐
72e		Dodge Commando Truck			
	1982	'PEPSI'.................	Red and White body, Red/White/Blue decal, Superfast, 72 mm........	£2-4	☐
	1984	'KELLOGGS'.................	Red and White body...............	£2-4	☐
		wheel change:	With Gold hubs	£8-11	☐
	1984	'SMITHS CRISPS'.................	With 'crisp packet' design................	£8-11	☐
	1984	'STREETS ICE CREAM'....	Australian issue	£8-11	☐
	1985	'HERTZ'..................	All Yellow body	£1-3	☐
	1986	'ROYAL MAIL'.................	Red body................	£1-3	☐
	1987	'RISI'..................	All Yellow body................	£1-3	☐
	1987	'JETPRESS'.................	White body, Australian issue................	£8-11	☐
	1988	'YORKIE'.................	Blue body, Red/Yellow design, promotional...........	NRP	☐
	1988	'KIT KAT'.................	Red Body, Red/White design, promotional...........	NRP	☐
	1989	'MATCHBOX CONVENTION USA'	Red/White body	£4-6	☐
	1990	'C-PLUS ORANGE'	Green and Orange body...........	£4-6	☐
72f	1986	Sand Racer	US issue model	£3-5	☐
72g	1986	Ford 'SUPERVAN 2'	White/Blue body & tampo print, (includes Collector Card)........	£2-4	☐
	1987	colour change:.........	Mid or Dark Blue body................	£2-4	☐
	1988	design change:.........	White body, Blue/Red design 'STARFIRE'........	£2-4	☐
	1989	design change:.........	Yellow body with Green design 'BP', Dutch promotional	£2-4	☐
72h	1990	Sprint Racer	Red/Grey or Red/Silver body, racing number '2' in Yellow........	£1-3	☐

MB 73

73a	1959	R.A.F. 10 ton Refueller	(Leyland) Airforce-Blue body, roundel, 6 Grey plastic wheels, 66 mm.	£35-45	☐
		wheel change:...........	Same model but with Black plastic wheels................	£350-400	☐
73b	1962	Ferrari F1 Racing Car	Red body, Grey or White driver, RN '73', 'spoked' metal hubs, Black plastic tyres ...	£18-25	☐
73c	1968	Mercury Commuter.................	Metallic Lime Green body, Silver hubs, Black plastic tyres, 78 mm.	£8-12	☐
	1970	wheel change:.............	As previous model but with Superfast wheels	£8-12	☐
	1972	colour change:.............	Red body version, bonnet motif, filler cap on some	£6-10	☐
73d	1974	Weasel..................	Metallic Green body, Rolamatic, Superfast, 72 mm.	£2-4	☐
		colour change:.............	Dark Military Green body................	£50-60	☐
		colour change:.............	Light Military Green, Chrome hubs	£10-15	☐
	1989	colour change:.............	Camouflage paint finish	£2-4	☐
73e	1980	Ford Model 'A' Car.................	Cream body, Green chassis, spare wheel on some, Superfast........	£5-8	☐
	1981	colour change:.............	TT Green body and chassis, spare wheel on some, Superfast........	£4-6	☐
	1982	colour change:.............	Cream/Black body, Brown chassis, Orange tinted windows, Superfast........	£2-4	☐
	1984	colour change:.............	Brown body, Black wings & roof	£2-4	☐
	1985	colour change:.............	Red body................	£2-4	☐
	1986	colour change:.............	Black body, Yellow/Red 'fire' design................	£2-4	☐
		Promotional:.............	Metallic & non-metallic Green, 'CLIMAT' label	£25-30	☐
	1990	colour change:.............	Red/Green body, (Brooke Bond promotional)...........	£1-3	☐
73f	1989	TV News Truck	Blue/Grey body, Red camera, 'MB TV 75'...........	NRP	☐
	1991	design change:.............	White body, Blue roof with Red 'SKY SATELLITE TELEVISION'........	NRP	☐

MB 74

74a	1959	Mobile 'REFRESHMENTS' Bar	White body, Pale Blue base, Blue interior, opening hatch, Grey plastic wheels	£100-130	☐
		colour change:...........	Cream body, Light Blue base, Grey plastic wheels................	£90-120	☐
		colour change:............	Pink body, Light Blue base, Grey plastic wheels................	£180-220	☐
		colour change:.............	Silver body, Light Blue base, Grey plastic wheels................	£30-40	☐
		wheel change:.............	Silver body, Light Blue base, Silver plastic wheels................	£35-45	☐
		base change:.............	Silver body, Light Blue base, Black plastic wheels................	£300-350	☐
			Silver body, Sea Green or Dark Blue base	£60-75	☐
74b	1966	Daimler Fleetline Bus.................	Cream body, 'ESSO' decals................	£12-18	☐
			Cream body, 'ESSO' labels................	£25-35	☐
			Green body, 'ESSO' labels................	£15-20	☐
			Red body, 'ESSO' labels................	£25-35	☐
		Superfast wheels:	Red body, 'ESSO' labels................	£8-12	☐
			Pink body, 'ESSO' labels................	£15-20	☐
			Red body, 'INN ON THE PARK' labels	£70-80	☐
			Red body, 'THE BARON OF BEEF' labels	£75-90	☐
74c	1973	Tow Joe Breakdown Truck	Metallic Green body, Green jibs, 75 mm........	£4-8	☐
		colour change:.............	Metallic Green body, Red jibs................	£8-12	☐
			Metallic Green body, White jibs................	£75-90	☐
			Yellow body, Red jibs................	£8-12	☐
			Yellow body, Red jibs, 'HITCH HIKER' labels................	£60-80	☐
			Red body, Red or Green jibs, (TP issue)................	£120-150	☐
74e	1979	Cougar Villager	Metallic Green body, Yellow interior, 76 mm........	£5-8	☐
		variants:	Metallic Blue body, Orange/Yellow interior................	£5-8	☐
		Bulgarian issue:..........	Metallic Blue with Black interior	£5-8	☐
		Bulgarian issue:..........	Metallic Green with Black interior	£5-8	☐
		note:	Many other variations exist.		

Ref. No.	Year(s)	Model Type	*Matchbox Miniatures – continued*	Market Price Range	
74f	1982	'FIAT' Abarth........................	White body with *'Matchbox Toys'* logo, RN '45', Black interior, 76 mm........................	NGPP	☐
	1983	design change:............	White body, racing number '3', *'ALITALIA'*.	NRP	☐
	1987	Matchbox/Dinky issue: ..	White body, Yellow/Red design, bubble-packed................................	NRP	☐
74g	1984	Mustang..............................	(US issued model), Orange body, *'GT'* logo	£4-6	☐
	1986	colour change:............	Silver body, racing number '427'	NRP	☐
74h	1986	'TOYOTA' MR 2..................	White body, *'MR 2'* and *'PACE CAR'* logos, (with Collector Card)................	NRP	☐
	1987	Laser Wheel issue:	Metallic Blue body, *'MR 2'* logo	NRP	☐
74i	1989	Utility Truck......................	Green/White body, *'CHERRY PICKER'*.	NRP	☐
	1990	design change:............	Red bonnet with Grey cab and body plus White boom	NRP	☐
	1992	colour change:............	Yellow body with various Blue logos plus White boom	NRP	☐

MB 75

Ref. No.	Year(s)	Model Type		Market Price Range	
75a	1960	Ford Thunderbird	All models Cream body and Peach side panels		
			Blue base, Silver wheels	£30-35	☐
		base/wheel change:......	Blue-Green base, Silver wheels	£45-60	☐
			Black base, Silver wheels	£50-60	☐
			Black base, Grey wheels	£55-75	☐
			Black base, Black wheels	£180-220	☐
75b	1965	Ferrari Berlinetta......................	Metallic Green body, wire wheels, Silver base	£40-50	☐
			Metallic Green body, wire wheels, unpainted base	£10-15	☐
			Metallic Green body, Silver wheels with Black tyres	£12-18	☐
			Red body, Silver wheels with Black tyres	£350-400	☐
		Superfast wheels:	Metallic Green body	£80-120	☐
			Red body...	£20-25	☐
75c	1971	Alfa Carabo...........................	Pink body, Yellow baseplate, Superfast wheels, 76 mm.	£2-4	☐
		colour change:............	Red body, *'Streetcar'* design, Yellow baseplate.............	£2-4	☐
		note:...........................	There are many other variations.		
75d	1977	Seasprite Helicopter..................	Red and White body, *'Rescue'*, Black rotors, 74 mm.	£2-4	☐
75e	1982	'MB TV NEWS' Helicopter	Orange/White body fitted with tinted windows, 76 mm.	NRP	☐
75f	1983	'POLICE' Helicopter.................	Black/White body, Black rotors.............................	NRP	☐
	1984	colour change:............	Orange body, *'Rescue'* logo	NRP	☐
75g	1986	Ferrari Testarossa......................	Red or Silver body, Superfast wheels	NRP	☐
	1988	Laser Wheels issue:....	Red body with Ferrari badges on front & sides................	NRP	☐
	1989	Promotional:	Orange body, *'REDOXON'* on roof, (Hong Kong issue) ..	NRP	☐
75h	1985	Dodge Caravan........................	Black or Maroon body	NRP	☐

Early '1-75' Series Sets sold by Christie's, South Kensington, London.

Matchbox Gift Sets
and multi-model Packs

Ref. No.	Year(s)	Set Name	Contents	Market Price Range	

Presentation Sets

The first presentation set was sold in the USA in 1957 and consisted of an enlarged normal 'Matchbox' containing eight of the sixty-four models that Lesney manufactured at that time. The first sets were not sold in the UK until 1959.

PS 1	1957	Matchbox Presentation Set	Contains models 1 - 8 (only available in USA)...	**£500-600**	☐
PS 2	1957	Matchbox Presentation Set	Contains models 9 - 16 (only available in USA)...	**£500-600**	☐
PS 3	1957	Matchbox Presentation Set	Contains models 17 - 24 (only available in USA)...	**£500-600**	☐
PS 4	1957	Matchbox Presentation Set	Contains models 25 - 32 (only available in USA)...	**£500-600**	☐
PS 5	1957	Matchbox Presentation Set	Contains models 33 - 40 (only available in USA)...	**£500-600**	☐
PS 6	1957	Matchbox Presentation Set	Contains models 41 - 48 (only available in USA)...	**£500-600**	☐
PS 7	1957	Matchbox Presentation Set	Contains models 49 - 56 (only available in USA)...	**£500-600**	☐
PS 8	1957	Matchbox Presentation Set	Contains models 57 - 64 (only available in USA)...	**£500-600**	☐
PS 1	1959	Private Owner Set......................	Contains 19 MGA, 43 Hillman Minx, 45 Vauxhall Victor, A-3 Garage......................	**£150-175**	☐
PS 2	1959	Transporter and 4 Cars Set......	Contains 30 Ford, 31 Ford Station Wagon, 33 Ford Zodiac, 36 Austin A50 and an A-2 Transporter..	**£150-175**	☐
PS 3	1959	Transporter and 6 Cars Set......	Contains 22 Vauxhall Cresta, 32 Jaguar XK, 33 Ford Zodiac, 43 Hillman Minx, 44 Rolls-Royce Silver Cloud, 45 Vauxhall Victor and A-2 Transporter	**£200-250**	☐
PS 4	1959	Commercial Vehicle Set............	Contains No.5 Bus, 11 Petrol Tanker, 21 Long Distance Coach, 25 'Dunlop' Van, 35 Horse Box, 40 Bedford Tipper, 47 'Brooke Bond' Van, 60 Morris Pickup	**£400-450**	☐
PS 5	1959	Army Personnel Carrier Set	Contains M3 Personnel Carrier, 54 Saracen, 55 DUKW, 61 Ferret, 62 General Service Lorry, 63 Ambulance, M-3 Tank Transporter.......................	**£150-175**	☐

Gift Sets

The packaging for the first UK issued sets consisted of a frail blue box with a yellow lid panel on which were displayed (in red) the models which made up the set. Sets in similar packaging were issued for the German market.

G 1	1960-61	Commercial Motor Set.............	Contains: 5b 'Players Please', 47a 'Brooke Bond' Van, 69a 'Nestles' Van, 60a 'Builders Supply' Pick Up, 37a 'Coca Cola' Lorry (even load), 59a Ford 'Singer' Van, 20a 'Ever Ready' Truck, 51a Albion 'Portland Cement' Lorry. (All models in G 1 had Grey plastic wheels)	**£350-450**	☐
G 1	1962-63	Commercial Vehicle Set............	Contains 5c 'Visco-Static', 10c, 12b, 13c, 14c, 46b, 74a.............................	**£250-300**	☐
G 1	1965	Motorway Set.......................	Contains 6, 10, 13, 33, 34, 38, 48, 55, 71 and R-1 layout...........................	**£125-175**	☐
G 1	1967	Service Station Set..................	Contains Service Station, 32c, 13d, 64b..	**£45-55**	☐
G 1	1970	Service Station Set..................	Contains 13e, 32d, 15e and Service Station...	**£45-55**	☐
G 1	1981	Transporter Set.....................	Contains Transporter and 5 Superfast Cars...	**£15-20**	☐
G 1	1984	Transporter Set.....................	Contains K10 plus 4 cars..	**£8-11**	☐
G 2	1960-61	Car Transporter Set.................	Contains A-2 Transporter with cars 22, 25, 33, 39, 57 & 75.........................	**£175-225**	☐
G 2	1962-63	Car Transporter Set.................	Contains models 25b, 30b, 31b, 39b, 48b, 65b and Accessory Pack No.2	**£225-275**	☐
G 2	1965	Car Transporter Set.................	Contains 22c, 28c, 36c, 75b and Major Pack 8b.....................................	**£80-90**	☐
G 2	1967	Transporter Set.....................	Contains Transporter, 14d, 24c, 31c, 53c...	**£55-65**	☐
G 2	1970	Transporter Set.....................	Contains Transporter and 5 Superfast models.......................................	**£45-55**	☐
G 2	1973	Transporter Set.....................	Contains Transporter and 5 Superfast models.......................................	**£45-55**	☐
G 2	1981	Railway Set.........................	Contains 43e, 2 x 44e, 25f...	**£10-15**	☐
G 2	1987	Car Transporter Set.................	Contains K120 Transporter plus MB25 Audi Quattro, MB33 Renault 11, MB55 Ford Sierra 4x4, MB74 Toyota MR2, MB75 Ferrari Testarossa	**NGPP**	☐
G 3	1960-61	Building Constructors Set	Contains 2, 6, 15, 16, 18, 24, 28 and M-1..	**£150-175**	☐
G 3	1962-63	Constructional Plant Set	Contains 2, 6, 15, 16, 18, 24, 28 and M-1..	**£200-250**	☐
G 3	1963-64	Farm & Agricultural Set	Contains K3, K11, M5 & M7...	**£100-140**	☐
G 3	1965	Vacation Set	Contains 12c, 23c, 27d, 42b, 45b, 56b, 68b, and Sports Boat on Trailer	**£90-120**	☐
G 3	1968	Farm Set...........................	Contains 12c, 37d, 40c, 43c, 65c, 72b, 47c, 39c.....................................	**£55-65**	☐
G 3	1970	Racing Specials Set.................	Contains 5e, 20d, 45c, 56c, 52c, 68c..	**£45-55**	☐
G 3	1973	'WILD ONES' Set	Contains 5 Superfast Cars...	**£45-55**	☐
G 3	1981	Racing Car Set	Contains Transporter and 4 Racing Cars..	**£10-15**	☐
G 3	1987	JCB Gift Set........................	No details..	**NGPP**	☐
G 4	1960-61	Farm Set............................	Contains 12, 23, 31, 35, 50, 72 & M-7..	**£125-150**	☐
G 4	1963	Agricultural Implements and Farm Vehicles Set.................	Contains 12, 23, 31, 35, 50, 72 and M-7..	**£175-225**	☐
G 4	1963	Grand Prix Set......................	Contains 13, 14b, 19c, 41b, 47b, 52a, 32b, 73b, Major Pack No.1, R-4 Racetrack	**£300-350**	☐
G 4	1965	Racetrack Set.......................	Contains 13d, 19d Green, 19d Orange, 41c White, 41c Yellow, 52b Blue, 52b Red, 54b, Major Pack M-6 29c....................................	**£120-160**	☐
G 4	1968	Race 'N' Rally Set..................	Contains 19d Orange, 19d Green, 52b Blue, 52b Red, 29d, 3c, 41c, 67b, 25d, 8e	**£100-125**	☐
G 4	1970	Truck SuperSet.....................	Contains 47c, 63c, 58c, 49b, 16d, 21d, 11d, 51c......................................	**£55-65**	☐
G 4	1973	Team Matchbox Set	Contains Racing Car Transporter and 4 Racing Cars.................................	**£40-50**	☐
G 4	1981	Military Assault......................	Contains Landing Craft and 6 military models.......................................	**£10-15**	☐
G 5	1960-61	Military Vehicles....................	Contains 54, 62, 63, 64, 67, 68 and M-3..	**£125-150**	☐
G 5	1963	Army Gift Set.......................	Contains 54a, 62a, 63a, 67a, 68a, 64a and Major Pack No.3...........................	**£125-150**	☐
G 5	1965	Army Gift Set.......................	Contains 12, 49, 54, 61, 64, 67, M-3..	**£125-140**	☐
G 5	1965	Fire Station Set.....................	Contains Fire Station, 29c, 54b, 59c..	**£130-150**	☐
G 5	1981	Construction Set....................	Contains 5 construction models..	**£10-15**	☐

Ref. No.	Year(s)	Model Type	*Matchbox Gifts Sets – continued*	Market Price Range	
G 6	1965	Commercial Trucks Set	Contains 6, 15, 16, 17, 26, 30, 58 and 62	£90-120	☐
G 6	1966	Truck Set	Contains 16c, 17d, 25c, 26b, 30c, 69b, 70b, 71b	£90-120	☐
G 6	1970	Truck Set	Contains 1e, 10d, 21d, 30c, 60b, 70b, 49b, 26c	£65-75	☐
G 6	1973	Drag Race Set	Contains 6 Superfast Cars	£40-50	☐
G 6	1981	Farm Set	Contains 6 farming models	£10-15	☐
G 7	1973	Ferry Boat	Contains Plastic Boat and 4 Superfast Cars	£15-20	☐
G 7	1978	Car Ferry Set	Contains 3 Cars and Sports Boat	£15-20	☐
G 7	1981	Emergency Set	Contains 5 Rescue models	£10-15	☐
G 7	1984	Emergency Set	Contains models 8, 12, 22, 57, 75	£8-11	☐
G 8	1984	Turbo Charged Set	Contains Turbo Charger plus 7, 9, 52, 60 and 68	£8-11	☐
G 9	1963	Major Series Set	Contains Major Packs 1, 2, 4 and 6	£150-200	☐
G 9	1965	Service Station Set	Contains 13, 33, 71, A-1, MG-1	£65-75	☐
G 10	1963	Service Station Set	Contains Service Station, 13c, 25b, 31b, and Accessory Pack No.1	£65-75	☐
G 10	1965	Fire Station Set	Contains MF-1, 14, 59, 2 of No.9	£65-75	☐
G 10	1986	'PAN-AM' Set	Contains 10, 54, 64, 65 and 'Sky-Buster' Boeing	£15-18	☐
G 11	1978	Strike Force Set	Contains 6 Army Vehicles	£45-50	☐
G 11	1986	'LUFTHANSA' Set	Contains 30, 54, 59, 65 and 'Sky-Buster' A300 Airbus	£15-18	☐
G 12	1978	Rescue Set	Contains 6 Rescue Vehicles	£20-30	☐
G 13	1978	Construction Set	Contains 6 Construction Vehicles	£20-25	☐
G 14	1978	Grand Prix Set	Contains Transporter and 4 Racing Cars	£20-25	☐
G 15	1978	Transporter Set	Contains Transporter and 5 Superfast Cars	£20-25	☐
G 40	1988	40 years Set..................	Contains Aveling Barford Road Roller, London Bus, Horse Drawn Milk Float, Massey Harris Tractor, Dennis Fire Engine. (These models may be distinguished from the original issues as they have 'Made in China' cast into the underside).	£8-12	☐
	1960-61	Garage Set 'C'	Contains 8 various models, a garage, R-1 (roadway), A-1 Esso pumps, A-2 Transporter and M-6 'Pickfords'	£300-350	☐

'Motorcity' Sets and Accessories Introduced in 1988

MC 1		Car Wash....................	with two Miniatures	NRP	☐
MC 2		Petrol Station...............	with two Miniatures	NRP	☐
MC 3		Pit Stop......................	with two Miniatures	NRP	☐
MC 4		Garage	with two Miniatures	NRP	☐
MC 5		Construction Crane	with MB 23	NRP	☐
MC 6		Conveyor Loader...........	with MB 9, 23, 29 and 32	NRP	☐
MC 7	1990	Farm Set	Contains Convoy CY20 Kenworth Tipper, MB27 Jeep (and Horsebox), TP103, TP108, and Harrow and Combine Harvester.	NRP	☐
MC 8	1990	Construction Set............	Convoy Peterbilt Low Loader plus Yellow Miniatures MB 9, 19, 23, 32, 42, 48	NRP	☐
MC 9		Gear Shift Garage	Gear lever operates car lift and 4 other functions.	NRP	☐
MC 10		10 Pack	10 assorted Miniatures	NRP	☐
MC 11		Car Transporter Set........	Contains CY1 Car Transporter plus two MB37 Escort Cabriolet (1 Red, 1 Blue)......	NRP	☐
MC 12		Aerobatic Team Set	Contains CY21 DAF Transporter plus MB57 and MB 75 Helicopters	NRP	☐
MC 13		'POLICE' Set	Contains Convoy Kenworth Low Loader plus Miniatures MB51 Ford Police Car ('G12' logo), MB61 and MB75 Helicopter	NRP	☐
MC 15	1990	Fire Set	Contains CY13 Fire Engine plus Miniatures MB13, MB16, MB18, MB54 Pumper, Skybuster SB26 'FIRE'.	NRP	☐
MC 17		British Airways Set	Contains 747 Airliner and Concorde plus 3 Miniatures	NRP	☐
MC 18	1990	Ferrari Set	Contains CY24 plus MB70e, MB70f, MB75 and MB14.	NRP	☐
MC 19	1990	British Airways	A Sky-Busters set	NRP	☐
MC 20		20 Pack	Contains 20 assorted Miniatures	NRP	☐
MC 23		Porsche Set	Contains CY24 plus MB3, MB7, MB41 & MB59	NRP	☐
MC 24		Red Arrows Set	See the 'Colour Section' picture.	NRP	☐
MC 30		30 Pack	Contains 30 assorted Miniatures	NRP	☐
MC 50		Bucket of Cars..............	Contains 50 assorted Miniatures	NRP	☐
MC 100		Garage Set	A complete mini-garage and equipment	NRP	☐
MC 150		Airport Set	Contains complete mini-airport layout and outfit	NRP	☐
MC 155		Motorcity Airport	International airport plus two airliners	NRP	☐
MC 160		Red Arrows Squadron HQ	Includes HQ building, control tower and two 'Red Arrows' (Skybusters)........	NRP	☐
MC 200		Playtrack	Includes bridge, petrol station, road signs, etc	NRP	☐
MC 250		Railway Set	no details	NRP	☐
MC 300		Playtrack	Includes car park and accessories	NRP	☐
MC 330		Playtrack	Minitronic unit with voice and sound effects	NRP	☐
MC 370		Super Spin Car Wash	Conveyor belt moves cars under water spray	NRP	☐
MC 400		Playtrack	Includes garage, car park and accessories	NRP	☐
MC 410		Deluxe Playtrack Set	Includes working bridge, dual lane track and accessories	NRP	☐
MC 420		High Rise Run	A multi-storey car park with super fast roll-down ramps	NRP	☐
MC 500		Multi-Storey Car Park	With working lift and roll-down ramps plus accessories	NRP	☐
MC 510		Transport Set	Roadway, buildings, roadway track, train, carriages, goods yard, airport, playmat	NRP	☐
MC 520	1992	Construction Zone...........	A complete building set with crane, scaffolding and playmat.	NRP	☐
MC 550	1992	Electronic Service Centre........	A complete Matchbox garage with electronic sound effects	NRP	☐
MC 560		Intercom City	Computerised communications system with sounds and voices, plus 4 models	NRP	☐
MC 570		Message Vehicles Sets...........	Four sets of vehicles which activate different sounds and messages when used with Intercom City	NRP	☐
MC 580		Intercom City Grand Prix Set	Similar system to MC 560 plus 3 racing cars	NRP	☐
MC 585		Intercom City Mega Set	Super Pack as per MC 560	NRP	☐
MC 590		Intercom City Airport Set	Similar to MC 560 plus 2 vehicles and an airliner	NRP	☐
MC 610		Container Port..............	Includes dockside equipment	NRP	☐
MC 620		Construction Yard..........	Yard with working features	NRP	☐

MC 630		Fold 'n' Go Garage..................	Includes garage plus pumps, parking lot and moving barriers	NRP ☐
MC 640		Fold 'n' Go Garage..................	Includes ramps, multi-level parking, moving lift and barriers	NRP ☐
MC 660		Electronic Rescue Centre	Portable Rescue Unit with building, 2 working sirens, search beam, lights, etc	NRP ☐
MC 700		Mini Tronics Sets	1: Car Wash, 2: Petrol Station, 3: Construction Site, 4: Conveyor Site	NRP ☐
MC 803		Circus Set...................................	CY24 *'Circus'*, MB16 and caravan, animal cage truck plus 2 horses	NRP ☐
MC 804		Circus Set...................................	Big Top, tent, CY24 *'Circus'*, MB16 and caravan, animal cage truck, Skybusters biplane, Model 'A' car, booking office van	NRP ☐

Miscellaneous Sets

C 6		Japanese Emergency Gift Set	All Japanese Set	£15-20 ☐
C 11		Japanese Airport Gift Set.........	Japanese Foam Pump, Ikarus Coach & Aircraft	£20-25 ☐
		Japanese Cars Gift Set	JPS Lotus, Volkswagen, Gold Rolls-Royce and Mercedes	£30-35 ☐
		Las Vegas Dodge Set	Car and Van	£120-140 ☐
MG 9		Gear Shift Garage	Gear lever operates car lift and 4 other functions	NRP ☐
MP 804	1990	Porsche Set	Contains MB3 (911 Turbo), MB7 (959), MB59 (944 Turbo)	NRP ☐
SS 100		Smash 'n' Crash.......................	Action Playset with two vehicles	NRP ☐
		Multi-Pack Gift Sets.................	Contains 5 Superfast models............................	£15-20 ☐
		'Days Of Thunder'	Film-related sets issued in the US only:	
			i) Modified MB10 Buick Le Sabre in 5 liveries	NGPP ☐
			ii) Modified MB54f Chevrolet Lumina in 5 liveries	NGPP ☐

Early Accessory Packs

A1a	1957	'ESSO' Petrol Pump Set............	Red pumps, White figure	£15-20 ☐
A1b	1963	'BP' Petrol Pump Set................	White pumps, Yellow/White decal	£15-20 ☐
A2	1957	Car Transporter........................	1st type: All Blue body with *'MATCHBOX'* logo.................	£35-40 ☐
			2nd type: Red cab, Grey trailer, *'MATCHBOX'* logo.................	£100-130 ☐
A3	1957	Garage	Yellow/Green/Red, opening doors, all metal	£15-20 ☐
A4	1960	Road Signs Set	Eight Red/White/Black signs *'Lesney'* on base..................	£15-20 ☐
A5	1960	'HOME STORES'....................	Food shop with window display and opening door	£20-25 ☐

Note: In 1959 the first of a continuing series of 'MATCHBOX GARAGES' was issued (MG1A). In 1963 a 'MATCHBOX FIRE STATION' was issued (MF1A). The models are made in plastic and a price of **£35 - £45** should be expected on each.

Major Series models

M 1 (a)	1958	Caterpillar Earthmover	Yellow body, Silver metal wheels, crimped or rounded axles, Black plastic wheels. 99 mm.. £25-35	☐
M 1 (b)	1963	'BP' Petrol Tanker....................	Green/Yellow/White main body, tinted windows, Knobby or fine Black plastic wheels, 102 mm. £30-35	☐
M 2 (a)	1958	Bedford Articulated Truck 'WALLS ICE CREAM'..........	Pale Blue cab & chassis, Cream detachable trailer, metal wheels, crimped axles, 101 mm... £60-70	☐
	1959	Wheel change	As above with Grey plastic wheels £50-60	☐
	1959-61	Colour change	As previous but with Off-White trailer, crimped or rounded axles £50-60	☐
M 2 (b)	1961	York Trailer 'DAVIES TYRES'	Orange cab, Silver Grey trailer, Knobby Grey, Black or Fine plastic wheels, Clear (early) or Green windows............................. £40-50	☐
M 2 (c)	1964	'LEP INTERNATIONAL TRANSPORT'	Same castings as M 2(b) with Silver cab and Maroon trailer, Fine Black wheels £40-50	☐
M 3	1959	Centurion Tank on Transporter..............................	Olive Green 'Mighty Antar' cab, transporter and tank. Metal (early), Grey or Black plastic tank rollers, knobby or fine (late) wheels, 155 mm. £40-50	☐
M 4 (a)	1959	Ruston Bucyrus Excavator.......	Maroon cab, Yellow boom/shovel, Red or Yellow '22-RB' side logo with small or large 'TAYLOR WOODROW' rear logo, 99 mm. £40-50	☐
M 4 (b)	1965	'FREUHOF' Hopper Train	Maroon tractor, 2 Silver hoppers, Red wheels, Black plastic tyres, 286 m. £50-55	☐
M 5	1959	'MASSEY FERGUSON 780' Combine Harvester	Red body, Tan driver, Red (early) or unpainted metal, or Yellow plastic steering wheel, '780 SPECIAL' logo on sides. Various front and rear wheel types, Yellow blades, 117 mm. £50-60	☐
M 6 (a)	1960	'PICKFORDS' Transporter	Dark Blue tractor, Maroon or Dark Red low-loader, Knobby or fine Black plastic wheels, 279 mm. £50-60	☐
		Colour change....................	Light Blue tractor, Dark Red low-loader £50-60	☐
		Colour change....................	Light or Dark Blue tractor, Bright Red low loader £80-90	☐
M 6 (b)	1966	'BP Racing Transporter'	Green body, Yellow/Green decal, Red hubs, Black plastic tyres, 127 mm.............. £35-40	☐
M 7	1960	'Jennings' Cattle Truck............	Red cab, Light Tan box trailer, Grey plastic wheels, 121 mm.................. £30-45	☐
			Red cab & ramp, Dark Tan box trailer, Grey plastic wheels £40-45	☐
			As previous model but with Black plastic wheels £50-55	☐
M 8 (a)	1961	'MOBILGAS' Petrol Tanker.....	Red cab and tank trailer with *'MOBILGAS'* logo in Dark Blue/White, Knobby Grey or Black or fine Black wheels, 99 mm. £60-70	☐
M 8 (b)	1964	'FARNBOROUGH-MEASHAM' Car Transporter..	Guy Warrier with Turquoise tractor and Orange trailer with *'CAR AUCTION COLLECTION'* logo in Black (early) or White. Grey or Black tyres, 209 mm. £40-45	☐
M 9	1962	Inter-State Double Freighter	Dark Blue cab, Two Silver trailers, *'COOPER-JARRETT INC'* logo in Dark Blue on Yellow background........................... £50-60	☐
		Logo change....................	Dark Blue cab, Two Silver trailers with *'COOPER-JARRETT INTERNATIONAL'* logo in Dark Blue on Orange background................... £60-70	☐
M 10	1962	Whitlock Dinkum Dumper	Yellow body, *'DD70'*, unpainted or Red hubs, 108 mm. £20-25	☐

'Two Packs', '900' Series, 'Twin Packs', 'Team Matchbox'

Ref. No.	Year(s)	Model Type	Model Features and Size	Market Price Range	

The 'Two Pack' series was launched in 1976. Each issue consists of two 'Miniatures' but with new 'TP' numbers on the base.
The series was renamed the '900 Series' in 1979 when the 'Long Haul Cab' vehicles were introduced as follows:

TP 22 Long Haul Double Container Truck,   TP 23 Long Haul Covered Container Truck,
TP 24 Long Haul Box Container Truck,   TP 25 Long Haul Pipe Truck

These models were popular and led to the introduction in 1982 of the 'Convoy' series which was based on Long Haul Trucks. This development resulted in the '900 Series' being renamed 'Two Packs'.

Ref. No.	Year(s)	Model Type	Model Features and Size	Market Price Range	
TP 1	1976	Mercedes Truck and Trailer	Blue/Yellow body, 'IMS' logo (Nos. 1e & 2d)	£10-15	☐
			Red/Yellow body, 'TRANSCONTINENTAL'	£5-10	☐
TP 2	1976	Mod Tractor and Hay trailer	Red tractor, Yellow trailer (Nos 25e & 40c)	£10-15	☐
TP 2	1979	Police Car and Fire Engine	Either 22e or 35c with 59d	£10-15	☐
TP 2	1981	'EXXON' Tanker	Red Cab and chassis, Red & White tank	£10-15	☐
TP 3	1976	Javelin & Pony Trailer	Green Javelin, Orange or Cream trailer, 2 horses	£10-15	☐
TP 3		French issue:	Jeep and pony trailer	£10-15	☐
TP 4	1976	Car and Caravan	Metallic Blue car, Yellow/Red caravan No. 57	£10-15	☐
TP 5	1976	Car towing Boat	Orange Ford Capri (other cars may be substituted)	£10-15	☐
	1981	colour change:	Blue car 'PHANTOM', and Blue boat & trailer	£10-15	☐
TP 5	1976	Lotus Set	2 Black 'JPS' Lotus racing cars	£20-25	☐
TP 6	1976	Breakdown Set	Nos. 61 or 74 with 15d Volkswagen or 65d Saab or 20e Range Rover	£10-15	☐
TP 7	1976	Emergency Set	'Stretcha Fetcha' No. 46 with either 59d or 64d	£10-15	☐
TP 7	1978	Jeep and Glider Set	Yellow Jeep No. 38c plus trailer	£10-15	☐
	1981	Red Jeep and trailer		£10-15	☐
TP 7	1978	Escort & Glider Set	No. 9f plus trailer	£10-15	☐
TP 8	1976	Bus & Hovercraft	No. 17d (with 'CARNABY St.' labels), and No. 72c	£10-15	☐
TP 8	1977	Field Car & Motorcycle	Orange No. 18c (with Silver base), plus Honda 38c	£10-15	☐
	1981	colour change:	Yellow car and trailer, Green motor-cycle	£10-15	☐
TP 9	1978	Field Car & Racing Car	No.18c with 'Team Matchbox' No.24	£10-15	☐
	1981	colour change:	Orange car and racing car	£10-15	☐
TP 10	1978	Ambulance & Fire Chief	Mercedes Ambulance & Fire Chief's car with 'Fire' labels, (No.59d with 3c)	£10-15	☐
TP 11	1977	Jeep and Motorcycle	Military Green No.38c with 'JEEP' on baseplate, plus 18f	£25-35	☐
		model change:	As previous model but with No.2c plus 18f Hondarora	£10-15	☐
TP 11	1979	Tractor & Hay Trailer	Red tractor and trailer Nos.25e and 40c	£10-15	☐
	1981	colour change:	Green tractor, Yellow trailer	£10-15	☐
TP 12	1977	Military Police & Field Car	Dark Military Green 'POLICE' labels (Nos.20e and 18c)	£25-35	☐
			As previous model but with 'AMBULANCE' labels	£25-35	☐
TP 12	1977	Field Car & VW Ambulance	Military Green	£25-35	☐
TP 13	1977	Weasel & Stoat	Dark Military Green	£100-125	☐
TP 13	1978	Unimog & Gun	No.49b in Military Green plus 32e	£10-15	☐
TP 14	1977	Tanker & Badger	Dark Military Green, (French flag on tanker)	£50-60	☐
TP 14	1978	Ambulance & Staff Car	Mercedes Ambulance No.3c plus No.46, both in Military-Green	£10-15	☐
TP 15	1977	Mercedes Truck & Trailer	Military Green Nos.1e and 2d, 'USA 48350' labels	£35-40	☐
TP 16	1977	Dump Truck & Bulldozer	28d Mack truck in Dark Military Green	£35-40	☐
		colour change:	In normal Military Green livery	£10-15	☐
TP 16	1979	Wreck Truck & Stalwart	Military Green finish Nos.71c and 61b	£10-15	☐
TP 16	1980	Artic Truck & Trailer	Yellow/Blue body for each model	£10-15	☐
			Red/Silver body for each model	£20-25	☐
TP 17	1979	Tanker and Trailer	Red/White body with 'CHEVRON' logo (No.63)	£10-15	☐
		colour change:	White/Yellow body with 'SHELL' logo (No.63)	£5-10	☐
TP 18	1979	'Water Sporter'	Red 7e Volkswagen Golf, Red/White 5f Seafire Motor Boat	£5-10	☐
TP 19	1980	Cattle Truck & Trailer	Red/Cream body for each model, plus 2 cows	£5-10	☐
TP 20	1980	Shunter & Side Tipper	Cream/Red 24e Diesel Shunter, Red or Black side tipper	£5-10	☐
	1981		Yellow/Red bodies, 'D1496-RF' logo	£5-10	☐
TP 21	1980	Datsun & M/C Trailer	Metallic Blue 24f (Datsun 280 ZX) with 3 Cream or Red motor-bikes	£5-10	☐
TP 21	1980	Citroën & M/C Trailer	Metallic Blue 12f with roof-rack, 3 Cream or Red motor-bikes	£5-10	☐
TP 22	1980	Container Truck	Metallic Red cab, Cream containers	£5-10	☐
	1981	with logo:	As previous model but with 'OCL' logo in Blue	£5-10	☐
TP 23	1980	Covered Truck	Red/White body, (articulated vehicle) 'FIRESTONE'	£5-10	☐
TP 24	1980	Box Truck	All Red body, 'FIRESTONE' in White, 8 wheels	£10-15	☐
		colour change:	Yellow cab, Yellow box, 'KODAK', 8 wheels	£150-175	☐
		colour change:	Cream cab, Red trailer base 'MATCHBOX'	£5-10	☐
		colour change:	Cream cab, Black trailer base 'MATCHBOX'	£8-12	☐
		colour change:	Red cab, Red trailer base	£8-12	☐
TP 25	1980	Pipe Truck	Metallic Green cab, Black trailer base, 3 Red pipes	£5-10	☐
		colour change:	Yellow cab version	£16-20	☐
TP 26	1981	Boat Transporter	Blue cab, Silver trailer, Red/Cream boat	£5-10	☐
TP 27	1981	Steam loco & Caboose	Green/Black logo, Green/Cream/Black Caboose	£5-10	☐
TP 28	1982	Cortina & Caravan	Bronze/White 25d, Red/White 'SUN SET' caravan 57d	£5-10	☐
TP 29	1982	Flareside Pickup & Boat	Blue 57f plus Blue/White boat	£5-10	☐
TP 30	1982	Datsun and Speed Boat	Silver/Red 24f, Yellow/Black 5f	£5-10	☐
TP 31	1982	Citroën & M/C Trailer	Yellow 12f and trailer with 3 Red bikes	£5-10	☐
TP 32	1982	Wreck Truck & Dodge	Green 61d with Orange/Blue 1g Dodge Challenger, 'Revin' Rebel'	£5-10	☐
TP 102	1984	Escort & Pony Trailer	Green Escort and 'SEAGULL' trailer	£5-10	☐
TP 103	1984	Cattle Truck & Trailer	Yellow cab and chassis, Brown cages, 4 cows	£5-8	☐

Ref. No.	Year(s)	Model Type	Matchbox Miniatures — Twin Packs – continued	Market Price Range	
TP 103	1987	new design:	Blue truck and trailer with Brown stake sides, plus 4 Black cows	£5-8	☐
TP 103	1989	new design:	Green truck and trailer with Yellow stake sides, plus 4 Black cows	£5-8	☐
TP 106	1984	Renault 5 & M/C Trailer	Black car, Yellow/Red panels, Yellow/Red motor-cycle trailer....................................	£5-10	☐
TP 106	1987	new design:	White/Orange/Black car 'Scrambles', White trailer, 3 motorbikes..............................	£5-10	☐
TP 107	1984	Datsun & Caravan	Silver/Blue car, White caravan..	£5-10	☐
TP 108	1984	Tractor & Hay Trailer.............	Blue tractor, Red/Black trailer..	£5-10	☐
TP 108	1987	new design:	Orange tractor and trailer with Black raves...	£5-10	☐
TP 108	1989	new design:	Green tractor, Yellow trailer with Black raves..	£5-10	☐
TP 109	1984	Citroën & Boat....................	White/Blue car, Black/White boat, Red trailer...	£5-10	☐
TP 110	1984	Matra Rancho & Boat	Black Rancho, Yellow logo, Orange inflatable..	£5-10	☐
TP 110	1987	new design:	Red Rancho, 'SURF 2' logo, Black boat on White trailer..	£5-10	☐
TP 111	1984	Cortina & Horsebox................	Red car, Yellow 'SILVERSHOES' horsebox, 2 horses...	£5-10	☐
TP 112	1985	Unimog & Trailer.................	Yellow body, White covers, Red 'ALPINE RESCUE'...	£5-10	☐
TP 112	1987	new design:	Red truck and trailer, White rear covers, 'UNFALL - BETTUNG'...................................	£5-10	☐
TP 112	1989	new design:	White truck and trailer, Orange rear covers, Blue 'GB 5' logo..................................	£5-10	☐
TP 113	1985	Porsche & Caravan................	Black car, White/Orange caravan..	£5-10	☐
TP 114	1986	VW Golf and Horsebox	Black car, Beige/Brown horsebox 'Silvershoes', 2 White horses.................................	£5-10	☐
TP 115	1987	Ford Escort and Boat	White car with 'XR4i' logo, plus White/Blue boat on trailer...................................	£5-10	☐
TP 116	1987	'Holiday Club'...................	Yellow vehicle 'HOLIDAY CLUB' plus trailer with Green '500' logo..............................	£5-10	☐
TP 117	1987	Mounted Police Land Rover	White 'POLICE' Land Rover and horsebox with 2 Black horses....................................	£5-10	☐
TP 117	1989	Mercedes G Wagon and Horsebox.	Green/White 'POLITIE' car and horsebox with 2 Black horses....................................	£5-10	☐
TP 118	1987	BMW and Glider...................	Red/White car and glider trailer, White glider...	£5-10	☐
TP 119	1987	Flareside and Seafire	Blue/Yellow vehicle and motorboat with 'FORD' and '60' logos..................................	£5-10	☐
TP 120	1989	VW Golf and Inflatable	Blue/Silver car 'GTI', Orange boat on trailer..	£5-10	☐
TP 121	1989	Land Rover and Seafire	White and Red vehicle and speedboat...	£5-10	☐
TP 122	1989	Porsche and Glider...............	Blue and Yellow car and glider trailer, White Glider..	£5-10	☐
TP 123	1989	BMW and Caravan.................	Metallic Blue car, Grey caravan with Red design on lower part.................................	£5-10	☐
TP 124	1989	Zoo Truck, Caravan Trailer.....	White and Red truck and caravan, 'All Stars Circus' logo......................................	£5-10	☐
TP 124	1991	Locomotive and Carriage........	Green and Cream loco and carriage with British Railways crest.................................	£5-10	☐
TP 125	1991	Shunter and Tipper	Yellow and Red models with Red logo on shunter..	£5-10	☐
TP 127	1991	BMW and Dinghy.................	White open top car plus Blue dinghy on White trailer..	£5-10	☐
TP 128	1992	Dodge Truck and Trailer	Red truck and trailer with White rear covers, 'Big Top Circus'................................	£5-10	☐
TP 129	1992	Isuzu and Powerboat.............	Red and White models with Gold logo and Blue stripes..	£5-10	☐
TP 130	1992	Land Rover and Pony Trailer...	Green and White models plus 2 Black horses...	£5-10	☐
TP 131	1992	G Wagon and Dinghy..............	White and Orange models with Blue 'Marine Rescue' logos.......................................	£5-10	☐
TP 131	1992	G Wagon and Dinghy..............	White and Orange models with Blue 'Marine Rescue' logos.......................................	£5-10	☐

Matchbox 'King-Size' Models

Following the successful sales of Major Series, Lesney Products decided to further develop the range by introducing a larger scale toy and a suitable name was 'King-Size'. Ultimately the popular Major Models were themselves built into the King-Size series when the Major Model series was discontinued in 1966.

Ref. No.	Year(s)	Model Type	Model Features and Size	Market Price Range	
K1-1	1960	Hydraulic Shovel	All Yellow body, Grey plastic wheels, 'WEATHERILL'...	£25-30	☐
K1-2	1963	Tipper Truck	Red cab and chassis, Orange tipper, 8 wheels, 'HOVERINGHAM'	£30-35	☐
			N.B. 'HOVERINGHAM GRAVELS LTD' issued models to customers in their own outer box.		
K1-3	1970	Excavator.........................	Red body, Silver shovel, tinted windows, 'O & K' logo, Black plastic tyres	£20-25	☐
K2-1	1960	Dumper Truck....................	Red body, 'MUIR HILL 14B', Black or Green, metal wheels	£25-30	☐
K2-2	1964	Dumper Truck....................	Yellow body, 'KW DART' logo, 6 Red wheels, Black plastic tyres	£25-30	☐
K2-3	1968	Scammell Wreck Truck	White body, Red jib & wheels, Grey hook, 'ESSO' logo..	£30-35	☐
		colour change:..........	Gold body version..	£30-35	☐
K3-1	1960	Caterpillar Bulldozer	Yellow body, Red engine, Grey metal rollers...	£25-30	☐
		colour change:	As previous model but with Red metal rollers...	£25-30	☐
		colour change:	As previous model but with Yellow metal rollers..	£25-30	☐
K3-2	1965	Tractor Shovel	Orange body, Red wheels 'HATRA'...	£25-30	☐
K3-3	1970	Tractor & Trailer.................	Each has Red body, Yellow trim, 'MASSEY FERGUSON' logo......................................	£25-30	☐
K4-1	1960	Tractor	Red body, Green wheels, 'McCORMICK INTERNATIONAL'..	£30-35	☐
		colour change:	As previous model with Orange or Red wheel hubs..	£25-30	☐
K4-2	1967	G.M.C. Tractor & Hoppers	Dark Red cab, 2 Silver hoppers, 'FREUHOF' logo..	£50-55	☐
K4-3	1969	Leyland Tipper	Dark Red cab and chassis, Silver tipper 'W. WATES'..	£25-30	☐
		colour change:	As previous model but with Yellow/Green body colours	£25-30	☐
		colour change:	With Red cab and chassis, Green tipper	£25-30	☐
		colour change:	With Blue cab and chassis, Silver tipper 'Miner' label	£25-30	☐
		colour change:	With Silver tipper and 'LE TRANSPORT' logo	£30-35	☐
K5-1	1961	Tipper Truck	Yellow body and tipper, Red wheels, 'FODEN' logo..	£25-30	☐
K5-2	1967	Racing Car Transporter	Green body, Silver drop down rear door, Red wheels..	£35-40	☐
K5-3	1970	Tractor and Trailer..............	Each has Yellow body, Red chassis, 'MUIR HILL'..	£25-30	☐
K6-1	1961	Earth Scraper	Orange body, Red engine, 'ALLIS CHALMERS'...	£30-35	☐
K6-2	1967	Mercedes Ambulance	White body, Silver grille, Red badge, ambulance-man, stretcher.............................	£25-30	☐
K7-1	1961	Rear Dumper......................	Yellow body, Red engine, 'CURTISS-WRIGHT'..	£25-30	☐
K7-2	1967	Refuse Truck	Red body and wheels 'CLEANSING DEPARTMENT'..	£25-30	☐
		colour change:..........	Blue body version...	£25-30	☐
K8-1	1962	Prime Mover & Transporter with Crawler Tractor........	Orange bodies, Yellow tractor 'LAING' logo in Black/Yellow, (6 x 6 wheels)..................	£75-80	☐
K8-2	1967	Guy Warrior Transporter........	Blue cab, Yellow car transporter 'FARNBOROUGH - MEASHAM'....................................	£45-50	☐
		colour change:.........	Orange cab, Orange or Yellow transporter	£45-50	☐

Ref. No.	Year(s)	Model Type	Matchbox 'King Size' – continued	Market Price Range	
K8-3	1970	'CATERPILLAR TRAXCAVATOR'	Yellow body and shovel, Blue or White driver	£30-35	☐
K9-1		Diesel Road Roller	Green body, Red wheels and driver 'AVELING BARFORD'	£25-30	☐
K9-2	1967	Combine Harvester	Red body, Yellow blades and wheels, 'CLAAS'	£25-30	☐
		colour change:	Green body, Red blades and wheels 'CLAAS'	£25-30	☐
K10-1	1963	Tractor Shovel	Blue-Green body, Red seat and wheels 'AVELING BARFORD'	£25-30	☐
K10-2	1966	Pipe Truck	Yellow body, Red wheels and pipes	£25-30	☐
		colour change:	('Super-Kings' issue) Purple body, Grey or Yellow pipes	£20-25	☐
K11-1	1963	Tractor & Trailer	Blue tractor, Grey/Blue trailer 'FORDSON SUPER MAJOR'	£30-35	☐
K11-2	1969	DAF Car Transporter	Yellow body, Yellow/Red decks, 'DAF' logo	£25-30	☐
		colour change:	Metallic Blue body, Gold trailer decks	£25-30	☐
K12-1	1963	Breakdown Truck	Green body, Yellow jib, 'MATCHBOX SERVICE STATION'	£35-40	☐
K12-2	1969	Scammell Crane Truck	Yellow body and chassis, 'LAING' on crane	£25-30	☐
K13-1	1963	Concrete Truck	Orange body and barrel, 'READYMIX' logo	£35-40	☐
		logo change:	As previous model but with 'RMC' logo	£35-40	☐
K14-1	1964	Jumbo Crane	Yellow body and crane, 'TAYLOR JUMBO CRANE'	£25-30	☐
K15-1	1964	Merryweather Fire Engine	Red body, Silver ladder, 'KENT FIRE BRIGADE'	£35-40	☐
K16-1	1966	Tractor & Twin Tippers	Green cab, Yellow tippers, 'DODGE TRUCKS' in Red	NGPP	☐
		colour change:	Yellow cab, Blue tippers same logo (22w)	£35-40	☐
K17-1	1967	Low Loader & Bulldozer	Green cab and loader, Red/Yellow Bulldozer	£24-26	☐
K18-1	1966	Artic Horse Box	Red cab, Brown box, 4 White horses 'ASCOT STABLES'	£25-30	☐
K19-1	1967	Scammell Tipper	Red body, Yellow tipper, Silver trim	£25-30	☐
K20-1	1968	Tractor Transporter	Red body, Yellow rack, 3 Blue tractors (39c)	£30-35	☐
		colour change:	As previous model but with Orange tractors	£70-75	☐
K21-1	1969	Mercury Cougar	Gold body, Cream or Red seats	NGPP	☐
K22-1	1969	Dodge Charger	Blue body, Yellow seats	NGPP	☐
K23-1	1969	Mercury 'POLICE' Car	White body with 'HIGHWAY PATROL' logo	NGPP	☐
K24-1	1969	Lamborghini Miura	Red body, Cream seats	NGPP	☐

GIFT SETS   (King-Size models)

	1963	King-Size Set	Contains K1-1, K2-1, K3-1, K5-1, K6-1	£60-65	☐
	1965	Construction Set	Contains K16-1, K7-1, K10-1, K13-1, K14-1	£75-80	☐
	1966	King-Size Set	Contains K16-1, K11-1, K12-1, K15-1	£40-45	☐

'Super-Kings' and 'Speed-Kings' 1971–92

After 1970 the 'King Size' range developed into the larger 'Super-Kings' Series. They were fitted with extra wide speed slick tyres to give them extra power, extra speed. During the period 1971-79 certain issues were sold as 'SPEED KINGS' and retailed in different coloured packaging. These have been identified in the listings by the abbreviation (SPK).

Individual model variations have been identified by the listing of either its colour, advertisement or logo.

Market Price Range. In general 'SUPERKINGS' are not very collectable and most models may be purchased for under £25. We regret we are unable to provide more specific information on the individual model prices. The editor would welcome details and prices of rare issues.

N.B. The Super-King listings represent the best if somewhat limited information that we have available. Further information on the rare issues and price levels would be welcomed.

N.B. 'BATTLE-KINGS' and 'SEA-KINGS' form part of the 'SUPER-KING' issues and are listed separately at the end of the section.

K2	1977	'24 HOUR' Car Recovery Vehicle	☐	K15	1973	Londoner Bus issues: Main advert 'HARRODS – ENTER A DIFFERENT	
K?	199?	Mod Tractor and Trailer	☐			WORLD', 'CARNABY STREET',	
K3	1980	Grain Transporter 'KELLOGGS'	☐			'SILVER JUBILEE', 'HARRODS –	
K4	1974	Big Tipper	☐			MORE THAN MONEY', 'LONDON	
K5	1972	Muir Hill Tractor and Trailer	☐			DUNGEON', 'HAMLEYS – FINEST	
K6	1971	Cement Mixer	☐			TOY SHOP', 'ROYAL WEDDING	
K6	1974	Motor Cycle Transporter 'HONDA'	☐			1981', 'LONDON WIDE TOUR',	
K7	1973	'TEAM MATCHBOX' Transporter	☐			'ARABIC SCRIPT' (not issued),	
K8	1981	Animal Transporter 'ANITRAN'	☐			'TELEGRAPH & ARGUS',	
K9	1973	Fire Tender 'DENVER'	☐			MACLEANS TOOTHPASTE',	
K10	1976	'AUTO TRANSPORT' Transporter	☐			'HERITAGE OF ENGLAND',	
K10	1982	Bedford 'COURIER' Transporter	☐			'BUTTERKIST', 'TOURIST	
K11	1976	'SHELL RECOVERY' Truck	☐			LONDON', 'FIRESTONE',	
K11	1981	Dodge Van Issues:-				'CHESTERFIELD 1984', 'LONDON	
		'MICHELIN', 'SUCHARD EXPRESS',				PLANETARIUM', 'PETTICOAT	
		'FRANKFURTER ALLGEMAINE', &				LANE', 'NESTLES MILKY BAR'	☐
		'FRANCESOIR'	☐			German Issues:	
K12	1975	Hercules 'LAING' Crane	☐			i) 'BERLIN IST EINE REISE WERT'	
K13	1971	DAF Building Transporter	☐			– 'BERLIN IS WORTH A TRIP'	☐
K13	1976	Aircraft Transporter	☐			ii) '1237 BESUCHEN SIE BERLIN	
K14	1971	Scammell Freight Liner 'LEP'	☐			HAMPSTADT DER DDR 1987' –	
K14	1977	'SHELL' Breakdown Truck	☐			'BERLIN CAPITAL OF THE GDR –	
K15	1971	Merryweather 'KENT' Fire Engine	☐			750 YEARS (1987)	☐

Ref. No.	Year(s)	Model Type	Market Price Range
K16	1974	Ford LTS Tankers, various issues:- 'TEXAXO', 'CHEMCO', 'BP', 'LEP', 'ARAL', 'SHELL', 'EXXON', 'TOTAL' and 'U.S. MATCHBOX CLUB' (NGPP), 'QUAKER STATE' and 'Battle Kings' issue. N.B. Some of these issues are scarce.	□
K17		Container Trucks 'DBP', 'PENGUIN', '7 UP' & 'GENTRANSCO' etc.	□
K18	1974	Tipper Truck 'TARMAC', 'US STEEL', 'HOCH & TIEF'	□
K19	1979	Security Truck 'GROUP 4' & 'FORT KNOX'	□
K20	1973	Cargo Hauler	□
	1979	Peterbilt 'HEAVY DUTY' Wrecker	□
K21	1971	Cougar Dragster (SPK)	□
	1974	Tractor Transporter	□
	1979	Ford Transcontinental Truck 'CONTINENTAL', 'POLARA', 'SUNKIST'	□
K22	1971	Dodge Dragster (SPK)	□
	1974	Hovercraft 'SEASPEED', 'HOVERLLOYD'	□
K23	1971	Mercury 'POLICE' Car (SPK)	□
	1974	Low Loader 'HOCH & TIEF'	□
K24	1971	Lamborghini Muira, Red or Blue/ Yellow	□
	1977	Scammel Truck issues:- 'LONDON TO GENEVA', 'MICHELIN', 'GENTRANSCO', 'BAUKNECT'	□
K25	1977	Powerboat & Trailer, 'SEABURST', 'CHRYSLER'	□
	1978	'MUIRHILL' Digger & Plough	□
K26	1971	Mercedes Ambulance (SPK)	□
K26	1978	Bedford Cement Truck, 'McALPINE', 'HOCH & TIEF'	□
K27	1971	Camping Cruiser	□
	1978	Powerboat Transporter 'EMBASSY', 'MISS SOLO'	□
K28	1971	Drag Pack (SPK)	□
	1978	Bedford Skip Truck, 'HOCH & TIEF', 'HALES'	□
K29	1971	Muira 'SEABURST' Set (SPK)	□
	1977	Ford Delivery Van, 'U-HAUL', 'AVIS', 'MR SOFTY', 'BASSETTS', 'TAA'	□
K30	1972	Mercedes C111, Gold, Lime or Blue	□
	1978	Unimog/Compressor	□
K31	1972	Bertone Runabout (SPK)	□
K31	1978	Peterbilt Refrigeration Truck 'CHRISTIAN SALVESON', 'PEPSI', 'IGLOO', 'GERVAIS GLACE', 'DR KOCH'S TRINK', 'DURA PENTA' (South African), 'BURGER KING' etc.	□
K32		No details of models issued	□
K33	1978	Cargo Hauler	□
K34	1972	Thunderclap (SPK)	□
	1979	Pallet Truck	□
K35	1972	Lightning (SPK)	□
	1979	Massey Ferguson Tractor & Trailer	□
K36	1972	Bandolero (SPK)	□
	1978	'LAING' Transporter	□
K37	1973	Sandcat, Orange or Gold (SPK)	□
	1979	Leyland Tipper 'LAING'	□
K38	1974	Gus's Gulpher (SPK)	□
	1980	Dodge 'AMBULANCE'	□
K39	1973	'MILLIGANS MILL' (SPK)	□
	1980	ERF Fire Engine (County)	
K40	1973	Blaze Trailer 'FIRE CHIEF' (SPK)	□
	1980	Ford Drinks Truck 'PEPSI'	□
K41	1973	Fuzz Buggy 'POLICE' (SPK)	□
	1978	Brabham F1 (SPK)	□
	1981	JCB Excavator	□
K42	1973	Nissan 270X (SPK)	□
	1979	Traxcavator Road Ripper	□
K43	1973	'CAMBUSTER' (SPK)	□
	1980/3	Mercedes Log Transporter	□
K44	1973	'BAZOOKA' (SPK)	□
	1978	Surtees F1	□
	1981/3	Bridge Transporter	□
K45	1973/8	Marauder (SPK)	□
K46	1974	Racing Car pack with K34 and K35	□
K47	1973	Easy Rider Tricycle (SPK)	□
K48	1974/8	Mercedes 350 SLC, Bronze or White (SPK)	□
K49	1973	Ambulance (SPK)	□
	1874	'MALTESER' Truck	□
K50	1974	Street Rod (SPK)	□
K51	1973	Barracuda, Blue or White (SPK)	□
K52	1973/8	Datsun Rally Car (SPK) Yellow, Silver or Green 'CIBIE'	□
K53	1976	Hot Fire Engine (SPK)	□
K54	1976	A.M.X. Javelin (SPK)	□
K55	1976/8	Corvette 'CAPER CART' (SPK) Blue or Red	□
K56	1976	Maserati Bora, Silver or Blue (SPK)	□
K57	1976	Javelin Drag Racing Set, K38 & K39 (SPK)	□
K58	1976/8	Corvette Power Boat Set, Blue or Red, K45 etc. (SPK)	□
K59	1976	Ford Capri MkII, White or Beige	□
K60	1976/8	Ford Mustang, Metallic Turquoise or White (SPK)	□
K61	1976	Mercedes 'POLICE' Car (SPK)	□
	1978	Mercedes 'POLIZEI' Car (SPK)	□
K62	1977	Doctors Car (SPK)	□
K63	1977	Mercedes 'Binz' 'AMBULANCE' (SPK)	□
K64	1978	'FIRE CONTROL' Range Rover	□
K65	1978	Plymouth Mountain Rescue i) 'EMERGENCY RESUCE'	□
		ii) 'BERGRETTUNG WACHT'	□
K66	1979	Jaguar XJ12 'POLICE' Set	□
K67	1978	Dodge Monaco (SPK) i) 'FIRE CHIEF'	□
		ii) 'HACKENSACK'	□
K68	1978	Dodge Monaco and Trailer (SPK)	□
K69	1978	Jaguar XJ12 and Caravan (SPK) Blue and Cream, or Red and White	□
	1980	Dodge Monaco and Caravan (SPK)	□
K70	1979	Porsche Turbo, Green or Black	□
K71	1979	Porsche 'POLIZEI' Set	□
K72	1979	Brabham F1, Red or Green	□
K73	1979	Surtess F1, White or Tan	□
K74	1979	Volvo Estate	□
K75	1979	Airport 'FIRE' Rescue issues:- 'AIRPORT FIRE TENDER', 'FLUGHAFEN-FEURWEHR', 'SECURITE AEROPORT'	□
K76	1979	Volvo Rally Set 'CIBIE'	□
K77	1979	Rescue Vehicle: 'STRASSEN SERVICE', 'SECOURS ROUTIER', 'HIGHWAY RESCUE'	□
K78	1979/83	U.S. Police Car, 'POLICE', 'POLIZEI' or 'CITY POLICE'	□
K79	1979	U.S. Taxi '75c FIRST ¼ MILE'	□
K80	1980	Dodge Custom Van	□
K81	1981	'SUZUKI' Motor Cycle	□
K82	1981	'BMW' Motor Cycle	□
K83	1981	'HARLEY DAVIDSON' 'POLICE' Motor Cycle	□
K84	1981	Peugeot 305 'EXPO' or 'ELF' logos	□
K85	1988	Audi Quattro Rally	□
K86	1982	VW Gold 'SHELL'	□
K87	1982	'MF595' Tractor & Rake	□
K88	1981	Security Van (Money Box) 'VOLKSBANK' or 'SAVE YOUR MONEY'	□
K89	1981	Forrestry Set 'KIELDER'	□
K90	1982	Matro Rancho 'TRANSGLOBE'	□
K91	1982	Motor Cycle Racing Set	□
K92	1982	Ford Helicopter Transporter	□
K93	1982	Road Lamp Maintenance Set	□
K95	1982	Audi Quattro, 'H. MIKKOLA', 'PACE' or 'PIRELLI'	□
K96	1983	Volvo 'AMBULANCE'	□
K97	1983	'POLICE' Range Rover	□
K98	1983	'PORSCHE 944'	□
K99	1979/83	'POLIZEI' Range Rover	□
K100	1983	Ford Sierra 4i	□
K101-K115		Battle Kings — See separate listing.	
K101	1983	Racing Porsche	□
K102	1983	Race Support Set	□
K103	1983	Peterbilt Tanker Truck 'COMET'	□
K104	1983	Rancho Rescue Set 'COASTGUARD'	□
k105	1983/5	Peterbilt Tipper, White or Yellow with 'TAYLOR WOODROW'	□
K106	1983	Aircraft Transporter 'ACES'	□
K107	1983	'SPEARHEADS' Launch Transporter	□

Ref. No.	Year(s)	Model Type		Ref. No.	Year(s)	Model Type	
K108	1983	Digger/Plough Transporter	☐	K156	1988	Porsche 911 Rally	☐
K109	1983	'SHELL' Petrol Tanker	☐	K157	1988	Porsche 944 Rally	☐
K110	1984	Fire Engine	☐	K158	1988	Sierra XR4i Pace Car	☐
K111	1985	Peterbilt Refuse Truck	☐	K159	1988	'PORSCHE' Racing Car Transporter	☐
K112	1985	Peterbilt 'FIRE' Spotter	☐	K160	1988	'MATCHBOX' Racing Car	
K113	1985	Garage Transporter	☐			Transporter	☐
K114	1985	Mobile Crane	☐	K161	1992	Rolls Royce Silver Spirit	☐
K115	1985	Mercedes Benz 190E 2.3/16V	☐	K162	1992	Ford Sierra Cosworth 'TEXACO' or	
	1989	Mercedes Benz Rally 'FUJI'	☐			'GEMINI'	☐
K116	1985	Racing Car Transporter	☐	K163	1990	'SCHMIDT' Snow Plough	☐
K117	1985	Bulldozer Transport 'TAYLOR		K164	1991	'SAFARI' Range Rover	☐
		WOODROW'	☐	K165	1990	'POLICE' Range Rover	☐
K118	1985	Road Set K30 and K21	☐	K166	1992	Mercedes 190E 'TAXI'	☐
K119	1985	'FIRE' Set with K110	☐	K167	1991	Ford Transit 'SURF N' SUN'	☐
K120	1986	Bedford Car Transporter	☐	K168	1992	Porsche 911 'CARRERA 4'	☐
K121	1986	Peterbilt Rescue Truck	☐	K171	1991	Toyoga 'Hi Lux' Pick Up	☐
K122	1987	DAF Road Train 'EUROTRANS'	☐	K172	1992	Mercedes Benz 560SL	☐
K123	1987	Leyland Cement Truck	☐	K173	1992	Lamborghini 'DIABLO'	☐
K124	1987	Mercedes '7 UP' Truck	☐	K175	1992	'SUZUKI' Santana	☐
K126	1987	DAF Helicopter 'RN' Transporter	☐				
K127	1987	Peterbilt Tanker 'TOTAL' or 'GETTY'					
		(US)	☐				
K128	1987	DAF Aircraft Transporter	☐				
K129	1987	Powerlaunch Transporter					
		'SPEARHEAD' or 'COASTGUARD'	☐				
K130	1987	'PLANT HIRE' Transporter	☐				
K131	1987	'TEXACO' Petrol Tanker	☐				
K132	1987	'FIRE' Engine	☐				
K133	1987/89	'REFUSE CITY' Track, Red or White	☐				
K134	1987	'FIRE' Spotters Plane Transporter	☐				
K135	1987	Garage Transporter 'TEXACO'	☐				
K136	1987	'FERRARI' Racing Car Transporter	☐				
K139	1987	'WIMPEY' Tipper Truck	☐				
K140	1987	Car 'RECOVERY' Vehicle	☐				
K141	1987	Skip Truck 'ECD'	☐				
K142	1987	BMW 'POLIZEI' Car	☐				
	1990	BMW 'POLICE' Car	☐				
	1990	BMW 'PACE' Car	☐				
K143	1987	'EMERGENCY' Van	☐				
K144	1987/90	Land Rover 'FRANKFURT' or 'ROAD					
		MAINTENANCE'	☐				
K145	1988	'IVECO' Tipper/Tractor	☐				
K146	1988	Jaguar XJ6	☐				
K147	1988	BMW 750iL	☐				
K148	1988	Crane Truck 'PEX'	☐				
K149	1988	Ferrari Testarossa	☐				
K150	1989	Leyland Truck	☐				
K151	1988	Skip Truck	☐				
K152	1988	Audi Quattro Saloon	☐				
K153	1988	Jaguar XJ6 'POLICE'	☐				
K154	1988	BMW 750iL 'POLIZEI'	☐				
K155	1988	'FERRARI' Testarossa Rally Car	☐				

Battle Kings issued 1974

Models packed in window boxes. They include 3 plastic soldiers.
Market Price Range £8-15

K101	Sherman Tank		K110	Recovery Vehicle
K102	M48 AS Tank		K111	Missile Launcher
K103	Chieftain Tank		K112	DAF Ambulance
K104	King Tiger Tank		K113	Military Crane Truck
K105	Hover Raider		K114	Army Aircraft Transporter
K106	Tank Transporter		K115	Army Petrol Tanker
K107	155mm Gun		K116	Troop Carrier & Howitzer
K108	Half Track		K117	Rocket Launcher
K109	Sheridan Tank		K118	Army Helicopter

Sea Kings issued 1976

Models packed in window boxes
Market Price Range £8-12

K301	Frigate 'F109'		K306	Convoy Escort 'F101'
K302	Corvette 'C70'		K307	Helicopter Carrier with
K303	Battleship '110'			2 Helicopters
K304	Aircraft Carrier with 4		K308	Guided Missile Destroyer
	aircraft '36'		K309	Submarine '117'
K305	Submarine Chaser 'C17'		K310	Anti Aircraft Carrier

SuperKing – Big 'MX' Models

These SuperKing models were powered by an Activator Gun which plugged into the vehicles and activated the mechanisms. The models were issued in their own packaging 1972-4.

Market Price Range £15-20

BM1	Incinerator Site and Refuse Truck (K17)	BM 4	Mechanical Coal Delivery Hopper and Tipper Truck (K4 Leyland Tipper)
BM 2	Mechanised Tractor Plant and Winch Transport (K20 Tractor Transporter)	BM 5	Mechanical Quarry Site and Traxcavator (K8 Traxcavator)
BM 3	Mechanised Crane Truck and Building Site (K12 Scammell Crane)	BM 6	Fire Rescue Scene with mechanised Fire Engine (K15 Merryweather Fire Engine)

Convoy Series

The model range was launched in 1982 and the early issues were made in England before manufacture was transferred to Macau. Many variations exist particularly in the U.S.A. where they have been used for promotional purposes linked to NASCAR truck racing. For a listing of the many variations available contact **Carr Collectables, PO Box 44, Ongar, Essex CM5 9AP. Tel: (01277) 364970.** The basic listing of models issued up to 1988 is as follows:

CY1	Kenworth Boat Transporter	CY13	Peterbilt Fire Engine
CY2	Kenworth Rocket Transporter	CY14	Kenworth Boat Transporter (MB 45e)
CY3	Peterbilt Container Truck	CY15	Peterbilt Tracking Vehicle
CY4	Kenworth Boat Transporter (MB 41f)	CY16	Scania Box Truck
CY5	Peterbilt Covered Truck	CY17	Scania Petrol Tanker
CY6	Kenworth Horse Box	CY18	Scania Container Truck
CY7	Peterbilt Petrol Tanker	CY19	Peterbilt Box Car
CY8	Kenworth Box Truck (MB 45e)	CY20a	Scania Tipper
CY9	Kenworth Box Truck (MB 41f)	CY20b	Kenworth Tipper
CY10	Kenworth Racing Transporter (MB 66f)	CY21	DAF Aircraft Transporter
CY11	Kenworth Helicopter Transporter (MB 75e)	CY22	DAF Power Boat Transporter
CY12	Kenworth Aircraft Transporter	CY23	Scania Covered Truck

CY24   DAF Box Car
CY25   DAF Box Truck
CY26   DAF Container Truck
CY27   Mack Box Truck
CY28   Mack Container Truck
CY29   Mack Aircraft Transporter
CY35   Mack Tanker
CY36   Kenworth Box Car
CY104   Kenworth Aerodyne Cab and Box Car Trailer

CY105   Kenworth Aerodyne Tanker
CY106   Peterbilt Tipper Truck
CY107   Mack CH-600 Box Car
CY109   Ford Aeromax Box Car
CY110   Kenworth Box Car
CY201   Fire Rescue Set
CY202   Police Set
CY203   Construction Set
CY204   NASA Set

N.B. See also issues listed in the Tyco Matchbox section.

Pictures taken from the 1967 Matchbox Catalogue.

Matchbox Catalogues

Issue Date	Publication	Cover Details	Market Price Range	
1957	Folded Leaflet	Yellow cover has Blue edging and depicts No.1 Diesel Roller. Colour pictures of nos. 1 - 42 of '1-75' series	£50-75	☐
1957	Folded Leaflet	Blue/Yellow cover featuring MOY No.1 Allchin 7nhp Traction Engine 1st series box. Contents list first nine Yesteryears.	£75-100	☐
1958	16-page catalogue	Cover features Rolls-Royce (44), emerging from box. Contents illustrate models 1 - 60 in colour, plus early 'Major Packs' and Accessory Packs	£50-75	☐
	Reprints	Catalogue reprinted for DTE in 1982.	£15-20	☐
1959	Folded Leaflet	Features first fourteen Models Of Yesteryear in colour	£75-100	☐
1959	16-page catalogue	Same cover as 1958 catalogue with '1959 Edition'. Lists 1-75's, Major Packs and accessories. Colour pictures	£50-75	☐
1959	24-page catalogue	'UK' & '2d' on cover featuring MOY No.9, 1-75 series, No.'43', and Accessory No.'2'. Colour contents show 1-75's Nos 1 - 72 and MOY 1 - 14 plus Accessories and Major Packs..	£50-75	☐
1960	32-page catalogue	'UK' & '3d' on cover featuring logo *ALL THE MATCHBOX POCKET TOYS BY LESNEY* plus semi-circle picture of MOY & 1-75's. Contents illustrate all ranges.	£50-75	☐
1961	32-page catalogue	*International Pocket Catalogue* on cover with picture of 1-75 model No.5 Bus. New style smaller catalogue listing all issues in colour plus International price list.	£50-75	☐
1962	20-page catalogue	'2d', *International Pocket Catalogue* and *1962 Edition* on cover. All issues listed, European price list included.	£35-45	☐
1963	20-page catalogue	No.53 Mercedes-Benz printed on cover with '2d' and *1963 Edition*. Contents include good Gift Set pictures and listings.	£10-14	☐
1964	32-page catalogue	'3d' on cover depicting Blue Mk.10 Jaguar (No.28). *1964 Matchbox Prices* on back cover. Contents include superb Gift Set pictures and listings.	£8-11	☐
1965	32-page catalogue	Cover features Motor Racing Cars. *1965 Matchbox Prices* on back cover. Excellent full colour Gift Set pictures. (Price 3d)	£8-11	☐
1966	40-page catalogue	London scene and *Price 3d* on cover. Excellent pictures of mid-sixties Gift Sets plus history of Matchbox.	£8-11	☐
1967	40-page catalogue	Cover features flags and 1-75 issues, *Price 3d*. Contents list and depict Veteran Car Gifts	£8-11	☐
1968	40-page catalogue	1968 car picture & *Price 3d* on cover. Includes details of manufacturing processes.	£8-11	☐
1969	48-page catalogue	Cover features Motorway scene. Contents include detailed history of the real cars making up the MOY range.	£8-11	☐
	2nd edition:	A second edition of the 1969 catalogue includes the first reference to *Superfast* issues	£8-11	☐
1970	64-page catalogue	Only drawings of models (no photographs) throughout. Superfast track featured. '6d', *MATCHBOX SUPERFAST* and a collage of models on cover.	£5-8	☐
1971	64-page catalogue	'2$p' on Blue/Red cover with scorpion design. 'Speed Kings' listed plus pictures of first Superfast Gift Sets.	£5-8	☐
1972	72-page catalogue	Yellow *MATCHBOX* and '3p' on cover. Contents feature launch of 'Scream'n Demon' bikes and excellent Gift Set pictures.	£5-8	☐
1973	80-page catalogue	'5p' and '1973' on cover of the largest Matchbox catalogue produced. Contents include good 'Super Kings' and Aircraft Kit listing.	£5-8	☐
1974	64-page catalogue	'2p' and '1974' on cover. Includes first 'SKYBUSTERS' listing.	£5-8	☐
1975	64-page catalogue	'2p' and '1975' on cover. Contents feature 'Rolamatics' and 'Battle Kings'	£5-8	☐
1976	64-page catalogue	'1976' on cover. Contents feature 'Sea Kings' plus 'Baby Dolls' & 'Disco Girl Dolls'	£5-8	☐
1977	80-page catalogue	'1977' on cover. Contents list the 'Two Pack' (TP) range of 1-75's. Good Gift Set pictures and listings of 1-75's.	£5-8	☐
1978	64-page catalogue	'1978' on cover. Includes good 'SKYBUSTERS' and 1-75 Gift Set pictures.	£5-8	☐
1979-80	80-page catalogue	'5p' and '1979-80' on cover. The contents feature good pictures of Gift Sets G1 - G8. '900' TP series introduced.	£4-6	☐
1980-81	80-page catalogue	'5p' on cover. All ranges listed including 'Walt Disney' & 'Power Track' equipment	£3-4	☐
1981-82	64-page catalogue	'5p' and '1981-82' on cover. 'Adventure 2000' space models pictured. 'Playtrack', 'Popeye' and 'Streak Sets' listed.	£2-3	☐
1982-83	64-page catalogue	'1982-83' on cover. 'Convoy' series introduced, good MOY pictures, 'Streak Sets' listed.	£2-3	☐
1984	64-page catalogue	'1984' on cover. 'MATCHBOX SPECIALS' introduced, good Gift Set pictures, 'Burnin' Key Cars', 'Rough Riders' and 'Lock Ups' listed.	£2-3	☐
1985	48-page catalogue	'1985' & 'chequered flag' design on cover. All ranges listed plus introduction of 'Trickshifters', 'Power Blasters', 'Matchmates' and 'Carry Cases'. (Printed in Italy)	£1-2	☐
1986	48-page catalogue	'1986' on cover. 'High Riders', 'Twin-Pack' and 'Action Packs' listed inside. 'Motor City' feature introduced	£1-2	☐
1987	72-page catalogue	'1987' on cover. Listing includes 'Superfast Lasers', 'Pocket Rockets', 'Speed Riders', 'Streak Racing', 'Hot Rod Racers', 'Turbo 2', 'Turbo Specials' and 'Demolition Cars'.	£1-2	☐
1988	88-page catalogue	'1988' on cover. Listing includes Miniatures Gift Sets pictures, 'Lasers', 'Super GT Sport' and 'Super Miniatures', 'Team Convoy', 'Road Blasters', 'Motor City' and 'Action Matchbox'. Also includes 'MICA' and 'Junior Matchbox Club' membership details.	£1-2	☐
1989	80-page catalogue	'1989' on cover. Listings include 'Miniatures', 'Twin-Pack', 'Motor City' Gift Sets, 'Dinky Collection', 'World Class', 'Conn-Nect-Ables', 'Flashbacks', 'Super ColourChangers' and 'Skybusters ColourChangers'.	50p	☐
1990	48-page catalogue	'1990' on cover. Contents include 'Superfast Minis' listing plus normal range of products.	50p	☐
1991	56-page catalogue	'1991' on cover. Includes 'Graffic Traffic', 'Action Series', 'Lightning Series', 'Matchbox 2000' range and Matchbox 'Railways'.	£1-3	☐
1991	A4 leaflet	Full-colour sheet with MOY on one side and the Dinky Collection on the other	50p	☐

Overseas Catalogue Editions

During the 1960's there were normally six editions of each catalogue; British, International, U.S.A., German, French and French-Canadian. The catalogues were usually of the same format as the UK editions but with the appropriate language and currency. *INTERNATIONAL CATALOGUE* was shown on the front cover together with the edition, e.g. *'EDITION FRANCAISE', 'INTERNATIONAL'* or *'U.S.A. EDITION'*. The 1960 'International Pocket Catalogue' listed the national prices for every product in Australia, Austria, Belgium, Spain, Denmark, Eire, France, Germany, Great Britain, Holland, Hong Kong, Italy, Kenya & East Africa, Singapore & Malaysia, South Africa, Sweden and Switzerland. From 1972 the country-specific editions only listed the model range available in that country.
Market Price Range - Prices are equivalent to those asked for UK editions.

Other Matchbox literature

'Mike and The Modelman' (1st edition 1970), was a childrens' book issued by Lesney telling the Matchbox story. A copy in perfect condition should cost between **£10 - £15**.

Trade Catalogues have been published for many years and occasionally become available for sale. Those before 1970 are scarce and no value information is possible at present. Those from the 1970-80 period tend to be in the region of **£10-15** while post-1980 editions sell for **£2-5** depending on content and condition.

The Matchbox Collectors Passport (introduced in 1987), also served as a catalogue providing a full colour listing of the MOY range available in the years in which it was current. In 1991 the Dinky Collection then available was also pictured with the Special Editions and the Passport scheme model offer.

Lesney Pub Signs c. 1970? All NGPP

"The Cock", "Swan", "Lion", "Unicorn", "Bull", "Rose & Crown", "Pig & Whistle", "George & Dragon", "Dick Turpin", "Britannia", "The Volunteer". The Editor would welcome information on the signs and details of prices.

TYCO-Matchbox issues

The following listings are in respect of the intended new release programme as shown in the 1993 Trade Catalogue. However, it is possible that not all the models listed will be released. See the 1994 'Model Price Review' for the latest news of actual issues.

MW 500 'Motor Show' Series

Two models alternately displayed in a showcase setting with a mirror-back finish and plinth.

Showcase 1	1993	2 BMWs	A Red '5' series and a White '850i'	NRP	☐
Showcase 2	1993	2 Lamborghinis	A Yellow 'Diablo' plus a Green 'Countach'	NRP	☐
Showcase 3	1993	2 Ferraris	A 'Testarossa' and an 'F-40' (both Red)	NRP	☐
Showcase 4	1993	2 Mercedes-Benz	A Metallic Bronze 'SEL' plus a Red '500 SL'	NRP	☐
Showcase 5	1993	2 Porsches	A Red '959' and a White '911'	NRP	☐
Showcase 6	1993	2 Jaguars	A Blue 'XJ-6' and a Metallic Silver 'XJ-220'	NRP	☐

'Masterclass' series 1:24 scale

'In a class of its own'. Each model has highly detailed features and is packaged in an excellent box.

LS 001	1993	Jaguar XJ-220	Silver body	NRP	☐
LS 002	1993	Lamborghini Diablo	Red body	NRP	☐
LS 003	1993	Porsche 911 Carrera Cabriolet..		NRP	☐

Farming Series (Miniatures) Farming Action Packs

1	1993	Tractor and Seeder	plus 2 cows	NRP	☐
2	1993	Tractor and Trailer	plus 3 pigs	NRP	☐
3	1993	Kenworth Horsebox	plus 4 horses	NRP	☐
4	1993	Tractor-Shovel	and Tiptrailer plus 3 sheep	NRP	☐
5	1993	Ford Tractor	plus Haytrailer and 2 horses	NRP	☐
6	1993	Ford Tractor	and Rotovator plus 8 ducks	NRP	☐
FM 110	1993	Mobile Farm Set	Contains 2 Tractors, Trailer, Harrow, Land Rover and accessories	NRP	☐
FM 120	1993	Farm Yard Set	Contains 2 Tractors, Combine Harvester, Horsebox, farm equipment, animals, accessories	NRP	☐
FM 130	1993	Big Farm Set	Contains Barn, Grain Silo, Land Rover & Pony Trailer, 2 Tractors, 2 Trailers, Tanker, Horsebox, Seeder, Harrow, accessories	NRP	☐

Farming Series (Large Scale) Each vehicle includes working features

FM 1	1993	Range Rover	Green body with *'ORGANIC FARMS'* logo, plus farmer, dog and 2 sheep	NRP	☐
FM 2	1993	Muir Tractor & Back Shovel	Green/Yellow tractor plus 8 chickens	NRP	☐
FM 3	1993	Shovel Tractor	Red/White/Silver tractor plus 3 pigs	NRP	☐
FM 4	1993	Toyota Hilux	Red body, Brown load plus cow and 2 milkchurns	NRP	☐
FM 5	1993	Muir Tractor & Trailer	Green/Yellow tractor/trailer with log load	NRP	☐
FM 6	1993	Massey Ferguson Tractor	Red/White tractor, Red/Brown trailer with 4 crates	NRP	☐
FM 7	1993	Massey Ferguson Tractor	Green/Black tractor plus Yellow/Green implement	NRP	☐
FM 9	1993	Farm Set	Models FM 1 to FM 7 combined	NRP	☐

Construction Series (Miniatures and Convoys)

'ACTION TEAM'

CS 81	1992	Bulldozer & Tractor Shovel	Miniatures plus signs	NRP	☐
CS 82	1992	Tipper & Excavator	Miniatures plus scaffolding and 2 ladders	NRP	☐
CS 83	1992	Road Roller & Crane	Miniatures plus 8 bollards	NRP	☐

'TRUCK TEAM'

CS 61	1992	Transporter & Shovel	Convoy Mack Transporter plus Shovel and 8 bollards	NRP	☐
CS 62	1992	Pipe Transporter	Convoy Mack Pipe Transporter plus 2 road signs	NRP	☐
CS 63	1992	Kenworth Tipper	Convoy Kenworth Tipper plus 2 road signs	NRP	☐
CS 64	1992	Grove Crane	plus 8 bollards	NRP	☐
CS 71	1993	Mobile Squad Set	Contains Convoy Kenworth Transporter plus Miniatures 11, 25 and 45	NRP	☐
CS 75	1993	Heavy Duty Squad	Contains Grove Crane plus Miniatures 5, 19, 23, 25, 45, in Red/Yellow	NRP	☐
CS 90	1992	Carry Pack	30 pieces including vehicles and accessories from previous sets	NRP	☐

Construction Series (Large Scale) Highly detailed Construction Vehicles

Ref. No.	Year(s)	Model Type	Description	Market Price Range	
CS 1	1993	Bulldozer	Yellow/Red body and shovel	NRP	☐
CS 2	1993	Leyland Cement Truck	Yellow body, Grey barrel, Red/White stripe design	NRP	☐
CS 4	1993	Skip Truck	Yellow/Red body and skip plus Red/White stripe design	NRP	☐
CS 5	1993	Unimog Tar Sprayer	Yellow/Red body with Red/White stripe design	NRP	☐
CS 6	1993	Tipper Truck	Yellow/Red body with Red/White stripe design	NRP	☐
CS 7	1993	Digger and Plough	Yellow/Red body with Red/White stripe design	NRP	☐
CS 8	1993	Mobile Crane	Yellow/Red body with Red/White stripe design	NRP	☐
CS 9	1993	JCB 808 Excavator	Yellow/Red body, Black tracks, Red/White stripe design	NRP	☐
CS 10	1993	Digger Transporter	Yellow/Red models with No.'9' on digger engine	NRP	☐
CS 11	1993	Pipe Transporter	Yellow/Red vehicle with 3 Grey plastic pipes	NRP	☐

'Emergency' Series (Miniatures and Convoys)

'ACTION TEAM'

Ref. No.	Year(s)	Model Type	Description	Market Price Range	
EM 81	1992	Snorkel and Foam Pumper	MB13 Snorkel plus MB 54 Pumper	NRP	☐
EM 82	1992	Matra Rancho and Truck	Matra Rancho 'Rescue' plus Ford Wreck Truck	NRP	☐
EM 83	1992	Ambulance & Power Truck	American Ambulance plus MB 50 Auxiliary Power Truck	NRP	☐

'TRUCK TEAM'

Ref. No.	Year(s)	Model Type	Description	Market Price Range	
EM 61	1992	Helicopter Transporter	Mack Helicopter Transporter (CY29) 'Police' plus road signs	NRP	☐
EM 62	1992	Fire Engine	Red CY13 with Blue 'FIRE' logo	NRP	☐
EM 63	1992	Coastguard Launch Transporter	White/Red CY22 with 'RESCUE' logo	NRP	☐
EM 64	1992	Peterbilt Rescue Centre	CY15 with road signs	NRP	☐
EM 71	1992	Helicopter Transporter	CY29 with MB18 and MB1 plus road signs	NRP	☐
EM 72	1992	Helicopter Transporter	CY29 with MB18 and Mercedes 280 GE, German issue	NRP	☐
EM 74	1992	Helicopter Transporter	CY29 with MB18 and Land Rover, Dutch issue	NRP	☐
EM 75	1992	Action 'FIRE' Set	CY13 plus TP131, MB18, MB51, MB 75 Helicopter	NRP	☐
EM 80	1992	30 Carry Pack	30 pieces including vehicles and accessories from previous sets	NRP	☐

'Emergency' Series (Large Scale) 'Emergency Vehicles to the Rescue!'

Ref. No.	Year(s)	Model Type	Description	Market Price Range	
EM 1	1993	US 'POLICE' Car	Yellow body with Blue stripe, '69' logo on roof	NRP	☐
EM 2	1993	Matra Rancho	Red body with White design and 'Fire Control Unit' logo	NRP	☐
EM 3	1993	Jaguar XJ-6 'POLICE'	White body with Red side stripe and lightbar on roof	NRP	☐
EM 4	1993	BMW 730 'POLICE'	White body with Red side stripe and 2 Blue roof lights	NRP	☐
EM 5	1993	Fire Engine	Red body with White extending ladders, '201 FIRE' logo	NRP	☐
EM 6	1993	Range Rover 'POLICE'	White body with Red side stripe and one Blue light	NRP	☐
EM 7	1993	Transit 'Air Ambulance'	White body, Yellow/Red stripe, Red cross, 2 Blue lights	NRP	☐
EM 8	1993	PB Wreck Truck & Car	Black/White truck 'POLICE', plus Silver Porsche 959	NRP	☐
EM 9	1993	Helicopter Transporter	White/Blue vehicle and White 'Coastguard' helicopter	NRP	☐
EM 10	1993	Snorkel Fire Engine	Red/White body 'County Fire' logo, plus a fireman	NRP	☐
EM 11	1993	Fire Spotter Plane	Red vehicle with Yellow 'FIRE' logo, plus Silver/Red spotter plane	NRP	☐
EM 12	1993	Power Launch Transporter	White/Blue vehicle with 'Coastguard' logo, plus Orange/White boat	NRP	☐
EM 13	1993	Helicopter	Red/Yellow helicopter with Yellow 'FIRE' logo	NRP	☐
EM 14	1993	Suzuki Santana	White body, Orange/Blue design, Blue 'POLICE' logo	NRP	☐

SB 830 - Airforce Series,   SB 840 - Airport Series   see the Skybusters listing (below)

Harley-Davidson Motor Cycle Series

Ref. No.	Year(s)	Model Type	Description	Market Price Range	
HD 210	1993	4 Motor Cycles Set	Includes Silver/Red, Silver/Turquoise, Silver/Blue and All-Silver models with 'Rev-Up' action	NRP	☐
HD 230	1993	Road Riders Set	Yellow/Silver motor cycle plus Black 'Harley-Davidson' transporter	NRP	☐
HD 250	1993	Hog Riders Set	Includes high detail Red/Silver and Blue/Silver motor cycles	NRP	☐

WS 700 'World Sports' Series 'The Greatest Sports Cars in the World'

Ref. No.	Year(s)	Model Type	Description	Market Price Range	
i)	1993	Ferrari 512 BB	White/Black body with Pink 'flame' design	NRP	☐
ii)	1993	Porsche 959	White body with 'KONI' logo and 'PORSCHE 959'	NRP	☐
iii)	1993	Ferrari F4	Red body with Yellow/Black Ferrari emblem	NRP	☐
iv)	1993	Jaguar XJ-220	Red body	NRP	☐
v)	1993	Ford Thunderbird	Black body, RN '28', 'HAVOLINE' logo	NRP	☐
vi)	1993	Chevrolet Lumina	Black body, RN '3', 'GOODRICH' logo	NRP	☐

WS 100 'World Class' Series 'The Finest Saloon Cars in the World'

Ref. No.	Year(s)	Model Type	Description	Market Price Range	
WS 101	1993	Porsche 944	Yellow body, Black opening tailgate	NRP	☐
WS 102	1993	Mercedes-Benz 190	Metallic Silver body	NRP	☐
WS 103	1993	Jaguar	White body	NRP	☐
WS 104	1993	BMW 750	Metallic Blue body	NRP	☐
WS 105	1993	Ferrari Testarossa	All Red body	NRP	☐
WS 106	1993	Lamborghini Diablo	Yellow body, Red 'DIABLO' logo, 'J68 TGL' registration	NRP	☐
WS 107	1993	Ford Sierra Cosworth	Black body, Red 'TEXACO' logo	NRP	☐
WS 108	1993	Ford Sierra Cosworth	White body, RN '1', 'GEMINI' logo	NRP	☐
WS 109	1993	Porsche 911 Carrera	Red body, Black 'CARRERA' logo	NRP	☐
WS 110	1993	Mercedes-Benz 500 SL	Metallic Brown body	NRP	☐

WS 50 'World Class' Series The Worlds Greatest High Performance Vehicles

1	1993	Porsche 928S....................	Metallic Grey, Black chassis, 928 on door	NRP ☐
2	1993	Lamborghini Countach	Yellow, Yellow chassis, LP5000S in Red on door	NRP ☐
3	1993	Mercedes AMG 560 SEC.........	White, Black chassis, AMG in blue on front wing	NRP ☐
4	1993	Corvette Roadster	Metallic Blue, Blue chassis, open top, Corvette in Red on door	NRP ☐
5	1993	Porsche 966 Turbo	Black, Black chassis, 944 Turbo in Yellow on door	NRP ☐
6	1993	Ferrari Testarossa................	Red, Red chassis, Black intake strips on doors	NRP ☐
7	1993	Ferrari 308 GTB....................	Red, red chassis	NRP ☐
8	1993	Porsche 959............................	Grey, Black chassis, Porsche in Yellow on door............................	NRP ☐

'City Life' Series   Detailed city service-vehicles

CL 1	1993	London Bus & Taxi	Red Londoner Bus with 'The Planetarium' logo, plus MB4 taxi	NRP ☐
CL 2	1993	Refuse Truck	All White body, 'ABF HAMBURG' logo	NRP ☐
CL 3	1993	Leyland Recovery Truck	White/Blue body, six-wheel truck with ramp	NRP ☐
CL 4	1993	Leyland Skip Truck.................	Red cab and chassis, Yellow skip	NRP ☐
CL 5	1993	Iveco Petrol Tanker	Red cab and tank with 'TEXACO' logo	NRP ☐

TR 50   'Transporters' Series   'The Kings of the Highway'

TR 1	1993	DAF Car Transporter	Yellow cab and rear, 'EXPRESS COURIER' logo	NRP ☐
TR 2	1993	Container Truck	Blue/White cab and rear, 'MATEY BUBBLE BATH' logo...........	NRP ☐
TR 3	1993	Helicopter Transporter	Blue transporter with 'RN' logo, plus Blue/Orange helicopter.........	NRP ☐
TR 4	1993	Mercedes Petrol Tanker	White cab and tank, 'TOTAL' logo	NRP ☐
TR 5	1993	DAF Aircraft Transporter	Blue/White 'ALPHA ONE' aircraft on White/Red trailer...............	NRP ☐
TR 6	1993	Mercedes Racing Car Transporter	White and Dark Blue body with 'GOODYEAR' logo	NRP ☐

'Matchbox Originals' Series

Each model perfectly duplicated from the original Matchbox classics and packed in a replica 'MOKO LESNEY' box.

SERIES I

1	1993	Diesel Road Roller	Blue body, Red wheels, Gold trim	NRP ☐
4	1993	Massey Harris Tractor	Green body, Cream driver, Silver wheels	NRP ☐
5	1993	London Bus	Red body, Silver wheels, 'MATCHBOX ORIGINALS' logo	NRP ☐
7	1993	Horse-Drawn Milk Float	Blue body, White driver and milk crates, Brown horse	NRP ☐
9	1993	Dennis Fire Escape....................	Red body, Yellow ladder wheels, Silver road wheels	NRP ☐

SERIES II

6	1993	Quarry Truck...........................	Blue cab with Grey tipper	NRP ☐
13	1993	Bedford Wreck Truck..............	Red body, Yellow crane and hook	NRP ☐
19	1993	MG 'TD' Midget......................	Dark Green body, White driver, Grey wheels...............................	NRP ☐
26	1993	E.R.F. Cement Mixer...............	Orange body, Grey wheels and mixer barrel	NRP ☐
32	1993	Jaguar XK-140	Black body, Grey wheels	NRP ☐

'Thunderbirds' Series   'International Rescue Services'

TB 1	1993	Thunderbird I..........................	Pilot Scott Tracey, Steel Grey/Blue/Red model, bubble-pack	NRP ☐
TB 2	1993	Thunderbird II.........................	Pilot Virgil Tracey, Green/Red model plus Yellow Thunderbird IV	NRP ☐
TB 3	1993	Thunderbird III	Astronaut Alan Tracey, Red/Black model with No.'3' logo............	NRP ☐
TB 4	1993	Lady Penelope's 'FAB 1'..........	Pink 'Rolls-Royce' with Silver radiator, Cream interior	NRP ☐
TB 79	1993	Thunderbirds Action Set	Redesigned Thunderbirds I, II, III & IV with powerful wind-back motors....	NRP ☐
TB 700	1993	Thunderbirds Rescue Pack........	Contains the entire Thunderbirds diecast model range......................	NRP ☐
TB 710	1993	Tracey Island Electronic Playset...................................	All the Thunderbirds models, with voice commands and rocket sounds	NRP ☐
TB 720	1993	Thunderbirds II Playset............	Thunderbirds II and IV models with voice commands and rocket sounds	NRP ☐
TB 750	1993	Thunderbirds Figures	95 mm. tall figures of Parker, John, Virgil, Jeff, Brains, Lady Penelope, Hood, Alan, Scott, Gordon..	NRP ☐

'Stingray' Series   'Defends the World from the evil Aquaphibians'

SR 200	1993	Stingray and Terrafish..............	Blue/Silver/Yellow 'Stingray', plus Green/Silver Terrafish............	NRP ☐
SR 210	1993	Marineville...............................	Stingray HQ. Contains 2 'Wasp' rockets plus 'Stingray' model	NRP ☐
SR 220	1993	Stingray Action Playset	Highly detailed 'Stingray' model with lift-off top, fires torpedoes. Colours as SR 200	NRP ☐
SR 250	1993	Stingray Figures.......................	Commander Shore, Titan, Marina, Captain Troy Tempest...............	NRP ☐

'Swop Tops' Series   Exotic cars which switch from classic hardtops to sporting convertibles

1	1993	Nissan 300 ZX........................	Deep Pink body with Blue '300 ZX'	NRP ☐
2	1993	Porsche 968............................	Dark Red body, Black top with Silver 'PORSCHE' logo	NRP ☐
3	1993	Corvette	Pink/White/Blue body with Black 'CORVETTE' logo	NRP ☐
4	1993	Ford Mustang GT....................	Yellow body with Black 'MUSTANG' logo	NRP ☐
5	1993	Ferrari Testarossa...................	Red body with 2 Ferrari emblems in Yellow/Black	NRP ☐
6	1993	Mercedes-Benz 500 SL	Silver body with Black lower part	NRP ☐

'The Nigel Mansell Collection'

Three sets make up the collection and each contains one of the following four models - MB 246 Nigel Mansell's Car,   MB 14 Grand Prix Racing Car (a Red Ferrari),   MB 57 Mission Helicopter (Yellow/Blue/White),   and MB 68 Chevy Van (White/Yellow/Blue).

NM 820	1993	Grand Prix Set.........................	Contains MB 246, MB 68, MB 57, and MB 70................................	NRP ☐
NM 830	1993	Formula 1 Set..........................	Contains MB 246, MB 68, MB 74, plus CY24 DAF Box Car with MB 57	NRP ☐
NM 860	1993	Williams F1 Transporter	Contains MB 246 plus the Superkings Iveco Transporter	NRP ☐

Nascar Racing Cars 1992 onwards

Matchbox Miniatures issued in the U.S.A. linked to Nascar Racing. The models are used for promotional purposes and include:
Pontiac Grand Prix, Ford Thunderbird, Dale Earnhardt Lumina and Chevrolet Lumina. Several variations exist and these may be obtained from specialist Matchbox dealers such as: **Carr Collectables, PO Box 44, Ongar, Essex. Tel: (01277-364970)**.

Skybusters Aircraft series introduced in 1973

SB 1	Lear Jet	SB 17	Ramrod	SB 35	Mil Mi Hind-D
SB 2	Corsair A7D	SB 18	Wildwind	SB 36	F-117a Stealth
SB 3	A300 Airbus	SB 19	Piper Comanche	SB 38	BAE 146 Airliner
SB 4	Mirage F1	SB 20	Helicopter	SB 39	Boeing Stearman Biplane
SB 5	Starfighter F104	SB 21	Lightning	SB 40b	Boeing 737-300
SB 6	MIG 21	SB 22	Tornado		
SB 7	Junkers	SB 23	Supersonic Jet	**Skybusters Gift Sets**	
SB 8	Spitfire	SB 24	F16 Fighter	and sets containing Skybusters	
SB 9	Cessna 402	SB 25	Helicopter	G 5	'Federal Express'
SB 10	Boeing 747	SB 26	Cessna Float Wing	G 6	'Virgin Airways'
SB 11	Alpha Jet	SB 27	Harrier Jet	G 8a	Thunderjets
SB 12	Skyhawk A-4F	SB 28	A300 Airbus	G 8b	Thunderjets
SB 12	Pitts Special	SB 29	SR-71 Blackbird	G 10	'Pan Am' Set
SB 12	Mission Helicopter	SB 30	F14 Tomcat	G 11	'Lufthansa' Set
SB 13	Douglas DC-10	SB 31	Boeing 747-400	G 18	Sky Giants
SB 14	Cessna 210	SB 32	A10 Thunderbolt	CY108	Lowloader & Hawk
SB 15	Phantom F4E	SB 33	Bell Jet Ranger	MC 17	'British Airways'
SB 16	Corsair	SB 34	Lockheed A130	MC 24	'Red Arrows' Set

Many variations of this popular series exist and collectors requiring full details and prices should obtain a copy of the 'Model Price Review' which includes a full collectors listing and price guide. Copies available direct from Swapmeet Publications.

'My First Matchbox' series

A range of pre-school miniatures using existing models in bright new colours. The twenty-three models introduced from 1990 are:

2	Rover Sterling	20	4 x 4 Jeep (with roof)	51	Combine Harvester
4	FX4-R Taxi	21	Chevy Breakdown Van	52	Police Launch
5	Peterbilt Tanker	26	Volvo Tilt Truck	57	Dump Truck
6	F1 Racing Car	40	Horse Box	64	Bulldozer
8	Astra Car	43	0-4-0 Locomotive	74	Utility Truck
17	Titan Bus	44	Railway Coach	75	Helicopter
18	Fire Engine	47	School Bus	75	Ferrari Testarossa
19	Peterbilt Cement Truck	49	Peugeot Quasar		

Matchbox 1-75 Models issued 1983 - 1990

The object of this Catalogue is to provide collectors with basic identification of models and their market prices. For collectors requiring a more detailed tabulation of the 900 variations of 1-75 models issued in this 7 year period we would recommend an excellent checklist which can be obtained from MICA member Geoffrey Leake, 38 Park Avenue, Worcester, WR3 7AH, England. (Remember to include a SAE if requesting details).

Super GT Miniatures Issued 1988 onwards

This was a budget range of 40 different vehicles sold in singles, doubles and packs of ten (no individual reference numbers).

Superfast 'Laser Wheels' issues 1987 - 1989

The 'laser' wheel discs flash different colours as they reflect the light.

LW1	'POLICE' Car	White, *'RADAR'*	LW18	Firebird Racer	Blue/Yellow
LW2	1982 Firebird	Blue body	LW19	Fiero Racer	Yellow, RN '10'
LW3	Porsche 928	Blue/White, RN '28'	LW20	Nissan 300 ZX Turbo	Red body
LW4	Daytona Turbo 2	White/Blue	LW21	Camaro Iroc Z	Red, RN '12'
LW5	A.M.G. Mercedes	Red *'A.M.G.'*	LW22	Toyota 'MR2'	Blue body
LW6	Porsche 935	Red, RN '35'	LW23	Ferrari Testarossa	Red body
LW7	Sierra XR4	Green, *'RS'*	LW24	Quasar	Dark Blue/Red
LW8	1962 Corvette	Green, RN '11'	LW25	Buick Le Sabre	Red, *'KEN WELLS'*
LW9	Datsun 280 ZX Turbo	Yellow	LW26	Cadillac Allante	Black body
LW10	Turbo Corvette	Black, *'TURBO'*	LW27	Saab 9000 Turbo	Red, RN '3'
LW11	Ferrari 308 GTB	Yellow, *'FERRARI'*	LW28	Rover Sterling	White/Red/Blue
LW12	Chevy Stock Car	Red, RN '21'	LW29	T-Bird Turbo Coupé	Bronze, RN '56'
LW13	1984 Corvette	Red, RN '7'	LW30	Volvo 480 ES	White, *'480'* logo
LW14	BMW Cabriolet 323i	White body			
LW15	Escort Cabriolet XR3i	Blue, RN '3'			
LW16	Sauber Group C Racer	Yellow, RN '2'	LW100	Big Bang Launcher	Car launch system
LW17	Lamborghini Countach	White/Blue, RN '2'	LW200	Laser 2000 Race Set	Launcher, Speedtrack, 1 Car
			LW300	Laser Jet Launcher	Shoots car across floor

Lesney Products - Souvenirs

Prices are in the region of £20-35 for most of those listed.

005	London Bus on tray
014	Rolls-Royce on Blue ash tray
016	Boeing 747 on ash tray
018	Rolls-Royce on ash tray
019	Rolls-Royce on ceramic 'office tidy'
024	Rolls-Royce on stainless-steel ash tray
121	Rolls-Royce on cigarette box
123	Packard on trinket box
127	1922 London Bus on trinket box
205	Boeing 747 on onyx penstand

206	Crossley coal truck on onyx penstand
211	Spitfire on penstand
212	Concorde on penstand
221	Packard on double penstand
222	Concorde on double penstand
302	Rolls-Royce on pipe-rack
505	Rolls-Royce Vintage Car double gift pack
621	Street Rod on penstand/calendar
623	Concorde on penstand/calendar
624	Rolls-Royce on penstand/calendar

Walt Disney Characters
A series of models produced by Lesney in 1971 and again in 1979.

The models are quite collectable and prices range from **£15** to **£25**.

Space Series 1971 issues, (127 mm.)

W1	Astrocar with Donald Duck
W2	Astrotracker with Mickey Mouse
W3	Astrocat with Mickey Mouse

Hot Rod Series 1971 issues, (127 mm.)

W7	Hotcar with Donald Duck
W8	Dragon with Mickey Mouse
W9	Fun Bug with Donald Duck

Disney Characters 1979, (73 mm.)

WD1-A	Mickey Mouse Fire Engine
WD2-A	Donald Duck's Beach Buggy
WD3-A	Goofy's Beetle (ears attached to shoulders on some)
WD4-A	Minnie Mouse Lincoln
WD5-A	Mickey Mouse Jeep:
i)	'Mickey Mouse' logo on bonnet
ii)	'Mickeys Mail Jeep' on bonnet
iii)	'Police' logo/crest on bonnet
WD6-A	Donald Duck's Jeep
WD7-A	Pinnochio's Travelling Theatre
WD8-A	Jimminy Cricket's Old Timer
WD9-A	Goofy's Sports Car
WD10-A	Goofy's Train
WD11-A	Donald Duck's Ice Cream Van
WD12-A	Mickey Mouse Corvette

'Adventure 2000' models
Space age models (issued 1977-82), and based on the year 2000. Three plastic spacemen with guns were included with each model.

K2001	Radar Command	Contains Metallic Green tracked vehicles with *'2000'* logo
K2002	Flight Hunter	Contains Metallic Green vehicle with Red wings and *'2000'* logo
K2003	Crusader	Contains Metallic Green vehicle on Black tracks, 2 Red guns
K2004	Rocket Striker	Contains Green/Red rocket-firing vehicle (Black tracks), plus 3 rockets
K2005	Command Force	Contains K2004 plus MB2 Hovercraft and 2 smaller vehicles (MB59 & MB68)
K2006	Shuttle Launcher	Metallic Blue body, Black tracks, Orange launcher, White shuttle, *'2000'*

Note: In 1980 some of the models were issued in Metallic Blue but apart from the Shuttle Launcher no details are available. The models were featured for the last time in the 1981/82 catalogue. Price range **£10 - £15**.

MATCHBOX AUCTION RESULTS

MOKO Boxed

MKS = Moko script boxed, MK = Moko boxed, LCP = Lesney coloured picture box, MW = metal wheels, GMW = Grey metal wheels, SP = Silver plastic wheels, BPW = Black plastic wheels, MS = 'Moko' in script letters, LD = Lesney drawing box.

Vectis Model Auction Results

MATCHBOX 1-75 SERIES

MB4C Triumph Motor Cycle Combination Light metallic blue, A to A + **£35**

MB5A London Bus 'Buy Matchbox series' Red/GMW/gold trim, 52 mm., A MS boxed, scarce **£60**

MB17A Bedford Removals Van Light blue, silver trim, GMW, A to A +**£130**

MB17B Bedford Removals Van Light green, GMW, 'Removals' outlined in black, rear cab windows, B+ to A **£40**

MB17C Austin Taxi maroon, GPW, A to A+ in B+ to A box.............**£40**

MB22B Vauxhall Cresta, Met. dull pink/blue, green lower sides, GPW, hook, A to A+ in B+ to A box **£90**

MB32A Jaguar XK140 Red/GPW, A to A +, LD boxed, very scarce**Not Sold** **Estimate £125-£150**

MB32A Jaguar XK120 red, Moko boxed **£100**

MB39A Ford Zodiac Convertible Peach/light brown driver, interior, base & hook, GMW, silver trim, B+ **£130**

MB46A Morris Minor 1000 Dark green, GMW, A apart from one rear window chip & biro '46' on one side of box **£38**

MB46A Morris Minor 1000 blue, GPW **£80**

MB47A Trojan Van 'BROOKE BOND TEA', red, GMW, A to A+ in B+ to A box **£35**

MB58A AEC Coach 'BEA' Dark blue, GPW, single line advert in white, A**£40**

MB59A Ford Thames Van 'SINGER' Light green, GPW, A to A + ...**£35**

MB59A Ford Thames Van A to A + ...**£35**

MB59A Ford Thames Van, but dark green, GPW, A **£140**

MB71A Military Water Truck BPW with Matchbox collectors badge, A to A+ **£35**

MB74A Mobile Canteen Off white/light blue base, GPW, B, decals are A, box is A to A+ **£55**

MB74A Mobile Canteen pink body **£140**

4B Massey Harris Tractor red, tan driver, gold rear wheels, solid metal front wheels, A to A + ...**£45**

7A Horse Drawn Milk Float orange body & side letters, white driver, grey plastic wheels, very scarce, A unboxed **£30**

MB46A Morris Minor 1000 blue, GPW, good C in B+ MK boxed, scarce**£50**

MB46B 'Beales' Removal Van unboxed **£75**

COLOURED PICTURE BOXES

MB36B Lambretta Scooter & Sidecar Met. light green, BPW, A to A + ..**£35**

MB37B 'COCA COLA' Lorry Yellow, even crates, large rear decal, BPW, A to A+ **£50**

MB46B 'PICKFORDS' Removal Van green, 3 line advert, BPW, A to A +**£32**

MB47B Commer Mobile Shop 'LYONS' Cream, BPW, A.....................**£45**

MB62B Commer TV Van 'RENTASET' Cream/red plastic parts all still attached to sprue, A to A+ in B box, Plus **MB62B Another** but 'RADIO RENTALS', A in B 'Rentaset' box **£70**

MB66B Harley Davidson Motorcycle & Sidecar, Met. bronze, A to A +, scarce **£70**

75B Ferrari Berlinetta red, silver hubs, A to A +, very rare wheel variation**£300**

LESNEY

Muffin the Mule B to B+ with all strings & Rings, in B+ box, very scarce**£280**

Covered Wagon green/white, two red barrels, six brown horses,m driver, A apart from 'box wear', to outside edge barrel, pic box is B, rare.....................**£130**

Bread Bait Press Trade display box for 12 with 8 A to A + boxed and one A to A+ unboxed, trade box is C, very rare...**£170**

Large Coronation Coach with Queen alone, gold finish with horses and riders, lovely B + to A with inner card support for draw bar in brilliant A picture box, could hardly be bettered, scarce...**£200**

MODELS OF YESTERYEAR

FIRST SERIES – all boxed

Y7 Jacobs Biscuit Van Cream roof, reddish brown body & radiator surround, grey metal wheels, one very small chip on side of roof otherwise A +, line drawing box is C **£40**

Y11 Aveling & Porter Steam Roller black flywheel & roof supports, A in A line drawing box **£65**

Y12 Horse Drawn Bus light brown horses/white manes & tails, A in A + picture box **£50**

Y14 'Duke of Connaught' Locomotive Gold boiler door, A + in B + picture box **£65**

Y2 'B' Type Bus unpainted wheels, 8 small windows, A...........................**£55**

Y3 'E' Type Tram unpainted metal wheels, white roof, A drawing box....**£60**

Y4 Sentinel 'Sand & Gravel', A **£50**

Y4 Sentinel black plastic wheels, scarce, A...**£160**

Y7 Leyland Lorry 'Jacobs', dark brown, cream roof, A **£80**

Y9 Showman's Engine maroon, cream roof, A in B + box **£75**

Y12 Horse Drawn Bus, A **£60**

Y13 'Santa Fe' picture boxed, scarce box **£50**

SECOND & THIRD SERIES

Y4 Shand Mason Fire Engine London Fire Brigade, blackish horses, gold helmets, thin braces on boiler base, A in B background picture box **£65**

Y4 Shand Mason Fire Engine London Fire Brigade, blackish horses/thick braces to boiler base/unpainted firemen still attached to sprue (very rare), A + in A + background picture box **£100**

Y5 Straw Boxed (1) 'Merita' (2) 'Langendorf' (3) 'Taystee' all A, scarce set of 3 USA code two models...**£75**

Y13 Crossley 'UK Matchbox' scarce code two **£100**

Y1 Allchin Traction Engine with straight red treads.............................**£105**

Y4 Shand Mason Fire Engine 'London Fire Brigade', gold helmets, silver boiler **£110**

Code 2 'UK Matchbox Club'...**£120**

Lacy Scott Auction Results

Y9-4 Leyland Cub Fire Engine **£50**

Y16-5 Scammell 100 Ton Truck-Trailer with G.E.R. loco **£62**

EARLY LESNEY

Large Coronation Coach with King and Queen.....................................**£460**

Christies, South Kensington Auction Results

Early Lesney orange large scale 'Scale Model Milk Cart' in original box **£220**

Wallis & Wallis Auction Results

LESNEY

Coronation Coach finished in gilt plating with figure of Queen Elizabeth II in coach drawn by 8 horses with 4 postillion riders, original box, GC to VGC**£110**

Coronation Coach finished in gold paint with two figures of King and Queen, drawn by 8 horses with 4 postillion riders, original box, VGC to Mint. One of only 300 models produced in 1952 with figures of the King...................**£500**

WHEN REPLYING TO ADVERTISEMENTS PLEASE MENTION JOHN RAMSAY'S CATALOGUE

Y-12 **1899 London Horse-Bus** 3¼ ins. 83mm. 100-1 4/–

Y-8 **1914 Sunbeam Motor-cycle with Milford Sidecar** 2⅝ ins. 67mm. 34-1 4/6

Y-11 **1912 Packard Landaulet** 3¼ ins. 82mm. 50-1 5/–

Matchbox
Models of Yesteryear

The objective of this listing is to provide guidance in respect of all the main model variations. Collectors requiring details of the many minor variations issued should obtain a copy of the excellent reference book produced by the Matchbox Club, namely 'The Yesteryear Book 1956-1993', which contains fine pictures of all issues. See the Matchbox Club page for details.

Common features. Many models have common identifying features and these are shown below to avoid unnecessary repetition in the Features column.

Model name and number. Both **'Models of Yesteryear'** & **'Made in England by Lesney'** are cast underneath all models issued up to the end of 1982. With the change of ownership this was replaced by **'Matchbox Intl Ltd.'** From 1987 **'Made in Macau'** appears on the base. All models have their 'Y' number shown underneath.

Wheels. All the wheels prior to 1970 were of metal construction. From 1972 (approximately), plastic wheels were used on all models. Nevertheless the models issued at this changeover period are to be found with either metal or plastic wheels. The varieties of wheels are:

Metal Spoked Wheels
Metal or Plastic Spoked Wheels
Plastic Bolt Head Wheels
Plastic Spoked Wheels
Solid Spoked Wheels

Scale of models ranges from 1:34 to 1:130 across the range. The scale of each model is usually shown on its box.

Logos and designs. The early models had waterslide transfers. Labels have also been used and currently models are tampo printed.

Catalogue listings. Do not place too much reliance on the model colours shown in catalogues. Very often the pictures shown are from mock-ups in colours never actually issued. E.g., the 1969 catalogue showed a picture of a blue Y-5 Peugeot that was issued in yellow. Similarly the 1973 catalogue showed a silver Hispano Suiza which was then issued in Red.

Bumpers, dashboards, headlights, radiator shells and windscreens. All assumed to be of metal construction prior to 1974 (approx.), after which plastic was increasingly used.

Base plate and chassis are usually of metal construction. Exceptions include the Y30 Mack Truck.

Tyres are of treaded black plastic unless otherwise indicated.

Seats are all made of plastic unless otherwise indicated.

Boxes

1956-57	All card box with just a plain black number shown on box ends. Line drawing of model on the front of box.
1957-60	All card box with line drawing of model used for first 15 models issued, blue number shown on white circle on endflap
1960-61	As first box but with a red number. All card box with coloured picture of the model (3 varieties of this box exist). All card box with model pictures on the box endflaps.
1968-69	Pink and yellow box with clear window.
1968-70	As previous box with hanging display card (developed in the US market and led to blister-pack design).
1969-70	Mauve and yellow box with window.
1974-78	'Woodgrain' window box in various colours
1979-83	'Straw' (light cream), window box.
1984-90	'Red' (maroon), window box.
1990	'New-style red'. Bigger, folded clear plastic
1993-94	New style direct mail high quality card boxes with full colour box model picture designs.

Matchbox Models of Yesteryear

Ref. No.	Year(s)	Model Type		Model Features and Size	Market Price Range	
Y1-1		**ALLCHIN TRACTION ENGINE**		Scale 1:80. The main variations are the rear wheel treads, the early models having a straight-across pattern, the second a diagonal and the third a smooth tread		
	1956		1	Green body, Red wheels (10 spokes front, 16 rear, unpainted 'straight across' treads), copper boiler door, 9 slats on cab floor, full Gold trim	**£175-200**	☐
			2	Same as version 1 but rear wheels with unpainted 'diagonal' treads, Copper boiler	**£70-90**	☐
			3	As 2 but Red diagonal rear wheel treads	**£100-135**	☐
			4	As 2 Dark or Bright Red diagonal treads	**£120-170**	☐
			5	As 2 but painted or unpainted rear treads, Gold boiler door	**£70-90**	☐
			6	As 5 but with Mid-Green boiler door	**£400-600**	☐
			7	As 6 but with rivetted axles and less Gold trim	**£200-250**	☐
	1983		8	As version 7 but with Gold boiler door	**£70-90**	☐
			9	As version 8 but with 11 slats to cab floor	**£70-90**	☐
			10	As 9 but with Silver boiler door	**£100-125**	☐
			11	As 10 but smooth unpainted wheel treads, Gold boiler door	**£500-750**	☐
Y1-2	1964	**1911 MODEL 'T' FORD**	1	Henry Ford's famous car in a scale 1:42. Red body and steering wheel, smooth Black roof and seats, single-lever handbrake, Brass trim, two holes in baseplate, 14 mm. brass wheels	**£14-16**	☐
			2	As version 1 but with twin-lever handbrake	**£140-150**	☐
			3	As 1 but without holes in baseplate	**£14-16**	☐
			4	As 3 but Black steering wheel and column	**£14-16**	☐
			5	As version 4 but 11 mm. brass wheels	**£14-16**	☐
			6	As 4 but with Black 'textured' plastic roof	**£150-200**	☐
	1974		7	Cream body, Red wings, bare metal windscreen frame, Chrome 12-spoke wheels, Dark Red textured roof. Seats & grille may be Red, Dark Red or Black	**£10-14**	☐
			8	As 7 but seats and textured roof in Black	**£140-160**	☐
			9	As version 8 but brass windscreen surround	**£40-50**	☐

Ref. No.	Year(s)	Model Type	*Matchbox Models of Yesteryear – continued*	Market Price Range	
	1975	10.............	White body, Red wings, bare metal windscreen frame, Red or Dark Red textured roof, Chrome 12-spoke wheels, Black seats and grille	£15-20	☐
		11.............	As 10 but Red seats, textured roof, 12 or 24-spoked Chrome wheels	£10-14	☐
	1984	12.............	Gloss Black body, Gold trim on running boards, Gold wheels, Fawn seats, 'LIMITED EDITION' under roof and baseplate, in 'Connoisseurs' set......................	GSP	☐
Y1-3		**1936 SS 100 JAGUAR**	The model (in a scale of 1:38) is of a two-seater sports car with metal body and folded-down hood in black plastic. It has chrome 24-spoke wheels, radiator and headlights, and a spare wheel on the petrol tank.		
	1977	1...............	White body and chassis with small sidelights (2 mm.), 'Lesney' on baseplate..............	£155-175	☐
		2...............	As 1 but with large sidelights (4 mm.), on front mudguards	£8-11	☐
	1978	3...............	As 2 (with large sidelights), but Steel-Grey body and chassis......................................	£50-60	☐
	1979	4...............	As 2 but Light Steel Blue body, 24-spoke or 12-spoke or solid chrome wheels, with plain or whitewall tyres..	£8-10	☐
		5...............	As 4 (24 or 12-spoke wheels), plus 5 ribs under running boards..............................	£6-8	☐
	1981	6...............	As version 5 but Dark Green body...	£5-7	☐
	1986	7...............	As 5 but Talbot Yellow body and chassis, whitewall tyres, 'Lesney England' base......	£60-80	☐
		8...............	As 7 but (Yellow), body components oversprayed Dark Green..................................	£12-15	☐
	1987	9...............	As 7 but Darker Yellow body and chassis, baseplate reads 'MATCHBOX INT'L (c) 1977, MADE IN MACAU'. Diorama box	£4-6	☐
Y1-G	1991	10.............	Red body, Black seats, Brown steering wheel, 'MADE IN CHINA' on baseplate	£4-6	☐
		11.............	Unpainted pewter version on wooden plinth (1991/1992 UK Passport Scheme)..........	£35-45	☐
Y2-1		**1911 'B' TYPE LONDON BUS**	The scale of this vintage bus model is 1:100 and its diecast driver may be found in any shade of mid or dark blue, sometimes black.		
	1956	1...............	Red body, Grey wheels (8 spokes front, 16 rear), Silver radiator, 4 small window frames above 4 main window frames, 'GENERAL'..	£150-200	☐
		2...............	As 1 but with 8 small window frames above 4 main window frames............................	£75-95	☐
		3...............	As 2 but minor changes, e.g. Black wheels and rivetted axles	£75-95	☐

The first fifteen models. Picture supplied by Wallis & Wallis, West Street Auction Galleries, Lewes, Sussex BN7 2NJ and reproduced by their kind permission.

Y2-2

1911 RENAULT TWO SEATER .... Scale 1:40. (The Red pigment in the seats is prone to fading in bright light.

	1963	1...............	Metallic Green body. Windscreen, lights, handbrake & 4-prong spare wheel carrier in Silver. Windscreen panel is above bonnet and radiator	£60-80 ☐
		2...............	As 1 but windscreen, lights, 4-prong spare wheel carrier etc in brass trim	£40-50 ☐
		3...............	As 2 but windscreen panel runs down sides of bonnet	£10-15 ☐
		4...............	As 3 but spare wheel carrier with 3 prongs, brass plating	£10-15 ☐
	1965	5...............	As 4 but with Black plastic steering wheel and column	£8-11 ☐

Y2-3

1914 PRINCE HENRY VAUXHALL .... An open car modelled in 1:47 scale with a metal body and plastic seats and steering wheel. The radiator surround, headlights, windscreen and toolbox are gold trimmed. It has 24-spoke wheels with a spare on the offside unless described differently.

	1970	1...............	Red body, Silver bonnet, Red radiator grille, Brass 26-spoke wheels & tank	£12-15 ☐
		2...............	As version 1 but with Copper petrol tank	£90-110 ☐
		3...............	As version 1 with Black radiator grille	£10-13 ☐
	1975	4...............	Blue body, Silver bonnet, Cream seats, Brass tank, Chrome 24-spoke wheels	£10-13 ☐
		5...............	As version 4 but with Copper petrol tank	£25-35 ☐
		6...............	As 4 (Brass tank), but with additional lateral floor braces	£8-11 ☐
		7...............	As 6 (with floor braces), but with Copper petrol tank	£20-30 ☐
		8...............	As 7 but with Red seats, (2,000 only, distributed in E.Europe)	£600-700 ☐
		9...............	As 6 (Cream seats), but with Chrome 12-spoke wheels	£6-8 ☐
	1979	10...............	Red body, Black chassis, Red 12-spoke wheels, small spare wheel rivet	£6-8 ☐
	1984	11...............	As 10 but Lighter Red body, large headed rivet retains spare wheel	£6-8 ☐

Y2-4

1930 4½ LITRE BENTLEY ...... Based on the 1930 Le Mans winning car, this model is in 1:40 scale.

	1985	1...............	Dark Green body, Green 24-spoke wheels, spare on nearside, Chrome trim, Brown seats & straps. Union Jack on sides, 'MADE IN ENGLAND' on base	£3-5 ☐
		2...............	As version 1 but dark Green Nylon mudguards	£10-15 ☐
		3...............	As 2 but light Brown bonnet straps, dashboard and seats	£4-6 ☐
	1988	4...............	As 3 but lighter Green body and wheels, 'MADE IN MACAU' on base	£4-6 ☐
	1990	5...............	Dark Blue body and wheels, Tan steering wheel and column, RN '7'	£10-15 ☐
		6...............	As 5 but with hole cast in base for self-tapping screw	£6-8 ☐
		7...............	As 6 but with Olive-Green steering wheel and column	£6-8 ☐
	1992	8...............	Maroon body, Chrome wheels, Black seats, wings, straps & folded hood	£4-6 ☐

Y3-1

1907 'E' CLASS TRAMCAR .... All versions have a bright Red body with Yellow 'LONDON TRANSPORT' fleetname and 'NEWS OF THE WORLD' decals. Scale 1:130.

	1956	1...............	Cream roof, Silver trim, thin Grey cow-catcher and unpainted wheels, cut-out in luggage area beneath the stairs	£200-275 ☐
		2...............	Same as 1 but with double thick cow-catcher brace	£90-110 ☐
		3...............	Same as 2 but with Powder Grey base plate and Silver trim	£200-275 ☐
		4...............	Same as 3 (with Powder Grey base plate), but with Gold trim	£200-275 ☐
		5...............	With no cut-out beneath the stairs, Cream or White roof, metal or Black plastic wheels	£70-80 ☐
	1985	6...............	As 5 but Black plastic wheels and White cow-catcher	£90-110 ☐

Y3-2

1910 BENZ LIMOUSINE .... The model has a metal body with Dark Green or Dark Red seats and radiator grille, Brass trim and spare tyre mounted on handbrake casting. Scale 1:54.

	1965	1...............	Cream body, Dark Green roof, Cream metal steering wheel, Green or Red seats	£50-60 ☐
		2...............	As 1 but with 'Chartreuse' Yellow roof	£200-250 ☐
	1969	3...............	As 2 but with Light Green body, Dark Green roof. (Black grilles exist)	£200-250 ☐
		4...............	Light Green body (as 3), but with 'Chartreuse' roof	£30-35 ☐
		5...............	As 4 but with Black plastic steering wheel	£30-35 ☐
		6...............	As version 5 but with Matt Black roof	£100-125 ☐
		7...............	Metallic Dark Green body with Matt Black roof	£10-15 ☐
		8...............	Metallic Dark Green body with Chartreuse roof	£200-250 ☐
		9...............	Black body and roof, Blue side panels, 'LIMITED EDITION' on baseplate, in 'Connoisseurs' set	GSP ☐

Y3-3

1934 RILEY MPH .... A two-seater sports car model with a metal body, plastic seats and steering wheel, Chrome radiator surround, windscreen, headlights and wheels. Scale 1:35.

	1973	1...............	Metallic Purple/Red body and chassis with Black seats and grille, Chrome 12-spoke wheels	£150-200 ☐
		2...............	As 1 but seats and grille in White and with 12 or 24-spoke wheels	£20-25 ☐
		3...............	As 2 but reddish-Purple body and chassis	£8-11 ☐
		4...............	As version 2 but with Dark Red body and chassis	£8-11 ☐
		5...............	As 4 but Light Red body & chassis, Red 12-spoke wheels	£30-40 ☐
	1979	6...............	Light Blue body, White seats and grille, 24-spoke wheels, RN '6' or '9'	£6-8 ☐
		7...............	As 6 but with RN '3' on door	£15-20 ☐
		8...............	As version 6 but with Red 12-spoke wheels	£15-20 ☐
		9...............	As version 8 but with racing number '6'	£15-20 ☐

Y3-4

1912 FORD MODEL 'T' TANKER .... The model features a small tanker with an all metal body and tank with simulated brass filler pipes and 12-spoke plastic wheels. Scale 1:35.

	1981	'BP'	1	Dark Green body, Black chassis, White roof, Red tank, Gold trim, Gold 'BP' logo on tank with Black shadow effect, '1978 No. Y12' on baseplate	£110-120 ☐
			2...............	As version 1 but baseplate number blanked-out	£4-6 ☐
			3...............	As 2 but without the shadow effect around the 'BP' logo	£4-6 ☐

Ref. No.	Year(s)	Model Type		*Matchbox Models of Yesteryear – continued*	Market Price Range	
			4...............	As version 3 but matt-Black filler caps..	£45-55	☐
			5...............	As 3 but with Gold 12-spoke wheels...	£15-20	☐
			6...............	As 3 but Chrome 12-spoke wheels, with shadow effect............	£15-20	☐
	1982	'ZEROLENE'...........................		20,000 issued in UK, 15,000 issued elsewhere in Europe		
			1...............	Bright Green body, gloss-Black chassis, White logo. Brass 12-spoke wheels...............	£40-50	☐
			2...............	As version 1 but matt-Black chassis..	£40-50	☐
			3...............	As version 1 but with Red 12-spoke wheels............................	£50-75	☐
	1983	'EXPRESS DAIRY'.................		90,000 made.		
			1...............	Blue body, Gloss Black lower body, White roof and logo, brass trim........................	£4-6	☐
			2...............	As 1 but with Red 12-spoke wheels...	£8-10	☐
			3...............	As 1 but with Chrome 12-spoke wheels.....................................	£6-8	☐
	1984	'CARNATION'.........................		This model has different prints below each cab window.		
			1...............	Cream body, Plum Red tank & chassis, Red 12-spoke wheels, White-wall tyres.........	NRP	☐
			2...............	As version 1 but with Red 24-spoke wheels..............................	£8-12	☐
			3...............	As 1 but with Gold 12-spoke wheels and Black tyres...............	£8-12	☐
	1986		4...............	As 1 but Plum-coloured 12-spoke wheels, modified baseplate..............	£25-30	☐
	1985	'MOBILOIL'............................		40,000 issued in UK, 40,000 elswhere.		
				Blue body and tank, Red bonnet and wheels, White logo, Red design.......................	£4-6	☐
	1986	'CASTROL'.............................		109,000 made.		
			1...............	Dark Green body and tank, White roof, Black chassis, Tan seats, Plum 12-spoke wheels, Gold grille, 'LESNEY PRODUCTS & Co.Ltd. (c) 1978' on base	£8-10	☐
			2...............	As 1 but 'MATCHBOX INT'L (c) 1985' on base........................	£6-9	☐
			3...............	As 2 but with Chrome radiator grille...	£20-30	☐
			4...............	As version 2 but with Black seats...	£20-30	☐
			5...............	As 2 but with Gold 12-spoke wheels, 'MATCHBOX 1986 ENGLAND' base............	£4-6	☐
	1986	'RED CROWN'......................		35,000 issued in UK, 35,000 elswhere.		
			1...............	Red body, tank and side panels, Gold 12-spoke wheels with Black tyres, 'MATCHBOX INT'L (c) 1986 MADE IN ENGLAND LIMITED EDITION' on base..........................	£6-8	☐
			2...............	with 'LESNEY PRODUCTS & Co.Ltd. (c) 1978 MADE IN ENGLAND' on base...	£10-15	☐
			3...............	As version 2 but with 'MATCHBOX 1985 ENGLAND' on base.....	£40-50	☐
	1989	'SHELL MOTOR SPIRIT'.......		Yellow body, White roof, Red 12-spoke wheels, 'MADE IN MACAU' on base.........	£4-6	☐
Y4-1		**SENTINEL STEAM WAGON**...................................		**'SAND & GRAVEL SUPPLIES'**. Scale 1:100.		
	1956		1...............	Bright Blue body & tool-box, Black chassis & boiler, Grey metal spoked wheels, domed & crimped axles. Yellow logo with Red border	£80-90	☐
			2...............	As version 1 but with Gold tool-box..	£80-90	☐
			3...............	As 2 but with rivetted axles...	£90-110	☐
			4...............	As 3 but with Black plastic wheels (24 treads front & rear)........................	£160-190	☐
Y4-2		**SHAND MASON FIRE ENGINE**...................		All metal body and 2 horses with 3 plastic firemen, metal wheels (13 spokes front, 15 rear). Gold pump and boiler appliance. Scale 1:63.		
	1960	'KENT FIRE BRIGADE'				
			1...............	Bright Red body, 2 Grey horses with Grey manes, 2 locating hose locker ribs. Three firemen with Gold helmets and breastplates........................	£450-550	☐
			2...............	As version 1 but with White horses...	£125-150	☐
			3...............	As 2 but firemen have only Gold helmets, (plain breastplates)	£125-150	☐
	1963	'LONDON FIRE BRIGADE'..		'No.72'.		
			4...............	As 3 but with new logo as above and no locating hose locker ribs	£125-150	☐
			5...............	As 4 but Black horses with White manes..................................	£125-150	☐
			6...............	As 5 but Brown horses with White manes, fireman with no Gold trim........................	£325-375	☐
			7...............	As version 5 but with minor modifications...............................	£125-150	☐
Y4-3		**1909 OPEL CAR**......................		The model features an open fronted metal bodied car with plastic roof, seats and steering wheel. It has 12-spoked wheels. Scale 1:38.		
	1967		1...............	White body and chassis, smooth Tan roof, Brass trim and wheels with Maroon seats and grille..	£20-30	☐
			2...............	As 1 but with bright Red seats and grille..................................	£12-15	☐
			3...............	As 2 with no body pins and roof secured to seat.......................	£12-15	☐
			4...............	As version 3 but with Maroon seats..	£12-15	☐
			5...............	with window in rear of Tan textured roof, Bright Red or Maroon seats......................	£300-350	☐
	1974		6...............	Orange body with Black chassis and roof, White grille, Maroon seats, 12 or 24-spoke wheels..	£8-11	☐
	1984		7...............	Bright Red body with Darker Red lower body, Tan roof with 'LIMITED EDITION', in 'Connoisseurs' set.	GSP	☐
Y4-4		**1930 DUESENBERG 'J' TOWN CAR**......................		The model features a superb large car with an open drivers area and enclosed passenger seats. It has a metal body, plastic roof, seats and trunk, chrome spoked wheels and two spares set into the running boards. Scale 1:43		
	1976		1...............	White main body, Orange/Red lower body, Yellow roof and seats, small roof window, 'X' shaped roof support, hollow chrome horns...................	£1200-1500	☐
			2...............	As 1 but seats and roof in Black	£1200-1500	☐
	1976		3...............	Metallic Red body, Black roof with larger window, Black seats........................	£8-11	☐
			4...............	As 3 with solid horns and chrome 12-spoke wheels, Black tyres................	£8-11	☐
			5...............	As 4 but with Maroon seats and roof, Chrome 24-spoke wheels...................	£200-225	☐

Ref. No.	Year(s)	Model Type		*Matchbox Models of Yesteryear – continued*	Market Price Range	
	1979		6...............	Two-tone Green body and rear panel, Dark Green seats and roof.................................	**£60-75**	☐
			7...............	As 6 but rear body panel is in Metallic Light Green...	**£8-11**	☐
			8...............	As version 7 but with Black seats and roof...	**£8-11**	☐
	1983		9...............	As 3 but Dark Brown upper body, sides & chassis, Cream or Beige seats and roof, 24-spoke wheels, 'LESNEY' or 'MATCHBOX' base..	**£4-6**	☐
			10.............	As 9 but 'solid' chrome wheels with White-wall tyres..	**£4-6**	☐
			11.............	As version 9 but Brown seats and roof...	**£5-8**	☐
	1986		12.............	As 3 but Metallic Silver body, Royal-Blue chassis, wheels and (tampo-printed), side panels, 'MADE IN ENGLAND' on baseplate...	**£4-6**	☐
			13.............	As 12 but tampo-printed side panels are Dark Blue..	**£4-6**	☐
	1988		14.............	As 12 but darker Blue (side panels mask-sprayed), 'MADE IN MACAU'	**£4-6**	☐
	1989		15.............	Two-tone Blue, Tan steering wheel, improved detailing, no baseplate hole................	**£15-20**	☐
	1990		16.............	As 15 but with baseplate hole, White-wall tyres..	**NRP**	☐
			17.............	As 16 but with Olive-Green steering wheel	**£10-12**	☐
Y5-1		**1929 LE MANS BENTLEY**		A famous sports racing car modelled in a scale of 1:55.		
	1958		1...............	British Racing Green body and tonneau (which has Grey rear end), unpainted solid spoked wheels (spare on nearside), Silver radiator, RN '5', Red metal seats..............	**£90-110**	☐
			2...............	As 1 but with Green radiator grille..	**£90-110**	☐
			3...............	As version 2 but with Gold radiator surround..	**£160-180**	☐
			4...............	As 3 but with an all Green tonneau..	**£75-85**	☐
			5...............	Minor changes: Green radiator surround and steering wheel, rivetted axles	**£75-85**	☐
Y5-2		**1929 4½ LITRE BENTLEY**......		The model features a metal body with plastic seats and tonneau. It has Union Jacks and racing numbers on its sides, chrome trim, folded windscreen and silver 24-spoke wheels, (spare on nearside). Scale 1:52.		
	1962		1...............	Metallic 'Apple Green' body, Dark Green seats and tonneau, Black RN '5'	**£325-375**	☐
			2...............	As 1 but with Dark Red seats and tonneau...	**£325-375**	☐
			3...............	As 1 but British Racing Green body/seats, additional holes in baseplate	**£45-55**	☐
			4...............	As 3 but with Dark Red seats and tonneau...	**£50-60**	☐
			5...............	As 4 but seats and tonneau in bright Red plastic..	**£25-35**	☐
			6...............	As 5 but racing number '6' or '3' in White circle..	**£60-70**	☐
			7...............	As version 5 but no holes in baseplate...	**£20-30**	☐
			8...............	As version 7 but with racing number '5'..	**£20-30**	☐
Y5-3		**1907 PEUGEOT**......................		A large car modelled in a scale of 1:43 with metal body and plastic seats, grille and steering wheel. It has 12-spoke wheels and a spare tyre.		
	1969		1...............	All Yellow body, matt Black roof with Dark Orange windows, Red seats and grille, no front seat beading	**£90-110**	☐
			2...............	As version 1 but with seat beading, Dark or Pale Orange windows	**£8-11**	☐
			3...............	As version 2 but with clear windows..	**£180-200**	☐
	1974		4...............	Orange-Gold body, roof & wheels, matt Black lower body, Red seats & grille............	**£145-170**	☐
			5...............	As 4 with Matt Black roof, seats and grille, Chrome 12-spoke wheels	**£90-100**	☐
			6...............	As version 4 with Black seats and grille...	**£10-15**	☐
			7...............	As version 5 with Light Gold body and roof...	**£10-15**	☐
			8...............	As version 7 with clear windows, Chrome 12-spoke wheels.....................................	**£100-120**	☐
			9...............	As version 7 with clear windows, Chrome 24-spoke wheels.....................................	**£60-70**	☐
Y5-4		**1927 TALBOT VAN**		A model van in a scale of 1:47. It has a metal body with side windows, opening rear doors, plastic seats and steering wheel and spoked wheels.		
	1978	'LIPTON'S TEA'		(with Royal Crest)		
			1...............	Dark Green body and 12-spoke wheels, matt Black roof & lower body, Yellow logo & crest	**£30-40**	☐
			2...............	As version 1 but gloss Black chassis..	**£8-11**	☐
			3...............	As 2 but without Black 'shadow' effect to logo...	**£30-35**	☐
			4...............	With gloss Black chassis and either 12 or 24-spoke Chrome wheels	**£8-11**	☐
	1978 1978	'LIPTON'S TEA'		(without royal crest, with 'CITY ROAD' logo)		
			1...............	Dark Green body, Gloss Black chassis, Matt Black roof, Green 12-spoke wheels, Yellow logo with shadow effect...	**£20-30**	☐
			2...............	As 1 with Chrome 12 or 24-spoke wheels, no shadow effect....................................	**£9-12**	☐
			3...............	As version 2 but with Olive-Green 12-spoke wheels...	**£9-14**	☐
			4...............	As version 2 but Gloss Black roof...	**£15-20**	☐
	1979	'CHOCOLATE MENIER'		First issued in 'woodgrain' box with light blue labels bearing French text.		
			1...............	Royal Blue body, Black roof and chassis, Yellow logo, Chrome 12-spoke wheels.......	**£8-10**	☐
			2...............	As 1 but with Chrome 24-spoke wheels	**£10-15**	☐
			3...............	As 1 but with Off-White logo (both sides)..	**£16-18**	☐
			4...............	As 1 but Red or Dark Green 12-spoke or Red solid wheels.....................................	**£10-15**	☐
	1980	'TAYSTEE BREAD'				
			1...............	Yellow body, Black roof, Red wheels, whitewall tyres, Red/White design	**£4-6**	☐
			2...............	As version 1 but with Black lower body...	**£8-10**	☐
			3...............	As 1 but with Red solid wheels...	**£20-25**	☐
	1981	'NESTLES'				
			1...............	Blue body, Black roof and chassis, Red wheels, White-wall tyres............................	**£140-160**	☐
			2...............	As version 1 but with Dark Grey roof...	**£12-15**	☐
			3...............	As version 1 but with Light Grey roof...	**£40-50**	☐
	1982	'CHIVERS & SONS LTD'				
			1...............	Cream body & roof, Dark Green wings, Red or Dark Red wheels	**£4-6**	☐

Ref. No.	Year(s)	Model Type	Description	Market Price Range	
	1982	'WRIGHT'S SOAP'			
		1.............	Dark Brown body with Cream roof and chassis, Chrome 12-spoke wheels..................	£3-5	☐
		2.............	As version 1 but with Brass 12-spoke wheels..	£8-10	☐
	1983	'EVER READY BATTERIES'			
		1.............	Dark Blue body, White roof and Black chassis, Tan seats, White/Orange logo..........	£8-10	☐
		2.............	As version 1 but with Black seats..	£3-5	☐
	1984	'DUNLOP TYRES'			
		1.............	Black and Yellow, Dark Yellow 12-spoke wheels, Tan or Black seats	£4-6	☐
		2.............	Black and Yellow, Pale Yellow 12-spoke wheels, Tan or Black seats	£4-6	☐
	1985	'ROSES LIME JUICE'			
		1.............	Light Cream body, Green roof, chassis & wheels, 'MADE IN ENGLAND' on base	£8-10	☐
		2.............	As 1 (Black seats), but Pale Cream/Dark Green body & chassis	£8-10	☐
		3.............	As version 2 but with Tan seats...	£30-40	☐
		4.............	As version 1 but with Red 12-spoke wheels...	£15-20	☐
	1988	5.............	As 1 but 'MADE IN MACAU' on baseplate..	£15-20	☐
	1989	'LYLES SYRUP'			
		1.............	Green body, Black chassis, Gold wheels, White logo	£4-6	☐
		2.............	As 1 but with Black wheels, improved (softer) tyres...	£15-20	☐
Y5-5		**LEYLAND TITAN BUS**			
	1989	'ROBIN STARCH'..................	Green/Cream body in 'SOUTHDOWN' livery	£8-10	☐
	1990	'SWAN FOUNTPENS'	Blue/Cream. Passport Scheme model – originally only available unboxed in cabinet ..	NGPP	☐
			Models issued without cabinet in special box at 9th MICA UK CONVENTION 3/94 at Telford (1000 only)..	£50-60	☐
Y5-C	1991	'NEWCASTLE BROWN ALE'......................................	Maroon/Cream body, 'COVENTRY CORPORATION'...	£4-6	☐
Y6-1		**1916 A.E.C. 'Y' TYPE LORRY**	**'OSRAM LAMPS'. Scale 1:100.**		
	1957	1.............	Duck Egg Blue body, Grey metal spoked wheels (8 front/16 rear), White logo	£1000-1200	☐
	1957	2.............	Mid-Blue body, driver, steering wheel, grille, seat, Grey wheels..............................	£750-1000	☐
		3.............	As 1 but with Light Grey body, painted bonnet handles on some...........................	£120-130	☐
	1959	4.............	As 3 but Dark Grey body, with or without painted bonnet handles	£175-225	☐
	1961	5.............	As 4 but with unpainted bonnet handles and Black plastic wheels (having 24 treads front, 30 treads rear)..	£1000-1200	☐
Y6-2		**1926 TYPE 35 BUGATTI**........	The model (in a scale of 1:48) has a metal body and seats, Black baseplate and Gold 8-spoke wheels with a spare on the nearside. Racing number '6' may be upside-down and appear as '9'.		
	1961	1.............	Light Blue body, Grey tyres, Red floor, dashboard and RN '6', Gold radiator............	£80-100	☐
		2.............	As version 1 but with Black tyres, chrome or unpainted wheels	£30-40	☐
		3.............	As version 2 but with Blue radiator	£150-175	☐
		4.............	As 2 but with narrow wheel rims..	£30-40	☐
		5.............	As version 2 but with White dashboard and floor	£250-300	☐
	1965	6.............	Red body, White dashboard & floor, Black seats & tyres, Gold radiator....................	£30-40	☐
		7.............	As version 6 but with Red radiator	£80-100	☐
		8.............	As 6 but Black dashboard and floor	£250-300	☐
Y6-3		**1913 CADILLAC**	The model features a metal bodied two seater car with a plastic roof and seats. It has 12-spoke wheels with a spare at the rear. Scale 1:48.		
	1968	1.............	Light Gold body, smooth Dark Red hood, seats and grille, brass trim. (Hoods on early issues were not secured to windscreen)	£17-22	☐
		2.............	Dark Gold body, smooth Dark Red hood and seats..	£20-30	☐
		3.............	As 2 but with textured Dark Red roof, seats and grille...	£60-70	☐
		4.............	Dark Gold body, Bright Yellow seats and grille, textured Black hood........................	£60-70	☐
		5.............	Metallic Green body, Bright Yellow seats and grille, textured Black hood, Chrome 12-spoke wheels...	£14-17	☐
		6.............	As version 5 but with Light Green seats and grille..	£100-150	☐
		7.............	As version 5 but with Blue or Pink seats and grille...	£100-150	☐
Y6-4		**1920 ROLLS ROYCE FIRE ENGINE**	The model features a metal vehicle body with plastic ladders, brass 12-spoke wheels and trim, spare wheel mounted on offside. Scale 1:48. 1st type ladders have square ended lug, 2nd type larger round ended		
	1977	1.............	Bright Red body, White 1st type ladders, Gold 12-spoke wheels............................	£90-110	☐
		2.............	As version 1 but with Brown or Reddish-Brown ladder...	£70-80	☐
		3.............	As version 1 but with Chrome 24-spoke wheels..	£10-12	☐
		4.............	White or Brown 2nd type ladders, Y6 & Y7 on baseplate.......................................	£4-6	☐
	1983	5.............	Dull Red body, Red/Brown 2nd type ladders	£8-10	☐
		6.............	As version 5 but with Red 12-spoke wheels...	£8-10	☐
		7.............	As 6 but with Chrome 12-spoke wheels...	£4-6	☐
		8.............	As version 7 but crew seat in Black plastic	£4-6	☐
		9.............	As 7 but bright Red plastic front seat, Brown double 2nd type ladder......................	£250-300	☐
Y6-5		**1932 MERCEDES L5 LORRY**	A brewery truck capable of carrying 6 tons, modelled in 1:69 scale.		
	1988	'STUTTGARTER HOFBRAU'	Cream body, Red logo & wheels. Later issues have smooth truck body sides.............	£4-6	☐
	1992	'HOLSTEN-BIER'	White body and tilt, Red wheels, Red/Black logos. Not issued	£4-6	☐

Y7-1

FOUR TON LEYLAND
'W & R JACOB & Co.Ltd'....... *'by Royal Appointment to His Majesty the King'.* Scale 1:100.

	1957	1..............	Dark Brown body, White or Cream roof, metal wheels, Silver radiator......................	£90-110 ☐
		2..............	As versions 1 but with Light Brown body........................	£90-110 ☐
		3..............	As 2 but without *'By Royal Appointment to His Majesty the King'*............................	£600-800 ☐
		4..............	As 2 but with Reddish/Brown body and radiator surround...............................	£100-125 ☐
		5..............	As 3 but with Black plastic wheels (24 treads front, 32 treads rear).......................	£800-900 ☐

Y7-2

1913 MERCER
RACEABOUT...................... Scale 1:46. The main variations are with the mudguards and their chassis fittings. The first issues had no struts/strengtheners.

	1961	1..............	Lilac body, Brass 12-spoke wheels & trim, 2 spare wheels, no struts......................	£20-30 ☐
		2..............	As version 1 but with mudguard struts...............................	£20-30 ☐
		3..............	As 2 but Yellow body, Lilac grille, Brass 12-spoke wheels & trim...........................	£20-30 ☐
		4..............	As 2 but Yellow body and grille, Brass 12-spoke wheels & trim...............................	£30-35 ☐

Y7-3

1912 ROLLS ROYCE.............. A large car modelled in a scale of 1:48. It has a metal body open at the rear with plastic seats, a spare tyre on the offside and brass trim. Thirty-two variations of this model exist so only the main ones are listed. Normally all the fittings (including the fire extinguisher), are brass plated, however variations exist with copper plated extinguishers. Three types of spare tyre carrier exist.

	1968	1..............	Silver body, Red chassis & smooth roof, seats & grille, brass 12-spoke wheels...........	£20-25 ☐
		2..............	As 1 but with smooth Grey roof...............................	£20-25 ☐
		3..............	As 2 but with Yellow seats...............................	£300-350 ☐
		4..............	As 2 but with ribbed rear section to Grey roof...............................	£150-175 ☐
		5..............	As 4 but with ribbed rear section to Red roof...............................	£20-25 ☐
		6..............	As 5 but Gold body, Silver bonnet, Black or Red seats, Copper extinguisher...........	£150-200 ☐
	1973	7..............	Gold body & bonnet, ribbed Red roof, Chrome wheels, Dark Red seats & grille.......	£8-10 ☐
		8..............	As 7 but with Black seats & grille, Chrome 12-spoke wheels...............................	£8-10 ☐
		9..............	As 7 but with early spare tyre carrier, Black or Dark Red seats...............................	£40-50 ☐
		10............	As 7 but with Green seats and grille...............................	£100-150 ☐
		11............	As 7 but with Black seats & grille, Red 12-spoke wheels...............................	£30-35 ☐
		12............	Bright Yellow body, Black chassis & ribbed roof, Red 12-spoke wheels.......................	£10-15 ☐
		13............	As 11 but having Chrome wheels with either 12 or 24 spokes...............................	£20-25 ☐

Y7-4

1930 FORD MODEL 'A'
BREAKDOWN TRUCK .... This model, based on the Y21 Woody Wagon, has a metal body with a plastic roof and lifting gear. It has plastic solid wheels, whitewall tyres and a large plastic front bumper. It was made to a scale of 1:40.

'BARLOW MOTOR SALES'

	1985	1..............	Orange body, bumpers & wheels, Black roof & chassis, Dark Green crane.................	£8-10 ☐
		2..............	As 1 ('MADE IN ENGLAND' base), but Light Green crane...............................	£35-45 ☐
	1987	3..............	As 1 but 'MADE IN MACAU' on base...............................	£20-30 ☐
	1988	**'SHELL'**	Yellow body, Black chassis, Red/Black logo, 'MADE IN MACAU' base.................	£4-6 ☐

Y8-1

1926 MORRIS COWLEY .... The 'Bullnose Morris' was the first saloon car to appear in the series and was modelled in a scale of 1:50.

	1958	1..............	Tan body, Dark Brown chassis, metal wheels, domed/crimped axles....................	£85-95 ☐
		2..............	As 1 but with Dark Tan body and rivetted axles	£85-95 ☐

Y8-2

1914 SUNBEAM
MOTORCYCLE & SIDECAR Model features unusual plated finish and a scale of 1:34.

	1962	1..............	Chrome machine and sidecar, Black cycle seat, Dark Green sidecar seat....................	£40-50 ☐
		2..............	As 1 but all Gold machine and sidecar...............................	£500-600 ☐
		3..............	As version 1 but Emerald Green sidecar seat...............................	£250-350 ☐
	1967	4..............	As 1 but Black plastic sidecar seat	£300-400 ☐

Y8-3

1914 STUTZ......................... The model features a metal bodied two seater car with plastic seats and roof. It has a spare wheel at rear and brass trim. Scale 1:48

	1969	1..............	Metallic Red body, Tan smooth roof, Copper petrol tank, Green seats and grille	£13-18 ☐
		2..............	As 1 (12-spoke Brass wheels), but with Tan textured roof...............................	£40-50 ☐
		3..............	As version 1 but with Brass petrol tank...............................	£50-60 ☐
	1973	4..............	Metallic Blue body, Black roof, White seats & grille, Chrome 12-spoke wheels...........	£6-8 ☐
		5..............	As 4 but with Red seats and grille...............................	£30-40 ☐
		6..............	As version 4 but with Chrome 24-spoke wheels...............................	£6-8 ☐

Y8-4

1945 M.G. TC .... A two seater sports car modelled in a scale of 1:35. Many variations exist.

	1978	1..............	Dark Green body, Tan roof and seats, RN '3', Chrome 24-spoke wheels....................	£70-80 ☐
		2..............	As version 1 but with Red seats	£15-20 ☐
		3..............	As version 2 but with Red 12-spoke wheels...............................	£20-25 ☐
		4..............	As 3 but Pink or Black seats, Chrome 24-spoke wheels...............................	£35-50 ☐
	1981	5..............	Bright Red body, Black seats, Tan or Rust roof, Chrome 24-spoke wheels	£6-8 ☐
		6..............	As version 5 but with Bright Red seats...............................	£20-25 ☐
	1983	7..............	Mid-Blue body, Black seats, Tan roof, Chrome 24-spoke wheels	£6-8 ☐
		8..............	As 7 but with Fawn seats, Tan or Rust roof...............................	£6-8 ☐
	1984	9..............	Cream body, Dark Brown lower body, Tan seats and roof...............................	£6-8 ☐
		10............	As 9 but with Dark Tan seats & roof, Tan or Pink/Brown seats....................	£4-6 ☐

Y8-5

YORKSHIRE STEAM WAGON .... A 1917 steam lorry (with transverse boiler), modelled in a scale of 1:61.

1987	'JOHNNIE WALKER' 1	Dark 'strawberry'-Red body, Grey cab roof, Cream tilt, Black chimney. 'JOHNNIE WALKER WHISKY' in bright Red on tilt sides plus striding figure logo	£200-300
	2	As 1 but 'JOHNNIE WALKER WHISKY' in light or dark Maroon	£6-8
	3	As version 2 but with non-striding figure	£150-200
1989	'SAMUEL SMITH'	Green & Beige. Passport scheme model ONLY IN CABINET. (12,000 made)...........	£75-85
1989	'WILLIAM PRICHARD'	Dark Blue body, Grey cab roof, Cream wheels and sack load, White logo	£4-6
1992	'FYFFES'	Yellow body and wheels, Cream tilt & roof, Blue 'Banana Merchant' logo	£10-12

Y9-1

1924 FOWLER SHOWMANS ENGINE .... *'LESNEYS MODERN AMUSEMENTS'.* Scale 1:80. Different colour shades exist, not affecting price.

1958	1	Dark Maroon body with a Cream roof, Gold cylinder block & chimney, smooth Orange/Yellow metal wheels. Copper boiler door. Brass canopy supports	£150-180
	2	As 1 but Dark Maroon cylinder block, Copper or Gold boiler door	£75-90
	3	As 2 but Pale Maroon body; Copper, Gold or Silver boiler door	£75-90
	4	As 3 but Bright Red body with White roof & Silver boiler door	£75-90
	5	As 4 but modified Black base casting, Silver or Brass supports	£100-110
	6	As 4 but with 'T' shaped fire-box ends	£90-110

Y9-2

1912 SIMPLEX .... The model features a metal body with a plastic roof and seats. It has 12-spoke wheels and spare tyre on offside and was modelled in a scale of 1:48.

1968	1	Lime Green body, smooth Tan roof, Brass wheels & trim, Red seats and radiator	£30-40
	2	As version 1 but with Mid-Green body	£10-15
	3	As version 2 but with textured Tan roof	£40-50
1970	4	Dark Metallic Gold body, Dark Red wings, seats and grille, Black textured roof	£25-35
	5	As 4 but with Chrome 12-spoke wheels	£25-35
	6	As 5 but Metallic Mid-Gold body	NGPP
1973	7	Bright Red body, Black textured roof, Brass trim, Yellow seats & grille	£13-16
1979	8	Dark Red body, Black chassis, textured Yellow or Black roof, Yellow seats & grille, Red wheels	£8-11
1986	9	Yellow body, Black chassis & grille, textured Yellow or Black roof, Brown seats, Gold 12-spoke wheels	£4-6
	10	As version 9 but Dark Yellow body	£4-6

Y9-3

1920 3-Ton LEYLAND LORRY .... *'LUFF & SONS'.* Featuring a high-sided lorry in a scale of 1:62. It has a plastic underframe, mudguards and front bumper, solid wheels and tyres.

1985	1	Dark Green body, Red chassis & wings, Pale Tan seats, Black grille	£20-30
	2	As 1 but with 'mushroom' coloured seats	£20-30
	3	As version 1 but with Black wings, Red seats	£80-100
	4	As version 3 but with Red radiator grille	£80-100

Y9-4

1936 LEYLAND 'CUB' FIRE ENGINE FK-7 .... Special Limited Edition model in 1:49 scale. 60,000 produced.

1989	1	Red body & wheels, Black roof, detachable Brown extending ladders	£40-50

Y10-1

1908 'GRAND PRIX' MERCEDES .... An early 12-litre chain-driven racing car modelled in a scale of 1:54

1958	1	Cream body, Pale Green seats, plated 12-spoke wheels, crimped axles	£60-70
	2	As 1 but with White body	£160-180
	3	As 1 but tooling insert modification to seat side, unplated wheels	£60-70
	4	As 2 but with Dark Green seats, crimped or rivetted axles	£60-70
	5	As 2 but Dark Green seats, White trim, rivetted axles	£130-140

Y10-2

1928 MERCEDES BENZ 36-220 .... The model features a metal body with one or two spare wheels, plastic seats and tonneau and spoked wheels. It was modelled in 1:52 scale.

1963	1	White body, Black seats & tonneau, 2 spare wheels, Silver trim, 2 holes in base	£800-1000
	2	As version 1 but with Red seats and tonneau	£30-40
	3	As version 2 but with only one spare wheel	£15-20
	4	As 3 but there are no holes in the baseplate, 2 spare tyres	£40-50
	5	As 4 but there is only one spare tyre	£15-20

Y10-3

1906 ROLLS-ROYCE SILVER GHOST .... Open four seater car modelled in 1:51 scale. It has a spare tyre on the offside and 12-spoke wheels. Many variations exist.

1969	1	Metallic Lime body, Metallic Brown wings, Brass wheels & trim, Red seats & grille ..	£12-15
1974	2	White body, Metallic Purple wings, Chrome wheels, Red seats and grille	£9-12
	3	As 2 but with Red wings, Black seats and grille	£9-12
	4	As version 2 but with Red wheels	£9-12
1979	5	Metallic Silver body and wings, Black seats and grille, Chrome wheels........................	£6-9
	6	As 5 but Red seats, grille and wheels, plain or White-wall tyres.........................	£6-9
	7	As 6 but with Yellow seats and grille, plain or White-wall tyres.........................	£12-15
	8	As 5 but with White seats, Black grille, Red wheels	£150-200

Y10-4 1957 MASERATI 250 F............ One of four 'Grand Prix Yesteryears' modelled in a scale of 1:35.

           1................ Bright Red body, Chrome 12-spoke or Aluminium 24-spoke wheels, baseplate wording: 'MATCHBOX INT'L LTD MADE IN ENGLAND', Black RN '12'......... **£8-12** ☐

           2................ As 1 but '(c) 1986' added to baseplate legend, modified suspension .... **£4-6** ☐

Y10-5 1931 DIDDLER TROLLEY BUS

        'LONDON TRANSPORT' ... 55,000 of this Special Limited Edition were made (in Macau). The model (in a scale of 1:76) has no less than 36 separate components.
Red/Cream body, Grey roof, 'RONUK', 'JEYES', 'JOHNNIE WALKER' .... **£15-20** ☐

Y11-1 1920 AVELING & PORTER STEAM ROLLER................

    1958 A popular model in a scale of 1:80.

           1................ Mid-Green body, Brown or Black flywheel, Black or Green canopy supports, makers plate in Gold............... **£130-150** ☐

           2................ As 1 but makers plate not in Gold............... **£90-100** ☐

Y11-2 1912 PACKARD LANDAULET ....

             The model features a metal body with plastic seats and spare tyre on offside, heraldic shield logo, brass 12-spoke wheels. It was made in a scale of 1:50.

    1962   1................ Dark Red body, Black bonnet & seats, metal steering wheel .... **£25-35** ☐

           2................ Minor changes include 3-prong tyre carrier & plastic steering wheel .... **£10-15** ☐

           3................ As 2 but Orange-Red body, Black bonnet & plastic steering wheel .... **£20-25** ☐

    1984   4................ Cream body, Brown chassis, Black roof, baseplate logo '1984 LIMITED EDITION', in 'Connoisseurs' set...................... **GSP** ☐

Y11-3 1938 LAGONDA DROPHEAD COUPE ....

            The model features a luxury 4-seat tourer with spare wheel covers in each of the front wings. Made in the '0'-gauge scale of 1:43.

    1972   1................ Metallic Gold main body, metallic Purple lower body, Black seats & plastic parts ..... **£600-750** ☐

           2................ As 1 but Dark Red lower body, Brass 24-spoke wheels, bumpers & lugs .... **£250-300** ☐

           3................ As version 2 but with Strawberry-Red lower body.......................... **£250-300** ☐

           4................ As version 2 but Dark Maroon lower body............................ **£45-50** ☐

    1974   5................ Metallic Orange body, Gold wings, Black seats, Brass 24-spoke wheels.................... **£30-40** ☐

           6................ As version 5 but Metallic Copper body, Chrome 24-spoke wheels .... **£10-12** ☐

           7................ As 6 but Maroon seats and other plastic parts, Red 12-spoke wheels .... **£14-18** ☐

           8................ As 6 but seats, roof, trunk and grille are in bright Red plastic....................... **£200-250** ☐

    1979   9................ Cream body, Black wings, Maroon seats & grille, solid chrome wheels .... **£4-6** ☐

          10............ As version 9 but with Black radiator grille .... **£4-6** ☐

          11............ As 10 but with Chrome 24-spoke wheels and White-wall tyres................ **£4-6** ☐

          12............ As 10 but the seats, tonneau and trunk are in Brown .... **£4-6** ☐

          13............ As 12 but with Dark Red 12-spoke wheels, White-wall tyres................ **£4-6** ☐

          14............ As 12 but the seats, tonneau and trunk are in Black................... **£30-40** ☐

    1985   15............ Deep Red body, Black seats, Brass 24-spoke wheels, (in 'Father's Day' Set).............. **GSP** ☐

          16............ As 15 but with seats, hood and trunk in Dark Brown .... **£4-6** ☐

Y11-4 1932 BUGATTI Type 51 .... Scale 1:35. Wheels vary in brightness (not affecting price).

           1................ Blue body, Brown seats, painted bonnet straps, Grey exhaust pipes, RN '4' .... **£15-20** ☐

           2................ As 1 but wider rear axle housing and larger dashboard lug............... **£4-6** ☐

    1990 1927 BUGATTI Type 35 .... Blue body, Black seats, plastic bonnet straps, Chrome exhaust, RN '6'....................... **£4-6** ☐

Y12-1 1899 HORSE DRAWN BUS.... 'LIPTONS TEA'. The first horse-drawn model in the series, (scale 1:100).

    1959   1................ Red body, Black 16-spoke metal wheels, Beige driver and metal seats, Brown horses (White manes/tails, Gold collars), 'VICTORIA & KINGS-CROSS', single drawbar rivet.................. **£75-85** ☐

           2................ As 1 but Dark Brown horses, partial Gold collars .... **£75-85** ☐

Y12-2 1909 THOMAS FLYABOUT ... The model is scaled at 1:48 and features a metal body with plastic roof and seats, 12-spoke wheels, spare tyre on offside and Black plastic steering wheel.

    1967   1................ Metallic Blue body, smooth Tan hood, Brass wheels, Yellow seats & grille............... **£700-900** ☐

           2................ As 1 (roof fixed to body pins), but with Dark Red seats and radiator grille............... **£20-25** ☐

           3................ As 2 but the smooth Tan hood is fixed to seat pins .... **£10-15** ☐

           4................ As 3 but the Tan hood has a textured finish .... **£32-39** ☐

           5................ As 3 but Black textured hood, White seats .... **£20-25** ☐

           6............ Metallic Purple body, Black textured hood & grille, White seats, Chrome 12 or 24-spoke wheels................... **£12-15** ☐

           7................ As 6 but Dark Red seats, Chrome 12-spoke wheels .... **£20-25** ☐

           8................ Metallic Ruby Red body, Black textured roof & grille, White seats, Chrome 12 or 24-spoke wheels..................... **£15-20** ☐

Y12-3

1912 FORD MODEL 'T'
VAN .... This model is in a scale of 1:35 and features a metal bodied van with oval side windows and a ribbed roof. It has plastic seats (usually Black), 12 or 24-spoke wheels and left hand drive steering wheel. Three different types of rear door design were produced as illustrated:

1st Type

2nd Type

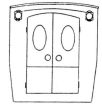

3rd Type cast in

1979	'COLMANS MUSTARD'	Yellow body, Matt-Black chassis and Black roof, Red or Black rear lights.		
	1...............	Type 1 Yellow doors, 12-spoke Red wheels, 'Y12' on base	**£6-8**	☐
	2...............	As version 1 but with Chrome 12-spoke wheels	**£6-8**	☐
	3...............	As version 1 but with Chrome 24-spoke wheels	**£20-25**	☐
	4...............	As 1 but with Black rear lights and Type 2 doors in Red	**£6-8**	☐
	5...............	As 4 but 'Y12' is not present on baseplate, Red rear lights	**£6-8**	☐
	6...............	As 5 but Gloss-Black roof, Black rear lights	**£20-25**	☐
1980	'COCA-COLA'	Off-White body, Black chassis and roof, Black or Red rear lights.		
	1...............	Type 1 doors in Red, 5 vertical Red body lines, Red 12-spoke wheels, plain tyres	**£250-300**	☐
	2...............	As 1 but with only 4 vertical Red body lines	**£35-45**	☐
	3...............	As 2 but Chrome 12 or 24-spoke wheels	**£50-60**	☐
	4...............	As 2 but Gold 12-spoke wheels, Red rear lights	**£50-60**	☐
1980	'SUZE'	Yellow body, Black chassis and matt Black roof, Black & Red logo.		
	1...............	Type 1 doors in Black, 'No. Y12' on baseplate, Red 12-spoke wheels	**£3-5**	☐
	2...............	As version 1 with Chrome 12 or 24-spoke wheels	**£3-5**	☐
	3...............	As 1 but with Red rear lights instead of Black	**£3-5**	☐
	4...............	As version 3 but with Type 2 doors in Black	**£30-40**	☐
	5...............	As 4 but 'No. Y12' blanked out from baseplate	**£3-5**	☐
	6...............	As 5 but with Type 2 doors in Red and with Gloss Black roof	**£110-120**	☐
1981	'SMITHS CRISPS'	Dark Blue body, White roof, Black chassis, Red 12-spoke wheels, whitewall tyres.		
	1...............	Type 1 doors and rear lights in White, Black seats, 'No. Y12' on baseplate ...	**£10-15**	☐
	2...............	As version 1 but with Tan seats	**£6-8**	☐
	3...............	As version 2 but without 'No. Y12' on baseplate	**£4-6**	☐
	4...............	As version 3 but with Type 2 doors in White	**£10-15**	☐
	5...............	As version 4 but with 'No. Y12' on baseplate	**£20-30**	☐
	Note:	500 'Code 3' issues of version 3 exist in 'Smiths Jubilee' livery.		
1981	'25th ANNIVERSARY OF YESTERYEARS'	(A white version of the standard box was provided for this model). Mid-Green body, darker Green chassis, Grey roof, Yellow 12-spoke wheels.		
	1...............	Type 2 doors in Silver-Grey, 'No Y12' on base, whitewall tyres, Silver '25' logo	**£3-5**	☐
	2...............	As version 1 but with Type 1 doors in Grey	**£400-500**	☐
	3...............	As version 1 but 'No. Y12' not present on baseplate	**£3-5**	☐
	4...............	As version 3 but Chrome or Red 12-spoke or Yellow 24-spoke wheels	**£8-11**	☐
1982	'BIRDS CUSTARD'	Blue body, Yellow roof, Black chassis, Red 12-spoke wheels, White-wall tyres		
	1...............	Type 2 doors in Yellow, Black seats, Chrome trim	**£6-8**	☐
	2...............	As version 1 but with a Metallic Blue body	**£40-50**	☐
	3...............	As version 1 but the seats are Tan plastic	**£6-8**	☐
	4...............	As version 1 with Yellow 12-spoke wheels	**£30-40**	☐
	5...............	As 3 (with Tan seats) but with Type 3 doors	**£6-8**	☐
	6...............	As 5 but with Black seats, Chrome trim, Chrome 12-spoke wheels	**£25-30**	☐
	7...............	As 5 but with Black seats	**£6-8**	☐
	8...............	As 6 (with Black seats), but with Brass radiator grille, windscreen and lamps	**£90-115**	☐
	9...............	As 1 but without tampo printing on rear doors	**NGPP**	☐
1982	'CEREBOS TABLE SALT'	Blue body, Black chassis, Red 12-spoke wheels, Black/White/Gold design		
	1...............	Yellow roof and type 2 doors, Brass trim, Black tyres and seats	**£180-200**	☐
	2...............	As 1 but with Chrome trim and White-wall tyres	**£180-200**	☐
	3...............	As 1 but with Gold 12-spoke wheels, Black or White-wall tyres	**£180-200**	☐
	4...............	As 1 but White roof, Gold trim, Black seats	**£3-5**	☐
	5...............	As 2 but White roof, Gold trim, Tan seats	**£60-70**	☐
1982	'ARNOTTS BISCUITS'	Orange/Red body, gloss Black chassis & roof, Gold trim & 12-spoke wheels.		
	1...............	Type 2 doors in Gold, label with Cream logo, wheatsheaf & parrot designs	**£180-200**	☐
	2...............	As version 1 but with Matt Black chassis and roof	**£180-200**	☐
	3...............	As version 1 but with double labels	**£180-200**	☐
	4...............	As version 2 but with double labels	**£180-200**	☐

Ref. No.	Year(s)	Model Type	*Matchbox Models of Yesteryear – continued*	Market Price Range	
	1982	'HARRODS EXPRESS DELIVERY'........	Dark Green body, Cream panel & roof, Black chassis, Gold 12-spoke wheels, in special Cream and Green version of the standard box.		
		1	Type 2 doors in White, Gold logo, Black seats	£6-8	☐
		2.............	As 1 but Type 3 doors and Green border around oval side windows....................	£6-8	☐
		3.............	As version 2 but the seats are in Tan plastic......................................	£6-8	☐
		4.............	As version 3 but the seats are in Pale Cream plastic...........................	£15-20	☐
	1983	'SUNLIGHT SEIFE'	Yellow body, Black chassis, roof and plastic seats, Red 12-spoke wheels.		
		1.............	Type 2 doors in Red, multicoloured design (on label) covers side window.................	£125-150	☐
	1983	'ROYAL MAIL'	Gold 'G R' logo and George V crown, Black chassis, roof & plastic seats.		
		1.............	Red, Type 2 doors printed in Yellow, Bright Red 12-spoke wheels, Gold trim............	£180-200	☐
		2.............	As version 1 but with Gold 12-spoke wheels	£180-200	☐
		3.............	As 1 but with Post-Office Red body, Type 3 doors, Bright Red 12-spoke wheels	£4-6	☐
		4.............	As version 3 but with Chrome trim...	£20-30	☐
		5.............	As 3 but with Gold trim, Chrome 24-spoke wheels...........................	£10-12	☐
	1983	'CAPTAIN MORGAN'...........	Black body and chassis, White roof, Gold 12-spoke wheels, Tan seat		
		1.............	Type 3 doors, Black 1-piece label (small 'rum', Gold border, 'pirate' cameo, White logo)	£3-5	☐
		2.............	As version 1 but Black seat, Bright Red 12-spoke wheels......................	£40-50	☐
		3.............	As version 1 but 2-piece label with large 'rum'	£3-5	☐
		4.............	As version 2 but 2-piece label with large 'rum'	£40-50	☐
	1983	'HOOVER'	Orange body, Black chassis and roof, Chrome trim. Special box.		
		1.............	Type 3 doors, Black rear lights and wheels, Black logo, lady/cleaner cameo	£3-5	☐
		2.............	As version 1 but with Tan seat	£20-30	☐
		3.............	As version 1 but with Black 24-spoke wheels..........................	£10-15	☐
	Note:.............		See also 'Code 2 models' section.		
	1984	'PEPSI-COLA'	White body, Red roof, rear lights & logo, Blue chassis, Chrome trim		
		1.............	Type 3 doors, Chrome 12-spoke wheels, 'LESNEY PRODUCTS 1978' on base.........	£3-5	☐
		2.............	As 1 but with Red 12-spoke wheels..................................	£3-5	☐
		3.............	As 1 but with Chrome 24-spoke wheels and White-wall tyres.......................	£3-5	☐
	1987	4.............	As 1 but with 'MATCHBOX INT.LTD (c) 1985' on baseplate.....................	£3-5	☐
	1985	'MOTOR 100'	Metallic Bronze body, Dark Brown chassis and roof and rear lights.		
		1.............	Type 3 doors, Red 12-spoke wheels, Red *'MOTOR 100'*. 'Globe' has Blue water & Cream land. With certificate 1-2,300	£25-40	☐
		2.............	As version 1 but without certificate...............................	£6-8	☐
		3.............	As version 2 but 'globe' has Cream water, Blue land........................	£200-250	☐
	1985	'IMBACH'..............................	A unique version of Y12-3 having an open truck body instead of a van.		
		1.............	Dark Blue body, Black chassis, Gold wheels, Tan seats, 65,000 made	£6-8	☐
		2.............	As version 1 but with Red 12-spoke wheels, Pinkish-Tan seats............	£8-11	☐
	1986	'H.J.HEINZ & Co'................	Model has Green 'gherkin' on roof, *'57 Varieties'* logo, Type 3 doors.		
		1.............	Greenish-Cream body, Dark Green chassis, Gold trim, Maroon 12-spoke wheels, *'Varieties'* printed with thin letters	£4-6	☐
		2.............	As version 1 but with *'Varieties'* printed with thick letters....................	£4-6	☐
		3.............	As version 1 but with Bright Red 12-spoke wheels............................	£4-6	☐
		4.............	As version 1 but with Chrome grille and trim	£4-6	☐
	1987	'ROSELLA'............................	Blue body, Yellow roof, Black chassis and seats, Type 3 doors.		
		1.............	Gold 12-spoke wheels and trim, Black tyres, 'MATCHBOX 1986' on base............	£5-7	☐
		2.............	As version 1 but with 'LIMITED EDITION' on base	£5-7	☐
		3.............	As version 1 but 'MATCHBOX 1985' on base..................................	£15-20	☐
		4.............	As 1 but 'LESNEY PRODUCTS & Co. Ltd (c) 1978' on base....................	£5-7	☐
		5.............	As 4 but with Maroon 12-spoke wheels, Black tyres.........................	£5-7	☐
Y12-4	1987	**1829 STEPHENSONS ROCKET**...................................	A Special Limited Edition of 60,000 pieces. Scale 1:64 ('S' gauge) Yellow ribbed engine, tender & barrel, Black chassis and components, White chimney, Gold trim. Yellow 12-spoke wheels on loco, 8-spoke on tender	£12-15	☐
Y12-5		**1937 G.M.C. Van**	A 1930s delivery van in a scale of 1:45. ('MADE IN MACAU' on base).		
	1988	'GOBLIN' 1	Black body, light Grey roof, 'acorn'-shaped headlights, solid Chrome wheels	£15-20	☐
		2.............	As version 1 but Black body and Black roof................................	£8-10	☐
		3.............	As version 2 but with streamlined headlights..........................	£3-5	☐
	1989	'BAXTERS' 1	Cream body, Green 'MACAU' base, 'acorn' shaped lights, Chrome wheels	£15-20	☐
		2.............	As version 1 but with streamlined headlights..........................	£3-5	☐
Y12-C	1991	'GOANNA' 1	Blue body, Black base ('MADE IN MACAU') Dark Red solid wheels. Advert is Bright Red/Dark Blue/White	£3-5	☐
		2.............	As version 1 but advert is Mid-Red/Mid-Blue/White, Mid-Red wheels..............	£3-5	☐
		3.............	As version 2 but advert is Orange-Red/Pale Blue/White	£3-5	☐
Y13-1		**1862 'SANTE FE' Locomotive** ..	A popular model (in a scale of 1:112) with hand-applied trim.		
	1959	1.............	Dark Green and Maroon body, metal wheels, Gold trim, Silver lens...........	£85-100	☐
		2.............	As 1 but no Gold trim on walkway.............................	£85-100	☐
		3.............	As 2 but Maroon headlight lens and no trim on condensers...................	£75-85	☐
		4.............	As version 3 but no Gold trim	£75-85	☐
		5.............	Light Green body, Maroon headlight lens, no Gold trim	£700-800	☐

Y13-2 — 1911 DAIMLER

The model features a metal body and 26-spoke wheels with plastic seats, external handbrake lever and spare wheel on offside. Modelled in 1:45 scale.

Year	No.	Description	Price	
1966	1	Yellow body, Black wings & seats, '1911 DAIMLER' & 'No. Y13' in 2 lines on base	£35-45	☐
	2	As version 1 but with Dark Red seats	£15-20	☐
	3	As 1 (Black seats), but with spare wheel open at base	£25-35	☐
	4	As 2 (Dark Red seats), but spare wheel open at base	£14-18	☐
	5	As 4 but steering wheel has 4 instead of 5 spokes, no pedals	£25-35	☐
	6	As 5 but '1911', 'DAIMLER' & 'No. Y13' in 3 lines on base	£30-35	☐
1984	7	Mid-Blue main body, Light Blue lower body 'LIMITED EDITION' on baseplate, in 'Connoisseurs' set	GSP	☐

Y13-3 — 1918 CROSSLEY

The model features a small metal truck with plastic cab cover & tilt. It has chrome spoked wheels with a spare on the offside. Scale 1:47.

Year	Type	No.	Description	Price	
1975	'R.A.F. TENDER'		Airforce Blue body, Red cross on White square label plus 'R.A.F.' roundel.		
		1	Flat baseplate with 'LTD' complete, Tan canopy, tilt and grille, Maroon seat	£325-375	☐
		2	As version 1 but seat in White plastic	£300-350	☐
		3	As 2 but additional brace to front wings, two side panel cleats	£40-50	☐
		4	As 3 but 2 discs (8 mm.), on baseplate and 'LTD' incomplete	£20-30	☐
		5	As version 4 but seat in Green plastic	£160-180	☐
		6	As version 4 but with 24-spoke Chrome wheels	£25-35	☐
		7	As version 4 but with Maroon seat	£25-35	☐
		8	As 6 but with Olive-Green cab cover, tilt and grille	£70-80	☐
		9	As version 8 but with 12-spoke Chrome wheels	£70-80	☐
		10	As 7 but with Black cab cover, tilt and grille	£300-350	☐
1979	'EVANS Bros COAL & COKE'		Dark Red body, Black lower body, seats and roof.		
		1	With 'CROSSLEY RAF TENDER' on baseplate, 24-spoke Chrome wheels	£50-60	☐
		2	As version 1 but with 12-spoke Chrome wheels	£15-20	☐
		3	As version 1 but with 12-spoke Red wheels	£50-60	☐
		4	As 3 but without 'RAF TENDER' on baseplate	£10-12	☐
		5	As 4 but brighter Red body and large Chrome stud on spare wheel	£15-20	☐

Y13-4 — 1918 CROSSLEY LORRY

Scale 1:47.

Year	Type	No.	Description	Price	
1983	'CARLSBERG'		Cream body, Black lower body, Green cab cover and tilt.		
		1	With Chrome 12-spoke wheels, Brass trim, Maroon seats, Green or Black grille, 'Lesney 1973 England' base	£6-8	☐
		2	As version 1 but with Brass 12-spoke wheels	£6-8	☐
		3	As version 2 but 'Matchbox 1973 England' on base	£3-5	☐
		4	As 3 but Darker Green grille, Gold 12-spoke wheels	£3-5	☐
1985	'WARINGS'	1	Dark Green body, textured cab cover and tilt in White plastic. White tilt labels with 'LONDON W.G. MADRID PARIS' in Brown	£5-7	☐
		2	As version 1 but with Cream labels	£5-7	☐
		3	As 1 (White labels), but textured Cream plastic cab cover and tilt	£5-7	☐
		4	As 3 (Cream cab cover and tilt) but labels are Cream	£5-7	☐
1985	'KOHLE & KOKS'				
		1	Lemon-Yellow body, Black cab roof, wheels, chassis & coal load	£3-5	☐
		2	As version 1 but with Dark Green 12-spoke wheels	£20-30	☐

Y14-1 — 1959 'DUKE OF CONNAUGHT' Locomotive (1903)

Scale 1:130.

No.	Description	Price	
1	Dark Green & Brown body, metal 12-spoked wheels, Gold trimmed sandbox on walkway (not joined to main wheel arch). Gold trim on other main features	£100-125	☐
2	As 1 but walkway sandbox has no Gold trim	£85-95	☐
3	As 2 but walkway boxes joined to main wheel arches	£85-100	☐
4	As version 3 but with combined wheels and axles	£85-100	☐
5	As version 4 but with boiler door in Silver	£100-110	☐

Y14-2 — 1911 MAXWELL ROADSTER

The model features a metal body, petrol tank and 12-spoke wheels with spare wheel on boot. It has plastic seats and roof and is modelled in a scale of 1:49.

Year	No.	Description	Price	
1965	1	Turquoise body, smooth Black roof, Red seats, Brass wheels, Brass petrol tank	£60-70	☐
	2	As version 1 but with Copper petrol tank	£8-12	☐
	3	As version 2 with textured roof	£8-12	☐
1984	4	Dark Cream body, Dark Green lower body, Brass 12-spoke wheels, Black textured roof with 'LIMITED EDITION' on underside, in 'Connoisseurs' set	GSP	☐

Y14-3 — 1931 STUTZ BEARCAT

The model features an open 2 seater tourer with metal body and plastic seats. It has Chrome 24-spoke wheels and 2 spares. Scale 1:44.

Year	No.	Description	Price	
1974	1	Metallic Light Green main body, Metallic Green lower body. Rear bumper open on left hand side, Red seats and grille, '1973' on baseplate	£100-125	☐
	2	As version 1 but rear bumper closed on both sides	£100-125	☐
	3	As version 2 with '1974' on baseplate	£5-7	☐
	4	As version 3 but with Dark Red seats	£75-100	☐
1979	5	Cream/Red body, Red door tops, Red seats and grille	£30-35	☐
	6	As version 5 but radiator grille in Black plastic	£25-35	☐
	7	As 5 but seats and grille are both in Maroon plastic	£25-35	☐
	8	As version 5 but with Cream door tops	£5-7	☐

	1981		9............ Cream and emerald-Green body, Black seats, Chrome 24-spoke wheels	**£6-8**	☐
			10............ As 8 but with Red 12-spoke wheels, White-wall tyres	**£15-20**	☐
	1985		11............ French Blue and Grey body, Brown or Beige seats	**£3-5**	☐
	1990		12............ Pale Cream/Blue, Dark Red seats, Tan or Olive steering wheel, Chrome 24-spoke wheels	**£3-5**	☐

Y14-4

		1936 E.R.A. Type R1-B............	A famous British racing car reproduced in a scale of 1:35.		
	1986		1............... Black body, Chrome 24-spoke wheels, RN '7', 'MADE IN ENGLAND' on base	**£3-5**	☐
			2............... As 1 but with 'aluminium' effect 24-spoke wheels	**£3-5**	☐
	1988	('Romulus')	3 .... Blue body, Dark Yellow chassis & springs, RN '4', 'MADE IN MACAU' on base ...	**£6-8**	☐
			4............... As version 3 but with darker Yellow chassis and springs	**£6-8**	☐

Y15-1

		1907 ROLLS-ROYCE SILVER GHOST	The first Yesteryear to be finished in metallic paint. Scale 1:55.		
	1960		1............... Metallic Light Green body, Silver 12-spoke wheels, Grey knobbly tyres, Black seats, Gold radiator, Silver number plate, Red rear light..	**£40-50**	☐
			2............... As 1 but Metallic Light Green rear lights and number plate	**£35-40**	☐
			3............... As version 2 but with Black knobbly tyres	**£15-20**	☐
			4............... As version 2 but with Black smooth tyres	**£15-20**	☐
			5............... As version 4 but with Gold 12-spoke wheels	**£15-20**	☐
			6............... As 5 but rear running boards filled-in, two holes in baseplate	**£15-20**	☐
			7............... As version 6 but with Green seats	**£50-60**	☐
			8............... As 6 but baseplate is extended and cross-member removed	**£15-20**	☐

Y15-2

		1930 PACKARD VICTORIA ...	The model features a metal body, 12 or 24-spoked wheels, with 2 spares (1 in each wing). It has a plastic roof and luggage trunk. Components are easily interchanged and many combinations exist (both fake and genuine). Scale 1:46.		
	1969		1............... Metallic brownish-Gold upper, dark Brown lower body, Maroon grille, seats and textured hood, Brass 24-spoke wheels, cross chassis brace	**£15-20**	☐
			2............... As 1 but Bright Red seats	**£15-20**	☐
			3............... As 2 but with Chrome 24-spoke wheels	**£40-50**	☐
	1974		4............... Metallic greenish-Gold body, dark Brown chassis, Maroon hood, Bright or Dark Red grille, Chrome 12 or 24-spoke wheels	**£10-15**	☐
			5............... As 4 but Black hood & trunk, Dark Red seats & grille, Chrome 24-spoke wheels	**NGPP**	☐
			6............... As 5 but with raised coachline round body rear, Black trunk..........................	**£50-60**	☐
			7............... As version 6 but with Gloss-Black chassis	**£200-250**	☐
			8............... Black body with Red panels, Black hood, Dark Red seats, solid Chrome wheels........	**£6-8**	☐
			9............... As 8 but White hood and Chrome solid or 24-spoke wheels	**£6-8**	☐
			10............. As version 9 but with Bright Red seats	**£30-35**	☐
	1984		11............. Dark Cream body, Brown or White textured hood, Red wheels, Mushroom seats......	**£6-8**	☐
			12............. As 11 but with Orange/Brown hood, Tan seats..	**£6-8**	☐

Y15-3

		1920 'Preston' type TRAM CAR........................	The model features a double decker tram with metal lower & upper decks, plastic window sections, chassis, roof, seats and staircase. Scale 1:87.		
	1987	'SWAN VESTAS'	1 .... Red body, White window sections, Grey chassis and roof, 'LONDON TRANSPORT'	**£3-5**	☐
			2............... As 1 but modified resistor box and letter 'A' added to baseplate	**NGPP**	☐
	1988	'SWAN SOAP'	1 .... Blue lower body & roof, Cream upper, 'DARLINGTON CORPORATION'	**£10-12**	☐
			2............... As 1 but additional letter 'A' on baseplate	**£3-5**	☐
	1989	'GOLDEN SHRED'	Cream upper & Orange lower body, 'PAISLEY DISTRICT TRAMWAYS'	**£3-5**	☐
Y15-D	1991	'ZEBRA GRATE POLISH'	Dark Brown body, Grey roof, 'NEWCASTLE CORPORATION TRANSPORT'	**£3-5**	☐
			2............... As version 1 but with Orange tampo print	**£3-5**	☐

Y16-1

		1904 SPYKER	Large open car with huge single headlamp and round grille. Scale 1:45.		
	1961		1............... Pale Cream body, Brass 12-spoke wheels, Grey knobbly tyres, Gold radiator surround, Green seats, spare wheel, curved brake/gear lever	**£200-250**	☐
			2............... As version 1 but with Pale Yellow body	**£50-60**	☐
			3............... As 2 but with Black knobbly tyres and straight brake/gear lever	**£25-30**	☐
			4............... As 3 but with two unthreaded holes in baseplate and 'MODELS OF YESTERYEAR No.16' removed, Brass 24-spoke wheels	**£90-110**	☐
			5............... As 3 but four braces on Gold wheels with fine tread tyres	**£25-30**	☐
			6............... As 5 but with Maroon body, Brass 12-spoke or Y6-2 Bugatti wheels. Brass headlamps, sidelights and radiator shell	**£1200-1500**	☐
			7............... As 6 but with Gold headlamps, sidelights and radiator shell	**£1200-1500**	☐
			N.B. Similar model sold at auction by Wallis and Wallis, Lewes on 7/6/93 for £1200.		
			8............... As version 5 but section between running boards and chassis filled in	**£25-30**	☐
			9............... As version 8 but finished in Dark Yellow	**£25-30**	☐
			10............. As version 9 but no Gold radiator shell	**£25-30**	☐

Y16-2

		1928 MERCEDES-BENZ SS COUPE............................	The model is in 1:45 scale and features a metal body with a spare wheel in each front wing, plastic roof & trunk, exposed manifold exhaust pipes in Brass.		
	1972		1............... Metallic Silver body, Metallic Red chassis/differential casting, Black grille, textured roof & smooth trunk, Brass 24-spoke wheels	**£50-75**	☐
			2............... As 1 but without the differential detail, Black trunk	**£25-30**	☐
	1974		3............... Metallic Lime Green body, Black textured roof, boot & seats, Chrome wheels	**£12-15**	☐
			4............... As version 3 but with Chrome 12-spoke wheels...	**£12-15**	☐
			5............... Metallic Light Green main body with 'Stutz Bearcat'-Green lower body, Chrome 24-spoke wheels..	**£200-250**	☐

Ref. No.	Year(s)	Model Type		Description	Market Price Range	
			6.............	As 3 with Dark Green seats, grille, textured roof & textured trunk............................	**£60-75**	☐
			7.............	As version 6 but with 12-spoke Chrome wheels..	**£45-60**	☐
			8.............	As 6 but the exhaust pipe is incorporated into baseplate casting.............................	**£55-65**	☐
			9.............	As 8 but with Black seats, grille, textured roof, textured trunk...............................	**£12-15**	☐
			10.............	As 9 but with Green 12-spoke wheels on plain Black tyres..	**£90-100**	☐
	1979		11.............	White body, Black textured roof, Chrome 24-spoke wheels and exhaust pipes, White-wall tyres...	**£6-8**	☐
			12.............	As version 11 but with Black chassis..	**£350-400**	☐
	1981		13.............	Mid-Blue body, Grey side panels, Black roof, Chrome 24-spoke wheels...................	**£5-7**	☐
			14.............	As 13 but with Red 12-spoke wheels, White-wall tyres...	**£14-18**	☐
			15.............	As 13 but with Duck Egg Blue body and side panels...	**£75-90**	☐
			16.............	As 13 but with milky-White body and side panels...	**£20-30**	☐
			17.............	As 13 but with Fawn body and side panels, Black or White-wall tyres......................	**£16-20**	☐
	1985		18.............	Bright Red body, Silver chassis, Red 24-spoke wheels, White-wall tyres....................	**£3-5**	☐
			19.............	As version 18 but with Red 12-spoke wheels..	**£3-5**	☐
	1990		20.............	Light Grey body, Black chassis, 24-spoke Chrome wheels, Tan steering wheel...........	**£3-5**	☐
			21.............	As 20 but with Olive-Green steering wheel with Black painted spokes......................	**£3-5**	☐
Y16-3		**1960 FERRARI DINO 246/V12**		One of four 'Grand Prix' Yesteryears modelled in a scale of 1:35.		
	1986		1	Bright Red body, Chrome 24-spoke wheels, Black RN '17' in White disc...................	**£15-20**	☐
			2.............	As version 1 but with wider brake drums...	**£3-5**	☐
			3.............	As version 2 but with aluminium-effect wheels...	**£10-15**	☐
Y16-4	1988	**1923 SCANIA-VABIS POST BUS**	1	Yellow body & skids, Grey roof, Brass trim and 12-spoke front wheels, Black rear wheels & track, Special Edition Model (60,000), Scale 1:49.	**£14-20**	☐
Y16-5	1989	**SCAMMELL 100 ton Truck and**		**Trailer with G.E.R. E4 Class 2-4-0 Locomotive** An impressive Special Limited Edition pair of models in 'S' gauge (1:64) Blue truck & trailer, White cab roofs & 'PICKFORDS' logo, Red chassis & wheels. Very dark Blue loco with Red bodylines, Gold trim & number '490'.........................	**£70-80**	☐
Y17-1		**1938 HISPANO SUIZA**		A stylish sports two-seater modelled in 1:48 scale.		
	1975		1.............	Dark Red body, Black wings, roof, seats & grille, Chrome 24-spoke wheels, 'LESNEY PRODUCTS & Co.Ltd. (c) 1973 MADE IN ENGLAND' on base...........	**£10-15**	☐
	1980		2.............	As 1 but Two-tone Metallic Silver Blue body, chassis and mudguards........................	**£6-8**	☐
			3.............	As 2 but with solid Chrome wheels and White-wall tyres...	**£6-8**	☐
			4.............	As version 3 but with Black chassis and mudguards..	**£6-8**	☐
	1981		5.............	As 4 but with Metallic Silver upper body, Powder-Blue sides....................................	**NGPP**	☐
			6.............	As 5 but with Metallic Silver chassis and mudguards..	**NGPP**	☐
	1986		7.............	Emerald Green body, Dark Green chassis & wings, Brass 24-spoke wheels, Black roof..	**NRP**	☐
			8.............	As version 7 but with Dark Green radiator grille...	**£10-12**	☐
			9.............	As 7 but 'MATCHBOX INTL' and 'MADE IN ENGLAND' on base..........................	**£20-30**	☐
			10.............	As 7 but 'MATCHBOX INTL' and 'MADE IN MACAU' on base............................	**£3-5**	☐
	1990		11.............	Metallic Green body with Pale Lime-Green panels, Pale Cream hood, Chrome 24-spoke wheels with White-wall flanges, 'MADE IN MACAU' on base....................	**£10-15**	☐
			12.............	As 11 but with cast hole in base for self-tapping screw..	**£5-7**	☐
			13.............	As version 12 but with Dark Lime-Green panels..	**£5-7**	☐
			14.............	As version 12 but the wheels are on press-fit axles..	**£10-12**	☐
Y18-1		**1937 CORD 812**		An unusual American car of the 1930s modelled in 1:48 scale.		
	1979		1.............	Bright Red body, Chrome 24-spoke wheels, White-wall tyres, White roof & seats, 'MADE IN ENGLAND (c) 1978 LESNEY PRODUCTS & Co.Ltd.' on base..........	**£6-8**	☐
			2.............	As version 1 but with Red solid wheels..	**£6-8**	☐
			3.............	As version 1 but with Chrome solid wheels..	**£3-5**	☐
			4.............	As 3 but with Dark Orange bonnet, front wings & baseplate....................................	**£3-5**	☐
	1981		5.............	As version 3 but darker Red body and grille...	**£6-8**	☐
	1983		6.............	As version 5 but Plum Red body..	**£6-8**	☐
			7.............	As version 6 but with Chrome 24-spoke wheels..	**£6-8**	☐
	1990		8.............	Yellow body, Brown hood, solid Chrome wheels, 'MADE IN MACAU' on base	**£6-8**	☐
Y18-2		**1918 ATKINSON 'D' TYPE STEAM WAGON**		The model (scaled at 1:60) has a metal body & plastic underframe, chrome chimney and boiler, and smooth plastic tyres on 8-spoke wheels.		
	1985	'LAKE GOLDSMITH'		Emerald Green body & wheels, Red underframe, Black rounded mudguards.............	**£6-8**	☐
	1986	'BLUE CIRCLE'	1	Pale Yellow body, Yellow wheels, Pale Blue logo, Black underframe.........................	**£6-8**	☐
			2.............	Deeper Yellow body, Darker Blue logo..	**£3-5**	☐
	1987	'BASS & Co'		Blue body with 7 barrels, Red transmission & wheels. (60,000 made).......................	**£6-8**	☐
	1988	'BURGHFIELD MILLS'		Red truck body and wheels, Black underframe, Yellow sack load..............................	**£3-5**	☐
Y19-1		**1936 AUBURN SPEEDSTER** ..		An American classic car in a scale of 1:42.		
	1979		1.............	Light Beige main body, bonnet & sides, Dark Brown wings & chassis, Dark Orange seats, Cherry-Red solid wheels, Black or WWT..	**£6-8**	☐
			2.............	As 1 but with Red solid wheels with Black or White-wall tyres.................................	**£6-8**	☐
			3.............	As version 2 but with Bright Red seats..	**£3-5**	☐
			4.............	As 1 but with very Dark Beige wings & chassis..	**£6-8**	☐

	1983		5...............	Light Cream body, Black wings, Bright Red seats, Red solid wheels, Black or White-wall tyres	**£12-15** ☐
			6...............	As version 6 but Off-White body, Black wings	**£3-5** ☐
			7...............	As 6 but with Red 12-spoke wheels, Black or White-wall tyres	**£3-5** ☐
	1985		8...............	White body & wings, Blue panels, seats & 24-spoke wheels	**£3-5** ☐
	1990		9...............	Dark Tan upper body & wings, Cream sides, Chrome 24-spoke wheels.............	**£3-5** ☐

Y19-2 1986 FOWLER B6 SHOWMANS ENGINE

				'Hey-Ho Come To The Fair'. Special Limited Edition of 65,000 models.	
			1...............	Blue body, Black smoke-box, White roof, Red wheels, Scale 1:68	**£30-35** ☐
			2...............	As 1 but with Off-White (almost Light Cream) roof	**£30-35** ☐

Y19-3 1929 MORRIS COWLEY VAN

				The model is in 1:39 scale and has a metal van body with oval side windows. It has 12-spoke wheels and a spare wheel on the nearside.	
	1987	'BRASSO'	1...............	Blue main body, Black wings, White roof, Red wheels, Chrome radiator	**£3-5** ☐
			2...............	As 1 but underside of roof has additional strengthening webs	**£3-5** ☐
			3...............	As 2 but darker Brown seats, press-fit wheels, screw hole in base, 'CHINA'	**£6-8** ☐
	1988	'MICHELIN'	1...............	Blue body, Black wings, Chrome wheels, Yellow roof & designs, *'Too small a tyre is soon ruined!'* on nearside, *'Pump up every Friday'* on offside	**£3-5** ☐
			2...............	As version 1 but with Lemon-Yellow designs	**£3-5** ☐
	1990	'J. SAINSBURY'	1...............	Brown body, Black wings, White roof, Chrome wheels & radiator, 'DELICIOUS DAIRY BUTTER' in Dark Blue on roof sides	**£3-5** ☐
			2...............	As 1 but 'DELICIOUS DAIRY BUTTER' in lighter shade of Blue	**£3-5** ☐

Y20-1 1981 1937 MERCEDES-BENZ 540K

				A luxurious open tourer modelled in 1:45 scale with opening dickey seat.	
			1...............	Metallic Silver body, Black wings, Chrome 24-spoke wheels, Red 28 mm. seats..........	**£8-11** ☐
			2...............	As 1 but with Red 30 mm. wide seats	**£6-8** ☐
			3...............	As version 2 but with Amber seats	**£6-8** ☐
			4...............	As version 2 but with Chrome solid wheels	**£6-8** ☐
			5...............	As version 2 but with Red 12-spoke wheels	**£6-8** ☐
	1985		6...............	White body with Red side stripe, seats and 24-spoke wheels	**£3-5** ☐
	1987		7...............	Bright Red body, Brown seats, Chrome 24-spoke wheels, White-wall tyres	**£6-8** ☐
	1989		8...............	Black body, Maroon seats, Chrome 24-spoke wheels, Tan steering wheel	**£15-20** ☐
	1990		9...............	As 8 but with cast hole in baseplate and '540K' nearer to rear axle	**£3-5** ☐
			10.............	As 9 but with press-fit Chrome 24-spoke wheels & White-wall flanges	**£3-5** ☐
			11.............	As 10 but with Light Olive-Green steering wheel	**£3-5** ☐

Y21-1 1930 FORD MODEL 'A' WOODY WAGON

				This model has metal bonnet, wings and baseplate but the main 'utility' body is in plastic. It has a Black roof and Chrome wheels. Scale 1:40. N.B. Box refers to '1927'	
	1981		1...............	Yellow bonnet, Dark Brown wings, Red seats, 24-spoke wheels, 'LESNEY' base.......	**£8-10** ☐
			2...............	As 1 but seats and steering wheel in Orange	**£35-45** ☐
			3...............	with Black chassis and 'FORD A' on base changed to 'FORD MODEL A'..............	**£20-25** ☐
			4...............	As 3 but Red seats & steering wheel, 'Matchbox 1981' on base	**£20-25** ☐
	1983		5...............	Dark Orange bonnet, Brown wings, Red seats, 12-spoke wheels, 'Matchbox' base	**£3-5** ☐

Y21-2 1930 FORD MODEL 'A' WOODY WAGON

				A development from Y21-1 with side windows filled in. Scale 1:40.	
	1983	'A & J BOX'	1...............	Copper bonnet, Dark Brown wings & chassis, White seats, Chrome 12-spoke wheels, White-wall tyres, 'LESNEY' base, windscreen without Chrome finish	**£8-10** ☐
			2...............	As 1 but the windscreen surround has Chrome finish	**£18-24** ☐
			3...............	As version 1 but Dark Orange bonnet	**£8-10** ☐
			4...............	As 1 with Yellow bonnet, Red seats, 24-spoke wheels, Black tyres.....................	**£35-45** ☐
			5...............	As 3 but 'MATCHBOX INT'L LTD' on underside of o/s running board	**£3-5** ☐
			6...............	As 5 but with Red seats, Chrome 12-spoke wheels, White-wall tyres	**£35-45** ☐
			7...............	Dark Orange or Copper bonnet, Off-White seats, 12 or 24-spoke wheels	**£8-10** ☐
	1985	'CARTERS SEEDS'	1.............	Blue bonnet, Black wings, Cream and Dark Blue wagon sides, Blue 'Carters', Brown seats, Chrome 12-spoke wheels, White-wall tyres	**£3-5** ☐
			2...............	As 1 but with Chrome 24-spoke wheels on White-wall tyres	**£3-5** ☐
			3...............	As 1 but White body panels, Pale Blue logo, Brown seats	**£8-10** ☐

Y21-3 AVELING AND PORTER ROAD ROLLER

				'James Young & Sons, Edinburgh' A Special Limited Edition of 60,000 models. Scale 1:60.	
	1987		1...............	Emerald Green body & wheels, very Light Grey roof & roller surfaces. Baseplate reads: '(C) 1987 Y21 MATCHBOX AVELING PORTER ROAD ROLLER'............	**£700-900** ☐
			2...............	As 1 but with Light Grey roof and mid-Grey roller surfaces............................	**£400-600** ☐
			3...............	As 2 but underside of roof has 'MATCHBOX INT'L LTD., MADE IN MACAU, LIMITED EDITION' cast-in	**£18-25** ☐

Y21-4 1988 1955 BMW 507

| | | | | Blue body, removable Black hood, opening bonnet, Chrome engine and solid wheels, '681 313', Special Limited Edition of 60,000 models. Scale 1:38 .... | **£8-10** ☐ |

Y21-5 1926 FORD Model 'TT' VAN

				A large van in 1:41 scale with a metal body and plastic underframe.	
	1989	'OSRAM'	1...............	Green body, Red roof and 12-spoke wheels, Grey seats, Chrome grille	**£8-10** ☐
			2...............	As 1 but with Black printed grille, lug under some cab roofs	**£20-30** ☐
	1990	'MY BREAD'	1...............	Beige body, Lilac-Grey seats, Red 12-spoke wheels	**£20-30** ☐
			2...............	As version 1 but with Mid-Grey seat	**£3-5** ☐
			3...............	As 1 but lighter Beige body, press-fit wheels	**£3-5** ☐
	1992	'DRAMBUIE'	1...............	Black body, Gold 12-spoke wheels, Red/Gold logo, heraldic shield on doors.............	**£6-8** ☐

Y22-1

FORD MODEL 'A' VAN .... Developed from the Y21-1 Woody Wagon, the model features an all metal van body with spare wheel on nearside. Scale 1:40.

1982	'OXO'	1	Red body & seats, Black smooth roof & wings, Chrome 24-spoke wheels	£70-80 □
		2	As version 1 but with Fawn seats	£6-8 □
		3	As 2 but raised edge to cab roof, Chrome 12-spoke wheels	£8-10 □
		4	As version 2 but with gloss Black roof	£12-14 □
		5	As 4 but 'MATCHBOX' on base instead of 'LESNEY'	£6-8 □
1984	'MAGGI SOUPS'	1	Yellow body, Black chassis, Red van roof, Chrome 24-spoke wheels, short 'Suppen & Speisen' logo, 'LESNEY' or 'MATCHBOX 1981' on base	£30-40 □
		2	As 1 but long 'Suppen & Speisen', 'LESNEY' on base, Chrome 24-spoke or Red 12-spoke wheels	£20-25 □
		3	As version 2 but with 'MATCHBOX 1981' on base	£6-8 □
1984	'TOBLERONE'	1	Beige body, Dark Brown wings, Red roof, Chrome 24-spoke wheels	£6-8 □
		2	As version 1 but with projecting edge on van roof	£3-5 □
1984	'PALM TOFFEE'	1	Off-White main body, Red wings and roof, Gold 24-spoke wheels, Black tyres	£3-5 □
1984	'POSTES CANADA POST	1	Red body, Black wings, special 'limited edition' box with English & French wording for issue in Canada.	£6-8 □
		2	As version 1 but packed in standard UK box	£3-5 □
1986	'SPRATTS'	1	Reddish-Brown body, Dark Brown wings, White roof, Chrome 24-spoke wheels	£3-5 □
1987	'LYONS TEA'	1	Dark Blue body, Black wings, White roof, Chrome 12-spoke wheels	£3-5 □
		2	As version 1 but with Light Gold wheels	£35-45 □
		3	As 1 but with bright Red 12-spoke wheels	£3-5 □
		4	As 1 but with press-fit wheels	£10-12 □
1989	'CHERRY BLOSSOM'	1	White body, Black roof & wings, Red wheels, 'MADE IN MACAU'	£3-5 □
		2	As 1 but 'MADE IN CHINA' on base which has cast screw-hole	£40-60 □
Y22-i	1991	'PRATTS OIL'	White body, Orange wheels, Black roof, 'Anglo-American Oil Co'	£3-5 □

Y23-1

1922 AEC OMNIBUS .... The model features a metal lower body, with a plastic staircase, upper deck, seats, safety bars and 12-spoke wheels on smooth black tyres. Scale 1:72.

1983	'SCHWEPPES'	1	Red main body and wheels, Black lower body, Dark, Mid or Light Brown seats and safety bars. Logo in Red on White label with round ends, Chrome grille	£120-130 □
		2	As version 1 but with Black and White label	£3-5 □
		3	As 2 but safety bars on 3 are mid-Brown, Light Brown on 4	£3-5 □
		4	As 3 but Red upper deck/single rail, White/Black logo on Yellow label	£3-5 □
		5	As version 4 but with unplated radiator surround	£8-10 □
1985	'R.A.C.'	Red main body, Black wings & chassis, Blue/White label, Chrome grille	£3-5 □
1985	'MAPLES'	Red main body, Black wings & chassis, (part of 'Fathers Day' gift set)	GSP □
1986	'HAIG'	1	Dark Brown lower body, Brown seats, Dark Red wheels	£3-5 □
		2	As version 1 but with Tan seats	£3-5 □
		3	As versions 1 & 2 but with Light Red wheels	£3-5 □
1988	'RICE KRISPIES	Red body, Black chassis, Gold 'GENERAL', 'KELLOGGS' logo on White panel	£3-5 □
1989	'LIFEBUOY SOAP'	1	Dark Blue/Cream body, Gold 'EAST SURREY' logo, 'COPTWORNE' destination	£3-5 □
		2	As version 1 but 'COPTHORNE' on destination board	£10-12 □

Y23-2

MACK BULLDOG TANKER .. A substantial model in 1:60 scale.

1989	'TEXACO'	1	Red body & wheels (12 mm. hub design at front), Black base	£15-20 □
		2	As 1 but 10 mm. hub design & larger centre recess in front wheels	£3-5 □
Y23-C	1991	'CONOCO'	Red body & wheels, White tank, Red logo, Black underframe	£3-5 □

Y24-1

1928 BUGATTI T44 .... One of the largest cars ever made, modelled in 1:72 scale.

1983		1	Black body, Yellow panels, Chrome 24-spoke wheels, Tan or Brown seats	£3-5 □
		2	As 1 but with Green or White seats	£100-150 □
		3	As 1 but rear number plate joined to mudguards	£6-8 □
1984		4	As 3 but with Pale Yellow panels with Black bar above handles	£6-8 □
		5	As version 4 but with White seats	£60-80 □
		6	As version 4 but with Black seats	£40-50 □
		7	As 6 but with Chrome 12-spoke wheels on Black tyres	£80-90 □
1987		8	Light Grey body, Red wings and chassis, Chrome solid wheels, Black tyres	£3-5 □
1990		9	Black body, Maroon panels, Chrome 24-spoke wheels, White-wall flanges	£3-5 □
		10	As version 9 but with Dark Red panels	£3-5 □
		11	As version 10 but with press-fit wheels	£3-5 □

Y25-1

1910 RENAULT 'AG' VAN ...... The model is in a scale of 1:38 and features an open cab with side mounted spare tyre.

1983	'PERRIER'	1	Two tone Green body, White seats & roof with 3 rear struts, raised sidelamp lens, open grab handles	£225-275 □
		2	As 1 but 4 struts at rear of roof rack	£3-5 □
		3	As version 2 but with Red seats	£6-8 □
		4	As 2 but with flat sidelamp lens	£3-5 □
1985		5	As 2 but with closed grab handles	£3-5 □
1985	'JAMES NEALE'	1	Yellow body & wheels, Blue chassis, White roof, 'closed' grab handles	£20-25 □
		2	As 1 but hole in right side of cab floor	£20-25 □
		3	As version 1 but with 'open' grab handles	£45-55 □
		4	As 3 but with hole in right side of cab floor	£45-55 □

Ref. No.	Year(s)	Model Type	*Matchbox Models of Yesteryear – continued*	Market Price Range	
		5............	As version 1 but with Navy Blue chassis and mudguards	£45-55	☐
		6............	As version 5 with 'open' grab handles..	£60-70	☐
	1985	'DUCKHAMS OILS'	Only available in 'Fathers Day' Gift Set (40,000 made).		
		1............	Metallic Silver body, Blue chassis, Red wheels, 'open' grab handles	GSP	☐
		2............	As version 1 but with 'closed' grab handles	£60-70	☐
	1985	'EAGLE PENCILS' 1	Light Blue body, Dark Blue wings/chassis, White roof, 'open' grab handles	NRP	☐
		2............	As version 1 but with 'closed' grab handles	£60-70	☐
		3............	As 1 but logos printed lighter, '1986' on base	£3-5	☐
		4............	As version 3 but with '1983' on base	£3-5	☐
	1986	'AMBULANCE'	Unique version of Y25 as a Special Limited Edition.		
		1............	Military-Green body & wheels, Black chassis, 'LIMITED EDITION' on base	£6-8	☐
		2............	As 1 but without 'LIMITED EDITION' on base	£6-8	☐
	1987	'TUNNOCKS' 1	Red body, Black chassis, seats and 12-spoke wheels, White roof, 'MATCHBOX 1986' on base, open grab handles, Brass trim	£8-10	☐
		2............	As 1 but with 'MATCHBOX 1986' on base	£3-5	☐
		3............	As version 1 but with Silver and Brass trim	£3-5	☐
		4............	As 2 but with Gold 12-spoke wheels	£40-60	☐
		5............	As 2 but with closed grab handles	£6-8	☐
	1987	'DELHAIZE' 1	Dark green body, White roof, Light Grey van sides with Gold logo...........	£10-15	☐
		2............	As 1 but with strengthened number plate braces	£3-5	☐
	1989	'SUCHARD CHOCOLATE'....	Lilac/White body, Brass trim, 'St.Bernard dog' design	£3-5	☐
Y26-1		**CROSSLEY DELIVERY TRUCK**	The model features a metal body with a plastic cab canopy and a plastic 3-barrel load. Note that the canopies and loads are easily interchangeable. Scale 1:47		
	1984	'LOWENBRAU' 1	Blue body, Tan canopy, 'RENAULT No.Y25 1983' on base, mid-Brown barrels.......	£60-75	☐
		2............	As 1 but baseplate reads: 'CROSSLEY No.Y13 1973'.	£40-50	☐
		3............	As 1 but baseplate reads:'CROSSLEY No.Y13/Y26 1973'	£3-5	☐
		4............	As version 3 but canopy in light Tan plastic.	£3-5	☐
	1986		5............ As 3 but Light Cream canopy and very Dark Brown barrels	£3-5	☐
	1986	'ROMFORD BREWERY' 1....	Black body & canopy, Brown chassis, Brass wheels, Brown seats	£3-5	☐
		2............	As version 1 but with Ruby Red seats	£8-10	☐
	1987	'GONZALEZ BYASS' 1	White body, Red wings & canopy, no 'SHERRY' on barrels, Brass wheels	£3-5	☐
		2............	As 1 but with 'SHERRY' in White on barrel sides	£3-5	☐
		3............	As version 2 but with Chrome 12-spoke wheels...	£3-5	☐
Y27-1		**1922 FODEN STEAM LORRY**	A popular model in 1:72 scale featuring a metal main body with a plastic tilt, cab roof & solid-tyred wheels, Black smoke-box with Gold chimney.		
	1984	'PICKFORDS' 1	Blue body, Red chassis & wheels, light Grey roof & tilt, baseplate reads: 'MATCHBOX INT'L LTD (C) 1984', truck body butted up to cab.	£20-25	☐
		2............	As 1 but front edge of truck body intrudes onto cab sides and ends 5 mm. from bottom of cab panel	£60-70	☐
		3............	As 2 but truck body extends to bottom of cab panel	£6-8	☐
		4............	As 3 but with Dark Grey cab roof & tilt	£6-8	☐
	1987		5............ As 4 but baseplate reads: 'MATCHBOX INT'L LTD (C) 1986'...............................	£6-8	☐
		6............	As 5 but with 'LIMITED EDITION' cast into shank of towing hook	£10-12	☐
		7............	As version 6 but with Dark Grey roof & tilt...	£10-12	☐
		8............	As version 5 but with Dark Grey roof & tilt...	£6-8	☐
		9............	As 5 or 8 but rivet without tow hook	£50-60	☐
	1985	'HOVIS'	Dark Brown truck body, Black lower body, Light Brown cab roof & canopy............	£5-8	☐
	1986	'TATE & LYLE'S' 1	Light Brown body, thick side panel dividing strut (under letter 'E' of 'TATE')...........	£17-24	☐
		2............	As 1 but with thinner strut giving a smoother side panel	£3-5	☐
	1986	'FRASERS'	Dark Green truck & trailer bodies, White tilts & cab roof, Red chassis. Special Limited Edition, box 'stretched' to accommodate trailer..	£15-25	☐
	1987	'SPILLERS' 1	Pale Cream body, Dark Green panels & chassis, Red wheels, Cream sack load	£3-5	☐
		2............	As 1 but tow-hook rivet is in centre of rear diagonal crossmembers	£15-20	☐
		3............	As version 1 but Mid-Green body panels...	£3-5	☐
	1989	'GUINNESS'...........................	Dark Blue lorry, Black roof & chassis, Red wheels, 5 barrels. (Also a PRM)............	£10-12	☐
	1990	'JOSEPH RANK' 1	Dark Green body, Brown chassis & cab roof, 2 holes cast in truck floor	£40-50	☐
		2............	As 1 but without holes in truck floor, Dark Brown cab roof..............................	£20-25	☐
		3............	As 2 but wheels have closed ended hubs (axle ends not visible)...........................	£3-5	☐
		4............	As version 3 but with Brown cab roof...	£3-5	☐
		5............	As 3 but with Dark Tan chassis, mudguards and water tank	£15-20	☐
	1992	'McMULLEN & SONS'	Black body, Red chassis & wheels, Gold logos, 5 barrels..	£15-20	☐
Y28-1		**1907 UNIC TAX**	The model is in 1:42 scale and features a metal body with a plastic roof, 12-spoke wheels, spare tyre attached to handbrake/gear lever casting.		
	1984		1............ Dark Red body, Black wings & roof, Red wheels, Tan seats, plastic meter	£3-5	☐
		2............	As 1 but with canopy securing pins at rear of body, metal meter..........................	£3-5	☐
		3............	As 2 but Dark Red or Maroon wheels...	£3-5	☐
	1987		4............ Dark Blue body, Black chassis and roof, Maroon wheels......................................	£3-5	☐
		5............	As version 4 but with Dark Red or Chrome 12-spoke wheels................................	£3-5	☐
Y28-C	1991		6............ White body, Black wings, roof, coachlining & 'LONDON', Brass 12-spoke wheels	£3-5	☐

Y29-1 — 1919 WALKER ELECTRIC VAN

The model has a metal body, plastic canopy/tilt, solid wheels. Scale 1:51.

1985	'HARRODS'	Olive-Green body, Cream canopy/tilt, Gold logo, smooth Black tyres, special Olive-Green version of standard box	£3-5 ☐
1986	'JOSEPH LUCAS'	Bright Green body and canopy/tilt, Red solid wheels, White logo	£3-5 ☐
1988	'HIS MASTERS VOICE'	(1) Dark Blue body and wheels, Grey canopy/tilt, 'Nipper' logo	£3-5 ☐
1989	'HARRODS' 1	Olive-Green, Pale Yellow panels, 'SPECIAL BREAD DELIVERY', Green box	£3-5 ☐
	2	As 1 but brighter Yellow panels, Green box	£3-5 ☐

Y30-1 — 1920 MACK TRUCK

Metal body, plastic chassis, roof and 5-spoke wheels. Scale 1:60.

1985	'ACORN STORAGE Co' 1	Blue main body, Grey cab and van roof, Dark Blue chassis & mudguards, Red seats, '1984 MADE IN ENGLAND' on baseplate	£3-5 ☐
	2	As 1 (Dark Blue chassis) but with Grey mudguards and cab steps	£14-17 ☐
	3	As 1 but with '1985 MADE IN ENGLAND' on baseplate	£14-17 ☐
	4	As 3 but with small retaining lug under roof front	£3-5 ☐
	5	Pale Grey body, Dark Grey van roof, '1985 MADE IN MACAU' on base	NGPP ☐
1985	'CONSOLIDATED' 1	Yellow body, Dark Brown chassis & mudguards, Tan canopy, Red wheels	£3-5 ☐
	2	As version 1 but Olive-Green canopy	£40-60 ☐
1987	'ARCTIC ICE CREAM'	Cream body & wheels, Dark Green chassis & mudguards, Beige roof	£3-5 ☐
1988	'KIWI POLISH' 1	Red body, Beige roof, very Dark Brown 'kiwi' design & logo coachlines	£3-5 ☐
	2	As 1 but with Light or Mid-Brown 'kiwi' design & logo coachlines	£3-5 ☐

Y31-1 — 1931 MORRIS COURIER VAN

A large van modelled in 1:59 scale without window glazing.

1990	'KEMPS BISCUITS' 1	Red body & wheels, Black mudguards, White roof, Gold design	£60-80 ☐
	2	Lighter Red body, horizontal body lines are 2 mm. short of vertical lines	£3-5 ☐
1992	'WEETABIX' 1	Yellow body, Black mudguards & bumper, Red wheels, Chrome radiator	£3-5 ☐

Y32-1 — YORKSHIRE STEAM WAGON

Based on Y8-5 (without tilt), and presented as a brewery vehicle. Scale 1:54.

1990	'SAMUEL SMITH' 1	Maroon body, White roof and 6-spoke wheels, 5 Brown barrels, 'Y8' on base	£5-7 ☐
	2	As version 1 but with Cream cab roof	£5-7 ☐
	3	As version 1 but with 'Y32' on base	£3-5 ☐
	4	As version 3 but with Cream cab roof	£3-5 ☐

Y33-1 — 1920 MACK AC TRUCK

A version of Y30-1 with doors and pneumatic tyres. Scale 1:60.

1990	'GOODYEAR' 1	Cambridge Blue body, Aqua Blue wheels, Dark Blue chassis, Grey roof	£40-60 ☐
	2	As version 1 but Aqua Blue body and wheels	£5-7 ☐

Y34-1 — 1990 — 1933 CADILLAC V-16

A magnificent car modelled in 1:46 scale with generous detailing.

	1	Navy Blue body, White hood, Light Olive-Green steering wheel, Chrome wheels	£40-60 ☐
	2	As version 1 but with Cream hood	£3-5 ☐
	3	As version 2 but with Brown steering wheel	£6-8 ☐
	4	White body, Navy Blue chassis, Black hood, Chrome wheels, White-wall flanges	£3-5 ☐

Y35-1 — 1930 FORD 'A' PICK-UP

Y7 and Y22 components provide the basis for this model in 1:40 scale.

1990	'W. CLIFFORD & SONS' 1	White/Black body, 5 milk-churns, Yellow wheels, 'Fresh Farm Milk' & logo in Red	£3-5 ☐
	2	As 1 but 'Fresh Farm Milk' and oval logos in Orange	NGPP ☐
1992	'AMBROSIA'	Blue/Cream body, 'From our Devon Creamery' logo	£10-12 ☐

Y36-1 — 1990 — 1936 ROLLS-ROYCE PHANTOM I

A 1:46 scale model based on a car once owned by Rudyard Kipling.

	1	Red body, Black roof, Chrome disc wheels, 'MADE IN CHINA' on base	£3-5 ☐
1992	2	As 1 but with Blue body, Black chassis & roof	£3-5 ☐

Y37-1 — 1931 GARRETT STEAM WAGON

Unusual steam wagon with vertical boiler, modelled in 1:59 scale.

1990	'CHUBB'S SAFE DEPOSITS'	Pale Blue body & wheels, White roof, 'MADE IN MACAU' on base	£6-8 ☐
1992	'MILKMAID'	Black cab & chassis, Pale Yellow sides to Cream box body, Red wheels	£15-20 ☐

Y38-1 — 1990 — 1920 ROLLS-ROYCE ARMOURED CAR

A Special Limited Edition model in 1:48 scale

	1	Light 'desert sand' body, Black gun, RAF roundels, 'HMAC AJAX'	£8-10 ☐
	2	As 1 but darker shade of 'desert sand' finish	£8-10 ☐

Y39-1 — 1990 — 1820 PASSENGER COACH

'York To London'. A Special Limited Edition model in 1:43 scale.

	1	Black body, Red doors, chassis & wheels, 4 diecast horses, 6 plastic figures	£18-25 ☐

Y40-1 — 1991 — 1931 MERCEDES-BENZ 770

A massive car (weighing more than 3 tonnes), modelled in 1:48 scale.

	1	Grey body, Blue hood, Chrome solid wheels with 2 spares, Maroon seats	£3-5 ☐

Y41-1 — 1932 MERCEDES L5 LORRY

A development from Y6-5 with the addition of a load. Scale 1:69.

1991	'HOWALDTSWERKE' 1	Olive-Green body, Grey roof & load, matt Silver radiator surround	£20-25 ☐
	2	As version 1 but with Chrome radiator surround	£3-7 ☐

Y42-1
1939 ALBION 10 ton CX27 ...... A 6-wheel heavy goods vehicle in a scale of 1:60.

1991   **'LIBBY'S'**   1 .... White cab, Blue flat-bed & wheels, 28 milk-churns, matt Silver radiator surround ...... **£8-10** ☐
  2 .... As version 1 but with Chrome radiator surround .... **£8-10** ☐

Y43-1   1991
1905 BUSCH STEAM FIRE ENGINE   1 .... Black body, Red wheels, 5 firemen, Special Edition model, scale 1:43 .... **£25-35** ☐
  2 .... As 1 but with Copper pipes and collars .... **£90-100** ☐

Y44-1   1991
1910 RENAULT T45 BUS   1 .. Yellow body, Black roof & wings, Red wheels, scale 1:38 .... **£8-10** ☐
  2 .... Same but bright Red roof (Est. 1,100 UK, 800 elswhere in Europe) .... **£70-90** ☐

Y45-1   1991
1930 BUGATTI ROYALE .... Black body with Blue bonnet sides, Chrome disc wheels, scale 1:46 .... **NRP** ☐

Y46-1   1991
1868 MERRYWEATHER FIRE ENGINE .... Red body & wheels, 3 firemen, 2 White horses, Special Edition model, scale 1:43 ...... **£25-30** ☐

Y47-A
1929 MORRIS COWLEY VAN .... Similar to Y19-2, but without the oval side windows. Scale 1:39.

1991   **'CHOCOLAT LINDT'** .... Black body, Yellow roof and logo, Chrome 12-spoke wheels .... **NRP** ☐

Y61   1992
1933 CADILLAC FIRE ENGINE .... Use of Y34 components has produced this Swiss fire appliance in 1:46 scale. Red body, Brown ladders on roof, *'Feuerweht Aarau'* logo on doors .... **£8-10** ☐

Y62   1992
1932 FORD 'AA' TRUCK .... A lorry developed from the Ford Model 'A' car, modelled in 1:46 scale. Lime Green body, Black chassis, Grey roof, Red wheels, Brown sack load .... **£10-12** ☐

Y63
1939 BEDFORD 'KD' TRUCK .... A popular subject presented in 1:46 scale.

1992   **'GEORGE FARRAR'** .... Red cab, Black chassis, Brown truck body, real stone load .... **£25-30** ☐

Y64   1992
1938 LINCOLN ZEPHYR .... A stylish car with a V12 4.4 litre engine, modelled in 1:43 scale. Off-White body, Brown seats, Cream folded hood & steering wheel .... **£8-10** ☐

Y65   1992
1928 AUSTIN 7 (Set) .... A Special Limited Edition Set comprising Austin 7 Van (Red body, 'CASTROL'), BMW Dixi 3/15 (Blue body, Black roof), ROSENGART 3-seater Tourer (White body). All three have Black chassis, Tan seats and Chrome wheels. Scale 1:43 .... **£25-30** ☐

Y66   1992
H.M. QUEEN ELIZABETH'S GOLD STATE COACH .... A Special Limited Edition model in 1:100 scale. Gold body and wheels, 8 Grey horses (4 with Red jacketed riders with Black boots and hats) Brown drawbar .... **£16-20** ☐

Models of Yesteryear   -   New Entries

Matchbox Collectibles

In 1993 Matchbox collectibles was launched to bring nostalgic die-cast Yesteryear models direct to adult collectors. The first models of all the new collection celebrated the most French of French vehicles, the Citroen, it's van affectionately known as the 'tin shed on wheels'. Available direct from Matchbox Collectibles and through a selected number of specialist collectibles centres.

HOW TO OBTAIN MATCHBOX COLLECTIBLES
Contact: Matchbox Collectibles (UK) Ltd, P.O. Box 35, Swift Park, Rugby, Warwickshire, CV21 1BR.

TASTE OF FRANCE SERIES issued 1993, 1947 Citroen Type H Van **£12-15**
YTF01 'EVIAN MINERAL WATER'
YTF02 'MARTELL COGNAC'
YTF03 'YOPLAIT YOGHURT'
YTF04 'MARCILLAT BRIE'
YTF05 'TAITTINGER CHAMPAGNE'
YTF06 'POMMERY MUSTARD'
YTF501 Two models set on wooden plinth **£24-27**

GREAT BEERS OF THE WORLD SERIES issued 1993/1994 **£9.95 each**
YGB01 1930 Ford A Van
YGB02 1926 TT Ford, "Becks" (Germany)
YGB03 1918 Atkinson Steam, "Swan" (Australia)
YGB04 1929 Morris Van, "Fullers" (England)
YGB05 1932 Ford AA Van, "Carlsberg" (Denmark)
YGB06 1932 Mercedes Truck, "Holsten" (Germany)
YGB07 1910 Renault Type AG Van,s "Kronenbourg" (France)
YGB08 1957 GMC Van, "Steinlager" (New Zealand)
YGB09 1920 Mack AC, "Moosehead" (Canada)

YGB10 1927 Talbot Van, "South Pacific" (New Guinea)
YGB11 1922 Foden Stream Wagon, "Whitbread" (England)
YGB12 1917 Yorkshire Steam Wagon, "Lowenbrau" (Germany)
YBG501 Twin model issue on Plinth **£25-28**

1995 'BEERS OF THE WORLD' ISSUES (YGB) £13-18
Ford AA 'CORONA'
Model T 'KIRIN'
Mercedes Lorry 'HENNINGER'
Morris 'CASCADE'
Garrett Steam 'FLOWERS'
Ford TT 'ANCHOR STEAM'
No other details available at time of going to print.

HORSE DRAWN CARRIAGE SERIES issued 1994 **£33-38**
YSH1 1900 Gypsy Caravan, 180 mm.
YSH2 1886 London Omnibus, 160 mm.
YSH3 1875 Wells Fargo Stage Coach, 200 mm.

THE GRAND CLASSICS COLLECTION issued 1994 **£12-15**
Y1-3 1936 SS Jaguar, Red with Black folded down hood
Y2-4 1930 Supercharged 4½ Litre Bentley, Dark Blue
Y4-4 1930 Duesenberg Model J Town Car. Two-tone Blue with Cream hood
Y34-1 1933 Cadillac 452 V16 Town Car, White with Black hood
Y36-1 1925 Rolls Royce Phantom 1, Red body, Black wings and roof (As below)
Y40-1 1931 Mercedes Benz 770, Grey body with Blue hood
Y45-1 1930 Bugatti Royale, Black/Royal Blue body

FIRE ENGINE SERIES issued 1994/95 **£18-20**
1 1932 Ford AA Fire Engine
2 1933 Cadillac V16 Fire Wagon
3 1920 Mack Fire Engine
4 1932 Mercedes Benz Ladder Truck
5 1939 Bedford Tanker Truck
6 1952 Land Rover Auxilliary

YY901 Petwer Jaguar on wooden base, issued 1994 .... **£26-29**
YCC01 CHRISTMAS TREASURES SET issued 1994
Four 1938 Austin 7 models in Christmas '1994' liveries of Red, Green, White/Blue and Blue **£18-20**

CLASSIC FIREFIGHTERS SERIES issued 1995
1880 Merryweather "Greenwich" Steam Fire Engine, 150 mm. **£39-42**
1905 Busch Self Propelled Fire Engine, 120 mm. **£39-42**

POWER OF THE PRESS SERIES issued 1995 YPP01-YPP08 **£13-15**
1 1948 Dodge RT Van 'NEW YORK TIMES' (USA)
2 1910 Renault Type AG Van 'LE FIGARO' (France)
3 1932 Mercedes Benz L5 Truck 'MORGENPOST' (Germany)
4 1935 Morris Courier 'THE TIMES' (Great Britain)
5 1932 Ford 'AA' 1½ Ton Truck 'LOS ANGELES TIMES' (USA)
6 1930 Ford Model 'A' Van 'WASHINGTON Post' (USA)
7 1923 AC Mack Truck 'PRAVDA' (Russia)
8 1937 GMC Van 'THE AUSTRALIAN' (Australia)

YSFE01 Legendary Fire Fighter Ahrens-Fox Quad, mounted on plinth **£60-65**

LATE 1995 RELEASE:- **THE KING OF THE AGE OF STEAM** 'THE 1925 CRESCENT LIMITED', HO Scale (1:87.1) 'PACIFIC TYPE' Locomotive and Tender. An authentic replica of a deluxe Pullman 4-6-2 locomotive which ran between Washington D.C. and New Orleans. Meticulously painted in lush 'Virginia Green' with highlights of white, brown and bright red. Gold trim and brass fittings. Fully operational. Comes with hardwood display base and certificate of authenticity. Price **£145 plus P&P**.

Models of Yesteryear - Gift Sets

Ref. No.	Year(s)	Set Name	Contents	Market Price Range	
G 6	1960	Gift Set	Contains Nos 1, 2, 5, 10 & 13	£325-375	☐
G 7	1960	Gift Set	Contains Nos 3, 8, 9, 12 & 14	£325-375	☐
G 6	1962	Veteran & Vintage Car Set	Contains Nos 5, 6, 7, 15 & 16	£325-375	☐
G 7	1962	Gift Set	Contains Nos 3, 4, 11, 12 & 13	£450-500	☐
G 7	1965	Veteran & Vintage Set	Contains Y2, Y5, Y10, Y15, Y16	£100-125	☐
G 7	1966	Gift Set	Contains Y1-2 Model T Ford, Y3-2 Benz, Y11-2 Packard, Y14-2 Maxwell	£75-100	☐
G 5	1968	Gift Set	Contains Y4-3 Opel White, Y6-3 Cadillac, Y9-2 Simplex Yellow Green, Y9-2 Simplex Green	£55-65	☐
G 5	1970-72	Gift Set	Contains Y8-3 Stutz Red, Y14 Maxwell, Y16-1 Spyker (Dark Yellow) Y7-3 Rolls Royce Silver and Red	£45-55	☐
Y-50	1982	Gift Set	Contains Y3-4 'BP' Tanker, Y5-4 Talbot Van 'Chivers', Y10-3 Rolls Royce, Y12-3 Model T Van, Y13-3 Crossley Coal Lorry	£35-40	☐
	1984	Connoisseurs Collection	Contains Y1-2 Black 1911 Model 'T' Ford. Y4-3 Red/Beige 1909 Opel. Y3-2 Blue/Black 1910 Benz Limousine, Y11-2 White/Black 1912 Packard Landaulet, Y13-2 Blue 1911 Daimler, Y14-2 Beige/Black 1911 Maxwell. 30,000 certificated & numbered sets issued in beechwood display case	£65-85	☐
	1985	'Fathers Day' Set	Y11-3 Red Lagonda, Y23-1 'MAPLES' Bus, Y25-1 Renault Van 'DUCKHAMS'	£15-18	☐
	1987	30 years Set (A)	Y6-4 Rolls Royce Fire Engine, Y25-1 'Eagle Pencils', Y29-1 'Harrods'	£15-20	☐
	1987	30 years Set (B)	Y4-4 Blue Duesenberg, Y28-1 Red Unic Taxi, Y29-1 'Harrods' Van	£15-20	☐
	1987	Starter Kit	(5 for 4 Set) Australian Gift Set	£25-30	☐
Y65	1992	**1928 AUSTIN 7 (Set)**	A Special Limited Edition Set comprising Austin 7 Van (Red body, 'CASTROL') BMW Dixi 3/15 (Blue body, Black roof) ROSENGART 3-seater Tourer (White body). All three have Black chassis, Tan seats and Chrome wheels. Scale 1:43	£25-30	☐

Models of Yesteryear 'Code 2' models

A system of categorising models has evolved among collectors to distinguish between authentic manufacturers output and acceptable but unauthorised alteration of their models for later resale. The explanation which follows refers to a coding system adopted generally (but not officially) throughout the model collecting fraternity in the UK and elswhere, and may be applied to models produced by any manufacturer.

CODE 1 Applies to models which have been originated and totally produced by an established manufacturer.
CODE 2 As CODE 1 but labelled or finished outside the factory WITH the manufacturer's permission.
CODE 3 Same as CODE 2 but model re-labelled, altered or re-worked WITHOUT authorization or permission from the manufacturer.

Ref. No.	Year(s)	Model Type	Model Features and Size	Market Price Range	
Y1-2	1976	**1911 MODEL 'T' FORD CAR**	Black body, textured roof, grille and seats, Chrome 12-spoke wheels, brass trim, bare windscreen frame. 900 models made for the USA.	£300-400	☐
Y5-4		**1927 TALBOT VAN**	With 12-spoke wheels and Chrome trim.		
	1978	'2nd A.I.M. CONVENTION'	Dark Green body & wheels, *'Toy Show, Harrisburgh PA. May 27, 28 1978'*.	£80-100	☐
	1981	'CRAWLEY SWAPMEET 1981'	Royal Blue body, Black roof & chassis, *'Follow Us To Crawley'*	£130-150	☐

Ref. No.	Year(s)	Model Type	Description	Market Price Range	
	1981	'VARIETY CLUB' 1	Yellow body & chassis, Black roof, Red wheels, *'Sunshine Coach Appeal'*	£180-200	☐
		2	As 1 but with Black chassis, mudguards and running boards	£180-200	☐
	1980	'MERITA BREAD'	Yellow body, Black roof, Red wheels, *'Old Fashioned Enriched Bread'*	£40-50	☐
	1980	'LANGENDORF'	Yellow body, Black roof, Red wheels, *'Old Fashioned Enriched Bread'*	£40-50	☐
	1980	'TAYSTEE BREAD'	Yellow body, Black roof, Red wheels and Pale Yellow *'Taystee'* on Red oval	£60-80	☐
	1981	'IRONBRIDGE' 1	Yellow body, matt Black roof, Red wheels, *'The Worlds First Iron Bridge'*	£150-175	☐
		2	As 1 with gloss Black chassis and mudguards	£140-160	☐
	1981	'BEES' 1	Yellow body, Black roof, Red wheels, White-wall tyres, *'Bees Art & Model Service'*	£85-100	☐
		2	As 1 but Black chassis & mudguards	£85-100	☐
		3	As 1 but with plain tyres	£85-100	☐
	1981	'DUTCH MATCHBOX MEET'	Blue & Grey body, Black roof & chassis, *'Stoevclaar'*, with Certificate	£200-250	☐
		'LAWRENCE FRASER TOYS'	Blue body, Black roof and wings, Pale Blue/White logo	£300-400	☐
Y7-3	1982	**1912 ROLLS-ROYCE**	Celebrating the wedding of Prince Charles and Princess Diana		
			Bright Yellow body, Black roof & chassis, Red wheels, *'Duchy Of Cornwall'*	£140-180	☐
Y12-3		**FORD MODEL 'T' VAN**			
	1981	'BANG & OLUFSEN'	White body, Red bonnet, Black roof & chassis, with certificate	£300-400	☐
	1981	'RAYLEIGH SWAPMEET'	Yellow body, Black roof, *'Model Collectors Extravaganza'*	£75-90	☐
	1982	'CADA TOYS'	Yellow body, Black chassis, roof & side panels, *'Cada Toys Have Moved'*	£160-180	☐
	1982	'DEANS of LEEDS'	Yellow body, Black roof, Red *'Deans for Toys'*, telephone no. on some	£100-130	☐
	1980	'CAMBERLEY NEWS'	Yellow body, Black roof, *'75th Anniversary'*, 750 made	£120-140	☐
	1983	'HOOVER' 1	Blue body, White roof, Black chassis, WITH CERTIFICATE	£600-800	☐
		2	As version 1 but without certificate	£300-350	☐
Y13-3		**1918 CROSSLEY**			
	1979	'U.K. MATCHBOX CLUB'	Red body & wheels, Yellow tilt & canopy, *'800 Members'*	£175-225	☐
	1981	'ASPECTS and IMAGES'	Red body & wheels, Light Brown tilt & canopy	£140-160	☐
	1981	'SURREY MODEL FAIR'	Red body, Grey cover, *'Tangley Model Workshop'*	£140-160	☐
Y21-5	1992	**1926 FORD 'TT' VAN** 'ANTIQUES ROADSHOW'	Black body, Gold 12-spoke wheels, *'The Next Generation - BBC'*	£600-1000	☐
	1992	'MODELS of AUSTRALIA ART SET'	2 models. 1: Royal Blue body, 'Jenny Kee' and face logos (multicoloured one side, Gold outline other side). 2: Dark Green body, 'Pro Hart' and insect design (multicoloured one side, Gold outline other side). 1,000 numbered sets, special box	£600-800	☐
Y47-A		**1929 MORRIS VAN**			
	1991	'ANTIQUES ROADSHOW'	Black body, Yellow roof, Chrome 12-spoke wheels, *'Going Live - BBC Television'*	£600-1000	☐

1990 USA Enhanced Models ('Great Motor Cars of the Century')

Because of the poor wholesale distribution in the USA and a consequent lack of market penetration, a series of twelve models was offered direct to the public via Matchbox Collectibles.

The models were enhanced by giving them detailed dashboards, number plates and rear lights plus mask-sprayed trim and authentic colours. They were issued in white cardboard boxes with black printing which had no need of a screw to retain the model. Models destined for the USA therefore did not have a screw hole cast in the base.

The twelve models included two new issues (Rolls Royce Phantom I and Cadillac V16) and ten re-colours: Y4-4 Duesenberg 'J' Town Car, Y20-1 1937 Mercedes 540K, Y-17 Hispano-Suiza, Y19-1 Auburn Speedster, Y18-1 Cord 812, Y24-1 Bugatti Type 44, Y14-3 Stutz Bearcat, Y6-2 Bugatti Type 35, Y16-2 Mercedes Benz SS Coupé, Y2-4 Bentley.

The models were also sold through retail outlets outside the USA but in the standard 'new style red' boxes which required a cast hole in each base for a self-tapping screw. Total production was 25,000 for UK collectors and a similar amount for those elsewhere in the world.

Models of Yesteryear Giftware series

Models specially plated to adorn giftware (e.g. cigarette boxes, ashtrays, penstands, boxes and pipestands). Non-plated versions of the models listed will also be found with the two baseplate holes used for fixing the plated models to the various items.

SILVER PLATED MODELS

Y1-2	1911 Model 'T' Ford	£20-30	☐
Y2-2	1911 Renault 2 seater	£20-30	☐
Y2-3	1914 Prince Henry Vauxhall	£20-30	☐
Y3-3	1934 Riley M.P.H.	£20-30	☐
Y4-3	1909 Opel Coupé	£20-30	☐
Y5-2	1929 4.2 Litre Bentley	£30-40	☐
Y6-2	1926 Type 35 Bugatti	£75-95	☐
Y7-2	1913 Mercer Raceabout	£45-65	☐
Y7-3	1912 Rolls-Royce	£20-30	☐
Y10-2	1928 Mercedes-Benz 36-220	£30-40	☐
Y10-3	1906 Rolls-Royce	£20-30	☐
Y12-2	1909 Thomas Flyabout	£20-30	☐
Y13-2	1911 Daimler	£20-30	☐
Y13-3	1918 Crossley	£175-225	☐
Y14-2	1911 Maxwell Roadster	£15-20	☐
Y15-1	1907 Rolls-Royce Silver Ghost	£15-20	☐

GOLD PLATED MODELS

Y1-2	1911 Model 'T' Ford	£30-40	☐
Y2-3	1914 Prince Henry Vauxhall	£15-20	☐
Y4-3	1909 Opel Coupé	£15-20	☐
Y5-2	1929 4.2 Litre Bentley	£35-40	☐
Y7-2	1913 Mercer Raceabout	£100-120	☐
Y7-3	1912 Rolls-Royce	£15-20	☐
Y10-2	1928 Mercedes-Benz 36-220	£75-95	☐
Y10-3	1906 Rolls-Royce	£20-30	☐
Y12-2	1909 Thomas Flyabout	£20-30	☐
Y13-2	1911 Daimler	£20-30	☐
Y13-3	1918 Crossley	£200-250	☐
Y14-2	1911 Maxwell Roadster	£15-20	☐
Y15-1	1907 Rolls-Royce Silver Ghost	£40-50	☐

Prices for plated models. The market for plated models is quite a small one. Consequently it is difficult to give a more precise or smaller range of likely prices. Some dealers put a high price on plated models when they get them and simply wait till a determined buyer appears even if this takes a long time. Others offer them for sale at a much lower price just to pass them on quickly. The lower prices are usually to be seen at swapmeets. However, in the case of rarer issues, it really is a case of the collector having to pay the price being asked as a similar model may not be seen again for some time.

Gold plated sets:

GOLDEN VETERAN Set with 3 models, Y7-3, Y13-2, Y14-2.. £50-65 ☐
HERITAGE GIFTS with 2 models Y7-3, Y10-3... £35-50 ☐

Models of Yesteryear Game

A rare Furnel Developments Ltd *'THE LONDON TO BRIGHTON VETERAN CAR GAME'* comprising MOY models:- Rolls Royce Silver Ghost, 1904 Spyker. Cards, plastic roadway, die shakers. Issued around 1960's. Game only sold at Mobil Oil Company petrol stations. .... Sold by Christies in 1994 for **£198**

Models of Yesteryear Car Game.
Sold by Christie's, South Kensington in December 1994 for £198.

Matchbox Trade Display Stands

Since the first wooden display stand was issued in the 1950s with the logo *'FROM 1/6 YOUR MATCHBOX TOYS'* a large variety of display units have been released. In the 4th Edition (page 183), a large representation of the 1964 trade display units is shown. All are very scarce and are keenly sought after by collectors. Various pieces are on display in the Chester Toy Museum Matchbox collection. In addition many of the rare early dealer display units are pictured in the excellent book 'Collecting Matchbox Diecast Toys' details of which are at the end of the chapter.

Collectors Passport Scheme 1988 - 1991

In 1987 Matchbox launched a promotional scheme designed to encourage regular purchases from its nationwide 'Appointed Stockists'. MOY collectors were issued with a 'passport' which was stamped each time they purchased a model. The purchase of six normal 1987 issues plus three Special Edition models, qualified the collector to buy a special framed cabinet containing the component parts of the Preston Type Tramcar (in its original standard issue livery). This special framed cabinet was only obtainable under the passport scheme. The scheme continued in 1988-89 and 1989-90 with models Y8-5 and Y5-5 respectively but these were in a livery unique to the promotion (they were not available as standard issues).

In the 1991 continuation of the scheme, Yesteryears were joined by Matchbox Dinky and purchase of either type of model gained a passport stamp. A complete passport now required the purchase of ten standard models plus either of the 1991 Special Editions (Y43 or Y46 Fire Engines). Application could then be made for the 'Exclusive Pewter Model of the 1936 Jaguar SS100' (a re-worked Y1-3 on a wooden plinth).

Y15-3	1987-88	Preston Type Tram Car	'SWAN VESTAS', Red/Cream livery, complete model plus components	£60-75	☐
Y8	1988-89	Yorkshire Steam Wagon	'SAMUEL SMITH'S', Green/Beige livery, complete model plus components	£75-85	☐
Y5	1989-90	1930 Leyland Titan Bus	'SWAN FOUNTPENS', Blue livery, complete model plus components	£45-55	☐
Y1-3	1990-91	1936 Jaguar SS100	Solid pewter (unpainted), body/seats/wheels/tyres, wooden plinth, special box	£25-35	☐

Acknowledgements

The Editor would like to express his thanks to the following collectors/dealers for new information received:-
Hardy Ristau, Germany; Chris Stonor, Collectors Gazette; Gerry Savage, Model & Collectors Mart; R. Boulter, Norfolk; Brad Partridge, Australia; Jim Whitaker, Bamford Toy Museum, Rochdale; John Clarke of Cambridgeshire; Roy Levy of London; Peter Bailey of Warwickshire; Barry Thompson, Gloucs.; Alan Latham, Kent, Bob Scott, Yeovil; Ethan Enzer, New York; Marcus Beagham, London; John Marshall, California; Paul Carr, Carr Collectables. Bob Ewers, Maidenhead; Mr R. Smith, Dover; Ray Holcroft, Lancs.

The Matchbox International Collectors Association (MICA)

M.I.C.A. was founded in 1985 and provides its members with a bi-monthly magazine which is full of useful information about past, present and future issues across the whole Matchbox and 'Dinky Collection' range of products.
All aspects of collecting are included and cover such topics as new releases, variations, past issues and a members advertisement section etc.
Once a year a social convention is held where talks on Matchbox are held and Matchbox auctions take place. A special 'members model' is issued to commemorate the event.

HOW TO JOIN

● THE USA, CANADA, MEXICO and SOUTH AMERICA

The Membership Secretary, PO Box 28072, Waterloo, Ontario, Canada N2L 6JB
Telephone: 519 885-0529

● AUSTRALIA, NEW ZEALAND AND SOUTH PACIFIC

The Membership Secretary, PO Box 1026, Baulkham Hills, NSW 2153, Australia

● UNITED KINGDOM, EUROPE and REST OF THE WORLD

The Membership Secretary, 13a, Lower Bridge Street Row, Chester CH1 1RS.
Telephone: (01244) 346297

Please note that all enquiries requiring a response must contain a stamped self-addressed envelope.

Recommended reading for Matchbox collectors:

'The Yesteryear Book 1956-1993'
Kevin McGimpsey and Stewart Orr, joint editors of the MICA magazine, assisted by several club members have produced the ultimate book for collectors of Models of Yesteryear. It contains 250 pages packed with full details of every variation issued plus superb colour photographs and International model values. Contact Major Productions, 13a, Lower Bridge Street Row, Chester, CH1 1RS.

'Collecting Matchbox Diecast Toys - The First Forty Years'
This important book was published in 1989 and contains chapters on every aspect of Matchbox production since 1947, with MICA members providing much of the technical input. Now out of print.

MORESTONE, MODERN PRODUCTS, BUDGIE and SEEROL

The following history and listings have been provided by Robert Newson.

The history of these makes is a fascinating story of inter-linked companies, take-overs and bankruptcies reflecting the ups and downs of the toy trade. In the late 1940s Morris & Stone was a toy wholesaler selling the products of many small toy manufacturers including those from Modern Products who had started as die-casters. Morris and Stone decided to have their own exclusive 'Morestone' branded lines and some were made by Modern Products, who increasingly relied on Morestone for the sole marketing and distribution of their toys. Morestone continued to use several suppliers but in 1954 set up a die-casting company jointly with Rodney Smith (one of the founders of Lesney Products).

From the mid-1950s to 1966 the Morestone and Budgie ranges contained models that came either from the in-house factory or from Modern Products. Morestone's production expanded with new ranges of models, such as the 'Noddy' and 'Big-Ears' vehicles in 1956 and the Esso Petrol Pump Series of miniatures, launched at Christmas of that year. In 1958, the 'Trucks of the World International Series' was introduced, but only ran to three models.

Some of the earlier Morestone and Modern Products models were re-issued as part of the Budgie range which was introduced in 1959. Model numbers were allocated in 1960 and new additions to the range continued every year up to 1966. During 1961, Morris & Stone was taken over by S. Guiterman & Co. Ltd., who changed the name of their new subsidiary to Budgie Models Ltd. Although the range included many interesting and unusual subjects, they failed to compete with Corgi, Dinky and Matchbox, and losses in Budgie Models Ltd. contributed to losses in the Guiterman group. In March 1966 these companies went into voluntary liquidation.

Modern Products was badly hit by this but eventually were able to set up a new company called Budgie Models (Continuation) Ltd and purchase the Budgie trade mark from the receiver. They wanted the Budgie dies as well, but these were destroyed in a fire while negotiations were in progress. The only dies to survive were those in their own factory. Thus the main range of Budgie commercial vehicles came to an end in 1966.

Modern Products continued to produce the Budgie miniatures, mainly for the USA, until 1969 when the stronger competition this time was from Mattel's 'Hot Wheels'. Modern Products' direction for the 1970s was to produce models for H. Seener Ltd., distributors of toys and souvenirs to London's tourist shops. The old Budgie Routemaster bus was reintroduced for Seener, followed by a new FX4 Taxi and Rolls-Royce Silver Cloud.

In 1983, following the death of one of the partners in Modern Products, the business was sold to a neighbouring engineering company called Starcourt Ltd (some boxes say Merracroft Ltd - an associate company of Starcourt). The new owners reintroduced several models from the original moulds, starting with the Aveling Barford Road Roller. However, a disagreement developed with Seener who withdrew the dies for the Taxi and Rolls-Royce (which he had paid for) and arranged for these to be made by Corgi together with a completely new Routemaster bus. These 'Seerol' models appeared in 1985 and are still available. Starcourt ceased toy production in 1985.

Some unpainted castings for no.204 Volkswagen Pick-Up and some empty boxes were sold to a Dutch firm and have since appeared in various liveries. These are classed as 'Code 3' models and have not been listed. The die-casting moulds were sold to Autocraft (Dave Gilbert) in 1988, and these include most of the 1950s Modern Products and part of the 1960s Budgie range. Autocraft are now in the process of adapting dies for a range of some 35 various models. Only one model has so far been reintroduced - a run of 1000 of no.258 Daimler Ambulance in kit form.

A complete history of these companies and their products is contained in the book 'Budgie Models' by Robert Newson. This hardback book also has full descriptions of all the models, 58 pages of colour photographs illustrating over 180 models, and reproductions of Budgie leaflets.

Morestone and Modern Products

Ref. No.	Year(s)	Model Type	Model Features and Size	Market Price Range	
	c.1946	Racing Car	Red, Dark Blue, Dark Green or Light Brown. One piece casting including driver. No identification on model. 135 mm.	£30-40	☐
	c.1947	Stage Coach with 4 horses	English mail coach with driver and trunk, Yellow body, Red wheels, 173 mm. 'Ye Olde Coach & Four' on box	£100-150	☐
	c.1948-56	Fire Escape (large)	Brass bell and wheel hubs. Base consists of sump and prop shaft only. Extending wheeled escape ladder. 108 mm. (excluding ladder)	£60-80	☐
	c.1950	Fire Escape (smaller)	Plain flat base, wheeled escape ladder, 66 mm. (excluding ladder)	£60-80	☐
	c.1948	Fire Engine	Clockwork motor and bell underneath, 'Morestone Series' cast-in, 135 mm.	£80-90	☐
	c.1948-58	0-6-0 Tank Locomotive	Green or Red, 'British Railways' cast in, re-issued as Budgie 224, 119 mm.	£25-35	☐
	1949-51	Horse Drawn Snack Bar	'SAM'S' cast on side below counter, removable roof, separate man, tea urn and two mugs, 117 mm. Wide range of colours	£65-85	☐
	1949-59	Horse Drawn Hansom Cab	Black/Yellow, driver, elastic band for reins, 118 mm. (re-issued as Budgie 100)	£50-70	☐
	c.1948-61	Horse Drawn Covered Wagon with Four Horses	Green, Red or Orange, driver, cloth canopy plain or printed with 'Thundering Hooves & Blazing Guns on the Western Trail', or 'Walt Disney's Davy Crockett Frontier Wagon' or 'Last of the Mohicans Chingachgook Hawkeye', later with 2 barrels, 'Made in England' cast transversely under, 190 mm. (Budgie 404)	£70-90	☐
	1949	'Wells Fargo' Stage Coach with two 'Galloping' Horses	Brown/Yellow, driver and guard, eccentric wheel for 'galloping' effect, some with 'Copyright F.W. Birch & Co.' cast inside, 164 mm.	£70-90	☐
	c.1950	'Wells Fargo' Stage Coach	Various colours, four horses, driver, 172 mm.	£70-90	☐
	1952-58	Stage Coach with 2 horses	Red or Orange (no lettering), Black plastic horses, wheels, figures, 165 mm.	£70-90	☐
	1954-59	Horse Drawn Covered Wagon with Six Horses	Red, Yellow wheels, printed cloth canopy 'The Wild West Land of Buffalo & Covered Wagon', driver, 2 barrels, 'Made in England' cast transversely under, 265 mm.	£70-90	☐

285

Ref. No.	Year(s)	Model Type	*Morestone and Modern Products – continued*	Market Price Range	
	1950-51	Road Sweeper	'City Cleansing Dept.' cast-in, clockwork motor in some, 91 mm.	**£80-100**	☐
	c.1950	Compressor	With man and pneumatic drill. No identification cast on model. 76 mm.	**£40-50**	☐
	1953	State Landau with 6 horses	Coronation souvenir, 3 figures cast-in. No identification on model. 111 mm.	**£30-40**	☐
	1953	Prime Mover with Trailer	Red prime mover, 'British Road Services', 'NO 311' and 'MAX 20 MPH' cast-in, Black plastic wheels, 83 mm. Orange plastic trailer, 136 mm.	**£100-125**	☐
	1953	Sleigh with Father Xmas	One reindeer. No identification on model. About 140 mm.	**£65-85**	☐
	1953-55	RAC Motorcycle and Sidecar	Cast wheels/tyres & rider, no windscreen, hinged lid on sidecar, 70 mm.	**£75-100**	☐
	1954-55	AA Motorcycle and Sidecar	Cast wheels/tyres & rider, windscreen, non-opening sidecar, separate rails, 70 mm.	**£75-100**	☐
	1956-57	RAC Motorcycle and Sidecar	Cast rider, windscreen, separate rails & hinged lid on sidecar, steering front forks, rubber tyres, plain number plates, 82 mm.	**£75-100**	☐
	1956-57	AA Motorcycle and Sidecar	Cast rider, windscreen, separate rails & hinged lid on sidecar, steering front forks, rubber tyres, plain number plates, 82 mm.	**£75-100**	☐
	1956-57	Solo Motorcycle	Cast rider, steering front forks, rubber tyres, plain number plates, 82 mm. 4 versions: Police Patrol, Despatch Rider, GPO Messenger and TT Rider.	**£50-75**	☐
	1954-55	Horse Drawn Gipsy Caravan	Yellow/Green, tinplate roof and base, separate driver & rear steps, 190 mm.	**£200-250**	☐
	1954-56	Bedford Dormobile	Red or Green body. 90 mm.	**£100-125**	☐
	1955-58	Leyland Double Deck Bus	Route '7', 103 mm. 'Motor Oil - ESSO - Petrol', Red body	**£70-80**	☐
			'Finest Petrol - ESSO - in the World', Red or Green body	**£70-80**	☐
			'ESSO - for Happy Motoring - ESSO', Red body	**£70-80**	☐
	1955-56	Aveling-Barford Road Roller	Green, Yellow or Red, driver, 117 mm. Re-issued as Budgie 701	**£30-40**	☐
	1955-59	Wolseley 6/80 Police Car	Black, loudspeaker, aerial, 113 mm. No maker's name. (Budgie 246)	**£50-60**	☐
1	1955-57	Foden 8-wheel Petrol Tanker	Red body, 'Motor Oil Esso Petrol' transfers, 136 mm.	**£175-200**	☐
2	1955-56	Foden 8-wheel Open Lorry	Light brown cab and chassis, Red truck body, 138 mm.	**£125-150**	☐
3	1955-56	Foden Flat Lorry with chains	Green cab and 8-wheel chassis, Beige flatbed, brass chain, 138 mm.	**£125-150**	☐
4	1955-57	Foden 8-wheel Flat Lorry	Yellow or Orange cab and chassis, Grey flatbed, 138 mm.	**£125-150**	☐
	1956-57	Bedford Car Transporter	Orange cab, Grey trailer, collapsible top deck, 2 loading ramps, 243 mm.	**£75-90**	☐
	1956	Daimler Ambulance	White or Cream body (no transfers), Silver base, opening rear doors, no maker's name, 110 mm. Re-issued as Budgie 258	**£75-90**	☐
	1955-57	AA Land Rover (large)	Yellow/Black, 'AA ROAD SERVICE' cast-in, opening rear doors, driver, passenger, 108 mm.	**£100-125**	☐
	1957-58	AA Land Rover (medium)	Yellow/Black, driver, 79 mm. 'AA ROAD SERVICE' transfers, no rear windows.	**£100-125**	☐
			Same but 'AA ROAD SERVICE' cast-in, two rear windows.	**£100-125**	☐
	1958	Military Police Land Rover	Olive Green, driver, 'MP Military Police' cast on sides, 79 mm.	**£150-200**	☐
	1958	Breakdown Service Land Rover	Red body, driver, 'Breakdown Service Unit' cast on sides, 79 mm.	**£75-100**	☐
	1958	Foden Dumper	Orange cab and chassis, Grey dumper, 108 mm. Re-issued as Budgie 226	**£30-40**	☐

Morestone 'Trucks of the World International Series'

Ref. No.	Year(s)	Model Type		Market Price Range	
	1958	Klöckner Side Tipper	Red cab, Black chassis, Cream tipper, 81 mm. (with 'Driving Licence')	**£40-50**	☐
	1958	Scammell Articulated Tanker	Orange cab, Cream tank. 'LIQUID IN BULK' cast on sides, 114 mm.	**£35-45**	☐
	1958	International Articulated Refrigerator Lorry	Red/Blue cab, Silver trailer, 'COAST to COAST REFRIGERATION' transfers, 153 mm. Re-issued as Budgie 202	**£35-45**	☐

'Noddy' items by Morestone and Budgie

Ref. No.	Year(s)	Model Type	Model Features and Size	Market Price Range	
			The Noddy items were given numbers when incorporated in the Budgie range around 1960.		
301	1956-61	Noddy and his Car (large)	Yellow/Red, windscreen, solid rubber wheels, metal or plastic 'Noddy', 98 mm.	**£100-150**	☐
	1957-58	Big Ears on Bicycle (large)	Red bicycle (64 mm.), metal 'Big Ears' with legs that move as the model is pushed along. No maker's name on model.	**£125-175**	☐
	c.1959	Clown on Bicycle (large)	Metallic Light Brown bicycle (64 mm. as previous model), metal clown figure with moving legs. No maker's name on model	**£100-125**	☐
	1958	Noddy's Garage Set	331 Noddy's Car & 'Esso' series nos. 7, 13, 16 & 20. Box folds into garage	**£150-175**	☐
303	c.1961	Noddy and his Car (large) with Big Ears	As 301 but with additional metal Big Ears Figure	**£125-175**	☐
305	1959-61	Noddy's Gift Box	Contains numbers 331, 333 and plastic Mr. Plod the Policeman	**£150-200**	☐
307	1959-61	Locomotive and Wagon with Noddy & Big Ears	Yellow loco with red cab. Red wagon. Plastic figures, 104 mm.	**£100-125**	☐
309	c.1961	Noddy and Locomotive	As no.307 but without wagon, 57 mm.	**£60-80**	☐
311	1960-61	Noddy on Bicycle with Trailer	Yellow bicycle, red trailer, plastic figure, 81 mm.	**£80-100**	☐
331	1958-61	Noddy and his Car (small)	Yellow car, red base and wheels, plastic figure, 52 mm.	**£80-100**	☐
333	1958-61	Big Ears on Bicycle (small)	Red. No maker's name on model. Plastic figure, 48 mm.	**£80-100**	☐

Morestone and Budgie Miniatures

Ref. No.	Year(s)	Model Type	Model Features and Size	Market Price Range	
			The miniatures were packaged in 'Esso' Petrol Pump boxes from 1956 to around 1959, then in Budgie bubble packs with a yellow backing card till 1964, and from 1965 in bubble packs with a blue backing card. In the early 1960s conventional boxes marked 'Mobile Vehicle Series' or 'Modern Vehicle Series' were also used.		
1	1956-58	AA Motorcycle and Sidecar	Rider, separate windscreen, 'MADE IN ENGLAND' under sidecar lid, 46 mm.	**£30-40**	☐
2	1956-58	RAC Motorcycle and Sidecar	Rider, separate windscreen. 'MADE IN ENGLAND' under sidecar lid, 46 mm.	**£30-40**	☐
3	1956-58	AA Land Rover	'AA ROAD SERVICE' cast-in, spare wheel (on bonnet) on some, 54 mm.	**£25-35**	☐

Ref. No.	Year(s)	Model Type	Description	Market Price Range	
4	1956-58	AA Bedford Van	AA badge and 'ROAD SERVICE' cast-in, 57 mm.	£25-35	☐
5	1956-70	Wolseley 6/80 Police Car	Black or green body, 65 mm.	£15-20	☐
6	1956-58	Cooper-Bristol Racing Car	Blue or Dark Blue body, Off-White base and driver, 58 mm.	£15-20	☐
7	1956-65	Mercedes-Benz Racing Car	Silver body, Red base and driver, 60 mm.	£15-20	☐
8	1956-70	Volkswagen 1200 Saloon	Metallic Light Blue body, 58 mm.	£15-20	☐
9	1956-58	Maudslay Horse Box	Red body, 'HORSE BOX SERVICE' cast-in, 57 mm.	£20-30	☐
10	1956-58	Karrier GPO Telephones Van	Dark green body, 57 mm.	£20-30	☐
11	1957-65	Morris Commercial Van	Red body, 'ROYAL MAIL' and 'E-II-R' cast-in, 58 mm.	£15-20	☐
12	1957-70	Volkswagen Microbus	Light Brown, Pale Blue or Metallic Dark Blue, 61 mm.	£15-20	☐
13	1957-64	Austin FX3 Taxi	Black body, Silver base and driver, 58 mm.	£15-20	☐
14	1957-70	Packard Convertible	Beige body, Red base and seats, Light Brown or Gold driver, 66 mm.	£15-20	☐
15	1957-70	Austin A95 Westminster Countryman	Blue or Orange, (Silver flash on some); or Metallic Mauve, 66 mm.	£15-20	☐
16	1957-64	Austin-Healey 100	Red body, Off-White base and driver, 57 mm.	£20-25	☐
17	1957-58	Ford Thames 5 cwt. Van	Blue body, 60 mm.	£40-50	☐
18	1957-66	Foden Dumper	Red cab and chassis, Lemon-Yellow or Grey dumper, 60 mm.	£14-18	☐
19	1957-70	Rover 105R	Green or Gold body, 65 mm.	£10-15	☐
20	1957-64	Plymouth Belvedere Convertible	Pale Pink or White body, Red base and driver, 64 mm.	£20-30	☐
20	1968-70	Austin A95 Westminster Emergency Vehicle	White with Orange beacon & 'EMERGENCY' transfer, Red base, 66 mm.	£35-45	☐
21	1963-66	Bedford TK Tipper Lorry	Dark Green tipper. Yellow, Off-White or Orange cab, 58 mm.	£15-20	☐
21	1968-70	Oldsmobile Town Sedan	Gold body, 66 mm.	£20-25	☐
22	1963-66	Bedford TK Crane Lorry	Dark Green cab, Orange crane, Orange or Dark Green platform, 56 mm.	£15-20	☐
22	1968-70	Cattle Transporter	Adapted from no.58. Light Brown body, Dark Brown rear door, 61 mm.	£20-25	☐
23	1963-66	Bedford TK Cement Mixer	Off-White mixer. Green, Yellow, Red or Orange cab & chassis, 59 mm.	£15-20	☐
24	1963-66	Bedford TK Refuse Lorry	Green, Orange, Red or Yellow cab, Silver back, 59 mm.	£15-20	☐
25	1963-66	Bedford TK Cattle Lorry	Light brown body. Off-White, Orange or Yellow cab, 58 mm.	£15-20	☐
26	1963-66	Aveling-Barford Road Roller	Similar to Lesney Matchbox no.1c. Green body, Red wheels, 55 mm.	£10-15	☐
27	1963-70	Wolseley 6/80 Fire Chief Car	Same as no.5 with altered base lettering. Red body, 65 mm.	£15-20	☐

50 - 55 These models were designated the 'Road Tanker Series'.

50	1963-66	'BP Racing Service' Tanker	Green with White tank, 61 mm.	£15-20	☐
51	1963-66	'Shell' Tanker	Yellow, 61 mm.	£15-20	☐
52	1963-64	'Shell BP' Tanker	Green or Yellow; White tank, 61 mm.	£15-20	☐
53	1963-66	'National' Tanker	Blue with Yellow tank, 61 mm.	£15-20	☐
54	1963-66	'BP' Tanker	Green with White tank, 61 mm.	£15-20	☐
55	1963-66	'Mobil' Tanker	Red body, 61 mm.	£15-20	☐
56	1966 & 1968-70	GMC Box Van	'HERTZ TRUCK RENTAL' transfers and 'TRUCK RENTAL' cast-in. Light Green or Pale Blue body, 61 mm.	£15-20	☐
57	1966-70	International Parcels Van	Green body, sliding door. 'REA EXPRESS' transfers, 67 mm.	£15-20	☐
58	1966-70	'Modern Removals' Van	'MODERN REMOVALS' transfers. Light Brown or Metallic Green, 61 mm.	£15-20	☐
59	1967-70	AEC Merryweather Fire Engine	Copied from Lesney Matchbox no.9c. Red body, Gold ladder, 65 mm.	£15-20	☐
60	1966-70	Rover 105R Squad Car	As no.19 but with altered base lettering. Black or Red body, 65 mm.	£15-20	☐
61	1966-70	Austin A95 Westminster Countryman 'Q Car'	As no.15 but with altered base lettering. Black or Metallic Dark Blue body, 66 mm.	£15-20	☐

Sets of 3 Vehicles   (Bubble-packed)

94	1966	Interpol Set	Intended to contain no.5 Police Car, 60 Squad Car, 61 Q Car. Not issued	NPP	☐
95	1966	Road Haulage Set	Intended to contain no.56 Hertz Van, 57 REA Van, 58 Removals Van. Not issued	NPP	☐
96	1965-66	Road Construction Set	Contains no.18 Dumper, 23 Cement Mixer, 26 Road Roller	£50-75	☐
97	1965-66	Truck Set	Contains no.21 Tipper, 22 Crane, 25 Cattle Lorry	£50-75	☐
98	1965-66	Utility Vehicle Set	Contains no.12 VW Microbus, 24 Refuse Lorry, 55 Mobil Tanker	£50-75	☐
99	1965-66	Traffic Set	Contains no.8 Volkswagen, 15 Austin, 27 Fire Chief	£50-75	☐
95	1968-70	Town Set	Contains no.20 Emergency Vehicle, 21 Oldsmobile, 56 Hertz Van	£50-75	☐
96	1967-70	Service Set	Contains no.5 Police Car, 19 Rover, 59 Fire Engine	£50-75	☐
97	1967-70	Truck Set	Contains no.12 VW Microbus, 57 REA Van, 58 Removals Van	£50-75	☐
98	1967-70	Utility Vehicle Set	Contains no.27 Fire Chief, 60 Squad Car, 61 Q Car	£50-75	☐
99	1967-70	Traffic Set	Contains no.8 Volkswagen, 14 Packard, 15 Austin	£50-75	☐

Gift Sets

No.8	1962	Gift Set No.8	Contains numbers 5, 8, 11, 12, 13, 15, 18 and 19	£100-130	☐
No.12	1962	Gift Set No.12	Contains 5, 7, 8, 11, 12, 13, 14, 15, 16, 18, 19 and 20 (Plymouth)	£120-150	☐

Collectors Notes

Budgie Models

Ref. No.	Year(s)	Model Type	Model Features and Size	Market Price Range	
100	1972-84	Horse Drawn Hansom Cab......	With driver, elastic band for reins. Re-issue of a Morestone/Modern Products model. 'Gold' plated or Metallic Light Brown, 118 mm.	£10-15	☐
101	1977-84	Austin FX4 Taxi	Also issued as no.703. Re-issued by Seerol. Black or Maroon body. 106 mm.	£10-15	☐
101	1984	Austin FX4 Taxi	Silver body, 'LONDON VINTAGE TAXI ASSOCIATION'. Limited (1,000) commemorative marking 25 years of the FX4. Normal box.	£20-25	☐
102	1981-84	Rolls-Royce Silver Cloud	Re-issued by Seerol. Gold (painted or 'plated'), Black, Silver, Cream, Red, Blue, Metallic Light Blue, Metallic Turquoise or Metallic Dark Pink, 107 mm.	£15-20	☐
202	1959-66	International Articulated Refrigerator Lorry	Re-issued 'Trucks of the World' model. Red/Blue or Red cab (windows later). Silver trailer, 'COAST TO COAST REFRIGERATION', 153 mm.	£40-50	☐
204	1959-64	Volkswagen Pick-Up	Blue body, Cream base, cloth tilt 'EXPRESS DELIVERY', 92 mm.	£35-45	☐
206	1959-64	Leyland Hippo Coal Lorry	Green or Orange cab, Light Brown body, 'COAL AND COKE' cast-in, coal load, 92 mm.	£45-55	☐
208	1959-61	RAF Personnel Carrier	RAF blue, roundels, White tilt. 'A MORESTONE PRODUCT', 104 mm.	£90-120	☐
210	1959-61	US Army Personnel Carrier	As 208 but Army brown body with star, Light Brown tilt, 104 mm.	£90-120	☐
212	1959-61	British Army Personnel Carrier	As 208 but Dark Green with Red/Yellow square, Light Brown tilt, 104 mm.	£90-120	☐
214	1959-64	Thornycroft Mobile Crane.......	Red cab and chassis, Yellow crane engine, Light Blue crane, 100 mm.	£50-60	☐
216	1959-64	Renault Truck	Yellow cab, Red body. Cloth tilt, 'FRESH FRUIT DAILY', 103 mm.	£35-45	☐
218	1959-63	Seddon 'Jumbo' Mobile Traffic Control Unit..........	Yellow cab and trailer with Black flash and catwalk. 'AUTOMOBILE ASSOCIATION' and AA badge transfers, 168 mm.	£100-120	☐
220	1959-66	Leyland Hippo Cattle Transporter.............	Orange cab, Light Brown body, Dark Brown base and ramp, 97 mm.	£35-45	☐
222	1959-65	International Tank Transporter with Centurion Tank	Army brown with star transfers. Cab as no.202. 155 mm. (with ramps up)	£45-55	☐
224	1959-66	0-6-0 Tank Locomotive	As Modern Products model. Red, 'BRITISH RAILWAYS' cast-in, 119 mm.	£25-35	☐
224	1971-84	0-6-0 Tank Locomotive	Red, Metallic Brown, Black or Dark Green, 'BRITISH RAILWAYS' on transfers or labels, 119 mm.	£10-15	☐
226	1959-66	Foden Dumper	Re-issue of a Morestone model. Orange cab and chassis, Grey dumper. 'BUD 123' number plate transfers, 108 mm.	£30-40	☐
228	1959-64	Karrier Bantam Bottle Lorry	Orange-Yellow, 12 maroon plastic crates. 'DRINK COCA-COLA' transfers, 'COMMER LOW LOADER' cast underneath, 134 mm.	£120-140	☐
230	1959-66	Seddon Timber Transporter......	Orange cab (no windows), or Green cab (with windows), Yellow trailer with 5 logs (wood dowel). 178 mm. (fully extended)	£45-55	☐
232	1960-66	Seddon Low Loader	Red cab (windows later), Orange trailer, 3 wooden cable drums. 167 mm.	£60-70	☐
234	1960-65	International Low Loader with Caterpillar Tractor.....	Orange cab, Light Brown trailer, Orange tractor, 155 mm. (with ramps up)	£40-50	☐
236	1960-66 and 1969-84	AEC Routemaster Bus.............	Also issued as nos.704, 705 and 706. All models have destination transfers for route '9' and 'LONDON TRANSPORT' transfers or labels. Most versions came with or without windows. 108 mm.		
			Red, 'Esso GOLDEN Esso'........	£10-20	☐
			Red, 'Esso UNIFLO - the tuned motor oil'.	£10-20	☐
			Red, 'GO ESSO - BUY ESSO - DRIVE ESSO'.	£10-20	☐
			Red, 'UNIFLO sae 10W/50 Motor Oil'.	£10-20	☐
			Red, Green or Gold, 'Houses of Parliament Tower Bridge'.	£10-20	☐
236	1973	Promotional issue:	Red body (with windows), 'Sheraton-Heathrow Hotel' on sides, 'OPENING 1st FEBRUARY 1973' on roof, Special box.	£60-70	☐
238	1960-63	Scammell Scarab Van...............	Crimson/Cream cab & trailer. 'BRITISH RAILWAYS' and 'CADBURYS', 150 mm. N.B. Chocolate Bar picture may be vertical or horizontal.	£75-85	☐
238	1964-66	Scammell Scarab Van...............	Yellow cab, Black chassis, Yellow trailer. 'Railfreight', 'CADBURYS', 150 mm.	£65-75	☐
238	1985	Scammell Scarab Van...............	Maroon cab, Maroon/Cream trailer. 'BRITISH RAILWAYS' and 'CADBURYS'	£15-20	☐
238	1985	Scammell Scarab Van...............	Yellow cab and trailer. 'Railfreight' and 'CADBURYS' transfers. Most of these were issued in original 1960s boxes. 150 mm.	£15-20	☐
240	1960-64	Scammell Scarab Wagon..........	Red/Cream cab, Yellow chassis, Red trailer, Green cloth tilt, 150 mm.	£55-65	☐
242	1960-66	Euclid Dumper	Red cab, Orange chassis and dumper. 114 mm.	£35-45	☐
244	1961-65	Morris Breakdown Lorry..........	Blue body, Yellow base, tool box and jib. 'BUDGIE SERVICE', 120 mm.	£45-55	☐
246	1960-64	Wolseley 6/80 Police Car.........	Re-issued Modern Products model. Black, loudspeaker, aerial, 'BUDGIE TOYS' cast under, 'POLICE' transfers on grille and body, 104 mm.	£35-45	☐
246	1983	Wolseley 6/80 Police Car.........	Light Blue, 'POLICE' labels, spotlights & roof sign replace the loudspeaker & aerial. Trial run of models - did not go into full production........	£45-55	☐
248	1961	Stage Coach with 4 horses	Listed on this number as 'Available later', but issued as no. 434.		
250	....	....	This number was used for packs of one dozen of the Budgie miniatures		
252	1961-63	Austin Articulated Lorry with Railway Container	Crimson cab, Cream load, windows, 'BRITISH RAILWAYS' transfers, 128 mm.	£65-75	☐
	1964	design change:	Crimson cab, Blue load, windows, 'Door to Door' transfers, 128 mm.	£75-85	☐
254	1961-64	AEC Merryweather Fire Escape.......................	Red, windows, Silver extending turntable ladder. 97 mm. (excluding ladder)	£65-75	☐
256	1961-64	Foden Aircraft Refuelling Tanker 'Pluto'	Red, with windows. 'ESSO AVIATION PRODUCTS' transfers, 149 mm.	£100-125	☐
258	1961-63	Daimler Ambulance	Re-issued Modern Products model. Cream body, Red base ('BUDGIE TOYS' cast-in), 'AMBULANCE' and 'EMERGENCY' transfers, 110 mm.	£65-75	☐
258	1991	Daimler Ambulance Kit...........	Re-issued as a kit of unpainted castings (by Autocraft).	£10-20	☐
260	1962	Ruston-Bucyrus Excavator.......	Yellow/Red cab, '10-RB', Beige or Olive-Green base and jib, 73 mm.	£100-125	☐
262	1962-64	Racing Motorcycle	No maker's name on model. Unpainted cycle, tinplate fairing in Metallic Blue, Metallic Lilac, Metallic Brown or Lime Green, Black plastic rider, 104 mm.	£75-100	☐
264	1962-64	Racing Motorcycle & Sidecar ...	Cycle as 262, sidecar and tinplate fairing in Metallic Blue, Metallic Pinkish-Red, Metallic Green, Metallic Lilac, Metallic Brown or Lime Green. Black plastic rider and passenger, no maker's name, 104 mm.	£75-100	☐

Budgie Listings continued on page 289 after colour section

PICTURE PRIDE DISPLAYS

SPOT ON MODELS

L-R from the bottom: Tommy Spot gift Sets, 801, 802, 805, 806, Gift Set 702 and Tommy Spot Set 803.

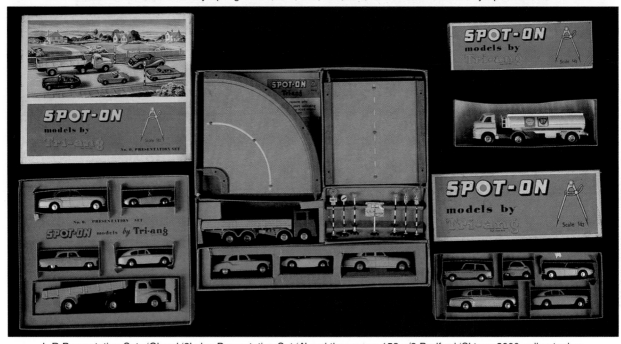

L-R Presentation Sets 'O' and '2' plus Presentation Set 'A' and the scarce 158 a/2 Bedford 'S' type 2000 gallon tanker.
Pictures kindly supplied by Christies of South Kensington, London and reproduced by their kind permission

SPOT ON MODELS

New Zealand issue. Note the special box and the N102 number

116 Caterpillar D 9 Bulldozer

Pictures kindly supplied by Gerry Savage of Model & Collectors Mart

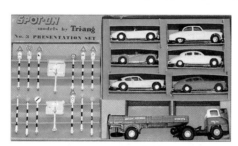

3 Presentation Set sold by Vectis Model Auctions (£1,300)

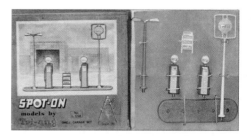

172A 'Shell' Garage Set. *Picture supplied by Vectis Model Auctions*

103 Colour Variations Metallic Silver/Blue, Metallic Silver/Black, Metallic Silver/Green

Note the 102 Bentley Saloon variations (bottom left) and the three 156 Mulliner Coach variations

The pictures at the bottom of the page were kindly supplied by Bruce Sterling of New York and reproduced by his kind permission

MORESTONE SERIES

Picture supplied by Patrick Talbot

Model sold by Vectis Model
Auctions (£160)
Excellent condition

Picture supplied by Patrick Talbot

BUDGIE TOYS

292 Leyland Bulk Milk Tanker

296 The rare Washington D.C. variation

228 Karrier Bantam — Rare mint example.
Picture supplied by Christies, South Kensington, London

272 Supercar

SHACKLETON TOYS

Foden FG 6 wheel Tipper Lorry (£400)

Trailer (£160)

Foden FG 6 wheel Platform Lorry (£540)

Above models sold by Vectis Model Auctions at their Guildford Saleroom in May 1995

BENBROS QUALITOYS

The Benbros Qualitoy pictures kindly supplied by Mr Patrick Talbot to whom the Editor wishes to express his thanks

BRITAINS

L-R Set 1552 'Royal Mail' Van (£1800), Set 154 Corporation Type Motor Ambulance (£700), Set 90 F 'Davis Estates Ltd',
Yellow Builders Four Wheeled Lorry (£1800)

Models sold by Christies, South Kensington, London in June, 1995 and the pictures reproduced by their kind permission

Rare model colour variations as sold by Christies at their 1994 Britains Archive sale

MISCELLANEOUS MODELS — CORGI TOYS

226 Morris Mini Minors × 3 i) Light Blue ii) Metallic Maroon iii) Sky Blue (£280), iv) 227 Morris Mini Cooper (£180), v) 'Wickerwork' Mini and vi) Mini Countryman 'Surfer' (£210)

Gift Set 23 (£300)

Chitty Chitty Bang Bang (£170)

L-R i) 300 Austin Healey, ii) 301 Triumph TR2, iii) 302 MG, MGA, iv) 309 Aston Martin DB4, v) 318 Lotus Elan

Mettoy B.O.A.C. Van (£320)

497 'Man From Uncle' Dark blue, with box packing (£110)

327 MGB GT & 345 MGC GT Competition

Mettoy 'Castoys' Marks & Spencer Issue 'Vanwall'.
Picture kindly supplied by Ray Strutt of Collectors Gazette

Models on this page were sold in May, 1995 by Vectis Model Auctions at their Guildford saleroom and the prices realised have been shown where available. At the time of the sale the condition of the models/boxes was excellent.

MISCELLANEOUS MODELS — DINKY TOYS

L-R 101 Sunbeam Alpine (Touring Finish) (2) i) Turquoise (£160), ii) Deep Pink (£160), 102 MG Midget Sports (Touring Finish) (2) i) Light Green (£230), ii) Orange (£170), 103 Austin Healey Sports (Touring Finish) Cream (£210)

L-R 104 Aston Martin (Touring Finish) (2) i) Salmon Pink (£180), ii) Light Blue (£180), 105 Triumph TR2 Sports (Touring Finish) (2), i) Grey (£150), ii) Lemon (£150), 103 Austin Healey '100' Sports Red (£210)

L-R 106 Austin A90 Atlantic Tourer (4), i) Black (£120), ii) Blue/Red (£110), iii) Blue/Dark Blue (£160), iv) Pink (£210) plus 2 × 107 Sunbeam Alpine Sports (Competition Finish) in Blue/Cream and Maroon/Blue liveries (no prices available)

159 Morris Oxford Green/Cream (£230)

159 Morris Oxford Deep Pink/Cream (£160)

159 Morris Oxford. Rare Pale Brown (£1700)

178 Plymouth Plaza Light Blue/White (£280)

396 Oldsmobile. Export Only Issue Sand Body (£260)

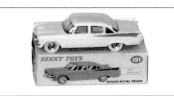

118 Dodge Royal Sedan Light Cream/Blue Flash (£370)

Models on this page sold by Vectis Model Auctions at their Guildford saleroom, and the prices realised have been shown where available. At the time of the sale the condition of the models/boxes was excellent.

Ref. No.	Year(s)	Model Type	Description	Market Price Range	
266	1962-64	Motorcycle & Delivery Sidecar	Blue cycle as 262, Red sidecar, 'EXPRESS DELIVERY' cast-in, no maker's name, Black plastic rider. 108 mm.	£75-100	□
268	1962-64	AA Land Rover	Different from Morestone AA Land Rovers. Yellow body, Black roof, windows, opening rear doors, 'AA ROAD SERVICE' transfers, 97 mm.	£125-150	□
270	1962-66	Leyland Articulated Tanker	Red, windows, 'ESSO PETROLEUM COMPANY LTD' labels, 132 mm.	£50-60	□
272	1962-64	Supercar	From TV series. Red/Silver body, Red wings (or colours reversed), clear plastic canopy, 'SUPERCAR' transfers, 122 mm.	£175-225	□
274	1962-66	Ford Thames Refuse Lorry	Blue cab/Silver body, or Yellow cab/Metallic blue body, windows, 101 mm.	£45-55	□
276	1962-66	Bedford LWB Tipper	Red cab with windows, Yellow tipper, 'HAM RIVER GRIT', 128 mm.	£40-80	□
278	1963-64	RAC Land Rover	Casting as 268, Blue, windows, 'RAC RADIO RESCUE' transfers, 97 mm.	£125-150	□
280	1963-64	AEC Super Fueller Tanker	White cab & trailer, windows, Green base & canopy, 'AIR BP', 219 mm.	£300-400	□
282	1963-66	Euclid Scraper	Yellow or Lime Green, windscreen, 'EUCLID', Black plastic wheels, 163 mm.	£35-45	□
284	1962	Euclid Crawler Tractor	Not issued	NPP	□
286	1962	Euclid Bulldozer	Not issued	NPP	□
288	1963-66	Leyland Bulk Flour Tanker	Red cab, windows, Off-White silos, Yellow hopppers, 'BULK FLOUR', 107 mm.	£45-55	□
290	1963-64	Bedford Ice Cream Van	No maker's name on model. Blue body and base, windows, 'Tonibell' transfers, Pink plastic cow on roof, 103 mm.	£85-110	□
292	1963-66	Leyland Bulk Milk Tanker	Blue or Red cab, windows, White tank, 'MILK', 107 mm.	£45-55	□
294	1963-66	Bedford TK Horse Box	Off-White cab, windows, Brown body, Light Brown doors. 2 Brown plastic horses. 'EPSOM STABLE' transfer, 109 mm.	£45-55	□
296	1963-66	Motorway Express Coach	Midland Red livery: Red body, Black roof, 'BIRMINGHAM-LONDON MOTORWAY EXPRESS' transfers, windows, 121 mm.	£70-85	□
		USA livery:	Light Blue body, Cream roof, 'WASHINGTON D.C.' and 'BLUE LINE SIGHTSEEING CO.' transfers, phone number 'LA9-7755' at rear	£300-400	□
298	1963-66	Alvis Salamander Crash Tender	Red body, windows, Silver plastic ladder, Yellow engine cover at rear, Black plastic wheels. 'FIRE SERVICE' transfers, 92 mm.	£100-125	□
300	1963-65	Lewin Sweepmaster	Blue/Silver, windows, Black plastic wheels, Black sweeping brush, 99 mm.	£45-55	□
302	1963-66	Commer Cabin Service Lift Truck	Blue cab, windows, Silver body, 'BOAC CABIN SERVICES', 104 mm.	£45-55	□
304	1964-66	Bedford TK Glass Transporter	Off-white cab and chassis, windows, Green body. 'TOWER GLASS CO.' transfers. Four clear plastic 'glass' sheets, 108 mm.	£45-55	□
306	1964-66	Fiat Tractor with Shovel	Orange tractor, Metallic Blue shovel, 108 mm.	£75-100	□
308	1964-66	Seddon Pitt Alligator Low Loader	Green cab, windows, Yellow trailer with Black ramp, 163 mm.	£45-55	□
310	1964-66	Leyland Cement Mixer	Orange cab, windows, Silver mixer, 'INVICTA Construction Co.', 98 mm.	£45-55	□
312	1964-66	Bedford Super Tipmaster	Dark Green cab, windows, Silver tipper. 'SUPER TIP-MASTER', 127 mm.	£45-55	□
314	1965-66	Fiat Tractor with Dozer Blade	As 306 but enclosed cab, Orange tractor, Metallic Blue blade, 81 mm.	£45-55	□
316	1965-66	Albion Overhead Maintenance Vehicle	Green body, windows, Silver/Black boom assembly, 107 mm.	£40-50	□
318	1965-66	Euclid Mammoth Articulated Dumper	Modified from no.242. Green cab, Yellow chassis, Orange tipper, 201 mm.	£75-95	□
322	1965-66	Scammell Routeman Pneumajector Transporter	Light Blue cab, Cream or White tipping tank, 'THE ATLAS CARRIER CO.', 111 mm.	£50-60	□
324	1965-66	Douglas Prospector Duomatic Tipper	Tips in two directions. Blue cab and chassis, windows, Grey tipper, 112 mm.	£55-65	□
326	1965-66	Scammell Highwayman Gas Transporter	Green cab, windows, Dark Green trailer, 6 White/Red gas cylinders, 146 mm.	£125-150	□
328	1966	Scammell Handyman Artic.	Planned but not issued	NPP	
330	1966	Land Rover	Modified 268, planned but not issued	NPP	
332	1966	'Kenning' Breakdown Lorry	Planned but not issued	NPP	
334	1966	Austin Gipsy Fire Tender	Planned but not issued	NPP	
404	1960-61	Horse Drawn Covered Wagon	with Four Horses. For details see Morestone and Modern Products entry.		
410	1961	Stage Coach with 4 Horses	Blue or 'Gold plated' coach, no lettering cast on sides but 'WELLS FARGO STAGE COACH' and 'A BUDGIE TOY' cast underneath, plastic horses and driver, bubble-packed, 114 mm.	£70-90	□
430	1960-61	Wagon Train Set	Contains 3 of no.432 plus 2 more horses with riders, bubble-packed	£100-150	□
432	1960-61	Horse Drawn Covered Wagon with Two Horses	Red wagon, ('A BUDGIE TOY' on floor), Grey, White or Lemon metal canopy, 2 barrels, plastic horses, driver and passenger, bubble packed, 82 mm.	£35-45	□
434	1961	Stage Coach with 4 Horses	'WELLS FARGO' above windows, 'STAGE LINES' on doors, luggage cast on roof, Red or Blue, plastic horses and driver, 189 mm.	£70-90	□
452	1958-63	AA Motorcycle & Sidecar	Initially in Morestone box. Windscreen, plastic rider, integral rails & hinged lid on sidecar, steerable, rubber tyres, plain number plates, 82 mm.	£75-100	□
452	1964-66	AA Motorcycle & Sidecar	New design. Sidecar with transfers and 'BUDGIE' underneath, plastic rider, windscreen and leg guards, plain number plates, 84 mm.	£75-100	□
454	1958-63	RAC Motorcycle & Sidecar	Initially in Morestone box. Windscreen, plastic rider, integral rails & hinged lid on sidecar, steerable, rubber tyres, plain number plates, 82 mm.	£75-100	□
454	1964-66	RAC Motorcycle & Sidecar	New design. Sidecar with transfers and 'BUDGIE' underneath, plastic rider, windscreen and leg guards, plain number plates, 84 mm.	£75-100	□
456	1958-66	Solo Motorcycle	Initially in Morestone boxes. Two casting versions as 452 and 454 above but 'Silver plated'. Plastic riders:		
			Police Patrol (Blue uniform)	£40-50	□
			Despatch Rider (Light Brown uniform)	£40-50	□
			GPO Messenger (Light Blue uniform)	£40-50	□
			'Tourist Trophy' Rider (White racing overalls)	£40-50	□
701	1983	Aveling-Barford Road Roller	Re-issued Modern Products model. Dark Green body cast in two halves, Silver/Red wheels, very Dark Blue driver, 117 mm.	£10-15	□
702	1984-85	Scammell Scarab Van	Re-issue of 238		
			Very Dark Blue cab and trailer, White 'RN' on doors, 'ROYAL NAVY' on tilt	£15-20	□
			Very Dark Blue cab and trailer, 'HALLS MENTHO-LYPTUS' labels	£15-20	□
			Maroon cab and trailer, 'LMS LIVERPOOL ROAD' transfers	£15-20	□
			Maroon cab and trailer, 'SPRATTS BONIO' transfers	£15-20	□
			Maroon cab and trailer, 'REA EXPRESS' transfers	£15-20	□

Ref. No.	Year(s)	Model Type	*Budgie Models – continued*	Market Price Range	
703	1984	Austin FX4 Taxi	As no.101 but in window box packaging. Black, Silver, Metallic Dark Pink, Gold, Dark Green, Light Grey or White body, 106 mm...	£15-20	☐
		AEC Routemaster Bus.............	Casting as no. 236.		
704	1984	'SHOP LINKER'	Yellow and Red body, windows, 'SHOP LINKER' labels, 108 mm............................	£8-11	☐
705	1984	'25 FAITHFUL YEARS'.....	Silver body, with windows, '25 FAITHFUL YEARS' labels, 108 mm...........................	£8-11	☐
706	1984	'WATFORD FA CUP FINAL'....................................	Yellow and Red body, windows, 'Watford FA Cup Final '84' labels, 108 mm.	£8-11	☐

Gift Sets

Ref. No.	Year(s)	Model Type		Market Price Range	
No. 4	1961	Gift Set No.4	Contains four models. Price depends on contents which vary.......................................	£125-165	☐
No. 5	1961	Gift Set No.5	Contains five models. Price depends on contents which vary....................................	£150-200	☐

Seerol Models

	Year	Model	Details	Price	
	1985	Austin FX4 Taxi	Re-issue of Budgie no.101 with amended base lettering and low friction wheels. Black body, 106 mm. Still available...	£3-5	☐
	1985	Rolls-Royce Silver Cloud	Re-issued Budgie 102, amended lettering, low friction wheels. Black, Silver, White, Yellow, Dark Blue, Pink or Maroon, 107 mm. Still available...........................	£3-5	☐
	1985	AEC Routemaster Bus..............	New design, 1:76 scale, 108 mm., still available.		
			Red, Light Green or Dark Green, 'Houses of Parliament Tower Bridge' labels	£8-11	☐
			Red, 'The Original London Transport Sightseeing Tour' labels................................	£8-11	☐
			Red, 'Greetings from London' tampo print..	£3-5	☐
			Red, 'Tower of London' tampo print..	£3-5	☐
			Red, 'Petticoat Lane' tampo print..	£3-5	☐
			Red, 'Buckingham Palace' tampo print...	£3-5	☐

Budgie Leaflets and Catalogues

A leaflet was included in the box with most Budgie Toys. Dates are not shown on any except the 1963 and 1964 catalogues.

Ref. No.	Year(s)	Publication	Cover Features & Details	Market Price Range	
	1959	Leaflet	Printed on one side only. 'Budgie Toys Speak for Themselves' at top.		
		1st version:	Includes the 6-horse Covered Wagon	£10-20	☐
		2nd version:.............	Timber Transporter replaces the Covered Wagon	£10-20	☐
	1960	Leaflet	Printed on both sides. 'Budgie Toys Speak for Themselves' on front, 'Budgie Toys for Girls and Boys' on reverse	£10-20	☐
	1961	Leaflet	'Budgie Toys Speak for Themselves' on Black background	£5-10	☐
	1961	Trade catalogue	Fold-out leaflet showing Noddy items, Wagon Train and Budgie miniatures as well as the main Budgie range. Separate price list marked 'Price List 1961' showing wholesale and retail prices	£30-40	☐
	1962	Leaflet	'Die-Cast Models by Budgie They Speak for Themselves' on Black background.		
		1st version:	268 AA Land Rover on front, 258 Daimler Ambulance on reverse.........................	£5-10	☐
		2nd version:.............	214 Mobile Crane on front, 266 Express Delivery Motorcycle on reverse..................	£5-10	☐
	1963	Leaflet	'Die-Cast Models by Budgie They Speak for Themselves' on Black background.		
		1st version:	278 RAC Land Rover on front, 258 Daimler Ambulance on reverse.........................	£5-10	☐
		2nd version:.............	278 RAC Land Rover on front, 266 Express Delivery Motorcycle on reverse	£5-10	☐
	1963	Trade Catalogue (8 pages)	Landscape format, includes retail price list	£30-40	☐
	1964	Trade Catalogue (8 pages)	'Budgie Models' on cover (portrait format). Includes retail price list	£30-40	☐

Models sold at auction by Vectis Model Auctions 1994-95

All boxed in excellent condition.

Morestone

c1954	Horse Drawn Covered Wagon, 6 horses..........................	£180
c1954	Horse Drawn Gipsy Caravan...	£250
c1954	Bedford Dormobile..	£130
c1955	No1 Foden 'ESSO' Petrol Tanker	£220
	No2 Foden Long Distance Wagon	£160
	No3 Foden Chain Lorry	£160
	No4 Foden 8-wheel Flat bed...	£140
c1956	'AA' Land Rover, 108 mm...	£140
c1957	'AA' Land Rover, 79 mm...	£200
c1958	'MILITARY POLICE' Land Rover (unboxed)	£115
	Group of six 'ESSO PETROL PUMP SERIES'	£130

Budgie

208	RAF Personnel Carrier	£130
218	'AA' Mobile Traffic Unit	£120
228	'COCA COLA' Truck	£120
256	'Pluto' Refuelling Tanker	£75
260	Ruston Bucyrus	£90
272	Mike Mercury's Supercar	£220
278	'RAC' 'RADIO RESCUE' Land Rover..........................	£130
296	Unboxed US issue 'Blue Line' Coach	£230
298	Alvis Salamander Fire Truck	£140
326	Unboxed Gas Pipe Truck..	£100
280	'AIR BP' Superfueller...	£300

SCAMOLD RACING CARS

Manufactured 1939-50 by Scale Models Ltd from whose title the model name was obtained. The models are extremely accurate 1/35 diecast scale models, with their original measurements being taken from the real racing cars at the famous Brooklands race track. Pre-war boxes state 'MANUFACTURED BY SCALE MODELS LTD, BROOKLANDS TRACK, WEYBRIDGE, ENG.'. This was dropped after the war.

The model details and castings are outstanding, with features such as removable exhausts, spring suspension, steering wheels and dashboards. In addition the back axle could be exchanged for one containing a clockwork motor which was wound up by a long starting handle. The wheel axles were crimped and the hubs were either brass (early) or aluminium (later) plus black treaded rubber tyres.

101	1939-50	ERA Racing Car	Blue (Light or Dark), Green (Light or Dark), Yellow, White or Black body	**£90-120**	☐
103	1939-50	Maserati Racing Car	Red, Blue, Green (Mid or Dark), Silver body	**£90-100**	☐
105	1939-50	Alfa Racing Car	Green (Mid or Dark), Silver, White or Blue	**£90-120**	☐

SHACKLETON MODELS

The company was formed by Maurice Shackleton and traded as James Shackleton & Sons Ltd. from 1939 to 1952. They had premises in Cheshire and originally produced wooden toys such as lorries and dolls houses. The toy lorries were only made pre-war and had four wheels, a simple wooden chassis and body with a green name badge on the rear of the cab, and were fitted with a highly detailed aluminium radiator grille. Known models are a Chain Lorry, Breakdown Lorry and a Sided Wagon. Their price today is around £100 each.

In 1948 having expanded its staff to nearly 40 people, the company started to produce diecast constructional models based on the Foden FG six-wheel platform lorry. The models consisted of separate parts all of which were, incredibly, made 'in house', including the clockwork motor, its key, and the wheels and tyres. The model was advertised in the 'Meccano Magazine' with the slogan 'You can dismantle it - Just like the real thing', and it was originally priced at £2/19/6. Eventually the range was extended to include a Dyson Drawbar Trailer and a Foden Tipper. Each model was packed in its own distinctive box which displayed a black and white picture of the model inside.

In 1952, whilst in the midst of producing the David Brown Trackmaster 30" Tractor, a shortage of materials coupled with difficult trading conditions brought about the end of the company. The unique models produced by the Shackleton company are now highly collectable and difficult to find.

Ref. No.	Year(s)	Model Type	Model Features and Size	Market Price Range	
i)	1948-52	Foden FG 6-wheel Platform Lorry	Yellow, Blue, Grey or Green body with Red wings, Grey chassis and Red or Grey fuel tanks, 12½ inches (305 mm.) long, initially in Blue/Yellow box, later in mottled Green box, (20,000 made)	**£200-300**	☐
			Same colours as above but with Grey or Black wings and Red chassis	**£300-400**	☐
			Same casting but with Red, Orange or Brown cab	**£300-400**	☐
Note. Box difficult to find: Blue box with paper label having picture of chassis.					
ii)	1949-52	Dyson 8-ton Drawbar Trailer	Yellow, Blue, Grey or Green body, packed in Red and Yellow box, (15,000)	**£100-150**	☐
iii)	1950-52	Foden FG 6-wheel Tipper Lorry	Yellow, Blue, Grey or Green body with Red wings, Grey chassis and Red or Grey fuel tanks, Silver wheels, (5,000)	**£300-400**	☐
			As previous models but with Grey wings and Red chassis	**£300-400**	☐
			As previous models but with Blue wings, Grey chassis, Grey wheels	**£300-400**	☐
			Orange or Red body	**£300-400**	☐
iv)	1952	David Brown Trackmaster 30" Tractor	No details available of body colours but the model had Black rubber tracks, exhaust pipe and headlights. It is thought that only 50 models were sold.	**£750-950**	☐
Note: It is known that some prototype models were made of Ploughs and Harrows, though it is not known if any were produced for sale.					
v)	1958-60	Foden S.21 8-wheel Platform Lorry	Dark Blue, Dark Green or Light Turquoise fibreglass cab with Red metal chassis and wheels, wooden flatbed, length overall 18½ inches (470 mm.), plastic injection moulded springs and axle parts, powered by 'Minimax' electric motor. (250 made as a promotional for Foden)	**£750-950**	☐

The information in this listing has been taken from an original article written by John Ormandy in the 'Modellers World' magazine, Volumes 12 and 13, and is used by kind permission of the Editors, Mike and Sue Richardson. Robert Taylor provided additional information.

Shackleton Toy

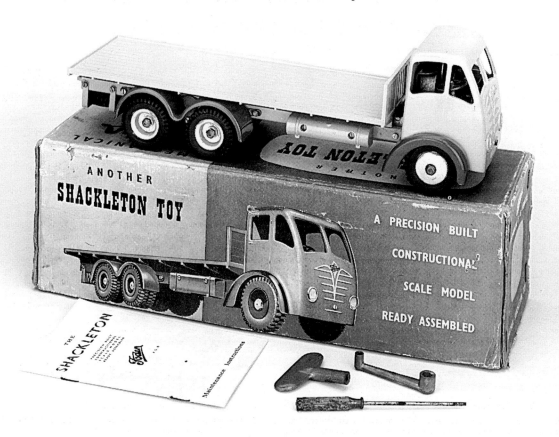

Foden F G Truck plus accessories.
Picture kindly supplied by Christie's, South Kensington, London.

Taylor & Barrett

Leyland Lion c.1934 with Birch Bros. bodyword. Picture supplied by Frank Wright of Kent.

Taylor and Barrett Lead Vehicles and the Postwar Re-issues

by Mike Richardson

The firm of Taylor and Barrett dates from the early 1920s when they started producing mainly figures but with a few odd carts. The vehicles themselves were only introduced in about 1935. These were rather crude by comparison with the Dinky Toys of the day as the lead gravity casting process was incapable of working to the fine limits possible with pressure diecasting as used by Meccano Ltd. The majority of the vehicles use a basic chassis incorporating the bonnet and wings. Different bodies are attached to this base unit by tabs and a radiator is plugged into the front. Some versions have the grille cast integrally with the bonnet, and most of these use plain metal wheels instead of having rubber tyres. These vehicles have a tremendous amount of charm as toys while they are only a generic representation of the types of vans and small trucks of the time. A wide variety of types were made including petrol tankers, a pick-up truck and a couple of mail vans. The breakdown truck is particularly attractive with a working crane on the rear. These toys were made until the production was halted in 1940 when the factory was bombed out of existence. All salvageable tools, moulds and stock was moved to a new location in North Finchley but production stopped very soon after because of the munitions requirements of the war effort.

During the war the tools were split between the Taylors and the Barretts for safe keeping but they did not join up again afterwards and two separate companies, F.G.Taylor & Sons and A.Barrett & Sons, started up in 1945. The main part of the range, the small commercial vehicles and the cars, does not seem to have survived the War, only the trolley buses, which became Barretts, and the Leyland coach which appeared in one-piece casting form as a Taylor. It is interesting to note that the trolleybus carries a route board '621 Finchley' which probably means that they went past the factory.

A range of very nice fire engines came along in the late 1930s with a super turntable ladder appliance as the top of the range. These were longer than the main range and had many parts. To mark the advent of the Home Office Fire Precautions scheme (where fire appliances were made available to local areas by central government), Taylor and Barrett painted their range in grey as well as the more traditional red. These grey models are highly sought after now. Personnel were also available to go with these fire engines. A Decontamination Squad being a particular favourite with their gas masks and chemical-proof overalls. There is also a fire engine in the short chassis range but it is not very impressive.

The trolley buses came in two sizes. The large one has a separate driver figure (and conductor as well in the T & B version but not the later Barrett), and the body is in two pieces, upper and lower decks. The small one is in one piece and has no driver. Needless to say there is a vast difference in the values of the two sizes.

There are generic cars, roadster, coup, saloon, on the short base but there is also quite a good model of the 1935 Singer Airstream saloon. This is also the poor man's Chrysler Airflow but never really caught on, the styling made the car look too tall to be appealing. A rather crude one-piece Austin Seven racer was the final car but this was to a larger scale.

Dinky Toys were not the only factory to make a model of the Air Mail Service Car based on the Morris Commercial chassis. T & B also made one and a nice chunky toy it is too. A couple of aeroplanes, a De Havilland Comet and an air liner, completed the range of powered vehicles. A modified version of the Comet seems to have been made by Barrett later but it differs a lot from the T & B, which is a much better model.

Some of the moulds were still around a few years ago and some attempts were made to make models again. These were fairly unsuccessful as casting techniques had changed and the new metals did not have the same flow characteristics as the early lead. Some models are definitely known to have been re-made as they have been seen at a swapmeet some time back, so collectors are advised to be wary.

Editor's note: All the models are rare - any auction prices that become available will be published in the next 'Model Price Review'.

The following listing is of models issued by Taylor and Barrett between 1920 and 1939. Post war production was split between F. G. Taylor & Sons and A. Barrett & Sons, each firm inheriting some moulds and continuing to make some but not all of the models until about 1952.
(FGT) = produced by F. G. Taylor after 1945, (AB) = produced by A. Barrett after 1945

No.	Description	Price
14	Trotting Pony Racer (FGT)	NGPP
15	Turntable Fire Escape (AB)	NGPP
16	Fire Engine and Escape (FGT)	NGPP
17	Fire Engine and Men (FGT)	NGPP
20	Horse Drawn Water Cart (FGT)	NGPP
21	Horse Drawn Brewer's Cart (FGT)	NGPP
22	Horse Drawn Window Cleaner's Cart (FGT)	NGPP
23	Horse Drawn Baker's Cart (FGT)	NGPP
26	Roman Chariot (FGT)	NGPP
27	Donkey Drawn Coster Cart with Dog and Boy (FGT)	NGPP
28	Donkey Drawn Coster Cart, Plants load, Walking Coster (FGT)	NGPP
28a	Donkey Drawn Coster Cart, Vegetable load, Walking Coster (FGT)	NGPP
29	Ice Cream Bicycle, 'ICE BRICKS' logo (FGT)	NGPP
36	Milk Float and Milkman (AB)	NGPP
42	Fire Escape and Team of Firemen (FGT)	NGPP
43	Air and Land Postal Service Set (-)	NGPP
49	Street Cleaning Barrow with two Bins (FGT)	NGPP
92	Llama Cart (FGT)	NGPP
92a	Donkey Cart (FGT)	NGPP
109	Pony Drawn Governor's Cart (AB)	NGPP
109a	Pony Drawn Cart (AB)	NGPP
111	Saloon Car (-)	NGPP
112	Transport Lorry (-)	NGPP
113	'ROYAL MAIL' Van (-)	NGPP
114	'AMBULANCE', Grey (Wartime civilian) (-)	NGPP
114a	'AMBULANCE', Khaki (Army) (-)	NGPP
115	Sports Car (-)	NGPP
116	Coupé (-)	NGPP
117	'AMBULANCE', (Street, civilian) (-)	NGPP
119	Racer (AB)	NGPP
120	Fire Engine (AB)	NGPP
123	Atlanta Touring Plane (AB)	NGPP
124	'AIR MAIL' Van (AB)	NGPP
128	Petrol Tanker (-)	NGPP
129	Breakdown Lorry (-)	NGPP
137	DH 'Comet' Aeroplane (AB)	NGPP
138	'AIR MAIL' Streamline Van (-)	NGPP
139	Saloon Car (-)	NGPP
152	Streamline Motor Coach (-)	NGPP
163	Streamline Fire Engine (-)	NGPP
197	Trolley Bus (small) (AB)	NGPP
204	Trolley Bus (large) (AB)	NGPP
302	Horse Drawn Covered Wagon (-)	NGPP
304	Sledge and Dogs (-)	NGPP
306	Aeroplane Set (Comet and Atlanta aircraft and pilots) (FGT)	NGPP
307	Fire Brigade Set (-)	NGPP
310	Rickshaw pulled by Chinese Coolie (FGT)	NGPP
311	Light Trailer Fire Pump in Action Set (-) (see black/white picture)	NGPP
?	Space Ship (-)	NGPP
?	Coronation Coach (small) (AB)	NGPP
?	State Landau Coach (-)	NGPP
?	Farmer's Gig (FGT)	NGPP
?	Farm Cart with Trotting Horse (-)	NGPP
?	Mobile Animal Trailer and Vet (-)	NGPP
No ref	Racing Car, Red body with 'MG Magnette' cast into side, 110 mm. 'FGT & SONS'	NGPP
No ref	Petrol Pumps, Black/White with rubber hoses (T&B)	NGPP

The listing has been compiled from original manufacturer's records by Mr Norman Joplin to whom the Editor would like to express his grateful thanks. Thanks are also due to Mr J.R. Anderson of Queensland, Australia and Ross Kennett of Roscoes Relics, South Australia, Australia for kindly sending new model information.

TIMPO TOYS

Robert Newson has provided this history and listing of cast metal Timpo motor vehicles.

The name Timpo comes from 'Toy Importers Ltd'. It was only with the outbreak of war in 1939 that Timpo started to manufacture their own lines, when importing became impossible. A few vehicles were made in 1940-41, but the main Timpo range started in 1946. The models were cheap and sturdy, if somewhat crude, and many have survived. Relatively few suffer from metal fatigue.

In 1949 Timpo advertised "faithful replicas of famous delivery services" and introduced several vans with attractive advertising liveries. An AEC Monarch lorry in the livery of Vaux brewery was introduced around 1950, and this was a far better model than the earlier toys. Sadly it was not the first of a new range – the 1951-2 ban on the use of zinc meant that Timpo discontinued all their diecast vehicles. Some of the dies were subsequently sold to Benbros, including the AEC lorry.

Timpo Toys are very rarely seen in mint condition, and prices are therefore quoted for good original condition.

Dates given are the approximate year of introduction.

Year	Model Type	Model Features and Size	Market Price Range	
1940	MG Record Car	Hollow-cast lead. Red, TIMPO TOYS cast on side, 98 mm.	£20-25	☐
1940	Streamlined Saloon	Separate body and chassis. Timpo in script underneath. 99 mm.	£30-40	☐
1940	Pick-Up Truck	Separate body and chassis. Timpo in script underneath. Re-issued post-war with name blanked out. 97 mm.	£30-40	☐
1940	Four-light Saloon	Possibly re-issue of a Goody Toy. Details unknown	NGPP	☐
1946	MG Record Car	Zinc diecast. TIMPO TOYS cast at rear on offside. 97 mm.	£10-15	☐
1946	'American Star' Racer	Star transfer on each side, 101 mm.	£10-15	☐
1946	'Timpo Saloon'	Possibly a Morris 8. 93 mm	£10-15	☐
1946	Austin 16 Saloon	Black. TIMPO TOYS underneath. 96 mm.	£30-40	☐
		Re-issued by Betal in three versions:		
		1. No name on model, brass wheel hubs	£30-40	☐
		2. A BETAL PRODUCT under roof, tin base with friction motor, brass wheel hubs	£30-40	☐
		3. As 2. but with plastic body rather than diecast	NGPP	☐
1946	MG Midget	Composition wheels. 82 mm.	£15-20	☐
1946	Packard Saloon	Fitted with aluminium baseplate and friction motor from 1948. 113 mm.	£10-15	☐
1946	Speed of the Wind Record Car	Similar to the Dinky Toy. 99 mm.	£10-15	☐
1947	Alvis 14 Saloon	A big four-light saloon. 106 mm.	£15-20	☐
1947	'Utility Van'	Fitted with aluminium baseplate and friction motor from 1948. 102 mm. (early casting) or 104 mm. (later casting).		
		1. No transfers, numerous colours, without motor	£10-15	☐
		2. Black, TYRESOLES SERVICE transfers, no motor	£30-40	☐
		3. "HIS MASTER'S VOICE" transfers, pale Yellow, Orange-Yellow, pale Blue or Green, with or without motor	£30-40	☐
1947	Articulated Petrol Tanker	No transfers. Re-issued by Benbros. 149 mm.	£10-15	☐
1947	Lincoln Convertible	A very approximate model of the 1942 Lincoln. Aluminium baseplate and windscreen. Most models in single colours (many different). Late version in cream with blue seats. 115 mm.	£15-20	☐
1947	Armstrong-Siddeley Hurricane	A coupe with top up. 105 mm.	£15-20	☐
1947	Streamlined Fire Engine	Red, two Yellow aluminium ladders. Fitted with aluminium baseplate and friction motor in 1949. 105 mm.	£25-30	☐
1947	Articulated Box Van	Re-issued by Benbros. 146 mm		
		1. Green, Blue or Red trailer with TIMPO TOYS transfers	£25-30	☐
		2. Black cab and trailer with Grey roof, Red wheel hubs, PICKFORDS transfers	£25-30	☐
		3. Orange cab and trailer, Black roof, UNITED DAIRIES transfers	£30-40	☐
		4. Light Blue cab, Light Blue and Cream trailer, WALL'S ICE CREAM transfers	£30-40	☐
		5. Dark Blue cab and trailer with off-White roof, LYONS TEA transfers	£30-40	☐
		6. Pale Yellow cab and trailer, transfers with BISHOPS MOVE logo and BISHOP & SONS DEPOSITORIES LTD. 10-12 BELGRAVE ROAD LONDON, S.W.1.	£30-40	☐
		7. Pale Yellow cab and trailer, transfers with BISHOPS MOVE logo and JOHN H. LUNN LTD. 6 HOPE CRESCENT EDINBURGH	£30-40	☐
1947	'London Taxi'	Cast in two parts. 94 mm.	£20-25	☐
1947	Alvis 14 Police Car	Police sign and loudspeakers at front of roof, wire aerial behind. Black. 106 mm.	£20-25	☐
1947	Articulated Low Loader	Re-issued by Benbros. 168 mm.	£10-15	☐
1947	Buick Saloon	A very crude model. Composition wheels. 99 mm.	£10-15	☐
1947	Pick-Up Truck	With eight cast-in barrels. 104 mm.	£15-20	☐
1947	Forward Control Tipper Lorry	Cream cab and chassis, Red tipper. 101 mm.	£15-20	☐
1947	Forward Control Luton Van	Same chassis as the tipper. 97 mm.		
		1. No transfers, Black lower half, Light Blue upper half	£15-20	☐
		2. Dark Blue, SMITH'S CRISPS transfers	£30-40	☐
		3. Brown, W.D. & H.O. WILLS transfers	£30-40	☐
1949	Forward Control Box Van	Same chassis as above. Re-issued by Benbros. 96 mm. Dark Blue, CHIVERS JELLIES transfers	£30-40	☐
1949	Normal Control Box Van	Later models with aluminium baseplate and friction motor. 105 mm.		
		1. Dark Blue with White roof, EVER READY transfers, with or without motor.	£25-30	☐
		2. Green, GOLDEN SHRED transfers, with motor	£30-40	☐
1949	Normal Control Petrol Tanker	Red, paper labels reading MOTOR OIL ESSO PETROL. Re-issued by Benbros. 116 mm.	£30-40	☐
1950	AEC Monarch Brewery Lorry	Red. VAUX cast on headboard behind cab, SUNDERLAND cast on cab sides. Brown hollow-cast barrels with VAUX cast on ends. Re-issued by Benbros without the headboard and with other changes. 129 mm.	£50-60	☐

TRI-ANG
SPOT-ON
MODELS

INTRODUCTION

Spot-On Models were introduced in 1959 by Tri-ang Toys to gain a foothold in that area of the market dominated at the time by Dinky Toys and their recently established rivals Corgi Toys.

Tri-ang realised that they had to offer not only a range of features similar to those on their competitors products but something more besides. They decided that collectors would appreciate models that were all made to the same precise scale right across the range. They would thus look right together and qualify as models as much as toys. Most Dinky and Corgi cars were made to a scale of 1:43 (with a few exceptions). Tri-ang advertised the precise nature of their (larger) chosen scale as being 'spot-on' at 1:42.

A large modern factory in Belfast, Northern Ireland, produced the models. A coloured picture of the real vehicle was included in the box of most early issues. Well over a hundred different models were designed and production continued till about the time that Tri-ang bought up Dinky Toys in 1967. It has been confirmed for us by Mr Richard Lines (of Tri-ang's parent company Lines Brothers), that the Spot-On company was wound up as a normal business process and not (as was previously thought) as a result of fire damage. After the cessation of UK production, some Spot-On dies went to New Zealand where some interesting versions were produced for a couple of years.

All Spot-On models are highly collectable today particularly commercial vehicles, buses and the Presentation and Gift Sets.

Spot-On model identification

Makers Name and Trade Mark are clearly marked on base of the model ('SPOT-ON' and 'Models by Tri-ang'). Some New Zealand produced versions have nothing at all on the base.

Model name is shown on base, for example: 'Ford Zodiac' (except some New Zealand versions).

Model number is usually shown on box but not always on the model.

Scale of models is 1:42 (with very few exceptions) and is usually (but not always) shown on the base.

Wheel hubs on cars are usually spun or turned aluminium with a raised 'hub cap'.

Wheel hubs on trucks are usually diecast and more accurate representations of the real things. Rear twin wheels have special 'double tyres'.

Number plates are represented on most Spot-On models with the exception of those having plastic chassis (such as 266 Bull Nose Morris and 279 MG Midget). The same numbers were used on different models. Multiple numbers used on same models see the 122 'UNITED DAIRIES' Milk Float. Please advise the editor of Number Plates not listed.

Windscreens and windows are included in all vehicle models.

Dashboards fully detailed on sports cars.

Tyres are of black rubber on all the vehicle models.

Other features include seats and steering wheel on most models, suspension on most cars, driver, other figures and lorry loads with some.

Colours are all listed where known though different and previously unknown colours still come to light occasionally.

Prices shown in the 'Market Price Range' column are for mint models in pristine boxes. These models are hence their high market prices. The condition of models generally encountered usually tends towards the average and consequently command lower prices. Similarly, rare colours or combinations of colours puts the price into the higher part of the range with common colours achieving a more moderate price level.

Spot-On Cars

Ref. No.	Year(s)	Model Type	Model Features and Size	Market Price Range	
100	1959	Ford Zodiac (without lights).....	Red/Cream or Blue/Cream body, 107 mm.	£60-80	☐
			Red or Cream body, 'WD 131'.	£60-80	☐
			Light Blue, Yellow, Salmon-Pink or Green body, 'LBL 100'	£65-90	☐
			Bluish-Grey and Brownish-Pink body	£75-100	☐
			Grey/Blue body	£65-90	☐
100sl	1959	Ford Zodiac with lights.............	Grey/Turquoise or Grey/Pink body, 'TRI 100' or 'LBL 100'	£75-90	☐
			Grey/White, Grey/Light Blue, or Green/White body..............................	£65-85	☐
			Yellow/White, Grey/Green, or Two-tone Blue body	£65-85	☐
101	1959	Armstrong Siddeley 236 Sapphire	Blue/Grey, Turquoise/Black, Blue/Black, Pink or Mauve body, 'TRI 101'. 108 mm. ..	£100-130	☐
			Metallic Green, Metallic Green/Black, or Bluish-Grey	£65-95	☐
			Light Blue body, 'NML 119'	£95-120	☐
			Light Blue/Black, Grey/Black body..	£95-120	☐
			Pale Green/Metallic Charcoal, or Deep Lilac/Black roof	£80-100	☐
			Cream/Metallic Charcoal or Metallic Blue/Black	£65-95	☐
			Yellow body, Black roof	£150-175	☐
102	1959	Bentley Continental 4-door Sports...................................	Metallic Green/Silver 'SGM 102', or Metallic Grey/Blue. 127 mm.	£100-130	☐
			Metallic Maroon/Silver, 'BML 821'	£175-195	☐
			Two-tone Grey or Silver/Grey, 'LBL 100' or Green/Grey, 'BTW 115'........	£95-120	☐
			Silver/Light Blue or Grey/Light Blue body	£120-145	☐

Ref. No.	Year(s)	Model Type	Description	Market Price Range	
103	1959	Rolls Royce Silver Wraith........	Metallic Silver and Maroon body (White seats), Metallic Silver and Metallic Light Blue (Cream seats), or Metallic Silver and Metallic Green body, 'LTP 103' or 'FTZ 102', 131 mm.	£140-180	☐
104	1959	M.G. 'MGA' Sports Car:..........	Beige or Blue body, 'BMP 104', 95 mm.	£100-140	☐
			Red body (Grey seats), 'PZL 108', or Pale Blue (White seats)..........	£110-135	☐
			Turquoise 'BMP 104', or Cream body (White seats)..........	£100-130	☐
			Salmon Pink (Grey seats), or Bluish-Green (Lemon seats)..........	£140-170	☐
			Deep Green body (White seats), 'SGM 102'	£175-200	☐
105	1959	Austin Healey 100/6	Yellow (White or Grey seats), Grey (Red seats), Beige (Grey seats), 'VYD 131', 89 mm.	£130-160	☐
			Blue, Green, Cream, Turquoise, Metallic Blue, Metallic Green, or Pink body..........	£125-155	☐
			Light Blue body (Royal Blue seats) 'LXQ 111' or 'SLT 105'..........	£150-180	☐
107	1960	Jaguar XK-SS..........	Metallic Blue body, Lemon seats, Black folded hood..........	£150-195	☐
			Cream or Red body, ('FTZ 107'), or Light Green body, ('WTB 647')..........	£100-140	☐
			Dark Olive (Light Grey seats/hood), or Pale Blue (Pale Grey seats/hood)..........	£150-175	☐
			Lilac body with Grey seats, Black folded hood..........	£175-225	☐
			Light Blue with Dark Blue seats and folded hood..........	£135-195	☐
			Light Grey body, Pale Blue seats and folded hood..........	£195-235	☐
108	1960	Triumph TR3a Sports	Light Blue or Red body, Grey seats, 'WTB 647'. 88 mm.	£100-140	☐
			Cream body with Dark Brown seats, 'PZL 108'..........	£175-200	☐
			Light Brown body (White seats), or Pale Green body (Grey seats), 'DVM 163'..........	£140-160	☐
			Sea Green body with Grey seats..........	£120-150	☐
			Grey body (White seats), or Metallic Green (Lemon seats)..........	£125-160	☐
112	1960	Jensen 541.....................	Grey, Mauve, Pink, Red/Black or Metallic Green body, 'AOU 218', 106 mm.	£100-125	☐
			Light Blue or Pale Green or Metallic Blue body	£100-125	☐
			Lemon body (Black roof), or Yellow body (Red seats)..........	£100-125	☐
113	1960	Aston Martin DB3 Saloon........	Light Blue, Grey, Red, 'BTW 115', Light or Dark Green body, 104 mm.	£125-150	☐
			Very Pale Pink or Deep Pink body	£100-130	☐
			Deep Lilac or Light Brown body	£140-160	☐
			White or Metallic Dark Green body	£130-160	☐
			Metallic Silver Blue body..........	£130-160	☐
			Yellow body, Lemon interior, Red steering wheel	£175-225	☐
114	1960	Jaguar 3.4 Mark 1 Saloon........	Metallic Blue, Maroon, Mauve, Metallic Green, or Pink, 108 mm.	£125-150	☐
			Light Grey or Mid-Green body	£140-175	☐
			Light Blue, Yellow or Red body	£110-140	☐
			White body	£160-180	☐
115	1960	Bristol 406 Saloon	Orange, Red, or Grey body, 116 mm.	£100-130	☐
			Metallic Dark Steel body	£160-180	☐
			Yellow or Metallic Greenbody	£100-160	☐
118	1960	BMW Isetta Bubble Car	Pale Blue, Beige or Turquoise, 'BML 112' or 'CMO 118' or 'LBL 100', 56 mm.	£65-75	☐
			Green or Metallic Green, Red, Pink or Yellow body	£75-95	☐
119	1960	Meadows Frisky Sport	Orange/Grey, Blue/Grey or Turquoise/Grey, 'MIP 119' or 'OVM 163'	£45-65	☐
			Red/Light Grey, Red/Black, or Light Blue/White, 69 mm.	£75-95	☐
			Bluish-Green/Black 'PZL 108', or Red/White body	£80-100	☐
120	1960	Fiat Multipla Estate	Blue (Cream seats), or Mauve (Red seats), 'TXY 120', 85 mm.	£70-80	☐
			Pink, Light Blue 'GTM 742', Yellow, Red or Dark Red body	£85-105	☐
			Sea Green or Pale Green body	£95-115	☐
131	1960	Goggomobil 'Super' Regent	Grey/Black, Yellow/Black, Mauve/Black, Blue/Grey, Blue, Green, Grey, Red or Turquoise, 'SGM 102' or 'VYD 121'..........	£60-70	☐
			Metallic Green, Beige, Light Grey, Pink or Deep Salmon Pink body, 'GTM 110'	£55-65	☐
			Light Blue/Black, Red/Black, Dark Blue/Black, Green/Black, 70 mm.	£55-65	☐
154	1961	Austin A40 Farina Saloon	Green, Grey, White, Blue/White or Grey/Blue, 'SGM 102'	£50-60	☐
			Light Grey, Metallic Blue, Beige, Light Blue or Turquoise body, 'AXM 124'	£55-75	☐
			Red/Black, Blue/Black, Green/Black, Lavender/Black, 88 mm.	£60-80	☐
	1966/7	'MAGGI' Promotional..............	Red body, Cream interior, 'MAGGI' in Yellow on front doors, Reg No 'FTZ 107'. Housed in special Red/yellow box with leaflet	£400-500	☐
157	1963	Rover 3-litre (without lights).....	Mid Blue, Mauve 'LXQ 218' or Yellow, 'BTW 115' or 'TRL 157'..........	£70-90	☐
			Grey, Pale Grey, Sea Green, Dark Green, Light Blue, 107 mm.	£85-115	☐
			Dark Blue or Dark Grey body	£120-150	☐
			White body	£95-125	☐
157sl	1963	Rover 3-litre with lights	Mid Blue, Mauve, Red or Yellow 'BTW 115'..........	£90-120	☐
			Grey, Pale Grey, Sea Green, Dark Green, Light Blue, 107 mm.	£85-115	☐
			Dark Blue or Dark Grey body	£120-150	☐
			White body	£95-125	☐
165/1	1961	Vauxhall PA Cresta Saloon	Beige, Red, Maroon, Pink, Turquoise or Yellow, 'WXD 219', 115 mm.	£80-100	☐
			Blue, Light Blue, Grey or Light Grey	£90-120	☐
			Plum Red or Sea Green body	£100-120	☐
165/2	1961	PA Cresta with roof rack	Beige, Red, Maroon, Pink, Turquoise or Yellow, 'JPO 113', 115 mm.	£80-100	☐
			Blue, Light Blue, Grey or Light Grey	£90-120	☐
			Plum Red or Sea green body	£110-140	☐
166	1962	Renault Floride Convertible......	Blue, Green or Grey body, 'SLT 105' or 'MLP 110', 101 mm.	£70-90	☐
			Dark Red, White 'SMP 104', or Yellow body	£80-100	☐
183	1963	Humber Super Snipe Estate	Beige/White, Blue/White, Green/White, Blue/Black, Beige, Blue, Metallic Bronze or TT-Blue, with or without wing mirrors	£90-120	☐
184	1963	Austin A60 (with skis)..............	Beige, Green or White body, 'LBL 100', 106 mm.	£65-85	☐
			Red, Light Blue or Light Grey (Grey rack)	£75-100	☐
			Lime Green or Greyish-Blue (Black or Grey roof-rack)	£85-120	☐
185	1963	Fiat 500..........	Light Blue, Green, Red 'TPO 106' or Grey body, 'TXY 120'..........	£80-100	☐
191	1963	Sunbeam Alpine Convertible.....	Beige, Mid-Blue, Green, Red, Mauve, Pink or Yellow, 'SLT 105', 95 mm.	£65-85	☐
			Turquoise or Grey (Cream seats), or Light Blue (White seats)	£90-110	☐
			Deep Salmon Pink or White with Red seats	£100-130	☐

Ref. No.	Year(s)	Model Type		Market Price Range	
191/1	1963	Sunbeam Alpine Hardtop	Red/White, Turquoise/White, Blue/Black, Blue/Cream, Beige/White, Grey/Black body and hardtop, 'BML 112', 95 mm.	£65-85	☐
			Dark Green (Red seats), or Metallic Green/Black 'VYD 131'	£95-130	☐
			Pink (Cream seats)	£85-120	☐
			Mauve (Cream seats), or Yellow body (Cream seats)	£120-140	☐
			Light Blue, Light Blue/White, Pale Blue/White	£80-110	☐
193	1963	N.S.U. Prinz	Turquoise, Beige, Pale Blue, Light or Dark Blue, Cream, Grey or Red body, 'PJL 114' or 'AXM 154', 84 mm.	£50-70	☐
			White body	£80-90	☐
195	1963	Volkswagen Rally Car.............	Beige, Cream, Maroon, or Orange body, roof light, flags on bonnet, racing number '9' or '23', 110 mm.	£140-170	☐
			Red body, racing number '11'	£240-280	☐
			Light Blue ('6'), Turquoise ('9'), or Metallic Bronze	£175-220	☐
210	1960	Morris Mini Minor..................	Shown catalogue but not issued	NPP	☐
211	1963	Austin Seven (Mini)	Light Blue, Grey, Red or Yellow body, 'LRT 145' or 'WTB 511', 73 mm.	£120-150	☐
			Pink body	£200-250	☐
			White body 'DVM 163'	£160-180	☐
213	1963	Ford Anglia Saloon.................	Cream, Grey or White body 'MLP 119', 95 mm.	£70-90	☐
			Turquoise, Light Blue, Dark Blue or Pink 'PJL 114'	£130-160	☐
215	1961	Daimler Dart SP250	Beige, Green or Yellow body, 'MLP 119', 75 mm.	£80-120	☐
			White (Red seats), or Light Blue (Blue seats)	£140-160	☐
			Turquoise (White seats), or Red (Cream seats)	£90-125	☐
216	1963	Volvo 122s	Red or Orange body, 'VYD 131', sliding roof, 110 mm.	£80-100	☐
			Blue, Grey, Turquoise, Yellow Ochre, Dark Green or Lime Green	£90-125	☐
217	1963	Jaguar 'E' Type	Beige, Cream, Light or Dark Green, Red, White or Yellow/Black, 'PML 511'	£90-120	☐
			Mid-Blue or Light Grey body	£95-130	☐
			Light Blue body	£200-240	☐
218	1963	Jaguar Mk.10...........................	Metallic Brown, Blue, Bronze or White, 'RBG 218', 122 mm.	£90-120	☐
			Dark or Mid-Green	£110-150	☐
219	1963	Austin-Healey Sprite Mk.III	Red (White seats), Blue (Red seats), Beige (White seats); Grey driver, Yellow scarf, 'WXD 219' or 'CMO 118' or 'VYD 131', 84 mm.	£80-100	☐
			Off-White or Light Blue body 'FTZ 107'	£95-125	☐
259	1963	Ford Consul Classic	White (Blue seats), Beige (White seats); or Blue, Light Blue, Red, Grey or Green body, 'PZL 108' or 'WTB 925' or 'RDG 151', 105 mm.	£80-100	☐
260	1963	Royal Rolls-Royce Phantom V	Maroon body, Blue interior, 2 flags on roof, Queen & Prince Philip in rear seats, driver & passenger in front. 143 mm.	£300-400	☐
261	1963	Volvo P1800	1: bonnet & boot open, spare wheel, Light Blue, Red, Turquoise 'LMB 134'	£80-100	☐
			2: only bonnet opens, Blue, Grey or Metallic Bronze 'PML 571'	£80-100	☐
262	1963	Morris 1100	Dark Blue or Red (Grey seats), Green or Beige (Red seats), 'LXQ 216', 89 mm.	£60-80	☐
			Lime Green or Light Blue body 'LRT 145'	£65-85	☐
263	1964	Bentley 4½ Litre (Supercharged)	Green body, Union Jack, racing number '27', '11' or '15' 'YU 3250', 108 mm.	£55-75	☐
266	1965	Bull Nose Morris 1923	Red/Black or Yellow/Black, Brown driver, (scale 1:48) 'IB 2009'	£40-50	☐
267	1964	M.G. 1100 Saloon	White/Dark Green (Red seats), Red (Cream seats), or Green (Red seats), or Red/White or Beige/Cream, 'PML 511', 88 mm.	£55-70	☐
			Royal Blue/White, 'LBL 100', Red interior	£350-450	☐
268	1965	Vauxhall PB Cresta	Shown in catalogue but not issued under this number, see 280	NPP	☐
270	1965	Ford Zephyr 6 Mk.III..............	Blue, Cream, Green, Greyish-Green or Grey (Red seats); or Red (Grey seats), 'LXO 913' or 'TXY 120' or 'KTJ 578' or 'VYD 131' or 'FTZ 107', 110 mm.	£65-90	☐
274	1965	Morris 1100 and Canoe............	Green, Grey, Light Blue, Dark Blue or Red car, Brown canoe on roof, 'DCY 472' ...	£45-65	☐
			Light Blue or Two-tone Green (Red canoe) or Red (Red/White canoe)	£60-85	☐
			Light Blue body 'OCY 472C' with Blue/Red canoe, Orange paddle (Set 703)	GSP	☐
276	1964	Jaguar 'S' type	Metallic Gold body, 'RBG 218' or 'VYD 131', 114 mm.	£120-150	☐
			Metallic Green	£120-150	☐
278	1965	Mercedes-Benz 230 SL	Metallic Red, Cream, or Maroon body, 'RVN 163', or 'NVM 278', 100 mm.	£75-100	☐
			Metallic Blue or Metallic Bronze	£85-115	☐
279	1965	M.G. PB Midget 1935..............	Dark Blue or Red body, Black wings & seats, 'CMY 749', 79 mm.	£50-65	☐
280	1963	Vauxhall PB Cresta	Red/Beige, Dark Blue/Cream or Grey/Green body 'VCS 165' or 'BVM 163'	£55-70	☐
281	1966	M.G. Midget Mk.II...................	Blue or Red body, Driver with scarf, 'GTM 742', 83 mm.	£75-100	☐
		New Zealand issue:........	Dark Green body, boxed in striped, N.Z. box	£150-200	☐
286	1965	Austin 1800.............................	Light or Dark Blue, Cream, Green or Beige (all with Red seats); or Red (Grey seats), 'BVM 163' or 'VCS 165', 100 mm.	£60-75	☐
287	1965	Hillman Minx (with roof-rack) and Luggage......................	Pale Green, Beige, Cream or Green (all with Red seats) Red (Grey seats) or Greyish-Green body, 'NTB 647' or 'LXQ 973', Two brown suitcases, 84 mm.	£60-85	☐
287/1	1965	Hillman Minx (with roof rack)	Same details as 287	£60-85	☐
289	1963	Morris Minor 1000..................	Metallic Blue or Light Blue body 'VYD 131'	£120-150	☐
			Red or Metallic Green body 'PML 511'	£160-200	☐
306	1964	Humber Super Snipe Estate	Same casting as 183 but with roof-rack and two suitcases.		
			Beige 'LBL 100', Blue, Green or Red body, 'SQM 501', 113 mm.	£100-140	☐
			Metallic Bronze	£100-150	☐
			Light Blue (White roof-rack) or Turquoise (White roof-rack) 'LBL 100'	£110-145	☐
			White and Turquoise body, Grey roof-rack, 113 mm.	£120-140	☐
			Blue body, White roof	£120-140	☐
307	1965	Volkswagen Beetle 1200	Metallic Blue or Metallic Dark Red body, 'RBG 218', 110 mm.	£145-195	☐
308	1965	Land Rover & Trailer	Green with Tan plastic canopy, 'VGS 165', trailer has Brown plastic body	£50-60	☐
401	1966	Volkswagen Variant with Skis ..	(New Zealand issue). Dark Blue body, roof rack, 'FYS 799' or 'EDU 458C', 100 mm. Boxed in striped N.Z. box	£500-750	☐
405	1966	'B.E.A.' Vauxhall Cresta	Dark Grey body with Red 'B.E.A.' logo.	£60-70	☐
407	1966	Mercedes-Benz 230 SL	Brown body, Red interior, Boot rack and luggage, 'WTR 647', 103 mm.	£50-60	☐
408	1966	Renault Caravelle	Not issued.	NPP	☐

Ref. No.	Year(s)	Model Type	*Tri-ang Spot-On Cars – continued*	Market Price Range	
410	1966	Austin 1800 and Rowboat	Green, Blue, Beige or Red car with Red or Orange boat on roof, 'ETW 566B' or 'DRX 257C'	£60-70	☐
401/1	1967	VW Variant Estate Car	Dark Blue body, White plastic opening tailgate	NGPP	☐

MAGICAR SERIES

Ref. No.	Year(s)	Model Type		Market Price Range	
501	1965	Jaguar Mk10............................	Blue or Green body, never seen sold	NGPP	☐
502	1965	Rolls Royce Silver Cloud MkIII.....................................	Blue or Red body, never seen sold	NGPP	☐
503	1965	Bentley S3 Saloon.....................	Blue or Red body, never seen sold	NGPP	☐
504		Ferrari Superfast	Blue or Red, never seen sold	NGPP	☐
505	1966	Batmobile.................................	Black body with Batman and Robin figures	£150-175	☐
		Tric Trac car............................	Plastic bodied racing car, never seen sold	NGPP	☐

Spot-On Commercial Vehicles and Vans

Ref. No.	Year(s)	Model Type	Model Features and Size	Market Price Range	
106a/0c	1960	Austin Prime Mover with MGA Sports Car in Crate	Light Blue, 'TPO 106', Dark Blue, or Orange cab. 234 mm..........................	£350-400	☐
106a/1	1959	Austin Prime Mover and Flat Float with Sides	Light Blue, Green or Orange cab and float sides, 234 mm................	£170-200	☐
106a/1c	1960	Austin Prime Mover and Float with Crate Load	Light Blue, Green or Orange cab. 234 mm..............................	£200-250	☐
			Turquoise body	£225-300	☐
CB106	1961-62	Four Wheel Trailer....................	Turquoise or Red body, Drop down tailboard, for use with E.R.F. & A.E.C. lorries, 'TRAILER' & '30' signs on rear	£50-60	☐
109/2	1960	E.R.F. 68g with Flat Float	Turquoise, Orange or Blue body, 'LTP 103', 210 mm.	£160-190	☐
109/2p	1960	E.R.F. 68g and Flat Float (without Sides, with Planks)..	Turquoise body with Black cab roof, Turquoise body or Yellow body. 210 mm.	£160-190	☐
109/3	1960	E.R.F. 68g and Flat Float (with Sides)........................	Dark Blue cab (Pale Blue float), Yellow body (Metallic Grey roof), Green body (Green roof), Blue body or Green body (Black roof), 'PLM 109', 210 mm................	£160-190	☐
			Deep Blue body (Silver chassis), or Orange-Red (Light Grey chassis).........................	£250-300	☐
			Lemon, Pale Green or Turquoise body, Silver chassis..........................	£190-250	☐
109/3b	1960	E.R.F. with sides, Barrel load...	Turquoise, Light Blue or Red body with or without Silver float bed, Drop down tailboard, ten Brown plastic barrels, 210 mm..........................	£200-300	☐
110/2	1960	A.E.C. Mammoth Major 8 and Flat Float (without sides) ..	Red, Blue or Maroon body (with or without Black roof), 210 mm.	£170-200	☐
110/2b	1960	A.E.C. Mammoth Major 8 'London Brick Co Ltd'.........	Red body, Black cab roof, Brown 'brick' load, 210 mm.	£200-250	☐
110/3	1960	A.E.C. Mammoth Major 8 'British Road Services'.........	Red body, with or without Black cab roof. 210 mm.	£200-250	☐
110/3d	1962	A.E.C. Mammoth Major 8 and Oil Drums Load.........	Red body, Black cab roof, Silver trim. 'GTM 110', 210 mm..........................	£300-400	☐
110/4	1961	A.E.C. Mammoth Major 8 'SHELL-BP' Tanker	Green cab, Red tank, Black chassis and catwalk, 'TXY 120', 210 mm...............	£400-500	☐
110/4	1963	A.E.C. Mammoth Major 8 'SHELL-BP' Tanker	Yellow cab, White/Yellow tank, Silver chassis and catwalk, 'RFS 166', 210 mm........	£500-750	☐
111/30g	1962	Ford Thames with Garage Kit..	Orange cab and truck body, Silver chassis. 'LBL 100', 219 mm.	£250-300	☐
			Light Blue cab and truck body, White garage	£250-300	☐
111/a0t	1961	Ford Thames Trader with Three Log Load	Two tone Blue or Red cab and truck body, 3 logs, 219 mm.........................	£250-300	☐
			Light Blue cab and truck body..	£200-275	☐
			Light Yellow cab and truck body..	£300-375	☐
111a/1	1959	Ford Thames Trader 'British Railways'	Maroon and White body, '4884 BG M' on cab and 'M 1741 GT6' logo on trailer. 'LXQ 111', 219 mm.	£200-250	☐
111a/1	1960	Ford Thames Trader 'R.Hall & Son Ltd. Fulham'	Green body, logo on door. Doubtful if model issued.	NPP	☐
111a/1s	1960	Ford Thames with Sack Load...	Dark Blue cab, Pale Blue truck body, Black chassis, 'LXQ 111', 219 mm.	£250-300	☐
			Light Blue and Silver	£275-325	☐
			Bluish-Green body (N.B. Load is 8 plastic sacks)...................................	£300-350	☐
117	1963	'JONES' Mobile Crane	Cream cab & jib, Red body & wheels, Black chassis, Grey base, 'WTB 117'...............	£150-200	☐
			Dark Red cab & body, White jib, Light Grey chassis & base, Silver wheels................	£300-400	☐
122	1961	'UNITED DAIRIES' Milk Float	Red/White body, chains, *'Lada and New Yoghurt'*, 'LTP 103' or 'LBL 100' or 'TPO 106' or 'JPO 113' or 'DVM 163', 98 mm.	£75-95	☐
158a/2	1961	Bedford 'S' Type 2000 Gallon 'SHELL-BP' Tanker	Green cab, Red tank, Black chassis, 'P33A37' logo. 202 mm.........................	£450-500	☐
			'PETROLEUM PRODUCTS' logo on tank		
158a/2	1962	Bedford 'S' Type 2000 Gallon 'SHELL-BP' Tanker	Yellow cab, White tank, Silver trim, 'P33A37' logo. 'PJL 114', 202 mm.	£800-1000	☐
158a/2C	1961	Bedford Low Loader................	Red low-loader with cable drum load. Doubtful if issued............................	NPP	☐

298

Ref. No.	Year(s)	Model Type	*Tri-ang Spot-on Commercial Vehicles – continued*	Market Price Range	
161	1961	Land Rover (long wheelbase)....	Grey/White, Light Grey/White or Blue/White, 108 mm.	£65-80	☐
210	1961	Morris Mini Van	Bright Yellow, seats/steering wheel, suspension	£90-120	☐
210/1	1962	Morris Mini Van 'Royal Mail'	Red body, Post Office crest, 'E-II-R', suspension, 'LXQ 193'.	£70-90	☐
210/2	1962	'Mini Van 'P.O. Telephones'.....	Olive-Green body, Gold crown logo & *TELEPHONE MANAGER*, 'MLP 119'......	£90-100	☐
258	1963	'R.A.C.' Land Rover................	Dark Blue body, *RADIO RESCUE*, 'LTP 103', 108 mm.	£90-120	☐
265	1964	'TONIBELL' Ice Cream Van....	Blue body, thick Red flash, attendant, *Soft Ice Cream*, 'GTM 742', *TONIBELL* logo on doors, 107 mm.	£90-125	☐
		New Zealand issue:.......	Blue body, thin Red flash, *TONIBELL* logo beneath hatch	£125-150	☐
271	1965	'EXPRESS DAIRIES' Milk Float	Blue/White body, 3 wheels, driver, *Drink Express Milk*.	£90-120	☐
273	1965	Commer Van 'SECURITY EXPRESS' ...	Green/Gold, driver and seated guard, coin slot in roof, 'RBG 218', 126 mm...........	£80-100	☐
308	1965	Land Rover and Trailer	Green body, Beige hood, Brown trailer, 107 mm.	£70-80	☐
315	1965	'GLASS & HOLMES' Commer Van.....................	Blue/Yellow, ladder, figures, *Window Cleaning Company Est 1891*	£80-100	☐
402	1966	Crash Service Land Rover	Orange body, *MOTORWAYS CRASH SERVICE*, logo in Blue, 125 mm.	£70-90	☐
404	1966	Morris Mini Van	Yellow body, suspension, ladder, figure, 79 mm.	£300-350	☐
404/1	1966	Morris Mini Van 'SHELL'	As previous model but without ladder and figure	£400-500	☐
404/2	1966	Morris Mini Van 'AA'	Shown in 1966 catalogue but never seen	NGPP	☐

Spot-On Buses, Coaches and Taxis

Ref. No.	Year(s)	Model Type		Market Price Range	
145	1963	Routemaster Bus	Red 'London Transport' bus, route '284', *Ovaltine - The Worlds Best Nightcap*, 198 mm.		
			1st type has chrome moulded radiator, 'BML 112'............................	£500-600	☐
			2nd type has transfer print on plastic background, 'LTR 145'...............	£400-500	☐
155	1961	Austin FX4 Taxi	Maroon body, Cream steering wheel, Green base 'PQT 155', Tin hubcaps.......	NGPP	☐
			Black body, Red steering wheel, Grey base, 'SLT 105'.	£65-80	☐
156	1961	Mulliner Luxury Coach.............	Pale Blue/Grey, Red flash, *Triang Tours*, 'LMC 156', 213 mm.	£300-400	☐
			Yellow/White body, Brown side flash	£1000-1250	☐
			Sea Green/Cream, Red flash	£400-500	☐
			Silver/Red/Dark Blue	£250-350	☐

Miscellaneous Spot-On models

Military and R.A.F. models

Ref. No.	Year(s)	Model Type		Market Price Range	
415	1965	R.A.F. Land Rover..................	Blue/Grey, R.A.F. roundel, hose/pump/attendant, 111 mm.	£80-100	☐
416	1965	Leyland Army Ambulance	Olive Green body. Not issued..	NPP	☐
417	1965	Military 'FIELD KITCHEN' ...	Olive Green body, squadron markings, suspension, 108 mm.	£100-125	☐
418	1965	Leyland Military Bus..............	Olive Green body, *Army Personnel*. Not issued	NPP	☐
419	1965	Land Rover and Missile Carrier...................	Olive Green body, 3 White Missiles	£200-250	☐

Roadmaking vehicles and Tractors

Ref. No.	Year(s)	Model Type		Market Price Range	
116	1959	Caterpillar Tractor D9	Brown/Silver body, Black rubber tracks, 153 mm............................ 'CATERPILLAR' on front & sides of engine and on working blade plus 'CAT D9' on rearside	£500-750	☐
123	1959	Bamford Excavator	Red/Yellow, *J.C.B.*. Intended model but not issued	NPP	☐
137	1962	'MASSEY FERGUSON 65' Tractor................................	Red/Silver/Blue body, smooth front tyres, treaded rear tyres, 79 mm........	£500-750	☐

Three of a kind: No.122 'UNITED DAIRIES' Milk Floats with Red bodies. Note the different registration numbers. Picture kindly supplied by Christie's of South Kensington, London and reproduced by their kind permission.

Fire, Police and Ambulance models

Ref. No.	Year(s)	Model Type	Description	Market Price Range	
207	1964	Wadham Ambulance with stretcher patient	Cream body without Red crosses, *'ACCIDENT'* & *'AMBULANCE'* sign, 'LBL 100'	£200-300	☐
			White body with Red crosses, *'ACCIDENT'* & *'AMBULANCE'* sign, 'BML 112'	£350-450	☐
256	1966	Jaguar 3.4 'POLICE' Car	White or Black. Very few with undamaged aerial or roof sign, 'SGM 102'	£200-275	☐
309	1965	Police 'Z' Car	Ford Zephyr police car from the BBC-TV series 'Z-Cars', 'TXY 120'		
			1st type with aerial and 'POLICE' sign, White body	£100-130	☐
			2nd type with no aerial or police sign, Black body	£600-700	☐
			2nd type, White body	£500-600	☐
316	1966	'FIRE DEPT' Land Rover	Red body, suspension, 2 firemen, 112 mm.	£80-100	☐
402	1966	Land Rover 'MOTORWAYS'	Orange/Blue body, hook, Blue 'CRASH SERVICE' logo	£70-90	☐
409	1966	Leyland 'Black Maria'	Blue body, *'Police'*, policeman & villain. Not issued	NPP	☐

Caravans, Boats, Motor Scooter

Ref. No.	Year(s)	Model Type	Description	Market Price Range	
135	1961	14ft Sailing Dinghy/Trailer	Blue/Grey, Dark Blue/Red, Dark Blue/White or Red/White boat (with or without cover), plastic trailer 117 mm.	£40-55	☐
135	1964	14ft GP Sailing Dinghy	Brown or Yellow boat on trailer, 128 mm.	£35-45	☐
139	1960	Eccles E.16 Caravan	Blue body, White roof, 146 mm.	NPP	☐
229	1966	Lambretta	Blue body, Red or White rear casing, 'GCM 229'	£150-200	☐
264	1962	Tourist Caravan	Blue body, White roof, 152 mm.	£45-55	☐

'Cotswold Village' series

Buildings and larger items:

1 School, 2a Haystack, 3 'Cornerstones' Cottage, 4 'Fourways' Cottage, 'The Cot' Cottage, 5 Antique Shop, General Store, 7 Bourton Town Hall, 8 Barn, 9 Public House, 10 Farm House, 11 Manor House, 12 Post Office, 13 Church, 14 Forge

Miscellaneous items:

Stocks, Memorial Stone, Set of Trees, Stone Bridge Sides

All the 'Cotswold Village' items are rare and it is suggested that larger buildings (church, shop, etc) are likely to be in the region of **£100 - £150**, while smaller buildings and miscellaneous items might be anything from **£10 - £50** depending on size, complexity, etc. Note however that these price levels can only be applied to items in pristine condition having no appreciable 'sag' or softness caused by ageing or sunlight.

Garage and Equipment

Ref. No.	Model Type	Description	Market Price Range	
L146/7/8	'SHELL' items	L146 Lamp standard, L147 'SHELL' sign, L148 Red/Yellow petrol pump. Each	£10-15	☐
L148	Trade pack	Blue card box containing 6 of L148 pumps	£80-100	☐
L149	Oil Dispenser Rack		£10-15	☐
L159	'BP' Lamp Standard		£10-15	☐
162	'BP' or 'SHELL' Filling Station		£35-45	☐
162/1/2/3	Garages	Each	£15-20	☐
163	'BP' Petrol Pump		£10-15	☐
164	'BP' Forecourt Sign		£10-15	☐
172a	'SHELL' Garage Set		£50-75	☐
172b	'BP' Garage Set		£50-75	☐

Road Signs and accessories (see also Gift Sets)

Ref. No.	Model Type	Description	Market Price Range	
	Road Traffic Signs	Twenty different signs were issued, each	£10-15	☐
L1271/	Road Direction Signs	/1 Portsmouth, /2 Guildford, /3 Bristol, /4 Birmingham, /5 Biggar, /6 Dumfries	£10-15	☐
	Bus Stops	No details available	£10-15	☐
	Road sections	Straights, curves, T-junctions. Each	£6-8	☐
	Plastic Figures	In groups set on a card. Figures include Garage Personnel, Newspaperman, Milkman, Postman, Doctor, Policeman, Schoolboys, Children, 3 Roadmen & Brazier or 3 Roadmen & Road Drill/Planks/Walls. Per card	£5-10	☐

Spot-On Presentation and Gift Sets

Ref. No.	Year(s)	Set Name	Contents	Market Price Range	

Presentation Sets

Ref. No.	Year(s)	Set Name	Contents	Market Price Range	
A	1960	Presentation Set 'A'	102 Bentley (Lilac/Silver), 108 Triumph TR3 (Green body, Grey seats), 114 Jaguar 3.4 (Green), 118 BMW Isetta (Pale Green), 154 Austin A40 (Red/Black)	£350-400	☐
No.0	1960	Presentation Set	106a/1 Austin Prime-Mover and Flat Float, 100 Ford Zodiac, 103 Rolls-Royce Silver Wraith, 104 MGA and 113 Aston Martin	£500-600	☐
No.1	1960	Presentation Set	100 Ford Zodiac, 101 Armstrong-Siddely, 103 Rolls-Royce and 104 MGA	£600-700	☐
No.2	1960	Presentation Set	109/3 ERF with Flat Float, 101 Armstrong-Siddely, 102 Bentley Continental and 105 Austin-Healey 100/6	£600-700	☐
No.3	1960	Presentation Set	Contains 111a/1 Ford Thames Trader, 101 Armstrong-Siddely, 104 MGA, 108 Triumph TR3a, 112 Jensen 541, 113 Aston Martin, 114 Jaguar 3.4	£600-750	☐
No.4	1960	Presentation Set	106a/1 Austin Prime-Mover and Flat Float, 109/3 ERF with Flat Float, 100 Ford Zodiac, 107 Jaguar XK-SS, 112 Jensen 541	£400-500	☐

Ref. No.	Year(s)	Model Type	*Tri-ang Spot-On Gift Sets – continued*	Market Price Range	
No.4a	1963	Presentation Set	Contains 104 MGA, 105 Austin-Healey, 107 Jaguar XK-SS and 108 Triumph TR3a	£400-500	☐
No.5		Presentation Set	118 BMW Isetta, 119 Meadows Frisky Sport and 131 Goggomobil Super Regent	£200-250	☐
No.6		'Miniature' Presentation Set	131 Goggomobil, 185 Fiat 500, 193 NSU Prinz and 211 Austin Seven	£300-400	☐
			Variation with 210/1 *'ROYAL MAIL'* Van instead of 193 NSU Prinz	£300-400	☐
No.6a		'Miniature' Presentation Set	131 Goggomobil, 185 Fiat 500, 119 Meadows Frisky and 211 Austin Seven	£350-450	☐
No.7		Rally Presentation Set	Contains 166 Renault Floride, 191 Sunbeam Alpine, 211 Austin Seven, 213 Ford Anglia, 215 Daimler Dart, 217 Jaguar 'E'-type	£500-600	☐
No.8		Presentation Set	Contains 157 Rover 3 litre, 191 Sunbeam Alpine, 213 Ford Anglia, 216 Volvo 122s, 258 RAC Land Rover	£500-600	☐
No.9		Presentation Set	Contains 122 Milk Float, 145 Routemaster Bus, 193 NSU Prinz, 207 Wadham Ambulance, 211 Austin Seven, 256 Jaguar Police Car	NGPP	☐
No.10		Presentation Set	Contains 122 Austin Seven, 145 Routemaster Bus, 157 Rover 3 litre, 158a/2 Bedford Tanker, 165 Vauxhall Cresta, 166 Renault Floride, 185 Fiat 500, 211 Austin Seven, 215 Daimler Dart and 262 Morris 1100	£400-500	☐
No.14		Presentation Set	Contains 211 Austin 7 Mini, 154 Austin A40, 156 Mullinee Coach, 191/1 Sunbeam Alpine (Hardtop), 122 'UNITED DAIRIES' Milk Float, 157sl Rover 3 Litre with lights	£500-600	☐
173		Terrapin Building Set	A constructional set	£20-30	☐
208/a		Road Construction Set	4 workmen, brazier, hut, poles, road sections and 18 other small items	£125-175	☐
259		Garage Set	A constructional set	£20-30	☐
701		'His, Her's, Junior's' Set	219 Austin-Healey Sprite, 267 MG 1100, 280 Vauxhall PB Cresta, in 'window' box	£200-250	☐
702		Gift Set 702	270 Zephyr Six, 274 Morris 1100 and canoe, 286 Austin 1800 and 135 Dinghy	£200-250	☐
702(a)		Gift Set 702	195 VW Rally, 217 Jaguar 'E' type, 261 Volvo P1800, 287 Hillman Minx	£300-350	☐
212	1963	Car, Dinghy & Trailer Set	Contains 165 Vauxhall PA Cresta and 135 GP Dinghy	£125-150	☐
269	1965	Ford Zephyr Six and Caravan	Contains 270 plus 264 Caravan. 262 mm.	£125-175	☐
308	1965	Land Rover and Trailer	Green bodywork, Fawn cover, 'LTR 145', 170 mm.	£65-85	☐
406	1966	Hillman Minx and Dinghy Set	Contains 287 Hillman Minx and 135 GP Dinghy and trailer. Various colours	£70-95	☐

N.B. Early Sets should contain Picture cards, Fleet owners and Magazine Club leaflets.

'Tommy Spot' series Gift Sets (all include a building kit and Tommy Spot figure)

801		Home with Tommy Spot	287 Hillman Minx (with Mr Spot), 270 Ford Zephyr Six with driver	£200-275	☐
802		Cops 'n Robbers with Tommy Spot	309 BBC-TV 'Z-Car' with driver & criminal, 276 Jaguar & driver	£275-350	☐
803		Superville Garage with Tommy Spot	286 Austin 1800 with driver, 279 MG Midget, 2 garage workers	£200-275	☐
804		Sailing with Tommy Spot	280 Vauxhall PB Cresta and sailing dinghy with Tommy and Mr Spot	£150-225	☐
805		Fire with Tommy Spot	316 Fire Dept Land Rover and trailer, two firefighters	£195-260	☐
806		Royal Occasion with Tommy Spot	260 Royal Rolls-Royce with chauffeur and royal passengers, 6 guardsmen	£450-650	☐
807		Pit stop with Tommy Spot	Mercedes-Benz 230 SL and Jaguar 'S', 2 racing drivers	£300-400	☐
808		Motorway Rescue with Tommy Spot	402 'Crash Service' Land Rover and mechanic, A.A. van & man	£400-500	☐

Spot-On New Zealand Issues

When Tri-ang took over the production of Dinky Toys in 1967 they stopped production of Spot-On Models in the United Kingdom. Fourteen models were subsequently produced by the Tri-ang Pedigree company of New Zealand from the original dies sent out from the U.K. New Zealand production lasted just 2 years and ceased in 1969/70. The New Zealand model reference numbers were different to their U.K. counterparts as listed in the Spot-On 7th Edition catalogue. Extras such as roof racks and luggage were not included with N.Z. issues. The following listing first appeared in 'Mini Cars' ('The News Sheet for Caledonian Autominologists'), dated September 1972 and was prepared by Eric Brockie in New Zealand. Thanks are due to James McLachlan (Club Secretary) for his kind permission to reproduce the listing.
N.B. Housed in Special striped New Zealand boxes.

UK Ref. No.	NZ Ref No.	Model	Difference from UK version	NZ Colour
289	101	Morris Minor 1000	Not manufactured in New Zealand	?
219	102	Austin-Healey Sprite	Same as UK issue	White
281	103	MG Midget	No Policeman included	Dark Green
404	104	Morris Mini Van	No 'Shell' logo ladder or mechanism	Yellow
267	105	MG 1100	Single colour only	Green
262	106	Morris 1100	Same as UK issue	Blue
287/406	107	Hillman Minx	No roof rack or dinghy	Green
280	108	Vauxhall Cresta	Single colour only	Blue
276	109	Jaguar 'S' type	Same as UK issue	Blue
286	110	Austin 1800	No lady driver or schoolboy	Light Brown
270	111	Ford Zephyr 6	Same as UK issue	White
308	112	Land Rover	No trailer included	Green
407	114	Mercedes-Benz 230 SL	Not manufactured in New Zealand	-
401	115	Volkswagen Variant	No roof rack or skis	Blue
279	116	MG PB Midget	Same as UK issue	Blue & Black
265	117	'TONIBELL' Ice Cream Van	Same as UK issue	Turquoise
402	118	Crash Service Land Rover	Same as UK issue	Orange & Blue
316	119	Fire Dept Land Rover	No Firemen	Red
415	120	R.A.F. Land Rover	Not manufactured in New Zealand	

PRICES OF NEW ZEALAND ISSUES— All scarce — All NGPP
N.B. Wallis & Wallis sold 401 VW Variant for £500 in 1993.

Spot-On Catalogues, Leaflets and Pictures

Ref. No.	Year(s)	Publication	Cover Features & Details	Market Price Range	
Catalogues					
	1959	Early issue...........................	Red cover featuring a Target plus the dividers and diagram of Rolls Royce 'LTP 103'. Wording:- '1/42' & 'SPOT ON MODELS BY TRIANG'. Contains 8 pages	£30-40	☐
	1959	'1st Edition'	Village scene with Spot-On buildings and models, 'Tri-ang' logo in bright red '6d', 'Dividers', 'SCALE 1/42'. Thick numbered pages with superb pictures.......................	£30-40	☐
	1960	'2nd Edition'.......................	Same cover as 1st Edition. 'Tri-ang' logo in maroon, '6d'. Pages not numbered but models displayed same as 1st Edition..	£30-40	☐
	1961	'3rd Edition'	Same as 2nd Edition	£25-35	☐
5a7383/DP	1963	'4th Edition'	Royal Rolls-Royce on cover, '3d', Page 19 lists the new type Presentation Sets 5-10, 14 plus boxes.	£20-30	☐
	1964	'5th Edition'.......................	Blue Austin 1800 (286) on cover, '2d', concertina type leaflet featuring new type of Black/Red window boxes for Gift Sets and single models..	£20-£30	☐
	1965	'6th Edition'.......................	Cover again features 286 Austin 1800 plus 289 Morris Minor, '2d', concertina type leaflet which includes 'Tommy Spot' and 'Magicar' listings and pictures	£20-30	☐
	1966	'7th Edition'.......................	Booklet type featuring 407 Mercedes 230 SL and 287 Hillman Minx, '6d', 'Tommy Spot' featured with 'Royal Occasion' set and Car Spotters guide................................	£20-30	☐

Leaflets and Model Pictures

The early 'blue boxes' for cars and small commercial vehicles and the early card boxes for the large commercial vehicles, contained a model picture and a Yellow/Blue/White leaflet listing the models available. Prices of model picture cards can vary depending on the rarity of the model itself within a price range from £5 to £25. Spot-On 'Picture wallets' are to be found at £15-20.

It should be noted that no 'blue box' model or early large commercial boxed model is complete without the model picture.

Leaflets are not uncommon and may be obtained for £2-3.

Trade Display Material

Electric revolving Trade Display Unit ....   **£300-400**   ☐

Spot-On Models Auction Results

VECTIS MODEL AUCTION RESULTS

108 Triumph TR3 Turquoise/grey seats/spun wheels, A scarce picture boxed with leaflet **£140**

100 Ford Zodiac Cream, lovely B+ in B+ box with picture **£50**

191 Sunbeam Alpine Convertible Red/white interior/spun wheels, A in B+ to A picture box **£100**

109/3 ERF 68G with flat float, all light green, A with B inner lining and box, scarce **£190**

109/3B ERF with barrel load, turquoise/silver float, A with 9 plastic barrels, inner lining is B+ box is B **£190**

109/3b ERF but deep turquoise/silver/9 barrels, A, inner lining is B, box is B+, very scarce **£180**

1102/2 AEC Mammoth Major 8 with flat float, dark plum red B+ with inner lining & early catalogue-leaflet in B to C box, rare **£180**

107 Jaguar XK SS met. pale blue/cream seats, B+ in B box with picture **£80**

195 VW Rally 'Beetle' light brown/No 6/ bonnet flags/roof light & spare wheel, B+ boxed with picture, very rare colour **£160**

195 VW Rally 'Beetle' grey B+ to A in B box with picture **£130**

219 Austin Healey Sprite white/driver A in C window box with A shaped inner lining **£90**

260 Royal Rolls Phantom maroon with all parts, B+ rigid perspex boxed, scarce **£220**

106 A/OC Austin Prime Mover deep blue red MGA in crate B+ to A with front end, some crate transfer details missing, box is B+ apart from surface tear each end from removal of sellotape, scarce **£250**

110/3 AEC Mammoth Major 8 'British Road Services' orange/red B+ but missing spare wheel in C box, scarce **£260**

154 Austin A40 'MAGGI' red/cream interior/'Maggi' in yellow on front doors/FTZ 107 Reg. No. B+ in exceptionally rare special red & yellow standard shape card box with 'Maggi Soups make meals marvellous' B to C with picture card and leaflet, RARE PROMOTIONAL MODEL given to the vendor by his older brother c.1966/7 when the latter worked for Nestles the owners of Maggi Soups — only the second boxed model we have seen and this is in better condition **£620**

215 Daimler Dart SP250 white/cream interior B+ in C to D box (printed end flap replaced by 'plain' original, rare colour combination) **£95**

113 Aston Martin DB3 dark red, A with PC&L in B+ box showing correct Red Spot **£120**

114 Jaguar 3.4 light grey, A (rear of boot is B+ in B box; end flap repairs and Green Spot) scarce **£100**

115 Bristol 406 met. deep green, A with correct spot on box, scarce **£85**

267 MG1100 two tone brown A in C box **£90**

287 Hillman Minx Deluxe off white, A to A+ in B box **£60**

289 Morris Minor 1000 met green A to A+ in B box, rare **£160**

210/1 'Royal Mail' Mini Van red B+ in C picture box, very scarce **£120**

271 Express Dairy Van navy blue/white/plastic crates, fitted/driver, B picture boxed, scarce **£70**

402 'Crash Service' Land Rover orange/blue jib, A to A+ in B+ window box **£80**

404 Morris Mini Van yellow with man and silver ladder, garage forecourt inner scene, all A to A+ in B+ window box, very rare **£440**

106A/1 Austin Prime Mover with flat float with sides, blue/silver, A apart from faults to fixing unit, box B **£120**

109/3 ERF 68Glemon/black cab roof/silver float, B+ in early thinner cardboard box with PC **£160**

109/3B ERF with barrel load, turquoise/silver, 9 barrels appear to be in original tissue wrapper, A in B+ to A box with inner lining, very scarce **£350**

109/3B ERF with barrel load, deep turquoise/silver/9 barrels, A inner lining is B, box is B+ **£280**

110/2B AEC 'London Brick Co' dark red/black roof with 'Brick' load, B to B+ with C inner lining in B box **£200**

111A/IS Ford Thames Trader with sack load, mid blue with 9 brown plastic sacks, A with B inner lining, box lid is C **£310**

111A/OT Ford Thames Trader with lod load, orange cab and trailer/3 logs, B+ to A with B inner lining and box, rare **£330**

111/AOG Trader with garage kit, orange with plastic kit load, A to A+ to A inner lining in B to B+ box **£310**

117 Jones Mobile Crane red/black/cream cab and jib/red wheels, B+ (fault to 'Jones' decal) with inner lining in C box **£140**

117 Jones Mobile Crane orange-red/grey base/white cab and jib, B+ in C box **£170**

Road Signs Presentation SET of 18, B+ to A with inner lining, box lid is B, rare **£170**

Magicar No 905 Batmobile with Batman and Robin figures/instructions, all A to A+ in B window box with 'Batmobile' pictorial label, perspex has split **£170**

NEW ZEALAND 'SPOT-ON' ISSUES

YELLOW WINDOW TYPE BOXED

N102 Austin Healey Sprite white/red interior/driver, A, box is B .... **Not sold-Estimate £150-200**

N116 MG PB Sports dark blue/red seats and tonneau, A .... **Not sold-Estimate £150-200**

N118 Crash Service Land Rover orange/blue jib, B+, box virtually A but for split perspex **£150**

WALLIS & WALLIS AUCTION RESULTS

Ford Thames Trader with articulated flat float with sides, maroon and cream, 'British Railways' livery, original box, GC **£160**

Mulliner Coach (156) in silver and blue with red flash to sides, original box with paperwork and insert, VGC **£160**

Scarce Caterpillar D9 Bulldozer (116) yellow with silver fronted blade and black rubber tracks, original box with paperwork and insert, VGC to Mint .. **£420**

LACY & SCOTT AUCTION RESULTS

AEC Mammoth Major 8 with brick load, British Road Services (110/2B) some retouching, BDG **£165**

Tourist Caravan 18ft (264), BDG **£26**

Morris 110 with opening bonnet (262), BDG **£45**

A Miniature Presentation Set containing Goggomobile green GTM 110, (131), Fiat 500 red TPO 106 (185), Austin Seven (Mini) beige DVM 163 (211) and Morris Mini van 'Royal Mail', red LXQ 193 (BM). Sold at Sothebys in the Mint and Boxed Sale. Mint & Boxed label on base **£800**

A Sports Car Set containing MG MGA Sports Car, salmon pink BMP 104 (minor chips), Austin Healey 100/6, yellow LXQ 111 (105) (minor chips), Jaguar XK SS, green WTB 647 (107) (M), and Triumph TR 3A Sports, light blue DVM 163 (M), with leaflet, (B) **£500**

A no. O Presentation Set: Austin Prime Mover light blue TPO 106 (106A/1) (minor chips), Ford Zodiac grey and blue LBL 100 (100), Bentley Continental two tone grey BTW 115 (102), MGA Sports turquoise with grey seats, BMP 104 (104) and Aston Martin DB3 saloon deep pink BTW 115 (113) (BDM) **£580**

A No. 2 Presentation Set: ERF and flat float (with sides) pale blue, silver chassis, SGM 102 (no front number) (109/3) (some retouching), Armstrong Siddeley Sapphire metallic green (101) (M), Bentley Continental two tone grey LBL 100 (102) (M), MGA Sports Car red PZL 108 (104) (minor chips), 6 straight road sections, 4 curved, Guildford direction sign (2) and 6 road traffic signs (BDG-M) **£580**

A No. 14 Presentation Set: Austin A40 saloon red MLP 119 (154), Mulliner luxury coach LMC 156 (no front number) (156) (minor chips), Rover 3 litre light blue PZL 108 (157), Sunbeam Alpine hard top metallic green VYD 131 (191/2) (minor chips), Austin Seven (Mini) beige WTB 511 (211), 'United Dairies' milk float red/white LTP 103 (122) (slight chips), 8 road sections, 4 curves and 4 straights, Bristol road direction sign and 6 road traffic signs (BDM-G) **£920**

CHRISTIES AUCTION RESULTS
South Kensington, London

802 Cops and Robbers Set with Tommy Spot **£350**

803 Tommy Spot Garage Set **£240**

806 Royal Occasion Set with Tommy Spot **£220**

111A/OG Ford Thames Trader and Garage Kit **£170**

106A/OC Austin Prime Mover with MGA in crate **£240**

Gift Set 702 .... **£190**

O Presentation Set **£320**

PS7 Rally Presentation Set **£380**

Pale metallic blue 105 Austin-Healey 100-Six, in original box (E, box G-E)**£132**

Apple green 218 Jaguar Mk.10, with specification leaflet, in original box (E, box F-G, small tear) **£110**

Pale blue and black 191/1 Sunbeam Alpine Hardtop, with specification leaflet, in original box (E, box F-G, taped at one end) **£99**

Green 165 Vauxhall Cresta, with specification leaflet, in original box (E, box G) **£110**

Red 215 Daimler SP250 Dart, with specification sheet, in original box (E, box G) **£110**

Pake blue 219 Austin-Healey Sprite MkIII with red interior, in original box (E, box F-G) **£110**

A rare Spot-On No.256 Police Car, finished in white with roof sign, bell and aerial, in original box with Fleet-Owner's Club leaflet, 1963-1964 (E, box F-G) **£165**

Spot-On No.114 3.4 Litre Jaguars: red, pink and light blue, in original boxes with colour picture inserts, pink model with unused transfers and four-fold model listing (G, boxes G) **£264**

TRI-ANG
MINIC SHIPS
Accurately detailed waterline models

The models were in the shops between 1958 and 1964, a comparatively short life, but production figures must have been high and this factor coupled with 'low play value' (they could not be raced like Dinky Toys), has meant that a reasonable number have survived for collecting purposes.

Six sales catalogues were published which nowadays are quite hard to find. No single catalogue shows the full range as additions, deletions and alterations were a regular occurrence.

Minic ships were re-introduced in 1976 and they are listed here after the first issues.

General notes on specific models
M702, M703: Queens came with and without funnel detail
M708, M709: Towards the end of their run Saxonia and Ivernia were renamed Franconia and Carmania (following Cunards refurbishment of the actual ships). They kept their original catalogue number but their sterns were slightly recast at that time to remove cargo handling gear and add swimming pools. They were painted green with green masts. Only 480 of each were made and are very hard to find.

M716, M717: Port Auckland/Port Brisbane - short run resulting in scarce models.
M718, M719, M720: Amazon, Arlanza, Aragon - scarce.
M726 Pilot, **M727** Lifeboat - very hard to find.
M740 Barge, (designed to match up with M731 tugboat), appears in catalogue but was not issued.
M754 Commando ship. Same casting as other carriers, it was grey and had a helicopter landing deck (a sticker applied the full length of the ship). Not generally known and not appearing in any catalogues; very rare.
M783 Hampshire, **M784** Kent, **M785** Devonshire, **M786** London. Missile Destroyers in grey. Short run; hard to find.
M853 Factory, **M854** Tanker, **M880** Whales (white & grey); all hard to find.
Also produced but not appearing in any catalogue is the Helicopter. It is possible this was designed to go with the limited issue Commando ship. It is a very small and basic item manufactured to a very high technological standard by taking an M880 Whale and nailing a 4-blade rotor to its head (same rotor used on missile destroyer)!

Ocean Liners   1:1200 scale (1 in to 100 ft)

Ref. No.	Model Type	Model Features and Size	Market Price Range	
M701	R.M.S. 'Caronia'	Green body, one plain Red/Black or detailed funnel, one mast, 178 mm. 'Painted in the correct Cunard green she is a most striking vessel'	£35-45	☐
M702	R.M.S. 'Queen Elizabeth'	Black/White, 2 plain Red/Black or detailed funnels, 2 masts, 262 mm. 'The worlds largest ship and the pride of the Cunard fleet'	£55-65	☐
M703	R.M.S. 'Queen Mary'	Black/White, plain Red/Black or detailed funnels, 2 masts, 259 mm. 'Her three funnels make her the most easily recognisable'	£40-45	☐
M704	S.S. 'United States'	Black/White body, two Red/White/Blue funnels, 252 mm. 'The present holder of the Blue Riband of the Atlantic'	£35-45	☐
M705	R.M.S. 'Aquitania'	Black/White body, four Red/Black funnels, two masts, 231 mm.	£80-100	☐
M706	S.S. 'Nieuw Amsterdam'	Grey/White body, two Yellow funnels, two masts, 231 mm.	£45-55	☐
M707	S.S. 'France'	Black/White, 2 Red/Black funnels, 5 masts, 262 mm. 'The longest ship in the world 1035ft being 4ft longer than Queen Elizabeth'	£80-100	☐
M708	R.M.S. 'Saxonia'	Black/White body, one Red/Black or detailed funnel, nine masts.	£35-40	☐
M708/2	R.M.S. 'Franconia'	Green body, one Red/Black funnel, nine masts, 155 mm.	£500-550	☐
M709	R.M.S. 'Ivernia'	Black/White or Green body	£35-40	☐
M709/2	R.M.S. 'Carmania'	Green body, one Red/Black funnel, nine masts, 155 mm.	£500-550	☐
M710	R.M.S. 'Sylvania'	Black/White, one Red/Black funnel, nine masts, 155 mm.	£30-40	☐
M711	R.M.S. 'Carinthie'	Black/White, one Red/Black funnel, nine masts, 155 mm.	£35-40	☐
M712	N.S. 'Savannah'	White, no funnels (nuclear powered), four masts, 149 mm.	£45-50	☐
M713	S.S. 'Antilles'	Black/White, one Red/Black funnel, ten masts, 152 mm. All White body, one Red/Black funnel, ten masts	£45-60 / £65-70	☐
M714	'Flandre'	Black/White, one Red/Black funnel, ten masts, 152 mm. All White body, one Red/Black funnel, ten masts	£35-45 / £45-55	☐
M715	R.M.S. 'Canberra'	White body, one Yellow funnel, three masts, 189 mm.	£55-65	☐
M716	M.S. 'Port Brisbane'	Grey/White, one Red/Black funnel, eight masts, 140 mm.	£90-110	☐
M717	S.S. 'Port Auckland'	Grey/White, one Red/Black funnel, seven masts, 140 mm.	£90-120	☐
M718	R.M.S. 'Amazon'	White, Yellow funnel, 19 masts, 10 lifeboats, 149 mm.	£115-130	☐
M719	R.M.S. 'Arlanza'	White, Yellow funnel, 19 masts, 149 mm.	£130-150	☐
M720	R.M.S. 'Aragon'	White, Yellow funnel, 19 masts, 149 mm.	£115-130	☐
M721	R.M.S. 'Britannia' Royal Yacht	Blue/White body, Yellow/Black funnel, 3 masts, 105 mm.	£15-18	☐
M721/H	R.M.S. 'Britannia' Hospital Ship	White body, three masts, 105 mm.	£15-18	☐

CHANNEL ISLANDS STEAMERS

M722	'Isle of Jersey'	Black/White body, 2 Yellow/Black funnels, 2 masts, 78 mm.	£18-24	☐
M723	'Isle of Guernsey'	Black/White body, 2 Yellow/Black funnels, 2 masts, 78 mm.	£18-24	☐
M724	'Isle of Sark'	Black/White body, 2 Yellow/Black funnels, 2 masts, 78 mm.	£18-24	☐
M726	Pilot Boat	Black/White/Yellow body, 'PILOTS', 45 mm.	£65-75	☐
M727	Lifeboat	Blue body	£15-20	☐

PADDLE STEAMERS
All the Paddle Steamers are 78 mm. in length.

M728	'Britannia'	Black/White, 2 funnels (Black/Blue, Red/Black or Yellow/Black), 2 masts	£20-25	☐
M729	'Bristol Queen'	Black/White, 2 funnels (Black/Blue, Red/Black or Yellow/Black), 2 masts	£20-25	☐
M730	'Cardiff Queen'	Black/White, 2 funnels (Black/Blue, Red/Black or Yellow/Black), 2 masts	£20-25	☐

Ref. No.	Model Type	Tri-ang Minic Ships – continued	Market Price Range	
TUGBOATS				
M731	Tugboat	Black/Grey/Red body, Red/Black funnel, 38 mm.	**£5-7**	☐
M731	Tugboat	Black/Grey/Red body, Yellow/Black funnel, 38 mm.	**£5-7**	☐
M731	Tugboat	Black/Blue/Red body, Yellow/Black funnel, 38 mm.	**£5-7**	☐
M731	Tugboat	Black/Grey/Yellow body, Yellow/Black funnel, 38 mm.	**£5-7**	☐
M810	Navy Tug H.M.S. 'Turmoil'	Black/Blue or Grey body, Black funnel, 50 mm.	**£5-8**	☐
OIL TANKER				
M732	S.S. 'Varicella'	Black/White body, Black/Yellow funnel ('SHELL' logo), 2 masts, 169 mm.	**£20-30**	☐
WHALE FACTORY SHIPS				
M733	T.S.S. 'Vikingen'	Grey body, six masts, 125 mm.	**£25-30**	☐
M734	Whale Chaser	Grey body, Yellow/Black funnel, 39 mm.	**£12-15**	☐
LIGHTSHIPS				
M735	'SUNK'	Red body, White logo/name, 33 mm.	**£7-10**	☐
M736	'SHAMBLES'	Red body, White logo/name, 33 mm.	**£7-10**	☐
M737	'CORK'	Red body, White logo/name, 33 mm.	**£7-10**	☐
M738	'VARNE'	Red body, White logo/name, 33 mm.	**£7-10**	☐
M739	'St.GOWAN'	Red body, White logo/name, no number on base, 33 mm.	**£7-10**	☐

Warships   1:1200 scale (1 in to 100 ft)

Ref. No.	Model Type	Model Features and Size	Market Price Range	
BATTLESHIPS				
M741	H.M.S. 'Vanguard'	Grey or Blue body with two masts, 206 mm.	**£30-35**	☐
AIRCRAFT CARRIERS				
M751	H.M.S. 'Bulwark'	Grey or Blue body with one mast, 186 mm.	**£20-25**	☐
M752	H.M.S. 'Centaur'	Grey or Blue body with one mast	**£20-25**	☐
M753	H.M.S. 'Albion'	Grey or Blue body with one mast	**£20-25**	☐
COMMANDO SHIP				
M754	H.M.S. 'Albion'	Grey ship with 12 Cream or Brown plastic helicopters. 1000 models issued and given to H.M.S. 'Albion' crew members (Capt. Adams in command)	**£400-500**	☐
CRUISERS				
M761	H.M.S. 'Swiftsure'	Blue or Grey body with one crane jib, 145 mm.	**£15-18**	☐
M762	H.M.S. 'Superb'	Blue or Grey body with one crane jib, 145 mm.	**£15-18**	☐
DESTROYERS, FLEET ESCORT, 'DARING' CLASS				
M771	H.M.S. 'Daring'	Blue or Grey body with one mast, 98 mm.	**£5-8**	☐
M772	H.M.S. 'Diana'	Blue or Grey body with one mast, 98 mm.	**£5-8**	☐
M773	H.M.S. 'Dainty'	Blue or Grey body with one mast, 98 mm.	**£5-8**	☐
M774	H.M.S. 'Decoy'	Blue or Grey body with one mast, 98 mm.	**£5-8**	☐
DESTROYERS, FLEET, 'BATTLE' CLASS				
M779	H.M.S. 'Alamein'	Blue or Grey body with one mast, 97 mm.	**£5-8**	☐
M780	H.M.S. 'Jutland'	Blue or Grey body with one mast, 97 mm.	**£5-8**	☐
M781	H.M.S. 'Anzac'	Blue or Grey body with one mast, 97 mm.	**£5-8**	☐
M782	H.M.S. 'Tobruk'	Blue or Grey body with one mast, 97 mm.	**£5-8**	☐
DESTROYERS, GUIDED MISSILE, 'COUNTY' CLASS				
M783	H.M.S. 'Hampshire'	Grey body with two masts, 136 mm.	**£20-25**	☐
M784	H.M.S. 'Kent'	Grey body with two masts, 136 mm.	**£30-35**	☐
M785	H.M.S. 'Devonshire'	Grey body with two masts, 136 mm.	**£20-25**	☐
M786	H.M.S. 'London'	Grey body with two masts, 136 mm.	**£20-25**	☐
FRIGATES, FAST ANTI-SUBMARINE, 'V' CLASS				
M787	H.M.S. 'Vigilant'	Blue or Grey body with one mast, 92 mm.	**£5-8**	☐
M788	H.M.S. 'Venus'	Blue or Grey body with one mast, 92 mm.	**£5-8**	☐
M789	H.M.S. 'Virago'	Blue or Grey body with one mast, 92 mm.	**£5-8**	☐
M790	H.M.S. 'Volage'	Blue or Grey body with one mast, 92 mm.	**£5-8**	☐
FRIGATES, ANTI-SUBMARINE, 'WHITBY' CLASS				
M791	H.M.S. 'Whitby'	Blue or Grey body, 94 mm.	**£5-7**	☐
M792	H.M.S. 'Torquay'	Blue or Grey body, 94 mm.	**£5-7**	☐
M793	H.M.S. 'Blackpool'	Blue or Grey body, 94 mm.	**£5-7**	☐
M794	H.M.S. 'Tenby'	Blue or Grey body, 94 mm.	**£5-7**	☐
MINESWEEPERS, 'TON' CLASS				
M799	H.M.S. 'Repton'	Blue or Grey body	**£5-7**	☐
M800	H.M.S. 'Dufton'	Blue or Grey body	**£5-7**	☐
M801	H.M.S. 'Ashton'	Blue or Grey body	**£5-7**	☐
M802	H.M.S. 'Calton'	Blue or Grey body	**£5-7**	☐
M803	H.M.S. 'Picton'	Blue or Grey body	**£5-7**	☐
M804	H.M.S. 'Sefton'	Blue or Grey body	**£5-7**	☐
M805	H.M.S. 'Upton'	Blue or Grey body	**£5-7**	☐
M806	H.M.S. 'Weston'	Blue or Grey body	**£5-7**	☐
SUBMARINES, 'A' CLASS				
M817	Sub 'A' Class	Blue or Grey body, 61 mm.	**£5-7**	☐
M818	Sub Recon	Blue or Grey body, 61 mm.	**£7-10**	☐

DOCKSIDE ACCESSORIES and MISCELLANEOUS

Ref. No.	Model Type	Description	Price	
M827	Breakwater Straights	Grey	£3-4	☐
M828/L	Breakwater Angle, Left	Grey	50p	☐
M828/R	Breakwater Angle, Right	Grey	50p	☐
M829	Breakwater End	Grey	50p	☐
M836	Quay Straights	Tan	£3-4	☐
M837	Crane Units	Tan, Brown or Green cargo	£3-4	☐
M838	Storage Tanks	Grey/Silver and Red	£2-3	☐
M839	Customs Shed	Green	£3-4	☐
M840	Warehouse	Brown	£3-4	☐
M841	Ocean Terminal	White with Black windows	£5-6	☐
M842	Swing Bridge	Red, no description on base	£2-3	☐
M843	Terminal Extension	White with Black windows	£5-6	☐
M844	Lock Gates (pair)	Brown	£1-2	☐
M845	Landing Stages	Cream 'L' shaped, 1" in length	£0-0	☐
M846	Lift Bridge	Silver/Tan	£2-3	☐
M847	Pier centre section	White	£2-3	☐
M848	Pier entrance section	White	£2-3	☐
M849	Pier head	White	£12-14	☐
M850	Pier Shelter	Green, 35 mm.	£5-6	☐
M851	Pier archways			☐
M852	Pier Building	White/Blue/Green, Silver Cupola 'RESTAURANT' plus 'DANCING TONIGHT'	£2-3	☐
M853	Factory Unit	Pink and Buff with Black chimneys	£25-30	☐
M854	Tanker Wharf Straight	Cream and Red	£65-75	☐
M855	Tanker Wharf Berth	Red and Green or Cream and Green, Black plastic pipeline	£2-3	☐
M857	26" Sea	Blue plastic	£14-18	☐
M857	52" Sea	Blue plastic	£25-30	☐
M861	Lifeboat set	Grey with Blue shed and one lifeboat	£35-40	☐
M878	Lighthouse	White	£1-2	☐
M880	Whales	White or plain Grey	£12-15	☐
M882	Beacon	White/Red or Green	£1-2	☐
M884	Statue of Liberty	Green/Grey	£15-20	☐
M885	Floating Dock	Grey dock with four Black plastic cranes	£20-25	☐
M -	Helicopter	Cream or Brown plastic body	£20-25	☐

GIFT SETS and SPECIAL PRESENTATION PACKS

Ref. No.	Model Type	Description	Price	
M891	'Queen Elizabeth'	Gift Set	£75-100	☐
M892	'United States'	Gift Set	£150-175	☐
M893	'Task Force'	Gift Set	£30-40	☐
M894	'Royal Yacht'	Gift Set	£80-100	☐
M895	'Nieuw Amsterdam'	Gift Set	£600-700	☐
M702s	'Queen Elizabeth'	Presentation Set	£80-100	☐
M703s	'Queen Mary'	Presentation Set	£100-120	☐
M704s	'S.S. United States'	Presentation Set	£100-120	☐
M705s	'R.M.S. Aquitania'	Presentation Set	£125-150	☐
M707s	'S.S. France'	Presentation Set	£125-150	☐
M741s	'H.M.S. Vanguard'	Presentation Set	£50-60	☐

Hong Kong 'Blue Box' issues 1976 - 1980

Minic ships were re-introduced in 1976 and manufactured in Hong Kong. The colours are slightly different from the original models. All these 'second issues' were given wheels and have 'HONG KONG' on the base.

SINGLE BOXED MODELS

'Queen Mary', 'Queen Elizabeth', 'United States', 'Canberra', HMS 'Vanguard', HMS 'Bulwark', 'Missouri', 'Bismark', 'Scharnhorst', 'Yamato'. Each			£15-20	☐
	R.M.S. 'Canberra'		£25-30	☐

SETS OF MODELS

1	Fleet Anchorage Set		£25-30	☐
2	Quay Set		£25-30	☐
3a	Ocean Terminal Set	with box lid showing stern of R.M.S. 'Queen Mary'	£45-50	☐
3b	Ocean Terminal Set	with box lid showing bow of R.M.S. 'Queen Mary'	£35-40	☐
4	Naval Task Force Set	with H.M.S. 'Bulwark and H.M.S. 'Vanguard'	£35-40	☐
5	Naval Task Force Set	with ships 'Bismark' and 'Scharnhorst'	£50-55	☐

Minic Catalogues 1958-64

1	Leaflet	with first Minic Ships listed	£75-100	☐
2	Booklet	with first Minic Ships listed	£25-30	☐
3	Booklet	with Ships and other Tri-ang products	£60-75	☐
4	Booklet	with Minic Ships only	£25-30	☐
5	Booklet	with Minic Ships only	£25-30	☐
6	Booklet	with Tri-ang range	£30-35	☐
M862	Minic illustrated leaflet		£10-15	☐

Acknowledgements   Thanks are due to Richard Lines of Hornby Hobbies and Richard Capon of Colchester for their contribution to the Minic Ships listing and to John Wade of Cambridgeshire for new information supplied.

MODEL RAILWAYS
Die-cast Model Listings

HORNBY DUBLO
MODEL RAILWAYS 1938 - 1964

In any chronicle of the Meccano company the middle of the 1930s stands out as the golden years. Frank Hornby's burgeoning enterprise encompassed the famous Liverpool works, a French factory producing its own distinctly Gallic toys and models and a worldwide network of branches and agents with eager customers everywhere for the growing range of Dinky Toys, Meccano sets, and of course the famous Hornby Series gauge 'O' clockwork and electric trains.

Gauge 'O' (scaled at 7 mm. to the foot) had become the paramount model railway scale supplanting the earlier (and bigger) Victorian gauge '1' and Hornby was the premier British manufacturer of gauge 'O' ready-to-run trains. However, even smaller (and thus more convenient) model railways were being developed, mainly on the Continent, where as far back as 1921 Bing offered their 'table-top' clockwork railway in 'HO' gauge, with an electric version two years later. 'HO' indicates 'half-O' and is 3.5 mm. to the foot. Other 'HO' models appearing in the 1920s included the Trix-Twin sets which were imported from Germany to England by the British Bassett-Lowke company.

As not every Meccano boy lived in a large house capable of accommodating a reasonable size railway, even in gauge 'O', Meccano were doubtless urged by would-be customers and dealers alike to manufacture something a little smaller - a 'OO' railway - and given the Company's superb marketing skills, would have been quite aware of competitors' developments in the smaller scales. However it was not until 1938 that the first Hornby 'Dublo' models were announced, the decision to produce a 'OO' range having been taken a bare 9 months before. In true Meccano style the new range comprised not merely locomotive models but an extensive choice of goods rolling stock, passenger coaches, railway buildings and signals, as well as the requisite track and controllers.

In 1972 Tri-ang was acquired by the Dunbee-Combex-Marx firm and the Hornby name lives on today as 'Hornby Railways' manufactured by Hornby Hobbies Ltd., of Margate. Study of the present Hornby Railways catalogue reveals a stud of over 30 finely detailed 'OO' locomotives along with a comprehensive range of rolling stock and accessories, tempting railway modellers and collectors alike. In 1966 Mr G.Wrenn negotiated the purchase of many of the original Dublo tools from Tri-ang, and the firm of G. & R. Wrenn continued to employ these tools in producing diecast 'OO' models until 1992 when production ceased. A number of the original Hornby Dublo type locomotives (with detail improvements) feature in the Wrenn range and any prizes for 'OO' longevity must surely go to 'N2' tanks and the 'A4 Sir Nigel Gresley', both seeing the first light of day in 1938 and still available in Wrenn form over fifty years later!

The 5th Edition listings have been carefully amended and collectors will find several new important variations have been included. As always the Editor will be pleased to receive any new information.

1: **Locomotive models 1938 - 1964**
   - Steam Outline Locomotives
     (Clockwork)
     (Electrically powered)
   - Diesel, Diesel-Electric and Electric
     Outline Locomotives

2: **Rolling Stock 1938 - 1964**
   - Passenger Coaches
   - Vans and Wagons

3: **Gift Sets**

4: **Accessories**
   - 1938 - 1940
   - 1948 - 1958
   - 1959 - 1964

5: **Catalogues**

6: **Model Pricing Guidelines**

7: **Packaging and Box Types**
   - Locomotives
   - Passenger Coaches, Vans, Wagons

8: **Technical Notes**
   - Construction materials
   - Wheel arrangements
   - 'Totem' Motifs, '00' scale
   - Wheel and Coupling types

Abbreviations (Railway Companies, Pre-Nationalisation):
GWR = Great Western Railway,   LMS = London, Midland and Scottish Railway,
LNER = London and North Eastern Railway,   SR = Southern Railway

Abbreviations (Post-Nationalisation (1948) British Railways):
'WR = Western region,   MR = Midland Region,   ER = Eastern Region,   SR = Southern Region

Abbreviations:- Types of Electric Motors:
HS = Horseshoe Magnet Motor,   HI = Half Inch Block Magnet Motor,   RF = Ringfield Motor

Ref. No.	Year(s)	Type	Name	No.	Railway	Colour	2/3 Rail	Type of Motor	Market Price Range

Steam Outline Locomotives (Clockwork)

Ref. No.	Year(s)	Type	Name	No.	Railway	Colour	2/3 Rail	Type of Motor	Market Price Range
DL1	1938-41	4-6-2	'Sir Nigel Gresley'	4498	LNER	Blue			£750-1000 ☐
DL7	1938-40	0-6-2	Tank	2594	SR	Olive Green			£700-800 ☐
DL7	1938-40	0-6-2	Tank	6917	LMS	Black			£400-450 ☐
DL7	1938-40	0-6-2	Tank	2690	LNER	Black			£450-550 ☐
DL7	1938-40	0-6-2	Tank	6699	GWR	Green			£700-800 ☐

Steam Outline Locomotives (Electrically powered)

Identification: Early issues have a Gold block with Red line on the rear of the tender with logo 'HORNBY MECCANO LTD, Made in England'. Later issues have a Silver block with Red Line.

N.B. Pre-war locomotives and very early post-war issues have no model number beneath the running board – later post-war issues do. e.g. EDL7 etc.

Ref. No.	Year(s)	Type	Name	No.	Railway	Colour	2/3 Rail	Type of Motor	Market Price Range
EDL1	1938-41	4-6-2	'Sir Nigel Gresley'	4498	LNER	Blue	3	HS	£600-800 ☐
Note:	Pre-war model had full-depth valances over the wheels and simple push rod instead of valve gear								
EDL2	1938	4-6-2	'Duchess of Atholl'	6231	LMS	Maroon	3	HS	NGPP ☐
			N.B. Shown in Pre-war literature but never issued						
EDL7	1938-41	0-6-2	Tank	2594	SR	Olive Green	3	HS	£600-700 ☐
EDL7	1938-41	0-6-2	Tank	6917	LMS	Black	3	HS	£300-400 ☐
EDL7	1938-41	0-6-2	Tank	2690	LNER	Black	3	HS	£300-400 ☐
EDL7	1938-41	0-6-2	Tank	6699	GWR	Green	3	HS	£500-600 ☐
EDL1	1947-53	4-6-2	'Sir Nigel Gresley'	7	LNER	Blue	3	HS/HI	£125-150 ☐
			Binns Road Repair, Rare variation with EDL11 under cab roof, i.e. Silver King body						£250-350 ☐
EDL2	1947-53	4-6-2	'Duchess of Atholl'	6231	LMS	Maroon	3	HS/HI	£100-150 ☐
			Rare variation with Cream nameplate				3		£250-400 ☐
			Rare variation with projection under the offside name plate instead of the normal inlet				3		£250-400 ☐
			Rare variation with smoke deflectors on either side of front of boiler (EDL12 under cab roof)				3		£500-800 ☐
Note: This variation occurred when models were repaired at Binns Road and were fitted with new 'Duchess of Montrose' bodies painted in 'Duchess of Atholl' livery.									
EDL2	1952	4-6-2	'Canadian Pacific'	1215		Black		HI	£600-700 ☐
Notes: (1) - This model was made for the Canadian market. (2) - Replicas of the Canadian Pacific are currently made using Duchess of Atholl originals.									
EDL11	1953-54	4-6-2	'Silver King'	60010	BR	Gloss Green	1	HI	£150-175 ☐
EDL11	1954-58	4-6-2	'Silver King'	60016	BR	Matt Green	3	HI	£100-125 ☐
L11/3211	1958-63	4-6-2	'Mallard'	60022	BR	Matt Green	3	HI	£125-175 ☐
L11	1958-63	4-6-2	'Mallard'	60022	BR	Matt Green	3	HI	£125-175 ☐
3211	1962-63	4-6-2	'Mallard' (nickel plated wheels)	60022	BR	Matt Green	3	HI	£300-350 ☐
2211	1959-64	4-6-2	'Golden Fleece'	60030	BR	Matt Green	2	HI	£130-175 ☐
EDL12/	1953-54	4-6-2	'Duchess of Montrose'	46232	BR	Gloss Green	3	HI	£150-175 ☐
/3212	1954-58	4-6-2	'Duchess of Montrose'	46232	BR	Matt Green	3	HI	£95-125 ☐
		4-6-2	Binns Rd. repair variation, nickel plated wheels, plain Brown box	46232			3	HI	£125-150 ☐

The immediate post-war versions (listed below) were fitted with post-war automatic couplings requiring a chamfer in the front buffer beam:

Ref. No.	Year(s)	Type	Name	No.	Railway	Colour	2/3 Rail	Type of Motor	Market Price Range
EDL7	1947	0-6-2	Tank (with pre-war body)	2594	SR	Olive Green	3	HS	£550-700 ☐
EDL7	1948-53	0-6-2	Tank	2594	SR	Malachite version	3	HS/HI	£250-350 ☐
EDL7	1947-48	0-6-2	Tank (LMS in serif letters)	6917	LMS	Black	3	HS	£175-250 ☐
EDL7	1949-53	0-6-2	Tank (LMS in block letters)	6917	LMS	Black	3	HI	£50-100 ☐
EDL7	1947	0-6-2	Tank (pre-war body)	2690	LNER	Black	3	HS	NGPP ☐
EDL7	1947	0-6-2	Tank	9596	LNER	Black	3	HS	NGPP ☐
EDL7	1948-53	0-6-2	Tank	9596	LNER	Green	3	HS/HI	£125-175 ☐
EDL7	1947-53	0-6-2	Tank	6699	GWR	Green	3	HS/HI	£200-250 ☐
EDL7	1948?	0-6-2	Tank (Duchess of Atholl Engine No)	6231	GWR	Green	3	HI	NGPP ☐
EDL7	1953	0-6-2	Tank (only one known example)	E9560	BR ER	Green	3	HI	NGPP ☐
EDL7	1953-54	0-6-2	Tank (no coal in bunker)	69567	BR ER	Gloss Black	3	HI	£125-150 ☐
EDL17/ /L17	1954-58	0-6-2	Tank (no coal in bunker)	69567	BR ER	Matt Black	3	HI	£50-70 ☐
3217	1961-63	0-6-2	Tank (with coal in bunker)	69567	BR ER	Matt Black	3	HI	£200-300 ☐
2217	1960-63	0-6-2	Tank (small safety valve)	69550	BR ER	Matt Black	2	HI	£100-125 ☐
	1963-64	0-6-2	Tank (large safety valve)	69550	BR ER	Matt Black	2	HI	£125-150 ☐
EDLT20/ LT20/3220	1957-61	4-6-0	'Bristol Castle'	7013	BR WR	Matt Green	3	HI	£100-150 ☐
3221	1961-61	4-6-0	'Ludlow Castle'	5002	BR WR	Matt Green	3	RF	£400-450 ☐
2220	1959-59	4-6-0	'Denbigh Castle'	7032	BR WR	Matt Green	2	HI	£175-200 ☐
2221	1960-64	4-6-0	'Cardiff Castle'	4075	BR WR	Matt Green	2	RF	£150-175 ☐

Ref. No.	Year(s)	Type	*Hornby Dublo – continued*			Colour	2/3 Rail	Type of Motor	Market Price Range
EDL18	1954-58	2-6-4	Tank (1st issue in plain blue box)	80054	BR	Matt Black	3	HI	£175-200 ☐
EDL18	1955-58	2-6-4	Tank (2nd issue in picture box)	80054	BR	Matt Black	3	HI	£125-150 ☐
3218	1961-63	2-6-4	Tank	80059	BR	Matt Black	3	HI	£350-400 ☐
2218	1959-64	2-6-4	Tank	80033	BR	Matt Black	2	HI	£95-125 ☐
3225/ /LT25	1958-61	2-8-0	BR Class 8F	48158	BR	Matt Black	3	HI	£125-150 ☐
3224	1961-63	2-8-0	BR Class 8F	48094	BR	Matt Black	3	RF	£350-450 ☐
2225	1959-59	2-8-0	BR Class 8F	48109	BR	Matt Black	2	HI	£180-225 ☐
2224	1960-64	2-8-0	BR Class 8F	48073	BR	Matt Black	2	RF	£125-160 ☐
2226	1959-64	4-6-2	'City of London'	46245	BR MR	Maroon	2	HI	£125-175 ☐
3226	1961-63	4-6-2	'City of Liverpool'	46247	BR MR	Maroon	3	HI	£450-600 ☐
*2206	1959-64	0-6-0	Tank, Class R1 (Plastic bodies)	31337	BR SR	Black	2	HI	£60-80 ☐

Normal buffers nickel plated but the Red plastic versions sell for 75% more.

*2207	1959-64	0-6-0	Tank, Class R1 (Plastic bodied)	31340	BR SR	Green	2	HI	£50-70 ☐
2235	1961-64	4-6-2	'Barnstaple'	34005	BR SR	Matt Green	2	RF	£125-175 ☐
3235	1961-63	4-6-2	'Dorchester'	34042	BR SR	Matt Green	3	RF	£325-400 ☐

Diesel, Diesel-Electric and Electric Outline Locomotives

Ref. No.	Year(s)	Type	Description		Colour		2/3 Rail	Type of Motor	Market Price Range
*L30/3230	1958-62	D8000	Diesel-Electric 1000 loco, 'Bo-Bo' (Blue striped box)	BR	Green	HI	2		£75-125 ☐
*2230	1959-62	D8017	Diesel-Electric 1000 loco, (picture box)	BR	Green	2	HI		£75-125 ☐
*2230	1959-62	D8017	Diesel-Electric 1000 loco, (Red box)	BR	Green	2	HI		£75-125 ☐
*L30/2230			Versions of the above locos, without buffers but otherwise identical, were produced for the Canadian market						NGPP ☐
*2231	1960-64	0-6-0	Diesel-Electric shunter	D3302	BR	Green	2	RF	£60-85 ☐
*3231	1961-63	0-6-0	Diesel-Electric shunter	D3763	BR	Green	3	RF	£150-195 ☐

Note: Variations are available with split coupling rods on each side. Expect them to be **£20 to £25 more.**

2232	1961-64	'Co-Co'	Deltic Class 3300 hp Diesel-Electric	none	BR	Green	2	RF	£100-120 ☐
3232	1961-63	'Co-Co'	Deltic Class 3300 hp Diesel-Electric	none	BR	Green	3	RF	£120-135 ☐
2234	1962-64	'Co-Co'	Deltic 'Crepello' 3300 hp Diesel-Electric	D9012	BR	Green	2	RF	£125-250 ☐
3234	1962-63	'Co-Co'	Deltic 'St.Paddy' 3300 hp Diesel-Electric	D9001	BR	Green	3	RF	£275-350 ☐
2233	1961-64	'Co-Bo'	1200 hp Diesel-Electric loco	D5702	BR	Green	2	RF	£110-140 ☐
			As above a version exists which has a working light at the non driving end						NGPP ☐
3233	1961-64	'Co-Bo'	1200 hp Diesel-Electric loco	D5713	BR	Green	3	RF	£150-175 ☐
2250	1962-64	....	Suburban Electric loco (Drive Coach and Trailer Car)	S65326	BR SR	Green	2	RF	£250-300 ☐
3250	1962-63	....	Suburban Electric loco (Drive Coach and Trailer Car)	S65326	BR SR	Green	3	RF	£250-350 ☐

Note: Both the above sets were sold with dummy Driving Coach Trailer S77511.

*2245	1964	'Bo-Bo'	3300 hp Electric locomotive with twin overhead pantographs	E3002	BR	Blue	RF,2	....	£400-500 ☐

* Note: These models have moulded plastic bodies with diecast metal chassis

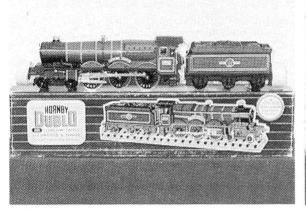

3R 'Ludlow Castle'

3R 'Dorchester'

Ref. No.	Year(s)	Type & Export No.		Railway	No.	Livery & Box Ref.	Market Price Range	

Passenger Coaches (pre-war Three-Rail)

Ref. No.	Year(s)	Type & Export No.		Railway	No.	Livery & Box Ref.	Market Price Range	
D1	1938-40	Corridor Coach	1st/3rd	LNER	42759	Teak finish with White roof (D251)	£100-150	☐
D2	1938-40	Two Coach Articulated Unit			45401		£650-850	☐
			All 3rd and Brake 3rd ...	LNER	45402	Teak finish with White roof (D252)		☐
D3	-	Corridor Coach	1st/3rd	LMS	4183	Maroon body, Silver Grey roof (not issued pre-war)	NGPP	☐
			Brake/3rd	LMS	26133	Maroon body, Silver Grey roof (not issued pre-war)	NGPP	☐

Passenger Coaches (post-war Three-Rail)

Ref. No.	Year(s)	Type & Export No.		Railway	No.	Livery & Box Ref.	Market Price Range	
D1	1948-53	Corridor Coach	1st/3rd	LNER	42759	Teak finish with Brown coach ends (32010)............	£30-40	☐
	1953-55		All 3rd	LNER	45401	Teak finish with Brown coach ends (DR361 & 32012)	£50-70	☐
						with Grey roof (similar to D11)	£75-100	☐
	1948-53		Brake 3rd	LNER	45402	Teak finish, Brown or Teak coach ends (DR361 & 32011)	£40-60	☐
D2	1948-49	Two Coach Articulated Unit			45401			☐
			All 3rd and Brake 3rd ...	LNER	45402	Teak finish with White roof (D252) post-war model was only listed for sale overseas	£750-1000	☐
D3	1949-53	Corridor Coach	1st/3rd	LMS	4183	Maroon body, Silver-Grey or Grey roof (DR363 & 32015)	£40-60	☐
			Brake/3rd	LMS	26133	Maroon body, Silver-Grey or Grey roof (32016)	£40-60	☐
D11	1953-56	Corridor Coach	1st/3rd	BR (E)	E42759E	Red & Cream body, Grey roof, tinplate windows (32013)	£20-35	☐
			Brake/3rd	BR (E)	E45402E	Red & Cream body, Grey roof, tinplate windows (32014)	£20-35	☐
D12	1953-56	Corridor Coach	1st/3rd	BR (M)	M4183	Red & Cream body, Grey roof, transparent windows (32017)	£20-25	☐
			Brake/3rd	BR (M)	M26143	Red & Cream body, Grey roof, transparent windows (32018)	£20-25	☐
32017	1956-58	Corridor Coach	1st/2nd	BR (M)	M4183	Red & Cream body, Grey roof, transparent windows (32017)	£20-25	☐
			1st/3rd	BR (M)	M4183	As previous model but with Black coach ends (32017)..	£25-35	☐
32018	1956-58	Corridor Coach	Brake/2nd	BR(LMR)	M26143	Red & Cream body, Grey roof, transparent windows (32018)	£20-25	☐
			Brake/3rd	BR(LMR)	M26143	As previous model but with Black coach ends (32018)..	£25-35	☐
D13	1954-56	Suburban Coach	1st/3rd	BR	....	Maroon body, Grey roof, tinplate windows (32091)......	£20-25	☐
			Brake/3rd	BR	....	Maroon body, Grey roof, tinplate windows (32091)......	£20-25	☐
32090	1956-57	Suburban Coach	1st/2nd	BR	....	Maroon body, Grey roof, tinplate windows (32090)......	£20-25	☐
			1st/3rd	BR	....	Maroon body, Grey roof, tinplate windows (32090)......	£20-25	☐
32091	1956-57	Suburban Coach	Brake/2nd	BR	....	Maroon body, Grey roof, tinplate windows (32091)......	£20-25	☐
			Brake/3rd	BR	....	Maroon body, Grey roof, tinplate windows (32091)......	£20-25	☐
D14	1956-57	Suburban Coach	1st/3rd	BR	....	Maroon body, Grey roof, transparent windows (32092) with windows at one end (as brake van)...........	£20-25	☐
			Brake/3rd	BR	....	Maroon body, Grey roof, transparent windows (32093).........................	£20-25	☐
32092	1956-58	Suburban Coach	1st/2nd	BR	....	Maroon body, Grey roof, transparent windows (32092).........................	£20-25	☐
32093	1956-58	Suburban Coach	Brake/2nd	BR	....	Maroon body, Grey roof, transparent windows (32093).........................	£20-25	☐
D21	1957-58	Corridor Coach	1st/2nd	BR (W)	W15862	Brown/Cream body, Grey roof, transparent windows (32094).........................	£20-25	☐
			Brake/2nd ...	BR (W)	W34481	Brown/Cream body, Grey roof, transparent windows (32095).........................	£20-25	☐
32094	1957-58	Corridor Coach	1st/2nd	BR (W)	W15862	Brown/Cream body, Grey roof, transparent windows (32094).........................	£20-25	☐
32095	1957-58	Corridor Coach	Brake/2nd ...	BR (W)	W34481	Brown/Cream body, Grey roof, transparent windows (32095).........................	£20-25	☐
D22	1957-58	Corridor Coach	1st/2nd	BR (M)	M4193	Maroon body, Grey roof, transparent windows (32023).........................	£20-25	☐
			Brake/2nd ...	BR (M)	M26143	Maroon body, Grey roof, transparent windows (32023).........................	£20-25	☐
32022	1957-58	Corridor Coach	1st/2nd	BR (M)	M4193	Maroon body, Grey roof, transparent windows (32022).........................	£20-25	☐
32023	1957-58	Corridor Coach	Brake/2nd ...	BR (M)	M26143	Maroon body, Grey roof, transparent windows (32023).........................	£20-25	☐

Passenger Coaches (post-war Two-Rail)

Ref. No.	Year(s)	Type & Export No.		Railway	No.	Livery & Box Ref.	Market Price Range	
4005	1959-61	Corridor Coach	1st/3rd	BR (M)	M4183	Red & Cream body, Grey roof, transparent windows (36005).........................	£25-35	☐
4006	1959-61	Corridor Coach	Brake/2nd ...	BR (M)	M26143	Red & Cream body, Grey roof, transparent windows (36006).........................	£25-35	☐
4009	1959-61	Corridor Coach	1st/2nd	BR (W)	W15862	Brown & Cream body, Grey roof, transparent windows (36009).........................	£20-25	☐
4010	1959-61	Corridor Coach	Brake/2nd ...	BR (W)	W34481	Brown & Cream body, Grey roof, transparent windows (36010).........................	£20-25	☐
4013	1959-62	Corridor Coach	1st/2nd	BR (M)	M4193	Maroon body, Grey roof, transparent windows (36013).........................	£20-25	☐
4014	1959-61	Corridor Coach	Brake/2nd ...	BR (M)	M26143	Maroon body, Grey roof, transparent windows (36014).........................	£20-25	☐

Ref. No.	Year(s)	Type & Export No.			Description	Market Price Range	
4021	1959-64	Suburban Coach	1st/2nd	BR	....	Maroon body, Grey roof, transparent windows (36021)	**£20-25**	☐
4022	1959-64	Suburban Coach	Brake/2nd ...	BR	....	Maroon body, Grey roof, transparent windows (36022)	**£20-25**	☐
4025	1959-64	Suburban Coach	1st/2nd	BR (SR)	S41060	Green body, Grey roof, transparent windows (36025)...	**£25-35**	☐
4026	1959-64	Suburban Coach	Brake/2nd ...	BR (SR)	S43374	Green body, Grey roof, transparent windows (36026)...	**£25-35**	☐

Passenger Coaches (with 'Super Detail' features)

Ref. No.	Year(s)	Type & Export No.			Description	Market Price Range	
4035	1961-64	Pullman Car - First Class (4185)........	BR	ARIES	Brown & Cream body, Grey roof, transparent windows (36035)	**£40-50**	☐
4036	1961-64	Pullman Car - Second Class (4186).....	BR	Car 74	Brown & Cream body, Grey roof, transparent windows (36036)	**£40-50**	☐
4037	1961-64	Pullman Car - Brake/2nd (4187)	BR	Car 79	Brown & Cream body, Grey roof, transparent windows (36037)	**£40-50**	☐
4050	1960-64	Corridor Coach - 1st/2nd (4200)	BR (W)	W15870	Brown & Cream body, plastic roof, transparent windows (36050)	**£20-30**	☐
4051	1960-64	Corridor Coach - Brake/2nd (4201)	BR (W)	W34290	Brown & Cream body, plastic roof, transparent windows (36051)	**£20-30**	☐
4052	1961-64	Corridor Coach - 1st/2nd (4202)	BR (E)	E15770	Maroon body, Grey roof, transparent windows (36052)	**£20-30**	☐
4053	1961-64	Corridor Coach - Brake/2nd (4203)	BR (E)	E35173	Maroon body, Grey roof, transparent windows (36053)	**£20-30**	☐
4054	1962-64	Corridor Coach - 1st/2nd (4204)........	BR (SR)	S15573	Green body, Grey roof, transparent windows........	**£35-45**	☐
4055	1962-64	Corridor Coach - Brake/2nd (4205)	BR (SR)	S35001	Green body, Grey roof, transparent windows........	**£35-45**	☐
4060	1961-64	Open Corridor Coach - 1st (4210)	BR (W)	W3085	Brown & Cream body, Grey roof, transparent windows (36060)	**£25-30**	☐
4061	1961-64	Open Corridor Coach - 2nd (4211).....	BR (W)	W3984	Brown & Cream body, Grey roof, transparent windows (36061)	**£25-30**	☐
4062	1961-64	Open Corridor Coach - 1st (4212)	BR (M)	M3002	Maroon body, Grey plastic roof, transparent windows (36062)	**£25-35**	☐
4063	1961-64	Open Corridor Coach - 2nd (4213).....	BR (M)	M3716	Maroon body, Grey plastic roof, transparent windows (36063)	**£25-35**	☐
4075	1961-64	Passenger Brake Van (4225)	BR (E)	E81312	Maroon body, Grey roof, transparent windows (36075)	**£20-30**	☐
4076	1963-64	Six-wheel Passenger Brake..................	BR (M)	M32958	Maroon body, Grey roof, transparent windows (34076)..........	**£100-125**	☐
4081	1962-64	Suburban Coach - 1st/2nd (4231)........	BR (SR)	S46291	Green body, Grey roof, transparent windows (36081)...	**£50-70**	☐
4082	1962-64	Suburban Coach - Brake/2nd (4232)...	BR (SR)	543381	Green body, Grey roof, transparent windows (36082)...	**£50-70**	☐
4082	1962-64	variation:	BR (SR)	S43381	with correct coach number (rare) (36082)	**£110-130**	☐
4083	1962-64	Suburban Coach - 1st/2nd (4233)........	BR (M)	M41012	Maroon body, Grey roof, transparent windows (36083)	**£40-50**	☐
4084	1962-64	Suburban Coach - Brake/2nd (4234)...	BR (M)	M43277	Maroon body, Grey roof, transparent windows (36084)	**£40-50**	☐
4150	1962-64	Electric Driving Trailer Coach (4250)	BR (SR)	S77511	Green, Yellow band on drive end, Black rear panel......	**£110-130**	☐
4150	1962-64	variation:	BR (SR)	S77511	As previous model but Green inner panel on rear.........	**£130-150**	☐

Note: The Export issues packed in boxes displaying the special Export Numbers are rare - expect to pay an additional **£20 per issue.**

Restaurant Cars

Ref. No.	Year(s)	Type & Export No.			Description	Market Price Range	
D20	1957 only	Restaurant Car	BR (W)	W9562	Brown & Cream body, Grey roof, transparent windows (32097)	**£25-35**	☐
32096	1957-58	Restaurant Car	BR (W)	W9572	Brown & Cream body, Grey roof, transparent windows (32096)	**£25-35**	☐
32097	1957-58	Restaurant Car	BR (W)	W9562	Red & Cream body, Grey roof, transparent windows (32097)	**£25-35**	☐
4047	1959-64	Restaurant Car	BR (W)	W9572	Brown & Cream body, Grey roof, transparent windows (36047)	**£25-35**	☐
4048	1959-64	Restaurant Car	BR(LMR)	W9562	Red & Cream body, Grey roof, transparent windows (36048)	**£25-35**	☐
4049	1959-61	Restaurant Car	BR (M)	W9566W	Maroon body, Grey roof, transparent windows (Red frames)	**£25-35**	☐
4049	1961-64	Restaurant Car	BR (M)	W9566W	As previous model but with White window frames	**£25-35**	☐

Restaurant Cars and Sleeping Car ('Super Detail')

Ref. No.	Year(s)	Type & Export No.		Colour	Market Price Range	
4070	1963-64	Restaurant Car	BR (W) W1910	Brown & Cream body, Grey roof, transparent windows (34070)	£90-120	☐
4071	1963-64	Restaurant Car	BR (E) E1939	Maroon body, Grey roof, transparent windows (34071)	£120-180	☐
4078	1961-64	Sleeping Car (4228)	BR (W) W2402	Maroon body, Grey roof, transparent windows (36078)	£35-60	☐

Vans and Wagons (pre-war Three-Rail)

Model identification: All have White lettering and Black chassis unless shown differently. See 'Technical Notes' for types of wheels and couplings.

Ref. No.	Year(s)	Model Type	Colour	Market Price Range	
'Great Western Railway' - 'G.W.' issues					
D1	1938-40	Open Goods Wagon	Grey body	£25-35	☐
D1	1938-40	Goods Van	Grey body, White roof, *'RETURN TO G.W.R.'*	£55-75	☐
D1	1938-40	Goods Brake Van	Grey body, White roof, 'PARK ROYAL' logo	£45-65	☐
D1	1938-40	Coal Wagon	Grey body	£25-35	☐
D1	1938-40	Cattle Truck	Grey body, White roof	£25-35	☐
'London, Midland & Scottish' - 'L.M.S.' issues					
D1	1938-40	Open Goods Wagon	Bauxite Brown body	£25-35	☐
D1	1938-40	Goods Van	Bauxite Brown body, Silver-Grey roof	£25-35	☐
D1	1938-40	Goods Brake Van	Bauxite Brown body, Silver-Grey roof	£25-35	☐
D1	1938-40	Coal Wagon	Bauxite Brown body	£25-35	☐
D1	1938-40	'MEAT' Van	Bauxite Brown body, Silver Grey roof	£25-35	☐
D1	1938-40	Cattle Truck	Bauxite Brown body	£45-65	☐
D2	1938-40	High-Sided Coal Wagon	Bauxite Brown body	£25-35	☐
'London & North Eastern Railway' - 'N.E.' issues					
D1	1938-40	Open Goods Wagon	Grey body	£25-35	☐
D1	1938-40	Goods Van	Grey body, White roof	£25-35	☐
D1	1938-40	Goods Brake Van	Brown body, White roof	£25-35	☐
D1	1938-40	Coal Wagon	Grey body	£25-35	☐
D1	1938-40	'FISH' Van	Light Brown body, White roof	£25-35	☐
D1	1938-40	High Capacity Wagon	Brown body, White 'BRICK' and *'RETURN TO FLETTON'* logos, Black or Brown chassis	£60-75	☐
D1	1938-40	Horse Box	Teak body, White roof	£25-35	☐
D2	1938-40	High-Sided Wagon	Seven-plank Grey body	£40-50	☐
D2	1938-40	High-Sided Coal Wagon	Seven-plank Grey body	£40-50	☐
'Southern Railway' - 'S.R.' issues					
D1	1938-40	Open Goods Wagon	Chocolate Brown body	£40-50	☐
D1	1938-40	Goods Van	Chocolate Brown body, White roof	£75-85	☐
D1	1938-40	Goods Brake Van	Chocolate Brown body, White roof	£125-150	☐
D1	1938-40	Coal Wagon	Chocolate Brown body	£40-50	☐
Tank Wagons					
D1	1938-40	'ROYAL DAYLIGHT'	Red tank, Gold logo	£80-100	☐
D1	1938-40	'POWER ETHYL'	Green tank, White and Red logo and 'hand' motif	£80-100	☐
D1	1938-40	'ESSO'	Buff tank with Red stripe, Dark Blue logo with Red shadow	£80-100	☐

Vans and Wagons (post-war Pre-Nationalisation Liveries, Three-Rail)

Model identification: All have White lettering and Black chassis unless shown differently. See 'Technical Notes' for types of wheels and couplings.

Ref. No.	Year(s)	Model Type	Colour	Market Price Range	
'Great Western Railway' - 'G.W.' issues					
D1	1948-53	Open Goods Wagon	Grey body	£30-40	☐
D1	1948-53	Goods Van	Grey body, White roof, *'RETURN TO G.W.R.'*	£75-100	☐
D1	1948-53	Goods Brake Van	Grey-Green body, White roof, 'PARK ROYAL' logo	£70-90	☐
D1	1948-53	Coal Wagon	Grey body	£20-30	☐
D1	1948-53	Cattle Truck	Grey-Green body, White roof with 2 small windows	£20-30	☐
D1	1948-53	Cattle Truck	Grey-Green body, White roof with one long window	£40-60	☐
'London, Midland & Scottish' - 'L.M.S.' issues					
D1	1948-53	Open Goods Wagon	Bauxite Brown body	£30-40	☐
D1	1948-53	Goods Van	Bauxite Brown body, Silver-Grey or Grey roof	£15-20	☐
D1	1948-53	Goods Brake Van	Bauxite Brown body, Silver-Grey or Grey roof	£15-20	☐
D1	1948-53	Coal Wagon	Bauxite Brown body	£10-15	☐
D1	1948-53	Cattle Truck	Bauxite Brown body, Cream interior, 2 small windows, Silver-Grey roof	£100-130	☐
D1	1948-53	'MEAT' Van	Bauxite Brown body, Silver-Grey or Grey roof	£10-15	☐
D1	1948-53	High-sided Coal Wagon	Bauxite Brown body	£10-15	☐
D2	1948-53	High-sided Wagon	Bauxite Brown body	£10-15	☐

'London & North Eastern Railway' - 'N.E.' issues

Ref. No.	Year(s)	Model Type		Market Price Range	
D1	1948-53	Open Goods Wagon	Grey-Green or Grey body	£15-20	☐
D1	1948-53	Goods Van	Brown body, White roof	£15-20	☐
D1	1948-53	Goods Brake Van	Brown body, White roof	£15-20	☐
D1	1948-53	Coal Wagon	Grey-Green or Grey body	£15-20	☐
D1	1948-53	'FISH' Van	Brown body, White roof	£15-20	☐
D1	1948-53	High Capacity Wagon	Brown body with White 'BRICK' and *RETURN TO FLETTON* logos	£15-20	☐
D1	1948-53	Horse Box	Teak body, White roof	£15-20	☐
D2	1948-53	High-sided Coal Wagon	Seven-plank Grey-Green body	£50-60	☐
			As previous model but with seven-plank Grey body	£25-35	☐

'Southern Railway' - 'S.R.' issues

Ref. No.	Year(s)	Model Type		Market Price Range	
D1	1948-53	Five Plank Open Goods Wagon	Chocolate Brown body	£80-100	☐
D1	1948-53	Goods Van	Chocolate Brown body, White roof	£100-150	☐
D1	1948-53	Goods Brake Van	Chocolate Brown body, one window on end	£100-150	☐
D1	1948-53	Goods Brake Van	Chocolate Brown body, window each side of end door	£80-100	☐
D1	1948-53	Coal Wagon	Chocolate Brown body	£60-80	☐
D1	1948-53	'MEAT' Van	Buff body, Silver-Grey roof	£100-150	☐
D1	1948-53	'MEAT' Van	Buff body, White roof	£60-80	☐

Tank Wagons

Ref. No.	Year(s)	Model Type		Market Price Range	
D1	1948-53	'ROYAL DAYLIGHT'	Red tank, Gold logo, (no 'ESSO' or 'PARAFFIN' logos on tank sides)	£80-100	☐
D1	1948-53	'POWER PETROL'	Green tank, Silver logo, Red 'ETHYL' logos, White 'hand' design	£80-100	☐
D1	1948-53	'ESSO'	Buff tank with Red stripe, Dark Blue logo with Red shadow	£100-150	☐

Vans and Wagons
(post-Nationalisation 'British Rail' issues, Three-Rail)

Model identification: All have White lettering and Black chassis unless shown differently. See 'Technical Notes' for types of wheels and couplings. Models have a diecast chassis and a tinplate body.

Ref. No.	Year(s)	Model Type		Market Price Range	
D1/32020	1954-58	Cattle Truck	Brown body, Grey roof, metal wheels	£10-15	☐
32021	1958	Cattle Wagon	Brown body, Grey roof, spoked plastic wheels, plastic body	£10-15	☐
D1/32025/6	1954-58	Coal Wagon	Grey body, metal or spoked plastic wheels	£10-15	☐
D1/32035	1954-58	Fish Van	Brown body, Grey roof	£10-15	☐
D1/32040	1954-58	Goods Van	Brown body, Grey roof	£10-15	☐
D1/32044/5	1954-58	Goods Brake Van	All Grey body, Grey roof	£10-15	☐
32046	1954-58	Goods Brake Van	Brown body, Grey roof	£10-15	☐
D1/32047	1954-58	Goods Brake Van	All Grey body, 'PARK ROYAL' logo	£10-15	☐
32047	1954-58	Goods Brake Van	All Grey body, 'SOUTHALL' logo	£10-15	☐
D1/32049	1954-58	Caboose	Black body, 'CANADIAN PACIFIC RAILWAY' logo	£90-140	☐
D1/32050	1954-58	High Capacity Wagon	Brown body, 'BRICK - EMPTY TO FLETTON'	£10-15	☐
D1/32051	1954-58	30 ton Wagon	'BOGIE BOLSTER', Grey	£10-15	☐
D1/32058/ /32041	1954-58	Ventilated Van	Brown body, White or Grey roof	£10-15	☐
D1/32060	1954-58	Horse Box	Red body, Grey roof	£10-15	☐
D1/32065	1954-58	Meat Van	White body, Grey roof	£10-15	☐
D1/32067	1958	Bulk Grain Wagon	Grey body	£10-15	☐
D1/32068	1958	Salt Wagon	Yellow body, Grey roof, Red 'SAXA SALT' logo, plastic body	£10-15	☐
D1/32069	1958	'U.G.B.' Sand Wagon	Yellow body, Black 'United Glass Bottle Co.' logo, plastic body	£10-15	☐
32070	1953-55	Tank Wagon	Red tank, Red/White/Blue 'ESSO', Gold 'ROYAL DAYLIGHT', Black 'PARAFFIN' logos	£20-25	☐
D1/32076	1956-58	'TUBE' Wagon	Brown body	£10-15	☐
D1/32080	1954-56	Tank Wagon	Green tank with Gold/Yellow 'POWER PETROL' logo	£20-25	☐
D1/32081	1953-58	Tank Wagon	Silver-Grey tank, Red/White/Blue 'ESSO' logo	£15-20	☐
D1/32082	1955-58	Tank Wagon	Yellow tank, Red 'SHELL LUBRICATING OIL' logo	£20-25	☐
D1/32083	1955-57	Tank Wagon	Red tank, White 'VACUUM OIL COMPANY' logo plus 'MOBILGAS' & 'MOBILOIL' motifs	£25-35	☐
D1/32084	1956-57	'MOBIL' Tank Wagon	Red tank, White 'MOBIL OIL COMPANY LTD' logo plus 'MOBILOIL' & 'MOBILGAS' motifs	£25-35	☐
	1957-58		Red tank, Dark Blue 'MOBIL' logo on White background	£25-35	☐
D1/32086	1953-59	Low sided Wagon	'LIVERPOOL CABLES'	£10-15	☐
D1/32098	1957-59	TPO Mail Van	Maroon body, Grey roof, in box with catcher	£20-30	☐
D2/32030	1954-58	High-sided Coal Wagon	Grey body	£10-15	☐
D2/32052	1954-58	Double Bolster Wagon	Grey body	£10-15	☐
D2/32055	1954-58	High-sided Coal Wagon	Grey body	£10-15	☐
D2/32056	1954-58	Mineral Wagon	Grey body	£10-15	☐
	1953	New version	With labels at the wrong end	£25-40	☐

THREE RAIL - TWO RAIL TRANSITION 1958, Box numbering identification
The box numbers changed from their 3-rail reference numbers (e.g. 32048 WR) to their new 2-rail numbers, (32048 WR became 4312 WR, etc). The early models continued to be issued in blue boxes with white stripes and also displayed an 'SD6' number to denote that they were 'Super Detail' models. The 'SD6' reference only appeared on the blue/white box. Eventually the 'SD6' was dropped and the red box (with white lines) was introduced.

Vans and Wagons   ('British Rail' issues, Two-Rail)

Ref. No.	Year(s)	Model Type		Market Price Range	
4300	1961-64	Blue Spot Fish Van	White or Cream body, Grey roof, Blue spot, 'INSUL FISH' logo (SD)	£20-25	☐
4301	1962-64	Banana Van	Brown body, Grey roof with Yellow identification spot (SD)	£20-25	☐

Ref. No.	Year(s)	Model Type	*Hornby Dublo Vans and Wagons – continued*	Market Price Range	
4305	1960-64	Passenger Fruit Van	Maroon body, Black or Grey roof, (SD)	£25-35	☐
4310	1958-61	Goods Brake Van	Grey body & roof, (M730012), (SD)	£10-15	☐
	1962-64		Brown body, Grey roof, (M730973), (SD)	£35-40	☐
4311	1959-64	Goods Brake Van	Brown body, 'B.R.', (SD)	£10-15	☐
4312	1959-64	Goods Brake Van	Grey body, 'W.R.', (SD)	£10-15	☐
4313	1962-64	Gunpowder Van	Brown body, Grey roof, (SD)	£15-20	☐
4315	1960-64	'B.R.' Horse Box	Maroon body, Grey roof, Light Brown or Buff plastic horse, (SD)	£75-100	☐
4316	1960-64	'S.R.' Horse Box	Green body, Grey roof, Light Brown or Buff plastic horse, (SD)	£100-125	☐
4318	1961-62	Packing Van for Breakdown Train	Red body, Grey roof, (SD), with closed brake gear	£25-35	☐
	1962-64		With open brake gear	£40-50	☐
4320	1959-64	Refrigerator Van	White or Cream body, Grey roof, (SD)	£10-15	☐
4323	1961-64	'S.R.' Utility Van	Green body, Grey roof, (SD)	£35-45	☐
4325	1959-64	12 ton Ventilated Van	Brown body, White roof, (SD)	£7-9	☐
4401	1959-64	T.P.O. Mail Van	Maroon body, Grey roof, in box with catcher	£20-30	☐
4605	1959-64	40 ton Bogie Well Wagon	Grey body with White 'WELTROL' logo, (SD)	£10-15	☐
4610	1959-64	'BOGIE BOLSTER' Wagon	Grey body, (SD)	£10-15	☐
4615	1959-64	Double Bolster Wagon	with Timber Load, Grey body, Black base	£9-12	☐
4620	1959-61	Breakdown Crane Wagon	Red matt finish, White on Black 'No.133'	£40-50	☐
	1961-64		Red gloss finish, White on Black 'No.133'	£80-100	☐
4625	1959-64	20 ton Wagon	'BULK GRAIN', Grey body, (SD)	£10-15	☐
4626	1960-64	Bulk Cement Wagon	'PRESFLO', Bauxite Brown body, (SD)	£10-15	☐
4627	1960-64	'I.C.I.' 20 ton Salt Wagon	'BULK SALT', all-Blue body, (SD)	£10-15	☐
4630	1958-64	8 ton Cattle Wagon	Brown body, Grey roof, (SD)	£10-15	☐
4635	1958-64	13 ton Coal Wagon	Grey body, with coal load, (SD)	£15-20	☐
4640	1959-64	12 ton Steel Type Goods Wagon	Brown body, (SD)	£10-15	☐
4644	1963-64	21 ton Hopper Wagon	Grey body, (SD)	£75-100	☐
4645	1961-64	Low-sided Wagon	Brown body, (SD)	£10-15	☐
4646	1961-64	Low-sided Wagon	Grey body, 2 Yellow plastic cable drums, 'ALUMINUM WIRE AND CABLE Co'	£35-45	☐
4646	1959-62	Low-sided Wagon	Grey, 2 Black/Beige wooden cable drums, 'LIVERPOOL CABLES'	£9-12	☐
4647	1959-64	Low-sided Wagon	Brown body with Red/Grey container, 'BRITISH RAILWAYS', 'FURNITURE'	£9-12	☐
4648	1959-64	Low-sided Wagon	Brown body with White/Grey container, 'BRITISH RAILWAYS', 'INSUL-MEAT'	£9-12	☐
4649	1961-64	Low-sided Wagon	Brown body with Hornby Dublo tractor (Blue)	£35-45	☐
4652	1959-64	Machine Wagon	'LOWMAC', Brown body, (SD)	£10-15	☐
4654	1964	'RAIL CLEANING WAGON'	White logo on Black wagon plus six cleaning plugs, (SD), (900 only issued)	£300-500	☐
4655	1959	Mineral Wagon	Grey metal body with plastic disc type wheels, (SD)	£60-75	☐
	1959-62		As previous model but with Grey plastic body, plastic wheels, closed brake gear	£10-15	☐
	1962-64		With open brake gear	£18-23	☐
4656	1962-64	16 ton Mineral Wagon	Brown plastic body, plastic wheels	£30-45	☐
4657	1962-64	United Dairies Milk Tank	Six-wheeled 'Super Detail' vehicle		
			Off-White tank, Yellow 'U.D.' logo, High and Low supports	£25-55	☐
			Off-White tank, Yellow 'U.D.' logo, plus High supports	£25-35	☐
			Off-White tank, Yellow 'U.D.' logo, plus Low supports	£25-35	☐
			White tank, Yellow 'U.D.' logo, plus High and Low supports	£25-35	☐
			Cream tank, Yellow 'U.D.' logo, plus High supports	£35-45	☐
			Cream tank with High and Low supports	£35-45	☐
4658	1962-64	'PRESTWIN' Silo Wagon	Brown body, (SD)	£7-9	☐
4660	1962-64	'U.G.B.' Sand Wagon	Yellow body, Black 'United Glass Limited' logo, (SD)	£35-45	☐
	1959-62	Private Owners variation	Yellow body, Black 'United Glass Manufacturing Company Ltd' logo	£12-15	☐
	1961-62		As PO variation but with open brake gear	£15-25	☐
4665	1959-62	'SAXA SALT' Wagon	Yellow body, Grey roof, Red logo, (SD), with closed brake gear	£10-15	☐
	1962-64		With open brake gear	£20-25	☐
4670	1959-64	13 ton Standard Wagon	Grey body, (SD)	£10-15	☐
4675	1959-64	Tank Wagon	White Chlorine tank, Yellow top, Black 'I.C.I. motif and star, (SD)	£10-15	☐
4676	1959-62	Tank Wagon	Silver-Grey tank with two Red/White/Blue 'ESSO' motifs plus Black star, closed brake gear,(SD)	£10-15	☐
	1962-64		With open brake gear	£20-30	☐
4677	1959-62	Tank Wagon	Red tank with Dark Blue 'MOBIL' logo on White background, closed brake gear, (SD)	£15-20	☐
	1962-64		With open brake gear	£24-30	☐
4678	1959-62	Tank Wagon	Yellow tank with Red 'SHELL LUBRICATING OIL' logo, closed brake gear, (SD)	£15-20	☐
	1962-64		With open brake gear	£20-30	☐
4679	1959-64	Tank Wagon	Silver-Grey tank with Black 'TRAFFIC SERVICES Ltd' logo, 2 Black stars, (SD)	£15-20	☐
4680	1959-62	Tank Wagon	Black tank with Red 'ESSO' motif plus White 'ESSO PETROLEUM COMPANY LTD' logo and 2 Black stars, closed brake gear, (SD)	£20-30	☐
	1962-64		With open brake gear	£30-40	☐
4685	1959-64	Tank Wagon	Dark Blue 'I.C.I.' Caustic Liquor Bogie Wagon, (SD)	£65-85	☐
		variation:	As previous model but with Diamond bogies	£100-150	☐
4690	1959-60	Tube Wagon	Brown body with spoked wheels (SD6), but a red box was not issued with 4690 on it	£10-15	☐

Notes:

'SUPER DETAIL' - Models with the abbreviation '(SD)' have greatly enhanced 'SUPER DETAIL' features
'BLACK STARS' - Two Black stars on a wagon indicates that the vehicle can travel by the fastest freight train
'SILVER TANK' - A Tank Wagon painted Silver indicates that it is carrying an inflammable liquid

N.B. Screwed couplings indicate model is an Export issue and worth more (normal couplings rivetted). The exceptions to this rule are 4625 20 ton 'BULK GRAIN' & 4627 'ICI' Salt Wagon.

Other wagons will be found with open brake gear, but this does not greatly affect their value and their availability is equal to those with closed brake gear.

3: Gift Sets

Ref. No.	Year(s)	Set Name	Contents	Market Price Range	

Pre-war issues

Ref. No.	Year(s)	Set Name	Contents	Market Price Range	
DP1	1938-40	Clockwork Passenger Train Set..............	'L.N.E.R.' Contains DL1 'Sir Nigel Gresley' loco and tender plus two Articulated Coaches, 8 curved and 2 straight rails..........	£1000-1250	☐
DG7	1938-40	Clockwork Tank Goods Train Sets..............	'G.W.R.', 'L.M.S.', 'L.N.E.R.', 'S.R.' Contains DL7 Tank loco plus Open Wagon, Goods Van and Goods Brake Van..........	£300-900*	☐
EDP1	1938-40	Electric Passenger Train Set.....	'L.N.E.R.' Contains EDL1 'Sir Nigel Gresley' loco and tender plus two Articulated Coaches, 8 curved and 2 straight rails..........	£900-1250	☐
EDG7	1938-40	Electric Tank Goods Train Sets..............	'G.W.R.', 'L.M.S.', 'L.N.E.R.', 'S.R.' Contains EDL7 loco plus Open Wagon, Goods Wagon and Goods Brake Wagon..........	£300-900*	☐

* **Note:** The Market Price Range for these sets reflects the great variation in market prices for the individual locomotives (see the Locomotives listing).

Post-war issues (Pre-Nationalisation Liveries)

Ref. No.	Year(s)	Set Name	Contents	Market Price Range	
EDP1	1948-53	Electric Passenger Train Set.....	'L.N.E.R.' Contains EDL1 'Sir Nigel Gresley' loco and tender plus D1 1st/3rd and Brake/3rd Coaches..........	£150-200	☐
EDP2	1948-53	Passenger Set..........	'L.M.S.' Contains EDL2 'Duchess of Atholl' loco and tender plus D3 'L.M.S.' Coaches '3rd' and 'Brake 3rd'..........	£120-160	☐
EDP2	1948-53	Passenger Set..........	'CANADIAN PACIFIC' Contains EDL2 loco (1215) and tender plus D3 'L.M.S.' Coaches '3rd' and 'Brake 3rd'..........	£650-850	☐
EDG3	1948-53	Freight Train Set..........	'CANADIAN PACIFIC RAILWAY' Contains EDL2 loco and tender plus 32049 'C.P.' Caboose & D1 Bogie Bolster Wagon..........	£650-850	☐
EDG7	1948-53	Tank Goods Train Sets..........	'G.W.R.', 'L.M.S.', 'L.N.E.R.' or 'SOUTHERN' Contains EDL7 0-6-2 loco plus D1 Goods Van, D1 Open Wagon & D1 Goods Brake Wagon..........	£300-900*	☐

* **Note:** The Market Price Range for these sets reflects the great variation in market prices for the individual locomotives (see the Locomotives listing).

Post-Nationalisation 'British Railways' issues (Three-Rail)

Ref. No.	Year(s)	Set Name	Contents	Market Price Range	
EDP10	1954-58	Passenger Train Set 'B.R.'..........	EDL17 0-6-2 Tank loco (69567) D14 Suburban Coaches '1st/3rd' & 'Brake/3rd'..........	£100-125	☐
EDP11	1954-58	Passenger Train Set 'B.R.'..........	EDL11 'Silver King' loco and tender plus D11 Coaches '1st/2nd' & 'Brake/2nd'..........	£100-125	☐
EDP12	1954-58	Passenger Train Set 'B.R.'..........	EDL12 'Duchess of Montrose' (gloss finish) D11 Coaches '1st/2nd' & 'Brake/2nd'	£120-140	☐
			Same set but with matt finish locomotive..........	£90-105	☐
EDP13	1954-58	Tank Passenger Set 'B.R.'..........	EDL18 2-6-4 Tank loco (no.80054) plus D13 Suburban Coaches '1st/3rd' and 'Brake/3rd'..........	£100-125	☐
EDP14	1954-58	Passenger Train Set 'B.R.'..........	EDL18 2-6-4 Tank loco (no.80054) plus D14 Suburban Coaches '1st/2nd' & two 'Brake/3rd'..........	£120-140	☐
EDP15	1954-58	Passenger Train Set 'B.R.'..........	Contains EDP11 'Silver King' loco and tender plus D12 Coaches '1st/3rd' & 'Brake/3rd'..........	£100-125	☐
EDG16	1954-58	Tank Goods Set 'B.R.'..........	EDL17 0-6-2 Tank loco (no.69567) plus D1 issues: 2 Open Wagons and a Goods Brake Van..........	£100-125	☐
EDG17	1954-58	Tank Goods Set 'B.R.'..........	EDL17 0-6-2 Tank loco (no.69567) plus D1 issues: Meat Van, Open Wagon, 'MOBIL' Tank Wagon, Goods Brake Van..........	£100-125	☐
EDG18	1954-58	Tank Goods Set 'B.R.'..........	EDL18 2-6-4 Tank loco (no.80054) plus D1 issues: High Capacity Wagon, Bogie Bolster Wagon, Goods Brake Van..........	£100-125	☐
EDG19	1954-58	Tank Goods Set 'B.R.'..........	EDL18 2-6-4 Tank loco (no.80054) plus D1 issues: Ventilated Van, 'MOBIL' Tank Wagon, Double Bolster Wagon, Tube Wagon, Goods Brake Van..........	£130-150	☐
EDP20	1954-58	'BRISTOLIAN' Passenger Train Set..........	Contains LT 20 'Bristol Castle' loco and tender plus D21 Coaches '1st/2nd' & 'Brake/2nd'..........	£160-180	☐
EDP22	1954-58	Passenger Train Set 'B.R.'..........	Contains EDL12 'Duchess of Montrose' loco and tender plus D22 Coaches '1st/2nd' & 'Brake/2nd'..........	£100-125	☐
G 25	1954-58	Freight Train Set 'B.R.'..........	Contains: 3225/LT25 Class 8F loco (2-8-0, no.48158) plus D1 Refrigerated Van, 'WELTROL' Bogie Wagon, D1 'SHELL' Tank Wagon, D1 Open Wagon & Goods Brake Van..........	£100-125	☐

'British Railways' issues (Two-Rail)

Ref. No.	Year(s)	Set Name	Contents	Market Price Range	
2001	1959-64	Tank Goods Set..........	'Ready to Run' Black or Blue 0-4-0 Tank loco plus two open wagons and Goods Brake Van 'B.R.'..........	£75-100	☐
2004	1959-64	Diesel Shunter Goods Set..........	'Ready to Run' Contains Yellow 0-4-0 loco plus two open wagons and Goods Brake Van 'B.R.'..........	£50-75	☐
2006	1959-64	Southern Tank Goods Set..........	2207 Green loco (0-6-0, no.31340) plus 4660 'U.G.B.' Sand Wagon, 4646 Steel Goods Wagon, 4312 Goods Brake Van 'W.R.'..........	£100-125	☐
2007	1959-64	Southern Tank Passenger Set....	2207 Green loco (0-6-0, no.31340) plus 4025/6 Suburban Coaches '1st/2nd' & 'Brake/3rd'..........	£100-125	☐
2008	1959-64	Tank Goods Set..........	2206 Black loco (0-6-0, no.31337) plus 4660 'U.G.B.' Sand Wagon, 4640 Steel Goods Wagon, 4312 Goods Brake Van..........	£100-125	☐
2009	1959-64	Tank Passenger Set 'S.R.'..........	2206 Black loco (0-6-0, no.31337) plus 4025/6 Suburban Coaches '1st/2nd' & 'Brake/2nd' 'S.R.'..........	£100-125	☐
2015	1959-64	'The TALISMAN' Passenger Train Set 'E.R.'..........	2211 'Golden Fleece' loco and tender plus 4052/3 Coaches '1st/2nd B.R.' & 'Brake/2nd B.R.'..........	£200-300	☐
2016	1959-64	Tank Goods Set..........	2217 loco (0-6-2, no.69550) plus 4665 'SAXA SALT' Wagon, 4677 'MOBIL' Tank Wagon, 4646 Cable Wagon (2 drums), 4310 Goods Brake Van 'L.M.R.'..........	£100-125	☐
2019	1959-64	Tank Goods Set..........	2218 loco (2-6-4, 80033) 4648/9 Low-sided Wagons (Meat Container & Tractor) Double Bolster Wagon (Timber load) Goods Brake Van 'L.M.R.' or 'E.R.'..........	£100-125	☐

Ref. No.	Year(s)	Set Name		Market Price Range	
2020	1959-64	'TORBAY EXPRESS' Passenger Train Set 'W.R.'	2220 'Denbigh Castle' loco & tender, 4050/1 Coaches '1st/2nd' & 'Brake/2nd'	£200-250	☐
2021	1959-64	'RED DRAGON' Passenger Train Set	2221 'Cardiff Castle' loco and tender plus D1 or 4050/1 Coaches '1st/2nd' & 'Brake/2nd'	£200-250	☐
2022	1959-64	'THE CALEDONIAN' Passenger Train Set	2226 'City of London' loco and tender plus D22 Coaches '1st/2nd' & 'Brake/2nd'	£200-300	☐
			As previous set but with updated 4052/3 Coaches '1st/2nd' and 'Brake/2nd'	£200-300	☐
2024	1959-64	Express Goods Set 'L.M.R.'	Contains 2224 loco (2-8-0, no.48073) plus 4320 Refrigerator Van, 4605 Bogie Well Wagon, 4678 'SHELL' Tank Wagon, 4670 Standard Wagon, 4310 Goods Brake Van 'L.M.R.'	£100-125	☐
2025	1959-64	Express Goods Set 'L.M.R.'	2225 loco (2-8-0, no.48109) plus same rolling stock as set 2024	£200-250	☐
2030	1959-64	Diesel-Electric Goods Set	Contains 2230 'Bo-Bo' loco (no.8017) plus 4320 Refrigerator Van 'W.R.', 4625 Grain Wagon, 4325 Ventilated Wagon, 4310 Goods Brake Van 'L.M.R.'	£100-125	☐
2033	1959-64	Diesel-Electric Goods Set	2233 'Co-Bo' loco (no.D5702) plus same rolling stock as set 2030	£200-250	☐
2034	1959-64	'THE ROYAL SCOT' Passenger Train Set	2234 Deltic loco 'Crepello' plus 4052/3 Maroon Coaches '1st/2nd' and 'Brake/2nd'	£200-250	☐
2035	1959-64	'BOURNEMOUTH BELLE' Passenger Train Set	Contains 2235 'Barnstaple' loco and tender plus 4035/6/7 Pullman Coaches	£250-300	☐
2045	1959-64	3300 hp Electric Loco Set	Illustrated in 1964 catalogue but not issued	NPP	☐
2049	1959-64	Breakdown Train Set	Contains 2217 loco (0-6-2, no.69550) plus 69550 Crane, 4318 Packing Van and Brake/2nd Suburban Coach	£200-300	☐
2050	1959-64	Suburban Electric Train Set	Contains 2250 Drive Coach and Trailer Car 4150. Shown in Oct.1962 catalogue as 3 x Car Unit but only marketed as a 2 x Car Unit	£200-250	☐

GIFT SET ENCLOSURES: Operating instructions, Track Layout plans, 'Tested' label, Guarantee, Application form to join the 'Hornby Railway Club'.

4:   Accessories

Ref. No.	Year(s)	Accessory	Details	Market Price Range	

Pre-war accessories (1938 - 1940)

Ref. No.	Year(s)	Accessory	Details	Market Price Range	
D1	1938-40	Main Line Station Building	Cream with Red or Green roof, wooden construction	£200-250	☐
D1	1938-40	Goods Depot	Cream with Red or Green roof, wooden construction	£200-250	☐
D1	1938-40	Engine Shed	Cream with Red or Green roof, wooden construction	£200-250	☐
D1	1938-40	Signal Cabin	Cream with Red or Green roof, wooden construction	£50-75	☐
D2	1938-40	Station Building	Cream with Green roof, wooden construction	£300-400	☐
D2	1938-40	Arched roof	Wooden construction, perspex roof	£200-250	☐
D2	1938-40	Centre platform	Wooden construction	£30-40	☐
D2	1938-40	Side platform	Wooden construction	£30-40	☐
D2	1938-40	Centre platform ramps	Wooden construction	£20-30	☐
D2	1938-40	Side platform ramps	Wooden construction	£20-30	☐
D1	1938-40	Cardboard Tunnel (short)		£40-50	☐
D1	1938-40	Cardboard Tunnel (long)		£40-50	☐
D1	1938-40	Footbridge		£30-40	☐
D1	1938-40	Buffers (single)	or D2 Buffers (double)	£15-25	☐
D1	1938-40	Buffer Stops	Six in a box	£35-50	☐
D1	1938-40	Signal (single)	or D2 Signal (double) or D3 Signal (Junction)	£7-12	☐
D1	1938-40	Railway Staff	6 metal figures: Guard, Porter with luggage, Ticket Collector, Shunter, Engine Driver, Station Master	£75-100	☐
D2	1938-40	Railway Passengers	6 metal figures: 3 males, 3 females	£75-100	☐
	1938-40	Miscellaneous items	include transformers, electrically operated points, switches, etc.	£6-12	☐
	1938-40	'Clockwork' Track Points		£30-40	☐
	1938-40	'Clockwork' Track		£1-2	☐
	1938-40	Electric Track		£1-2	☐

Post-war accessories (1948 - 1958) Three-Rail

Ref. No.	Year(s)	Accessory	Details	Market Price Range	
D1	1948-58	Through Station	(Diecast Cream with Orange roof, Green doors and windows)	£50-70	☐
D1	1948-58	Island Platform	(Diecast Cream with Orange roof, Green doors and windows)	£30-40	☐
D1	1948-58	Platform extension	with wall for Through Station	£35-45	☐
D1	1948-58	Platform extension	with wall for Island Platform	£35-45	☐
D1	1948-58	Turntable (32180)	Metal, Grey-Green with Orange sideframes	£40-60	☐
D1	1948-58	Footbridge	All Cream three-piece construction	£20-30	☐
D1	1948-58	Level Crossing (3460 3 R)	Metal, White gates with Red warning circles, Green verges	£10-15	☐
		Plastic version:	Cream base & gates, White posts, Red warning circles	£25-35	☐
D1	1948-58	Girder Bridge	Diecast metal, Orange	£40-50	☐
D1	1948-58	T.P.O. Mail Van Set	with Mail Van, lineside apparatus and two mailbags	£20-30	☐
D1	1948-58	Loading Gauge		£10-15	☐
D1	1948-58	Water Crane	Brown	£5-10	☐
D1	1948-58	(051) Station Staff	6 metal figures: Guard, Porter, Ticket Collector, Shunter, Engine Driver, Station Master	£40-50	☐
D2	1948-58	(053) Passengers	6 metal figures: 3 males, 3 females	£40-50	☐
3450	1948-58	Buffers Stop	Box of 2	£10-15	☐

Signals and Switches

Ref. No.	Year(s)	Accessory	Details	Market Price Range	
32115	1948-58	Colour Light Signal ES6	'Home'	£7-12	☐
32116	1948-58	Colour Light Signal ES6	'Distant'	£7-12	☐
32117	1948-58	Colour Light Signal ES6	'Junction - Home'	£10-15	☐

Ref. No.	Year(s)	Accessory	Description	Market Price Range
D1	1948-58	Switch	Red, for electrically operated points and signals	£7-10 ☐
D2	1948-58	Switch	Black, for isolating rails	£7-10 ☐
G3	1948-58	Switch	Green, for coloured light signals (rare)	£20-30 ☐
ED1/5065	1948-58	Signal	Electrically operated, single arm, 'Home'	£7-12 ☐
ED1/5066	1948-58	Signal	Electrically operated, single arm, 'Distant'	£7-12 ☐
ED2/5070	1948-58	Signal	Electrically operated, double arm, 'Home - Distant'	£12-18 ☐
ED3/5075	1948-58	Junction Signal	Electrically operated, two arms, 'Home'	£12-18 ☐
ED3/5076	1948-58	Junction Signal	Electrically operated, two arms, 'Distant'	£12-18 ☐
D1/5050	1948-58	Signal	Hand operated, single arm, 'Home'	£10-15 ☐
D1/5051	1948-58	Signal	Hand operated, single arm, 'Distant'	£7-10 ☐
D2/5055	1948-58	Signal	Hand operated, double arm, 'Home - Distant'	£7-10 ☐
D3/5060	1948-58	Junction Signal	Hand operated, two arms, 'Home'	£12-18 ☐
D3/5061	1948-58	Junction Signal	Hand operated, two arms, 'Distant'	£12-18 ☐

Accessories (1959 - 1964) Two-Rail

Ref. No.	Year(s)	Accessory	Description	Market Price Range
050	1959-64	Railway Staff	12 moulded plastic figures	£100-125 ☐
052	1959-64	Railway Passengers	12 moulded plastic figures	£30-40 ☐
790	1959-64	Granite Chippings		£2-3 ☐
791	1959-64	Coal (imitation)	per bag	£2-3 ☐
1575	1959-64	Lighting Kit		£10-15 ☐
2400	1959-64	T.P.O. Mail Van Set	Mail Van plus lineside apparatus, two mailbags	£20-30 ☐
2450	1959-64	Buffers Stop		£10-15 ☐
2451	1959-64	Illuminated Buffers		£15-20 ☐
4620	1959-64	Breakdown Crane	Gloss or Matt, with 2 support wagons each with 2 screw jacks plus match truck (see Wagons listing)	£75-90 ☐
5005	1959-64	Engine Shed Kit - Two Road	Cream and Green with Grey roof	£60-70 ☐
5006	1959-64	Engine Shed Extension Kit		£20-30 ☐
5010	1959-64	Footbridge		£10-20 ☐
5015	1959-64	Girder Bridge	Red plastic (rare - only 3,000 made)	£300-400 ☐
5020	1959-64	Goods Depot Kit	Cream and Green, Grey roof, Red/Yellow static working jib	£30-50 ☐
5025	1959-64	Gradient and Mile Posts	Box of 12	£40-50 ☐
5030	1959-64	Island Platform Kit	Cream and Green, Grey roof	£30-40 ☐
5035	1959-64	Loading Gauge		£15-20 ☐
5037	1959-64	Lineside Notices	Box of six	£25-35 ☐
5040	1959-64	Platelayers' Hut	Box of 6	£25-35 ☐
5080	1959-64	Signal Cabin	Cream and Green, Orange roof	£10-20 ☐
		Rare variation:	As previous model but with Green roof	£150-200 ☐
5083	1959-64	Terminal and Through Station Composite Kit		£200-300 ☐
5084	1959-64	Station Canopy Extension Kit	(Tri-ang - Hornby). Box with large top opening, Red/Yellow printing. N.B. 5084 & R5084 also housed in 3rd type of Red box. (Triang Hornby)	£400-500 ☐
R5084	1959-64	Station Canopy Extension Kit	(late Tri-ang - Hornby). Plain White box, Black/White end labels	£200-300 ☐
5085	1959-64	Suburban Station Kit	Cream and Green with Grey roof	£30-40 ☐
5086	1959-64	Platform extension		£5-10 ☐
5087	1959-64	Platform Fence extension		£10-20 ☐
5089	1959-64	Platform Side extension		£20-30 ☐
5090	1959-64	Telegraph Poles	Box of 12	£50-75 ☐
5091/2	1959-64	Tunnel	Single or Double, price for either	£50-100 ☐
5094	1959-64	Tunnel Ends	Box of 6	£100-150 ☐
5095	1959-64	Water Crane	Buff	£35-45 ☐

Note: All the Building Kits in the listing above are of plastic construction.

5: Hornby Dublo Catalogues

Ref. No.	Year(s)	Publication	Cover Features & Details	Market Price Range	
7/938/185 UK	1938-39	Catalogue............................	First catalogue dedicated solely to Hornby Dublo. White cover with colour picture of pre-war layout and boy with flag and whistle plus man and seated boy. Lists all pre-war issues with prices and pictures.................	£75-100	☐
1/939/27	1939	Leaflet (one page)	Gives details of the new EDP2 'L.M.S.' Electric Passenger Set plus list of rolling stock and prices.................................	£15-20	☐
12/1039/70 UK	1939	Leaflet (8 pages).................	A large leaflet with Orange cover listing the entire pre-war range	£75-100	☐
7/1053/250	1953-54	Leaflet	Colour cover. Lists new 'B.R.' liveries	£30-40	☐
7/754/200	1954-55	Leaflet	Colour cover, products price list	£30-40	☐
7/755/550	1955-56	Leaflet	Colour cover depicting attractive layout. Includes superb colour pictures of entire range	£30-40	☐
7/556/500	1956-57	Leaflet	With colour picture of 'Duchess of Montrose'.	£30-40	☐
7/857/500	1957	Three-fold Leaflet	With excellent centre page layout spread (man with FIVE fingers pointing to layout)	£20-30	☐
7/858/500	1958	Three-fold Leaflet	Cover depicts 'Duchess of Montrose' 'ROYAL SCOT'	£15-25	☐
HD/CF/1	1959	Three-fold Leaflet	Cover depicts 2236 'City of London' 'THE CALEDONIAN'	£15-25	☐
18/259/300	1959	'Hornby Book of Trains'....	Cover shows green loco (4472) and price '1/6d'. 64 pages...................................	£10-15	☐
92016	1960	24 page Catalogue	The cover depicts a Blue 'English Electric' loco...	£10-15	☐
72236/02	1961	24 page Catalogue	Cover depicts D9002 Diesel Electric loco with excellent pictures of all items manufactured..	£10-15	☐
77250/02	1961	3 fold Leaflet......................	'City of Liverpool' (No.46247) on the cover	£7-12	☐
18/561/500	1961	24 page Catalogue	Cover picture shows 'Barnstaple' loco...	£10-15	☐
13/162/500	1962	28 page Catalogue	Cover picture shows 'Deltic' locomotive..	£10-15	☐
72245/02	1962	4 page Leaflet......................	Excellent cover picture shows the front ends of 'Barnstaple' and 'Crepello' locos	£10-15	☐
7/363/400 ?					
722257/02	1963	20 page Booklet..................	Pocket sized booklet depicting 'Kingfisher' loco, introduces the E3001 Loco with Pantographs...	£10-15	☐
13/464/100	1964	4-fold Leaflet......................	With view of two green locos	£10-15	☐
R 280 S	1965	Tri-ang and Hornby Dublo Amalgamation Issue	Night scene on cover	£10-15	☐

In addition to the foregoing basic listing of leaflets and catalogues dedicated to Hornby Dublo many other publications listed the products:
Meccano Magazines - pre-war and post-war
Meccano General Products catalogues
Large stores own catalogues - 'Hamleys', 'Gamages', 'Bentalls', etc.
Hornby 'Book of Trains' - pre-war and post-war
'Hornby Trains' leaflets and illustrated price lists - pre-war and post-war from 1948

6: Model Pricing Guidelines

Post-war Locomotives. All were issued both as individual models and in sets. Post-war re-issued models are priced at 20% less than pre-war examples.

Horseshoe (HS) and Half Inch (HI) Motors. Prices shown assume a Horseshoe Motor has been fitted. For Half Inch Motor deduct 15%.

Binns Road Repair Locomotives. Variations exist such as nickel silver wheels replacing alloy wheels and plastic wheels replacing small pony and bogie wheels. These variations could affect prices by up to 20%.

Early Boxes. Models EDL1 and EDL2 packed in light powder-blue boxes are priced at 33% more than those in dark blue boxes.

'Gloss' finished Locomotives. The only locomotives to be issued in a glossy paint livery were:
EDL11 'Silver King',   EDL12 'Duchess of Montrose',   N2 69567 Tank Locomotive.

Qualifying Standards. The prices shown in this Catalogue have been based on the following qualifying standards:
Locomotives to be in exceptional condition showing no signs of wear or fingerprints, to be in working order, and to be in its original box.
Boxes to be in pristine, unmarked condition, complete with any original packing or labelling. See the following section on 'Packaging'.

Prices for non-Mint or unboxed models. Models in near mint condition but unboxed are usually priced at approximately 60% to 70% of the mint and boxed price shown.

7: Packaging and Box types

Locomotives, pre-war packaging
A boxed model should include the original corrugated cardboard wrapper which displays a white 'Meccano' sticky label with red printing, plus a small sticker indicating the locomotive's livery. A further sticker indicates whether the model is 'Clockwork' or 'Electric'. The ends of the locomotive should be protected by cardboard core end rings.
Each locomotive was packed with a brown 'TESTED' label together with operating instructions, a track layout guide, plus an application form to join the 'Hornby Railway Company'. A guarantee was also enclosed with the number shown matching the number stamped on the bottom of the box.

Locomotives, post-war packaging
Packing materials should include a cover protector strip which covers the entire length of the boxed model, tucking into the box ends. The ends of the locomotive should be protected by engine housing cores plus top and bottom cardboard strip protectors.
Enclosed with the model should be operating instructions, a track layout leaflet/booklet and a guarantee with the number matching the number stamped on the bottom of the box.
Early post-war models were packed with a brown 'TESTED' label, later issues received just a white rubber stamped label and the last locomotives had a yellow/black label.

A combined 'TESTED AND GUARANTEED' certificate (ref. 16/500) was also used in the early post-war 'long box' sets (the certificate had blue printing on pale blue paper). All sets contained a 'TESTED' label.

Passenger Coaches, Vans and Wagons packaging

All models issued from 1938 until 1955 were housed in strong cardboard boxes. On the side of most boxes was printed a date manufacturing code together with a quantity code plus a prominent Box Number. D3 Corridor Coach, L.M.S. Brake/3rd for example: Box Number 'DR 363', Date '6 49' (June 1949) Manufacturing Code '3.5 N' (3,500). A printing reference was also shown - 'BWW9232'. Stamped on the box, usually on its back, was the date the model was actually issued - often some months later than the manufacturing date shown. It is not always possible to find the release date stamp. In addition the colours of the boxes and the colour of the box lettering were changed at regular intervals.

The main changes were as follows:

1938 - 1940	Pale blue boxes with dark blue printed letters
1948 - 1949	Pale blue boxes with dark blue printed letters. The first post-war models were issued in plain brown cardboard with blue printing.
1950 only	Grey-blue boxes with dark blue printed letters
1951 only	Grey-blue boxes with white printed letters
1952 - 1955	Dark blue boxes with white printed letters
1955 - 1958	Dark blue boxes with white parallel lines and without the date and manufacturing information. The box numbers continued to be shown and were prominently featured in catalogues. Pictures added to boxes in 1958 when 'Super Detail' models introduced.
1958 - 1964	Red boxes with white parallel lines and without date and manufacturing information.

NB Assembly dates and Packers' initials shown on the end flaps of some boxes, for example 'HG 358'.

Model and Box Numbers

When the Hornby Dublo range was launched in 1938 each model reference received a 'D' prefix. This referred to 'Dublo' in order to differentiate the models from existing Hornby trains. In addition each box (as described above) was given a separate reference number. This system continued until 1956 when the box number effectively became the catalogue number. As a consequence the models listed include both the original simple 'D' reference numbers and their box numbers. For the purposes of simplicity the models have been listed on a 'date of release' basis in this Catalogue.

The perfect Gauge "OO" railway!

HORNBY-DUBLO TRAINS

Hornby-Dublo Trains are unique in their scale accuracy and beauty of finish. The Locomotives are fitted with motors either clockwork or electric, of a power and reliability never before achieved in this gauge. The Remote Control of the Electric Locomotives is perfect—starting, stopping, reversing and speed regulation are all carried out by the movement of a single lever on a special Controller at the lineside.

The track consists of solid drawn brass rail, mounted on a realistic metal base with holes for screwing down to a baseboard for permanent layouts.

The underframes of the Vans and Wagons, and the bogies of the Passenger Coaches, are pressure die-cast. All vehicles are fitted with pressure die-cast wheels. Automatic couplings are fitted to all Coaches, Vans and Wagons.

The Main Line Station, which is constructed in wood, will accommodate a three-coach train, and by means of the printed slips provided can be named "Berwick" (L.N.E.R.), "Penrith" (L.M.S.), "Truro" (G.W.R.) and "Ashford" (S.R.). There are also an Island Platform and a Goods Depot.

The Hornby-Dublo Electric Trains operate on 12-volt Direct Current and are intended to be run from mains Alternating Current through a Dublo Transformer connected to a Dublo Controller. Where the mains supply is Direct Current, or where there is no mains current at all, the trains can be run from a 12-volt accumulator.

DO NOT MISS THIS !
● A Special Folder, printed in colour, is available giving details and prices of the complete Hornby-Dublo range. Free from any Meccano dealer, or direct from Meccano Ltd., Dept. M.R., Binns Road, Liverpool 13.

A CORNER OF A HORNBY-DUBLO RAILWAY LAYOUT SHOWING THE REMARKABLE REALISM OF THE NEW TRAINS.

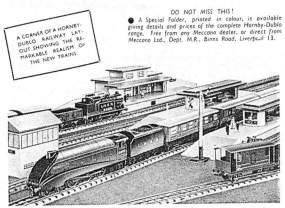

MANUFACTURED BY MECCANO LIMITED, LIVERPOOL

PASSENGER TRAIN SETS (ELECTRIC OR CLOCKWORK) L.N.E.R.
The trains in these sets, both Clockwork and Electric, consist of a perfect scale model of the famous L.N.E.R. stream-lined "Pacific" Locomotive "Sir Nigel Gresley," an eight-wheeled Tender, and a Two-Coach Articulated Unit of the standard L.N.E.R. type. Rails are included, and in the electric Sets there is a Controller that gives complete remote control, both of speed and reversing, and incorporates a circuit breaker.
ELECTRIC PASSENGER SET (L.N.E.R.) **Price 70s.**   CLOCKWORK PASSENGER SET (L.N.E.R.) **Price 39s. 6d.**

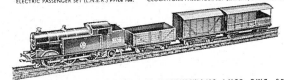

GOODS TRAIN SETS (ELECTRIC OR CLOCKWORK) L.M.S., L.N.E.R., G.W.R., S.R.
Each of these Sets includes a scale model of a six-coupled Tank Locomotive of the 0-6-2 type that is used by all four British groups. The trains consist of an Open Wagon, a Goods Van and a Brake Van. The Brake Vans are specially fine scale models of the latest types in use on the respective systems. Rails are included, and in the electric sets there is a Controller that gives complete remote control, both of speed and reversing and incorporates a circuit breaker.
ELECTRIC GOODS TRAIN SET. **Price 55s.**   CLOCKWORK GOODS TRAIN SET. **Price 27s. 6d.**
(L.M.S., L.N.E.R., G.W.R., S.R.)   (L.M.S., L.N.E.R., G.W.R., S.R.)

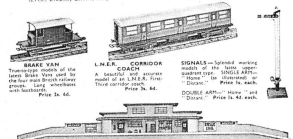

BRAKE VAN
True-to-type models of the latest Brake Vans used by the four main British railway groups. Long wheelbases with footboards.
Price 2s. 6d.

L.N.E.R. CORRIDOR COACH
A beautiful and accurate model of an L.N.E.R. First-Third corridor coach.
Price 3s. 6d.

SIGNALS — Splendid working models of the latest upperquadrant type. SINGLE ARM—"Home" (as illustrated) or "Distant." **Price 1s. each.**
DOUBLE ARM—"Home" and "Distant." **Price 1s. 4d. each.**

STATION
A model in wood of a station in modern style, attractively coloured, and long enough to accommodate a three-coach train. With it are packed printed gummed slips giving a choice of four names—"Berwick," L.N.E.R.; "Penrith," L.M.S.; "Truro," G.W.R.; "Ashford," S.R. **Price 7s. 6d.**

MANUFACTURED BY MECCANO LIMITED, LIVERPOOL

December, 1938 'Model Railway News' advertisement.

HORNBY DUBLO RAILWAYS

Picture taken from the 1957 Hornby Dublo Catalogue Ref: HD/CF/3 7/857/500

HORNBY DUBLO RAILWAYS

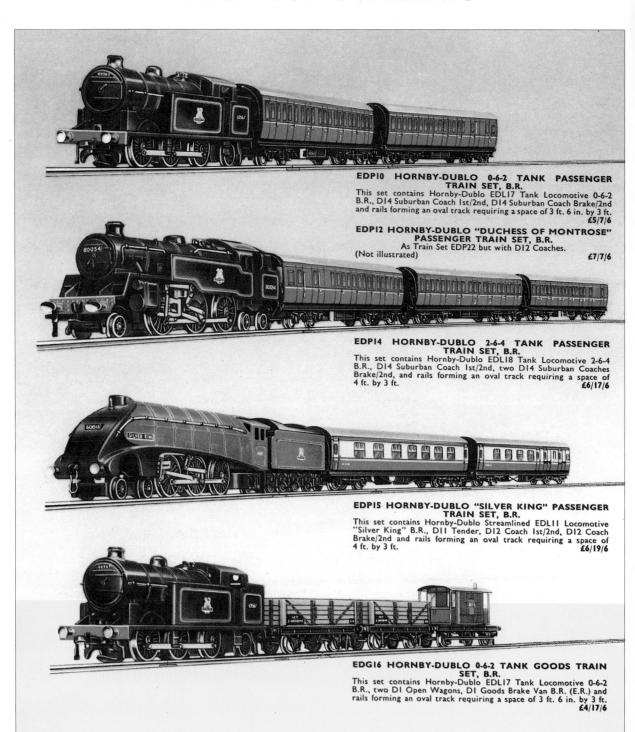

EDP10 HORNBY-DUBLO 0-6-2 TANK PASSENGER TRAIN SET, B.R.
This set contains Hornby-Dublo EDL17 Tank Locomotive 0-6-2 B.R., D14 Suburban Coach 1st/2nd, D14 Suburban Coach Brake/2nd and rails forming an oval track requiring a space of 3 ft. 6 in. by 3 ft.
£5/7/6

EDP12 HORNBY-DUBLO "DUCHESS OF MONTROSE" PASSENGER TRAIN SET, B.R.
As Train Set EDP22 but with D12 Coaches.
(Not illustrated)
£7/7/6

EDP14 HORNBY-DUBLO 2-6-4 TANK PASSENGER TRAIN SET, B.R.
This set contains Hornby-Dublo EDL18 Tank Locomotive 2-6-4 B.R., D14 Suburban Coach 1st/2nd, two D14 Suburban Coaches Brake/2nd, and rails forming an oval track requiring a space of 4 ft. by 3 ft.
£6/17/6

EDP15 HORNBY-DUBLO "SILVER KING" PASSENGER TRAIN SET, B.R.
This set contains Hornby-Dublo Streamlined EDL11 Locomotive "Silver King" B.R., D11 Tender, D12 Coach 1st/2nd, D12 Coach Brake/2nd and rails forming an oval track requiring a space of 4 ft. by 3 ft.
£6/19/6

EDG16 HORNBY-DUBLO 0-6-2 TANK GOODS TRAIN SET, B.R.
This set contains Hornby-Dublo EDL17 Tank Locomotive 0-6-2 B.R., two D1 Open Wagons, D1 Goods Brake Van B.R. (E.R.) and rails forming an oval track requiring a space of 3 ft. 6 in. by 3 ft.
£4/17/6

Picture taken from the 1957 Hornby Dublo Catalogue Ref: HD/CF/3 7/857/500

HORNBY DUBLO RAILWAYS

EDG17 HORNBY-DUBLO 0-6-2 TANK GOODS TRAIN SET, B.R.
This set contains Hornby-Dublo EDL17 Tank Locomotive 0-6-2 B.R., D1 Meat Van, D1 Open Wagon, D1 Tank Wagon "MOBIL", D1 Goods Brake Van B.R. (E.R.) and rails forming an oval track requiring a space of 3 ft. 6 in. by 3 ft.   £5/7/6

EDG18 HORNBY-DUBLO 2-6-4 TANK GOODS TRAIN SET, B.R.
As Train Set EDG19 but with a different selection of Rolling Stock. (Not illustrated)   £6/8/6

EDG19 HORNBY-DUBLO 2-6-4 TANK GOODS TRAIN SET, B.R.
This set contains Hornby-Dublo EDL18 Tank Locomotive 2-6-4 B.R., D1 Ventilated Van, D1 Tank Wagon "MOBIL", D2 Double Bolster Wagon, D1 20-ton Tube Wagon, D1 Goods Brake Van B.R. (L.M.R.) and rails forming an oval track requiring a space of 4 ft. by 3 ft.   £6/17/6

EDP20 HORNBY-DUBLO "BRISTOLIAN" PASSENGER TRAIN SET, B.R. (W.R.)
This set contains Hornby-Dublo EDLT20 Locomotive and Tender "Bristol Castle", D21 Coach 1st/2nd, D21 Coach Brake/2nd and rails forming an oval track requiring a space of 4 ft. by 3 ft.
Available later

EDP22 HORNBY-DUBLO "ROYAL SCOT" PASSENGER TRAIN SET, B.R. (L.M.R.)
This set contains Hornby-Dublo EDL12 Locomotive "Duchess of Montrose", D12 Tender, D22 Coach 1st/2nd, D22 Coach Brake/2nd and rails forming an oval track requiring a space of 4 ft. by 3 ft.   £7/7/6

Picture taken from the 1957 Hornby Dublo Catalogue Ref: HD/CF/3 7/857/500

HORNBY DUBLO RAILWAYS

LOCOMOTIVES AND TENDERS

Hornby-Dublo Locomotives are scale-proportioned models, finely-detailed, with accurate reproduction of valve gear. Suppressors are fitted which effectively counter interference with radio and television reception.

EDL12 Locomotive
"Duchess of Montrose"
£3/9/6
and
D12 Tender,
B.R. (L.M.R.) 11/6

EDL18 Tank Locomotive 2-6-4, B.R.
£3/9/6

EDLT20 Locomotive and Tender
"Bristol Castle" B.R. (W.R.).
Sold only as a unit
Available later

EDL17 Tank Locomotive 0-6-2 B.R.
£2/9/6

EDL11 Locomotive "Silver King"
£3/5/0
and **D11** Tender B.R. (E.R.) 10/6

Picture taken from the 1957 Hornby Dublo Catalogue Ref: HD/CF/3 7/857/500

WREN RAILWAYS

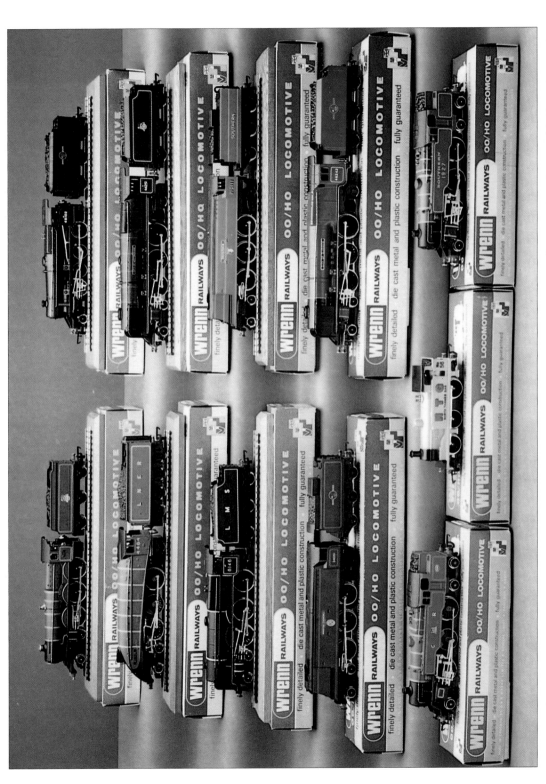

L-R Top Down: (1) 2400 Castle Class 4-6-0 'BR', '7007' 'Great Western' (2) W2409 Freight Locomotive '8F' Class '48102' 'BR' 2-8-0, (3) W2413 Locomotive '8P' Class 4-6-2 'LNER', 4464 'BITTERN', (4) W2414 Locomotive 'West Country/Merchant Navy Class '7P' Class 4-6-2, 'City of Nottingham', (5) W2403 'Royal Scot' Class 4-6-0 LMS '6146' 'The Rifle Brigade', (6) 2407 West Country/Merchant Navy Class '7P' Class 4-6-2 21C111 'Tavistock', (7) W2265 West Country/Merchant Navy '7P' Class 'BR', '34051', 'Winston Churchill', (8) 2316 City 8P Class 'BR', '46242' 'City of "Glasgow', (9) W2246 (4MT) Class Tank Locomotive 'CR' '2085', (10) 2202 'R1' Class 0-6-0 'NTG' '56', (11) W2245 (4MT) Class 2-6-4 'SR' '1927'
Picture kindly supplied by Barry Potter of Barry Potter Auctions, 25 The Green, Great Bowden, Leicestershire

v

WREN RAILWAYS

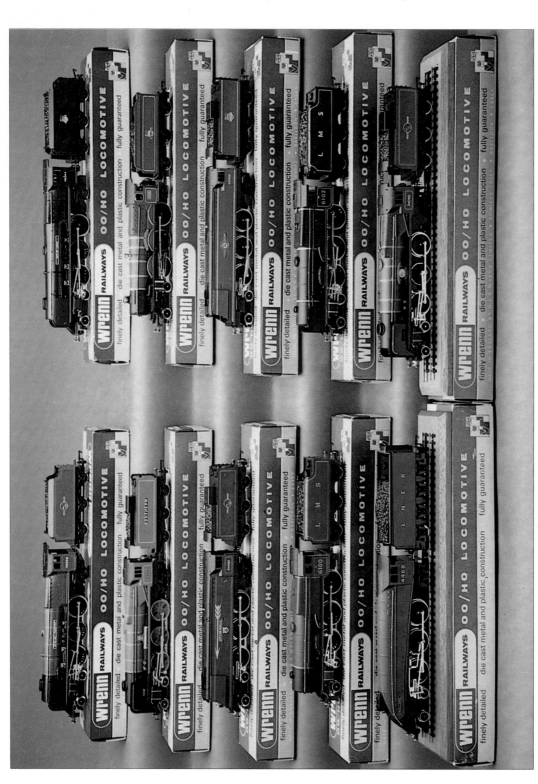

L-R Top Down: (1) W2314 City '8P' Class 4-6-2 'BR', '46244' 'City of Leeds'; (3) W2237 West Country/Merchant Navy '7P' Class 4-6-2 'Sir William Stanier', (2) 2311 City '8P' Class 'BR', '46256' 'Sir William Stanier', (2) 2311 City '8P' Class 'BR', '46256' 'Sir William Stanier', (4) W2223 Castle Class 4-6-0 'BR', '4802' 'Windsor Castle', (5) 2266a West Country/Merchant Navy '7P' Class 4-6-2 'Lyme Regis', '21C109' 'Lyme Regis', (4) W2223 Castle Class 4-6-0 'BR', '4802' 'Windsor Castle', (5) 2266a West Country/Merchant Navy '7P' Class 4-6-2 'City of Wells' (Golden Arrow) 'BR', '34092'; (6) N2267 West Country/Merchant Navy '7P' Class 4-6-2 'Lamport and Holt Line' 'BR', '35026'; (7) W2260 'Royal Scot' Class 4-6-0 'LMS', '6100', 'Royal Scot'; (8) 2261 'Royal Scot' Class 4-6-0 'LMS', '6102', (9) W2210 'A4" Class 4-6-2 'LNER', '4468', 'Mallard'; (10) W2402 West Country/Merchant Navy '7P' Class 4-6-2 'BR', '34090', 'Sir Eustace Missenden'

Picture kindly supplied by Barry Potter of Barry Potter Auctions, 25 The Green, Great Bowden, Leicestershire.

WREN RAILWAYS

W2213 (A4) Class 4-6-2 'NE', '4903' 'Peregrine'

W2224 (8F) Class 2-8-0 'BR', '48073'

2312 City (8P) Class 4-6-2 'BR', '46245' 'City of London'

2239 West County/Merchant Navy Class (7P) 4-6-2 'BR' '34028 R/B' 'Eddystone'

Pictures kindly supplied by Lacy Scott Model Auctions, 10 Risbygate St. Bury St. Edmunds and reproduced by their kind permission.

WREN RAILWAYS

W2212 (A4) Class 4-6-2 'LNER', '7', 'Sir Nigel Gresley'

2275 West Country/Merchant Navy (7P) Class 4-6-2 'BR', '34065' 'Hurricane'

2218 '4MT' Class 2-6-4 'BR' '80033'

W2221 'Castle Class' 'BR', '4075' 'Cardiff Castle'

Pictures kindly supplied by Lacy Scott Model Auctions, 10 Risbygate St. Bury St. Edmunds and reproduced by their kind permission.

8:   Technical Notes

Model construction materials

Locomotives: Die-cast zinc alloy bodies, wheels and chassis until 1958 when polystyrene features were introduced.

Coaches: The early coaches had die-cast bogies and wheels with lithographed tinplate bodies. From 1959 polystyrene ends, roofs and underframes were introduced.

Vans and Wagons: Die-cast underframes and wheels until 1958 when polystyrene introduced.

Locomotive wheel arrangements

Steam Locomotives are classed by the number of wheels in the order: Leading - Driving - Trailing. Some wheel arrangements have a general type name, for example 4-6-2 'Pacific', or 4-4-2 'Atlantic'. Two leading or trailing wheels are a 'pony truck'. Four leading or trailing wheels are a 'bogie truck'. Diesel and Electric engines have their own classifications.

'BO - BO'	A locomotive fitted with two pairs of wheels at both front and rear.
'CO - CO'	A locomotive fitted with three pairs of wheels at both front and rear (Deltic)
'CO - BO'	A locomotive with three pairs of wheels at the front and two pairs at the rear

'Totem' motifs

These refer to the motifs on 'British Railways' locomotive tenders.
1st type: Lion on a wheel,   2nd type: Lion on a Crown.
References to totems facing forwards or backwards indicate the direction the head of the lion is facing.
The tails of the lions in the 1st type of motif have four variations. Each variation is linked to a matching cab number design:
1:   Lion with thin short tail - small thin matching cab number
2:   Lion with thick short tail - small thick matching cab number
3:   Lion with thick long tail - large thick matching cab number
4:   Lion with thin long tail - large thin matching cab number

Hornby Dublo model scale

Double '0' ('00') scale is 4 mm. to the foot (1/76) and is thus slightly larger than the 3.5 mm. 'HO' scale, but still using the same 16.5 mm. rail gauge.

Wheel and Coupling types (Passenger Coaches, Vans and Wagons)

Types of wheels

1938 - 40	Wheels have an inner and outer axle rim and often show signs of fatigue. Axles held by single housing.
1948 - 53	Same as pre-war wheels in shape but not prone to fatigue. Axles retained by clips to mountings.
1953 - 58	Wheels have no pronounced inner or outer axle rim. Axles retained by mounting clips.
1958 - 64	Nylon 'disc' wheels with no spokes. Axles retained by mounting clips (used on coaches).
1958 - 64	Nylon wheel with eight spokes. Axles retained by mounting clips (used on vans and wagons).

Types of couplings

1938 - 40	A flat spring-steel coupling with an oval end plus a small chassis hook.
1948 - 54	A metal coupling with 'RD.No.848012' on shank and without patent ref. 'PAT NO 605283'.
1954 - 58	Same as previous coupling but with both Registered and Patent Numbers on shank.
1956 - 60	Same as previous coupling but with longer vertical 'hook-up' link.
1963 - 64	Same as previous coupling but finer and made of Nylon.

Hornby Dublo information sources:

The Swapmeet Toys and Models Ltd., the Dick Fawcett and Terry Durrant 'Hornby Dublo' collections,
Hornby Dublo catalogues 1938 - 1964,
models sold at Christies' London Auction sales,
models sold at Vectis, Guildford, Auction sales,
models sold at the regular Lacy Scott Auction sales in Bury St.Edmunds,
models sold at Phillips West Two, London, Auction sales, and Wallis & Wallis, Lewes, Sussex, sales.
models sold at Barry Potters Toy & Train Auctions, The Benn Hall, Rugby, Warks.

Acknowledgements

Chris Dyer of Somerset and Brian Secker of Trains & Olde Tyme Toys, Aylsham Road, Norwich for additional information.

Books and further information.

The following are recommended:
'The Hornby Dublo Post-war 3-Rail Collectors Guide' - Tony Oakes, Mayfield Publishing, 68, Main Road, Wynbunbury, Nantwich, Cheshire, CW5 7LS.
'Hornby Dublo Trains', Hornby Companion Series, Vol.3 - Michael J. Foster, Guild Publishing, London (by arrangement with New Cavendish Books).
The many monographs and notes published by the Dublo Circle of the Hornby Railway Collectors Association in the H.R.C.A. Journal.
Hornby Railway Collectors Association (H.R.C.A.)
Membership Secretary: Bob Field, 2 Ravensmore Road, Sherwood, Nottingham, NG5 2AH.

HORNBY DUBLO AUCTION RESULTS

Condition abbreviations: (P) Poor, (F) 'Fair, (G) Good, (E) Excellent, (M) Mint, (NPA) No price available
Gradings shown refer to condition of models. Boxes are all (G) to (E) unless otherwise described.

Locomotives and Train Sets sold at auction 1994 - 1995

Christies Auction Results

A pre-war Hornby Dublo electric EDL1 'Sir Nigel Gresley' Locomotive and post-war Tender, finished in blue LNER livery, locomotive with black wheels, tender post-war version, circa 1938, tender 1950 (G)..............................£165

A rare pre-war Hornby Dublo electric EDG7 LMS Goods Set, comprising Tank Locomotive 6917, Open Wagon, Goods Van and Guards Van, blue controller, oil, spanner, in original box, circa 1938 (F-G, box F-G, corners split, lacks engine cover)...£495

A rare pre-war Hornby Dublo electric EDG7 LNER Tank Goods Set, comprising Tank Locomotive 2690, Open Wagon, Goods Van, Brake Van, blue controller, oil, spanner, test guarantee, circa 1938, (F-G, box F-G, repairs to corners)£495

A rare pre-war Hornby Dublo clock-work DG7 GWR Tank Goods Set, comprising Tank Locomotive 6699, Open Wagon, Goods Van, Guards Van, oil, key, test and guarantee slip, in original box, circa 1938 (G, box P-F, corners damaged, some staining)..£880

A Hornby-Dublo EDG7 'Southern' Tank Goods Set, comprising Tank Locomotive 2594 with thin lettering, small windows, half-inch motor, Open Wagon, Goods Van, Brake Van, transformer and track, in original box. (F-G, on guard iron broken, box base P-F, lid P, two sides missing), LH and RH Points and Signal Cabin, in original boxes (G, boxes F)..........................£286

A Hornby-Dublo No. 3226 three-rail 4-6-2 'City of Liverpool' Locomotive and Tender in BR maroon livery, in picture box with instructions (G-E, box G, taped to ends)..£308

A Hornby-Dublo 3250 three-rail Electric Motor Coach Brake/2nd Power Car, in BR green livery (small glue mark to one side) and 4150 Electric Driving Trailer Coach in matching livery (small glue marks to both sides), both in original boxes (G, boxes F)...£286

A Hornby-Dublo No. 2250 BR(S) Electric Motor Coach Brake/2nd, with instructions, in original red and white striped picture box (G) and 4150 Suburban Driving Trailer Coach (G) and 2231 BR 0-6-0 Diesel-Electric Shunting Locomotive, in original red and white striped box with guarantee (G, box G)..£418

A Hornby-Dublo No. 2245 BR E3002 Bo-Bo pantograph Electric Locomotive, in original red and white striped box (box insert missing) and a spare E3002 body (F-G, box G)..£330

A Hornby-Dublo No. 4076 six-wheel Passenger Brake Van, in original red and white striped box (G-E, box G)...£121

A rare Hornby-Dublo D1 'Canadian Pacific Railway' Caboose,, in original blue box (G-E, box G)...£220

A Hornby-Dublo 4654 Rail Cleaning Wagon, (G) and another example (F, sides over-painted)..£286

A rare Hornby-Dublo EDP2 Canadian Pacific Railway Passenger Train Set with CPR Locomotive and Tender, two BR Midland cream and red Corridor Coaches and a quantity of track, in original box (G-E, box P, split sides)£660

WOODEN BUILDINGS

D1 Mainline Station green roof, original box dated 1·39 (E), box (F), and D1 Signal Cabin red roof (G-E) £209

D1 Two-Road Engine Shed original box dated 2·40 (G-E), box over (F-G) and D1 Goods Depot red roof (F-G)..£440

D1 Mainline Station green roof, original box dated 11·39 and D1 Island Platform blue walls and red roof, original box..£462

5080 Signal Cabin green roof, original box with end label, box lid dates 8·62 (E), box (F-G)...£143

EDL2 'Canadian Pacific' Three-Rail 4-6-2 Locomotive and tender 1215, LMS 1st, 3rd and 3rd/brake corridor, c.1953, locomotive (F), tender (G), coaches (G)..£385

3224 BR 8F 2-8-0 Freight Locomotive and tender in original box with guarantee slip and instructions, c.1961 (E), box (D)..£385

3211 Mallard Locomotive and tender with nickel silver wheels and two BR coaches, contained in P15 Flying Scotsman passenger set box, locomotive (G), coaches (F-G), box (P)..£176

2001 Two-Rail 'Ready-to-Run' Electric Train Set comprising black 0-4-0 Tank Locomotive, two open wagons, brake van, controller, track and 1963 catalogue, original box 1963-64 (E), box interior (G), exterior (F)...............................£176

5083 Terminal or Through Station Composite Set, plastic, previously assembled, original picture box (E), box (G)...£121

DL1 'Sir Nigel Gresley' Locomotive and tender, No 4498, c.1938, clockwork (F-G)..£286

D2 LNER Two-Coach Articulated Unit original box dated 12·38 (G-E, box E)..£308

3234 BR 'St paddy' Diesel-Electric Locomotive metal side frames, original box (E), box (G)...£242

BR(M) 'City of Liverpool Locomotive and tender, with tested tag and oil, original box (E), box (G) £330

3535 'Dorchester' Locomotive and tender, original box (F-G), box (P)...£187

2245 BR E3002 Bo-Bo Pantograph Electric Locomotive guarantee, original box (E), box (E)..£825

EDG7 LMS Electric Tank Goods Set comprising tank locomotive 6917, in wrapper (F-G), original set box with Meat van, c.1939, box (P)............£176

3224 BR 2-8-0 8F Locomotive and tender 48094, with instructions, guarantee, tag and oil in original blue and white striped box (G-E), box (G)..........£418

3235 BR(S) West Country 'Dorchester' Locomotive and tender, with instructions, guarantee, tag, oil, and amended oiling instructions in original blue and white striped box (E), box (G)...£242

3218 BR 2-6-4 Tank Locomotive 80059 with nickel silver wheels and revised chimney, instructions, guarantee, and oil, in original box (G-E), box (G)£418

An Artwork Board for box-lid for 3234 'St Paddy' Deltic Diesel-Electric Locomotive, pen ink, highlighting and body colour over photograph, with photographically-derived text and background and pen and ink circle 'Ring Field' details, rubber stamp 'Reduce 3 to 2' c.1962 ....£385

Lacy Scott Auction Results

80059 Tank Locomotive, 2-6-4 (G)..£250

2335 Locomotive and Tender, 4-6-2, West Country Barnstaple in export box (B-M)..£170

48073 Locomotive and Tender, 2-8-0 (B-G)....................................£55

SR Goods Brake Van, pre-war (F)...£30

GW Goods Wagons, pre-war 'Park Royal' brake van, a goods van and a 5-plank open wagon (F)...£28

Teak Coach 1st/3rd, pre-war, later wheels fitted and another with some dents (F)..£28

Locomotive and Tender, 'Sir Nigel Gresley', No. 7, 3R 4-6-2, individual boxes (B-G)...£100

4620 Breakdown Crane, complete with jacks (B-G)..........................£38

48094 Locomotive and Tender, BR 2-8-0 (B-G)...............................£340

Passenger Set, boxed, pre-war 3R EDPI comprising 4-6-2 locomotive and tender 'Sir Nigel Gresley' 4498, articulated coaches and track, bogies to tender and coaches disintegrated, with corridor connection, no controller (B,D,G,F,F)...£420

3234 Co Co Diesel Locomotive, 'St Paddy' with instructions, 3R (B-F), one coupling broken..£240

EDLT20 Locomotive and Tender, 'Bristol Castle', 3R 4-6-0 (B,D,G) £60

2594 Tank Goods Set, 3R, pre-war, ED7 with Southern tank locomotive, open wagon, goods wagon and brake van, controller and track (no oil bottle) with instructions and accessory leaflet 12/1039/70 (torn) (B,D,G).................£720

4498 Locomotive and Tender, 'Sir Nigel Gresley' EDLT11, pre-war, 3R, 4-6-2 in DL1 box, clockwork locomotive and tender, box (B-G)..............................£360

2-Coach Articulated Unit, pre-war, D2 in original light blue box dated 1948 (B-G)..£580

Locomotive and Tender, 'Bristol Castle', 3R 4-6-0 with instructions (B-G)£200

Wallis & Wallis Auction Results

4-6-2 SR West Country Locomotive and tender 'Dorchester' No 34042, dark green and black BR livery, original box (GC, VGC)..................................£155

4-6-0 Locomotive and tender 'Ludlow Castle' green BR livery, 5002 to footplate sides, associated box, (VGC)..£190

4-6-0 Locomotive 'Denbigh Castle' and tender in BR green and black livery, No 7032 to footplate sides, original box, (GC, VGC)....................................£105

Two 2-6-4 Class 4 Tank Locomotives both in BR livery, one a scarce No 80059 and the other No 80033 (VGC) £300

0-6-2 Tank Locomotive 'Southern 2594' dark green and black livery (GC, VGC)..£230

Deltic Diesel Electric Locomotive 'St Paddy' 2234, green BR livery, loco No D9001, original box, (VGC)..£150

3,300HP Electric Locomotive 2245, blue body, white roof operating pantographs, loco No E3002, original box (VGC-Mint)..............................£280

Two Car Southern Railway Electric Set consisting of an electric motor coach, brake/2nd and a similar trailer coach with interior fittings, original boxes, (VGC) £210

Barry Potter Auction Results

RAIL LOCOMOTIVES

4-6-0 Loco and Tender No.7013 'Bristol Castle' with instructions, near mint boxed-mint boxed **£120**

4-6-0 Loco and Tender No 7013 'Bristol Castle' with instructions, near mint boxed-mint boxed **£160**

Deltic Diesel Electric Loco 'St Paddy' with instruction, mint boxed **£360**

4-6-2 Loco and Tender No.34042 'Dorchester' with instructions, near mint boxed-mint boxed **£360**

4-6-2 Loco and Tender No.34042 'Dorchester' with instructions, near mint boxed-mint boxed **£300**

0-6-2 Tank Loco No.60567 Late version with coal in bunker and nickel silver wheels, with instructions, near mint box-mint boxed **£520**

2-8-0 8F Loco and Tender No.48158 with instructions, near mint boxed-mint boxed **£150**

2-8-0 8F Loco and Tender No.48094 with instructions, mint boxed **£420**

4-6-2 Loco and Tender No.46247 'City of Liverpool' with instructions, mint boxed **£580**

0-6-0 Diesel Electric Shunting Loco with instructions, mint boxed **£170**

4-6-0 Loco and Tender No.5002 'Ludlow Castle' with instructions, near mint boxed-mint boxed **£420**

4-6-2 Loco and Tender No.60022 'Mallard' late version with picture box, nickel and thin handrail with instructions, mint boxed **£400**

2-6-4 Tank Loco No.80059 with instructions, mint boxed **£500**

2-6-4 Tank Loco No.80033 with instructions, mint boxed **£140**

Electric Motor Coach with instructions, mint boxed **£200**

2-8-0 8F Loco and Tender No.48073 with instructions, near mint boxed-mint boxed **£150**

Co-Bo Diesel Electric Loco with instructions and card retainers, mint boxed **£140**

4-6-2 Loco and Tender No.46245 'City of London' with instructions, mint boxed **£160**

Deltic Diesel Electric Loco 'Crepello' with instructions and card retainers, mint boxed **£130**

0-6-0 Diesel Electric Shunting Loco picture box, with instructions, mint boxed **£110**

0-6-0 Diesel Electric Shunting Loco plain red export box, with instructions, mint boxed **£310**

4-6-0 Loco and Tender No.4075 'Cardiff Castle' with instructions, near mint boxed-mint boxed **£170**

4-6-2 Loco and Tender No.34005 'Barnstaple' with instructions, near mint boxed-mint boxed **£190**

4-6-0 Loco and Tender No.7032 'Denbigh Castle' with instructions, mint boxed **£200**

4-6-2 Loco and Tender No.60030 'Golden Fleece' with instruction, mint boxed **£130**

2-8-0 8F Loco and Tender No.48109 with instructions, near mint boxed-mint boxed **£180**

3,300HP Electric Loco No.3002 with all instruction, mint boxed **£520**

2-6-4 Tank Loco BR Black No.80059, with instructions, near mint boxed**£360**

4-6-0 Loco & Tender BR Green No.5002 'Ludlow Castle', with instructions, mint boxed **630**

4-6-2 Loco & Tender BR Maroon No.46247 'City of Liverpool', with instructions, near mint boxed **£370**

2-8-0 8F Loco & Tender BR Black No.48094, with instructions, mint boxed**£350**

4-6-2 Loco & Tender BR Green No.60022 'Mallard', late version with nickel silver wheels and picture box, with instructions, mint boxed **£290**

4-6-2 Loco & Tender BR Green No.34042 'Dorchester', with instructions, near mint boxed **£210**

Deltic Diesel Electric Loco 'St. Paddy', with instructions, mint boxed **£380**

Pre-war Clockwork Gresley Set, with 4-6-2 Loco & Tender LNER Blue No.4498 'Sir Nigel Gresley', Clockwork, Pair of articulated coaches, track, key and oil. Box lid with complete picture, lacking lip, box base is worn but presentable. A very rare set, good plus boxed **£450**

Pre-war 0-6-2 Tank LNER Black No.2690, clockwork, excellent **£230**

Pre-war 0-6-2 Tank LMS Black No.6917, clockwork, good plus **£210**

Electric Twin Pantograph Loco No.E3002, complete with both instructions, guarantee and box insert, superb, mint boxed **£650**

Co Bo Diesel Electric Loco with instructions, still having card retailers strung around loco, mint boxed **£160**

Electric Motor Coach, SR Suburban 2nd Class Coach, Electric Driving Trailer Coach, all in reproduction boxes, all near mint boxed (3) **£180**

ROLLING STOCK

4150 Electric Driving Trailer Coach SR, mint boxed **£170**

4070 Restaurant Car WR mint boxed **£100**

4035 Pullmans Car 'Aries', 4036 Pullman Car 2nd Class and 4037 Pullmans Car Brake/2nd, mint boxed (3) **£85**

4052 Corridor Coach 1st/2nd BR, 4053 Brake/2nd Br, 4062 Open Corridor Coach 1st Class BR and 4063 2nd Class BR, mint boxed (4) **£110**

4050 Corridor Coach 1st/2nd WR, 4051 Brake/2nd WR, 4060 Open Corridor Coach 1st Class WR, and 4061 2nd Class WR, mint boxed (4) **£110**

4075 Passenger Brake Van BR, 4078 Composite Sleeping Car Br, 4054 Corridor Coach 1sr/2nd SR and 4055 Brake/2nd SR, mint boxed **£100**

Two 4083 Suburban Coaches 1st/2nd BR, 4084 Surburban Coach Brake/2nd BR, mint boxed (3) **£130**

Three 4081 Suburban Coaches 2nd Class SR, mint boxed (3) **£100**

Two 4081 Suburban Coaches 2nd Class SR, 4082 Suburban Coach Brake/2nd SR, near mint boxed (3) **£140**

4076 Six-wheeled Passenger Brake Van mint boxed **£85**

4685 Caustic Liquor Bogie Wagon mint boxed **£85**

4654 Rail Cleaning Wagon complete with instruction leaflet and six filter pads, mint boxed **£680**

4316 Horse Box SR, with horse, Also 4315 Horse Box BR, with horse, mint boxed (2) **£110**

4615 Double Bolster Wagon with timber load, **4615 Double Bolster Wagon** with tractor, **4605 40-Ton Bogie Well Wagon, 4610 Bogie Bolster Wagon, 4645 Low Sided Wagon** and **4652 Machine Wagon Lowmac,** mint boxed (6) **£140**

4676 Tank Wagon 'Esso', **4677 Tank Wagon** 'Mobil', **4678 Tank Wagon** 'Shell' and **4680 Tank Wagon** 'Esso' (fuel oil), mint boxed (4) **£85**

4646 Low Sided Wagon with Aluminium Cable Drums, **4647 Low Sided Wagon** with furniture container, **4648 Low Sided Wagon** with insulated meat container and **4658 Prestwin Silo Wagon** mint boxed (4) **£110**

4320 6-Ton Refrigerator Van WR, 4318 Packing Van for breakdown crane, **4665 Saxa Salt Wagon, 4301 Banana Van** and **4313 Gunpowder Van** mint boxed (5) **£85**

'Hornby Dublo' Shop Display Showcard circa 1960. The sign formed to give a 3D effect. Showing 'City of London' Locomotive passing under a footbridge. Very colourful and attractive, Good plus-Excellent **£260**

Two 4050 Corridor Coach 1st/2nd WR. Plus **Two 4052** 1st/2nd BR, mint boxed (4) **£80**

4187 Pullmans Car Brake/2nd, mint boxed. With **Two 4935 Pullmans Car 'Aries'** near mint boxed (3) **£48**

Two 4036 Pullmans Car 2nd Class, with **Two 4037 Pullmans Car Brake/2nd** mint boxed (4) **£60**

4070 Restaurant Car WR mint boxed **£80**

4685 Caustic Liquor Bogie Wagon rare version with diamond bogies, mint boxed **£220**

4076 Six-Wheeled Passenger Brake Van near mint boxed **£100**

5015 Plastic Girder Bridge mint boxed **£360**

Shop Display Illuminated Sign with 'Hornby Dublo' in large wooden letters above a glass panel lettered 'Made by Meccano Ltd, excellent plus **£400**

3 Rail 0-6-2 Tank Loco No.2594 Southern Malachite Green, near mint boxed **£250**

Pre War 0-6-2 Tank Loco. Clockwork LMS No.6917 Marked around keyhole, with key. Pale Blue Box, Good-Good plus boxed **£200**

Terminal or Through Station Composite Kit complete, very attractive in picture box, mint boxed **£360**

Vectis Models Auction Results

The letters A-E describes the conditions of each lot as follows:- A+ = As near mint or pristine condition; A = Virtually mint boxed; B+ = Model is near mint, box has very slight faults; B = Slight model or box faults; C = More obvious model chips and box faults inc. tears, but still complete; D = Same as C but box has one or more end flaps missing and model may have faded paint as well as chips; E = Model and box both have considerable faults.

D407 Main Line Station red roof, generally B to B+ **£180**

D403 Island Platform Red roof/two pale blue seats/semi-circular wall ends, also pale blue (scarce) 'Bovril' & 'Gold Flake' adverts, B+ to A **£160**

D402 Goods Depot Red roof/'Birds Custard' advert one end, B+ to A . **£110**

EDL7 0-6-2 Electric Tank Loco 'Southern 2594', Olive green inc. wheels, one rear disc trailing wheel has some fatigue, otherwise brilliant B+ to A with original packing ends and corrugated cardboard lining with green 'Electric' label, pale blue box covered in shrink wrap is C, rare **£500**

DL7 another but Clockwork 'L.M.S. 6917', Black, B to B unboxed, rare**£220**

DL7 another but Clockwork 'L.N.E.R. 2690', Black, B+ to A unboxed, rare **£220**

ELD7 another but 'G.W.R. logo/6699' Dark Green/gloss black/matt black wheels, good B, in shrink wrapped pale blue box (no front coupling) rare**£330**

EDL7 0-6-2 'Southern 2594', Dark Olive green/gold lettering & numbers sides, rear and front buffer beam/black wheels, no front coupling, C, rare **£180**

EDL7 another but Malachite Green body and wheels/yellow letters & numbers outlined in black on sides & hopper sides, and yellow numbers on rear and front buffer beam, front & rear couplings, B+ to A, scarce **£200**

EDL7 another but black 'L.N.E.R. 9596' in Gold outlined in red on sides and in gold on rear and front buffer beams, good B **£120**

ELD7 another but Apple Green (inc. wheels) and Silver 'Hornby' transfer on rear instead of previous Gold and 'TYPE EDL7' cast underneath, lovely B+ to A **£110**

3231 0-6-0 Diesel Shunter D3763, dark green, A **£100**

No.321 4-6-0 'Ludlow Castle' & Tender, B+ in C box with instructions**£250**

No.3224 another but 48094, A in B striped picture box showing correct number on loco **£300**

No.3225 4-6-2 'Dorchester 34042', BR Green, A in B to C striped picture box **£230**

No.3226 2-6-2 'City of Liverpool 46247', BR Maroon, A in B+ striped picture box **£340**

No.3233 Co-Bo Diesel Electric Loco BR Green D.5713, B to B+ in C striped picture box **£70**

No.3250 Suburban Electric Loco S.65326 BR SR Green/grey roof, B+ in C blue box with yellow picture lid **£120**

No.2220 4-6-0 'Denbigh Castle 7032', BR Green, lovely A in B+ plain red box **£160**

No.2235 4-6-2 'Barnstaple 34005', BR Green, lovely A in B+ box **£120**

EDG7 Tank Goods Train with Black 0-6-2 'LMS 6917' Block letters, B+ to A with packing ends; L.M.S. Open Wagon, B+ to A; Goods Van & Goods Brake Van, both Silver roofs & about B, plus track and black controller, interesting box lid has large coloured 'O Gauge' Type picture and 'Hornby-Dublo' in red/yellow letters on blue label, scarce early 1948 set **£160**

D1/32049 Canadian Pacific 437270 Caboose, black B+ to A unboxed ..**£140**

Group of Six unboxed 'S.R.' Issues (1) Five Plank Open Wagon, B+; (2) & (3) Goods Van one B to B+ the other C; (4) Goods Brake van, two end windows, B; (5) & (6) Meat Van, white roof, one B the other C, scarce lot **£210**

Group of Three Red/White striped boxed: (1) No. 4049 Restaurant Car, reddish maroon/grey, A; (2) No.4075 Passenger Brake Van, A; Plus (3) No.4071 B.R. (E) Restaurant Car E1939, A but in 4049 box, scarce group **£120**

Group of Six Red/White striped boxed Tank Wagons inc. 'Chlorine', 'Mobil', 'Esso', 'Esso' on replaced frame & wheels, 'Traffic Services' and U.D. Cream Tank, all about A apart from second 'Esso', plus No.4318 Packing Van, A and No.4620 Breakdown Crane, B to B+ in C red/white striped box **£120**

Group of 14 Red/white striped boxed two rail issues inc. Gunpowder Van (2), Good Brake, Banana Van, Low Sided Wagon with (loose) tractor, ICI Salt, Passenger Fruit Van etc., all about A, some box faults **£120**

No.4315 Horse Box (B.R.) with two Horses, A to A+ in B+ Red/White striped box, scarce, plus No.4685 Caustic Liquor Bogie Wagon, A to A+ in B+ to A box **£85**

No.4070 Restaurant Car W.R. W1910, B+ boxed **£75**

No.4071 Restaurant Car B.R. (E) E1939, A in B box **£95**

No.5083 Terminal or Through Station Composite Kit with Lights, appears complete & unassembled in C box, rare **£270**

WHEN REPLYING TO ADVERTISEMENTS PLEASE MENTION JOHN RAMSAY'S CATALOGUE

BARRY POTTER AUCTIONS

Buying or Selling - There is a great deal on offer

Colour Illustrated Catalogue containing at least 500 quality lots,
all with estimated prices, as well as results from the previous Auction.

All lots are accurately described with clear condition descriptions.

All items are treated with care, and insured from collection,
to fully supervised viewing on Sale day.

Saturday Auctions at The Benn Hall, Rugby.
A superb venue close to the M1 and M6, with excellent parking.

You can have absolute confidence in our handling of your collection
and be certain that our Auction will achieve the best possible result for you.
All transactions are confidential.

The quality and variety at our Auctions is considerable

At our 5 Auctions in 1995 we have sold:

**Over 300 Hornby and Bassett-Lowke O Gauge Locomotives,
over 400 Wrenn and over 150 Hornby Dublo Locomotives,
over 200 Trix Locomotives, over 2000 Dinky, Corgi Toys,
countless other Diecast Models, Trains and Tinplate Toys**

Our 1996 Auction dates are Saturdays:
10th February, 13th April, 29th June,
21st September, 30th November.

Colour Illustrated Catalogues are only £3 post paid.
For £15 you will receive a Catalogue for each of our
next 6 Sales, a month before each Auction.
This service is £18 for Europe, £20 outside Europe.

**Barry Potter Auctions, 13 Yew Tree Lane,
Spratton, Northampton. NN6 8HL.
Telephone either Barry or Ellis Potter
on 01604 770025 or 01604 846688.**

WHEN REPLYING TO ADVERTISEMENTS PLEASE MENTION JOHN RAMSAY'S CATALOGUE

Lone Star Railways

Robert Newson has provided this information and listing of Lone Star's miniature railway items.

The series was launched in 1957 as a push-along railway system called "Lone Star Locos". All items were to 000 scale and the track gauge was 8.25 mm, exactly half of 00 gauge. The rolling stock and track were made entirely of diecast metal, and were reasonably accurate models, giving a range which today is quite collectable.

In 1960 an electric system called "Treble-O-Lectric" was introduced. This used many of the same basic models as the Lone Star Locos (which continued in production) but modified for electric operation. The track gauge was the international standard N gauge (9 mm) and the rolling stock had Tri-ang type couplings in place of the hook and eye couplings of the Lone Star Locos. Also plastic wheels were fitted so as not to short-circuit the track! New diesel locomotives were introduced since the push-along locomotives were too small to accommodate a motor.

In 1962 the range of American rolling stock in the Treble-O-Lectric series was expanded with several new liveries. Also in that year the Lone Star Locos were issued in new blister packs numbered from 50 to 84.

A range of buildings called "Gulliver County" was introduced in 1963 to complement the various railway models. These were one-piece vinyl mouldings. Also new was a set of five diecast road vehicles. In 1964 rolling stock in Canadian liveries was introduced.

In 1966 the push-along range was re-launched as "Treble-O-Trains". The rolling stock was now the same as Treble-O-Lectric (but non-motorised) i.e. with Tri-ang type couplings and plastic wheels. The track was moulded in grey plastic rather than the diecast track of the Lone Star Locos.

The Treble-O-Lectric range continued unchanged for several more years and was still available in 1970 but was discontinued fairly soon thereafter.

The various series have overlapping number ranges and many items appear in more than one series. For example the signal box in the different types of packaging was numbered 33, 80, EL.152 or 92, yet the model stayed the same throughout! Market Price Range – Lone Star Railway models are not highly collectable and therefore models may be obtained at a low cost.

Lone Star Locos – Card Boxes

1. 0-6-0 Class 3F Tank Loco
2. 2-6-2 Class 3 Tank Loco
3. Open Goods Wagon (2)
4. Midland Region Coach
5. Straight track
6. Curved track
7. 0-6-0 Diesel Shunting Loco
8. 4-6-2 Class A4 Gresley Loco
9. Tender for no.8
10. 4-6-2 Class 8P Loco Princess Royal
11. Tender for no.10
12. U.S. Diesel Loco
13. Brake Van
14. Cattle Wagon
15. "U.D." Tank Wagon
16. "B.P." Tank Wagon
17. "Shell" Tank Wagon
18. Goods Van (2)
19. B.R. Mk.I Composite Coach
20. Points (1 LH, 1 RH)
21. Crossovers (2)
22. Sleeper built buffer (3)
23. Re-railer track (3)
24. Station and platform
25. Flat Wagon (3)
26. U.S. Passenger Coach
27. Girder Bridge with Piers
28. Incline piers (6)
29. Plastic Trees (3)
30. Telegraph Poles (plastic)
31. Fences and Gates (plastic)
32. Semaphore signals (2)
33. Signal box

Lone Star Locos – Blister Packed

50. 0-6-0 Class 3F Tank Loco with track
51. 2-6-2 Class 3 Tank Loco with track
52. 0-6-0 Diesel Shunting Loco with track
53. 4-6-2 Class A4 Gresley Loco
54. 4-6-2- Class 8P Loco Princess Royal
55. Tender for no. 53 with 2 straight tracks
56. Tender for no. 54 with 2 straight tracks
57. Midland Region Coach with track
58. B.R. MkI Composite Coach
59. Brake Van and Flat Wagon
60. Cattle Wagon and Open Goods Wagon
61. "U.D." Tanker with straight track
62. "B.P." Tanker and Flat Wagon
63. "Shell" Tanker with re-railer track
64. Goods Van and Open Goods Wagon
65. 100 ton Breakdown Crane Wagon
66. U.S. Diesel Loco
67. U.S. Passenger Coach
68. Bogie Flat Wagon with track
69. Bogie Tank Wagon
70. U.S. Caboose
71. U.S. Box Car
72. Straight track (5)
73. Curved track (5)
74. Points (1 LH, 1 RH) and track (2)
75. Re-railer track (4)
76. Crossover (1), Buffer (2) and track (2)
77. Level crossing and re-railer track
78. Girder Bridge with Piers
79. Incline Piers (6)
80. Signal box and Signal
81. Signals (3)
82. Plastic trees (5)
83. Telegraph Poles, Fences and Gates
84. Station and Platform

Treble-O-Lectric – Card Boxes

Note: In order to concentrate on the more collectable items, track and spare parts have not been listed.

EL.50 Standard Goods Set
EL.51 Standard Passenger Set
EL.52 Goods Set with Accessories
EL.53 Passenger Set with Accessories
EL.54 Transcontinental Passenger Set
EL.55 Transcontinental Goods Set
EL.56 B.R. De Luxe Scenic Set
EL.60 D5000 Diesel Loco
EL.60A D5000 Diesel Loco (non-motorised)
EL.61 D5900 Diesel Loco
EL.61A D5900 Diesel Loco (non-motorised)
EL.62 U.S. F.7 Diesel Loco "Union Pacific"
EL.62A U.S. F.7 Diesel Loco "Union Pacific" (non-motorised)
EL.63 U.S. F.7 Diesel Loco "New Haven"
EL.64 U.S. F.7 Diesel Loco "Chesapeake & Ohio"
EL.65 U.S. F.7 Diesel Loco "Kansas City Southern"
EL.66 U.S. 0-8-0 Baldwin Steam Loco and Tender "Union Pacific"
EL.67 F.7 Diesel Loco "Canadian Pacific"
EL.68 F.7 Diesel Loco "Canadian National"
EL.70 Mk.I Composite Coach – maroon
EL.71 Mk.I Brake End Coach – maroon
EL.72 U.S. Coach "Union Pacific"
EL.73 U.S. Vista Dome Coach "Union Pacific"
EL.74 Mk.I Composite Coach – green
EL.75 Mk.I Brake End Coach – green
EL.76 U.S. Coach "New Haven"
EL.77 U.S. Vista Dome Coach "New Haven"
EL.78 U.S. Coach "Pullman"
EL.79 U.S. Vista Dome Coach "Pullman"
EL.80 Brake Van
EL.81 "Shell' Tank Wagon
EL.82 "B.P." Tank Wagon
EL.83 "U.D." Tank Wagon

EL.84 Cattle Wagon
EL.85 Open Goods Wagon
EL.86 Goods Van
EL.87 U.S. Box Car "Union Pacific"
EL.88 100 ton Breakdown Crane Wagon
EL.89 Bogie Flat Wagon with Citroen DS19 and Land Rover
EL.90 Bogie Tank Wagon "Mobilgas"
EL.91 U.S. Caboose "Union Pacific"
EL.92 U.S. Box Car "Boston & Maine"
EL.93 U.S. Box Car "New Haven"
EL.94 U.S. Box Car "Santa Fe"
EL.95 Bogie Tank Wagon "Texaco"
EL.96 Bogie Flat Wagon with Austin Articulated Lorry
EL.97 U.S. Caboose "New Haven"
EL.98 U.S. Caboose "Chesapeake & Ohio"
EL.99 U.S. Caboose "Kansas City Southern"
EL.130 "Canadian Pacific" Coach
EL.131 "Canadian Pacific" Vista Dome Coach
EL.132 "Canadian National" Coach
EL.133 "Canadian National" Vista Dome Coach
EL.140 Box Car "Canadian Pacific"
EL.141 Caboose "Canadian Pacific"
EL.142 Refrigerated Box Car "Canadian National"
EL.143 Caboose "Canadian National"
EL.150 Station and Platform
EL.151 Platform Extension with Lamp Standards
EL.152 Signal Box
EL.153 Semaphore Signal – Home (2)
EL.154 Semaphore Signal – Distant (2)
EL.155 Rail built buffer (3)
EL.156 Girder Bridger and Piers

EL.157 Incline Piers (6)
EL.158S Incline tray – straight
EL.158C Incline tray – curved
EL.159 Telegraph Poles (28)
EL.160 Fences (24) and Gates (4)
EL.161 Trees (plastic) (3)
EL.162 Tunnel
EL.163 Footbridge
EL.164 Level crossing with Barriers
EL.165 Loading gauge (3)
EL.166 Colour Light Signals (3)
EL.167 Set of 12 plastic figures (unpainted)
EL.168 Set of five road vehicles: Citroen DS19, Land Rover, Dennis Fire Engine, Austin Articulated Flat Lorry, AEC Regal IV Single Deck Bus.
EL.169A Bridge Girder
EL.169B Bridge Pier
EL.177 Scenic Baseboard

Gulliver County Buildings

1320 Inn
1321 Church
1322 Fire Station
1323 Ranch Style Bungalow
1324 Shop and Car Park
1325 Garage Service Station
1326 Pair of Shops
1327 Two Storey House with Garage
1328 Thatched Cottage
1340 Twin Falls Station
       Scenic Village Set

Treble-O-Trains – Blister Packed

74. U.S. Diesel Loco "Union Pacific"
75. D5900 Diesel Loco
76. U.S. Baldwin 0-8-0 Steam Loco (without tender)
77. B.R. Mk.I Composite Coach
78. U.S. Passenger Coach
79. U.S. Box Car "New Haven"
80. Bogie Tank Wagon "Shell"

81. Bogie Flat Wagon with Citroen DS19 and Land Rover
82. 100 ton Breakdown Crane Wagon
83. U.S. Caboose "New Haven"
84. Cattle Wagon and Brake Van
85. Curved track (6)
86. Straight track (6)

87. Trees (6)
88. Level crossing with Barriers and track
89. Figures, Telegraph Poles, Fences and Gates
90. Footbridge
91. 0-6-0 Tank Loco and Open Goods Wagon
92. Signal Box and Colour Light Signals (2)

Master Models – OO Gauge Layout Accessories

Diecast models manufactured in England during the 1950's – 'A Wardie Product'. The following information and illustrations have been obtained from the 1951 Gamages Book of Model Trains, Boats, Aircraft etc.

In addition to the 'W.H. SMITH' Bookstall listed – at least two other station stalls were issued – 'FINLAY' the tobacconists stall and 'WALTONS LTD' fruit stall.

THESE MASTER MODELS ARE SCALED FOR OO GAUGE LAYOUTS

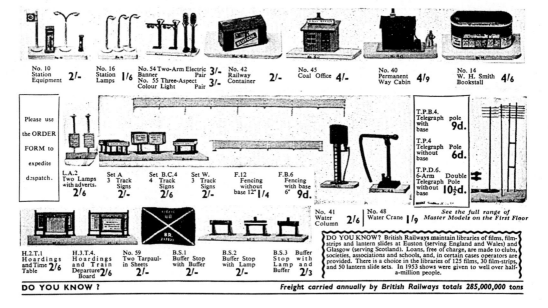

No. 10 Station Equipment 2/-
No. 16 Station Lamps 1/6
No. 54 Two-Arm Electric Banner Pair 3/-
No. 55 Three-Aspect Colour Light Pair 3/-
No. 42 Railway Container 2/-
No. 45 Coal Office 4/-
No. 40 Permanent Way Cabin 4/9
No. 14 W. H. Smith Bookstall 4/6

Please use the ORDER FORM to expedite despatch.

L.A.2 Two Lamps with adverts. 2/6
Set A 3 Track Signs 2/-
Set B.C.4 4 Track Signs 2/6
Set W. 3 Track Signs 2/-
F.12 Fencing without base 12" 1/4
F.B.6 Fencing with base 6" 9d.

T.P.B.4. Telegraph pole with base 9d.
T.P.4 Telegraph Pole without base 6d.
T.P.D.6. 6-Arm Double Telegraph Pole without base 10½d.

No. 41 Water Column 2/6
No. 48 Water Crane 1/9
See the full range of Master Models on the First Floor

H.2.T.1 Hoardings and Time Table 2/6
H.3.T.4. Hoardings and Train Departure Board 2/6
No. 59 Two Tarpaulin Sheets 2/-
B.S.1 Buffer Stop with Buffer 2/-
B.S.2 Buffer Stop with Lamp 2/-
B.S.3 Buffer Stop with Lamp and Buffer 2/3

DO YOU KNOW? British Railways maintain libraries of films, filmstrips and lantern slides at Euston (serving England and Wales) and Glasgow (serving Scotland). Loans, free of charge, are made to clubs, societies, associations and schools, and, in certain cases operators are provided. There is a choice in the libraries of 125 films, 30 film-strips, and 50 lantern slide sets. In 1953 shows were given to well over half-a-million people.

DO YOU KNOW ?   *Freight carried annually by British Railways totals 285,000,000 tons*

Master Models continued

A FULL RANGE OF 'MASTER MODELS' THAT WILL

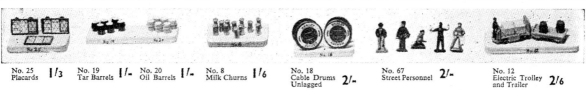

No. 25 Placards **1/3**	No. 19 Tar Barrels **1/-**	No. 20 Oil Barrels **1/-**	No. 8 Milk Churns **1/6**	No. 18 Cable Drums Unlagged **2/-**	No. 67 Street Personnel **2/-**	No. 12 Electric Trolley and Trailer **2/6**

No. 57 Crew Unloading Trucks **2/6**	No. 3 Assorted Figures **2/-**	No. 2 Railway Passengers **2/-**	No. 23 Track Party Repair **2/-**	No. 4 Seated Figures (No seat) **2/-** No. 75. With Seat **2/6**	No. 1 Railway Staff **2/-**	No. 5 Seated Figures (Seat not included) **2/-**

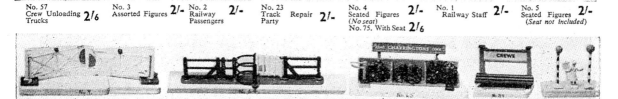

● *All goods delivered free in our own extensive van area.*

No. 9 Level Crossing Gates, Single Track. **3/-**	No. 76 Level Crossing Gates, Double Track. **3/9**	No. 64 Wicket Gates **2/6**	*Model Dept. First Floor*	No. 65 Charringtons Coal Bunkers, Scale and Coalman **4/-**	No. 39 Station Name and Seat **2/-**	No. 69 Belisha Set Crossing **1/6**

NEW MODELS

No. 77 Girder Bridge for Double Track. **12/9**	No. 68 Girder Bridge for Single Track. **10/6**	No. 70 Bus Shelter **2/6**	No. 72 Gent's Toilet **4/6**	No. 73 Pit Workers **2/-**	No. 74 6in. Fence **6d.**	No. 78 Sitting Army Figures (No Seat) **2/-**	No. 79 Sitting Naval Figures (No Seat) **2/-**

PUT THE 'FINISHING TOUCH' TO YOUR LAYOUT

No. 15 Two Telephone Kiosks **2/-**	No. 66 Two Station Clocks **1/6**	No. 31 Enquiry Kiosks **2/-**	No. 32 Lagged Cable Drums **2/-**	H.1/T.3 Small Hoarding, Large Time Table **2/6**	No. 33 6 Esso Oil Drums **2/-**	No. 34 Watchman's Hut and Workman **2/6**	No. 24 Police Boxes **2/-**

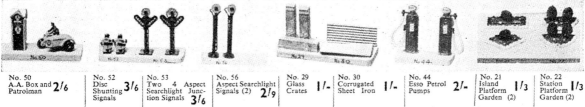

No. 50 A.A. Box and Patrolman **2/6**	No. 52 Disc Shunting Signals **3/6**	No. 53 Two 4 Aspect Searchlight Junction Signals **3/6**	No. 56 Aspect Searchlight Signals (2) **2/9**	No. 29 Glass Crates **1/-**	No. 30 Corrugated Sheet Iron **1/-**	No. 44 Esso Petrol Pumps **2/-**	No. 21 Island Platform Garden (2) **1/3**	No. 22 Station Platform Garden (2) **1/3**

No. 35 Cable Laying Party **2/6**	No. 38 Sand Bin and Fire Buckets **2/-**	No. 7 Platform Accessories **2/-**	No. 26 Sleeper Buffer **2/-**	No. 27 Scale, Weights, Light Luggage **1/-**	No. 43 Cycle Rack, 4 Cycles **2/-**	No. 62 Police Box and Patrolman **2/-**	No. 63 Two Oval Pillar Boxes **1/6**

WRENN RAILWAYS

OO/HO gauge scale models manufactured by
G and R Wrenn Ltd, Bowlers Croft, Basildon, Essex, England.

STEAM OUTLINE LOCOMOTIVES, 1968-1992

Technical specifications:

Wrenn Locomotives are mostly constructed with die-cast metal bodies. The models have fine body detailing, individual hand rails and nickel-plated driving wheels. The locomotives are in a large part hand-finished. Painted parts have been twice stove-enamelled; crests and linings are in authentic colours. Tri-ang type couplings are fitted as standard but Hornby-Dublo type are included with all locomotives. Wrenn locomotives are modelled in 4mm. to the foot scale (1:76) and are suitable for use on OO/HO track systems of 16.5mm. (0.650″) gauge.

N.B. This introduction has been extracted from the description provided in the first edition Wrenn catalogue (1973).

BR = British Railways, GWR = Great Western Railway, GW = Great Western, LMS = London, Midland and Scottish, WD = War Department, LNER = London and North Eastern Railway, NE = North Eastern, MR = Midland Region, WR = Western Region, NCB = National Coal Board, NTG = North Thames Gas, SR = Southern Railways (or Southern Region), SE & CR = South East and Chatham Railway, R/B = rebuilt, MPR = market price range, NGPP = no grading possible at present.

Locomotives, 'Castle' Class (4-6-0)

Ref. no.	Livery	Loco number	Colour	Loco name, notes	MPR	
W 2221	BR	4075	Green	'Cardiff Castle'	£80-100	☐
W 2221b	BR	5023	Light Green	'Brecon Castle'	£120-140	☐
W 2221k	GWR	4075	Green	'Cardiff Castle', (kit)	£400-500	☐
W 2221a	BR	7013	Green	'Bristol Castle'	£90-110	☐
W 2222	GWR	7002	Green	'Devizes Castle'	£80-100	☐
W 2223	BR	4082	Blue	'Windsor Castle'	£120-140	☐
W 2247	GWR	7029	Green	'Clun Castle'	£100-120	☐
W 2247a	BR	7029	Green	'Clun Castle'	£130-150	☐
W 2284	BR	5090	Green	'Neath Abbey'	£130-150	☐
W 2400	BR	7007	Green	'Great Western'	£350-400	☐
W 2417	BR	5034	Green	'Corfe Castle'	£350-400	☐

Locomotives, 'Coronation' (7P) Class (4-6-2)

W 2300	–	–		'Princess' (unpainted kit)	£350-400	☐
W 2301	LMS	6221	Blue	'Queen Elizabeth'	£450-500	☐
W 2301a	LMS	6220	Blue	'Coronation'	£650-750	☐
W 2302	LMS	6244	Maroon	'King George VI'	£450-500	☐
W 2302a	LMS	6228	Maroon	'Duchess of Rutland'	£750-850	☐

Locomotives, 'City' (8P) Class (4-6-2)

W 2226	BR	46245	Maroon	'City of London'	£100-130	☐
W 2226m2	BR	46245	Maroon	'City of London', (5-pole)	£130-150	☐
W 2226a	BR	46238	Maroon	'City of Carlisle'	£300-350	☐
W 2226am2	BR	46238	Maroon	'City of Carlisle', (5-pole)	£350-380	☐
W 2227	LMS	6254	Black	'City of Stoke-on-Trent'	£100-120	☐
W 2227a	LMS	6256	Black	'Sir William Stanier'	£160-180	☐
W 2227am2	LMS	6256	Black	'Sir William Stanier', (5-pole)	£200-220	☐
W 2228	BR	46235	Green	'City of Birmingham'	£100-120	☐
W 2228m2	BR	46235	Green	'City of Birmingham', (5-pole)	£140-160	☐
W 2228a	BR	46241	Green	'City of Edinburgh'	£250-275	☐
W 2228am2	BR	46241	Green	'City of Edinburgh', (5-pole)	£300-325	☐
W 2229	BR	46242	Blue	'City of Glasgow'	£100-120	☐
W 2229a	BR	46246	Blue	'City of Manchester'	£300-350	☐
W 2241	LMS	6229	Black	'Duchess of Hamilton'	£100-120	☐
W 2241m2	LMS	6229	Black	'Duchess of Hamilton', (5-pole)	£130-150	☐
W 2241a	LMS	6225	Black	'Duchess of Gloucester'	£240-260	☐
W 2241am2	LMS	6225	Black	'Duchess of Gloucester', (5-pole)	£260-280	☐
W 2242	LMS	6247	Maroon	'City of Liverpool'	£100-120	☐
W 2264	BR	46229	Maroon	'Duchess of Hamilton'	£300-350	☐
W 2285	LMS	6221	Maroon	'Queen Elizabeth'	£240-260	☐
W 2286	BR	46252	Black	'City of Leicester'	£220-250	☐
W 2294	LMS	6234	Grey	'Duchess of Abercorn'	£240-260	☐
W 2299	BR	46221	Green	'Queen Elizabeth'	£250-300	☐
W 2304	BR	46244	Maroon	'City of Leeds' (with alternative 'KG VI' plates)	£300-325	☐
W 2304	BR	46244	Maroon	'King George V'	£300-325	☐
W 2311	BR	46244	Black	'City of Leeds' (unlined, with wrong number)	£250-300	☐
W 2312	BR	46245	Green	'City of London'	£400-500	☐
W 2313	BR	46234	Green	'Duchess of Abercorn'	£400-500	☐
W 2314	BR	46256	Green	'Sir William Stanier'	£500-600	☐
W 2315	BR	46242	Maroon	'City of Glasgow'	£300-350	☐
W 2316	BR	46242	Green	'City of Glasgow'	£300-350	☐
W 2401	LMS	6223	Maroon	'Princess Alice'	£350-400	☐
W 2405	BR	46231	Green	'Duchess of Atholl'	£350-400	☐
W 2414	BR	46251	Black	'City of Nottingham'	£350-400	☐

Locomotives, 'Royal Scot' Class (4-6-0)

Ref. no.	Livery	Loco number		Name	Price	
W 2260	LMS	6100	Maroon	'Royal Scot'	£180-200	☐
W 2260-5P	LMS	6100	Maroon	'Royal Scot', (5-pole)	£220-240	☐
W 2260a	LMS	6141	Maroon	'Caledonian'	£240-260	☐
W 2261	LMS	6012	Black	'Black Watch'	£180-200	☐
W 2261-5P	LMS	6102	Black	'Black Watch', (5-pole)	£220-240	☐
W 2261a	LMS	6160	Black	'Queen Victoria's Riflemen'	£240-260	☐
W 2262	BR	46110	Green	'Grenadier Guardsman'	£180-200	☐
W 2262a	BR	46148	Green	'Manchester Regiment', (5-pole)	£240-260	☐
W 2273	BR	46159	Blue	'The Royal Air Force', (5-pole)	£250-280	☐
W 2274	LMS	6125	Maroon	'Lancashire Witch', (5-pole)	£240-260	☐
W 2288	BR	46159	Green	'The Royal Air Force'	£250-280	☐
W 2293	LMS	6141	Black	'Caledonian' (gloss or matt)	£240-260	☐
W 2298	BR	46100	Green	'Royal Scot'	£400-500	☐
W 2403	LMS	6146	Black	'The Rifle Brigade'	£300-350	☐

Locomotives, 'A4' Class (4-6-2)

Ref. no.	Livery	Loco number		Name	Price	
W 2209	LNER	4482	Green	'Golden Eagle'	£120-140	☐
W 2209a	LNER	4495	Green	'Great Snipe'	£140-160	☐
W 2209am2	LNER	4495	Green	'Great Snipe', (5-pole)	£140-160	☐
W 2210	LNER	4468	Blue	'Mallard'	£140-160	☐
W 2210am2	LNER	4495	Blue	'Golden Fleece', (5-pole)	£200-220	☐
W 2211	BR	60022	Green	'Mallard'	£80-100	☐
W 2211a	BR	60014	Green	'Silver Link'	£140-160	☐
W 2212	LNER	7	Blue	'Sir Nigel Gresley'	£80-100	☐
W 2212a	LNER	4498	Blue	'Sir Nigel Gresley'	£160-180	☐
W 2212am2	LNER	4498	Blue	'Sir Nigel Gresley', (5-pole)	£160-180	☐
W 2213	NE	4903	Black	'Peregrine'	£120-140	☐
W 2213a	NE	4900	Black	'Gannet'	£120-140	☐
W 2282	NE	4463	Black	'Sparrow Hawk'	£180-200	☐
W 2283	LNER	4493	Grey	'Woodcock'	£180-200	☐
W 2295m2	LNER	4489	Blue	'Dominion of Canada'	£300-350	☐
W 2306	BR	60010	Green	'Dominion of Canada'	£300-350	☐
W 2310	LNER	4498	Blue	'Sir Nigel Gresley'	£220-250	☐
W 2413	LNER	4464	Green	'Bittern'	£350-400	☐

Locomotive, 'West Country/Merchant Navy' (7P) Class (4-6-2)

Ref. no.	Livery	Loco number		Name	Price	
W 2235	BR	34005 R/B	Green	'Barnstaple'	£140-160	☐
W 2236	BR	34042 R/B	Green	'Dorchester'	£140-160	☐
W 2236a	BR	34016 R/B	Green	'Bodmin'	£240-260	☐
W 2237	SR	21C109 R/B	Green	'Lyme Regis'	£120-140	☐
W 2238	BR	35028 R/B	Green	'Clan Line'	£200-220	☐
W 2239	BR	34028 R/B	Green	'Eddystone'	£200-220	☐
W 2265	BR	34051	Green	'Winston Churchill'	£270-300	☐
W 2265a	SR	21C155	Green	'Fighter Pilot' (Golden Arrow)	£300-350	☐
W 2265ax	SR	21C155	Green	'Fighter Pilot'	£400-500	☐
W 2266	SR	21C103	Green	'Plymouth'	£240-260	☐
W 2266ax	BR	34092	Green	'City of Wells'	£300-350	☐
W 2266a	BR	34092	Green	'City of Wells' (Golden Arrow)	£300-350	☐
W 2267	BR	35026	Blue	'Lamport and Holt Line'	£300-350	☐
W 2267a	BR	35026	Green	'Lamport and Holt Line'	£400-500	☐
W 2268	BR	34004	Blue	'Yoevil', (5-pole)	£300-350	☐
W 2268a	BR	34004	Green	'Yoevil'	£350-400	☐
W 2269	BR	34053 R/B	Green	'Sir Keith Park' (Golden Arrow)	£300-350	☐
W 2269x	BR	34053 R/B	Green	'Sir Keith Park'	£300-350	☐
W 2275	BR	34065	Green	'Hurricane', (5-pole)	£450-500	☐
W 2276	SR	21C 101	Green	'Exeter' (Golden Arrow), (5-pole)	£600-700	☐
W 2276x	SR	21C 101	Green	'Exeter', (5-pole)	£400-500	☐
W 2277	BR	34066	Green	'Spitfire'	£400-450	☐
W 2278	SR	21C 13	Black	'Blue Funnel Line'	£400-450	☐
W 2278a	SR	21C 13	Green	'Blue Funnel Line'	£400-450	☐
W 2287	BR	34036 R/B	Green	'Westward Ho!'	£400-450	☐
W 2289	SR	21C 5	Black	'Canadian Pacific Line'	£500-600	☐
W 2290	SR	21C 5	Green	'Canadian Pacific Line'	£500-600	☐
W 2291	BR	34010	Green	'Sidmouth'	£350-400	☐
W 2296	BR	34021 R/B	Green	'Dartmoor'	£500-600	☐
W 2297	BR	35010 R/B	Green	'Blue Star Line'	£500-600	☐
W 2305	SR	21C 107	Green	'Wadebridge'	£500-600	☐
W 2309	BR	34036 R/B	Black	'Westward Ho!' (unlined)	£600-700	☐
W 2402	BR	34090 R/B	Green	'Sir Eustace Missenden'	£400-450	☐
W 2407	SR	21C 111	Green	'Tavistock'	£400-450	☐
W 2411	BR	35003	Blue	'Royal Mail Line'	£400-450	☐
W 2412	BR	34020	Green	'Seaton'	£350-400	☐
W 2415	BR	34052 R/B	Green	'Lord Dowding'	£350-400	☐
W 2416	BR	34057	Green	'Biggin Hill'	£350-400	☐

Tank Locomotives, 'R1' Class (0-6-0)

Ref. no.	Livery	Loco number			Price	
W 2201	ESSO	38	Blue		£50-60	☐
W 2201a	SE & CR	69	Green		£140-160	☐
W 2202	NTG	56	Yellow		£50-60	☐
W 2203	SHELL		Silver		£50-60	☐

Ref. no.	Livery	Loco number			Market Price Range
W 2204	LMS	7420	Maroon		£40-50 ☐
W 2205	BR	31337	Black		£40-50 ☐
W 2205	BR	31340	Black		£50-60 ☐
W 2205a	BR	31047	Black		£150-180 ☐
W 2206	BR	31340	Green		£40-50 ☐
W 2206	BR	31337	Green		£50-60 ☐
W 2206a	BR	31128	Green		£150-180 ☐
W 2207	SR	1127	Olive Green		£40-50 ☐
W 2207a	SR	1152	Olive Green		£150-180 ☐
W 2408			Gold plated	(non-powered)	£140-160 ☐
W 2410	SR	1047	Green		£600-900 ☐

Tank Locomotives, 'N2' Class (0-6-2)

Ref. no.	Livery	Loco number			Market Price Range
W 2214	LMS	2274	Maroon		£50-60 ☐
W 2215	LMS	2385	Black		£50-60 ☐
W 2215a	LMS	2248	Black		£150-180 ☐
W 2216	BR	69550	Black		£50-60 ☐
W 2216a	BR	69496	Black		£200-250 ☐
W 2217	LNER	9522	Green		£50-60 ☐
W 2217a	LNER	2690	Black		£240-260 ☐
W 2280	GWR	8230	Green		£240-260 ☐
W 2292	SR	2752	Dark Green		£240-260 ☐
W 2292	SR	2752	Light Green		£240-260 ☐

Freight Locomotives, '8F' Class (2-8-0)

Ref. no.	Livery	Loco number			Market Price Range
W 2224	BR	48073	Black		£80-100 ☐
W 2224a	BR	48290	Black		£200-220 ☐
W 2225	LMS	8042	Black		£80-100 ☐
W 2225a	LMS	8233	Black		£200-220 ☐
W 2240	LNER	3144	Black		£90-110 ☐
W 2272	LMS	8016	Maroon		£120-140 ☐
W 2281	WD	302	Grey		£160-180 ☐
W 2308	BR	48290	Green		£250-300 ☐
W 2409	BR	48102	Black		£350-400 ☐

Tank Locomotives, '4MT' Class (2-6-4)

Ref. no.	Livery	Loco number			Market Price Range
W 2218	BR	80033	Black		£80-100 ☐
W 2218	BR	80054	Black		£140-160 ☐
W 2218a	BR	80064	Black		£140-160 ☐
W 2218a	BR	80079	Black		£140-160 ☐
W 2219	LMS	2679	Maroon		£80-100 ☐
W 2220	GWR	8230	Green		£120-130 ☐
W 2245	SR	1927	Green		£120-130 ☐
W 2246	CR	2085	Blue		£240-260 ☐
W 2270	BR	80135	Green		£200-220 ☐
W 2271	LNER	9025	Green		£180-200 ☐
W 2279	BR	80151	Black	(5-pole)	£150-180 ☐
W 2307	BR	80079	Black	(unlined)	£200-220 ☐
W 2406	BR	80120	Black		£300-350 ☐

Diesel-Electric Locomotives, 'BO-BO' Class 20 (4-4)

Ref. no.	Livery	Loco number			Market Price Range
W 2230	BR	D8017	Green		£50-70 ☐
W 2230a	BR	20-008	Blue		£50-70 ☐
W 2230b	BR	8003	Blue		£50-70 ☐
W 2230bnp	BR	D8015	Blue	(non-powered)	£70-80 ☐
W 2230np	BR	D8010	Green	(non-powered)	£70-80 ☐
W 2230rf	BR	20-132	Grey	'RAILFREIGHT'	£225-250 ☐

Diesel-Electric Shunters, '08' Class (0-6-0)

Ref. no.	Livery	Loco number			Market Price Range
W 2231	BR	D3763	Green		£60-70 ☐
W 2231np	BR	D3768	Green	(non-powered)	£70-80 ☐
W 2232	BR	D3464	Blue		£60-70 ☐
W 2232np	BR	D3523	Blue	(non-powered)	£70-80 ☐
W 2232a	BR	08 762	Blue		£200-250 ☐
W 2233	LMS	7124	Black		£50-60 ☐
W 2234		72	Red	'N.C.B.'	£60-70 ☐
W 2243	LMS		Yellow	'DUNLOP'	£70-80 ☐

'Brighton Belle' Two-Car Sets

Ref. no.	Livery	Loco number			Market Price Range
W 3004/5	BR		Blue/Grey		£180-200 ☐
W 3004/5a	BR		Blue/Grey	'150 Years'	£250-300 ☐
W 3306/7	Pullman		Brown/Cream	(Set 3051, 1988-89)	£250-300 ☐
W 3006/7	Pullman		Brown/Cream	(Set 3052, 1990-91)	£180-200 ☐
W 3006/7a	Pullman		Brown/Cream	'150 Years' (1990-91)	£250-300 ☐

Wrenn TRAIN SETS

Ref. no.					Market Price Range
001	'BR' Goods Set		0-6-0 Locomotive, Two Wagons, Guards Van, track oval		£100-140 ☐
002	'BR' Freight Set		2-6-4 Locomotive, three Wagons, Guards Van, track oval		£150-200 ☐
003	'BR' Pullman Set		West Country Locomotive, two Pullman cars, track oval		£200-250 ☐

WRENN ROLLING STOCK

PASSENGER COACHES – PULLMAN CARS, 1968-1992

'Super Detail' bodies in high impact polystyrene, with die-cast bogies for stability, fitted with metal-tyred wheels and pin-point axles for extra smooth and friction-free running. Interior fitted with seats, tables and lamps.

N.B. This description has been extracted from the first and second edition Wrenn catalogues (1973-74).

Ref. no.	Type	Livery	Name, notes	MPR	
W 6000	Brake/2nd	Brown/Cream	'Car No.77'	£25-30	☐
W 6000a	Brake/2nd	Brown/Cream	'Car No.79'	£25-30	☐
W 6001	2nd class	Brown/Cream	'Car No.73'	£25-30	☐
W 6001	2nd class	Brown/Cream	'Car No.74'	£35-40	☐
W 6001a	Parlour car	Brown/Cream	'Car No.87'	£25-30	☐
W 6001b	Parlour car	Brown/Cream	'Car No.86'	£25-30	☐
W 6001ag	1st class	Brown/Cream	'AGATHA'	£30-35	☐
W 6001s	1st class	Brown/Cream	'SHEILA'	£40-50	☐
W 6001u	1st class	Brown/Cream	'URSULA'	£30-35	☐
W 6002	1st class	Brown/Cream	'ARIES'	£30-35	☐
W 6002a	1st class	Brown/Cream	'AUDREY'	£30-35	☐
W 6002b	1st class	Brown/Cream	'BELINDA'	£35-40	☐
W 6002v		Brown/Cream	'VERA'	£30-35	☐
W 6002d	1st class	Brown/Cream	'DORIS'	£35-40	☐
W 6002h	1st class	Brown/Cream	'HAZEL'	£30-35	☐
W 6002c	1st class	Brown/Cream	'CARINA'	£40-50	☐
W 6003	Brake/2nd	Blue/Grey (BR)	'S 308 S', (BR log on some)'	£25-30	☐
W 6004	2nd class	Blue/Grey (BR)	'S 302 S', (BR logo on some)	£30-35	☐
W 6004a	Parlour car	Blue/Grey (BR)	'S 287 S', ('Brighton Belle')	£30-35	☐
W 6005	1st class	Blue/Grey (BR)	'S 301 S', ('Golden Arrow')	£30-35	☐
W 6005a	1st class	Blue/Grey (BR)	'S 284 S', ('Brighton Belle')	£30-35	☐
W 6005a	1st class	Blue/Grey (BR)	'S 280 S', ('Brighton Belle')	£30-35	☐
W 6006	Brake/2nd	Green (SR)	'1708'	£25-30	☐
W 6007	2nd class	Green (SR)	'2523'	£25-30	☐
W 6008	1st class	Green (SR)	'1245'	£25-30	☐
W 6009	Brake/2nd	Red (LMS)	'2370'	£25-30	☐
W 6010	2nd class	Red (LMS)	'3459'	£25-30	☐
W 6011	1st class	Red (LMS)	'1046'	£25-30	☐
W 6012	1st class	Brown/Cream	'PEGASUS', ('Golden Arrow')	£30-35	☐
W 6012a	1st class	Brown/Cream	'CECILIA', ('Golden Arrow')	£35-40	☐
W 6012b	1st class	Brown/Cream	'ARIES', ('Golden Arrow')	£35-40	☐
W 6012c	1st class	Brown/Cream	'CYGNUS', ('Golden Arrow')	£40-50	☐
W 6101c	Parlour car	Brown/Cream	'83', (limited edition)	£70-80	☐
W 6102e	1st class	Brown/Cream	'EVADNE', (limited edition)	£70-80	☐

PRIVATE-OWNER and STANDARD WAGONS, 1968-1992

A fine and very extensive range of 'OO/HO' smooth running wagons each with extremely colourful private-owner markings. The bodies are of high-impact polystyrene, some have opening doors, and with the exception of the all-plastic models have detailed die-cast under frames. Tri-ang couplings are fitted and Hornby-Dublo conversion kits are available. Colours of some wagons may be subject to change without notice.

N.B. This information has been extracted from the description provided in the first and second edition Wrenn catalogues (1973-74).

Wheels were initially made entirely of plastic; metal wheels were introduced in 1972. Various shades of grey predominate as the roof colour of a vehicle which has one; the few exceptions are shown below. Note that large shade differences exist in body colours as well, and colour of lettering also varies in shade and intensity. These differences are the result of normal mass-production techniques and do not affect the collectability or price of the model wagons.

Manufacturers name shown on boxes: **'Wrenn OO/HO'** (1968-1969), **'Tri-ang Wrenn'** (1970-1972), **'Wrenn Railways'** (1973-1992).

Ref. no.	Item	Running no.	Body main colour	Lettering colours	MPR	
W 4300p	Fish Van 'FINDUS FOODS'	E87231	White	Red/Blue	£10-15	☐
W 4301p	Banana Van 'FYFFES'	B881867	Brown	Blue/White	£10-15	☐
W 4301p	Banana Van 'FYFFES'	B881867	Green	Blue/White	£10-15	☐
W 4305p	Long Fruit 'D' Van 'BABYCHAM'	W2910	Maroon	Red/Black/Yellow	£10-15	☐
W 4305x	Long Fruit 'D' Van/Passenger	W2910	Maroon		£10-15	☐
W 4310	Brake/Goods Van, 'BR' (ER)	B950350	Brown (matt or gloss)		£10-15	☐
W 4311p	Guards Van, LMS	M730973	Brown		£10-15	☐
W 4311x	Guards Van, 'BR' (MR)	M730973	Brown		£10-15	☐
W 4312	Guards Van, 'BR' (MR)	(Dublo mould faulty, not issued)				☐
W 4313	Gunpowder Van, 'BR'	B887002	Brown		£10-15	☐
W 4313p	Gunpowder Van, 'STANDARD FIREWORKS'	B887002	Brown	Red/White	£20-25	☐
W 4313p	Gunpowder Van, 'STANDARD FIREWORKS'	B887002	Green	Red/White	£20-25	☐
W 4315p	Horse Box, 'FOXHUNTER CHAMPIONSHIPS'	E96435	Green	Red/Bright Yellow	£20-25	☐

333

Ref. no.	Item				Market Price Range
W 4315p	Horse Box, 'Royden Stables Brighton Oct 6-11'	E96435	Green	Red/Pale yellow	£10-15 ☐
W 4315p	Horse Box, 'Royden Stables Brighton Oct 6-11'	E96435	Green	Red/Green	£40-50 ☐
W 4315p	Horse Box, 'Royden Stables' (no date/place)	E96435	Green	Red/Bright Yellow	£25-30 ☐
W 4315x	Horse Box, 'Royden Stables' (no date/place)	E96435	Green	Red/Bright Yellow	£25-30 ☐
W 4316	Horse Box, 'BR'	E96435	Maroon		£20-25 ☐
W 4317	Ventilated Van 'WALLS'	DE545523	Bright Red	Dull Yellow	£10-15 ☐
W 4318p	Ventilated Van 'PEEK FREANS'	DE545523	Brown	White	£10-15 ☐
W 4318p	Ventilated Van 'PEEK FREANS'	B757051	Brown	Pale White	£10-15 ☐
W 4318p	Ventilated Van 'WALLS'	DE545523	Dull Red	Bright Yellow	£10-15 ☐
W 4318pa	Ventilated Van 'PEEK FREANS'	DE545523	Dark Grey	White	£10-15 ☐
W 4318x	Ventilated Van 'BR'	B757051	Dark Brown		£10-15 ☐
W 4318x	Ventilated Van 'BR'	DE545523	Bright Red		£10-15 ☐
W 4320p	Refrigerator Van 'ESKIMO FOODS'	W59850	Off-White	Red/Black	£10-15 ☐
W 4320x	Refrigerator Van 'BR'	W59850	Off-White		£10-15 ☐
W 4323	Utility Van 'BR'	S 2380 S	Green		£10-15 ☐
W 4323	Utility Van 'SOUTHERN'	S 2380 S	Green	Yellow	£10-15 ☐
W 4324	Utility Van 'BR'	S 2380 S	Bright Blue		£10-15 ☐
W 4325	Ventilated Van 'OXO'	DE545523	White	Light Red	£10-15 ☐
W 4325	Ventilated Van 'OXO'	DE545523	White	Red	£10-15 ☐
W 4600	Ore Wagon with load 'CLAY CROSS'		Light Grey	White/Red	£10-15 ☐
W 4625p	20-ton Bulk Grain Wagon 'BR'	B885040	Light Grey		£10-15 ☐
W 4626p	Cement Wagon 'BLUE CIRLE'		Dark Grey	Yellow/Blue	£10-15 ☐
W 4627p	Salt Wagon 'CEREBOS'		Grey	Blue	£10-15 ☐
W 4630	8-ton Cattle Wagon 'BR'	B893344	Brown		£10-15 ☐
W 4630a	8-ton Cattle Wagon 'GW'	103240	Mid-Grey		£10-15 ☐
W 4635p	12-ton Coal Wagon 'HIGGS LONDON'	85	Brown	Red/White	£10-15 ☐
W 4635p	12-ton Coal Wagon 'HIGGS LONDON'	85	Orange	Red/White	£10-15 ☐
W 4635p	12-ton Coal Wagon 'HIGGS LONDON'	85	Dark Green	Red/White	£25-30 ☐
W 4635p	12-ton Coal Wagon 'HIGGS LONDON'	85	Grey	Red/White	£10-15 ☐
W 4640	Goods Wagon, Steel-type	B466865	Brown		£10-15 ☐
W 4640	Goods Wagon, Steel-type	B466865	Buff		£10-15 ☐
W 4644	Hopper Wagon with load	B414029	Grey		£10-15 ☐
W 4644	Hopper Wagon, no load	B414029	Grey		£10-15 ☐
W 4652	Machine Wagon 'LOWMAC', 'BR'	B904631	Gloss r matt Brown		£10-15 ☐
W 4652	Machine Wagon 'LORIOT', 'GW'	43260	Dark Grey		£10-15 ☐
W 4652p	Lowmac Wagon 'AUTO DISTRIBUTORS' (with Minix model Ford Anglia and Caravan, colours vary)		Brown	Turquoise/White/Black	£70-80 ☐
W 4655	16-ton Mineral Wagon 'BR'	B54884	Grey		£10-15 ☐
W 4655a	16-ton Mineral Wagon 'BR'	B550200	Dark Brown		£10-15 ☐
W 4655L	16-ton Mineral Wagon with load 'BR'	B54884	Grey		£10-15 ☐
W 4657	Milk Tanker (6 wheels) 'UNITED DAIRIES'		White	Yellow/Black	£10-15 ☐
W 4658	Prestwin Wagon 'FISONS'	B873000	Red-Brown	White/Black	£10-15 ☐
W 4658x	Silo Wagon 'PRESTWIN', 'BR'	B873000	Red-Brown	White	£10-15 ☐
W 4660p	Open Wagon 'TWININGS'	95	Brown	White/Black	£10-15 ☐
W 4660p	Open Wagon 'TWININGS'	95	Orange	White/Black	£10-15 ☐
W 4665	Salt Wagon 'SAXA'	248	Primrose	Red/Black	£10-15 ☐
W 4665p	Salt Wagon 'SAXA'	248	Yellow	Red/Black	£10-15 ☐
W 4665p	Salt Wagon 'SAXA'	248	Orange	Red/Black	£10-15 ☐
W 4666	Salt Wagon 'SIFTA'	125	Bright Blue	Silver/Pink/Black	£10-15 ☐
W 5000	Coal Wagon 'BLY & Co'		Dark Green	Yellow/White/Black	£10-15 ☐
W 5001	Blue Spot Fish Van 'ROSS FISHERIES'	E87231	White	Red/Blue/White	£10-15 ☐
W 5001x	Blue Spot Fish Van 'BR'	E87231	White		£10-15 ☐
W 5001x	Blue Spot Fish Van 'ROSS FISHERIES'	E87231	Cream		£10-15 ☐
W 5002	Horsebox 'SELSDON STABLES'	E96435	Maroon	Yellow	£15-20 ☐
W 5003	Tank Wagon (6-wheels) 'GUINNESS'		Silver	Red/White/Yellow	£20-25 ☐
W 5004	Ventilated Van 'DUNLOP'	B757051	Yellow	Red/White/Black	£10-15 ☐
W 5004	Ventilated Van 'DUNLOP'	DE545543	Yellow	Red/White/Black	£10-15 ☐
W 5004	Ventilated Van 'DUNLOP' (slogan reversed)	DE545543	Yellow	Red/White/Black	£10-15 ☐
W 5005	Cement Wagon 'TUNNEL'		Grey	Red/Whitre	£10-15 ☐
W 5005	Cement Wagon 'TUNNEL'		Red	Red/White	£10-15 ☐
W 5005x	Cement Wagon		Mid-Grey		£10-15 ☐
W 5006	Ore Wagon with load 'SOUTHDOWN'	17	Grey	Black/Green/Red/White	£10-15 ☐
W 5006	Ore Wagon with load 'SOUTHDOWN'	17	Blue	Black/Green/Red/White	£10-15 ☐
W 5007	Banana Van 'GEEST'	B881867	Brown	Yellow/Blue/White	£10-15 ☐
W 5007a	Banana Van 'GEEST'	B881902	Grey	Yellow/Blue/White	£10-15 ☐
W 5007x	Banana Van 'BR' (no Yellow spot)	B881902	Brown		£10-15 ☐
W 5007x	Banana Van 'BR' (with Yellow spot)	B881902		Brown	£10-15 ☐
W 5008	Open Wagon 'HARRIS'	14	Black	White	£10-15 ☐
W 5009	Gunpowder Van 'BSA'	B887002	Brown	Red/Black/Yellow	£10-15 ☐
W 5010	Ventilated Van 'ROBERTSONS'	B757051	Grey (White roof)	Blue/Yellow/Red/Black	£10-15 ☐
W 5010	Ventilated Van 'ROBERTSONS'	DE545533	Grey	Blue/Yellow/Red/Black	£10-15 ☐
W 5010	Ventilated Van 'ROBERTSONS'	57	Brown Grey	Blue/Yellow/Red/Black	£10-15 ☐

Ref. no.	Item				Market Price Range	
W 5011	Ventilated Van 'WATNEYS'	B757051	Red	White	£10-15	☐
W 5011x	Ventilated Van 'BR'	DE545553	Red		£10-15	☐
W 5012	Express Parcels Van 'BR'	E87003	'BR' Blue/Grey		£10-15	☐
W 5013	Tanker Wagon 'ST IVEL'		White (terra-cotta roof)	Blue/White	£15-20	☐
W 5013a	Tanker Wagon 'ST IVEL GOLD'		White	Blue/White/Red	£50-60	☐
W 5014	Six-wheel Passenger/Brake 'STOVE'	Not manufactured due to tinprinting required.				
W 5015	Ore Wagon with load 'HINCHLEY'	14	Blue	Blue/Black/Yellow	£10-15	☐
W 5015	Ore Wagon with load 'HINCHLEY'	14	Grey	Blue/Black/Yellow	£10-15	☐
W 5016	Cement Wagon 'BLUE CIRCLE'		Grey	Blue/Yellow	£10-15	☐
W 5016	Cement Wagon 'BLUE CIRCLE'		Yellow	Blue/Yellow	£10-15	☐
W 5017	Ore Wagon with load 'PYCROFT'		Pale Green	Red/Grey	£10-15	☐
W 5017	Ore Wagon with load 'PYCROFT'		Black	Red/Grey	£10-15	☐
W 5017	Ore Wagon with load 'PYCROFT'		Grey	Red/Grey	£10-15	☐
W 5018	Salt Wagon 'STAR SALT'	105(white)	Red	Yellow/White/Black	£10-15	☐
W 5018	Salt Wagon 'STAR SALT'	105(blue)	Red	Yellow/White/Black	£10-15	☐
W 5019	Refrigerator Van 'GW'	59828	White	Red	£10-15	☐
W 5019	Refrigerator Van 'BR'	W59850	White		£10-15	☐
W 5020	Bulk Grain Wagon 'KELLOGGS'	B885040	Grey	White/Red/Yellow	£10-15	☐
W 5021	Salt Wagon 'CEREBOS'		Red	Blue/White/Yellow	£10-15	☐
W 5022	Banana Van 'FYFFES'	B881867	Yellow	Blue/White	£10-15	☐
W 5023	Tanker Wagon 'Milk Marketing Board'		Bright Blue	White	£20-25	☐
W 5024	Salt Wagon 'COLMANS' (no 'Liverpool')	15	Yellow	Black/White/Yellow	£10-15	☐
W 5024	Salt Wagon 'COLMANS'	15	Yellow	Black/White/Yellow	£10-15	☐
W 5024	Salt Wagon 'COLMANS'	15	Light Grey	Black/White/Yellow	£10-15	☐
W 5024	Salt Wagon 'COLMANS'	15	Light Grey	White/Black/Yellow	£10-15	☐
W 5025	Ore Wagon with load 'CARTER'	7	Black	Red/White/Black	£10-15	☐
W 5026	Mineral Wagon 'PARK WARD'	7	Brown	White/Black	£10-15	☐
W 5027	Refrigerator Van 'CARR & Co'	W59850	Pale Green	Red/White/Black	£10-15	☐
W 5027	Refrigerator Van (no name)	W59850	All Pale Green		£10-15	☐
W 5028	Banana Van 'NE'	159611	Grey	White	£10-15	☐
W 5029	Steel Open Wagon 'GW'	110265	Dark Grey	White	£10-15	☐
W 5029	Steel Open Wagon with load 'GW'	110265	Dark Grey	White	£10-15	☐
W 5030	Ventilated Van 'LMS'	59673	Red	White	£10-15	☐
W 5031	Goods Guards Van 'NE'	128105	Light Grey (White roof)	White	£10-15	☐
W 5032	Plank Wagon with load 'LMS'	24361	Red (White load)	White	£10-15	☐
W 5032	Plank Wagon with load 'LMS'	24361	Red (Black load)	White	£10-15	☐
W 5033	Ventilated Van 'SR'	41596	Brown	White	£10-15	☐
W 5034	Steel Wagon with load 'NTG'	B486863	Yellow	Red/Yellow/Black	£10-15	☐
W 5034	Steel Wagon (no load) 'NTG'	B486863	Buff	Red/White/Black	£10-15	☐
W 5035	Hopper Wagon with load 'NCB'	128	Dark Green	White	£10-15	☐
W 5036	Hopper Wagon with load 'HOVERINGHAM'	230	Terra-cotta	White	£10-15	☐
W 5036	Hopper Wagon (no load) 'HOVERINGHAM'	230	Terra-cotta	White	£10-15	☐
W 5037	Goods Guards Van 'GW'	Dublo mould faulty – not issued				
W 5038	Goods Guards Van 'SR'	32831	Dark Brown	White	£10-15	☐
W 5039	Petrol Tank Wagon 'ESSO'		Silver	Red/White/Blue	£10-15	☐
W 5040	Petrol Tank Wagon 'SHELL'		Yellow	Red and Black only	£10-15	☐
W 5040	Petrol Tank Wagon 'SHELL'		Yellow	Red/Black/White	£10-15	☐
W 5041	Petrol Tank Wagon 'MOBIL'		Dark Red	Red/White/Blue	£10-15	☐
W 5042	Petrol Tank Wagon 'ESSO'	3300	Dark Turquoise	Red/White/Yellow	£10-15	☐
W 5043	Coal Wagon 'AYR CO-OP'	67	Black	Red/White	£10-15	☐
W 5044	6w Tanker Wagon 'DOUBLE DIAMOND'		Terra-cotta	Red/White/Black	£20-25	☐
W 5045	Grain Wagon 'QUAKER OATS'		Terra-cotta	Blue/Red/White/Yellow	£10-15	☐
W 5046	Ventilated Van 'WALLS'	57	Brown	Red/Orange	£10-15	☐
W 5046	Ventilated Van 'WALLS'	B757051	Brown	Red/Yellow	£10-15	☐
W 5046	Ventilated Van 'WALLS'	DE545523	Red	Yellow	£10-15	☐
W 5047	Ventilated Van 'BISTO'	25	Stone (White roof)	Red/Black/Green/White	£10-15	☐
W 5048	Coal Wagon with load 'CRAMSTON'	347	Terra-Cotta	White/Black	£10-15	☐
W 5049	Long Fruit Van 'GW'	27614	Dark Brown	Pale Yellow or White	£10-15	☐
W 5050	Fish Van 'NORTH SEA FISH'	E67840	'BR' Blue/Grey	White/Red.	£15-20	☐
W 5051	Mineral Wagon (open) 'SHELL'		Silver	Red/White/Yellow	£20-25	☐
W 5051a	Mineral Wagon (open) 'ESSO'		Silver	Red/White/Blue	£20-25	☐
W 5052	Refrigerator Van 'YOUNGS'	78	White	Red	£10-15	☐
W 5053	Utility Van 'BR'	E37232	Brown		£10-15	☐
W 5054	Ventilated Van 'DECCA'	DE545543	Yellow Grey	Blue/White	£10-15	☐
W 5054	Ventilated Van (no name)	DE545543	Yellow Yellow		£10-15	☐
W 5055	Long Fruit Van 'BR'	W28720	'BR' Blue		£10-15	☐
W 5056	Hopper Wagon with load 'TARMAC'	M82	Stone	White/Black	£10-15	☐
W 5057	Gunpowder Van GPV 'BR'	W105780	Black/Black	Red/White	£10-15	☐
W 5058	Fruit Van 'GW'	38200	Grey/White	White	£10-15	☐
W 5059	Flat Wagon with large tyres 'AUTO SPARES'	115	Terra-cotta	Cream	£20-25	☐
W 5060	Low-sided Wagon	B459325	Grey		£10-15	☐
W 5061	Petrol Tank Wagon 'SHELL-BP'		Stone	Red/Yellow/Black/White	£10-15	☐
W 5062	Petrol Tank Wagon 'ROYAL DAYLIGHT'		Black	White	£10-15	☐
W 5063	Banana Van 'TROPICAL FRUIT'	M40	Light Grey	Yellow/Light Blue	£10-15	☐

Ref. no.	Item				Market Price Range	
W 5064	Fish Van 'B.R.T.'	E67840	Stone/White	White/Red/Black	£10-15	☐
W 5065	Insulated Van 'BIRDS-EYE'	312	'BR' Blue/White	Red/White	£10-15	☐
W 5066	6w Tanker Wagon 'SKOL BEER'		Terra-cotta	Red/Black/Yellow/White	£20-25	☐
W 5067	Plank Wagon with load 'AMOS BENBOW'	3	Grey and Black	White/Black	£10-15	☐
W 5068	Hopper Wagon 'CHARRINGTONS'	B421818	Grey	Black	£10-15	☐
W 5069	Plank Wagon with load 'BRITISH SODA'	14	Terra-cotta	White	£10-15	☐
W 5069	Plank Wagon with load (no name)		Terra-cotta		£10-15	☐
W 5070	Salt Wagon 'DISTILLERS Co'	87	Light Grey	White/Black	£10-15	☐
W 5071	Bulk Grain Wagon 'BASS CHARRINGTON'	24	Maroon	White	£10-15	☐
W 5072	Bulk Cement Wagon 'BLUE CIRCLE'		Grey	Blue/White/Yellow	£10-15	☐
W 5073	Steel Wagon 'BRITISH ANTHRACITE'	4253	Terra-cotta	White/Green	£10-15	☐
W 5074	Coal Wagon with load 'BASSETTS'	77	Grey	White	£10-15	☐
W 5075	Coal Wagon with load 'TWININGS'	95	Brown	White (or Black/White)	£10-15	☐
W 5076	Petrol Tank Wagon 'POWER ETHYL'		Green	White/Red/Black	£10-15	☐
W 5077	Tank Wagon 'UNITED MOLASSES'	18	Maroon	White	£10-15	☐
W 5078	Hopper wagon 'WILTON QUARRIES'	Not manufactured.				
W 5079	Hopper Wagon 'NE'	174369	Dark Grey	White	£10-15	☐
W 5079	Hopper Wagon 'NE'	174369	Light Grey	White	£10-15	☐
W 5080	Bulk Cement Wagon 'RUGBY CEMENT'	17	Grey	Black/White/Orange	£15-20	☐
W 5081	Bulk Cement Wagon 'PRESFLOW', 'BR'	72	Chocolate	White	£10-15	☐
W 5082	Hopper Wagon with load 'SYKES'	7	Light Grey	Red/White	£10-15	☐
W 5083	Fruit Van 'BR'	B872181	Brown		£10-15	☐
W 5084	Bulk Cement Wagon 'BULK CEMENT', 'BR'	52	Terra-cotta	Black	£10-15	☐
W 5085	Utility Van 'LMS'	M527071	Maroon		£25-30	☐
W 5086	6w Tanker Wagon 'CO-OP MILK'	172	White	Pale Blue	£40-50	☐
W 5087	Parcels Van 'RED STAR'	E87003	'BR' Blue/Grey	Red/White	£15-20	☐
W 5088	Hopper Wagon 'BRITISH GAS'	142	Dark	White	£15-20	☐
W 5089	Refrigerator Van 'INSUL-MEAT'	105721	Grey	White	£15-20	☐
W 5090	Goods Brake Van 'BR' (MR)	B950127	Grey		£15-20	☐
W 5090	Goods Brake Van 'BR' (MR)	M730012	Grey		£15-20	☐
W 5091	6w Tanker Wagon 'UNIGATE'	220	White	Blue/White/Red	£50-60	☐
W 5092	Bulk Cement Wagon 'READYMIX'	68	Mid-Grey	Black/Orange	£25-30	☐
W 5093	Tank Wagon 'ICI CHLORINE'	163	Black	White	£15-20	☐
W 5094	Ventilated Van 'GW'	W145207	Light Grey	White	£15-20	☐
W 5095	6w Tanker Wagon 'EXPRESS DAIRIES'	50	Bright Blue	White	£25-30	☐
W 5096	5-plank Wagon 'A. BRAMLEY'	6	Brown	Black/White	£25-30	☐
W 5097	5-plank Wagon 'WEBSTER'	47	Dark Green	Red/White	£25-30	☐
W 5098	Hopper Wagon 'BRITISH STEEL'	28	Brown	White	£25-30	☐
W 5099	Goods Brake Van (short wheel-base) 'BR'	B950231	Brown		£25-30	☐
W 5099a	Goods Brake Van (short wheel-base) 'BR'	B932103	Grey		£25-30	☐
W 5100	Ventilated Van 'WRENN RAILWAYS'	W145207	Grey	White/Black/Yellow	£20-25	☐
W 5100a	Ventilated Van 'WRENN RAILWAYS'	W145207	Brown	White/Black/Yellow	£30-35	☐
W 5101	Salt Wagon 'ICI BULK SALT'	25	Light Grey	White	£30-35	☐
W 5102	Gunpowder Van 'BR'	B887002	Brown		£30-35	☐
W 5103	Lowmac Wagon with load	B904631	Brown	(Brown or 'Stone' load)	£30-40	☐
W 5103	Lowmac Wagon 'CEMENT', with load	B904631	Brown	Black	£50-60	☐
W 5104	Tank Wagon 'BULK FLOUR', 'BR'	20	White	Black	£50-60	☐
W 5105	Banana Van 'JAFFA'	B881902	Grey	Green/Yellow	£50-60	☐
W 5106	High-sided Wagon 'HUGHES'	29	Grey	White/Black	£30-40	☐
W 5107	5-plank Wagon 'CONSOLIDATED FISH'	76	Grey	White/Black	£30-40	☐
W 5108	Long Fruit Van 'BR'	B517112	Light Grey		£30-40	☐
W 5109	5-plank Wagon 'BARNSLEY COLLIERIES'	350	Terra-cotta	White	£50-60	☐
W 5110	Tank Wagon 'BRITISH SUGAR'	23	Dark Red	White	£50-60	☐
W 5111	Hopper Wagon 'WEAVER TRANSPORT'	152	Chocolate	White	£50-60	☐
W 5112	Ore Wagon with load 'CLAY CROSS'		Black	Red/White/Black	£50-60	☐
W 5113	Cattle wagon 'MANOR FARM'	50	Brown	White	£50-60	☐

Note: Items W5109 to W5113 inclusive are the over-run of these Limited Edition Wagons:

Limited Edition Wagons with numbered certificates
(W5500-5502 – only 500 of each. W5503-5504 – only 350 of each)

W 5500	5-plank Wagon 'BARNSLEY COLLIERIES'	350	Terra-cotta	White	£50-60	☐
W 5501	Tank Wagon 'BRITISH SUGAR'	23	Dark Red	White	£50-60	☐
W 5502	Hopper Wagon 'WEAVER TRANSPORT'	152	Chocolate	White	£50-60	☐
W 5503	Ore Wagon with load 'CLAY CROSS'		Black	Red/White/Black	£50-60	☐
W 5504	Cattle Wagon 'MANOR FARM'	50	Brown	White	£50-60	☐

Acknowledgements: The editor is indebted to Dave Jowett, ably assisted by Stewart Bean and Harry Walker for the preparation of the listings. The editor also wishes to express his thanks to Barry Potter for supplying technical information and catalogue pictures.

Wrenn Auction Results

BARRY POTTER AUCTIONS
25 The Green, Great Bowden, Leicestershire, LE16 7EU

2400 4-6-0 Loco and Tender No 7007 'Great Western'. The very first Limited Edition to celebrate the Great Western 150th Anniversary, near mint boxed **£360**

2302/A 4-6-2 Loco and Tender Coronation Class, LMS Maroon 'King George VI', mint boxed **£560**

2417 4-6-0 Loco and Tender BR Green No.5034 'Corfe Castle' Limited Edition, mint boxed **£300**

2404 4-6-2 Loco and Tender LNER Blue No.4468 'Mallard' Limited Edition, mint boxed **£180**

2403 4-6-0 Loco and Tender Royal Scot Class LMS Black No.6146 'The Rifle Brigade' Limited Edition, mint boxed **£170**

2403 4-6-0 Loco and Tender Royal Scot Class LMS Black No.6146 'The Rifle Brigade' Limited Edition, mint boxed **£190**

2407 4-6-2 Loco and Tender SR Green No.21c11 streamlined 'Tavistock' Limited Edition, mint boxed **£430**

2409 2-8-0 8F Loco and Tender BR Black No.48102, Limited Edition, mint boxed **£310**

2217 2-6-4 Tank Loco LNER Green No.9025, mint boxed **£230**

2214 0-6-2 Tank Loco LSM Maroon No.2274, near mint boxed **£44**

2217 0-6-2 Tank Loco LNER Green No.9522, mint boxed **£50**

2221 4-6-0 Loco and Tender BR Light green No.5023, near mint boxed. **£130**

2294 4-6-2 Loco and Tender LMS Grey No.6234 'Duchess of Abercorn', mint boxed **£250**

2210 4-6-0 Loco and Tender LNER Blue No.4468 'Mallard', mint boxed **£140**

2221 4-6-0 Loco and Tender BR Light Green No.5023 'Brecon Castle', near mint boxed **£130**

2225 2-8-0 8F Loco and Tender BR Blue No.8042, mint boxed **£75**

2223 4-6-0 Loco and Tender BR Blue No.4082 'Windsor Castle', mint boxed **£130**

2240 2-8-0 8F Loco and TenderLNER Black No.3144, mint boxed **£85**

2241 4-6-2 Loco and Tender LMS Black No.6229 'Duchess of Hamilton', mint boxed **£120**

2217 0-6-2 Tank Loco LNER Green No.9522, mint boxed **£55**

2219 2-6-4 Tank Loco LMS Maroon No.2679, near mint boxed **£50**

2207 0-6-0 Tank Loco SR Green No.1127, mint boxed **£40**

2227/A 4-6-2 Loco and Tender LMS Black No.6256 'Sir William A. Stainer FRS', mint boxed **£160**

2237 4-6-2 Loco and Tender West Country. Southern Green No.21c109 'Lyme Regis' Minor dent to cab roof, otherwise, near mint boxed**Not Sold Estimate £130-£150**

2283 4-6-2 Loco and Tender LNER Grey No.4489 'Woodcock', near mint boxed **£170**

2287 4-6-2 Loco and Tender BR Green No.34036 'Westward Ho', mint boxed **£370**

2274 4-6-0 Loco and Tender LMS Maroon No.6125 'Lancashire Witch' 5 pole motor, near mint boxed **£160**

2296 4-6-2 Loco and Tender Rebuilt West Country BR Green No.34021 'Dartmoor', mint boxed **£510**

2293 4-6-0 Loco and Tender Royal Scot Class LMS Wartime Black No.6141 'Caledonian', near mint boxed **£170**

2316 4-6-2 Loco and Tender BR Green No.46242 'City of Glasgow' Reputedly the last model made by Wrenn only 70 were made, mint boxed **£300**

2289 4-6-2 Loco and Tender SR Black Merchant Navy No.21C5 'Canadian Pacific', mint boxed **£600**

2212A 4-6-2 Loco and Tender LNER Blue No.4498 'Sir Nigel Gresley', mint boxed **£120**

2309 4-6-2 Loco and Tender Rebuilt West Country BR Black No.34036 'Westward Ho', mint boxed **£300**

2265/A 4-6-2 Loco and Tender Merchant Navy SR Green No.21C155 'Fighter Pilot' with golden arrows to side and front, flags to front, mint boxed .. **£490**

2281 2-8-0 8F Loco and Tender In war Department Grey 'WD' on tender 302 on cabside, mint boxed **£160**

2299 4-6-2 Loco and Tender BR Green No.46221 'Queen Elizabeth', mint boxed **£170**

2311 4-6-2 Loco and Tender BR Black No.46244 'City of Leeds', mint boxed **£190**

2304 4-6-2 Loco and Tender BR Maroon No.46244 'City of Leeds' with optional King George VI nameplates, mint boxed **£200**

2224 2-8-0 8F Loco and Tender BR Black No.48073, near mint boxed **£80**

2265 4-6-2 Loco and Tender Streamlined BR Green No.34051 'Winston Churchill', near mint boxed **£290**

2246 2-6-4 Loco and Tender Caledonian Railway Blue No.2085, mint boxed **£280**

2217 0-6-2 Tank Logo LNER Green No.9522, near mint boxed **£80**

2230 BO BO Diesel Electric Loco BR Blue, No.D80013, near mint boxed**£50**

2226 4-6-2 Loco and Tender BR Maroon No.46245 'City of London', mint boxed **£140**

2240 2-8-0 8F Loco and Tender LNER Black No.3144, near mint boxed . **£90**

2230 BO BO Diesel Electric Loco BR Green No.D8017 no couplings, good plus boxed Wrenn Horsebox, SR Utility Van, Fish Van, all excellent plus boxed (4) **£70**

3006/7 Pullmans 'Brighton Bell' Brown cream 2 car set comprising motorised coach and dummy end with three additional Pullmans Coaches 'Audrey', 'Vera' and 'Aries', mint boxed **£220**

2218 2-6-4 Tank Loco BR Black No.80033, near mint boxed **£65**

4-6-0 Loco and Tender BR Blue 'Windsor Castle' Wrongly numbered box, near mint boxed **£80**

2240 2-8-0 8F Loco and Tender LNER Black No.3144, mint boxed **£75**

2225 2-8-0 8F Loco and Tender LMS No.8042, mint boxed **£90**

2242 4-6-2 Loco and Tender LMS Maroon No.6247 'City of Liverpool', mint boxed **£120**

2211/A 4-6-2 Loco and Tender No.4482 'Golden Eagle', near mint boxed**£140**

4-6-2 Loco and Tender No.4482 'Golden Eagle', near mint boxed **£95**

4-6-2 Loco and Tender BR Green No. 34042 'Dorchester', near mint **£85**

2226 4-6-2 Loco and Tender No.46245 Maroon 'City of London', mint boxed **£95**

2212 4-6-2 Loco and Tender LNER Blue No.7 'Sir Nigel Gresley', mint boxed **£110**

2213 4-6-2 Loco and Tender NE Black No.4903 'Peregrine', mint boxed **£100**

2221/A 4-6-0 Loco and Tender BR Green No. 7013 'Bristle Castle', near mint boxed **£120**

2229 4-6-2 Loco and Tender BR Blue No.46242 'City of Glasgow', mint boxed **£125**

2227/A 4-6-2 Loco and Tender LMS Black No.6256 'Sir William A Stainer FRS', near mint boxed **£170**

2213/A 4-6-2 Loco and Tender NE Black No.4900 'Gannet' with instructions, mint boxed **£130**

2272 2-8-0 8F Loco and Tender LMS Maroon No.8016, mint boxed **£140**

2228 4-6-2 Loco and Tender BR Green No.46235 'City of Birmingham', mint boxed **£140**

2209/A 4-6-2 Loco and Tender LNER Green No.4495 'Great Snipe', near mint boxed **£100**

2238 4-6-2 Loco and Tender BR Green No.35028 Clan Line, mint boxed**£180**

4-6-2 Loco and Tender West Country SR Green, No.21C109 'Lyme Regis', mint boxed **£150**

2211 4-6-2 Loco and Tender BR Green No.60022 'Mallard', mint boxed **£110**

2242 4-6-2 Loco and Tender LMS Maroon No.6247 'City of Liverpool', near mint boxed **£100**

2204 0-6-0 Tank Loco LMS Maroon No.7420, near mint boxed, with **4-6-0 Loco and Tender** nicely repainted GWR Green 'Lockheed Hudson' No.5081 Incorect Wrenn Box (2) **£70**

2237 4-6-2 Loco and Tender West Country No.21C109 Southern 'Lyme Regis', near mint boxed **£110**

2238 4-6-2 Loco and Tender Merchant Navy BR Green No. 35028 Clan Line, near mint boxed **£130**

Pullmans Boxed Set No.WP100 Comprising 4-6-0 **Loco and Tender** 'Cardiff Castle' and 3 Pullmans Coaches, Excellent Plus, near mint boxed **£150**

Boxed Freight Set No.2 with LMS 2-6-4 Maroon **Tank Loco** No.2679 4 Wagons and Trackwork, near mint boxed **£100**

4 SR Utility Vans with 6 good Brake Vans, apart from 1 missing coupling, all mint boxed (10) **£48**

Pullmans Coaches 'Aries', 'Vera', 'Audrey', 'Car No.77', 'Car No.87', mint boxed (5) **£120**

Pullman Coaches 'Vera', 'Audrey', two 'Car No.73'. With SR Utility Van, Horse box, some damage to boxes, excellent near mint boxed, 9 packets of Wrenn Track Screws (16) **£80**

18 Various Wagons including Fruit Van GW, Coal Wagon 'Cramston', Fish Van 'Findus', Black Gunpowder Van and Hopper Wagon 'Hoveringham', all mint boxed (18) **£100**

6 Pullman Coaches 'Cecila', 'Vera', '2 Aries', 'Parlour Car' and Brake/2nd, mint boxed (6) **£90**

6 Southern Coaches two first class, two second class and two brake/2nd, mint boxed (6) **£120**

5 LMS Coaches two first class, two brake/2nd and one second class, and a blue Pullmans brake/2nd coach, mint boxed (6) **£95**

Pullmans 'Brighton Belle' Five Car Set comprising motorised 'Car No.91', 'Car No.73', 'Hazel' and 'Doris', mint boxed (5) **£120**

Blue Pullmans 'Brighton Belle' Five Car Set comprising motor and dummy tailer cars and three coaches, mint boxed (5) **£150**

2209/A 4-6-2 Loco and Tender LNER Green No.4495 'Great Snipe', mint boxed **£130**

2211/A 4-6-2 Loco and Tender No.60014 'Silver Link', mint boxed. **Not Sold Estimate £120-£150**

2216 0-6-2 Tank Loco BR Black No.69550, mint boxed **£75**

2218 2-6-4 Tank Loco BR Black No.80033, near mint boxed**Not Sold Estimate £90-£120**

2220 2-6-4 Tank Loco GWR Green No.8230 with instructions, near mint boxed **£80**

2224 2-8-0 8F Loco and Tender No.48073 with instructions, mint boxed **£110**

2227 4-6-2 Loco and Tender LMS Black No.6254 'City of Stoke on Trent', near mint boxed **£120**

2227/A 4-6-2 Loco and Tender 8P LMS Black No.6256 'Sir William A. Stanier' F.R.S., mint boxed **£130**

2228/A 4-6-2 Loco and Tender BR Green No. 46241 'City of Edinburgh' wrong box base, excellent boxed **£130**

2235 4-6-0 Loco and Tender BR Green No.34016 'Bodmin' with instructions, near mint boxed **£140**

2236/A 4-6-2 Loco and Tender BR Green No.34016 'Barnstaple' with instructions, near mint boxed **£240**

2239 4-6-2 Loco and Tender Green No.34028 'Eddystone', mint boxed .. **£180**

2241/A 4-6-2 Loco and Tender LMS Black No.6225 'Duchess of Gloucester', mint boxed **£150**

2245 2-6-4 Tank Loco SR Green 'Southern 1927', mint boxed.............**£120**

2247 4-6-0 Loco and Tender 'Clun Castle', mint boxed...........**£120**

2260 4-6-0 Loco and Tender LMS Maroon No.6100 'Royal Scot', mint boxed **£200**

2261 4-6-0 Loco and Tender LMS Black No.6102 'Black Watch', mint boxed **£140**

2262 4-6-0 Loco and Tender BR Green No.46110 'Grenadier Guardsman', mint boxed **£140**

2264 4-6-2 Loco and Tender BR Maroon No.46229 'Duchess of Hamilton', mint boxed **£330**

2266/A 4-6-2 Loco and Tender BR Green 'City of Wells', near mint boxed**£210**

2270 2-6-4 Tank Loco BR Green No.80135, mint boxed **£100**

2273 4-6-0 Loco and Tender Blue Royal Scot 'The Royal Air Force', near mint boxed **£190**

2279 2-6-4 Tank Loco BR Black 5P No.80151, mint boxed **£110**

2282 4-6-2 Loco and Tender NE Black No.4463 'Sparrow Hawk', near mint box **£110**

2284 4-6-0 Castle Loco and Tender 'Neath Abbey', mint boxed.............**£130**

2285 2-6-2 Loco and Tender LMS Maroon No.6221 'Queen Elizabeth', mint boxed **£120**

2286 4-6-2 Loco and Tender BR Black No.46252 'City of Leicester', mint boxed **£120**

2301 4-6-2 Loco and Tender LMS Blue Coronation No.6211 'Queen Elizabeth', near mint boxed...........**£440**

2302 4-6-2 Loco and Tender LMS Red Coronation No.6244 'King George VI', mint boxed **£520**

2304 4-6-2 Loco and Tender BR Red No.46244 'King George VI', mint boxed **£160**

2306 4-6-2 Loco and Tender BR Green No.60010 'Dominion of Canada', mint boxed **£160**

2308 2-8-0 8F Loco and Tender BR Green No.48290, mint boxed **£120**

2312 4-6-2 Loco and Tender BR Green No.46234 'Duchess of Abercorn', mint boxed **£330**

2412 4-6-2 Loco and Tender BR Green No.34020 'Seaton' Limited Edition with stand, Certificate, mint boxed **£400**

2413 4-6-2 Loco and Tender LNER Green No.4464 'Bittern' Limited Edition with stand, Certificate, mint boxed **£280**

2414 4-6-2 Loco and Tender BR Black No.46251 'City of Nottingham' Limited Edition with stand, Certificate, mint boxed **£210**

2415 4-6-2 Loco and Tender BR Green No.34052 'Lord Dowding' Limited Edition with stand, Certificate, mint boxed **£400**

2216 2-6-2 Tank Loco BR Black No.80033, near mint boxed...................**£60**

2301 4-6-2 Loco and Tender Coronation Class 'Queen Elizabeth' LMS Blue No.6221, mint boxed ....**Not Sold Estimate £500-£600**

2408 0-6-0 Tank Loco 'Jubilee' Limited Edition to commemorate the Hornby Dublo 50th Anniversary, a non powered model with a 24 carat plated body, mint boxed **£160**

2406 2-6-4 Tank Loco Br Black No.80120 Limited Edition, mint boxed **£280**

2404 4-6-2 Loco and Tender LNER Blue No.4468 'Mallard' Limited Edition with stand and instructions, mint boxed **£330**

2405 4-6-2 Loco and Tender BR Green No.46231 'Duchess of Atholl' Limited Edition with stand, certificate and instructions, mint boxed **£340**

2402 4-6-2 Loco and Tender BR Green No.34090 'Sir Eustace Missenden' Limited Edition, mint boxed **£400**

2401 4-6-2 Loco and Tender LMS Maroon No.6223 'Princess Alice' Limited

Edition, mint boxed...........**£350**

2416 4-6-0 Loco and Tender BR Green No.34057 'Biggin Hill' Limited Edition, mint boxed **£400**

2267 4-6-2 Loco and Tender Merchant Navy Class BR Blue No.35026 'Lamport and Holt Line', near mint boxed **£250**

2261A 4-6-0 Loco and Tender LMS Black No.6160 'Queen Victoria's Rifleman', mint boxed **£180**

2262 4-6-0 Loco and Tender BR Green No.46110 'Grenadier Guardsman' with instructions, mint boxed ....**Not Sold Estimate £180-£220**

2262/A 4-6-2 Loco and Tender BR Green No.46148 'The Manchester Regiment', Excellent plus boxed ....**Not Sold Estimate £120-£160**

2278 4-6-2 Loco and Tender Southern Black Merchant Navy No.21C13 'Blue Funnel', mint boxed **£390**

2288 4-6-0 Loco and Tender BR Green No.46159 'The Royal Air Force', mint boxed **£220**

2411 4-6-2 Loco and Tender BR Blue Merchant Navy No.35003 'Royal Mail' Limited Edition with stand and certificate, mint boxed **£430**

2290 4-6-2 Loco and Tender Southern Green Merchant Navy No.21C5 'Canadian Pacific', mint boxed **£400**

2236 4-6-0 Loco and Tender BR Green No.34032 'Dorchester', mint boxed**£150**

2291 4-6-2 Loco and Tender BR Green No.34010 'Sidmouth', mint boxed**£370**

2305 4-6-2 Loco and Tender Southern Green No.21C107 'Wadebridge', mint boxed **£520**

Barry Potter Auction – June 1995

2402 4-6-2 Loco & Tender BR Green No.34090 'Sir Eustace Missenden', Limited Edition, complete with stand, certificate and instructions, near mint boxed **£360**

2404 4-6-2 Loco & Tender LNER Blue No.4468 'Mallard', Limited Edition, complete with stand, certificate and instructions, mint boxed...........**£390**

The Brighton Belle 2 Car Pullman Set, Blue and Grey, lacking one white internal box sleeve, near mint boxed **£140**

2267 4-6-2 Loco & Tender BR Blue No.35026 'Lamport & Holt Line', with instructions, mint boxed **£360**

2313 4-6-2 Loco & Tender BR Green No.46234 'Duchess of Abercorn', with instructions, mint boxed **£510**

2316 4-6-2 Loco & Tender BR Green No.46242 'City of Glasgow', with instructions, mint boxed **£420**

2314 4-6-2 Loco & Tender BR Green No.46256 'Sir William A. Stanier F.R.S.', with instructions, mint boxed **£680**

2285 4-6-2 Loco & Tender BR Green No.34051 'Winston Churchill', with instructions, mint boxed **£340**

2265/A 4-6-2 Loco & Tender Southern Green No.21C155 'Fighter Pilot', with Golden Arrows to sides and flags to front, with instructions, near mint boxed **£310**

2237 4-6-2 Loco & Tender Southern Green No.21C109 'Lyme Regis', with instructions, mint boxed **£160**

2260 4-6-0 Loco & Tender LMS Maroon No.6100 'Royal Scot', with instructions and optional smoke deflectors, mint boxed **£160**

2246 2-6-4 Tank Caledonian Blue No.2085, with instructions, mint boxed**£200**

2266 4-6-2 Loco & Tender Southern Green No.21C103 'Plymouth', with instructions, near mint boxed **£230**

2236/A 4-6-2 Loco & Tender BR Green No.34092 'City of Wells' with Golden Arrows to sides and flags to front, with instructions, mint boxed **£330**

2238 4-6-2 Loco & Tender BR Green No.35028 'Clanline', mint boxed.. **£160**

Wagons. 3 'Robertsons', 'Bass Charington', 'St. Ivel', Tanker, 'Hinchley' Ore, 5 SR Ventilated, 2 'Pycroft' Ore, 'Guiness' Tanker, 3 LMS Ventilated, 4 Red Ventilated, 2 'Watneys' Ventilated, 3 'Dunlop', 'Sifta Salt', 'Tunnel Bulk Cement', 2 'Walls Bacon', 'Double Diamond' Tanker, 2 Brake Vans, SR Brake Van, (1 box perspex damaged), all mint boxed (34)...........**£200**

2 Southern Green Coaches (1st Class and Brake/2nd), Esso Tanker, All excellent plus boxed. Catalogues – 2nd, 3rd, 4th, 5th Editions, 3 Price Lists, instruction sheets, track booklet, all excellent (12) **£90**

Wallis & Wallis, Lewes, Sussex
Late July 1995

A scarce Wrenn OO The Brighton Belle, 2 car set in original boxes and packing. VGC to mint, boxes light age wear and marking...................**£240**

A Wrenn OO gauge 4-6-2 rebuilt West Country Lyme Regis (W2237), in original box and packing, VGC to mint **£150**

A Wrenn OO gauge 4-6-2 West Country class Plymouth (W2266), in original box, VGC to mint, very slight rubs to box corners...............**£250**

A desirable Wrenn OO gauge rebuilt West Country 4-6-2 Bodmin and tender (W2236/a) in original box. VGC, box corners slight wear...........**£250**

THE TOYFAIR WORLD
Toyfair Organisers and the Fairs they arrange:

Julie and John Webb, (01526) 398198
Alexandra Palace, Alfreton, Bacup, Beverley, Bishops Stortford, Borehamwood, Bradford, Brentwood, Bury St.Edmunds, Cambridge, Cleethorpes, Colchester, Colne, Cradley Heath, Doncaster, Donington Park, Droitwich, Dulwich, Edmonton, Gateshead, Halifax, Heanor, Heywood, Huddersfield, Huntingdon, Ipswich, Keighley, Kings Lynn, Leeds, Leeds, Lincoln, Long Eaton, Mansfield, Mildenhall, Morley, NEC-Birmingham, Newark, Normanton, Norwich, Peterborough, Rayleigh, Rotherham, Southend, St.Neots, Swaffham, Telford, Wakefield, Wales (Royal Welsh Showground, Bulith Wells), Walsall, Wisbech, Wymondham, York Racecourse.

Barry Potter, (01604) 770025, (mobile: 0850-434902)
Birmingham, Coventry, Dunstable, Harrogate, Loughborough, Luton, Market Harborough, Rugby, Sandown, Stevenage, Solihull, Stoneleigh, Sutton Coldfield,

Dennis Wright, (01335) 342093, Buxton Toyfair

Trevor Morgan, (01242) 524644 (eve), (mobile: 0831-499754),
Bath, Bristol, Cheltenham, Gloucester, Reading.

Mike Spencer (01622) 735396) and Geoff Martin, (01732) 840787
Brighton, Crawley, Croydon, Ditton, Dorking, Lancing, London (Eltham), Mitcham, Tunbridge Wells, Woolwich, Worthing.

Gainsborough Swapmeets, (01427) 611225,
Gainsborough, Lincolnshire

John Moore Fairs, (01455) 636003,
Atherstone, Burton-on-Trent, Coalville, Coventry, Derby, Grantham, Hinckley, Oakham, Stafford, Stone

Leslie Johnson Collectors Toy Fairs, (01708) 348144,
Basildon, Dartford, Croydon, Gravesend, Harrogate, Hatfield, Ilford, Kingston, London, Northwood, Upminster.

Keith Manning, (01372) 725063,
Eastleigh, Guildford, Havant.

Richard or Joyce Atkins, (01869) 347489,
Banbury, Malvern, Oxford, Salisbury, Sevenoaks, Swindon, Worcester, Leamington Spa.

Bulldog Toyfairs (Stu Vowles), (01373) 452857, (mobile: 0585-944002),
Ascot, Bridgewater, Cirencester, Exeter, Newbury, Shepton Mallet, Weymouth.

Maidenhead Static Model Club, (01256) 819141,
Windsor International Swapmeet.

P. Hallam, (01270) 878519,
Chester, Stoke, Wolverhampton.

Dee Thomas, (01202) 521686, Bournemouth.

BB Models, (01295) 711741, Witney.

Tim Mohon, (01665) 711799 (day), (01665) 711000 (eve),
Darlington, Middlesbrough, Newcastle, Tynemouth.

Cliff Maddock, (01734) 833062,
Reading ('The Big Southern Vintage Toy Fair').

Northern Toyfairs (David Hinam), (01246) 232832,
Barnsley, Bradford, Chesterfield, Dewsbury, Halifax, Harlow, Hull, Leicester, Ossett, Scunthorpe, Sheffield, Stockport, Wakefield, Wetherby, Wolverhampton.

Eagle Promotions, (01623) 635005 and (01427) 617417,
Uttoxeter Racecourse.

Alan Whitehead, (01204) 364646 or 491763,
Bolton Fleamarket and Autojumble.

Mid Kent Toy Fair and Auto Jumble, (01622) 753783,
Maidstone, Mid Kent, Weald of Kent.

Emporium Fairs, (01202) 743742,
Ferndown, Weymouth.

Stuart and Kevin, (01244) 346297,
Farnham Maltings, Telford (MICA Toyfair)

Mike Rooum, (0171) 499 0482,
Bristol, Gloucester.

Bruce and Pam King Doll Fairs, (01480) 216372,
Elvaston Castle, Linton, Market Harborough, Wakefield.

Transtar Promotions (Geoff & Linda Price), (0121) 502 3713,
Birmingham, Brierley Hill, Cannock, Leicester, Stoke-on-Trent, Stourbridge, Walsall Wood, West Bromwich, Wolverhampton.

Colin Penn, (0181) 888 4485,
Brentwood, Enfield, Hornchurch, Merton, Rochford, Selsdon, Wimbledon.

Nick Sandys, (01704) 548477,
Carlisle, Garstand, Northwich, Ormskirk.

P.Levinson, (0181) 205 1518,
Beaconsfield, Elstree, Wembley.

3 Counties Toyfairs (Ian Shave), (01923) 263145,
Biggleswade, Letchworth, Milton Keynes, Ruislip, St. Albans, Welwyn.

Collectors Toys and Train Fairs, (01753) 642067,
Uxbridge, Middlesex.

Bill Bourne, (01277) 624937,
Chelmsford, Southend.

Norman Joplin, (01670) 714522,
British Toy Soldier and Figure Show, Royal National Hotel, London.

Ashford Model Collectors Club, (01233) 641636,
Ashford, Canterbury.

Toyman Fairs, (01992) 620376,
Bromley, Chalfont St. Peter, Cuffley, Hertford, Orpington, Richmond.

Ian Wakefield, (01159) 892128,
Nottingham Toy and Train Fair.

B. Mclaren, (01324) 31012, Falkirk.

Dave Jones (Central Fairs), Julie (01543) 371123,
Aldridge, Burton-on-Trent, Hagley, Hinckley.

Scotsman Fairs (George Mann), (01505) 862533, or Scotsmann Models (0141) 552 6759,

Clive Read, (01594) 542855, Cardiff Toy Fair.

Chris and Penny Dyer, (01634) 702757),
Minehead Toy and Train Sale.

Regal Fairs, (01242) 577853, (mobile: 0850-300636),
Science Museum, Wroughton Airfield, Swindon.

N. Thomas, (01179) 325780, Chippenham, Nailsea.

Viv and Barry Stockton, (0151) 334 3362,
Altrincham, Barton, Blackpool, Southport, Warrington, Wigan Pier, Wirral.

Gray and Di, (01322) 439981,
Eltham Toy and Train Collectors Fair, Lea, London.

Iain Hines, (0181) 898 0681 (or Tricia (01753) 545383),
Heathrow International.

A. S. Models and Toys, (01215) 577073,
Bromsgrove, Cannock, Spetchley, Stoke-on-Trent, Telford.

Coventry Diecast Model Club, (01203) 418027,
Coventry Toy Fairs.

RCSW Swapmeets (L. Kenwood), (01734) 733690,
Cardiff, Newport, Reading, Southampton, Winchester.

Bluebell Railway, (01903) 244655, Horsted Keynes

Re-Rail (Geoff Rudin), (01744) 885005,
Accrington, Blackburn, Haydock, Leyland, Manchester, St. Helens, Ulverston.

Dennis Green, Denvor Promotions, (01844) 343198, (mobile: 0378-119603, Aylesbury, Bucks.

Keynote Promotions, (01376) 510663, (mobile: 0860-448359),
London Harrow.

D & J Fairs, (01159) 231639 (Dave Jowett),
Alexandra Palace, NEC Birmingham, Nottingham, Doncaster, Donington, London Lee Valley, Telford.

M & J Fairs, (01756) 717494 (day), (01756) 799358 (eve),
Skipton Toy and Train Fair.

P & R Toyfairs, (01623) 870666, (mobile: 0973-291652),
Grantham, Nottingham, Redditch, Stafford, Stoke-on-Trent.

Steel Promotions, (01617) 969538,
Leeds (Pudsey), Pontefract, Rochdale.

John Bartrum, (0181) 200 5020, Holt (Norfolk).

Corgi Collector Club Annual Toyfair, (01533) 826666,
Donnington Park.

Ray Strutt, (01825) 768776, Modelex Annual Show.

Abbreviations

A
A.E.C.   Associated Equipment Company
AA   Anti-aircraft (or Automobile Association)
A.A.   Automobile Association
ABC   (ABC-TV) Associated British Cinemas (Television)
A.C.   Auto-Carriers
A.F.S.   Auxilliary Fire Service
AMC   American Motor Corporation
APC   Armoured Personnel Carrier
ATV   Associated Television

B
BA   British Airways
BAC   British Airways Corporation
BBC   British Broadcasting Corporation
BEA   British European Airways
BFPO   British Forces Post Office
bhp   Brake horsepower
BLMC   British Leyland Motor Corporation
BMC   British Motor Corporation
BMW   Bayrische Motoren-Werke
B.O.A.C.   British Overseas Airways
BP   British Petroleum
BR   British Railways
BRM   British Racing Motors
BRS   British Road Services
B.S.M.   British School of Motoring

C
CA   A type of Bedford van
CF   A type of Bedford van
CHEVVY   (or Chevy) Chevrolet
CLE   Certificated Limited Edition
cv   chevaux-vapeur (a measure of power)
C.W.S.   Co-operative Wholesale Society
cwt.   hundred-weight

D
DD   Double-decker
DG   (Lledo Models of) Days Gone
DH   De Havilland
Dk.   Dark (shade of colour)
DTB   'Dinky Toys' on base
DUKW   An amphibious vehicle developed by General Motors in wartime. The letters are not initials or an abbreviation but are simply part of an early drawing-office reference.

E
E   East
EEC   European Economic Community
E.F.E.   Exclusive First Editions
e.g.   exempli gratia (for example)
EMI   Electrical & Musical Industries Ltd
ER   Elizabetha Regina, (E II R, Queen Elizabeth II) or Eastern Region
ERA   English Racing Automobiles
ERF   Edwin Richard Foden
Est.   Established (or estimate/d)

F
Fiat   (or FIAT) Fabbrica Italiana Automobile Torino
fig(s)   figure(s)

G
GB   Green box
G.B.   Great Britain
GBT   Globe-Trotter
GER   Great Eastern Railway
GMC   General Motors Corporation
GP   Grand Prix
GPO   General Post Office
GR   Georgius Rex

GS   Gift Set
GSP   Gift Set price
GTO   Gran Turismo Omologato
GTV   Gran Turismo Veloce
GUS   Great Universal Stores
GWR   Great Western Railway

H
HM   His/Her Majesty
HMAC   His Majesty's Armoured Car
HMS   His/Her Majesty's Ship
H.M.V.   'His Masters Voice'
hp   horse-power
H.W.M.   Hersham & Walton Motors

I
IBM   International Business Machines
ICI   Imperial Chemical Industries
INTER   (or INTL) International
I.O.M.   Isle of Man

J
JB   James Bond
JCB   Joseph C. Bamford
J.M.T.   Jersey Motor Transport

K
K.D.F.   Kraft durch Freude
K.L.G.   Kenelm Lee Guinness
K.L.M.   Koninklijke Luchtvaart Maatschappij NV (Dutch airline)

L
L.A.P.D.   Los Angeles Police Department
LE   Limited Edition
LM   Le Mans
LMS   London Midland & Scottish Railway
LNER   London & North Eastern Railway
LNWR   London & North Western Railway
loco   locomotive
logo   lettering, trademark or advertising design
LP   Lledo Promotional
LT   London Transport
Lt.   Light (shade of colour)
Ltd.   Limited (Limited Liability Company)
LWB   Long wheel-base

M
MB   Matchbox
Met.   Metallic
MG   A make of car, derived from 'Morris Garages'
MGA, MGB   types of MG car
MGC   A type of MG car
M.I.C.A.   Matchbox International Collectors Association
mm.   millimetres
MOY   Models Of Yesteryear
MPR   Market Price Range
MR   Midland Region

N
N   North
NAAFI   Navy, Army & Air Force Institutes
N.A.S.A.   National Aeronautics & Space Administration
NB   nota bene (mark well)
NCL   National Carriers Limited
NCO   Non-Commissioned Officer
NCP   National Car Parks
NEC   National Exhibition Centre
NGPP   No guide price at present
nhp   (or n.h.p.) Nominal horsepower
No.   Number
NOR   Number of rails
NOV   Number of variations

NPE   No price estimate
NPP   No price possible
NRP   Normal retail price
NS   (or n/s) Nearside
NSPCC   National Society for the Prevention of Cruelty to Children

O
OPO   On-pack offer
OS   (or o/s) Offside

P
PB   Propeller blade(s)
PLC   Public Limited Company (see also Ltd.)
P.M.G   Post Master General (Australia)
PO   Post Office
PRM   Promotional model
PSV   Public service vehicle
P.T.T.   Postes-Telephones-Telegraphes

R
RAC   (or R.A.C.) Royal Automobile Club
RAF   (or R.A.F.) Royal Air Force
R.C.M.P.   Royal Canadian Mounted Police
RF   'Ring-field' motor
RHD   Right-hand drive
RM   Routemaster (bus)
RN(s)   Racing or Rally number(s)
RNLI   Royal National Life-boat Institution
RT   Route

S
S   South
SBRW   Solid black rubber wheels
SBX   Special box
SD   'Super Detail' (Hornby Dublo)
S.F.F.D.   San Francisco Fire Department
S.F.P.D.   San Francisco Police Department
SR   Southern Railway, Southern Region
St.   Saint or Street
STP   Scientifically-Treated Petroleum
SWB   Short wheel-base
SWRW   Solid white rubber wheels

T
TBA   'To be announced'
TC   Twin carburettors
TDF   Tour De France
TK   Type of Bedford truck
TS   'Touring Secours'
TT   Two-tone (or Tourist Trophy)
TV   Television
TWA   Trans-World Airlines

U
UB   Unboxed
UK   United Kingdom
UN   United Nations
US   United States (of America)
USA   United States of America
USAAF   United States Army Air Force
USAF   United States Air Force
USS   United Space Starship

V
VW   Volkswagen

W
W   West
WR   Western Region

Y
YB   Yellow box
YMCA   Young Mens Christian Association

TOY and MODEL MUSEUMS

Arundel Toy and Military Museum High Street, Arundel, Sussex. Old toys, dolls, games, etc.

Bamford Toy Museum 19 Tyrone Road, Rochdale, Lancs. Tel (01706) 360002. A superb display of rare toys and items of interest.

Chester Toy Museum 13a Lower Bridge Street Row, Chester CH1 1RJ. Open most days. Matchbox Toys (particularly 1-75 series and Models of Yesteryear). Fine collection of Dinky Toys and general toys also on display.

Corgi Toy Collection The Corgi Company has permanent collections of its past products. Part is displayed at the Corgi Heritage Centre, Heyden, Rochdale, Lancs., and part at the British Motor Industries Heritage Trust Museum, Gaydon, near Warwick.

David Cooke Dinky Toys Collection Bressingham Steam Museum, Bressingham, Norfolk. Superb collection of rare Dinky Toys. Open April-October.

House on Hill Toy Museum Stansted, Essex. One of the largest toy displays in the UK.

Ironbridge Toy Museum Shropshire Excellent display of all groups of toys and models.

Lamberhurst Toy and Train Museum Forstal Farm, Gaudhurst Road, Lamberhurst, Kent. An excellent day out for the whole family. Mixed collection.

London Toy and Model Museum 21 Craven Hill, London W2 3EN. Open most days. General collection of toys and models.

Merley House Model Museum Merley, Wimborne, Dorset.
Open Easter till end of September (telephone 01202 - 886533). Most model ranges represented, very good display of railway and white-metal models.

Museum of British Road Transport Hales Sreet, Coventry, CV1 1PN. Home of the world famous 'TIATSA' collection. Open daily 10:00 - 4:30 (telephone 01203 - 832425).

Nostalgia Toy Museum High Street, Godshill, Isle of Wight (telephone 01983 - 821296)

Sussex Toy and Model Museum 52-55 Trafalgar Street, Brighton, East Sussex, BN1 4EB. Open most days (telephone 01273 - 749494). The museum is close to Brighton Station and has a good selection of toys and models.

Tintagel Toy Museum, Tintagel, Cornwall. Excellent display of toys and models.

Vintage Toy and Train Museum, 1st Floor, Field's Department Store, Market Place, Sidmouth, Devon, EX10 8LU. Easter to October. Strong on railway models (particularly Hornby) plus unusual selections of Dinky Toys.

MODEL CLUBS

Maidenhead Static Model Club 21a High Street, West Wickham, Kent, BR4 0LP. The oldest and widest-based toy and model collectors club. Founded in 1969. WINDSOR SWAPMEET organisers. 12 magazines a year. Monthly meetings, Trips, Quizzes, Discounts, Promotions, Charity fund raising. Telephone (01895) 673386.

The Coventry Diecast Model Club 22 Edingale Road, Walsgrave Park, Coventry, CV2 2RF. The fastest growing club in the country! Six quality magazines a year, monthly meetings, lectures, outings, discounts, badges, stickers, ties, Club models, etc.

Ulster Model Club D. R. Nicholl, 74 Old Westland Road, Belfast, BT14 6TE.

Ashford Model Collectors Club Towers Garage Showroom, Faversham Road, Ashford, Kent. Telephone (01233) 641636.

Havant Model Club Havant, Hampshire.

East Anglian Diecast Model Club David Cooke, Norwich (01603) 300800. Club meetings at 'The Norfolk Dumpling', Hall Road, Norwich, last Tuesday of every month (except December).
new members welcome!

Beccles Model Club Frank Clarke, 1 St Marys Road, Beccles, Suffolk, NR34 9NQ. Thriving club with varied and regular programme of events.

Corgi Toys Numerical Index

Corgi Toys Numerical Index – continued

Dinky Toys Numerical Index

346

Sale & Purchase Record

DATE	MODELS BOUGHT OR SOLD	PRICE

N.B. Extra pages may be obtained by photocopying this page

Collector's Notes

Index to Advertisers

The advertisers index has been compiled as an extra service for catalogue users. Whilst every care has been taken in compiling the listing, the publishers cannot accept responsibility for any errors or omissions. Similarly, the publisher cannot accept responsibility for errors in the advertisements or for unsolicited photographs or illustrations.